C0-BXA-253

ANIMAL AGENTS AND VECTORS OF HUMAN DISEASE

By Ernest Carroll Faust, M.A., Ph.D.

The William Vincent Professor of Tropical Diseases and Hygiene and Head, Division of Parasitology, Department of Tropical Medicine and Public Health, The Tulane University of Louisiana, New Orleans, Louisiana; Consultant, Armed Forces Institute of Pathology; Consultant, U. S. Public Health Service; Member, Expert Panel on Parasitic Diseases, World Health Organization; Member, Committee on Revision U. S. Pharmacopeia, 1950-1960.

216 Text figures, 9 Plates, Including One in Color

LEA & FEBIGER

PHILADELPHIA

1955

Library of Congress Card Catalog Number: 55-6379

Printed in the United States of America

To My Wife

LOLA SWIFT FAUST

This Volume is Affectionately Dedicated

Preface

The scope of this volume is the area involving animal agents and vectors and their relationship to human disease. While the information presented is in no sense exhaustive, it provides broad coverage of the subject, including the etiology, epidemiology, pathogenesis, symptomatology, diagnosis and control of this group of infections. The contents should therefore be stimulating and useful to the zoölogist, epidemiologist, pathologist, clinician, laboratory diagnostician and public health worker.

Synoptic tables are provided in the introductory chapters to acquaint the reader with similarities and differences among the diseases produced or transmitted by animals. These data are supplemented by specific information in subsequent chapters where each agent or vector is considered. The most useful diagnostic procedures are presented separately under "Diagnostic Aids." Many illustrations have been introduced to aid in an understanding of the morphologic features of the organisms involved and the clinical aspects of the diseases which they produce. Although it has not been feasible to list all of the source references cited in the text, a number of the more valuable ones will be found at the end of each chapter, for assistance to persons who are interested in making a more thorough study of a particular infection.

Thanks are extended to colleagues who have made helpful suggestions, and particularly to those who have furnished illustrative material. Acknowledgement is also made to authors and publishers for use of numerous engravings. Gratitude is expressed to Lea & Febiger for sympathetic, patient and intelligent coöperation during the publication of this volume.

Ernest Carroll Faust

New Orleans, La.

Contents

Section 1. General Information and Orientation

Important General References to the Literature

ASH, J. E., and SPITZ, S. 1945. *Pathology of Tropical Diseases. An Atlas.* 350 pp. W. B. Saunders Co., Philadelphia.

BELDING, D. L. 1952. *Textbook of Clinical Parasitology.* 1139 pp. Appleton-Century-Crofts, New York.

BOYD, M. F. (Editor). 1949. *Malariology. A Comprehensive Survey of All Aspects of This Group of Diseases from a Global Standpoint.* Vols. I and II. 1643 pp. W. B. Saunders Co., Philadelphia.

BRUMPT, E. 1949. *Précis de Parasitologie.* 6th ed. Vols. I and II. 2138 pp. Masson & Cie., Paris.

CHANDLER, A. C. 1949. *Introduction to Parasitology, with Special Reference to the Parasites of Man.* 8th ed. 756 pp. John Wiley & Sons, New York.

CRAIG, C. F. 1944. *The Etiology, Diagnosis and Treatment of Amebiasis.* 332 pp. Williams & Wilkins Co., Baltimore.

CRAIG, C. F., and FAUST, E. C. 1951. *Clinical Parasitology.* 5th ed. 1032 pp. Lea & Febiger, Philadelphia.

FAUST, E. C. 1949. *Human Helminthology.* 3rd ed. 744 pp. Lea & Febiger, Philadelphia.

HOARE, C. A. 1950. *Medical Protozoology.* 334 pp. Williams & Wilkins Co., Baltimore.

HULL, T. G. 1954. *Diseases Transmitted from Animals to Man.* 4th ed. 720 pp. Charles C Thomas, Springfield (Ill.).

KUDO, R. R. 1954. *Protozoology.* 6th ed. 966 pp. Charles C Thomas, Publisher, Springfield, Ill.

MACKIE, T. T., HUNTER, G. W., III, and WORTH, C. B. 1954. *A Manual of Tropical Medicine.* 2nd ed. 907 pp. W. B. Saunders Co., Philadelphia.

MATHESON, R. 1950. *Medical Entomology.* 2nd ed. 612 pp. Comstock Publ. Co., Ithaca (N. Y.).

MOST, H., Editor. 1951. *Parasitic Infections in Man.* 229 pp. Columbia Univ. Press, New York.

RUSSELL, P. F. 1952. *Malaria. Basic Principles Briefly Stated.* 210 pp. Oxford Univ. Press, London.

Animal Agents and Vectors of Human Disease

SECTION I

General Information and Orientation

Chapter 1

Introduction

PARASITISM constitutes one of the major phenomena of the living world. All around us there is unmistakable evidence of its existence—vegetation attacked by fungi, bacteria, viruses, nematodes, mites and insects, and animal forms from the simplest one-cell organisms to man himself providing shelter and food for an almost uncountable number of plant and animal parasites. Yet parasitism varies widely in degree and in its effects on the host.

The mosquito which takes a blood meal from man is a very casual parasite in contrast to the hookworm which is securely anchored to the intestinal mucosa and sucks blood. The colon ameba, *Endamoeba coli*, like many enteric bacteria, is an apparently harmless guest, while its relative, *Endamoeba histolytica*, has the capacity to invade tissues and to produce severe damage. Another ameba, *Endamoeba moshkovskii*, which is almost indistinguishable morphologically from *E. histolytica*, has been recovered only from sewage and is apparently unable to adapt itself to a parasitic life.

An interesting example of facility in adaptation is the threadworm, *Strongyloides stercoralis*. Ordinarily this delicate roundworm spends most of its existence as a tissue parasite of the human small intestine, with a relatively short developmental period outside the body in moist earth. But under certain favorable environmental conditions it may continue to live and multiply for many generations in the soil, or it may continue exclusively as a tissue parasite without an extrinsic phase.

Certain groups of animals have become irreversibly "fixed" in parasitism. All members of the Sporozoa (malaria parasites, coccidia, etc.) and of the tapeworms and digenetic trematodes are adapted exclusively to parasitism. Their existence is no longer facultative but is strictly obligative.

HOST-PARASITE RELATIONSHIP

A truly successful parasite is one which has developed a state of equilibrium with its host, so that no detectable damage is produced which endangers the health or life of the host. In a suitable host the parasite may obtain food and shelter without any evidence of trauma or toxicity; or the damage produced may be so slight that repair and functional readjustment keep pace with the injury. These types of host-parasite relationship normally produce no manifestations of disease. In contrast, when the parasite gets out of control its insult to the host characteristically evokes symptoms, in other words, a state of disease. Emphasis in this text will be placed on those parasites which produce disease, with particular reference to the human host.

VECTORS OF DISEASE

Many animals may not be parasites themselves and yet may be very important in the transmission of disease. The arthropods (insects, ticks, mites, etc.) constitute the largest single group of vectors of infectious agents. One thinks of mosquitoes in malaria, yellow fever, dengue and filariasis, of body lice in epidemic typhus and relapsing fever, and of ticks in Rocky Mountain spotted fever. In a broader sense, animal and plant tissues in or on which the parasite temporarily resides may be considered as passive transfer agents, for example, pork infected with the larval stage of *Trichinella spiralis* or *Tænia solium*, fresh-water fishes with the second-stage larvas of the fish tapeworm, *Diphyllobothrium latum*, and water cress on which the larval stage of the sheep liver fluke, *Fasciola hepatica*, has become encysted.

There are many disease-producing organisms which are mechanically transferred by flies, cockroaches and other filth feeders to human food and drink or directly to the skin and mucous membranes. This category includes the agents of many infectious enteric diseases, such as typhoid fever, the dysenteries and cholera; likewise the microörganisms of tetanus, anthrax, epidemic conjunctivitis and possibly trachoma and yaws.

FACTORS RESPONSIBLE FOR PARASITIC DISEASES OF MAN

Most parasitic diseases are more common and produce a greater burden on human productiveness and happiness in warm climates than in the cooler temperate zones, but there are notable exceptions. Many of these diseases result from human habits of food and drink, others from bathing customs and still others from overcrowding, but all can be traced to breaches in sanitary practice. Another large group of diseases are due to bites of insects and other arthropods which are biological vectors of pathogens.

EFFECTS OF ANIMAL PARASITES ON HUMAN ECONOMY

Human economy is penalized severely as a result of parasitic diseases. Certain aspects of the damage produced are measured in terms of morbidity and mortality, and the economic loss due to illness in terms of reduced productivity on the farm and in the factory; but there is no comparable method for evaluating human suffering *per se* from infection with malaria, amebiasis, ascariasis, hookworm disease or blood-fluke infection.

THE SOLUTION

Disease in the individual may be lessened and at times eradicated by chemotherapeutic measures, particularly with the development of more effective and more specific drugs. Yet, even if all parasitic diseases were amenable to treatment and there were enough physicians to carry out the treatment, this method of control by itself could not eradicate any infectious disease from a given area or a given population. One must turn to a larger horizon, that of preventive medicine to realize the desired goal. For each disease there must be accurate information on how the disease is propagated. Then for each community practical ways and means must be discovered to break the chain of transmission: by immunization, provided a satisfactory vaccine has been developed; or safe food and drink may be made available; or measures may be employed to eliminate an arthropod vector or reduce its numbers below the level required for transmission. Another important preventative consists in the sanitary disposal of human excreta. Moreover, chemoprophylaxis is at times very valuable in connection with one or more of the above-mentioned procedures. Finally, the ultimate goal is the education of the population in better methods of individual and group hygiene.

SUMMARY

1. Parasitism is an important fact of life.
2. Successful parasitism is one in which little or no damage accrues to the host. This is optimal parasite-host adaptation. Failure to achieve such an equilibrium produces disease in the host, varying greatly in degree.
3. Many animals, particularly the insects and their relatives, while not in themselves important parasites, are essential transmitters of many etiologic agents of disease.
4. Multiple factors are responsible for parasitic diseases of man.
5. There is no adequate measure of the amount of human waste and suffering resulting from parasitic infection.
6. The solution lies primarily in prevention rather than in curative medicine.

HISTORICAL MILEPOSTS IN MEDICAL PARASITOLOGY

Year	*Subject*	*Discoverer*
1379	Discovery of sheep liver fluke, *Fasciola hepatica*	Jehan de Brie
1687	Recognition that the larval tapeworm, cysticercus, is an animal form	Redi
1843	Discovery that a hookworm, *Ancylostoma duodenale*, causes anemia	Dubini
1851	Discovery that a blood fluke, *Schistosoma hæmatobium*, causes Egyptian hematuria	Bilharz
1852–1863	Elucidation of the life cycles of *Echinococcus granulosus*, *Taenia solium* and *Taenia saginata*	von Siebold, Küchenmeister; Leuckart; Naunyn
1855–1859	Demonstration of the life cycle of *Trichinella spiralis*	Leuckart; Virchow
1875	Discovery of *Endamoeba histolytica* and demonstration that it is a causative agent of dysentery	Lösch
1878	Demonstration that a domestic mosquito, *Culex quinquefasciatus*, is an intermediate host of Bancroft's filaria worm	Manson
1880	Discovery of the malaria parasites in human red blood corpuscles	Laveran
1883	Elucidation of the life cycle of *Fasciola hepatica*	Leuckart; Thomas
1893	First demonstration of the arthropod transmission of a protozoan infection	Smith and Kilborne
1897–1905	Elucidation of the life cycle of a human hookworm, *Ancylostoma duodenale*	Looss
1897	Transmission of the parasite of bird malaria by *Culex* mosquitoes	Ross
1898–1899	Transmission of the parasites of human malaria by *Anopheles* mosquitoes	Grassi, Bignami and Bastianelli; Ross
1900	Conclusive experimental proof that *Aëdes* is the transmitter of urban yellow fever, confirming the earlier work of Carlos Finlay	Reed, Carroll, Agramonte and Lazear
1903	Proof that *Trypanosoma gambiense* is transmitted by the tsetse fly, *Glossina palpalis*	Bruce and Nabarro
1905	Proof that the spirochete of relapsing fever in Africa is transmitted by a tick, *Ornithodoros moubata*	Dutton and Todd
1906–1908	Conclusive evidence that bubonic plague is commonly transmitted by the tropical rat flea, *Xenopsylla cheopis*	Indian Plague Commission
1909	Demonstration that epidemic typhus fever is transmitted by the human body louse	Nicolle
1909	Discovery that the blood-sucking bug, *Panstrongylus megistus*, transmits *Trypanosoma cruzi*	Chagas
1913	Final experimental evidence that a snail is the required intermediate host of *Schistosoma japonicum*	Miyairi and Suzuki

1917	Elucidation of the complete life cycle of the fish tapeworm of man, *Diphyllobothrium latum*	Rosen and Janicki
1920–1921	Elucidation of the life cycle of *Ascaris lumbricoides*	Ransom and Foster
1930—	Synthesis of several drugs (quinacrine, 4-aminoquinolines, chlorguanide, daraprim and 8-aminoquinolines) which are more valuable than quinine in the suppression and cure of malaria	Various German, American and British investigators
1931	Development of a successful vaccine for yellow fever	Sawyer and associates
1933	Discovery of enzoötic ("jungle") yellow fever in South America and Africa	Soper and other investigators
1935	Proof of pre-erythrocytic stages of malaria parasites in the fixed tissue cells of birds, mammals and man	Huff and Bloom; Raffaële; James and Tate; Kikuth and Mudrow; Adler and Tchernowitz; Fairley; Shortt and colleagues
1943—	Development of DDT, benzene hexachloride (Gammexane) and other arthropod toxicants as effective chemical agents for control of typhus fever, bubonic plague, malaria and other mosquito-transmitted diseases, leishmaniasis, Chagas' disease, etc.	Many laboratory and field workers

REFERENCES

BAER, J. G. 1951. *Ecology of Animal Parasites.* 224 pp. Univ. of Illinois Press, Urbana.

BISHOPP, F. C., and PHILIP, C. B. 1952. Carriers of Human Diseases, from *Insects,* Year Book of Agr., Washington, D. C. pp. 147–160.

BRAND, TH. VON. 1948. The Physiology of Helminth Parasites in Relation to Disease. Proc. 4th International Congr. Trop. Med. & Malaria, 984–991.

———1951. Physiology of Blood Parasites, in *Parasitic Infections in Man,* Harry Most, Editor. Columbia Univ. Press, New York. pp. 90–113.

BUEDING, E. 1949. Metabolism of Parasitic Helminths. Physiol. Rev., *29,* 195–218.

FAUST, E. C., SCOTT, L. C., and SWARTZWELDER, J. C. 1934. Influence of Certain Food Stuffs on Lesions of *Endamœba Histolytica* Infection. Proc. Soc. Exp. Biol. & Med., *32,* 540–542.

McCOY, O. R. 1937. The Physiology of the Helminth Parasites. Physiol. Rev., *15,* 221–240.

SMYTH, J. D. 1947. The Physiology of Tapeworms. Biol. Rev., *22,* 214–238.

STEINHAUS, E. A. 1947. *Insect Microbiology.* 763 pp. Comstock Publ. Co., Ithaca (N. Y.).

WENRICH, D. H. 1935. Host Parasite Relations. Proc. Am. Phil. Soc., *75,* 605–650.

Chapter 2

The Natural History and Epidemiology of Animal Parasites

NATURAL HISTORY is a comprehensive term. It includes both the life history of organisms and the environment in which they live. It involves the metabolic processes which sustain life and the methods of reproduction by which each species maintains its kind. It takes account of competition among different organisms and adaptations to changes in climatic and edaphic conditions.

The natural history of animal parasites is particularly interesting and intriguing. These parasites were originally free-living organisms. While some groups of parasites have free-living present-day relatives, others have become so intimately parasitic that they have become profoundly modified in structure and metabolic characteristics.

The disease-producing animal parasites of man are too frequently considered either as organisms separate from their environment, *viz.*, from a zoölogical viewpoint, or from a strictly clinical viewpoint, *viz.*, the symptoms they evoke, methods for diagnosis of the disease, and its treatment. The more dynamic concept of agents of disease requires an understanding of how these parasites propagate, how infection is produced, how the parasite affects the tissues of its host, how this tissue damage produces symptoms, why certain chemotherapeutics are selectively harmful to the pathogen, and how measures may be developed to control the parasite. Students of the basic principles of parasitism, clinicians and sanitarians must all understand the essential facts concerning the etiologic agents and the environment in which they and their hosts exist.

Summary information on the natural history of the more important protozoan and helminthic parasites of man is provided in Table 1 (pp. 16-19).

EPIDEMIOLOGY

Epidemiology is the science which is concerned with the propagation of human disease. It includes the disease-producing agents for which man is the principal or sole susceptible host and those in which animals serve as reservoirs of the parasites.

Disease with continued prevalence in a human community is *endemic;* if the prevalence is high it is *hyperendemic;* if it appears only occasionally it is *sporadic*, and if it develops as a sharp outbreak it is *epidemic*. Comparable terms for disease in an animal community are *enzoötic*, *hyperenzoötic*, *sporadic* and *epizoötic* respectively.

The importance of a particular disease in a geographic area is evaluated by different types of information. Impressions are unreliable. Morbidity and mortality records compiled by bureaus of vital statistics provide only a general idea of the number of individuals suffering and dying from the disease, and these may not be representative. The prevalence of a particular disease may have been discovered during a survey undertaken in special groups of the population, such as children of school age, adult males in military service, groups in eleemosynary institutions, or patients in special wards of a hospital. Whatever the source of the data, it is necessary to determine both the accuracy of the diagnosis and how representative the sampling is of the population as a whole. The figures obtained from such sources are not usable until they are properly related to the total number of inhabitants of the geographic area from which the statistics were obtained, or at least the total number of individuals in the surveyed group.

EPIDEMIOLOGIC SURVEYS

In undertaking a survey to determine the prevalence and importance of a particular disease it is desirable to obtain beforehand as much available information as possible concerning the existence of the disease in the area to be studied, whether it is an autochthonous infection of long-standing or one introduced in recent years; whether it is endemic or is epidemic, and whether it occurs predominantly in any particular segment of the population.

A comprehensive survey should be planned so that the data can be properly evaluated, *e. g.*, statistically analyzed. The time has long since passed when trial and error methods are sanctioned.

In the field of parasitology, in which animals are either the etiologic agents or are vectors of pathogenic microörganisms, a number of surveys serve as useful patterns for conducting epidemiologic investigations. Hookworm infection, ascariasis, amebiasis, malaria, yellow fever and murine typhus fever are good examples.

In the case of hookworm infection and ascariasis, the disposal of human excreta and physiographic and climatic conditions favoring the extrinsic development of the parasite were found to constitute basic information; in amebiasis water supplies, food and food handlers, filth flies and particularly direct person-to-person methods of exposure provided valuable clues; in malaria and yellow fever the prevalence of breeding places of the respective mosquito transmitters were found to be as important epidemiologically as the development of the pathogen in the human host.

Murine typhus was first differentiated as a disease epidemiologically distinct from other rickettsioses partly because it occurred in certain occupational groups of the population. It was found to be present in rats which infested the wharves and nearby buildings of seaport towns, from whence it was carried inland by these rats, and transmitted from rat to rat and from rat to man by rat fleas.

Surveys to determine the prevalence of a disease must also determine its geographic extent. Individually or in combination, physiographic and climatic factors commonly play significant rôles in the distribution of disease. Likewise agricultural and domestic pursuits, irrigation, food habits, methods of disposal of human excreta and religious practices—all these require careful study and analysis as potential epidemiologic determinants.

Table 1. Natural History of the More Important

Parasite	*Geographic Distribution*	*Usual Infective Stage*	*Portal of Entry*
PROTOZOA			
Endamoeba histolytica	cosmopolitan; most common in warm climates	cyst	mouth[1]
Endamoeba coli	cosmopolitan; most common in warm climates	cyst	mouth[1]
Balantidium coli	cosmopolitan; most common in warm climates	cyst	mouth[1]
Giardia lamblia	cosmopolitan; most common in warm climates	cyst	mouth[1]
Trichomonas vaginalis	relatively common, in males and females	trophozoite (only stage known)	vulva[1] or urethra
Leishmania tropica	W. India, Middle East, Near East, N. Africa	leptomonas	skin[2]
Leishmania brasiliensis	W. Hemisphere from Sou. Mexico to N. Argentina	leptomonas	skin[2]
Leishmania donovani	China, India, Africa, Mediterranean area, S. America	leptomonas	skin[2]
Trypanosoma gambiense	West and Central Africa	metacyclic trypanosome	skin[2]
Trypanosoma rhodesiense	Central and East Africa	metacyclic trypanosome	skin[2]
Trypanosoma cruzi	Western Hemisphere	metacyclic trypanosome	skin[3]
Plasmodium vivax	warm climates (at least during summer)	sporozoite	skin[2]
Plasmodium falciparum	warm climates	sporozoite	skin[2]
Plasmodium malariae	warm climates	sporozoite	skin[2]
Toxoplasma gondii	cosmopolitan	trophozoite?	mouth?
NEMATODES			
Enterobius vermicularis	cosmopolitan; common in children	fully embryonated egg	mouth[1]
Trichocephalus trichiurus (*Trichuris trichiura*)	warm, moist climates	fully embryonated egg	mouth[1]
Ascaris lumbricoides	cosmopolitan; more common in warm climates	fully embryonated egg	mouth[1]
Necator americanus	common in warm climates	filariform larva	skin[1]
Ancylostoma duodenale	Palearctic Region, W. South America	filariform larva	skin[1]

[1] By direct or indirect contact with body excreta containing the parasite.

[2] From proboscis of insect vector at time of skin puncture to obtain blood or tissue juice from host.

Protozoan and Helminthic Parasites of Man

Location in Man		*Usual Reservoir Hosts of Definitive Stage*	*Other Obligate Hosts and Vectors*
Primary Site	*Secondary Sites*		
wall, large int.	other viscera, skin	monkeys, dogs, rats	none
lumen, large int.	none	monkeys	none
wall, large int.	none	pigs, monkeys	none
in duodenal crypts	gall bladder	none	none
in vaginal folds	bladder, prostate	none	none
skin	mucous membranes (rare)	dogs, rodents	sand-fly (*Phlebotomus*)
skin	mucous membranes (common)	dogs, possibly other mammals	sand-fly (*Phlebotomus*)
skin (temporary)	reticulo-endothelium (fundamental)	dogs, rodents	sand-fly (*Phlebotomus*)
skin (temporary)	blood, lymph nodes, c.n.s.	cattle?	tsetse-fly (*Glossina*)
skin (temporary)	blood, lymph nodes	wild game mammals	tsetse-fly (*Glossina*)
skin	intracellular in viscera	many mammals	triatomid bugs
exo-erythrocytic foci	r.b.c.	none	*Anopheles* mosquitoes
exo-erythrocytic foci	r.b.c.	none	*Anopheles* mosquitoes
exo-erythrocyric foci	r.b.c.	none	*Anopheles* mosquitoes
reticulo-endothelium	brain, retina	many mammals and birds	none known
attached, cecum and appendix	female genital tract	none	none
attached, cecum and appendix	colon, rectum	pigs?	none
lumen sm. int.	various viscera	pigs?	none
attached, sm. int.	none	none	none
attached, sm. int.	none	none	none

[3] From feces of insect vector while feeding on blood or tissue juice of host.
[4] From infected food or contaminated water taken into the mouth.
[5] In contact with infested water.

Table 1. Natural History of the More Important

Parasite	*Geographic Distribution*	*Usual Infective Stage*	*Portal of Entry*
Ancylostoma braziliense	limited distribution in warm climates	filariform larva	skin[1]
Strongyloides stercoralis	common in warm, moist climates	filariform larva	skin[1]
Trichinella spiralis	cosmopolitan; common in United States	larva encysted in pork	mouth[4]
Wuchereria bancrofti	throughout warm climates	filariform larva	skin[2]
Onchocerca volvulus	tropical Africa, Mexico, Guatemala, eastern Venezuela	filariform larva	skin[2]
Loa loa	tropical Africa	filariform larva	skin[2]
Dracunculus medinensis	warm climates, Eastern Hemisphere	2nd-stage larva in cyclops	mouth[4]
TAPEWORMS			
Taenia saginata	cosmopolitan in beef-eaters	cysticercus larva in beef	mouth[4]
Taenia solium	cosmopolitan in pork-eaters	(1) cysticercus larva in pork; (2) egg	mouth[1,4]
Echinococcus granulosus	cosmopolitan; common in sou. South America	egg in dog's excreta	mouth[1]
Hymenolepis nana	cosmopolitan in children in warm climates	egg	mouth[1]
Hymenolepis diminuta	cosmopolitan in warm cli mates (primarily)	larva in hemocele of rat flea	mouth[1]
Dipylidium caninum	cosmopolitan in warm climates (primarily)	larva in hemocele of dog flea	mouth[1]
Diphyllobothrium latum	north temperate zones; Chilean and Argentinean lakes	sparganum larva in fish flesh	mouth[4]
TREMATODES			
Fasciola hepatica	cosmopolitan in sheep-raising countries	larva encysted on water cress	mouth[4]
Fasciolopsis buski	Oriental countries	larva encysted on water plants	mouth[4]
Clonorchis sinensis	Sino-Japanese and Indo-Chinese areas	larva encysted in flesh of fresh-water fish	mouth[4]
Paragonimus westermani	Sino-Japanese areas, SW Pacific islands; northern S. America	larva encysted in soft tissues of crabs and crayfish	mouth[4]
Schistosoma japonicum	China, Japan, Philippines, Formosa, Celebes	cercaria free in fresh water	skin[5]
Schistosoma mansoni	Africa, Arabia, Brazil, Guianas, Venezuela, W. Indies	cercaria free in fresh water	skin[5]
Schistosoma hæmatobium	Africa, Near East, Middle East, southern Portugal	cercaria free in fresh water	skin[5]

Protozoan and Helminthic Parasites of Man (Concluded)

Location in Man		*Usual Reservoir Hosts of Definitive Stage*	*Other Obligate Hosts and Vectors*
Primary Site	*Secondary Sites*		
attached, sm. int. (rare in man)	none	dogs, cats	none
within intestinal mucosa	lungs	dogs, chimpanzees	none
in duodenal mucosa	larvas in migration, encysting in striped muscles	hogs, bears, walruses	none
lymphatics of lower trunk and legs	lymphatics of upper trunk	none	mosquitoes (*Aedes*, *Culex*, etc.,
in subcut. nodules	none known	none	coffee-fly (*Simulium*)
migrating in subcut. tissues	crossing front of eyes	none	mango-fly (*Chrysops*)
gravid ♀ migrates to skin	none known	fur-bearing mammals	Cyclops
attached, sm. int.	none known	none	cattle
attached, sm. int.	(cysticercus larvas in various viscera)	none	hogs
(adults only in sm. int. of canines)	(hydatid cysts in human viscera)	dogs and wild relatives	sheep, cattle, hogs (alternating with dogs)
attached, sm. int.	none known	rats? mice?	none
attached, sm. int.	none	rat, mouse	rodent fleas
attached, sm. int.	none	dog, cat	dog flea, cat flea, human flea
attached, sm. int.	none known	dogs, bears? cats?	(1) *Diaptomus*, *Cyclops;* (2) fresh-water fish
proximal bile ducts	abdominal wall, brain, etc.	herbivores	(1) snails; (2) moist vegetation
attached, duodenum [4]and jejunum	none	pigs	(1) snails; (2) water plants
distal bile ducts	pancreatic ducts (rare)	many fish-eating mammals	(1) snails; (2) fresh-water fishes
lungs near bronchioles	abdominal viscera, brain	felines	(1) snails; (2) crabs and crayfishes
mesenteric venules	liver, lungs, brain, etc.	many mammals	oncomelaniid snails
mesenteric venules	liver, lungs, etc.	monkeys (rarely)	planorbid snails
vesical venous plexus	pelvic organs, rectum, lungs, c.n.s.	none	bulinid snails

A disease may be transplanted vast distances by the migration of the human population. This is well illustrated by the diseases brought to the Western Hemisphere by the European discoverers and explorers, notably smallpox, measles and tuberculosis, all of which on introduction produced high mortality in the totally non-immune native Americans. Later, with the importation of Negro slaves, many of the diseases of Africa were brought to the Americas, *viz.*, malaria, hookworm disease, Bancroft's filariasis, Manson's schistosomiasis and yaws. Yellow fever may likewise have been introduced to tropical America from Africa. In 1899 plague was introduced for the first time into South America and possibly for the first time into the western part of the United States.

The primary goal of an epidemiologic survey is to elucidate the ways in which the disease has become established, how it is propagated, how human exposure occurs, and how significant the infection is in the life and economy of the population. However, such a survey fails in its purpose unless it provides practical measures for control of the disease.

EPIDEMIOLOGIC CLASSIFICATION OF PARASITIC DISEASES

Diseases may be classified according to (1) the systematic relationship of the etiologic agents, (2) the organs and tissues which are damaged and (3) the methods by which the etiologic agents gain access to the host's body. A concise systematic classification of the disease-producing agents of animal origin, together with important vectors of disease, is provided in Chapter 3, p. 25. Pathologic considerations are briefly discussed in Chapter 4, p. 36. In this chapter it is appropriate to classify these diseases from an epidemiologic point of view. The several categories may be outlined as follows.

I. Filth-borne or contaminative infections. Transfer of the pathogenic agent is direct from person to person, *via* fomites, or is air-borne, without intermediate host or extrinsic developmental stage. Examples: The pathogenic ameba (*Endamoeba histolytica*), the pathogenic ciliate (*Balantidium coli*), the duodenal flagellate (*Giardia lamblia*), the vaginal flagellate (*Trichomonas vaginalis*); likewise, the seatworm (*Enterobius vermicularis*), the dwarf tapeworm (*Hymenolepis nana*) and the pork tapeworm (*Tænia solium*, larval stage); and the mange mite (*Sarcoptes scabiei*), the body louse (*Pediculus corporis*), head louse (*Pediculus capitis*) and the pubic louse (*Phthirus pubis*), contracted by direct or indirect contamination.

II. Infection Contracted from Soil or Water. This method applies to several parasitic worms which necessarily or typically have required stage(s) of development in soil or water outside the body of man or other definitive host.

   A. *Entry via mouth* in infective egg stage. Examples: Giant intestinal roundworm (*Ascaris lumbricoides*) and whipworm (*Trichocephalus trichiurus*).

   B. *Entry via the skin* in infective larval stage. Examples from the soil (filariform larvas): Hookworms (*Necator americanus*, species of *Ancylostoma*), and the threadworm (*Strongyloides stercoralis*). Examples from water: Cercarial stage of blood flukes which have escaped from the molluscan intermediate host.

III. Food-borne Infections, in which the infective-stage intermediate host or vector is the natural food of man, consumed raw or inadequately processed. Examples: Trichina worm (*Trichinella spiralis*) and pork tapeworm (*Tænia solium*) in pork; beef tapeworm (*Tænia saginata*) in beef; Chinese liver fluke (*Clonorchis sinensis*), and fish tapeworm (*Diphyllobothrium latum*) in fresh-water fish; Oriental giant intestinal fluke (*Fasciolopsis buski*) and sheep liver fluke (*Fasciola hepatica*) encysted on aquatic plants.

IV. Arthropod-borne Infections, in which the arthropod is either (A) a biological vector, or (B) mechanical vector.

A. *The Arthropod as biological (essential) vector.* (1) The arthropod intermediate host accidently gets into the mouth and is swallowed, or (2) a blood-sucking arthropod introduces the parasite into or onto the skin at the time of feeding.

(1) Accidental ingestion of the arthropod intermediate host. Examples: Rat tapeworm (*Hymenolepis diminuta*) in rat fleas; dog tapeworm (*Dipylidium caninum*) in dog, cat, or human fleas, and the dragon worm (*Dracunculus medinensis*) in the water "flea" (*Cyclops*).

(2) Introduction of pathogen into or onto the skin by a blood-sucking arthropod. Examples: The malaria parasites (*Plasmodium* species) from *Anopheles* mosquitoes, the agents of cutaneous, muco-cutaneous and visceral leishmaniasis from sandflies, of African trypanosomiasis (*Trypanosoma gambiense* and *T. rhodesiense*) from tsetse flies, and American trypanosomiasis (*T. cruzi*) from blood-sucking (triatomid) bugs; various species of filarias from blood-sucking flies; the agents of yellow fever, dengue, encephalitis and encephalomyelitis from mosquitoes, and Colorado tick fever from hard-bodied ticks; the rickettsias causing tick-transmitted spotted-fever and Q fever from ticks, scrub typhus and rickettsial pox from rodent mites, classical epidemic typhus from human body lice and murine typhus from rat fleas; *Pasteurella pestis* from rodent fleas, and *P. tularensis* from many blood-sucking arthropods; the spirochetes causing epidemic relapsing fever from body lice and those causing endemic relapsing fever from soft-bodied ticks.

B. *The Arthropod as mechanical (accidental) vector.* Many microbial pathogens are carried mechanically to human food and drink or to the skin and mucous membranes by filth-feeding flies, cockroaches and possibly other arthropods, causing epidemics or sporadic cases of enteric diseases, ophthalmitis, tuberculosis, anthrax, tularemia, brucellosis and possibly yaws, poliomyelitis and trachoma.

V. Infestation by Arthropods. This parasitic relationship may be specific, semi-specific or accidental.

A. *Specific,* in which the arthropod has a required phase within the skin or underlying somatic tissues of the body. Examples: Mange mite (*Sarcoptes scabiei*), chigoe (*Tunga penetrans*) and several types of specific myiasis produced by fly larvas.

B. *Semi-specific and accidental,* in which larvas of flies, less frequently beetles and mites, produce incidental or occasionally severe damage.

VI. VENENATING ANIMALS. This category includes several phyla of the Animal Kingdom.

A. *Venom (or saliva) introduced through mouth parts* into the skin. Examples: Poisonous spiders, ticks, mites, many groups of blood-sucking insects, gila monsters and poisonous snakes.

B. *Venom introduced through caudal apparatus.* Examples: Scorpions, bees, wasps and ants.

C. *Venom in body hairs, spines or nettling apparatus.* Examples: Jelly fishes, sea urchins, urticating caterpillars, fishes with poison spines.

D. *Venom in body fluid* introduced when the venenating animal is crushed on the skin. Example: Blister beetles.

E. *Venom (or toxin) in viscera,* introduced when eaten. Example: Several species of fishes.

SUMMARY

1. The natural history of animal parasites is concerned with a broad spectrum of parasitic species, including those with close kin among free-living organisms and groups which have been greatly modified by their adaptations to parasitism. The term "natural history" includes the ways by which parasitic organisms live and propagate, how they gain entry to their hosts, cause damage to the host's tissues and produce symptoms.

2. Epidemiology is concerned with the propagation of human disease. Epidemiologic information should be accumulated so that it can be satisfactorily analyzed.

3. Epidemiologic surveys provide the necessary evidence to determine the importance of a disease in a community, a country or on a global basis. These surveys require careful planning and execution.

4. Diseases produced by animal parasites may be classified epidemiologically as follows: (1) Filth-borne or contaminative, (2) infections contracted from soil or water, (3) food-borne (not directly due to filth), (4) arthropod-borne, (5) infestations due to arthropods, and (6) venenation caused by animals.

REFERENCES

CORT, W. W. 1931. Recent Investigations on the Epidemiology of Human Ascariasis. J. Parasitol., *17*, 121–144.

CORT, W. W., *et al.:* 1921–1925. Investigations on the Control of Hookworm Disease. Am. J. Hyg., *1* to *5* (34 separate papers).

FAUST, E. C., and MELENEY, H. E. 1924. *Studies on Schistosomiasis Japonica.* 339 pp. Am. J. Hyg., Monogr. Ser. No. 3.

MCCOY, G. M., *et al.* 1936. *Epidemic Amebic Dysentery.* 187 pp. Nat'l Inst. Health Bull. No. 166, Washington, D. C.

SCOTT, H. H. 1943. The Influence of the Slave Trade in the Spread of Tropical Disease. Trans. R. Soc. Trop. Med. & Hyg., *37*, 169–188.

Shortt, H. E., and Garnham, P. P. C. 1948. The Pre-erythrocytic Development of *Plasmodium Cynomolgi* and *Plasmodium Vivax*. Trans. R. Soc. Trop. Med. & Hyg., *41*, 785–795.

Simmons, J. S., *et al.* 1944. *Global Epidemiology. A Geography of Disease and Sanitation.* Vol. I. 504 pp. India and the Far East; The Pacific Area. J. B. Lippincott Co., Philadelphia.

————. 1951. Vol. II. 652 pp. Africa and the Adjacent Islands. J. B. Lippincott Co., Philadelphia.

Strode, G. K., Editor. 1951. *Yellow Fever.* 710 pp. McGraw-Hill, New York.

Stoll, N. R. 1947. This Wormy World. J. Parasitol., *33*, 1–18.

Chapter 3

Etiologic Classification of Animal Agents and Vectors of Disease

ALTHOUGH the terms "agent" and "vector" convey entirely different ideas, etiologically all animal agents and vectors belong to the same category of living organisms, namely the ANIMAL KINGDOM. Hence they can be allocated to a classification according to their accepted systematic relationship. This classification is constructed according to a logical plan as recognized in the Rules of Zoölogical Nomenclature, beginning with major divisions (Sub-Kingdom, then Phylum) and extending through successive lesser divisions down to genus and species. The term "*species*" is employed to designate a population, the members of which have essentially the same genetic characters and are capable of continued reproduction of their kind, but usually can not interbreed with individuals of other species.

The use of combined genus and species names to designate a species, *viz.*, *Canis familiaris* for the domestic dog, is referred to as *binomial nomenclature*, which in zoölogical literature dates back to the tenth edition of Linnaeus' *Systema Naturae* (1758). Common names differ not only in different languages but at times among different persons speaking the same language; hence the need for a universally understood designation. The Rules of Nomenclature specify that the names used in classification must be of Greek or Latin derivation or, if from a non-classical language, they should have a classical ending. (Example of the former, *Endamœba histolytica*, and of the latter, *Leishmania donovani*.) The genus name is invariably a noun, while the species name may be an adjective, a noun in apposition with the generic name, or a noun in the genitive case. If an adjectival form, the species name must agree with the generic name in number and in gender. Examples of these three categories are: *Trypanosoma gambiense*, *Giardia lamblia* and *Plasmodium malariæ*. It is common practice for the scientific binomial to be printed in *Italics;* the genus name begins with a capital letter while the species name is typically all lower case. The author of a name, with the year of the designation, follows the name of the species in any complete nomenclatural citation. If the author designated the species but not the genus presently recognized, his name is given in parenthesis followed by the author who is credited with the allocation to the genus.

There are also regulations concerning priority of names. This serves to prevent the recognition of multiple scientific names for the same species. Difficulties arise when (1) persons fail to abide by the Rules, (2) the original description is inadequate, and (3) older valid names buried in the literature for many years are re-discovered and technically must replace names which have become well established in the literature.

The system of classification employed in this outline is an adaptation of "Zoölogical Names, a List of Phyla, Classes and Orders," prepared for Section F, American Association for the Advancement of Science, A. S. Pearse, Editor, Durham, North Carolina, 1949. Only those sub-groups will be included which contain etiologic agents, hosts or vectors of human parasites.

Species of importance in clinical and preventive (human) medicine are preceded by an asterisk (*), those of major importance by a solid disc (•). The letter "**A**" indicates a causative *agent*, the letter "**H**" an intermediate, alternate or reservoir *host*, and the letter "**V**" a *vector*. Those without * or • designation are parasites which are not commonly regarded as pathogenic.

SYSTEMATIC CLASSIFICATION OF ANIMAL AGENTS AND VECTORS OF HUMAN DISEASE

Kingdom: ANIMALIA Linnaeus, 1758

PHYLUM: **Protozoa** Goldfuss, 1817. Animals consisting of a single cell which performs all necessary functions of metabolism and reproduction.

CLASS: **Rhizopoda** von Siebold, 1845. Protozoa that move by means of *pseudopodia* (singular, *pseudopodium*), finger-like processes of the cytoplasm which are projected and retracted in response to external stimuli; reproduction wholly asexual.

FAMILY: *Amœbidæ* Bronn, 1859. (The amebas.)

A• *Endamœba histolytica* (Schaudinn, 1903) Hickson, 1909.
Endamœba coli (Grassi, 1879) Hickson, 1909.
Endamœba gingivalis (Gros, 1849) Smith and Barrett, 1914.
Endolimax nana (Wenyon and O'Connor, 1917) Brug, 1918.
Iodamœba bütschlii (von Prowazek, 1912) Dobell, 1919.
Dientamœba fragilis Jepps and Dobell, 1918.

CLASS: **Mastigophora** Diesing, 1865. (The flagellates.) Protozoa that move by means of thread-like filamentous processes of the ectoplasm called *flagella* (singular, *flagellum*); reproduction wholly asexual. The class contains two major physiologic groups of medical importance, (1) those living in the digestive tract and the vagina and (2) parasites of the blood stream and tissues of the body.

(1) Species living in the digestive tract and vagina; transmission from person to person without a vector.

A* *Giardia lamblia* Stiles, 1915.
Trichomonas hominis (Davaine, 1860) Leuckart, 1879.
Trichomonas tenax (O. F. Müller, 1773) Dobell, 1939.
A* *Trichomonas vaginalis* Donné, 1837.
Chilomastix mesnili (Wenyon, 1910) Alexeieff, 1912.
Embadomonas intestinalis Wenyon and O'Connor, 1917.
Enteromonas hominis da Fonseca, 1915.

(2) Parasites of the blood stream and tissues, requiring a blood-sucking insect as transmitter.

A• *Leishmania tropica* (Wright, 1903) Lühe, 1906.
A• *Leishmania brasiliensis* Vianna, 1911.
A• *Leishmania donovani* (Laveran and Mesnil, 1903) Ross, 1903.

A● *Trypanosoma gambiense* Dutton, 1902.

A● *Trypanosoma rhodesiense* Stephens and Fantham, 1910.

A● *Trypanosoma cruzi* Chagas, 1909.

CLASS: **Ciliata** Perty, 1952. Protozoa which move by means of delicate, short filamentous projections of the ectoplasm called *cilia* (singular, *cilium*); reproduction usually asexual. A single species parasitizes the human intestine.

A* *Balantidium coli* (Malmsten, 1857) Stein, 1862.

CLASS: **Sporozoa** Leuckart, 1879. Protozoa typically not provided with special organelles for locomotion; reproduction by alternating asexual multiplication (*schizogony*) and multiplication following sexual union (*sporogony*). The class contains two major groups of medical importance.

ORDER: **Coccidia** Leuckart, 1879. Sporozoa with alternation of asexual and sexual generations but requiring only one host; parasites of the intestinal epithelium and its outpocketings.

A* *Isospora belli*, Wenyon, 1923.

A* *Isospora hominis* (Rivolta, 1878) Dobell, 1919.

ORDER: **Hæmosporidia** Danilewsky, 1886. Sporozoa with alternation of asexual and sexual generations associated with alternation of hosts; adapted to intracellular parasitism in the fixed tissue cells and red blood corpuscles. All species parasitizing man belong to the genus *Plasmodium*, which designates the malaria parasites.

A● *Plasmodium vivax* (Grassi and Feletti, 1890) Labbé, 1899.

A● *Plasmodium falciparum* (Welch, 1897) Schaudinn, 1902.

A● *Plasmodium malariæ* (Laveran, 1881) Grassi and Feletti, 1890.

A* *Plasmodium ovale* Stephens, 1922.

Position Uncertain:

A● *Toxoplasma gondii* Nicolle and Manceaux, 1908.

PHYLUM: **Cœlenterata** Leuckart, 1848. Several species possess nettling substances elaborated in nematocyts.

A The Classes **Hydrozoa** (fresh-water polyps and jelly fishes), **Syphozoa** (large, frequently colonial jelly fishes) and **Anthozoa** (sea anemones and corals) each include a number of species which produce annoying urtication and occasionally dangerous systemic symptoms in persons bathing or swimming in infested water.

PHYLUM: **Platyhelminthes** Gegenbaur, 1859 (Flatworms). Many-celled animals, bilaterally symmetrical, usually flattened dorso-ventrally, with three body layers, lacking a body cavity, with bilaterally symmetrical excretory system ending in "flame cells" (*solenocytes*). The Class TURBELLARIA Ehrenberg, 1831 include almost exclusively free-living organisms which are typically covered with a ciliated epithelium. Certain stages of the two classes of parasitic flatworms, TREMATODA and CESTOIDEA, are structurally and phylogenetically related to the TURBELLARIA.

CLASS: **Trematoda** Rudolphi, 1808. Exclusively parasitic; definitive stage lacking ciliated covering; sucker(s) usually present; digestive canal present except in sporocyst generation of digenetic species; usually hermaphroditic.

SUB-CLASS: **Digenea** Carus, 1863. Almost all species endoparasitic; one or more suckers, of which one is always peri-oral; excretory opening in definitive stage median posterior in position; characterized by alternation of three or more generations and an alternation of two or more hosts, with intermediate stages in a mollusc; larva hatched from egg (*miracidium*) has a ciliated covering.

Family: *Schistosomatidæ* Looss, 1899 (Blood flukes).

Diecious worms, in which the mature female is held in the ventral sex canal of the male; typically present in portal-caval venous circulation of mammals and birds; cercarias fork-tailed, lacking a muscular pharynx; eggs non-operculate.

A● *Schistosoma japonicum* Katsurada, 1904.

A● *Schistosoma mansoni* Sambon, 1907.

A● *Schistosoma hæmatobium* (Bilharz, 1852), Weinland, 1858.

Family: *Clinostomatidæ* Lühe, 1901.

Adults hermaphroditic, flattened; typically in mouth, esophagus or respiratory tube of birds and reptiles; eggs operculate; cercarias fork-tailed, apharyngeal.

A *Clinostomum complanatum* (Rudolphi, 1809) Braun, 1901.

Family: *Fasciolidæ* Railliet, 1895. Large distomate trematodes parasitizing land and sea mammals; metacercarias encysted on vegetation (or in fish flesh) which is consumed raw by definitive hosts.

A* *Fasciola hepatica* Linnaeus, 1738. (Sheep liver fluke.)

A● *Fasciolopsis buski* (Lankester, 1857) Odhner, 1902. (Giant intestinal fluke.)

Family: *Echinostomatidæ* Looss, 1902. Medium to large distomate trematodes typically having a collar of spines around the oral sucker.

A* *Echinostoma ilocanum* (Garrison, 1908) Odhner, 1911, and several other species of *Echinostoma*.

A *Himasthla muehlensi* Vogel, 1933.

A *Paryphostomum sufrartyfex* (Lane, 1915) Bhalerao, 1931.

A *Echinochasmus perfoliatus* (von Rátz, 1908) Dietz, 1910.

Family: *Plagiorchiidæ* Lühe, 1901. Small to medium-sized distomate trematodes; cercaria with stylet in dorsal wall of oral sucker.

A *Plagiorchis javanensis* Sandground, 1940.

Family: *Dicrocœliidæ* (Looss, 1907) Odhner, 1910. Relatively small, usually flattened distomate trematodes, having testes in front of ovary; metacercarias develop in insects, which are sources of infection for definitive host.

A *Dicrocœlium dendriticum* (Rudolphi, 1818) Looss, 1899.

Family: *Opisthorchiidæ* Lühe, 1901. Flattened, delicate, usually lance-shaped distomate trematodes, commonly parasitic in bile ducts; metacercarias encysted in fish flesh.

A* *Opisthorchis felineus* (Rivolta, 1884) Blanchard, 1895.

A* *Opisthorchis viverrini* (Poirier, 1886). Stiles and Hassall, 1896.

A● *Clonorchis sinensis* (Cobbold, 1875) Looss, 1907.

Family: *Heterophyidæ* Odhner, 1914. Very small, oval, pear-shaped or elongated-oval distomate trematodes attached to intestinal mucosa; metacercarias encysted in fish flesh.

A* *Heterophyes heterophyes* (von Siebold, 1852) Stiles and Hassall, 1900, and other species of *Heterophyes*.

A* *Metagonimus yokogawai* Katsurada, 1912.

Family: *Troglotrematidæ* Odhner, 1914. Small to medium-sized fleshy distomate trematodes in intestine or other viscera; metacercarias encysted in fish flesh or crustaceans (crabs and crayfish).

A *Troglotrema salmincola* (Chapin, 1926) Witenberg, 1932.

A● *Paragonimus westermani* (Kerbert, 1878) Braun, 1899.

CLASS: **Cestoidea** (Rudolphi, 1808) Fuhrmann, 1931. Exclusively parasitic, adults hermaphroditic; ciliated epithelium when present confined to embryo hatched from egg; attachment organ (*scolex*) provided with suckers and frequently with hooklets; adult worm (*strobila*) in most species a chain of sexually complete units (*proglottids*).

SUB-CLASS: **Cestoda** (van Beneden, 1849) Monticelli, 1892, *emended* by Fuhrmann, 1931. Adult typically with scolex and a graded series of proglottids. Mature embryo developing within egg shell typically provided with (6, 3 pairs of) hooklets, hence an *oncosphere*.

ORDER: **Cyclophyllidea** Braun, 1900. Scolex with 4 sucking cups; eggs with mature embryo when laid.

Family: *Tæniidæ* Ludwig, 1886. Uterus blind, with median longitudinal pouch and lateral branches; eggs with a thick outer shell composed of a large number of truncated pyramids.

A* *Tænia saginata* Goeze, 1782. (Beef tapeworm.)

A● *Tænia solium* Linnaeus, 1758. (Pork tapeworm.)

A● *Echinococcus granulosus* (Batsch, 1786) Rudolphi, 1805. (Hydatid worm.)

Family: *Hymenolepididæ* Fuhrmann, 1907. Uterus sac-like; eggs with membranous outer shell.

A* *Hymenolepis nana* (von Siebold, 1852) Blanchard, 1891. (Dwarf tapeworm.)

A *Hymenolepis diminuta* (Rudolphi, 1819) Blanchard, 1891. (Rat tapeworm.)

Family: *Dilepididæ* Fuhrmann, 1907, *emended* by Lincicome, 1939. Uterus broken up into egg capsules; several eggs in each mother membrane.

A *Dipylidium caninum* (Linnaeus, 1758) Railliet, 1892. (Dog tapeworm.)

ORDER: **Pseudophyllidea** Carus, 1863. Scolex with 2 opposite sucking organs; eggs operculate, immature when laid.

Family: *Diphyllobothriidæ* Lühe, 1910. Scolex with one ventral and one dorsal longitudinal sucking groove; eggs mature in water and release a ciliated embryo which on ingestion by a copepod develops into first-stage (*procercoid*) larva.

A* *Diphyllobothrium latum* (Linnaeus, 1758) Lühe, 1910. (Fish tapeworm of man.)

A *Diphyllobothrium mansoni* (Cobbold, 1882) Joyeux, 1928. (Manson's tapeworm.)

PHYLUM: **Acanthocephala** (Rudolphi, 1809) Pearse, 1936.

Exclusively parasitic worms consisting of body proper and an anterior proboscis which is usually armed with spines and can be retracted into a sheath. Sexes separate. Embryo hatching from egg only after ingestion by an arthropod intermediate host.

A *Macracanthorhynchus hirudinaceus* (Pallas, 1781) Travassos, 1917. (Thorny-headed worm.)

A *Moniliformis moniliformis* (Bremser, 1811) Travassos, 1915. (Moniliform worm.)

PHYLUM: **Nematoda** (Rudolphi, 1808) Diesing, 1861, *emended* by Pearse, 1936. (True roundworms.) Unsegmented, bilaterally symmetrical, elongated cylindroidal worms, with definite longitudinal axis, complete digestive tract, body cavity not lined with mesothelium; sexes usually separate.

CLASS: **Aphasmidia** Chitwood and Chitwood, 1933. Nematodes *lacking phasmids* (caudal chemo-receptors.)

Family: *Trichinellidæ* Ward, 1907. Body thread-like, with delicate esophagus; females *viviparous;* adults in intestinal mucosa and larvas encapsulated in muscles of same host.

A● *Trichinella spiralis* (Owen, 1835) Railliet, 1895. (Trichina worm.)

Family: *Trichocephalidæ* Baird, 1853. Anterior portion of body capillary, posterior part relatively fleshy, in male coiled into a flattened spiral.

A* *Trichocephalus trichiurus* (Linnaeus, 1771) Blanchard, 1895; also designated as *Trichuris trichiura* (Linnaeus, 1771) Stiles, 1901. (Whipworm.)

CLASS: **Phasmidia** Chitwood and Chitwood, 1933. Nematodes *with phasmids* (caudal chemo-receptors).

ORDER: **Rhabditida** Chitwood, 1933. Mouth surrounded by 3 or 6 lips; esophagus muscular, with posterior bulb.

Family: *Strongyloididæ* Chitwood and McIntosh, 1934. Parasitic females *filariform;* free-living adults *rhabditoid.*

A* *Strongyloides stercoralis* (Bavay, 1877) Stiles and Hassall, 1902. (Thread worm.)

Family: *Strongylidæ* Baird, 1853. Oral capsule lacking teeth and cutting plates but with a ring of chitinous armature.

A *Ternidens deminutus* (Railliet and Henry, 1905) Railliet and Henry, 1909.

A *Œsophagostomum apiostomum* (Willach, 1891) Railliet and Henry, 1905. (Nodular worm.)

Family: *Syngamidæ* Leiper, 1912. Male permanently joined to female by fusion of genital openings.

A *Syngamus laryngeus* Railliet, 1899. (Throat worm.)

Family: *Ancylostomatidæ* (Looss, 1905) Lane, 1917, *emended* by Nicoll, 1927. Oral capsule well developed and armed with teeth or cutting plates; copulatory bursa of male well developed.

A● *Ancylostoma duodenale* (Dubini, 1843) Creplin, 1845. (Old World hookworm.)

A* *Ancylostoma braziliense* de Faria, 1910.

A● *Necator americanus* (Stiles, 1902) Stiles, 1903. (Tropical hookworm.)

Family: *Trichostrongylidæ* Leiper, 1912. Thread-like worms; males with conspicuous, large copulatory bursa.

A* *Trichostrongylus orientalis* Jimbo, 1914.

Family: *Metastrongylidæ* Leiper, 1907. Oral end reduced in size; posterior end of male with deformed copulatory bursa and very long copulatory spicules.

A *Metastrongylus elongatus* (Dujardin, 1845) Railliet and Henry, 1911.

Family: *Oxyuridæ* Cobbold, 1864. Small nematodes having a blister-like cuticular collar around the anterior end; females with long, pointed tail.

A● *Enterobius vermicularis* (Linnaeus, 1758) Leach, 1853 (Pinworm or seatworm.)

Family: *Ascarididæ* Baird, 1853. Fairly large to large, stout nematodes, with 3 conspicuous oral lips.

A● *Ascaris lumbricoides* Linnaeus, 1758. (Giant intestinal roundworm.)

ORDER: **Spirurida** Chitwood, 1933. Oral opening surrounded by 2 lateral pseudo-lips (or 6 rudimentary lips or lip-less).

Family: *Spiruridæ* Oerley, 1885. Mouth with 2 (or 4) tri-lobed lips and a distinct pre-esophageal vestibule; caudal wings (*alæ*) of male conspicuous; *oviparous.*

A *Gongylonema pulchrum* Molin, 1857. (Gullet worm.)

Family: *Gnathostomatidæ* Blanchard, 1895. Stout worms; mouth with 2 large tri-lobed lips; head separated from remainder of body by a distinct constriction; *oviparous.*

A *Gnathostoma spinigerum* Owen, 1836.

Family: *Physalopteridæ* Leiper, 1908. Mouth with 2 large, simple, triangular pseudo-lips surrounded by cuticular collar; *oviparous.*

A *Physaloptera caucasica* von Linstow, 1902.

Family: *Thelaziidæ* Railliet, 1916. Mouth without definite lips; *ovoviviparous.*

A *Thelazia callipæda* Railliet and Henry, 1910. (Oriental "eye worm.")

Family: *Acanthocheilonematidæ* Faust, 1939. Worms filariform; females giving birth to delicate thread-like embryos (*microfilarias*).

A● *Wuchereria bancrofti* (Cobbold, 1877) Seurat, 1921. (Bancroft's filaria.)

A* *Wuchereria malayi* (Brug, 1927) Rao and Maplestone, 1940. (Malayan filaria.)

A● *Onchocerca volvulus* (Leuckart, 1893) Railliet and Henry, 1910. (Convoluted filaria.)

A* *Acanthocheilonema perstans* (Manson, 1891) Railliet, Henry and Langeron, 1912. (Persistent filaria.)

A* *Acanthocheilonema streptocerca* (Macfie and Corson, 1922) Faust, 1949. (Crooked-tail filaria.)

A* *Mansonella ozzardi* (Manson, 1897) Faust, 1929. (Ozzard's filaria.)

A* *Dirofilaria immitis* (Leidy, 1856) Railliet and Henry, 1911. ("Cruel" filaria, dog heartworm.)

A* *Loa loa* (Cobbold, 1864) Castellani and Chalmers, 1913. (Loa worm or "eye worm.")

Family: *Dracunculidæ* Leiper, 1912. Females very much longer than males; *viviparous*, discharging larvas through rupture in body wall just behind the mouth.

A● *Dracunculus medinensis* (Linnaeus, 1758) Gallandant, 1773. (Dragon worm, Medina worm or Guinea worm.)

PHYLUM: **Nematomorpha** (Vejdovsky, 1886) *emended* by Potts, 1908, Ritchie, 1915 and Pearse, 1936. Unsegmented, bilaterally symmetrical, elongated, cylindroidal worms, with definite longitudinal axis; digestive tract atrophied in adults; body cavity lined with mesothelium; proboscis present in first larval stage.

CLASS: **Gordiacea** von Siebold, 1848. Gonads not continuous with their ducts; larval stage in insects; adults free in water. "Hair snakes," many species of which are *spurious parasites* of man.

PHYLUM: **Echinodermata** Laske, 1778. Unsegmented marine invertebrates with 5-radiate symmetry; probably descended from worms with bilateral symmetry.

CLASS: **Echinoidea** Bronn, 1860. Subspherical, completely covered with a calcareous shell; with complete digestive tract having mouth and anus opening at opposite poles; provided with articulated spines, serving as protection and for locomotion.

A The hollow sharp spines of a few species of sea urchins reportedly have poisonous content.

PHYLUM: **Annelida** Lamarck, 1809. Elongated invertebrate animals with bilateral symmetry and true segmentation (*metamerism*); body covering chitinous, not impregnated with lime; no true appendages.

CLASS: **Hirudinea** Lamarck, 1818. (Leeches.) Typically lacking segmental bristles; provided with a peri-oral and a posterior sucker.

A Many species infest man and animals.

PHYLUM: **Arthropoda** von Siebold and Stannius, 1845. Elongated invertebrates with bilateral symmetry, true segmentation (*metamerism*), jointed true appendages and a chitinous exoskeleton, which in many species is impregnated with lime.

SUPERCLASS: **Crustacea** Pennant, 1777. Species having typically 2 pairs of pre-oral antenna-like appendages and at least 3 pairs of post-oral jaw-like appendages; mostly aquatic, breathing entirely through gills.

CLASS: **Eucrustacea** Kingsley, 1894. Usually lacking abdominal appendages.

ORDER: **Eucopepoda** Claus, 1875. (Water "fleas.") Lacking compound eyes; females with egg sacs.

H* Species of *Diaptomus* and *Cyclops* are intermediate hosts of important human worm parasites.

ORDER: **Decapoda** Latreille, 1802. Large species. Thorax covered with a carapace; first pair of legs usually large, provided with conspicuous claws.

H* Several species of crabs and a few species of crayfishes are the second intermediate hosts of the lung fluke, *Paragonimus*.

CLASS: **Chilopoda** Latreille, 1802. (Centipedes.) Usually with one pair of legs for each segment behind the head; first pair of head appendages modified as poison claws.

A Several species puncture human skin and produce mild venenation.

CLASS: **Arachnida** Lamarck, 1815. Body divided into head-thorax (*cephalothorax*) and abdomen; with cheliceræ and lacking antennæ; adults with four pairs of thoracic legs.

ORDER: **Scorpiones** Latreille, 1810. (True scorpions). Body elongate; cephalothorax unsegmented; anterior 7 segments of abdomen broad, posterior segments narrowed, ending in a curved hollow stinger.

A● Many species are harmful, at times injecting venoms deadly to man.

ORDER: **Araneæ** Lamarck, 1818. (Spiders.) Cephalothorax distinctly constricted from unsegmented abdomen; first pair of preoral appendages (*cheliceræ*) modified as poison fangs.

A● Black-widow spider and several other species inject potent venom into human skin; at least one species produces an ulcerative dermatitis.

ORDER: **Acari** Leach, 1817. (Ticks and mites.) Head, thorax and abdomen united, without superficial evidence of segmentation; mouth provided with a median sub-oral piercing organ, the *hypostome;* adults with 4 pairs of legs, larvas with 3 pairs.

AV● Many recognized superfamilies of medical importance: some introduce poisonous substances into the skin; others infest the skin; still others are important biological vectors of microbial pathogens.

CLASS: **Pentastomida** Heymons, 1926. (Tongue worms.) Body elongate, tongue-like or cylindrical with annulations, but without separation into head, thorax and abdomen; head with 2 pairs of retractile claws.

A A few species, such as *Linguatula serrata* and *Armillifer moniliformis*, are internal parasites of man.

CLASS: **Insecta** Linnæus, 1758. (Insects.) Forms with distinct head, thorax and abdomen, and three pairs of thoracic legs. Many species of medical importance are grouped in the following orders.

ORDER: **Anoplura** Leach, 1815. (Sucking lice.) Wingless, body compressed dorso-ventrally, with mouth parts adapted for piercing and sucking.

AHV● *Pediculus corporis* (body louse), *P. capitis* (head louse) and *Phthirus pubis* (pubic or "crab" louse) produce annoying infestation. The body louse likewise is a very important disease vector.

ORDER: **Orthoptera** Latreille, 1796. (Grasshoppers, crickets, cockroaches, etc.) With 2 pairs of wings, the outer one of which is parchment-like; with mouth parts adapted for chewing.

HV A number of species are intermediate hosts of incidental human helminths. Cockroaches are mechanical vectors of several pathogenic organisms.

ORDER: **Heteroptera** Latreille, 1825. (True bugs.) Typically with 2 pairs of wings, but wingless in some families; body somewhat compressed dorso-ventrally; with mouth parts adapted for piercing and sucking.

HV* Bedbugs are serious but relatively innocuous pests; reduvioid ("assassin") bugs are vectors of Chagas' disease.

ORDER: **Diptera** Linnaeus, 1758. (Flies.) With one pair of wings, attached to second thoracic segment; with mouth parts adapted for sucking; saliva is allergenic for some persons.

AHV● Very important as vectors of a large number of human diseases.

ORDER: **Siphonaptera** Latreille, 1825. (Fleas.) Wingless, with body compressed laterally; with mouth parts adapted for piercing and sucking.

AHV● Several species are important transmitters of diseases to man; one species causes infestation of the skin.

ORDER: **Coleoptera** Linnaeus, 1758. (Beetles.) With 2 pairs of wings, of which the first pair are leathery; with mouth parts adapted for chewing.

AH Some species cause skin blisters; others are intermediate hosts of worms which occasionally parasitize man.

ORDER: **Hymenoptera** Linnaeus, 1758. (Bees, wasps, ants, etc.) With 2 pairs of membranous wings, mouth parts adapted for chewing and sucking; ovipositor in worker females is modified into a posterior sting apparatus.

A* Several species produce painful venenation, occasionally anaphylactic shock.

ORDER: **Lepidoptera** Linnaeus, 1758. (Moths and butterflies.) With 2 pairs of membranous wings covered with overlapping scales; with mouth parts adapted for sucking.

A The larvas (caterpillar stage) of many moths and one family of butterflies possess poisonous hollow hairs which produce troublesome nettling rash in contact with human skin and mucous membranes.

PHYLUM: **Mollusca** Linnaeus, 1758. Fleshy invertebrates lacking segmentation; with reduced body cavity; usually with an exoskeleton which frequently takes the form of a shell.

CLASS: **Gastropoda** Cuvier, 1798. (Snails.) With asymmetrical organization, a well-developed head having contractile tentacles, and a shell spirally coiled, at least in the larval stage.

ORDER: **Pectinobranchia** Cuvier, 1817. Operculate, with gills; radula with 7 rows of teeth.

H Many species of this order are essential intermediate hosts of important trematode parasites of man, *viz.*, *Paragonimus*, *Heterophyes*, *Echinostoma*, *Schistosoma japonicum*, *Clonorchis*, *Opisthorchis*, etc.

ORDER: **Pulmonata** (Cuvier, 1817) Ehrenberg, 1831.

Air-breathers, with lung and breathing tube, lacking gills and operculum.

H Many species of this order are essential intermediate hosts of important trematode parasites of man, *viz.*, *Fasciola*, *Fasciolopsis*, *Schistosoma mansoni*, *S. hæmatobium*, *Dicrocœlium*, etc.

A Marine snails of the genus *Conus* are provided with a poison gland and stinging apparatus and are known to inflict severe, occasionally fatal wounds.

CLASS: **Lamellibranchia** DeBlainville, 1924. (Bivalves.) Headless, with a covering of two valvate shells, united by a ligament.

H Several species of mussels, clams, limpets, etc. are essential intermediate host of less important trematode parasites of man.

PHYLUM: **Chordata** Haeckel, 1874. Possessing a notochord, an elastic rod derived from the endoderm, situated between the digestive tract and the nerve chord.

SUBPHYLUM: **Craniata** Lankester, 1877. (Vetebrates.) With segmentation evident in embryonic stages but demonstrable in mature stage only in internal organs.

SUPERCLASS: **Pisces** Linnaeus, 1758. (Fishes.) Aquatic forms having gills for respiration, with vertebral column, cranium, well-developed visceral skeleton, a pair each of pectoral and pelvic fins and unpaired fins supported by cartilaginous or bony skeleton.

CLASS: **Chondrichthyes** J. Müller, 1846. (Cartilaginous or elasmobranch fishes.) Head prolonged into a snout supported by a cartilaginous extension of the cranium; mouth ventral, transverse, at some distance from anterior end.

ORDER: **Selachii** Cuvier, 1829. With notochord more or less replaced by vertebral center.

A Several species of sting rays have a whip-like tail provided with a basal spine which inflicts serious wounds. Electric rays produce shock.

CLASS: **Osteichthyes** J. Müller, 1846. (Bony fishes.)

SUPERORDER: **Teleostei** Owen, 1847. (True bony fishes.) Having extensive ossification of skeleton; mouth always terminal.

H* Many species of bony fishes serve as second intermediate hosts of important trematode and tapeworm parasites of man.

A* Several species of bony fishes have poisonous spines and some have flesh which produces systemic intoxication.

SUPERCLASS: **Tetrapoda** Williston.

Possessing a pair of pectoral and a pair of pelvic limbs instead of fins.

CLASS: **Amphibia** Linnaeus, 1758. (Mud puppies, salamanders, frogs, toads, etc.) Paired fins replaced by jointed appendages, with toed feet often webbed between the digits.

H Species of amphibians serve as second intermediate hosts of several trematode and tapeworm parasites of man.

CLASS: **Reptilia** Laurenti, 1768. (Reptiles.) Amniotic vertebrates, *viz.*, with amnion and allantois in embryonic life; lacking branchial (gill) respiration; skin horny, provided with scales.

H Some species serve as second intermediate hosts of trematode and tapeworm parasites of man.

ORDER: **Squamata** Oppel, 1811. With scaly skin, transverse cloacal opening, and paired penial organ in male.

SUBORDER: **Lacertilia** Cuvier, 1834. (Lizards.) Usually distinguished from snakes by the possession of visible limbs; bones of jaw firmly united.

A The gila (pronounced *hela*) monsters produce moderate to severe venenation.

SUBORDER: **Serpentes** Linnaeus, 1758. (Snakes.) Usually distinguished by absence of visible limbs, large number of ribs in the trunk region and remarkable distensibility of the jaws.

A● Many species of "poisonous snakes," *viz.*, those possessing specialized maxillary fangs, are harmful and some are extremely dangerous.

CLASS: **Aves** Linnaeus, 1758. (Birds.) Amniotic vertebrates; body feathered, anterior limbs modified into wings; like reptiles in the possession of amnion and allantois in embryonic life.

H A few birds serve as second intermediate hosts or reservoirs of trematodes and tapeworms which occasionally parasitize man.

CLASS: **Mammalia** Linnaeus, 1758. (Mammals.) Amniotic vertebrates; skin provided with hair.

H● A very large number of mammals serve as intermediate hosts or reservoirs of animal and other parasites which produce human disease.

A Vampire bats feed on the blood of man, horses and cattle.

A The duck-billed platypus has a venenating apparatus.

REFERENCES

CHITWOOD, B. G. 1937. A Revised Classification of the Nematoda, in *Skrjabin Festschrift*, Moscow. pp. 69–79.

CRAIG, C. F., and FAUST, E. C. 1951. *Clinical Parasitology*. 5th ed. 1032 pp. Lea & Febiger, Philadelphia.

DOBELL, C. 1919. A Revision of the Coccidia Parasitic in Man. Parasitol., *11*, 147–197.

HARWOOD, P. D., CHITWOOD, B. G., and MCINTOSH, A. 1941. Report of the Committee on Nomenclature, American Society of Parasitologists. J. Parasitol., *27*, 279–282.

HERTIG, M., TALIAFERRO, W. H., and SCHWARTZ, B. 1937. Report of the Committee on Terminology, American Society of Parasitologists. J. Parasitol., *23*, 325–329.

INTERNATIONAL COMMISSION ON ZOÖLOGICAL NOMENCLATURE. 1926. Rules and Regulations. Proc. Biol. Soc. Washington, *39*, 75–104.

JAMES, M. T. 1947. *The Flies That Cause Myiasis in Man*. 175 pp. U. S. Dept. Agr. Misc. Publ. No. 631, Washington, D. C.

MOORE, J. P. 1918. The Leeches (Hirudinea), in Ward and Whipple's *Fresh-Water Biology*, pp. 648–660. John Wiley & Sons, New York.

PEARSE, A. S., Editor. 1949. Zoölogical Names. A List of Phyla, Classes and Orders. 24 pp. Durham (N. C.).

WENYON, C. M. 1926. *Protozoölogy*. 2 vols. 1563 pp. Baillière, Tindall & Cox, London.

Chapter 4

Pathogenesis and Symptomatology of Diseases Produced by Animal Agents

PATHOGENESIS

PARASITES or other agents which produce injury to their hosts are *pathogens*. The origin and development of this damage to the host's tissues is *pathogenesis*. As indicated in Chapter 1, the injury may be so slight that it can not be detected by subjective or objective evidences or it may be sufficient to evoke definite *symptoms*. The degree of injury to the host is dependent on a variety of factors, important among which are (1) the virulence of the agent, (2) the amount of the agent or its products in the inoculum, (3) the site of inoculation, (4) whether single or repeated exposure has occurred, (5) the type of injury produced, (6) tolerance of the host to the particular species or strain of the etiologic agent, and (7) general threshold of resistance on the part of the host.

Intrinsic Pathogenicity of the Agent.—Different strains of the same species of agent vary in their ability to produce injury to the same host. This is illustrated by *Endamœba histolytica*, some strains of which produce asymptomatic infection, others acute colitis. Likewise, tropical strains of the malaria parasite, *Plasmodium vivax*, are likely to become more firmly established, to produce more severe symptoms and to be more difficult to eradicate than temperate-zone strains of the same species.

Amount of the Inoculum.—In certain diseases the amount of inoculum and the concentration of the etiologic agent are related to the chances or degree of injury to the host. A heavy "dose" of cysts of *Endamœba histolytica* is much more likely to cause extensive tissue invasion and hence acute symptoms than a very few cysts of the same strain.

Site of Inoculation.—A majority of parasites gain entry by the oral or respiratory route, others actively enter the skin, and still others are introduced into or onto the skin by a biological vector. The normal host has to a certain degree developed adaptations to these routes of inoculation. Still another *entre* is trans-placentally from the mother to the unborn. This is rare in malaria but probably fairly common in toxoplasmosis.

Single or Repeated Inoculation.—A single light exposure may be abortive, that is, it may not "take." However, if repeated exposure occurs, even though each "dose" may be light, there is the chance that sooner or later infection will develop. In an amebiasis endemic area the likelihood of eventual infection is very good, no matter how careful the individual is in his personal hygiene. In several helminthic diseases earlier exposure and "take" may provide considerable resistance to subsequent infection. The phenomenon is probably immunologic in character but is usually and possibly never absolute in degree.

When living foreign protoplasm is introduced into the host's body, and especially if it multiplies within the tissues, it tends to stimulate production of antibody. Introduction of salivary secretions of certain arthropods may have a similar effect. Such substances may cause sensitization of host's tissues resulting in allergic and even anaphylactic phenomena.

Type of Injury Produced.—The injury may be traumatic, mechanical, lytic, intoxicative, allergenic, or a pathway may be opened for other pathogenic microörganisms to invade the tissues. Usually the amount of *traumatic damage* produced immediately at the site of active invasion or by the introduction of an infectious agent into the host is relatively slight, as, for example, when *Ascaris* larvas hatch from the egg in the duodenum and penetrate the intestinal wall, or hookworm larvas penetrate exposed skin. But there are notable exceptions. A considerable number of excysted *Trichinella* larvas will produce extensive tissue irritation as they enter duodenal mucosa. Likewise, myiasis-producing fly maggots frequently cause extensive, disfiguring lesions when they burrow into the tissues. Traumatic damage may be much more extensive as growing or multiplying stages of the parasite migrate through, or break out of confines in host's tissues. Examples are found in the escape of malaria parasites from red blood cells, in the rupture of pulmonary capillaries by nematode larvas, in damage caused by larvas and adult females of *Strongyloides stercoralis* in the intestinal mucosa and by young sheep liver flukes migrating through hepatic parenchyma.

Mechanical damage is concerned with blockage of important channels and encroachment on vital tissues. Malaria parasites in capillaries of the brain stop blood flow and produce cerebral anemia and hemorrhage. Bancroft's filaria worms block lymph flow. Cysts of larval tapeworms, notably of the hydatid worm (*Echinococcus granulosus*) and the pork tapeworm (*Tænia solium*), when lodged in the brain, cause severe symptoms due to the space they occupy, the tissues they destroy and the reactions they provoke.

Lytic damage is a third type. A number of animal parasites elaborate digestive enzymes in their cytoplasm (protozoa such as *Endamœba histolytica, Leishmania donovani, Toxoplasma gondii*) or in specialized glands (cercarias of blood flukes, adult hookworms), which enable them to digest host tissue.

Intoxicative and *allergenic injuries* result from the introduction into the body of specific secretions, such as venom, saliva or secretions and metabolic wastes elaborated by pathogenic agents that have gained entry to the body. These products may cause damage at the site of deposition on the skin or mucous membranes, with hemorrhage and with death of nearby cells, or they may be carried throughout the body by the lymphatics and blood vessels.

Bacteria and other secondary pathogens may enter the body as a result of lesions produced by animal agents or vectors of disease. This may be on the skin, *viz.*, "ground itch" following invasion of hookworm larvas into the skin, or in the intestinal tract following the development of ulcers by hookworms or other parasites which damage the epithelial covering of the digestive tract. Even the "bite" of a mosquito, in itself relatively innocuous, may provide opportunity for development of septicemia by a hemolytic streptococcus.

REACTION OF THE HOST TO INVASION

The host does not usually allow invasion to go unchallenged. Locally and systemically there are evidences of reaction. These are of two types, cellular and humoral.

At the site of invasion and where the parasite or its progeny is filtered out in the tissues, there is typically an infiltration of host's cells which have the function of phagocytosing the parasite or at least of surrounding it, and thus protecting the rest of the body from the injurious effects of the invader. Typically in parasitic diseases, unlike in bacterial infections, there is no remarkable response of neutrophilic leukocytes, but rather on the part of the macrophages, epithelioid cells and giant cells, and in the case of metazoan infections the eosinophilic leukocytes.

In the case of *Endamœba histolytica* there is essentially no host-tissue response to invasion of the wall of the large intestine, with resultant lytic destruction of the tissues. Only when the surface of the ulcer becomes more extensive and bacteria develop in the lesion is there an infiltration of neutrophilic leukocytes, called into action by the invading bacteria. However, if the amebas get into extra-intestinal sites *via* the blood stream or lymphatics and colonize in the liver, lungs, brain, or other visceral sites, leukocytic infiltration occurs. This appears to result not from the amebas themselves but from the amount of necrotic tissue caused by their lytic action.

The mechanism of response to *Leishmania donovani* or to the agent of Chagas' disease (*Trypanosoma cruzi*), is particularly interesting. Once these protozoan parasites enter the skin, they are engulfed by wandering histiocytes or fixed macrophages in nearby cutaneous lymph nodes. The parasites are not killed but proceed to multiply in these host cells until they burst; then the parasitic progeny are engulfed by other macrophages. This calls forth an abnormal production of macrophages and is responsible for a corresponding diminution in neutrophils, so that the body's first line of defense is greatly weakened and bacterial infection characteristically supervenes.

When the parasite or its products (eggs, larvas, etc.) are trapped in various tissues, the typical response is the production of a fibrotic capsule or the development of a pseudo-tubercle around each foreign object. If there are numerous infiltrated bodies near one another a granuloma may form around the entire mass.

Although much of this local tissue reaction is helpful in isolating and circumscribing the parasite, the end result may be more harmful than advantageous to the host. In kala-azar (see above) the production of excess macrophages, and the associated absolute decrease in production of neutrophils are definitely harmful to the host. Likewise, the extensive invasion of fibroblasts around infiltrated parasites or their products replaces active tissues and thus reduces the normal functioning of these tissues.

Systemically, the presence of the parasite stimulates certain cellular responses and antibody production. The former activity is found in the increase in the circulating blood of monocytes, lymphocytes, and, in most metazoan diseases, in excess production of eosinophils.

In all of these host reactions to animal parasites it appears that any immunity which is produced exists only as long as the parasite is alive (amebiasis, malaria), or its reproductive products remain in the tissues (blood-fluke infection, trichinosis). This is unlike certain acute viral diseases, such as smallpox, measles and yellow fever, in which immunity once developed remains relatively fast long after the agent itself has been eradicated.

PATHOGENESIS AS A DYNAMIC PROCESS

The inter-relationship of parasite and host is a vital one and the picture is never static.

If the parasite gains a foothold in the host, there is a contest between the two for mastery. At times the parasite develops overwhelmingly and produces so extensive damage that the host succumbs. At other times the host prevails and the parasite is vanquished. Probably more frequently than is realized an equilibrium is established so that both parasite and host survive without endangering the normal activities of either, and the host becomes a carrier without clinical evidence of the infection.

SYMPTOMATOLOGY

It is the purpose of this section of the text to show that the manifestations or other indications of ill health are the natural accompaniment of the pathologic changes which develop in these diseases. *The clinician starts with patients and not with agents of disease.* From the patient's complaint, his history and a careful physical examination, on the basis of training and experience the physician suspects that one or more etiologies are possible and by observation, clinical and laboratory aids he proceeds to narrow the possibilities to the most probable one.

At the time the physician sees the patient the infection may be in the incubation period, there may be prodromal symptoms, or the disease may be in its acute or chronic phase. More often than not in infections with animal parasites the clinical onset is gradual rather than sudden and there may be no acute manifestations, so that the infection has reached a chronic condition at the time of the patient's visit. All of this must be taken into consideration when an attempt is made to relate the symptomatic evidence to probable causes. Moreover, it is entirely possible that the symptoms elicited arise not from a single agent but from two or more, particularly if the condition is a chronic one.

Physicians who are well informed concerning the microbial agents of disease, their pathologic processes and how these are responsible for symptoms, usually feel less secure in the field of animal parasitology because only a smattering of knowledge has been obtained concerning these agents and their effects on the host. The information contained in this and in subsequent chapters dealing with specific animal agents of disease, their pathologic effects and clinical consequences, may help in solving the difficulty.

Summary information on the pathology and conspicuous symptoms of the more important animal agents of disease is incorporated in Table 2, while a list of important symptoms encountered in parasitic diseases, with the etiologic agents which may cause these symptoms, is provided in Table 3. The latter is arranged according to anatomical relationship of the symptoms, so as to be more useful to the clinician.

SUMMARY

1. Parasites or other agents which are injurious to their host are pathogens. The degree of damage produced may be inconsequential or it may evoke definite symptoms. Important factors which determine the degree of injury produced include (1) virulence of the agent, (2) amount of the agent in the inoculum, (3) site of inoculation, (4) number of successive exposures, (5) type of injury and (6) tolerance of the host to the particular species or strain of pathogenic agent.
2. The type of damage produced may be traumatic, mechanical (obstructive), lytic, intoxicative or allergenic. Each of these may operate separately or in combination with one or more of the other types.
3. The host's reaction to invasion by a pathogenic agent consists of cellular and humoral responses. Unlike the stimulus produced by bacteria, that caused by animal agents of disease usually consists of macrophage activity both locally and systemically. Metazoan agents characteristically call forth an increased production of eosinophils. Sensitization phenomena are frequently encountered in metazoan diseases.
4. Pathogenesis is a dynamic process, relating the injury produced in the host's tissues to their functioning.
5. Indications of ill health are the natural accompaniment of pathologic changes. The physician starts with the patient's symptoms and not with the agents of disease. He considers the several possible etiologies and then by special clinical and laboratory aids narrows these down to the most probable ones. He is more conscious of microbial than animal agents because of his training. This text provides useful information on animal-induced diseases.

Table 2. Pathologic Effects and Clinical Manifestations Produced by Animal Agents of Disease

Disease *Etiologic Agent*	*Clinical Name of Disease*	*Essential Pathologic Processes*	*Representative Clinical Manifestations*
PROTOZOA			
Endamœba histolytica	Amebiasis	Ulceration of wall of large intestine; at times formation of abscesses in the liver, lungs, brain, etc.; all resulting from tissue digestion (lytic necrosis)	Dysentery, diarrhea, appendicitis; symptoms suggesting peptic ulcer or gall-bladder disease; vague abdominal discomfort; asyndromic or asymptomatic state; hepatitis, liver abscess, pulmonary, cerebral or other localized symptoms
Balantidium coli	Balantidiasis	Ulceration of wall of large intestine	Dysentery, diarrhea or asyndromic state
Giardia lamblia	Giardiasis	Irritation of duodenal mucosa, with excess production of mucus	Mucous diarrhea, pain in the "pit of the stomach," or asymptomatic
Trichomonas vaginalis	Trichomonas vaginitis	Irritation of vaginal mucosa, with superficial erosion	Annoying profuse, creamy vaginal discharge
Leishmania tropica	Cutaneous leishmaniasis	Granulomas of skin	Local elevated ulcers having depressed centers
Leishmania brasiliensis	Muco-cutaneous leishmaniasis	(1) Primary ulceration and granulomas of the skin; later (2) ulceration of mucus membranes	(1) Primary eroding cutaneous ulcer; later (2) erosive ulceration of mucous membranes and underlying tissues
Leishmania donovani	Visceral leishmaniasis (kala-azar)	Multiplication of parasites in macrophages, causing hyperplasia of reticulo-endothelium and neutropenia	Undulant type of fever; enlarged liver and spleen; edema; monocytosis, neutropenia, anemia
Trypanosoma gambiense	Gambian trypanosomiasis	(1) Blood-stream infection→(2) lymph node invasion → (3) central nervous system invasion	(1) Septic type of fever→ (2) lymphadenitis→(3) symptoms referable to central nervous system
Trypanosoma rhodesiense	Rhodesian trypanosomiasis	(1) Blood-stream infection→(2) lymph node invasion	Fulminating toxic disease, rapidly fatal
Trypanosoma cruzi	Am. trypanosomiasis (Chagas' disease)	Primary lymph node enlargement due to parasite's invasion usually at outer canthus of eye; parasitemia; invasion, parasite multiplication and tissue destruction in myocardium, brain, reticulo-endothelium, endocrine organs, etc.	Edema at outer canthus of eye (Romaña's sign); typhoidal syndrome; myocarditis, brain symptoms, neutropenia, anemia, etc.

Table 2. Pathologic Effects and Clinical Manifestations Produced by Animal Agents of Disease.—(Continued)

Etiologic Agent	*Clinical Name of Disease*	*Essential Pathologic Processes*	*Representative Clinical Manifestations*
Plasmodium vivax	Vivax malaria	Invasion and destruction of red blood cells, with liberation of toxic metabolites; splenomegaly	Episodes of chills and fever, typically every 48 hrs., with remissions and relapses; anemia
Plasmodium falciparum	Falciparum malaria	Idem.; likewise embolic blocking of blood capillaries	Idem.; also symptoms referable to brain, lungs, kidneys, etc., resulting from capillary blocking
Plasmodium malariæ	Quartan malaria	Invasion and destruction of red blood cells, but more slowly and insidiously than in vivax malaria	Episodes of chills and fever, typically every 72 hrs., with remissions and relapses; anemia
Toxoplasma gondii	Toxoplasmosis	Granulomas developing around parasites in brain, retina, and in reticulo-endothelial tissues	Chorioretinitis, hydrocephaly in newborn; possibly exanthematous disease with fever; asyndromic or asymptomatic state
NEMATODES			
Ascaris lumbricoides	Ascariasis	Pneumonitis during larval migration through lungs; blockage and traumatic damage to intestines or elsewhere; or without evident tissue damage	Atypical pneumonia during migration through lungs; disturbed digestion, malnutrition; appendicitis, acute abdomen, or symptoms referable to liver, lungs or other ectopic locations; eosinophilia
Necator americanus, *Ancylostoma duodenale*	Hookworm infection	Ulceration of mucosa at sites of worms' attachment, and mechanical loss of blood from intestine	Anemia, cardiac enlargement and decompensation, malnutrition, stunting of growth, hookworm facies, eosinophilia
Ancylostoma braziliense	"Creeping eruption"	Injury and cellular reaction to filariform larvas crawling in serpentine tunnels through skin	Intense pruritus of invaded skin; septic condition of infected area
Strongyloides stercoralis	Strongyloidiasis	Traumatic damage to parasitized intestinal mucosa	Diarrhea frequently alternating with constipation; pain in the "pit of the stomach;" high eosinophilia; at times depressive mental state
Trichocephalus trichiurus	Whipworm infection	Traumatic damage at each site in cecum, appendix and colon where worm is attached	Variable, from asymptomatic to mucous diarrhea or dysentery or even prolapse of rectum; neurotoxic manifestations; eosinophilia

Enterobius vermicularis	Oxyuriasis (enterobiasis)	Irritation to mucosa of appendix and cecum; scarification of perianal and perineal skin, with bacterial invasion	Occasional appendicitis; intense itching of perianal and perineal skin; reflex nervous symptoms; degree of eosinophilia variable
Trichinella spiralis	Trichinosis	Severe irritation to duodenal mucosa, followed by intense inflammation of the striated muscles and myocardium, and possibly damage to brain capillaries	Syndrome of acute food poisoning, fever, then intense myositis, evidence of myocarditis and at times severe brain symptoms; intense eosinophilia
Wuchereria bancrofti, *Wuchereria malayi*	Bancroft's filariasis, Malayan filariasis	Lymphangitis and lymphadenitis, usually with subsequent fibrosis of involved organs and blockage of lymph flow	Raised, inflamed lymphatic tract, intensely painful, usually accompanied by fever; chronic stage having lymph varix, elephantoid enlargement of extremities or external genitalia; eosinophilia
Onchocerca volvulus	Onchocercosis	Subcutaneous fibrous nodule around parent worms; inflammatory reaction to migrating microfilarias	Visible or palpable nodules under the skin; dermatoglyphia; ocular opacities, eventually producing blindness; eosinophilia
Loa loa	Loaiasis ("eye-worm" infection)	Progressive inflamed tract in subcutaneous tissues immediately behind migrating worm; at times generalized inflamed, edematous skin	Evidence of worm at head of inflamed tract, or crossing in front of eye in corneal conjunctiva; at times urticaria and fever; eosinophilia
Dracunculus medinensis	Dracunculosis	Inflammation of tunneled tract in which gravid female is migrating to skin; skin blister where head of worm reaches epidermis	Hypersensitization reaction during migration of female worm; sepsis of tunnel after blister bursts in contact with water
CESTODES (Tapeworms)			
Tænia saginata	Beef tapeworm infection	Physical burden of mature worm occupying up to 2 liters mass in small intestine; occasional occlusion of appendix or ileum	Malnutrition; diarrhea; occasional acute abdomen or appendicitis; eosinophilia
Tænia solium	(1) Pork tapeworm infection (2) Cysticercosis (larval infection)	(1) Injury to intestinal mucosa at site of attachment (2) Inflammatory reaction to larva developing in brain, eyeball, heart muscles, etc.	(1) Diarrhea (2) Acute cardiac, cerebral or ocular symptoms Eosinophilia may occur in (1) or (2)

Table 2. Pathologic Effects and Clinical Manifestations Produced by Animal Agents of Disease.—(Continued)

Etiologic Agent	*Clinical Name of Disease*	*Essential Pathologic Processes*	*Representative Clinical Manifestations*
Echinococcus granulosus	Hydatid disease	Hydatid cyst may grow to size of football in liver, lungs and other viscera; may become malignant (alveolar) or erode osseous tissue	Symptoms referable to parasitized organ; if unilocular cyst bursts, anaphylaxis results; eosinophilia
Hymenolepis nana	Dwarf tapeworm infection	Large number of attached worms cause severe irritation to mucosa of small intestine	May produce mucous diarrhea; reflex nervous symptoms frequent in children; eosinophilia at times
Diphyllobothrium latum	Fish tapeworm infection	May induce primary anemia or systemic intoxication	Symptoms of primary anemia or moderate to severe systemic intoxication; eosinophilia at times
TREMATODES (Flukes)			
Fasciola hepatica	Sheep liver-fluke infection	Necrosis of liver parenchyma at time of migration of larvas from intestine; inflammation of proximal bile ducts and gall bladder	Acute hepatic disease, followed by cholecystitis or cholelithiasis; eosinophilia at times
Fasciolopsis buski	Fasciolopsiasis	Inflammation and ulceration of duodenal and jejunal mucosa	Symptoms mimicking peptic ulcer; indigestion; generalized edema; high eosinophilia, asthenia
Clonorchis sinensis, Opisthorchis felineus	Clonorchiasis and opisthorchiasis	Hyperplasia of distal bile ducts, with fibrosis and pressure necrosis of hepatic parenchyma	Cholecystitis or cholelithiasis; hepatic cirrhosis, occasionally with ascites; eosinophilia at times
Paragonimus westermani	Paragonimiasis (lung-fluke infection)	Peribronchial fibrous encapsulation of worms, with opening into bronchiole; or encapsulation of worms lodged in brain, abdominal viscera, etc.	Hemoptysis with minute rusty specks (worm's eggs) in discharge; or symptoms referable to worms lodged in ectopic sites
Schistosoma japonicum, S. mansoni	Intestinal schistosomiasis	Acute hepatitis; congested spleen, damage to intestine as eggs filter into lumen; later, pseudo-tubercle formation around eggs infiltrated in tissues of liver, intestines, etc.	Toxic manifestations with late afternoon fever; tender, palpable liver and spleen; diarrhea; high eosinophilia; later, portal cirrhosis with ascites, intestinal fibrosis, asthenia

Schistosoma hæmatobium	Vesical schistosomiasis	Lesions primarily confined to bladder and external genital organs resulting from infiltration and deposition of eggs in bladder lumen	Hematuria, bladder colic, eosinophilia; later, urethral stricture, possibly proctitis; septic complications
HIRUDINEA			
Limnatis nilotica	Internal hirudiniasis	Inflammation and congestion of nasopharynx, larynx, etc., blockage of trachea	Extreme pain from swollen sites where engorged leech is attached; suffocation if leech is inhaled into trachea
Tropical rainforest leeches	External hirudiniasis	Inflamed, indurated area around site of leech's puncture of skin to suck blood, with bloody-serous exudate	Evidence of trauma and swelling around each puncture site, with exudation of bloody serous fluid; little or no accompanying pain; occasionally aquatic leech may enter urethra of male bathing in infested water and produce painful occlusion, with anuria
ARTHROPODS			
Sarcoptes scabiei (scabic or mange mite)	Scabies or sarcoptic mange	Burrowing of female mites in serpiginous skin tunnels	Slightly raised, inflamed tunnels in skin, intensely pruritic, frequently secondarily infected from scratching
Tunga penetrans	Chigœ infestation	Enlarging burrow deep into the skin, containing female flea	Pea-sized tunnel in skin, usually between the toes, containing egg-laying female; painful and pruritic, commonly septic
Several species of filth flies (larval stage, *i.e.*, maggots)	Myiasis	Extensive traumatic damage, especially to skin and underlying tissues, as larvas invade, feed and grow	Disfiguring surface lesions with undermining burrows, commonly septic and containing foul-smelling, necrotic tissue and fluid
Bees, wasps, hornets and ants	Venenation caused by Hymenoptera	Local and at times systemic intoxication from injection of fluids through sting apparatus (modified ovipositor)	Symptoms of local and systemic intoxication, at times hypersensitization, especially "bee allergy"
Moths (larval stage)	Caterpillar urtication	Local urtication on skin and mucous membranes where poison hairs of caterpillars lodge or break off in the skin	Evidence of local inflammation, urtication and intense pruritus at site of injury to skin
Beetles	Beetle vesication (canthariasis)	Vesication at site on skin or mucous membranes where blister fluid is discharged	Development of blisters at site of injury to skin

Table 2. Pathologic Effects and Clinical Manifestations Produced by Animal Agents of Disease.—(Continued)

Etiologic Agent	*Clinical Name of Disease*	*Essential Pathologic Processes*	*Representative Clinical Manifestations*
Ticks, mites, blood-sucking flies, lice and fleas	Arthropod (*name of agent*) venenation	Local trauma (ticks, chigger mites, horse flies) at site of skin puncture; sensitization to specific foreign substances in salivary secretions	Evidence of inflammation at site of injury; tick paralysis; "serum sickness" and other manifestations of sensitization
Black-widow spider (*Latrodectus mactans*) and other spiders	Spider venenation (arachnidism)	Local inflammation, edema and induration; systemic reaction to neurotoxin introduced into skin through fangs	Sharp pain, with swelling at site where fangs penetrate skin; burning and aching of injured member; dizziness, weakness, tremors, abdominal cramps, cardiac, respiratory and c.n.s. symptoms
Scorpions	Scorpion venenation	Local inflammation, induration, edema and coagulative necrosis at site where caudal stinger introduces hemorrhagic and neurotoxic venom into the skin	Intense radiating, burning pain at site of injury; generalized numbness, throbbing, twitching, neuro-motor disturbances, respiratory paralysis; convulsions mimicking strychnine poisoning
OTHER ANIMAL AGENTS			
Coelenterates (hydras, jelly fishes)	Jelly-fish sting	Nettling rash, at times vesication, at multiple sites on skin in contact with the microscopic nematocyst hairs which discharge poison fluid	Intense stinging pain at each point of venenation; systemic reaction if the insult is excessive; frequently shock resulting from fear complex
Echinoderms	Sea-urchin venenation	Inflammation and induration of skin resulting from introduction of poison through hollow calcareous spines on the subglobose shell of certain sea urchins	Evidence of trauma and inflammatory reaction at site of skin puncture by spinose processes of the sea urchin
Fishes	Fish poisoning	(1) Acute food poisoning from consuming flesh of certain species of marine fishes (2) Trauma and local skin reaction to puncture by poison spines of several types of fishes	(1) Acute food poisoning syndrome (2) Local and systemic manifestations from injury of skin and systemic absorption of poison

Snakes and gila monsters	Snake and gila-monster venenation	Inflammation, hemorrhage and induration at site of "strike" by the reptile, with variable degree of systemic reaction depending on intrinsic properties, quantity, and whether the venom is primarily hemorrhagic or neurotoxic in character	Picture of local inflamed, indurated or hemorrhagic lesion at site of "strike"; damage proceeding centrally *via* lymphatics (or occasionally venous blood vessels), with extensive internal hemorrhage in viperine venenation, severe to fatal neurotoxic symptoms in venenation by cobras, adders, poisonous coral snakes and sea snakes; less serious systemic manifestations from gila monster venenation

Table 3. Manifestations of Disease Caused by Animal Agents

* Indicates a common symptom produced by this agent

Symptoms Referable to:	*Etiologic Agent*
I. DIGESTIVE TRACT	
Acute abdomen	*Ascaris lumbricoides*, **Fasciolopsis buski*, *Tænia saginata*
Appendicitis	*Ascaris lumbricoides*, **Endamœba histolytica*, *Enterobius vermicularis*, **Schistosoma japonicum*, **S. mansoni*, *Tænia saginata*, *T. solium*, *Trichocephalus trichiurus*
Diarrhea	**Balantidium coli*, *Diphyllobothrium latum*, **Endamœba histolytica*, **Fasciolopsis buski*, **Giardia lamblia*, *Hymenolepis nana*, **Schistosoma japonicum*, *S. mansoni*, **Strongyloides stercoralis*, *Trichocephalus trichiurus*
Dysentery	**Balantidium coli*, **Endamœba histolytica*, hookworms, *Leishmania donovani*, malaria parasites, **Schistosoma japonicum*, **S. mansoni*, *S. hæmatobium*, *Trichocephalus trichiurus*
Food poisoning syndrome	Fish poisoning; **Trichinella spiralis* (early stage)
Geophagia	*Hookworms
Glossitis	**Trichinella spiralis*
Hemorrhage, hematemesis	Hookworms, malaria parasites
melena	*Hookworms
(See also "Dysentery.")	
Indigestion	**Ascaris lumbricoides*, **Fasciolopsis buski*, *hookworms
Pain in the "pit of the stomach"	**Ascaris lumbricoides*, **Fasciolopsis buski*, *Giardia lamblia*, **Strongyloides stercoralis*, *Tænia saginata*
Peptic ulcer syndrome	**Endamœba histolytica*, *Fasciola hepatica*, **Fasciolopsis buski*

Table 3. Manifestations of Disease Caused by Animal Agents (Continued)

Symptoms Referable to:	Etiologic Agent
Proctitis	**Endamœba histolytica*, **Schistosoma japonicum*, **S. mansoni*, *S. hæmatobium*, *Trichocephalus trichiurus*
Prolapse of rectum	*Schistosoma japonicum*, **S. mansoni*, **Trichocephalus trichiurus* (heavy infection)
Stomatitis	*Gongylonema pulchrum*, *Gordius* spp. (rarely), *Leishmania brasiliensis*, *L. donovani*
II. LIVER	
Ascites	**Schistosoma japonicum*, **S. mansoni*, *Clonorchis sinensis* (rarely)
Gall-bladder disease	*Ascaris lumbricoides*, **Clonorchis sinensis*, **Endamœba histolytica* (referred symptom), **Fasciola hepatica*, *Giardia lamblia*
Hepatic cirrhosis	*Clonorchis sinensis*, **Fasciola hepatica*, *Opisthorchis felineus*, **Schistosoma japonicum*, **S. mansoni*
Hepatitis	*Ascaris lumbricoides*, **Endamœba histolytica*, *Fasciola hepatica*, **Schistosoma japonicum*, **S. mansoni*
Hepatomegaly	*Endamœba histolytica*, *hydatid of *Echinococcus granulosus*, **Leishmania donovani*, **Schistosoma japonicum*, **S. mansoni*, *Trypanosoma cruzi*
III. SPLEEN	
Splenomegaly	**Leishmania donovani*, *malaria parasites, *Schistosoma japonicum*, *S. mansoni*, *Trypanosoma cruzi*
IV. GENITO-URINARY ORGANS	
Blackwater fever	*Plasmodium falciparum*
Cervicitis	*Endamœba histolytica*, *Schistosoma hæmatobium*
Epididymitis	*Schistosoma hæmatobium*, **Wuchereria bancrofti*
Hematuria	*Dioctophyma renale* (rarely), **Schistosoma hæmatobium*
Hemoglobinuria	*Plasmodium falciparum*
Nephritis	Malaria parasites
Nycturia	*Enterobius vermicularis*
Nymphomania	*Enterobius vermicularis*
Salpingitis	*Enterobius vermicularis*
Urethritis	Aquatic leeches, **Schistosoma hæmatobium*
Urinary bladder disease	**Schistosoma hæmatobium*
Vaginitis	*Endamœba histolytica*, *Enterobius vermicularis*, **Schistosoma hæmatobium*, **Trichomonas vaginalis*
V. LUNGS AND PLEURAL CAVITY	
Asthma, bronchial	**Ascaris lumbricoides*; bees
Bronchitis	**Ascaris lumbricoides*, **Leishmania donovani*, *Strongyloides stercoralis*
Cyst, pulmonary	**Cysticercus cellulosæ*, *hydatid of *Echinococcus granulosus*
Emphysema	*Ascaris lumbricoides*, *Paragonimus westermani*
Hemorrhage, hemoptysis	**Paragonimus westermani*

Pleuropulmonary abscess	*Endamœba histolytica*
Pneumonia, atypical bronchial	**Ascaris lumbricoides*, **Leishmania donovani*, **Strongyloides stercoralis*
Suffocation	Leeches, especially **Limnatis nilotica; Syngamus laryngeus*
VI. HEART	
Cardiac disease	Bee sting, *hookworms, **Trichinella spiralis*, **Trypanosoma cruzi*
Myocarditis	**Trichinella spiralis*, **Trypanosoma cruzi*
VII. CENTRAL NERVOUS SYSTEM	
Brain abscess	*Cysticercus cellulosæ*, *Endamœba histolytica*, hydatid of *Echinococcus granulosus*, *Paragonimus westermani*
Calcification, cerebral	**Toxoplasma gondii*
Central nervous system disease	**Cysticercus cellulosæ*, *Endamœba histolytica*, hydatid of *Echinococcus granulosus*, malaria parasites (**Plasmodium falciparum*), *Schistosoma japonicum*, *S. mansoni*, **Toxoplasma gondii*, *Trichinella spiralis*, *Trypanosoma cruzi*, **T. gambiense*
Cyst, cerebral	**Cysticercus granulosus*, *hydatid of *Echinococcus granulosus*
Epilepsy, Jacksonian	**Cysticercus cellulosæ*, *hydatid of *Echinococcus granulosus*, **Paragonimus westermani*, **Schistosoma japonicum*
Hemorrhage, cerebral	Malaria parasites (**Plasmodium falciparum*), *Trichinella spiralis*
Hydrocephaly	*Toxoplasma gondii*
Myelitis, transverse	*Schistosoma mansoni*
Paralysis(monoplegia, diplegia,hemiplegia, quadriplegia)	**Cysticercus cellulosæ*, *hydatid of *Echinococcus granulosus*, **Paragonimus westermani*, **Schistosoma japonicum*
Reflex nervous symptoms	**Enterobius vermicularis*, **Hymenolepis nana*, **Strongyloides stercoralis*, *Tænia saginata*, **Trichocephalus trichiurus*
VIII. EYE	
Chorio-retinitis	Malaria parasites, **Toxoplasma gondii*
Conjunctivitis	*Ascaris lumbricoides*, blister beetles, caterpillars, *Leishmania tropica*, malaria parasites, **Thelazia californiensis*, *T. callipæda*, **Trichinella spiralis*, tropical leeches
Cyst, ocular	*Cysticercus cellulosæ*, hydatid of *Echinococcus granulosus*
Ophthalmitis	*Cysticercus cellulosæ*, hydatid of *Echinococcus granulosus*, larvas (maggots) of filth flies, larvas of hookworms and other nematodes not normally parasitic in man, **Loa loa*, malaria parasites, **Onchocerca volvulus*, **Trichinella spiralis*, **Toxoplasma gondii*, **Trypanosoma cruzi* (primary lesion, the *chagoma*)
Ophthalmomyiasis	Larvas (maggots) of several species of filth flies
Palpebral edema	**Fasciolopsis buski*, **Trichinella spiralis*, **Trypanosoma cruzi*, urticating caterpillars, vesicating beetles

Table 3. Manifestations of Disease Caused by Animal Agents (Continued)

Symptoms Referable to:	*Etiologic Agent*
IX. NASO-PHARYNX	
Nasopharyngeal inflammation, congestion and erosion	Leeches (**Limnatis nilotica*), *Leishmania brasiliensis*, maggots of sheep bot (*Œstrus ovis*).
X. CIRCULATORY SYSTEM	
Microfilaremia	*All species of filaria worms except *Onchocerca volvulus*
Parasitemia	*All species of filaria worms except *Onchocerca volvulus;* *malaria parasites, **Trypanosoma cruzi*, **T. gambiense*, **T. rhodesiense*
XI. BLOOD CELLS	
Anemia	*Diphyllobothrium latum*, *hookworms, **Leishmania donovani*, *malaria parasites, *Schistosoma japonicum*, *S. mansoni*, *Tænia saginata*, *Trichocephalus trichiurus*
macrocytic	*Diphyllobothrium latum*, hookworms (occasionally)
microcytic	*Hookworms, **Leishmania donovani*, *malaria parasites, *Schistosoma japonicum*, *S. mansoni*, *Strongyloides stercoralis*, tapeworms, *Trichocephalus trichiurus*
Eosinophilia	**Ascaris lumbricoides*, **Fasciolopsis buski*, *hookworms, **Schistosoma japonicum*, **S. mansoni*, **S. hæmatobium*, **Strongyloides stercoralis*, *tapeworms, **Trichinella spiralis*, **Wuchereria bancrofti* and other filaria worms
Leukocytosis	Acute stage of many helminthic infections; *Endamœba histolytica* (in extra-intestinal foci)
Monocytosis	Chronic stage of many helminthic diseases, **Leishmania donovani*, malaria parasites (chronic infection), *Trypanosoma cruzi*
Neutropenia	Chronic stage of many helminthic infections; **Leishmania donovani*, malaria parasites (chronic infection), *Trypanosoma cruzi*
XII. LYMPHATIC SYSTEM	
Lymphadenitis	**Leishmania donovani*, **Trypanosoma cruzi*, **T. gambiense*, **T. rhodesiense*, **Wuchereria bancrofti*, **W. malayi*
Lymphangitis	**Wuchereria bancrofti*, **W. malayi*
XIII. SKIN AND SUBCUTANEOUS TISSUES	
Cancrum oris	**Leishmania donovani*
Cutaneous lesions	**Ancylostoma braziliense* and other hookworms, **Demodex folliculorum*, *Endamœba histolytica*, **Gnathostoma spinigerum*, *larvas (maggots) of filth flies, *leeches, **Leishmania brasiliensis*, **L. tropica*, **Sarcoptes scabiei* and other mites, *Schistosoma* spp. (cercarias), *Strongyloides stercoralis*, *Tunga penetrans* (chigoe)
Cutaneous or subcutaneous migration	**Dracunculus medinensis*, *larvas of *Ancylostoma braziliense* and other hookworms, **Loa loa*, **Sarcoptes scabiei*

Dermatitis	*Ants, assassin bugs, *bees, *beetles, *blood-sucking flies, *caterpillars, *chiggers, *chigoe, *demodectic (follicular) mite, *flies, *gnats, *hookworm larvas, *hornets, *lice, *mange (sarcoptic) mites, *mosquitoes, *schistosome cercarias, **Strongyloides stercoralis*, *wasps
granulomatous	**Leishmania tropica*, **L. brasiliensis*
nodular	**Onchocerca volvulus*, **Tunga penetrans*
ulcerative	**Leishmania brasiliensis*
Dermatographia	**Onchocerca volvulus*, *Schistosoma japonicum*
Edema (See also "Palpebral edema.")	**Fasciolopsis buski*, **Leishmania donovani*, **Trichinella spiralis*
Hemorrhage, cutaneous	*Viperine snakes
Larva migrans, cutaneous	*Larvas of *Ancylostoma braziliense* and other species of *Ancylostoma*, *Bunostomum phlebotomum* (rarely), *Necator americanus* (occasionally), **Gnathostoma spinigerum*, larvas (maggots) of several species of filth flies
Mange, follicular	**Demodex folliculorum*
sarcoptic	**Sarcoptes scabiei*
Muco-cutaneous lesions	**Leishmania brasiliensis*
Pruritus, cutaneous	*Ancylostoma braziliense* and other species of hookworms (larval stage), **Sarcoptes scabiei*, **Tunga penetrans*
perianal and perineal	**Enterobius vermicularis*, tapeworms (proglottids)
Urtication and nettling rash	*Caterpillars, flesh of poisonous fishes, *jelly fishes
Vesication	*Blister beetles
XIV. MUSCULAR SYSTEM	
Myositis	**Trichinella spiralis* (migrating stage of larvas)
XV. SKELETAL SYSTEM	
Erosion of bone	Hydatid of *Echinococcus granulosus*
XVI. SENSITIZATION PHENOMENA	
Allergy	**Ascaris lumbricoides*, bees, blood-sucking arthropods (saliva), **Dracunculus medinensis*, *Enterobius vermicularis*, *Fasciolopsis buski*, *filaria worms, hookworms, larvas (maggots) of filth flies, malaria parasites, **Schistosoma japonicum*, *S. mansoni*, **Strongyloides stercoralis*, **Trichinella spiralis*, *Trichocephalus trichiurus*
Hypersensitization	**Ascaris lumbricoides*, bees, blood-sucking flies, **Dracunculus medinensis*, fleas, flies, lice, **Loa loa*, **Onchocerca volvulus*, **Wuchereria bancrofti*
Urticaria	*Loa loa*, **Onchocerca volvulus*, **Schistosoma japonicum*
XVII. VENENATION	
Venenation	Ants, *bees, blood-sucking insects (in saliva), *gila monsters, *marine fishes, mites, *scorpions, *spiders, ticks, *venomous snakes

Table 3. Manifestations of Disease Caused by Animal Agents (Concluded)

Symptoms Referable to:	*Etiologic Agent*
XVIII. General Systemic (not related to a single organ or system)	
Asthenia	*Ascaris lumbricoides*, **Fasciolopsis buski*, *hookworms, *Hymenolepis nana* (heavy infection), **Leishmania donovani*, malaria parasites (particularly **Plasmodium falciparum*), **Schistosoma japonicum*, *S. mansoni*, *S. hæmatobium*, *Strongyloides stercoralis*, *Tænia saginata*, *Trichocephalus trichiurus*
Chills and fever	Malaria parasites
Cyst, abdominal	*Hydatid of *Echinococcus granulosus*, *Paragonimus westermani*
Fever (See also "Chills and fever".)	**Endamœba histolytica* (in extra-intestinal foci), **Leishmania donovani*, *Loa loa*, **Schistosoma japonicum*, **S. mansoni*, **T. cruzi*, **T. gambiense*, **T. rhodesiense*, **Wuchereria bancrofti*, **W. malayi*
Hemorrhage, internal	*Viperine snakes
of mucous membranes	**Leishmania donovani*, malaria parasites
Larva migrans, internal	Species of roundworms not normally parasitic in man; immature *Gnathostoma spinigerum*
Malnutrition	*Ascaris lumbricoides*, **Fasciolopsis buski*, *hookworms, **Schistosoma japonicum*, **S. mansoni*, **Strongyloides stercoralis*, tapeworms, *Trichocephalus trichiurus*
Myiasis (of eye, intestines, nares, skin, etc.)	*Larvas (maggots) of several species of filth flies

REFERENCES

Bogen, E. 1926. Arachnidism. Arch. Int. Med., *38*, 623–632.

Cruz, W. O. 1948. Hookworm Anemia, a Deficiency Disease. Proc. 4th Int'l Congr. Trop. Med. & Malaria. pp. 1045–1054.

Culbertson, J. T. 1951. Immunologic Mechanisms in Parasitic Infections, in *Parasitic Infections in Man*, Harry Most, Editor. 229 pp. Columbia Univ. Press, New York.

Denhoff, E., and Laufer, M. W. 1948. Pinworm Infection and Childhood Behavior. Am. J. Dis. Child., *77*, 746–756.

Dew, H. R. 1928. *Hydatid Disease.* 429 pp. Sydney (Austral.).

Ewing, H. E. 1948. Observations on the Habits and the Injury Caused by the Bites and the Stings of Some Common North American Arthropods. Am. J. Trop. Med., *8*, 39–62.

Faust, E. C. 1948. An Inquiry into Ectopic Lesions in Schistosomiasis. Am. J. Trop. Med., *28*, 175–199.

————1954. *Amebiasis.* 154 pp. Charles C Thomas, Springfield (Ill.).

Jones, C. A. 1951. Clinical Studies in Human Strongyloidiasis. I. Semeiology. Gastroenterol., *16*, 743–756.

Maegraith, B., Jones, E. S., and Andrews, W. H. H. 1951. Pathological Processes in Malaria: Progress Report. Trans. R. Soc. Trop. Med. & Hyg., *45*, 15–42.

MELENEY, H. E., and FRYE, W. W. 1936. The Pathogenicity of *Endamœba Histolytica*. Trans. R. Soc. Trop. Med. & Hyg., *29*, 369–379.

MICHAEL, P. 1944. Filariasis Among Navy and Marine Personnel. Report of Laboratory Investigation. U. S. Naval Med. Bull., *42*, 1059–1074.

MILWIDSKY, H. 1945. The Surgical Complications of Ascariasis. Acta Med. Orientalia, *4*, 370–384.

NAPIER, L. E. 1946. *The Principles and Practice of Tropical Medicine*. 917 pp. Macmillan Co., New York.

RANSMEIER, J. C. 1946. Tick Paralysis in the Eastern United States. J. Pediatr., *34*, 298–308.

RHOADS, C. P., *et al.* 1934. Hookworm Anemia. Am. J. Hyg., *20*, 291–306.

SALZBERGER, M. 1928. Leeches as Foreign Bodies in the Upper Air Passages in Palestine. Laryngoscope, *38*, 27–32.

SHATTUCK, G. C. 1951. *Diseases of the Tropics*. 803 pp. Appleton-Century-Crofts, New York.

SODEMAN, W. A. 1950. Clinical Picture of Hepatic Amebiasis. Am. J. Trop. Med., *30*, 141–143.

Chapter 5

Diagnosis, Treatment and Prognosis

DIAGNOSIS

Diagnosis of animal agents of disease, like those of any other etiology, consists of clinical and laboratory procedures. The physician studies the patient, obtains as complete and accurate a history as is possible, makes necessary physical examination and carries out one or more essentially clinical tests. On the basis of these findings he arrives at a presumptive and tentative diagnosis.

The physician will want to obtain all of the laboratory assistance possible to support his clinical diagnosis. If the laboratory confirms his findings he develops more assurance in his diagnostic conclusions. If the laboratory provides only "negative" findings or indicates that other etiologic agents are present, he may need to revise his opinions. It is preferable for the laboratory report to state "parasites not found" rather than "negative," since the latter is an equivocal expression and may mislead the physician.

Relatively few parasitic disease syndromes are pathognomonic. Of this limited group possibly amebiasis of the liver is the best example. Practically all others, including amebic colitis and malaria, require laboratory confirmation. There are many instances in which clinical diagnosis of amebiasis, unsupported by laboratory findings, has mistakenly by-passed other enteric diseases for "amebic colitis;" and cases of "malaria," diagnosed solely on the basis of a history of "chills and fever," have at times proven to be typhoid fever or relapsing fever.

Laboratory examination is almost invariably essential for a definitive diagnosis of parasitic diseases. In every clinical laboratory there should therefore be at least one individual experienced in parasitologic diagnosis. This field requires special training, without which, just as in bacteriology and serology, the laboratory provides inadequate, if not inaccurate information. The director of the laboratory, usually a clinical pathologist and not a specialist in parasitology, should recognize the need for special training and have on his staff at least one properly qualified parasitology assistant.

Since the diagnosis of parasites constitutes only one of the several functions of the clinical laboratory and since the physician utilizes the laboratory in order to obtain full diagnostic aid for his patients, there must be close coöperation between the clinician and the laboratory. Hematologic and frequently bacteriologic or serologic technics are at times indicated to supplement parasitologic methods. The physician may request that all or only one of these supplementary services be carried out. Likewise, the director of the laboratory may request multiple specimens for examination or suggest that tests of other types be performed.

PLATE I

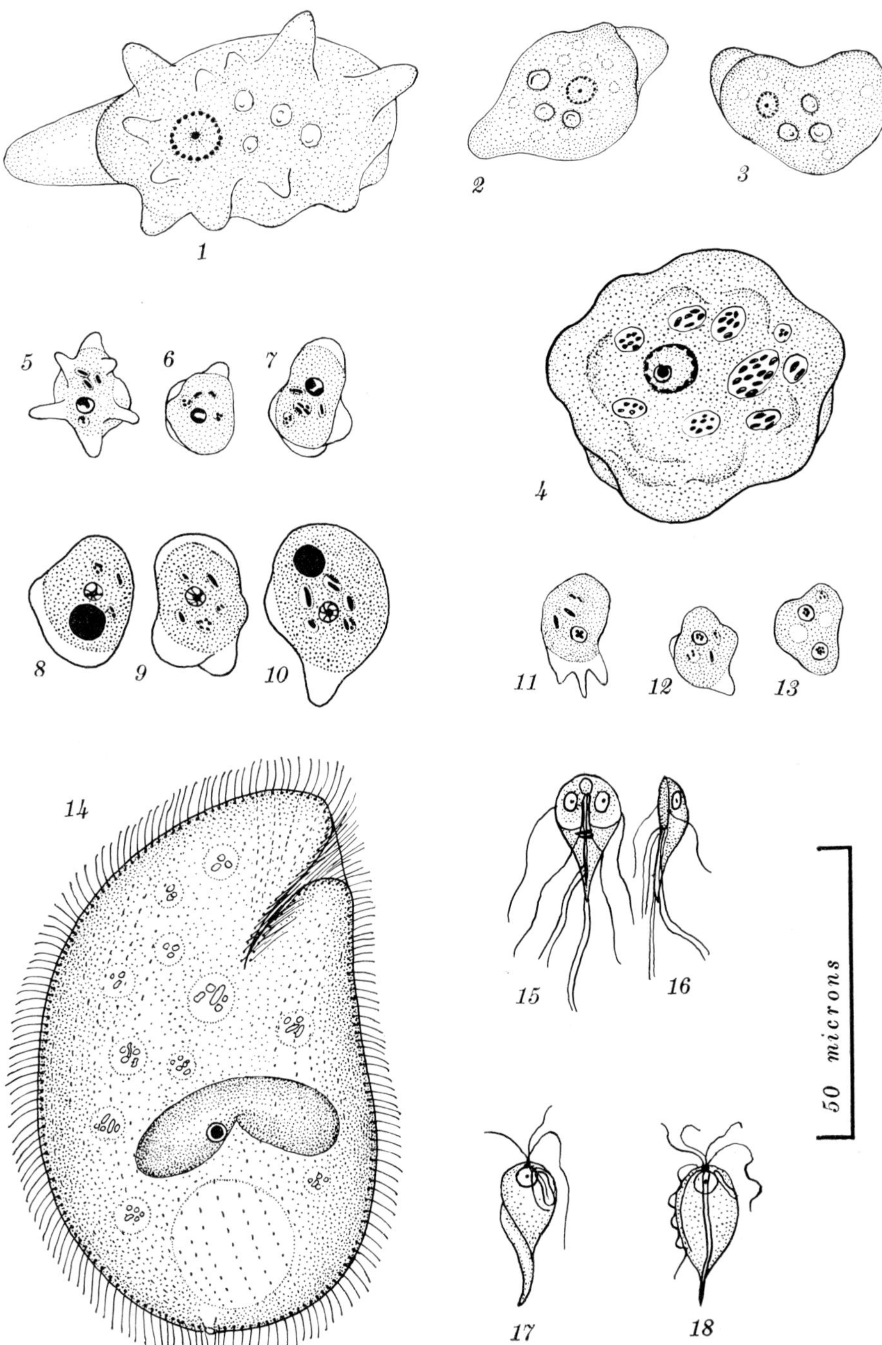

Trophozoites of Protozoa Commonly Occurring in Human Stools. *1, 2, 3, Endamoeba histolytica; 4, Endamoeba coli; 5, 6, 7, Endolimax nana; 8, 9, 10, Iodamoeba bütschlii; 11, 12, 13, Dientamoeba fragilis; 14, Balantidium coli; 15, 16, Giardia lamblia; 17, Chilomastix mesnili; 18, Trichomonas hominis.* (*1–13*, from Faust's *Amebiasis*, courtesy Charles C Thomas, Springfield, Ill.; *14*, after Faust, in Craig and Faust's *Clinical Parasitology*, Lea & Febiger, Philadelphia; *15–18*, original.)

PLATE II

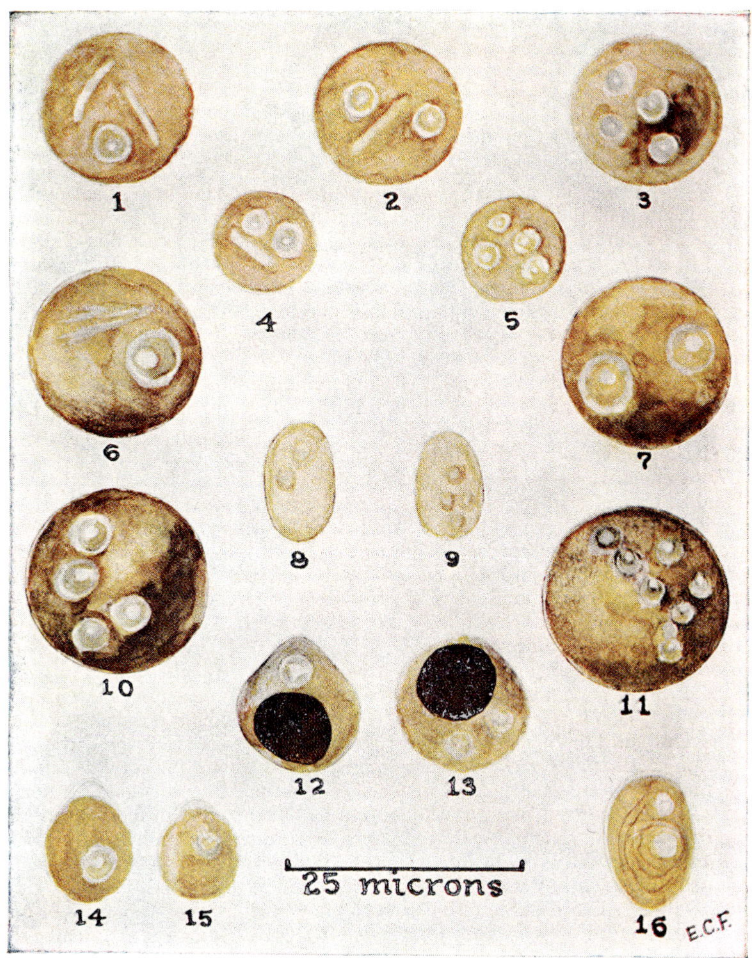

Cysts of Protozoa Commonly Occurring in Human Stools. Cysts of the common protozoa of man as seen in fresh fecal films stained with D'Antoni's iodine. The karyosome and peripheral chromatin, and at times the chromatoidal bars, stand out as practically unstained in contrast to the yellowish-brown of the cytoplasm; the glycogen in most species stains a diffuse mahogany brown, but in *Iodamoeba bütschlii* it is a densely-staining compact mass. *1–5,* cysts of *Endamoeba histolytica,* with chromatoidals; *3,* with diffuse glycogen mass. *8, 9,* cysts of *Endolimax nana. 12, 13,* cysts of *Iodamoeba bütschlii. 6, 7, 10, 11,* cysts of *Endamoeba coli,* with diffuse glycogen mass; *14, 15,* cysts of *Chilomastix mesnili; 16,* cyst of *Giardia lamblia.* (From chart prepared under the author's direction. The reproduction used here has been hand-colored to show the characteristic staining reaction of fresh cysts when treated with D'Antoni's iodine.) From Faust's *Amebiasis,* courtesy of Charles C Thomas, Springfield, Ill.)

(Legend for Plate III).

Eggs and Larvas of the More Common Helminth Parasites of Man. Diagnostic chart of the characteristic eggs and larvas of the more common helminths parasitizing man. *A*, *Ascaris lumbricoides* (giant intestinal roundworm), unsegmented fertile egg, usually with bile-stained outer shell, passed in feces; *B*, *A. lumbricoides*, infertile egg, usually with bile-stained outer shell, passed in feces; *C*, *Enterobius vermicularis* (pinworm or seatworm), with completely developed larva, usually deposited by the mother worm on the perianal or perineal skin; *D*, *Ancylostoma duodenale* ("Old World hookworm") or *Necator americanus* ("American hookworm"), early cleavage stage, passed in semiformed feces; *E*, *A. duodenale* ("Old World hookworm") or *N. americanus* ("American hookworm"), with completely developed first-stage (rhabditoid) larva, passed in constipated stool or developed in feces that have stood twenty-four to forty-eight hours in the laboratory; *F*, *A. duodenale* ("Old World hookworm") or *N. americanus* ("American hookworm"), anterior extremity of hatched rhabditoid larva, showing long, narrow, buccal cavity (contrast with anterior end of *G*); *G*, *Strongyloides stercoralis* (threadworm), rhabiditoid larva passed in feces or obtained by duodenal drainage, showing very short buccal cavity (contrast with *F*); *H*, *Trichostrongylus*, characteristic morula-stage egg passed in feces; *I*, *Trichocephalus trichiurus* (*Trichuris trichiura* or whipworm), with unsegmented embryo, usually with bile-stained outer shell, passed in feces; *J*, *Taenia saginata* (beef tapeworm) or *T. solium* (pork tapeworm), with fully embryonated oncosphere, with dark brown outer shell passed in feces; *K*, *Hymenolapis nana* (dwarf tapeworm), with fully embryonated oncosphere, passed in feces; *L*, *Hymenolepis diminuta* (rat tapeworm), with fully embryonated oncosphere, passed in feces; *M*, *Diphyllobothrium latum* (fish tapeworm), characteristically unembryonated as passed in feces; *N*, *Diphyllobothrium mansoni*, *D. erinacei*, *D. houghtoni* et al. of subgenus *Spirometra*, characteristically unembryonated, as passed in feces of definitive host; *O*, *Dipylidium caninum* (double-pored dog tapeworm), mother egg capsule containing several fully embryonated oncospheres, as passed in feces or expressed from disintegrating gravid proglottid; *P*, *Fasciolopsis buski* (giant intestinal fluke) or *Fasciola hepatica* (sheep liver fluke), unembryonated, as passed in feces or obtained by duodenal and/or biliary drainage; *Q*, *Dicrocoelium dendriticum*, with developed miracidium, passed in feces or obtained by duodenal or biliary drainage; *R*, *Heterophyes heterophyes*, with developed miracidium, passed in feces; *S*, *Metagonimus yokogawai*, with developed miracidium, passed in feces; *T*, *Opisthorchis felineus*, with developed miracidium, passed in feces or obtained by duodenal or biliary drainage; *U*, *Clonorchis sinensis* (Chinese liver fluke), with developed miracidium, passed in feces or obtained by duodenal or biliary drainage; *V*, *Paragonimus westermani* (Oriental lung fluke), unembryonated, recovered from sputum or swallowed and passed in feces; *W*, *Gastrodiscoides hominis*, unembryonated, passed in feces; *X*, *Schistosoma haematobium* (vesical blood fluke), with developed miracidium, passed in urine or at times in feces; *Y*, *Schistosoma mansoni* (Manson's blood fluke), with developed miracidium, passed in feces; *Z*, *Schistosoma japonicum* (Oriental blood fluke), with developed miracidium, passed in feces.

R, *S*, *T*, and *U*, × 666; all other figures, × 333. (From Faust's *Human Helminthology*, Lea & Febiger, Philadelphia.)

PLATE III

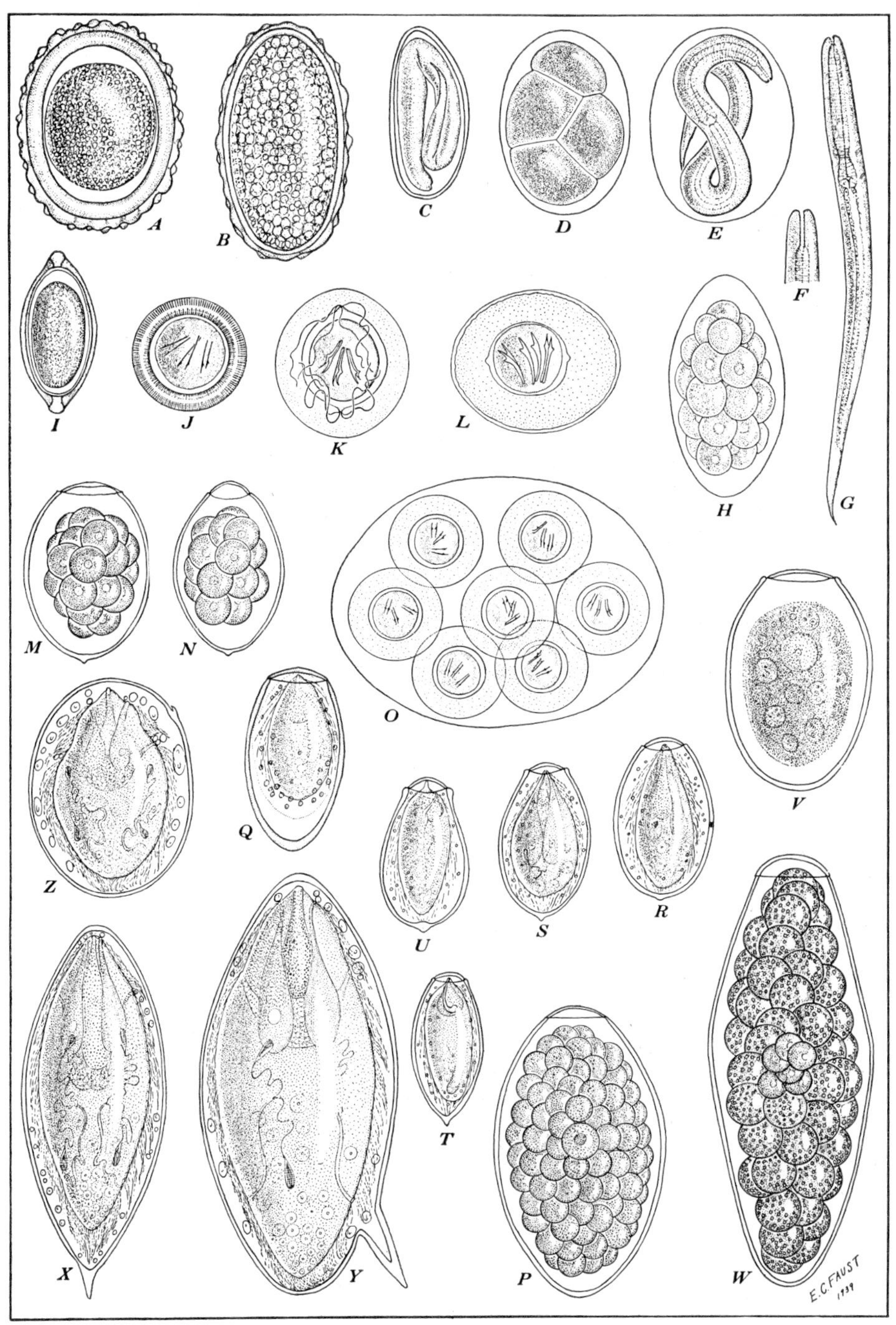

(*Legend on opposite page*).

Although the principal function of the laboratory is to confirm or redirect the physician with reference to his original clinical diagnosis, it has a very important additional function in making examinations during treatment and subsequently, to determine the efficacy of the treatment. If the parasites and symptoms are removed, the diagnosis has been justified. On the other hand, if the parasites disappear after treatment but the symptoms persist, then the parasites may not have been responsible for the symptoms. This brings the reader to an important conclusion, namely that the physician in charge of the patient is obliged to interpret the laboratory findings in the light of his clinical findings. Laboratory diagnoses should never be used without incorporating them into the total picture obtained in a study of the whole patient, since underlying asyndromic or asymptomatic disease may be more important than the readily discovered parasitic infection.

Summary information is provided in Table 4 concerning animal agents of disease and their stages found in various types of specimens obtained for etiologic diagnosis.

Table 4. Diagnostic Examination for Animal Agents of Disease

Legend: T, trophozoite; C, cyst; A, mature or adolescent form; E, egg; L, larva; Mf, microfilaria; P, proglottid; I, intracellular; F, free in plasma or interstitial fluid

Specimen to be Examined	*Agent and Stage to be Looked for*			
	Protozoa	*Helminths*	*Arthropods*	*Others*
STOOL	*Endamœba histolytica* (T, C), *Balantidium coli* (T, C), *Giardia lamblia* (T, C), *Isospora belli* and *I. hominis* (C) NOTE: Look for trophozoites of *E. histolytica, Balantidium coli* and *Giardia lamblia* in unformed stools, cysts in formed stools. These protozoa must be differentiated from the following non-pathogenic species commonly evacuated in the feces: *Endamœba coli, Endolimax nana, Iodamœba bütschlii, Dientamœba fragilis, Chilomastix mesnili, Trichomonas hominis* and other less common forms. (Consult Plate I, p. 55 for trophozoites. Plate II, between pp. 56 and 57 for cysts.)	*Ascaris lumbricoides* (A, E), *Necator americanus* and *Ancylostoma duodenale* (E), *Strongyloides stercoralis* (L), *Trichostrongylus* spp. (E), *Trichocephalus trichiurus* (E), *Enterobius vermicularis* (E, *uncommon*); *Tænia saginata* and *T. solium* (P; E, *uncommon*), *Hymenolepis nana* and *H. diminuta* (E), *Dipylidium caninum* (P), *Diphyllobothrium latum* (E); *Fasciola hepatica* (E), *Fasciolopsis buski* (E), echinostome flukes (E), heterophyid flukes (E), *Clonorchis sinensis* and *Opisthorchis felineus* (E), *Paragonimus westermani* (E), *Schistosoma japonicum* and *S. mansoni* (E), *S. hæmatobium* (E, occasionally). Consult Plate III, p. 57, for eggs of common helminths.	Filth flies (L) and beetles (L), the eggs or larvas of which are accidentally swallowed; mites ingested in cheese; larvas of myiasis-producing fly (*Sarcophaga hæmorrhoidalis*) (L)	

Table 4. Diagnostic Examination for Animal Agents of Disease.—(Continued)

Specimen to be Examined	*Agent and Stage to be Looked for*			
	Protozoa	*Helminths*	*Arthropods*	*Others*
ANAL SWAB	*Endamœba histolytica* (T, C), *Balantidium coli* (T, C)	*Strongyloides stercoralis* (L), *Enterobius vermicularis* (A, E), *Tænia* spp. (E), *Schistosoma japonicum* and *S. mansoni* (E)	Larvas of filth flies crawling out anus	
URINE, VAGINAL and PROSTATIC DISCHARGE	*Endamœba histolytica* (T, *rarely*), *Trichomonas vaginalis* (T)	Vinegar eel (*Turbatrix aceti*) (A, L), *Ascaris* (L, *rarely*), *Strongyloides* (L, *rarely*), *Trichinella* (L, *rarely*), *Dioctophyma renale* (E, *rarely*), *Schistosoma hæmatobium* (E), *S. mansoni* (E, *uncommon*)	Many species of filth flies accidently introduced *per urethram* (L)	
SPUTUM	*Endamœba histolytica* (T, *rarely*)	*Strongyloides stercoralis* (L, *uncommon*), scolices of *Echinococcus granulosus* (L, *uncommon*), *Paragonimus westermani* (E)		
BLOOD	*Leishmania donovani* (I, *in macrophages*), *Trypanosoma gambiense* and *T. rhodesiense* (F), *T. cruzi* (F; I, *in macrophages*), *Plasmodium* spp. (I; F, *rarely*), *Toxoplasma gondii* (I, *in macrophages, rarely*)	*Trichinella spiralis* (L, *rarely*), *Wuchereria bancrofti* and *W. malayi* (Mf), *Loa loa* (Mf), *Onchocerca volvulus* (Mf, *rarely*), *Acanthocheilonema* spp. (Mf), *Mansonella ozzardi* (Mf)		
SPINAL FLUID	*Trypanosoma gambiense* (F), *T. cruzi* (F, *rarely*)			
ASPIRATE, BIOPSY and NECROPSY SPECIMENS				
Proctoscopic	*Endamœba histolytica* (T, C), *Balantidium coli* (T, C)	*Trichocephalus trichiurus* (A, E)		
Duodenal	*Giardia lamblia* (T)	*Necator americanus* and *Ancylostoma duodenale* (E), *Strongyloides stercoralis* (L), *Tænia* spp. (E), *Hymenolepis* spp. (E), *Fasciola hepatica* (E), *Fasciolopsis buski* (E), echinostome flukes (E), heterophyid flukes (E), *Clonorchis sinensis* and *Opisthorchis* spp. (E)		

Hepatic	*Endamœba histolytica* (T), *Leishmania donovani* (I), *Trypanosoma cruzi* (I), *Plasmodium* spp. (I)	Non-human ascarids in visceral "larva migrans" (L), *Echinococcus granulosus* (L), *Fasciola hepatica* (A, E), *Clonorchis sinensis* and *Opisthorchis felineus* (A, E), *Schistosoma japonicum* and *S. mansoni* (A, E)		
Gall-Bladder and Common Duct	*Giardia lamblia* (T, *uncommon*)	*Fasciola hepatica* (A, E), *Clonorchis sinensis* and *Opisthorchis felineus* (A, E)		
Splenic	*Endamœba histolytica* (T, *rarely*), *Leishmania donovani* (I), *Trypanosoma cruzi* (I), *Plasmodium* spp. (I)	*Echinococcus granulosus* (L)		
Lymph Nodes and Lymphatic Vessels	*Leishmania donovani* (I), *Trypanosoma gambiense* and *T. rhodesiense* (F), *T. cruzi* (I), *Toxoplasma gondii* (I)	*Wuchereria bancrofti* and *W. malayi* (A, Mf), *Paragonimus westermani* (A, E, both *uncommon*), *Schistosoma* spp. (A, E)		
Pleuro-Pulmonary	*Endamœba histolytica* (T), *Plasmodium* spp. (I)	*Tænia solium* (L), *Echinococcus granulosus* (L), *Paragonimus westermani* (A, E)	*Linguatula serrata* (A, E, *uncommon*)	
Brain and Spinal Cord	*Endamœba histolytica* (T), *Trypanosoma gambiense* (F), *T. cruzi* (I), *Plasmodium* spp., (I), *Toxoplasma gondii* (I, F)	*Tænia solium* (L), *Echinococcus granulosus* (L), *Diphyllobothrium* sp. (L = *Sparganum proliferum*), *Paragonimus westermani* (A, E), *Schistosoma japonicum* and *S. mansoni* (A, *rarely*; E, *uncommon*)		
Eye	*Leishmania tropica*, *L. brasiliensis* and *L. donovani* (T), *Trypanosoma gambiense* and *T. rhodesiense* (F), *T. cruzi* (I), *Plasmodium* spp. (I), *Toxoplasma gondii* (I)	*Ascaris lumbricoides* (L), non-human roundworms producing nematode ophthalmitis (L), *Trichinella spiralis* (L), *Thelazia* spp. (A), *Wuchereria bancrofti*, *W. malayi*, *Onchocerca volvulus*, *Loa loa* and other filarias (Mf), *Loa loa* (A), *Tænia solium* (L), *Echinococcus granulosus* (L), *Diphyllobothrium mansoni* et al. (*Sparganum* L), *Schistosoma hæmatobium* (A, E), leeches (A, *uncommon*)	Toxic secretions of bees, wasps, hornets, ants, beetles, blood-sucking flies, fleas, pubic lice, mites and ticks; nettling hairs of caterpillars; myiasis-producing flies (L); beetles (L, *rarely*)	Nettling cells (nematocysts) of jelly fishes; venom of snakes sprayed on unprotected conjunctiva

Table 4. Diagnostic Examination for Animal Agents of Disease.—(Concluded)

Specimen to be Examined	Agent and Stage to be Looked for			
	Protozoa	*Helminths*	*Arthropods*	*Others*
Urinary Bladder, Vagina, Urethra, Epididymis, Prostate, Testes, etc.	*Endamœba histolytica* (T, *uncommon*), *Trichomonas vaginalis* (T)	*Wuchereria bancrofti* (A, Mf), *Echinococcus granulosus* (L), *Schistosoma hæmatobium* and *S. mansoni* (A, E), *S. japonicum* (E, *rarely*)		
Renal and Adrenal	*Trypanosoma cruzi* (I), *Plasmodium* spp. (I)	*Trichinella spiralis* (L), *Dioctophyma renale* (A, E, *rarely*)		
Cardiac (myocardium)	*Trypanosoma cruzi* (I)	*Trichinella spiralis* (L, *en transit*), *Tænia solium* (L), *Echinococcus granulosus* (L), *Schistosoma* spp. (E, *rarely*)		
Smooth and Striated Muscle (excluding Myocardium)		*Trichinella spiralis* (L, *encysted*), *Tænia solium* (L), *Echinococcus granulosus* (L)		
Bone		*Echinococcus granulosus* (L)		
Skin and Subcutaneous Tissues	*Endamœba histolytica* (T), *Leishmania tropica* and *L. brasiliensis* (I), *L. donovani* (I), *Trypanosoma cruzi* (I)	*Ancylostoma braziliense* (L), *A. caninum* (L, *uncommon*), *A. duodenale* (L, *uncommon*), *Necator americanus* (L, *uncommon*), *Bunostomum phlebotomum* (L, *rarely*), *Onchocerca volvulus* (Mf), *Loa loa* (A), *Dirofilaria repens* (A, *rarely*), *Dracunculus medinensis* (A), *Tænia solium* (L), species of non-human blood flukes producing "cercaria dermatitis" (L)	Toxic secretions of bees, wasps, hornets, ants, beetles, blood-sucking flies, fleas, lice, mites, and ticks; nettling hairs of caterpillars; myiasis-producing flies; trauma caused by hypostome of ticks; infestation by scabic mite, follicular mite, parasitoid mites, chigger mites and chigoe flea; venenation due to sting of scorpions and bite of venomous spiders	Nettling cells (nematocysts) of jelly fishes; local trauma, local and systemic poisoning produced by sea urchin spines and fish spines; "bites" of gila monsters and many species of venomous snakes

TREATMENT

Treatment of disease has a fourfold objective. The clinician has as his goal (1) specific therapy to eradicate the cause of the symptoms, (2) the alleviation of pain and other severe manifestations of disease and (3) therapeutic procedures directed against supervening agents. A fourth objective is chemotherapeutic prophylaxis.

In the case of animal agents of disease, the removal of the agent and its harmful products is most important for the individual patient. Thus, the administration of relatively specific, well-tolerated drugs which will destroy or evacuate the agent, or neutralize the effect of its secretions and excretions, is invariably indicated. At times, however, it is important to prescribe measures which are palliative or supportive, either preceding specific medication or concurrent with it, so that the patient may experience prompt relief. At other times effective treatment for a particular agent can better be accomplished if attention is also directed to the elimination of associated disease processes. These several etiologic components may be so intimately related that it is difficult to distinguish them.

Certain types of disease due to animal agents are not amenable to chemotherapy but are relieved by surgical intervention. The operation may be a very minor one, as, for example, extraction of the stinger of a honey bee or the removal of a chigoe from the skin; or it may call for skilled major surgery, as in the case of cysticercosis, hydatid cyst or parasitic granulomas of the brain, in acute abdomen due to ascariasis, or in suffocation resulting from the lodgment of a leech or *Ascaris* in the trachea.

Standard therapeutic procedures for the more important or more common diseases produced by animal agents are summarized in Table 5.

Table 5. Standard Therapeutics Procedures for the More Important or More Common Diseases Caused by Animal Agents

Disease	*Drug or Other Therapeutic Agent*	*Adult Dosage and Administration*	*Comments*	*Page Ref. in Text*
Protozoan				
Amebiasis				
Intestinal	(1) Chiniofon, 0.25 Gm. enteric tablets	(1) 3 to 4 t.i.d., *orally*, for 8–10 days, totaling 18 to 30 Gm.	May produce diarrhea	96
	(2) Diiodoquin hydroxyquinoline (Dicdoquin), 0.20 Gm. compressed tablets	(2) 3 to 4 t.i.d., *orally*, for 20 days, totaling 12 to 16 Gm.	No reported side effects	96
	(3) Carbarsone, 0.25 Gm. enteric tablets	(3) One b.i.d., *orally*, for 10 days, totaling 5 Gm.	May produce arsenical idiosyncrasies	96
	(4) Bismuth glycolylarsanilate (Milibis), 0.25 Gm. tablets	(4) 2 t.i.d., *orally*, for 7 days, totaling 10.5 Gm.	Usually well tolerated	97
	(5) Aureomycin, (chlortetracycline) capsules 0.25 Gm.	(5) 2 q.i.d., *orally*, for 7 days, totaling 14 Gm.	Usually well tolerated	97
	(6) Terramycin (oxytetracycline), 0.25 Gm. capsules	(6) 2 q.i.d., *orally*, for 10 days, totaling 20 Gm.	Usually well tolerated	97
	(7) Fumagillin, 10 mgm. tablets.	(7) 30–60 mgm. daily, *orally* for 10–14 days, totaling 0.3 to 0.84 Gm.	Usually well tolerated	97
	(8) Emetine hydrochloride, 6% aq. sol. in 1 cc. ampules (65 mgm.)	(8) One mgm./kilo body weight (but not to exceed total of 65 mgm.) daily, *intramuscularly*, for 3 or 4 days, maximum total 195 to 260 mgm.	Myocardial toxicant; *used only* for *symptomatic relief*	96

Table 5. Standard Therapeutics Procedures for the More Important or More Common Diseases Caused by Animal Agents.—(Continued)

Disease	*Drug or Other Therapeutic Agent*	*Adult Dosage and Administration*	*Comments*	*Page Ref. in Text*
Amebiasis				
Extra-intestinal	Chloroquine phosphate, 0.25 Gm. compressed tablets	One q.i.d., *orally*, for 2 days, then 1 b.i.d. for 2 to 3 weeks, totaling 9 to 12.5 Gm.	No known contraindication; most satisfactory in hepatic amebiasis	97
Balantidiasis	(1) Carbarsone, 0.25 Gm. enteric tablets	(1) One b.i.d., *orally*, for 10 to 20 days, totaling 5 to 10 Gm.	(See "Amebiasis, Intestinal.")	104
	(2) Aureomycin, 0.25 Gm. capsules	(2) As above in intestinal amebiasis	(See "Amebiasis, Intestinal.")	104
	(3) Terramycin, 0.25 Gm. capsules	(3) As above in intestinal amebiasis	(See "Amebiasis, Intestinal.")	104
Trichomonas Vaginitis	(1) Diodoquin, 0.20 Gm. compressed tablets	(1) 3 to 4 t.i.d., *orally*, for 20 days, totaling 12 to 16 Gm., in conjunction with (2) One diodoquin suppository inserted nightly into posterior fornix of vagina	To rectify vaginal pH introduce into vagina one capsule containing boric acid (0.3 Gm.), glucose (0.3 Gm.), and lactose (0.3 Gm.)	112
Giardiasis	Quinacrine (Atabrine), 0.1 Gm. compressed tablets	One t.i.d., orally, for 3 to 5 days, totaling 0.9 to 1.5 Gm.	Efficacious, usually well tolerated	107
Leishmaniasis				
Cutaneous	Neoantimosan (Fuadin), 6 to 7% aq. sol. in ampules	4 to 5 cc. twice weekly, *intramuscularly*, for 8 weeks, totaling about 4 to 5 Gm.	Relatively well tolerated	174
Mucocutaneous	(1) Neoantimosan, as above	(1) As above	Relatively well tolerated	178
	(2) Neostibosan, as below	(2) As below	Relatively well tolerated. Employed for secondary lesions in conjunction with sulfa drugs or antibiotics	178
Visceral	(1) Neostibosan, 5% aq. sol. in ampules	2 cc.→4 cc.→6 cc. daily, then 6 cc. daily, *intravenously* (or *intramuscularly*), until 48 to 80 cc., containing 2.4 to 4.0 Gm. has been administered	Fairly well tolerated	183
	(2) Urea stibamine, 5 to 10% aq. sol. freshly prepared each administration	1 cc.→2 cc.→3 or 4 cc. daily, *intravenously*, for 7 to 10 days, until 12 to 18 cc., containing 1.2 to 1.8 Gm. has been administered	Fairly well tolerated	183
	(3) 4:4′ diamidino-stilbene, 5% aq. sol.	1 cc.→2 cc. daily or on alternate days, *intravenously*, until 26 cc., containing 1.3 Gm. has been administered	*Only for cases refractory to antimony;* very toxic, at times producing facial neuropathy	183

Trypanosomiasis				
Gambian	(1) Tryparsamide, 20% aq. sol. in ampules	(1) 5 cc.→10 cc.→15 cc. weekly, then 15 cc. weekly, *intravenously,* until 120 to 400 cc., containing 24 to 80 Gm. has been administered	Development of severe neuritis or ophthalmitis during treatment requires immediate discontinuation	192
	(2) Naphuride Na, Suramin (Bayer 205), as below	(2) As below	Employed when tryparsamide is not tolerated	192
Rhodesian	Naphuride Na, Suramin (Bayer 205), 10% aq. sol. in ampules	10 cc. once or twice weekly, *intravenously,* until 70 to 100 cc., containing 7 to 10 Gm., has been administered	Effective only during early stage of disease	189
American (Chagas' disease)	None known			
Malaria				
Vivax	(1) Chloroquine phosphate (Aralen), 0.25 Gm. (0.15 Gm. base) tablets	A. SUPPRESSIVE: 2 weekly, *orally,* beginning 2 weeks before exposure and continuing during exposure period	Well tolerated	157
		B. CURATIVE: 4 *stat.* as loading dose, 2 6 hrs. later, then 2 daily × 2, totaling 2.5 Gm. (1.5 Gm. base)	Given in conjunction with primaquine. (See below.)	157
	(2) Amodiaquin dihydrochloride dihydrate (Camoquin), 0.25 Gm. (0.2 Gm. base) tablets	A. SUPPRESSIVE: 2 weekly, *orally,* as with chloroquine	Well tolerated	158
		B. CURATIVE: 3 *stat.* as loading dose, followed by suppressive therapy	Given in conjunction with primaquine. (See below.)	158
	(3) Primaquine diphosphate, 26.5 mgm. (15 mgm. base) tablets	One daily, *orally,* for 14 days, in conjunction with chloroquine or amodiaquin for *curative treatment*	To eradicate residual exo-erythrocytic foci	158
Falciparum	(1) Chloroquine, as above, or	A. SUPPRESSIVE: as above		
	(2) Amodiaquin, as above	B. CURATIVE: as above	In falciparum malaria primaquine is not required	
Quartan	(1) Chloroquine, as above (2) Amodiaquin, as above (3) Primaquine, as above in vivax malaria	A. SUPPRESSIVE: as above in vivax malaria B. CURATIVE: as above in vivax malaria	Requires primaquine (See above under "Vivax Malaria") to eradicate residual exo-erythrocytic foci	158
Toxoplasmosis	No curative therapy demonstrated; sulfa drugs and some antibiotics are partially suppressive			202

Table 5. Standard Therapeutics Procedures for the More Important or More Common Diseases Caused by Animal Agents.—(Continued)

Disease	*Drug or Other Therapeutic Agent*	*Adult Dosage and Administration*	*Comments*	*Page Ref. in Text*
Coccidiosis	None known		Complete bed rest and a bland diet are indicated	114
Helminthic				
Ascariasis	Hexylresorcinol crystoids (Crystoids anthelmintic), 0.1 or 0.2 Gm. hard gelatin capsules	One Gm. in one dose, *orally*, on empty stomach, preceded and followed by saline purgation in constipated patients	Acute intestinal obstruction contraindicates use of drug, may require surgical intervention	229
Hookworm Infection	Tetrachlorethylene, 0.5 or 1.0 cc. soft gelatin capsules	3 cc. in one dose, *orally*, on empty stomach, preceded and followed by saline purgation	If complicated with ascariasis, prescribe hexylresorcinol crystoids, as above	246
"*Creeping Eruption*"	Diethylcarbamazine (Hetrazan), 0.1 Gm. compressed tablets	1.0 to 2.0 mgm./kilo body weight, t.i.d., *orally*, for 10 to 20 days, totaling 4 to 8 Gm.	Possible mild sensitization reaction to dying worms	276
	Ethyl chloride spray	Spray inner end of tunnel to kill larval worm	Avoid deep burning of tissues	276
Strongyloidiasis	(1) Gentian violet med., 12 mgm. or 30 mgm. 1½-hr. coated tablets	60 mgm. t.i.d., *orally*, before meals for 16 days	May produce nausea and vomiting	258
	(2) Hetrazan, 0.1 Gm. compressed tablets	1.0 to 2.0 mgm./kilo body weight t.i.d., *orally*, for 10 to 20 days, totaling 4 to 8 Gm.	Possible mild sensitization reaction to dying worms	259
Whipworm Infection (trichocephaliasis or trichuriasis)	(1) 0.3 cc. oil of chenopodium + 2.7 tetrachlorethylene in soft gelatin capsules	3 cc. in one dose, *orally*, on empty stomach, preceded and followed by saline purgation	For effectiveness the cecal area must be free of feces and mucus	223
	(2) Hexylresorcinol, 1:300 in aq. sol. of 10% gum of acacia	300 to 600 cc., administered as *high retention enema*, nightly for 2 to 5 times	Particularly useful when the worms are attached all along the colon and rectum	223
Oxyuriasis (enterobiasis)	Gentian violet med., 12 mgm. or 30 mgm. 4-hr. coated tabs.	60 mgm. t.i.d., *orally*, before meals for 8 days, rest one week, then repeat	Treat all cases in family group simultaneously to prevent reinfection; severe nausea and vomiting require temporary discontinuation of treatment	217
	Piperazine hexahydate	25 to 37 mgm./kilo body weight b.i.d. in syrup, *orally*, for 7 days, rest one week, then repeat	Essentially nontoxic	218

Trichinosis	No specific therapy known		During initial stage daily or twice daily purgation with sodium sulfate sol. (30 Gm. in a glass of water) may dislodge adolescent females from duodenal mucosa, and considerably reduce pathologic effects	272
Bancroft's and *Malayan Filariasis*	Hetrazan, 0.1 Gm. compressed tablets	1.0 to 2.0 mg./kilo body weight, t.i.d., *orally*, for 20 or more days, totaling 4 to 8 Gm.	Sensitization to dying worms may be relieved with antihistaminics	299
Onchocercosis	Naphuride Na, Suramin (Bayer 205), 10% aq. sol. in ampules May be preceded with Hetrazan to kill microfilarias and reduce sensitization	20 mgm./kilo body weight weekly, *intravenously*, for 8 weeks	Excise parent tumors as soon as they appear	306
Loaiasis	Hetrazan, 0.1 Gm. compressed tablets	1.0 to 2.0 mgm./kilo body weight, t.i.d., *orally*, for 20 or more days	Sensitization to dying worms may be relieved with antihistaminics	310
Dracunculosis	Emulsion: Phenothiazine, 2 Gm. pulv., in 0.35 Gm. lanolin and 15 cc. sterile olive oil previously heated at 150° C. for one hr.; add 5 cc. sterile water, then 20 cc. sterile olive oil; autoclave at 115° C. for 30 minutes	Anesthetize worm's tract with procaine, then inject anthelmintic emulsion into and lateral to worm's pathway; massage briskly for 5 minutes, then grasp at head end of worm with forceps and remove by gentle traction	Administer epinephrin at time worm is migrating to skin to counteract hypersensitization reaction	315
Tæniasis				
Intestinal	Quinacrine (Atabrine), 0.1 Gm. compressed tablets	0.5 Gm. in one dose, *orally*, on empty stomach, with equal amount sodium bicarbonate, preceded and followed by saline purgation	May produce nausea and vomiting	331
Cysticercosis	Surgical removal indicated			
Hydatid Disease	Surgical removal if feasible; otherwise specific biotherapy		Biotherapy with hydatid antigen has been successful in inoperable cases	359
Dwarf Tapeworm Infection	Quinacrine (Atabrine), 0.1 Gm. compressed tablets	As in tæniasis, intestinal (See above)		
Fish Tapeworm Infection	Quinacrine (Atabrine), 0.1 Gm. compressed tablets	As in tæniasis, intestinal (See above)		
Sheep Liver-Fluke Infection	Emetine hydrochloride, 6% aq. sol. in 1 cc. ampules	One mgm./kilo body weight (but not to exceed 65 mgm.) daily, *intramuscularly*, for 10 to 12 days	Myocardial toxicant; keep patient in bed under close observation	383

Table 5. Standard Therapeutics Procedures for the More Important or More Common Diseases Caused by Animal Agents.—(Continued)

Disease	*Drug or Other Therapeutic Agent*	*Adult Dosage and Administration*	*Comments*	*Page Ref. in Text*
Fasciolopsiasis	Hexylresorcinol crystoids (Crystoids anthelmintic), 0.1 or 0.2 Gm. hard gelatin capsules	One Gm. in one dose, *orally*, on empty stomach, preceded and followed by saline purgation	No contraindication except in acute abdomen	372
Clonorchiasis and Opisthorchiasis	Gentian violet med., 12 mgm. or 30 mgm. 1½-hr. coated tablets	60 mgm. t.i.d., *orally*, before meals for 15–20 days	Effective only in early infections	390
Paragonimiasis	Emetine hydrochloride, aq. sol. in 1 cc. ampules	One mgm./kilo body weight (but not to exceed 65 mgm.) daily *intramuscularly*, for not more than 12 days	Myocardial toxicant; keep patient in bed under close observation	395
Schistosomiasis				
Intestinal (japonica and mansoni)	Sodium antimony tartrate or potassium antimony tartrate, ½% aq. sol.	8 cc.→12 cc.→16 cc. on alternate days first week, then 20→24 cc. three times weekly, *intravenously*, for total of 320 cc., containing 0.576 Gm. antimony	Introduce carefully into cubital vein and inject very slowly to avoid respiratory and hepatic irritation	414
Vesical	(1) As for intestinal schistosomiasis		Better tolerated than in intestinal schistosomiasis	
	(2) Lucanthone HCl (Miracil D), 0.1 Gm. compresses tablets	10–20 mgm./kilo body weight daily, *orally*, for 7–8 days	Rather poorly tolerated but treatment is soon completed; not as effective as antimony tartrates	425
Hirudiniasis				
External	Strong salt solution (brine)	Apply to site to release leech from its attachment to skin	Cauterize oozing lesion and cover with sterile dressing	448
Internal	Surgical intervention required		Irrigation of nasopharynx with strong saline solution may expel the worm	447
Arthropod Infestation				
Sarcoptic or *Demodectic Mange*	Benzene hexachloride (Gammexane), ½% in ointment base	Cleanse lesion with green soap and warm water; rub in ointment and leave overnight; put on clean clothing next morning; repeat treatment between 6th and 10th day to kill hatched young	Thoroughly sterilize all undergarments and bed linen in contact with lesions	465

Chigoe Infestation	Iodine tincture	Remove flea from lesion with sterile sharp needle; sterilize lesion with iodine or merthiolate solution	Treat dogs between toes to remove reservoir of infestation	504, 513
Myiasis	Surgical removal indicated	After removal of maggots and débridement, irrigate with antiseptic solution and apply sterile dressing	Intervention must be expeditious to prevent permanent disfigurement or even fatal outcome	505-512
Bee Sting	Epinephrin	Employ to counteract hypersensitization	As soon as possible desensitize with bee extract	482
Caterpillar Urtication	Calamine lotion	Apply *topically* to lesions on skin	If conjunctiva is involved, consult ophthalmologist first	480
Beetle Vesication	Calamine lotion	Apply *topically* to lesions on skin followed by dry sterile dressing		
Bite by ticks, mites, bloodsucking flies, biting, gnats, and fleas	Calamine lotion, or phenolated camphor sol. in pure mineral oil (Camphophenique)	Apply with cotton swab or rub into site of bite	Attached ticks should be anesthetized with ether or xylene and removed by gentle traction; chigger mites should be removed with sharp needle; sterile dressing may be needed	463, 467, 468, 484, 487, 496, 497, 498, 499
Pediculosis (Louse infestation), caused by				
Pediculus corporis	DDT, 2% powder in inert base	Dust body and clothing periodically	Mass treatment of entire infested group is indicated	484
P. capitis	Benzene hexachloride (Gammexane), ½% in ointment base	Rub onto all head hairs and into scalp; leave over night, then wash out; repeat if necessary	Treat all contacts simultaneously	484
Phthirus pubis	Benzene hexachloride (Gammexane), ½% in ointment base	Rub onto all infested areas; leave over night, then wash out	Treat all contacts simultaneously	485
Latrodectism (Spider poisoning)	Specific antivenin	Administer *intramuscularly*	Calcium gluconate, 10 cc. 10% sol., introduced slowly *intravenously* is indicated for supportive treatment. Cortisone is reportedly helpful	460
Scorpion Venenation	Univalent or polyvalent antivenin	Administer *intramuscularly*	Glucose, 10% sol., introduced slowly *intravenously*, topical ice packs and, at times, insulin, are helpful	457

Other Types of Poisoning				
Jelly-Fish Sting	Calamine lotion	Apply *topically* to skin lesions	Supportive treatment for shock may be indicated	554
Sea-Urchin Venenation	Calamine lotion	Apply *topically* to skin lesions	Apply sterile dressing to prevent bacterial infection	554
Fish Poisoning				
(1) From eating "poison" fish	Emetics and purgatives	Employ as in acute food poisoning	Supportive treatment may be indicated	559
(2) From venenation through spines	Calamine lotion and antiseptic dressing	Apply *topically* to injured sites	Supportive measures may be indicated if systemic intoxication occurs	560
Gila Monster Venenation	None available	Sterilize wound, keep open and apply aseptic dressing	Keep wound open and suck out as much venom as possible; employ	
Snake Venenation	Univalent or polyvalent antivenin	Introduce antivenin in 25 to 50 cc. amounts proximal to wound *intramuscularly* or subcutaneously (intravenously if the patient has developed severe neurotoxic manifestations); children require larger doses of antivenin than adults per kilo body weight	tourniquet to localize venom; apply ice pack topically; keep patient warm, use supportive measures and avoid alcoholic stimulants	570

Chemotherapeutic prophylaxis is an ultimate goal theoretically feasible in infections which solely affect man or are almost exclusively human. Where there are important reservoir hosts close to human beings other methods of control must be found. *Prophylaxis* means prevention. *Causal prophylaxis* means prevention of the development of the causative agent in the environment, elimination of exposure, or destruction of the agent after it has entered the body but before it has had time to produce damage by multiplication or by discharge of its irritating by-products. On the basis of these definitions no drug has been discovered which is a practical prophylactic against animal agents of disease.

PROGNOSIS

Prognosis is a forecast of the result. In medicine it is a prediction of the outcome of a disease. As in weather forecasting, so in medicine the prognostician bases his deductions principally on averages of evidence. Yet individuals vary, at times widely, from the average. Experience with patients added to scientific information frequently provides a more accurate prognosis than scientific deductions alone.

Prognosis varies not only with the individual but with the virulence of the particular type of the etiologic agent, the stage of the disease, available therapy, and the patient's "will" to survive. In severe epidemics prognosis is less favorable than in mildly endemic infections. Moreover prognosis may be good with respect to survival and poor when complete return to normal health is concerned, since the pathologic process in a chronic infection may have become so extensive that normal function is impossible, even though the individual may live for years.

The development of new drugs and biologicals has greatly improved the prognosis of many diseases. Wherever these therapeutics are available and are administered early enough in the progress of the disease, an otherwise unsatisfactory prognosis is transformed into a favorable one.

SUMMARY

1. Diagnosis of disease consists of clinical and laboratory procedures. In most diseases produced by animal agents clinical diagnosis is tentative and requires laboratory confirmation.
2. Laboratory diagnosis of parasitic diseases requires skilled technical assistants who have had special training and experience in this particular field. Yet their work should be carried out in close coöperation with that of other specialists in the laboratory.
3. The physician in charge of the patient has the primary responsibility for providing diagnostic material and in evaluating the laboratory findings in terms of the total information obtained on the patient.
4. Treatment of disease is directed towards eradication of the causative agent, alleviation of symptoms, elimination of supervening disease processes, and therapeutic control of disease in a community.
5. Chemotherapeutic prophylaxis is theoretically possible and is a highly desirable goal, but in a strict sense it has never been attained in diseases produced by animal agents.
6. Prognosis is forecasting results on the basis of average available information. With the development of many modern drugs and biologicals the prognosis in many diseases caused by animal agents has changed from unsatisfactory to very favorable.

REFERENCES

Alving, A. S., Arnold, J., and Robinson, D. H. 1952. Mass Therapy of Subclinical Vivax Malaria with Primaquine. J. Am. Med. Assn., *149*, 1558–1562.

Anderson, H. H., Bostick, W. L., and Johnstone, H. G. 1953. *Amebiasis: Pathology Diagnosis and Chemotherapy.* 393 pp. Charles C Thomas, Springfield (Ill.).

Bozicevich, J. 1951. Immunological Diagnosis of Parasitic Diseases, in *Parasitic Infections in Man,* Harry Most, Editor. 229 pp. Columbia Univ. Press, New York.

Brown, H. W. 1951. Therapy of Filariasis and the More Common Intestinal Helminths, in *Parasitic Infections in Man,* Harry Most, Editor. 229 pp. Columbia Univ. Press, New York.

Craig, C. F. 1948. *Laboratory Diagnosis of Protozoan Diseases.* 2nd ed. 384 pp. Lea & Febiger, Philadelphia.

Craig, C. F., and Faust, E. C. 1951. *Clinical Parasitology.* 5th ed. 1032 pp. Lea & Febiger, Philadelphia.

Faust, E. C. 1952. Modern Criteria for the Laboratory Diagnosis of Amebiasis. Am. J. Trop. Med. & Hyg., *1*, 140–145.

HEWITT, R., *et al.* 1950. The First Year's Results of a Mass Treatment Program with Hetrazan for the Control of Bancroftian Filariasis on St. Croix, American Virgin Islands. Am. J. Trop. Med., *30,* 443–452.

MACKIE, T. T., HUNTER, G. W., III, and WORTH, C. B. 1954. *A Manual of Tropical Medicine.* 2nd ed. 907 pp. W. B. Saunders Co., Philadelphia.

SABIN, A. B., and FELDMAN, H. A. 1949. Dyes as Microchemical Indicators of a New Immunity Phenomenon Affecting a Protozoön Parasite (Toxoplasma). Science, *108,* 660–663.

SEN GUPTA, P. C. 1944. The Value of the Complement Fixation Test in the Diagnosis of Kala-azar. Ind. Med. Gaz., *79,* 465–469.

SIMMONS, J. S., and GENTZKOW, C. J. 1955. *Medical and Public Health Laboratory Methods.* 6th ed. *In Press.* Lea & Febiger, Philadelphia.

SODEMAN, W. A. 1951. Some Recent Advances in the Diagnosis and Treatment of Amebiasis. Med. Ann. District of Columbia, *20,* 409–415.

TRUSSELL, R. E. 1947. *Trichomonas Vaginalis and Trichomoniasis.* 277 pp. Charles C Thomas, Springfield (Ill.).

Chapter 6

Control and Prevention

CONTROL means repression, restraint or management. When applied to disease, it implies a check on the disease process, either in the individual or in a population. If the causative agent is a pathogen which has invaded the host, control may refer to symptomatic relief or inhibition of the further activities of the agent, but not necessarily to its eradication. In public health the term "control" is applied when measures are taken to check an epidemic or to reduce the incidence of an important disease in a community.

In contrast to control of a disease already residing in an individual or a group, *prevention* is an interception or blockade set up between the causative agent and the host, so that the latter escapes exposure. Prevention is therefore primarily a public health concept, but clinically it is of the greatest significance since it protects the community and in doing so keeps the individual free of the disease.

Control and prevention have very wide applications in the field of animal agents and vectors of disease. Practically all methods and procedures which are effective in reducing and eradicating infectious diseases may be employed here, since all of these diseases are preventable. What, then, are the methods and how may they be effectively employed? These questions will be briefly considered under the following six main headings. Frequently satisfactory control and prevention are to be obtained only when two or more procedures are undertaken simultaneously.

1. *Water.*—Water intended for drinking should be potable; it is equally important that it be free of microscopic and macroscopic pathogens. Wherever water supplies are subject to pollution by man or animals it is necessary for them to be processed to make them safe for human consumption. Gross pollution of streams from community sewage requires sanitary disposal or sterilization before the effluent reaches the water supply. In most urban areas in the United States this is satisfactorily managed by municipal sanitary installations in so far as most enteric bacteria are concerned. In many other countries of the world this is not necessarily the case. Sewage-treatment plants as presently operated in the United States will not guarantee that the effluent is free of viable cysts of *Endamœba histolytica* or eggs of *Ascaris lumbricoides* and *Tænia* spp. Contamination of water supplies in rural areas from latrines or resulting from promiscuous defecation is a potential danger for which no eminently practical solution has yet been found.

The following animal agents or vectors of disease may at times be controlled by safe water supplies: *Endamœba histolytica, Schistosoma japonicum, S. mansoni, S. hæmatobium,* Cyclops infected with larvas of *Dracunculus medinensis,* and the leech *Limnatis nilotica.* In the case of *E. histoly-*

tica it has been demonstrated that cysts in feces highly diluted with fresh water survive considerable periods of time, and if there is heavy pollution with cysts such water supplies have been responsible for epidemics of amebic colitis. Correction of the cause has terminated exposure.

2. *Food.*—Human food may serve as a medium for exposure to animal agents of disease in two ways. In the first place, it may be directly contaminated with excreta, and thus be responsible for parasitic infections. Secondly, apparently clean food may contain developing stages of animal agents, as, for example, larvas of *Trichinella spiralis* and *Tænia solium* in pork, *T. saginata* in beef, several helminths in fresh-water fish, and *Fasciola hepatica* on water cress. In all instances thorough heating of these articles of food will safeguard the consumer.

3. *Personal and Group Hygiene.*—Lack of personal and group hygiene is responsible for many diseases caused by animal parasites. *Failure to observe personal cleanliness*, particularly with reference to habits of defecation and urination, thorough washing of the hands after defecation and before meals, bathing and frequent changing of underpants, is directly responsible for many parasitic infections. In mental hospitals and prisons, and likewise in children's homes and large families of low socio-economic status, group contact tends to increase exposure to these diseases, as it does to scabies and pediculosis.

Correction of faulty habits of personal and group hygiene constitutes a major objective in the prevention of diseases caused by animal parasites, yet it is the most difficult to accomplish of all public health programs. It requires coöperation of all members of a community and this, in turn, means public health education of the masses at a level which they can understand and with incentives which they can appreciate. This program should be integrated with an over-all plan to improve hygiene and sanitation in the home and the community. It will require years of patient, intelligent effort if the objectives are to be achieved.

4. *Arthropods and Arthropod-transmitted Diseases.*—This constitutes the largest single group of diseases subject to effective control. It is divided into two main categories, *viz.*, (*a*) diseases resulting directly from infestation or attack by the arthropod, and (*b*) those transmitted by the arthropod as vector. In both instances the attack is primarily on the arthropod, to kill it or reduce its numbers below the level of public health importance.

The majority of diseases due to arthropods consists of infections which the arthropod transmits either as an essential (biological) or casual (mechanical) vector. Important examples are malaria, yellow fever and several other viral diseases, filaria infections, the rickettsioses, plague and relapsing fever, all of which employ certain arthropods as essential hosts. Specific therapy administered to infected individuals will at times greatly reduce the amount of microörganisms which can be picked up by the arthropod from human hosts, yet the most effective attack in all of these diseases is against the arthropod transmitter.

Mechanical transmission of enteric and other infectious diseases by filth flies is controllable by effective reduction in the breeding of the flies. DDT and other insect toxicants are periodically useful when a concerted campaign is undertaken to cover an entire community but the rapid development of resistance by the flies to these insecticides indicates that reliance for control can not be placed solely on this procedure.

5. *Zoönotic Diseases.*—In a broad sense this comprehends all the diseases of animals. In the more usual sense it refers to those diseases of animals which are transmissible to man. Control of those which are arthropod-transmitted to man can be effected by attack on the arthropod (see above). In trematode diseases, all of which require some snail or other mollusc as intermediate host, the most practical way to break the cycle is by destruction of the mollusc, *i. e.*, by molluscicidal control. In other diseases more careful personal hygiene will have to be developed to avoid exposure.

6. *Immunization.*—Immunization has not been developed as a practical procedure in diseases due to animal agents.

THE CONTROL AND PREVENTIVE PROGRAM

Control must be considered as a tentative public health program; prevention is the ultimate objective. Neither can be achieved without adequate knowledge concerning the natural history and epidemiology of the diseases to be controlled, points which were particularly emphasized in Chapter 2 of this volume. Added to adequate knowledge must be experience in handling the preventive program. This means not only familiarity with the particular disease in general but more specifically in the environment, that is, the community in which the program is to be instituted. Since most human populations can not be coerced to coöperate in the control and prevention of disease, they must be gradually educated to see the usefulness to them of particular hygienic and sanitary measures.

Finally, projects undertaken to eradicate animal agents and vectors of disease should constitute an integral part of a comprehensive program of sanitation and health education in the community. In this way more funds and more personnel are made available, and success in obtaining the goal is likely to be achieved earlier and to be more permanent.

SUMMARY

1. Control of a disease, either in the individual or in a community, means repression but not necessarily eradication. Prevention implies protection from exposure. Both of these concepts have wide application in the field of animal agents and vectors of disease.

2. The principal means of controlling and preventing parasitic diseases consist in providing clean water and uncontaminated food supplies, public health education with particular reference to personal and group hygiene, attack on arthropod agents and vectors, reducing exposure to the diseases of animals which are transmissible to man, and immunization.

3. *Control* of diseases due to animal agents and vectors of disease *must be regarded as a temporary measure; prevention is the ultimate objective.* These projects should be incorporated in a comprehensive program of sanitation and health education in the community.

REFERENCES

Cannon, A. B., and McRae, M. E. 1948. Treatment of Scabies (with Kwell Ointment Containing Hexachlorocyclohexane). J. Am. Med. Assn., *138*, 557.

Departments of the Army, Navy and Air Force. 1951. Prevention and Control of Communicable Diseases of Man. Washington, D. C.

Good, N. E. 1950. Effectiveness of DDT Dusting in Controlling Rat Ectoparasites and Typhus Infection in Rats. Communicable Dis. Center Bull., Apr. 1950, pp. 5–11.

Hertig, M. 1949. Phlebotomus and Residual DDT in Greece and Italy. Am. J. Trop. Med., *29*, 773–800.

Machiavello, A. 1946. Plague Control with DDT and "1080"; Results Achieved in a Plague Epidemic at Tumbres, Peru, 1945. Am. J. Pub. Health, *36*, 942–954.

Mozley, A. 1952. *Molluscicides.* 87 pp. H. K. Lewis & Co., London.

Newton, W. L. 1950. Water Treatment Measures in Control of Amebiasis. Am. J. Trop. Med., *30*, 135–138.

Smith, C. N., and King, W. V. 1950. Field Studies of Tick Repellents. Am. J. Trop. Med., *30*, 97–102.

Soper, F. L., and Wilson, D. B. 1942. Species Eradication, a Practical Goal of Species Reduction in the Control of Mosquito-borne Diseases. J. Nat'l Malaria Soc., *1*, 24 pp.

Strode, G. K., *et al.* 1952. *Health Hints for the Tropics.* 23 pp. Suppl. to Trop. Med. & Hyg., News.

Wilcox, C. 1950. *Health and Disease in the Tropics.* 200 pp. Oxford Univ. Press, London. (Chapters on "Water Supplies," "Sewage and Refuse Disposal," "Personal Protection" and "Health Policies and Organization.")

Wolman, A. 1953. Financing Sanitary Works in the Tropics. Am. J. Trop. Med. & Hyg., *2*, 557–564.

SECTION II

Protozoan Agents of Disease

Chapter 7

Intestinal Protozoa and Related Species

(Amebas, Ciliates, Flagellates and Sporozoa)

EMPHASIS in this group of parasites will be placed on those species which are pathogenic agents. However, it will be necessary to include information on other species which require microscopic differentiation from those that produce disease.

For etiologic classification the reader is referred to Chapter 3, pages 25 to 35.

THE AMEBAS

General Description.—All amebas, whether parasitic or free-living, have an active stage, the *trophozoite;* many species also have an *encysted stage.* The trophozoite is a naked protoplast without a resistant cuticle or cell membrane. The central dynamic organelle is the *nucleus,* which is morphologically distinct in different genera and even in different species. The nucleus is situated within a granular *endoplasm,* which, in turn, is surrounded by a clear *ectoplasm.* The ameba exhibits motility by means of *pseudopodia* (singular, *pseudopodium*), finger-like extensions of the ectoplasm that are temporarily extended towards favorable stimuli in the immediate environment and retracted when the stimuli are unfavorable. In this way the trophozoite is constantly changing its shape. The pseudopodia may be relatively viscous, broadly rounded processes which typically extend only a short distance from the central mass of the organism (*Endamœba coli, Iodamœba bütschlii*); again they may be more fluid in consistency and have a longer axis with rounded tips (*Amœba proteus, Endamœba histolytica*) or they may be characterized as streaming thread-like extensions, as in *Actinophrys sol* (Order Heliozoa of the Rhizopoda). Some amebas have true locomotion (*E. histolytica*) while others appear to be practically stationary.

All amebas multiply by binary fission, during which the nucleus first divides into two, followed by a division of the protoplasm into two essentially equal portions, so that two asexual daughter amebas are produced with no residual material. This process continues indefinitely as long as the conditions in the environment are favorable. In the case of *Dientamœba fragilis* there are frequently two nuclei in the trophozoite.

In many species of free-living and parasitic amebas there is an encysted stage, an adaptation for survival under conditions not satisfactory for the trophozoite. Among the parasitic amebas this likewise provides an opportunity for transfer from one host to another. In preparation for encystation the ameba discharges any undigested material within its cytoplasm and rounds up (the *precyst*). Then it secretes a tough membrane or wall around itself and becomes the *cyst*. In some species (*Endamœba histolytica, E. coli, Endolimax nana,* etc.) nuclear division characteristic of the species takes place within the cyst. Later, when excystation occurs, there is compensatory division of the cytoplasm. In free-living species with thick cyst walls (*Hartmanella hyalina*) the encysted stage is quite resistant to

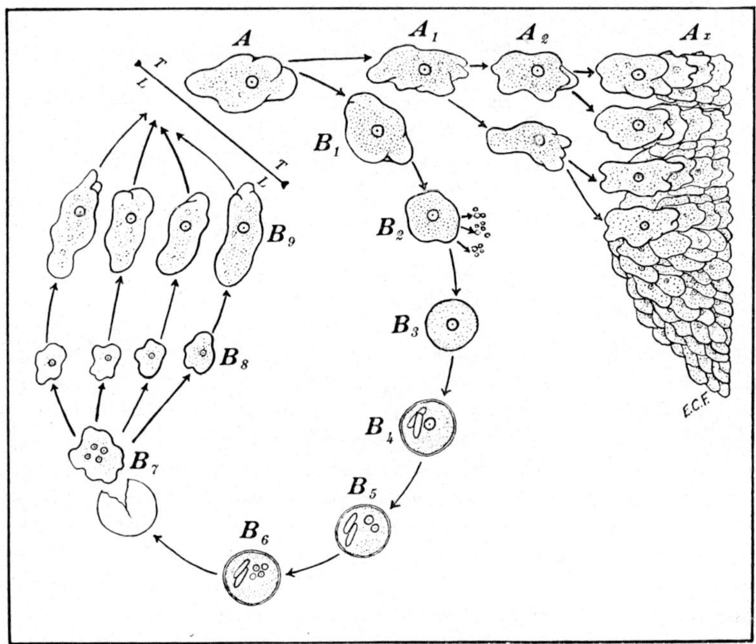

Fig. 1.—Successive stages in the life cycle of *Endamœba histolytica*. (From Faust's *Amebiasis*, courtesy of Charles C Thomas, Springfield, Ill.)

unfavorable conditions in the environment, and fair resistance to desiccation has been demonstrated for *Endamœba coli* (Reardon *et al.*, 1951). Although cysts of *E. histolytica* can survive for a considerable period when the excreta in which they are evacuated from the host are diluted with large volumes of fresh water, they rapidly succumb to desiccation and putrefaction.

Excystation of parasitic species takes place in nature only after viable cysts have been swallowed by an appropriate host and have reached a level in the intestinal tract where the digestive juices are neutral or slightly alkaline. At this time the imprisoned amebas become active and escape through a split in the cyst wall. The freed, typically multinucleate ameba (the *metacyst*) then divides into as many little amebas (*metacystic trophozoites*) as there are nuclei in the metacyst; or at times there may be a supernumerary division of nuclei during, or immediately following excystation, with a comparable increase in the number of metacystic trophozoites. These minute amebas now pass down to the cecal level in the large intestine, where they have an opportunity to grow to the size of normal trophozoites, and are ready to initiate a new life cycle. Figure 1 illustrates the full life cycle of *Endamœba histolytica*.

Two species of amebas parasitic in man have no cystic stage, *viz.*, *Endamœba gingivalis*, which lives in diseased tissues along the gingival margins of the gums, and *Dientamœba fragilis*, a lumen parasite of the large intestine. The former species is transmitted from person to person by droplet spray and by kissing; the exact method of transfer of *D. fragilis* has not been satisfactorily demonstrated.

The amebas which are today adapted to a parasitic existence were free-living organisms in previous times. They must have been ingested by a variety of hosts in contaminated water and during some of these contacts they were successful in developing satisfactory parasite-host relationships. *Endamœba moshkovskii*, a close relative of *E. histolytica* morphologically, has been found only in sewage and has not yet developed a parasitic mode of life. *Endamœba blattæ* is a natural parasite of the digestive tract of the cockroach. Several species of *Endamœba* occur as disease-producing agents in reptiles and amphibia, and other species parasitize cattle (*E. bovis*), sheep (*E. ovis*), pigs (*E. polecki*) and other mammals. *E. gingivalis* has become adapted to the human mouth, and *E. histolytica*, *E. coli*, *Endolimax nana*, *Iodamœba bütschlii* and *Dientamœba fragilis* to the large intestine of man, monkeys and occasionally other mammals. The mechanism of tissue-invasion by *E. histolytica* in its appropriate hosts and by other species of amebas in cold-blooded vertebrates is a more recent development than the establishment of these respective species as lumen parasites in their present-day natural hosts.

ENDAMŒBA HISTOLYTICA

Nomenclature

Endamœba histolytica has been referred to in the literature under a variety of names.

The authenticity of the generic name "*Endamœba*" for the species "*histolytica*" and "*coli*" is based on Opinion 99 of the International Commission on Zoölogical Nomenclature (published September 19, 1928), in which it was ruled that *Entamœba* Casagrandi and Barbagallo, 1895 is synonymous with *Endamœba* Leidy, 1879, and hence must be superseded by the latter. Many protozoölogists have insisted that *Endamœba*, created by Leidy for the cockroach ameba, species *blattæ*, is generically distinct from *Entamœba*, and have requested the Commission to reopen the case. Should a new Opinion be handed down favoring this view, the correct generic name for the species *histolytica* and *coli* will be *Entamœba*.

Historical Note

Endamœba histolytica was discovered and described in 1875 by Lösch, in the dysenteric stools of a patient seen in St. Petersburg. Although Lösch was able to produce dysentery in a dog by introducing the trophozoites intra-rectally and found lesions in the large intestine of the human subject at autopsy, he failed to comprehend the importance of his observations, namely that this ameba was the etiologic agent of the disease. Kartulis (1886, 1887, 1904) in Egypt, Hlava (1887) in Prague, and Councilman and Lafleur (1891) in Baltimore confirmed and amplified the findings of Lösch. Quincke and Roos (1903) and Huber (1903) described cysts of this species, while Strong (1901), Schaudinn (1903) and Walker and Sellards (1913) differentiated *E. histolytica* from *E. coli*. *E. histolytica* is widely distributed over the globe. Recent investigations have emphasized the importance of elucidating the metabolic activities of this ameba, as a means of discovering the mechanism by which it is able to invade tissues.

Epidemiology

Endamœba histolytica has been found to be a parasite of man in all areas of the world where careful coprologic examinations have been conducted. Due to greater opportunity for exposure the infection is usually more prevalent and produces more severe symptoms in warm climates, but in mental hospitals, prisons, children's homes and other restricted communities in cooler climates under poor hygienic conditions and close person-to-person contact the incidence is high compared with that of the general population of the same localities.

Persons of all races and ages, and of both sexes appear to be equally susceptible to infection and differences in distribution can be explained on the basis of differences in exposure. Infants are not as commonly infected as older children and young adults characteristically show a higher incidence than older persons.

Amebiasis, that is, infection with *E. histolytica,* is usually endemic, but epidemics of serious proportions have developed even in recent years in such communities as Chicago (Bundesen, 1934; Hardy, 1935), Tokyo (Ritchie and Davis, 1948), an Air Force Base in England, and a manufacturing plant in Indiana, as a result of gross contamination of water with viable cysts of this ameba.

Methods of Transmission of E. histolytica.—These are not fully known but the following are probably the most important: person-to-person contact, water, foodhandlers and filth flies. Person-to-person contamination has been demonstrated to be the most likely method in communities having poor personal and group hygiene. This has been studied in children's homes (Ivanhoe, 1943; Miller and Choquette, 1947), in mental hospitals (Reardon, 1941, Berberian *et al.*, 1952; Sodeman and Beaver, 1952), in rural populations in a temperate climate (Faust, 1930; Milam and Meleney, 1931; Owen *et al.*, 1934; Seckinger, 1936; Eyles *et al.*, 1953); foodhandlers (Bundesen *et al.*, 1933; Schoenleber, 1941; Earle, 1944), and throughout many tropical communities (Kofoid *et al.*, 1925; Williams and Thomas, 1930; Faust, 1931; Connell, 1933; Hegner *et al.*, 1940; Elsdon-Dew, 1949).

Grossly polluted water has been responsible for hyperendemic amebiasis in many tropical countries, while faulty supplies of drinking water have produced epidemics of amebiasis in temperate climates (McCoy *et al.*, 1936; Ritchie and Davis, 1948; Morton *et al.*, 1952). The hazard of exposure to amebic cysts in individual water supplies in rural areas is probably considerable but is not known.

Food is an important vehicle for the transmission of *E. histolytica* in most countries only in so far as it is handled by persons who are cyst passers and whose hands are contaminated with the cysts (Schoenleber, 1941).

Filth flies which breed in human excreta have been repeatedly demonstrated to ingest cysts of *E. histolytica* and later deposit them in a viable state in their vomit drops and fecal dejecta (Pipkin, 1949). These flies have also been incriminated as natural carriers (Buxton, 1920; Frye and Meleney, 1932), and circumstantially have been associated with epidemics of amebic dysentery (Craig, 1917; Roubaud, 1918). Cockroaches are also highly suspect as mechanical vectors of amebic cysts (MacFie, 1922; Téjera, 1926; Frye and Meleney, 1936).

Animal Reservoirs.—Many species of monkeys are natural hosts of strains of *E. histolytica* which are infective for man and appropriate laboratory animals. Yet this source of inoculum is small indeed compared with human sources of exposure. Dogs and rats have on occasion likewise been found infected but the number of these cases is entirely too small to account for the incidence in man. The overwhelming source of *E. histolytica* to which man is exposed is human in its origin.

The Inoculum.—The viable cyst of *E. histolytica* is the usual and probably the only type of inoculum which produces infection in man.

Exposure.—Exposure occurs by the oral route. In a lightly endemic area a single exposure may be inconsequential but repeated exposure may eventually allow colonization of the amebas in the large bowel. Wherever a heavy inoculum is taken into the mouth the chance of a "take" is greatly enhanced, particularly if the exposed individual has been intemperate in his eating and drinking habits and the particular strain of ameba is highly pathogenic. Natives in hyperendemic areas typically develop a tolerance to the autochthonous (*i. e.*, homologous) strains of *E. histolytica*, while newcomers to the region are usually susceptible and rather rapidly develop severe symptoms.

Morphology, Biology and Life Cycle

Endamœba histolytica passes through four distinct stages in a complete life cycle, *viz.*, the trophozoite, precyst, cyst and metacystic stage (Fig. 2). From a clinical and public health viewpoint only two of these are important, the trophozoite and the cyst.

The *trophozoite* (Fig. 2 *A*) in its natural environment in the large intestine and in extra-intestinal foci varies remarkably in size from 8 to 10 microns in diameter to 60 microns. Size differences are most likely related to metabolic activity of the trophozoite, depending on the immediate environmental conditions. In this connection Meleney and Zuckerman (1948) and the author (unpublished data) have demonstrated that significant size changes occur under different conditions of cultivation in the test tube, and Elsdon-Dew (1949) has shown that much larger trophozoites develop in the Bantus than in Hindus or whites in Durban, Natal.

The active trophozoite has a finely granular, somewhat viscous endoplasm and a limpid ectoplasm which has a grayish, glassy-green tinge when observed under the microscope. The pseudopodia are broadly finger-like.

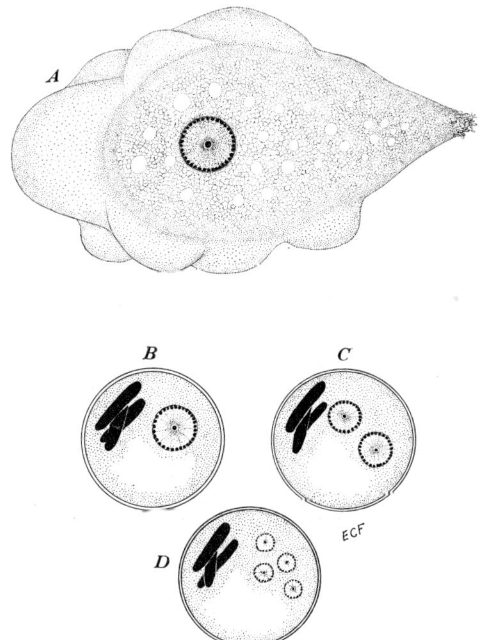

Fig. 2.—*Endamœba histolytica; A*, trophozoite, *B-D*, immature, maturing and ripe cysts. × 2000. (Original.)

During temporary progressive movement in one direction a single pseudopodium characteristically takes the lead, drawing the entire organism after it. At times the trailing end contains many bacteria which are dragged along in a temporary caudal pseudo-appendage. While in active locomotion, the nucleus is in advance of the center of mass; when the ameba becomes quiescent, the nucleus returns to a central position (Fig. 2).

The *nucleus* is spherical; its diameter is usually about one-fifth as large as the diameter of the quiescent ameba. It is surrounded by a delicate nuclear membrane, which is studded on its inner surface with minute granules having a chromatin-staining reaction. In the center of the nucleus there is a single dense, bead-like chromatin body, the *karyosome* (or endosome). Immediately around the karyosome there is an essentially unstained halo, and extending radially between this and the nuclear membrane there are several to many delicate achromatic (linin) fibrils, in the midst of a moderately dense nucleoplasm (Fig. 2 *A*).

E. histolytica is primarily, if not exclusively anaerobic in its metabolism. In appropriate culture media it grows and multiplies best at a temperature of about 37° C., under reduced oxygen tension. In the test tube it requires certain types of associated bacteria or other microörganisms for growth and multiplication, and this is apparently likewise a requisite while it is a lumen parasite in the mucosal crypts of the large intestine, utilizing mucus as its principal source of nourishment. However, as soon as it becomes established as a tissue parasite, it is able to develop normally in a bacteriologically sterile environment. Tissue invasion is accomplished by lytic and physical means. Lytic digestion of host cells provides food for the ameba

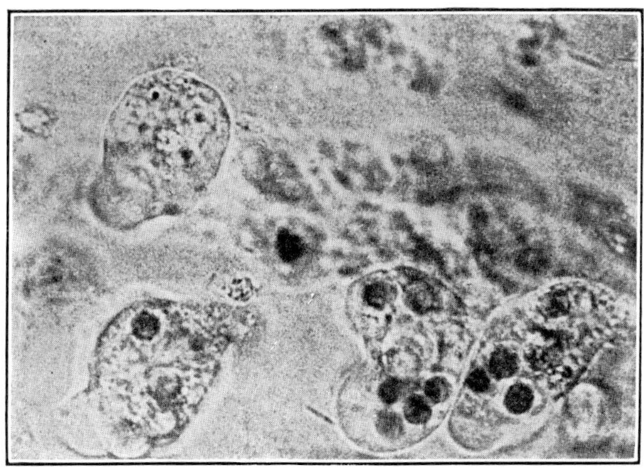

Fig. 3.—Trophozoites of *Endamœba histolytica* in dysenteric stool, unstained preparation, showing ingested red blood corpuscles. (From Medical Museum Collection, Armed Forces Institute of Pathology, in Craig and Faust's *Clinical Parasitology*, Lea & Febiger, Philadelphia.)

and allows it and its progeny to advance into the tissues. At times the trophozoite is seen lying between cells, suggesting that invasion may also be accomplished in part by forceful penetration.

In the host colonization occurs as a result of rapid and repeated binary fission. In this way it may produce superficial or deep ulceration of the intestinal wall, and may develop extensive secondary colonies in the liver and other extra-intestinal sites. Although this ameba is able to digest red blood corpuscles, these cells are apparently not required as food.

Encystation does not occur while E. histolytica is within the tissues, but only after the trophozoites have been extruded into the intestinal lumen and reach a level in the colon where dehydration of the stool is taking place. They encyst by discharging all undigested material, round up into a more condensed mass and secrete a cyst wall. Usually during this process diffuse glycogen within the protoplasm of the trophozoite becomes concentrated in a mass with hazy margins; chromatic material is concentrated into bars, rods or grape-like clusters in the cytoplasm of the cyst. Except for moderate reduction in size, the nucleus of the uninucleate cyst is morphologically identical with that of the trophozoite. Either before the stool is passed or soon thereafter the nucleus of the cyst divides into two, then each of the two daughter nuclei divides once again, so that the mature cyst usually has four nuclei (Fig. 2, *C*, *D*). Rarely a supernumerary nuclear division occurs, with a resultant 8-nucleate cyst.

If the stool is diarrheic, with or without blood and mucus, any *E. histolytica* trophozoites which are evacuated in the stool will remain unencysted.

Viable cysts of *E. histolytica* in the external environment are soon killed by drying, bacterial putrefaction of the medium, hypertonicity, direct sunlight and heat. They survive only in case the medium is diluted with large amounts of fresh water or as a result of their introduction within a few hours into the digestive tract of an appropriate new host. In case the latter condition is met, the cysts pass unchanged through the stomach into the small intestine. When they reach a level where the *p*H of the digestive juices is neutral or slightly alkaline, excystation occurs. First the encysted ameba becomes activated, stretches the cyst wall which splits open at a weak place, and the ameba slowly squeezes its way out of the wall. The 4-nucleate metacyst almost immediately undergoes cytoplasmic division, so that 4 little metacystic trophozoites are formed. These feed, grow to normal size and are ready to start a new cycle (see Fig. 1, p. 78).

It is most likely that in hosts with hyperacid intestinal juices excystation does not occur; likewise heavily-walled cysts may fail to excyst. These cysts will pass through the entire intestine and be evacuated in an unmodified condition. Once cysts have been formed in the lower colon, they will not excyst before evacuation in the stool (Swartzwelder, 1937).

Pathogenesis, Pathology and Symptomatology

Infection with *Endamœba histolytica* implies colonization. The rapidity with which colonization occurs and the depth of penetration of the intestinal wall depend to a considerable extent on the pathogenic capacity of the particular strain of *E. histolytica* at the time of exposure, whether or not the cuticular surface of the epithelium is intact, and probably also on the general resistance of the host to infection.

Some students of amebiasis working with experimental animals (Deschiens, 1937) believe that tissue invasion can not take place without associated pathogenic bacteria, but it has been demonstrated that this is not necessarily the case (Faust and Swartzwelder, 1935). Other workers in the field refer to "lumen amebas" and "tissue amebas" as intrinsically different organisms. They consider the lumen amebas to be essentially non-pathogenic and the tissue invaders to be pathogens. The evidence is based on experiments with laboratory animals, particularly the rhesus monkey (*Macaca mulatta*). No strain of *E. histolytica* has ever been proven to be non-pathogenic. While trophozoites of *E. histolytica* may temporarily lodge in the crypts of the large intestine, feeding on mucus and colonizing, the likelihood of lytic digestion of the intestinal epithelium and superficial tissue invasion is very considerable. If invasion fails to occur, it is highly probable that before long the organisms will be spontaneously eliminated.

Pathogenesis.—The first chance for *E. histolytica* to colonize in the intestine is at the cecal level (Fig. 4). If this does not occur then primary in-

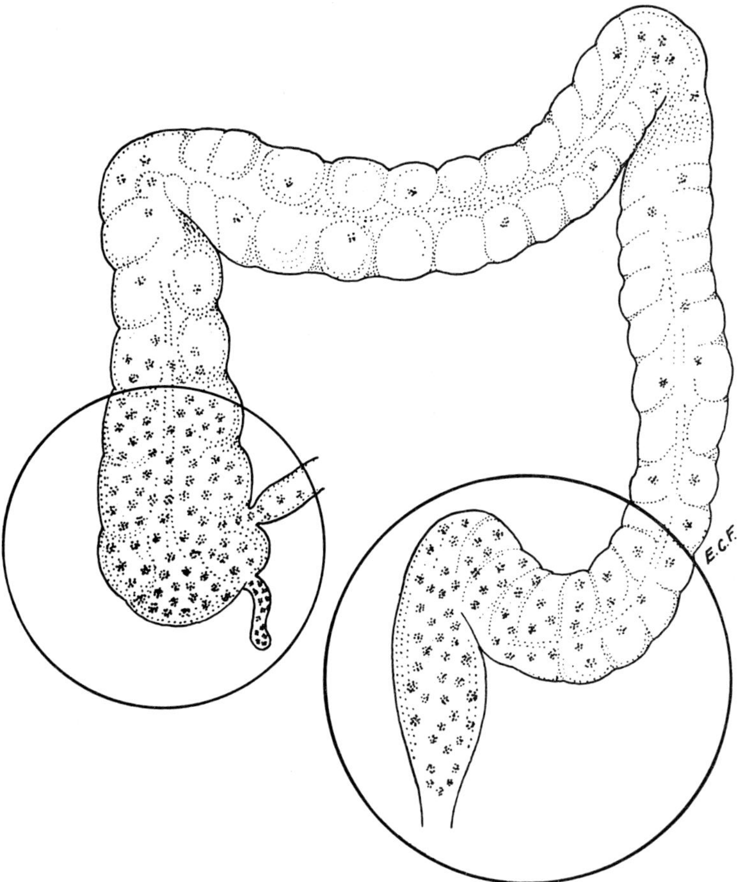

Fig. 4.—Diagram illustrating the relative numbers of accumulated amebic lesions in the large intestine. The most frequently invaded level is the cecal area and the second most common site, the sigmoido-rectal area. (After Faust, Transactions & Studies, College of Physicians of Philadelphia.)

fection may develop at a lower level of the large intestine, usually in the sigmoid colon or the rectum. The lesion produced as the ameba enters the wall is superficially a minute cavity resulting from lytic necrosis of the mucosa (Fig. 5). The increasing colony of amebas usually proceeds in a narrow channel down to the base of the mucosa where the lesion enlarges somewhat as the amebas reach the more resistant muscularis mucosæ. The invading organisms may not be able to penetrate this layer and will thus be confined to the epithelial layer. Moreover, repair may take place as rapidly as lytic necrosis occurs so that no essential functional damage is produced; and the repair process may dislodge the amebas and free the wall of the invaders (Fig. 6).

In many cases, the amebas gradually erode a passage through the muscularis mucosæ into the submucosa, where they are able to spread out

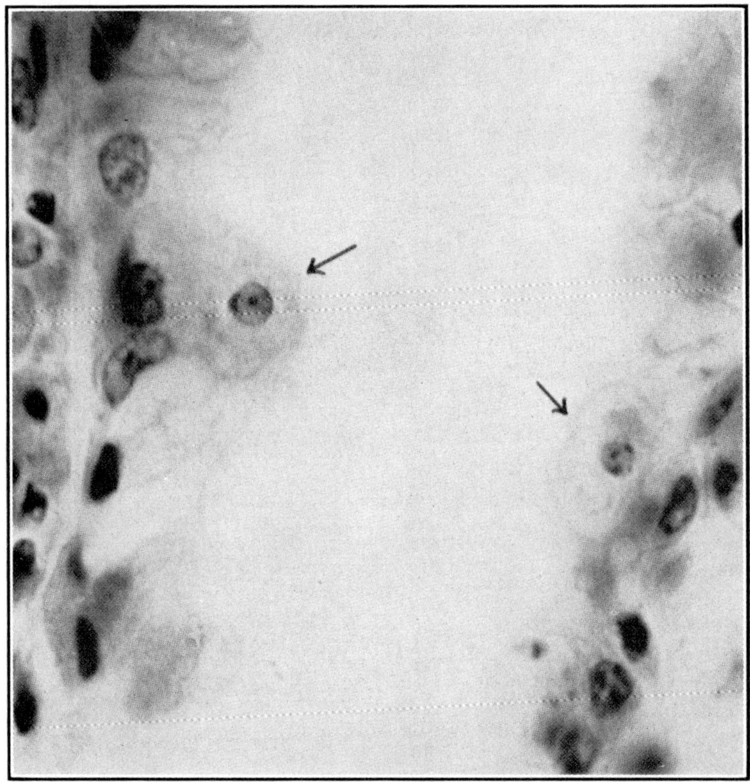

Fig. 5.—Photomicrograph of section of large intestine, showing early primary invasion of the mucosa by trophozoites of *Endamœba histolytica*. Two amebas are indicated by arrows. Note early lytic necrosis of epithelial cells on the surface and between the glands; likewise essential lack of host-cell reaction. × 470. (After James and Getz, in Craig's *Amebiasis and Amebic Dysentery*, courtesy of Charles C Thomas, Springfield, Ill.)

radially, producing an enlarged bottle base. Usually this primary lesion is not complicated by accompanying bacteria and there is essentially no tissue reaction to the amebic invasion.

From the submucosa the amebas may proceed into the muscular coats and may even erode a passage into the serosa, in which case they are likely to cause perforation. They may effect an entry into the mesenteric venules or lymphatics and be carried into the liver and other extra-intestinal organs. All soft extra-intestinal tissues are subject to infection, although the lesions develop most frequently in the liver, lungs, brain and skin, in the order named. *Wherever the amebic lesion develops outside the intestinal tract, it is without exception secondary to one or more lesions in the large intestine.*

Trophozoites squeezed out of the primary bottle-neck lesions by the peristaltic movements of the bowel pass down in the fecal stream and on

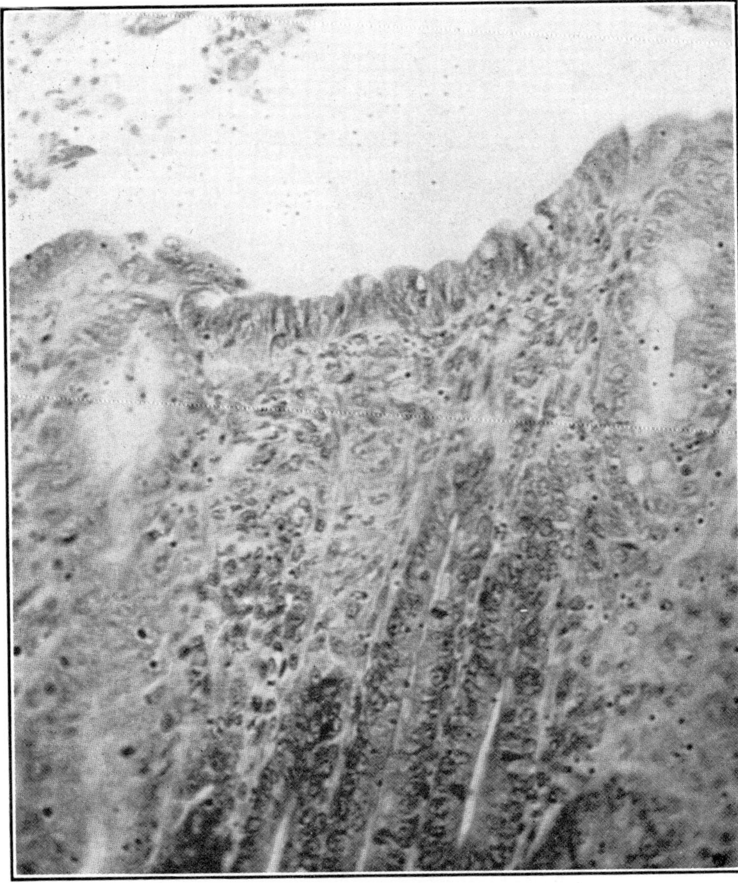

Fig. 6.—Repaired functioning epithelium of colon following spontaneous clearance of *E. histolytica* which had produced shallow ulceration. (Photomicrograph by Dr. John E. Tobie, in Faust's *Amebiasis*, courtesy of Charles C Thomas, Springfield, Ill.)

contact with the mucosa are enabled to produce necrotic ulceration at lower levels, particularly in the sigmoido-rectal area; or occasionally they may be regurgitated back into the distal portion of the ileum where they may colonize. Thus, as the infection progresses, additional sites of invasion are likely to develop, although on the average the cecal and then the sigmoido-rectal areas are those in which a majority of the lesions are found (Fig. 4).

As observed from the surface, the early uncomplicated amebic lesions are minute openings surrounded by a slightly raised yellowish ring (Fig. 7). They are separated from one another by undamaged mucosa, show no remarkable evidence of inflammatory reaction and fail to indicate the amount of subsurface tissue destruction which may be present.

The initial amebic lesion in the large intestine may maintain for some time a small surface opening leading into extensive subsurface enlargement, with tunnels connecting two or more separate lesions. Sooner or later the subsurface enlargement cuts off the arteriolar blood supply to the overlying layers and the surface sloughs off, leaving shaggy overhanging edges. Moreover, as the lesion becomes chronic it is invaded by bacteria which radically

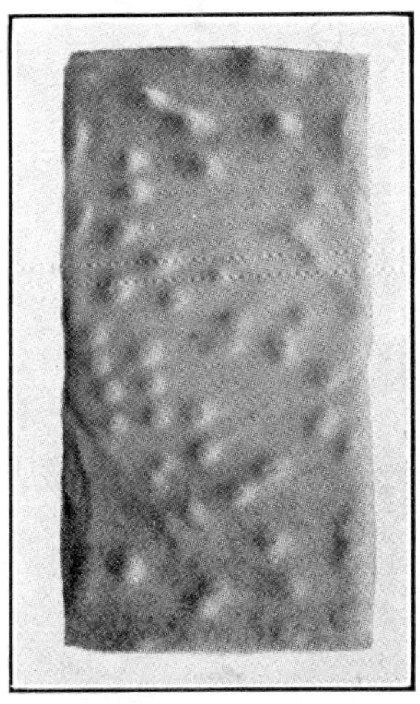

FIG. 7.—Surface view of numerous sites of entry of *Endamœba histolytica* into the colonic mucosa. (Photograph by Dr. John E. Tobie, in Faust's *Amebiasis*, courtesy of Charles C Thomas, Springfield, Ill.)

modify the gross and microscopic appearance of the ulcer. It is now infiltrated with neutrophilic leukocytes and fibroblasts, which tend to form a wall around the margin of the ulcer; and the overhanging edges become thickened (Fig. 8).

The extra-intestinal amebic lesion at first consists of a small focus where one or more amebas have become lodged in a vascular embolus and have proceeded to colonize, producing necrosis of the nearby host cells. In the liver, there is a tendency for these lesions to be multiple, but later one or at most a very few may become enlarged to develop into the so-called "amebic liver abscess" (Fig. 9). Although these lesions are usually bacteriologically sterile, the amount of tissue necrosis produced by the amebas characteristically stimulates both local and systemic neutrophilia in moderate amount.

The stool in an acute case of uncomplicated amebic colitis consists typically of unformed feces, tissue detritus, frequently many red blood cells which are at times rouletted together, and a minimum number of pus cells, together with active trophozoites of *E. histolytica.* In cecal amebiasis the stool is usually not dysenteric; in this form of amebiasis it will frequently contain numerous cysts of *E. histolytica,* but at times successively passed formed stools may be free of cysts or trophozoites.

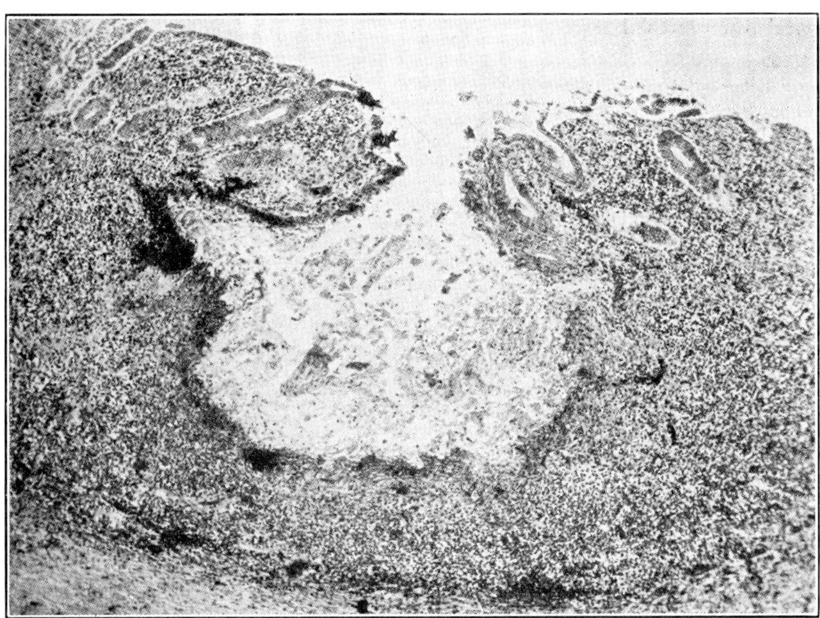

FIG. 8.—Chronic amebic ulcer of the colon involving the mucosa and submucosa. Extensive infiltration of the border of the lesion by neutrophils and fibrocytes suggests secondary bacterial invasion. (From Medical Museum Collection, Armed Forces Institute of Pathology, in Craig's *Amebiasis and Amebic Dysentery,* courtesy of Charles C Thomas, Springfield, Ill.)

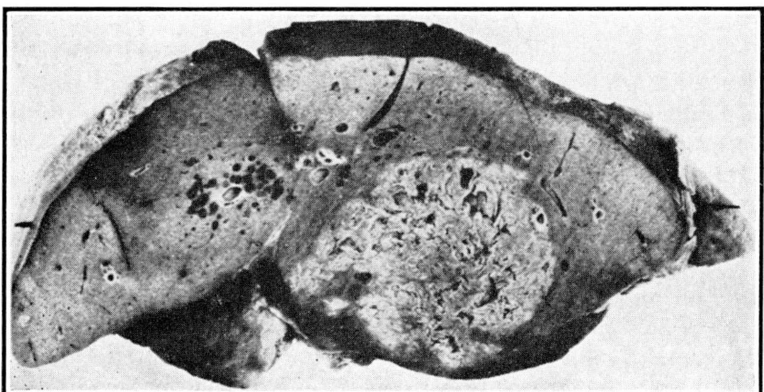

FIG. 9.—Section through an advanced amebic abscess of the liver. $\times \frac{1}{2}$. (Photograph, Medical Museum Collection, Armed Forces Institute of Pathology, in Craig and Faust's *Clinical Parasitology,* Lea & Febiger, Philadelphia.)

Symptomatology.—The clinical incubation period varies from a few days (O'Connor, 1934; Walker and Sellards, 1913) to three months or even a year (Craig, 1917) but averages about a month (Craig, 1944). And in many cases it is impossible to determine the interval between exposure and the first evidences of the disease. The *onset* is usually insidious, with a two- to three-day prodrome of vague intestinal discomfort and loose bowel movements, but occasionally it may be sudden, with precipitate development of dysentery (sigmoido-rectal syndrome) or acute appendiceal syndrome. In a high percentage of cases of hepatic amebiasis there is no previous history of the primary infection in the colon. A modern classification of the symptoms of amebiasis is summarized in the following outline (Faust, 1954).

I. **Amebiasis, Intestinal**
 A. Acute or Subacute (Primary Attack)
  1. Dysenteric or diarrheic
  2. Symptoms referable to cecal area
   Appendicitis syndrome
   Peptic ulcer or gall-bladder syndrome
  3. General abdominal discomfort and tenderness
 B. Chronic, usually with bouts of dysentery or diarrhea alternating with longer periods of constipation, or occasionally with continued diarrhea
 C. Asyndromic, without distinctive symptoms: including easy fatiguability, moderate loss of weight, possibly mental dullness
 D. Asymptomatic, without detectable symptoms; cysts of *Endamœba histolytica* passed in the stools

II. **Amebiasis, Extra-intestinal**
 A. Hepatic
  1. Mild hepatitis associated with symptomatic or asymptomatic amebic infection of the colon
  2. Acute amebic hepatitis syndrome
  3. Amebic liver abscess
 B. Symptoms referable to pleuro-pulmonary, cerebral, or other visceral sites
 C. Amebiasis Cutis

An examination of this clinical classification reveals an unusual amount of latitude in the symptoms of amebiasis, both with respect to the locations of the amebic lesions and the intensity or mildness of the symptoms, hence the appropriateness of the designation "protean." In some cases the symptoms are much more severe than the amount of pathology would seem to indicate; on the other hand, relatively mild symptoms may mask extensive pathology. Except in epidemics a majority of amebic infections will be chronic, asyndromic or asymptomatic. In chronic infections of the colon one must consider that a considerable proportion of the damage, and hence of the symptoms, may result from secondary bacterial invasion of the amebic ulcers. Moreover, it must always be remembered that amebiasis may be only one of two or more concurrent disease processes, as, for example, amebic colitis associated with shigellosis, salmonellosis, carcinoma, appendicitis of bacterial etiology, cholecystitis or true peptic ulcer. Furthermore, at times one or more amebic granulomas (amebomas) develop in the wall of the colon or rectum (Faust 1954).

Summary information on the symptoms in amebiasis is provided in Table 2, Chapter 4 (page 41). For more detailed information the reader is referred to the monographs by Craig (1944) and Faust (1954).

Table 6.—Differential Characteristics of Acute Amebic Colitis and Acute Shigellosis (From Craig and Faust's Clinical Parasitology, 1951)

	Amebiasis	*Shigellosis*
Epidemiology	Typically *endemic;* may be epidemic	Typically *epidemic*, but with endemic foci
	Onset insidious, preceded by diarrheal attacks	*Onset* acute
	Incubation period usually long and often indefinite; may be short in rare instances	*Incubation period* short, usually seven days or less
	Acute infections rare *in children*	Very common *in children*
Pathology	Superficial diffuse necrosis of mucous membrane absent; bottle-neck or crateriform ulcers characteristic and involving all coats of the intestine	Superficial necrosis of mucous membrane, diffuse in type, with characteristic ulcers
	Stools copious or small, consisting of blood, mucus, necrotic tissue cells and fecal material, but with few leukocytes; erythrocytes may be agglutinated and Charcot-Leyden crystals may be present; *E. histolytica* trophozoites may have ingested erythrocytes	*Stools* numerous and scant and filled with cellular exudate; pus cells numerous and erythrocytes not agglutinated; dysentery bacilli present, demonstrable on culture
	Blood shows *no leukocytosis* or one of mild degree; leukocytosis marked if amebic abscess of the liver is also present	*Marked leukocytosis* present at onset but disappears later
Symptomatology	Local abdominal tenderness over sigmoid, cecum or colon; no fever in most cases; tenesmus absent or moderate	Generalized abdominal tenderness; fever usually present; tenesmus severe
	Prostration, except in very acute cases, not evident	Prostration marked in most cases
	Emaciation not marked unless dysentery has continued for weeks	Emaciation usually marked
Complications	Severe hemorrhage, peritonitis, abscess of organs, especially of the liver	Polyarthritis may occur
Diagnostic tests	Blood serum negative for agglutination with dysentery bacilli	Blood serum positive for agglutination with one of the dysentery bacilli
	Therapeutic test with emetine results in disappearance of dysentery in a few days	Therapeutic test with emetine gives negative results
	Complement-fixation test for amebiasis positive	Complement-fixation test for amebiasis negative
Treatment	Treatment with emetine, chiniofon, diodoquin, carbarsone, etc., followed by improvement or cure	Treatment with these drugs has no effect upon the course of the infection

NOTE: It should not be forgotten that the dysenteric stage of amebiasis and shigellosis may in some instances coëxist.

Diagnosis

In intestinal amebiasis there is no definite pattern of symptoms, so that reliance must be placed on laboratory examination of specimens obtained from the patient.

Criteria for differentiating acute amebic colitis and acute shigellosis are compared in Table 6 (above).

Table 7.—*Differential Morphologic Characters Between Endamœba Histolytica and the Other Intestinal Amebas of Man*

	Endamœba histolytica	*Endamœba coli*	*Endolimax nana*	*Iodamœba bütschlii*	*Dientamœba fragilis*
	"Vegetative" or Trophozoite Stage. Unstained				
Size in microns	15 to 60μ	15 to 50μ	6 to 15μ	8 to 20μ	5 to 12μ
Motility	Active; progressive and directional	Sluggish; rarely progressive and directional	Sluggishly progressive	Sluggishly progressive	Active and progressive
Pseudopodia	Finger shaped; hyaline and glass-like; rapidly extruded	Shorter and more blunt; more granular; slowly extruded	Blunt and hyaline; very rapidly extruded	Blunt and hyaline; slowly extruded	Blunt and leaf-like; hyaline
Inclusions	Red blood corpuscles; no bacteria in fresh specimens	Bacteria and other material; no blood corpuscles	Bacteria; no blood corpuscles	Bacteria; no blood corpuscles	Bacteria; no blood corpuscles
Nucleus	Invisible usually	Visible rarely	Visible rarely	Invisible	Invisible
	"Vegetative" or Trophozoite Stage. Iron Hematoxylin Stain				
Nuclear membrane	Delicate; inner surface has single layer of minute chromatin dots	Thicker; inner surface lined with coarse chromatin dots	Intermediate in thickness; chromatin seldom present on inner surface	Thick; chromatin dots may be present on inner surface	Very delicate; no chromatin dots on inner surface
Karyosome	Minute and in center of nucleus	Much larger and eccentrically situated	Large and may be in center or to one side of center of nucleus	Large and granular, in center of nucleus or somewhat eccentrically placed	Large and composed of definite chromatin granules lying in a dimly stained matrix
Intranuclear chromatin	No chromatin between karyosome and nuclear membrane	Chromatin grains between karyosome and nuclear membrane	No chromatin between karyosome and nuclear membrane	....	No chromatin between karyosome and nuclear membrane
Inclusions	Red blood corpuscles; no bacteria unless degenerated	No red blood corpuscles; many bacteria and other material	No red blood corpuscles; many bacteria	No red blood corpuscles; bacteria	No red blood corpuscles; bacteria

		Cystic Stage. Iodine Smear Preparations			
Size in microns	3.5 to 20μ	10 to 33μ	5 to 14μ	5 to 20μ	No cysts have been demonstrated
Shape	Usually spherical	Usually spherical	Spherical, ovoidal or ellipsoidal	Irregular	
Cytoplasm	Bright greenish-yellow	Yellowish-brown	Pale green with numerous refractile vacuoles	Yellowish-green	
Glycogen mass	Diffuse and reddish-brown	Dark brown and indefinite central mass with indistinct border	Usually absent, brownish and either diffuse or defined	Usually present, dark brown and sharply outlined	
Nuclei	1 to 4; minute central karyosome very refractive; nuclear membrane beaded and refractive	1 to 8 or more; nuclear membrane refractive and granular; karyosome eccentric	1 to 4; indistinct	Indistinct; one usually present	
		Cystic Stage.	*Iron Hematoxylin Stain*		
Size in microns	6 to 20μ	10 to 33μ	5 to 14μ	5 to 20μ	No cysts have been found
Shape	Usually spherical	Spherical	Ovoidal or ellipsoidal	Irregular	
Cytoplasm	Alveolar, often vacuolated	Granular and vacuolated	Vacuolated with chromatin granules	Vacuolated, large glycogen vacuole usually present	
Chromatoidal bodies	Bar, oval or thick rod-like masses with rounded ends	Filamentous, thread-like or splinter-like with square or pointed ends	Small, spherical or baciliform, often in a vacuole	Usually absent; when present small round or granular	
Nuclei	1 to 4; delicate membrane lined with minute chromatin granules; karyosome minute central dot	1 to 8 or more; thick nuclear membrane lined with large dots of chromatin or irregular masses; karyosome eccentrically placed and large	1 to 4; nuclear membrane indistinct; karyosome in a single or divided mass on or near nuclear membrane	1, rarely 2; nuclear membrane very thin, often indistinct; karyosome placed centrally or laterally and surrounded by large granules	

The following methods of laboratory examination are employed for diagnosis of amebiasis: (A) Demonstration of *E. histolytica* from a stool, saline purge or enema specimen; from proctoscopic or other aspirates, or following test-tube cultivation of specimens submitted for laboratory study; (B) recognition of the organism in stained sections of tissue obtained at biopsy or autopsy, and (C) immunologic evidence from complement fixation, employing amebic antigen. Each of these will be considered briefly.

Stool, Purge and Enema Specimens.—Routine dependence for diagnosis is placed on stool specimens. Detailed description of modern methods of examination of the stool are found in the section on "TECHNICAL AIDS," pages 577 to 584, so that only general recommendations are necessary here. For satisfactory examination the stool specimen should be freshly passed into an uncontaminated container, and should be free of urine, oil, or fine particulate mineral material such as magnesia, kaolin, barium or bismuth. It is highly desirable that the unformed stool should be examined while still warm, or appropriately preserved in films (PVA or Lawless technic, pages 578 and 580) or in bulk (MIF technic, page 580) for subsequent examination, since this type of specimen is most likely to contain the trophozoite stage which rapidly degenerates and can not then be accurately diagnosed.

For convenience of the laboratory diagnostician the distinguishing morphologic differences between *Endamœba histolytica* and the other intestinal amebas of man are summarized in Table 7.

Saline purgation is valuable since it evacuates trophozoites from the cecal area at times when formed stools are consistently negative for *E. histolytica* cysts. If saline purgation is clinically contraindicated, a high lukewarm retention enema with physiologic salt solution will provide similar material. In both instances the portion to be examined consists of flecks of mucus and tissue detritus passed in the liquid portion of the evacuation. This should be unstained, mounted with a coverglass on a microscopic slide and examined before it has cooled.

Proctoscopic and Other Aspirates.—This type of specimen should be examined as an unstained direct-film preparation immediately after it has been obtained. Protoscopic aspirates from a suspected amebic ulcer of the rectum or adjacent segment of the colon invariably contain a variety of host-tissue cells which are very likely to be mistaken for amebas by the inexperienced examiner. Although cysts may be present in the material, there is no evidence that cysts are formed in the wall; a report of cysts from the tissues is therefore an indication of mistaken identification. Furthermore, a positive diagnosis of amebic trophozoites should be based only on definite evidence of typical *E. histolytica* motility. No other medium constitutes as prolific a source of mis-diagnosis as the proctoscopic aspirate. When the specimen is obtained from a liver, lung or other extra-intestinal abscess, it is preferable that it be aspirated from the margin of the abscess where amebic colonies are invading the as-yet-undamaged tissues.

Test-tube Cultivation.—Culture technic can not be justified for routine diagnostic purposes, particularly if cysts of *E. histolytica* can be demonstrated in direct fecal films or zinc sulfate concentrates. (See above.) However, active trophozoites may occasionally be grown in the test tube from purged, enema and aspirated material when direct microscopic examination has proven fruitless.

Stained Sections of Biopsied or Autopsied Material.—Punch biopsies from the rectum or sigmoid colon, liver or other organs and surgically-removed biopsies of the skin should be fixed immediately, preferably in Zenker's fixing fluid, processed according to approved technics, sectioned and stained with hematoxylin and eosin, for study of the architecture and histology of the lesion and with the hope of demonstrating *E. histolytica* trophozoites. After autopsy sections have been cut and stained by conventional hematoxylin-and-eosin methods they should be superstained with Best's carmine. Amebic trophozoites in the tissues will be stained a strawberry pink, due to diffuse glycogen in their cytoplasm. This staining reaction may be relied on for pathologic diagnosis of *E. histolytica*.

Complement Fixation.—In 1927, Craig published preliminary observations on the development of a complement-fixation test in amebiasis. In his hands this diagnostic method was highly specific. However, in the hands of other workers the test has produced inconsistent or equivocal results. Probably the most serious difficulty is failure to obtain antigen which is sufficiently potent. Bozicevich (1950) has provided evidence that the reaction is more likely to be positive or more strongly positive if it is prepared from the homologous strain of *E. histolytica*. Hussey and Brown (1950) found that the results of the test were more consistent with other standard diagnostic procedures when there were hepatic or other extra-intestinal lesions than in amebic colitis alone. Thus far the complement-fixation test has not become available as a routine diagnostic technic in the clinical laboratory.

Treatment

The earliest useful drug employed in the treatment of amebiasis was ipecacuanha, the anti-dysenteric properties of which were discovered by South American Indians. In 1912, Rogers, in India, demonstrated that emetine hydrochloride is highly effective in terminating attacks of acute amebic dysentery and in treating amebic liver abscess. In 1908, Deeks, in Panamá, employed bismuth subnitrate to control fulminating amebic colitis. In 1915, Du Mez, in the Philippines, first employed emetine bismuth iodide.

A milestone in anti-amebic therapy was reached when Mühlens and Menk (1921) introduced a new synthetic halogenated hydroxyquinoline, chiniofon (Yatren); this was followed by clinical investigation of two related compounds, vioform (David *et al.*, 1933) and diiodoquin (Silverman, 1937). Meanwhile Marchoux (1923) demonstrated the therapeutic usefulness of acetarsone, and Anderson and Reed (1931), of carbarsone. More recently Anderson *et al.* (1949) have shown that thioarsenites have superior anti-amebic properties and Dennis *et al.* (1949) have shown bismuth glycolarsanilate (Milibis) to be a very effective anti-amebic drug.

The advent of chloroquine as a satisfactory substitute for emetine in hepatic amebiasis (Conan, 1948) and of several antibiotics for treatment of intestinal amebiasis have greatly enlarged the therapeutic armamentarium in amebiasis.

Modern Anti-amebic Drugs

I. *Cephæline Alkaloids*

1. Emetine Hydrochloride U. S. P. (86.83% base) is employed for intramuscular injection. In some patients administration of recommended therapeutic doses (one mgm./kilo body weight per day but never more than 65 mgm. daily total) causes an acute fall in blood pressure, myocarditis, weakness, paralysis of skeletal muscles, nausea, vomiting and severe diarrhea. It is effective in terminating acute amebic colitis and in treatment of hepatic amebiasis but has a low rating in the cure of intestinal amebiasis. Patients should be kept in bed and carefully watched during treatment with this drug.
2. Emetine Bismuth Iodide (containing about 20% emetine and 20% bismuth) is administered orally. It has the same toxic potentialities as emetine hydrochloride, hence requires similar precautions.

II. *Halogenated Hydroxyquinolines*

1. Chiniofon U. S. P. *Proprietary names*: *Yatren*, *Anayodin.*

   Chiniofon contains about 28% iodine, its effective anti-amebic component. It is administered orally but may be employed in aqueous solution as a high retention enema.
2. Diiodoquin U. S. P. *Synonym:* diiodo-oxyquinoline. *Proprietary name:* Diodoquin.

   Diiodoquin is administered orally. It contains 63.9% iodine, is more effectively absorbed but acts more slowly than chiniofon; like chiniofon its value consists almost exclusively in killing the amebic trophozoites in the lumen and wall of the intestine.
3. Iodochlorohydroxyquine U. S. P. *Proprietary name:* Vioform.

   This drug is administered orally. It contains not less than 37.5% and not more than 41.5% iodine. Its properties are similar to those of chiniofon.

III. *Arsonic Acid Derivatives*

1. Acetarsone N. F. *Proprietary name:* Stovarsol.

   This drug is administered orally. It contains 27.23% metallic arsenic. Although its cure rate is fairly high, toxic reactions are pronounced.
2. Carbarsone U. S. P.

   This drug is administered orally. It contains 28.85% metallic arsenic. It has proven to be a consistently satisfactory anti-amebic preparation in carrier cases and is probably as lethal as chiniofon and diiodoquin to trophozoites in the intestinal wall, but equally ineffective in extra-intestinal amebiasis.
3. Thiocarbarsone. *Synonym:* Thioarsenite.

   This drug is administered orally. It has proven to be very effective in amebic colitis but is unsatisfactory for hepatic amebiasis. It has the same disadvantages of potential toxicity as other arsonic acid preparations.

4. Bismuth Glycolylarsanilate N. N. R. *Proprietary names:* Milibis, Wintodon, Wia.

This drug is administered orally. It contains 15.01% metallic arsenic and 41.88% metallic bismuth. It occasionally produces intestinal colic and diarrhea but is probably as well tolerated as carbarsone. It is very satisfactory for treating amebic colitis but is ineffective in hepatic amebiasis.

IV. 4-*Aminoquinolines*

1. Chloroquine Phosphate U. S. P. *Proprietary names:* Aralen, *et al.*

The diphosphate dihydrate (62% base) is administered orally, the hydrochloride (89% base) is for parenteral use. This drug in therapeutic amounts is well tolerated. It is most satisfactory in hepatic amebiasis but is relatively ineffective in curing amebic colitis.

V. *Antibiotics*

Some antibiotics, such as penicillin and streptomycin, are valuable adjuvants for treating bacterial complications of amebic lesions. Others, such as Terramycin, Aureomycin, bacitracin and fumagillin, have definite anti-amebic as well as antibacterial properties (Anderson, 1952; Frye *et al.*, 1952; Most *et al.*, 1952).

Standard anti-amebic drugs, their dosages and methods of administration, together with relevant comments, are provided in Table 5 (pages 63–64). On the average the employment of one of these drugs, or a combination of two or three whenever indicated, will eradicate *Endamœba histolytica* from the system; yet none of these chemotherapeutic agents alone or in combination can be guaranteed to produce etiologic cure in every instance. For this reason it seems wise to refer to them as "anti-amebic" rather than "amebicidal."

Surgical intervention in amebiasis is less frequent today than it was a quarter of a century ago. This is due to two causes: (1) Many cases of amebiasis are apprehended earlier and given appropriate medical therapy, so that they do not proceed to advanced stages requiring surgery, and (2) surgeons have become more conservative in amebiasis as they have in appendicitis vera. (Ochsner and DeBakey, 1939.)

As a result of better diagnostic methods, earlier recognition, development and availability of a considerable number of relatively specific anti-amebic drugs and better surgical technics, amebiasis today has a much more satisfactory prognosis than it had in former decades.

Control of Amebiasis

Success in the control of amebiasis requires that it be accepted as a public health problem of major importance. Its presence in the individual patient, whether in an active or carrier condition, and in each community at large, must be detected by reliable diagnostic procedures, so that its total incidence in the population and especially its high frequency in any particular group in the community are matters of official record in the vital statistics of the local and national health agencies. Today (Wright, 1950) only a small percentage of the total number of cases of amebiasis in the United States is reported to the National Bureau of Vital Statistics and relatively little dependence can be placed on their reliability.

The cause for endemic, hyperendemic or epidemic amebiasis in a population is to be found in its epidemiologic pattern, *viz.*, how the agent is maintained and propagated. Therefore, careful study must be made to determine whether water, food handlers, person-to-person contact, filth flies, or possibly reservoir hosts are the responsible factors. Then practical methods must be set up to rectify the difficulties.

In mental hospitals in cool or warm climates, as well as in restricted communities in temperate and tropical climates, chemotherapeutic prophylaxis has been demonstrated to be a valuable practical plan to control amebiasis (Berberian, Dennis and Korns, 1952; Sodeman and Beaver, 1952; Hoekenga, 1952; Yokogawa *et al.*, 1953). Mass therapy with modern anti-amebic drugs is administered to all persons in the group and all newcomers are required to take treatment. In this way the infection is eradicated and potential new sources are excluded.

OTHER AMEBAS OF THE DIGESTIVE TRACT

Endamœba gingivalis (Gros, 1849) Smith and Barrett, 1915.—This ameba is cosmopolitan in its distribution. It is a parasite of the mouth of man and other animals, including several species of monkeys, dogs and cats, and is most commonly found as a phagocyte in diseased gums and tonsils. Only the trophozoite stage has been described; the only plausible method of transmission is through droplet spraying of saliva or during more intimate oral contact of one person with another while kissing.

E. gingivalis (Fig. 10) measures 5 to 35 microns in diameter depending on its metabolic activity. In most respects it closely resembles *E. histolytica,* with a few to several finger-like pseudopodia, finely granular endoplasm and clear ectoplasm, but it apparently does not exhibit true progressive locomotion. The nucleus contains a small karyosome which is central or slightly eccentric in position and is surrounded by a thin halo. There are likewise numerous lenticular chromatin granules lying against the under surface of the nuclear membrane. Delicate achromatic fibrils extend from the center to the margin of the nucleus.

Endamœba coli (Grassi, 1879) Hickson, 1909.—This ameba has a world-wide distribution and is usually the most common amebic parasite of man. Although it is a harmless commensal of the lumen of the cecum and lower levels of the large intestine, its presence is concrete evidence that the host has ingested fecal material.

All typical life-cycle stages are found in *E. coli*, *viz.*, trophozoite, precyst, cyst and metacystic stages. The *trophozoite* (Fig. 11 *A*) measures 15 to 50 microns in diameter. It is a sluggish, quite viscous protoplast. The pseudopodia are broad, short, and do not typically extend any considerable distance from the main mass of protoplasm. This ameba does not exhibit progressive locomotion. The cytoplasm is dense and the non-granular ectoplasm is frequently poorly delimited from the coarsely granular endoplasm, while the nucleus is rarely distinguishable in the living organism. In stained preparations it is observed as a dense spherical mass, with a relatively large karyosome eccentrically placed and surrounded by a delicate halo. On the inner surface of the nuclear membrane there are coarse lenticular or plaque-like concentrates of chromatin. Bacteria and other enteric microbes, which are seen within food vacuoles, constitute the food of *E. coli*, although in a dysenteric menstruum this ameba will ingest red blood cells.

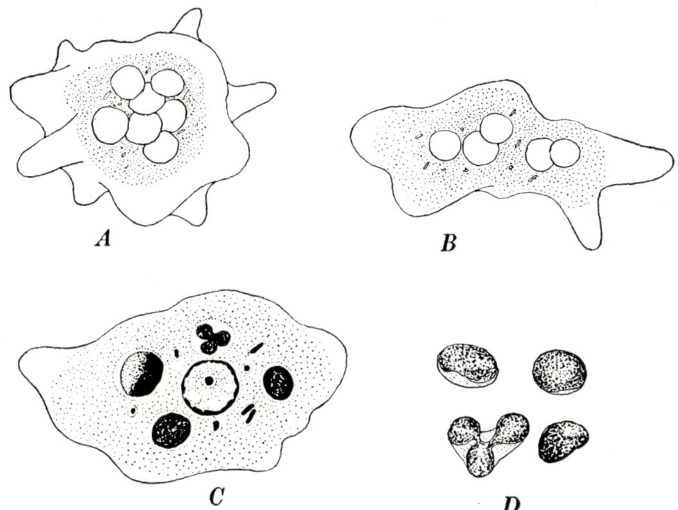

Fig. 10.—*Endamœba gingivalis.* Active trophozoites from gingival scrapings of individual having pyorrhea alveolaris. *A*, *B*, unstained living organisms; *C*, hematoxylin-stained specimen; *D*, characteristic nuclear débris of host cells in vacuoles of the ameba. × 1000. (After Faust, in Craig and Faust's *Clinical Parasitology*, Lea & Febiger, Philadelphia.)

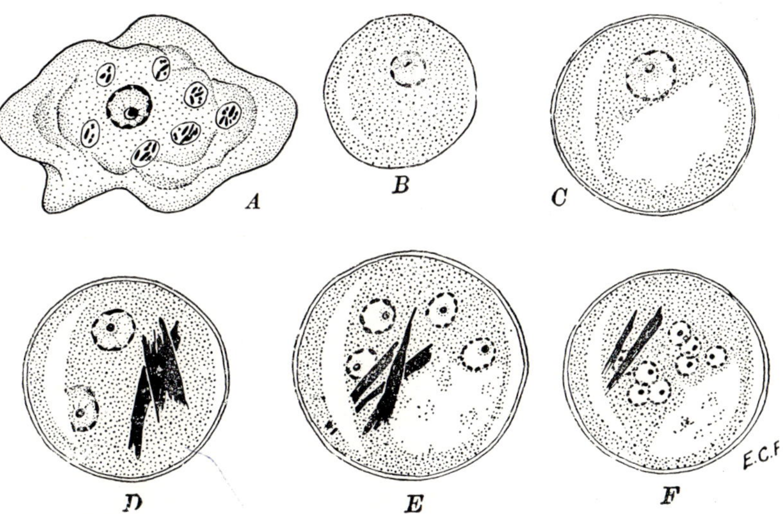

Fig. 11.—*Endamœba coli.* *A*, trophozoite with food inclusions; *B*, precyst; *C-F*, immature, maturing and ripe cysts, showing nuclear structure, characteristic chromatoidals and glycogen vacuoles. × 1000. (*A*, from Faust's *Amebiasis*, courtesy of Charles C Thomas, Springfield, Ill., *B-F*, after Faust, in Craig and Faust's *Clinical Parasitology*, Lea & Febiger, Philadelphia.)

Encystation occurs in a less dehydrated fecal medium than in the case of *E. histolytica*, so that trophozoites of *E. coli* are rarely seen in the stool except when it is frankly diarrheic. The cyst (10 to 33 microns in diameter) is usually larger than that of *E. histolytica*. When first formed the *cyst* (Fig. 11 *B*) has a single nucleus but as it matures it passes through successive stages with 2 to 8 nuclei (Fig. 11 *C*), occasionally reaching the extraordinary number of 16 to 32 or more. The cytoplasm of the cyst is densely granular and is free of undigested inclusions seen in the trophozoite. However, there are usually one or more dense masses of glycogen with foggy edges and sharp-ended chromatoidal splinters.

There is no clinical indication for treatment of persons harboring *Endamœba coli*, since it is non-pathogenic.

Endamœba polecki von Prowazek, 1912.—This intestinal ameba of the hog and rhesus monkey has been reported in isolated instances from man in California (Kessel and Johnstone, 1949) and Pakistan (Lubinsky, 1952). A third human infection has also been reported to the present author. The *trophozoite* resembles *E. coli* in its viscosity and sluggish movement, while the *cyst* is typically uninucleate and has an ovoidal inclusion body. The karyosome is made up of one or more chromatin granules disposed near the center of the nucleus and chromatin masses are present on the inner surface of the nuclear membrane.

Endamœba moshkovskii Tshalaia, 1941.—This species, which closely resembles *E. histolytica* in both *trophozoite* and *cystic stages* has been recovered from sewage in Moscow, U. S. A., England and São Paulo State, Brazil. Attempts to infect laboratory animals with this species have been unsuccessful.

Endolimax nana (Wenyon and O'Connor, 1917) Brug, 1918.—This species is world-wide in distribution and is frequently found in as high a frequency in any population as is *Endamœba coli*. It is a commensal in the lumen of the cecum and lower levels of the large intestine and produces no lesions, but like *E. coli* its presence indicates that polluted material has been ingested.

As the species name *nana* (*i. e.*, dwarf) suggests, this ameba is small compared with *E. histolytica* and *E. coli*, although large strains of *E. nana* may actually be larger than small-sized *E. histolytica*. The *trophozoite* (Fig. 12 *A*) measures 8 to 10 or more microns in diameter. The endoplasm is finely granular with numerous minute vacuoles, so that it has a foggy appearance. In contrast, the ectoplasm, with one or more short finger-like pseudopodia when the organism displays activity, is hyaline and almost transparent. The nucleus is ovoidal or subspherical. There is a relatively large karyosome, consisting of a mass of one or more granules, commonly eccentric in position, and anchored to the inner surface of the nuclear membrane by a few short fibrils. Stabler (1932) has also described minute chromatin granules on the inner surface of the nuclear membrane. The cytoplasm of the trophozoite contains several food vacuoles.

In preparation for encystation *E. nana* discards all undigested inclusions and consolidates into an ovoidal or subspherical mass. A delicate cyst wall is then secreted. During the ripening process of the cyst the nucleus undergoes binary division, and in turn the two nuclei divide to form four, the usual definitive number in the mature cyst (Fig. 12 *B*). Masses of glycogen with a hazy margin may obscure the nuclei. Chromatoidal bodies, if present in the cytoplasm, are coccoid or short curved rods. At times, even in iron-hematoxylin preparations, the cytoplasm may be foggy so that nuclear structure is not clear.

Iodamœba bütschlii (von Prowazek, 1911) Dobell, 1919.—This ameba is probably cosmopolitan in distribution but it is seldom as common as *E. histolytica, E. coli* and *Endolimax nana*. It is a harmless commensal living in the lumen of the large intestine. The trophozoite (Fig. 13 *A*) is sluggish, with little evidence of pseudopodial extension, and the thin layer of ectoplasm is not easily distinguished from the endoplasm except that the latter is denser and has a more viscous, granular composition. This trophozoite has a diameter of 8 to 20 microns. The nucleus is spherical, has a rather thick membrane, a karyosome which is central or somewhat eccentric in position and contains an inner granule surrounded by a number of poorly staining globules, all anchored to the nuclear membrane by radial filaments. Minute chromatin granules have also been described as lining the nuclear membrane. In addition to food-containing vacuoles this ameba is unique in its trophozoite stage in having in its cytoplasm one or two distinct rounded masses of glycogen. When the organism encysts it discharges undigested material, becomes somewhat condensed and secretes a cyst wall. The cyst (Fig. 13 *B*) is irregularly rounded, measures 5 to 18 microns in diameter, and usually contains only one nucleus (although rarely two nuclei have been observed).

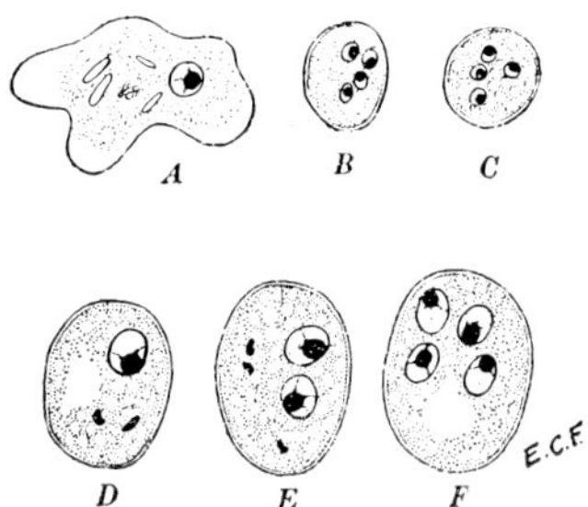

FIG. 12.—*Endolimax nana*. *A*, trophozoite; *B*, *C*, small race of cysts, with four nuclei; *D-F*, large race of cysts in successive stages of ripening. × 1000. (After Faust, in Craig and Faust's *Clinical Parasitology*, Lea & Febiger, Philadelphia.)

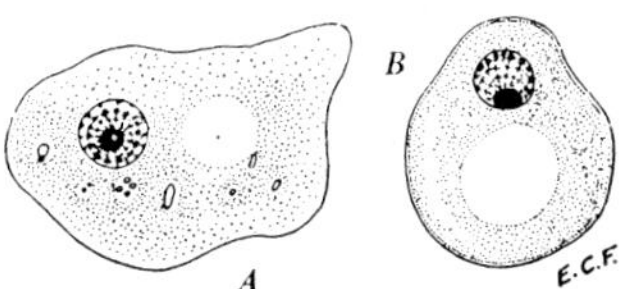

FIG. 13.—*Iodamœba bütschlii*. *A*, trophozoite; *B*, cyst. Note rounded glycogen vacuole present in both trophozoite and cyst. × 1000. (After Faust, in Craig and Faust's *Clinical Parasitology*, Lea & Febiger, Philadelphia.)

The clearly outlined glycogen mass which stains a deep mahogany brown with iodine readily differentiates *I. bütschlii* from the other intestinal amebas.

Dientamœba fragilis Jepps and Dobell, 1918.—This ameba has been described from many parts of the world but its minute size (usually 5 to 12 microns) and the fact that it exists only in the trophozoite stage have frequently caused it to be overlooked in coprologic examinations except when iron-hematoxylin preparations have been made and carefully searched under the oil-immersion objective. This organism is not a tissue invader but it lives typically in the mucosal crypts in intimate contact with the epithelium, at levels all the way from the cecum to the rectum. Although bacteria may be seen in its food vacuoles it seems probable that *D. fragilis* prefers mucus as its source of nourishment. The trophozoite (Fig. 14) is a delicate protoplast, with clear ectoplasm having very active lobulate hyaline pseudopodia and finely granular endoplasm. The nucleus is provided with a very thin spherical membrane that is sometimes not distinguishable even with good iron-hematoxylin staining. In its center there are at least four chromatin granules embedded in an achromatic matrix, with a few radiating fibrils extending to the nuclear membrane. Although uninucleate trophozoites are relatively common, there may be two nuclei, situated close together or widely separated.

Dientamœba fragilis is recovered both from formed and unformed stools but only when there are elements of mucus to which the organism adheres. Since encystation does not occur transmission must be accomplished in the trophozoite stage.

Several investigators (Gittings and Waltz, 1927; Hakansson, 1936; Wenrich, 1937, and Knoll and Howell, 1945) have attributed pathogenicity to *D. fragilis*, which has been the only identified organism associated with certain cases of anorexia, nausea, vomiting, low-grade fever, abdominal discomfort and diarrhea. Conclusive evidence of this causal relationship has not been demonstrated, but it is possible that *D. fragilis* at times produces a mild colitis comparable to the mucous duodenitis which may result from infection with *Giardia lamblia* (see below). At times it may be desirable to prescribe anti-amebic treatment as recommended for *Endamœba histolytica*. (See Table 5, page 63.)

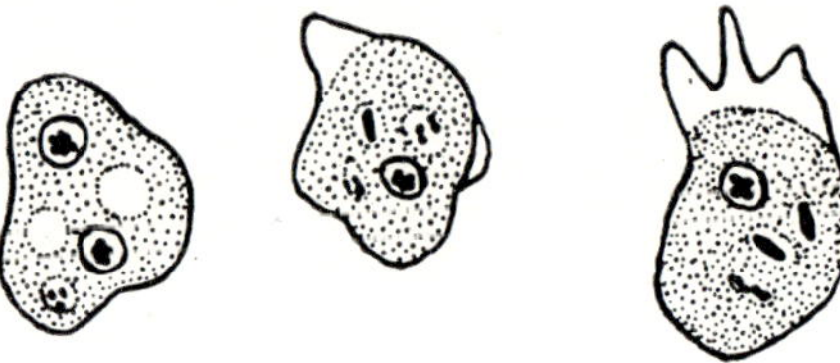

Fig. 14.—*Dientamœba fragilis*. Characteristic trophozoites. × 1600. (From Faust's *Amebiasis*, courtesy Charles C Thomas, Springfield, Ill.)

Coprozoic Amebas.—The following free-living, coprozoic amebas have been reported from time to time in specimens of human feces submitted for examination: *Dimastigamœba gruberi*, *Hartmanella hyalina*, *Sappinia diploides*, *Vahlkampfia lobospinosa* and *V. punctata*. (Consult Wenyon's *Protozoölogy*, 1926 or Kudo's *Protozoölogy*, 1954 for detailed description of these species.)

THE CILIATE PROTOZOA

Many ciliates exist as free-living infusoria and possibly even a larger number are parasites of the digestive tract of insects (*viz.*, termites and wood roaches) and vertebrates, particularly herbivorous mammals such as horses, cattle, sheep and goats. The body of these organisms is covered with parallel rows of short thread-like extensions of the ectoplasmic membrane called *cilia* (singular, *cilium*). Near the anterior end of the body there is a conical mouth, the *cytostome*, and at the opposite end an anal opening, the *cytopyge*. There are two types of nuclei, a larger, less dense *macronucleus* and nearby a small, dense *micronucleus* (or at times more than one). Multiplication is by transverse binary fission, with division of the cytoplasm following that of the nuclei. Many species also undergo conjugation, during which exchange of nuclei occurs. The only ciliate which is a *bona fide* parasite of man is *Balantidium coli*.

Balantidium coli (Malmsten, 1857) Stein, 1862.—This protozoön has a cosmopolitan distribution in hogs and is a common parasite of several species of monkeys. In man it is found mostly in warm climates, although human infections have also been reported from almost every country in the Northern and Southern Hemispheres outside the warm areas.

Epidemiology.—Exposure occurs from swallowing viable cysts of *B. coli.* The number of actual human infections with this parasite is few indeed compared with the opportunities for acquiring the infection from animal reservoirs. Probably man is relatively refractory to infection with the strains from these hosts, so that human infection develops only occasionally from this type of exposure. In contrast, once an infection has become established in man and the organism is adapted to the human intestine, it can be more easily transmitted from person to person, particularly in tropical communities and mental hospitals where personal and group hygiene is remarkably poor.

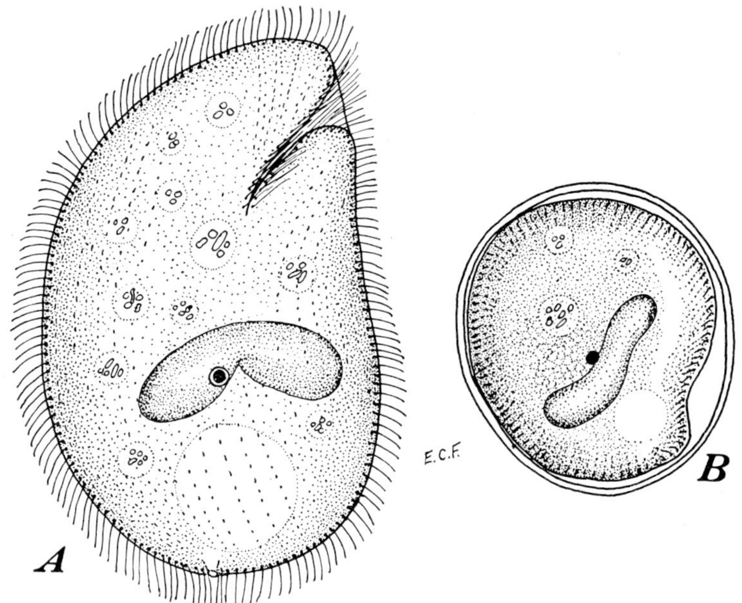

FIG. 15.—*Balantidium coli.* *A*, trophozoite; *B*, cyst. × 750. (After Faust, in Craig and Faust's *Clinical Parasitology*, Lea & Febiger, Philadelphia.)

Morphology, Biology and Life Cycle.—The organism has two stages, the trophozoite and the cyst. The trophozoite (Fig. 15*A*) is the largest of the protozoa parasitizing man. It is ovoidal, greenish-gray, covered with short cilia which are constantly in motion during life, and has a vigorous forward movement as it plows through even relatively thick liquid feces. It varies considerably in size (50 to 100 microns in length by 40 to 70 microns in breadth). The anterior end is somewhat conical and the posterior end broadly rounded. To one side of the anterior tip there is a funnel-shaped *peristome,* which leads into the *cytostome.* A minute *cytopyge* is situated at the opposite end. One, and at times two large *pulsating vacuoles* are found within the cytoplasm. The entire body is covered with a relatively tough pellicle. Slightly posterior to the equator of the organism there is an elongated kidney-shaped *macronucleus* and lying nearby on the concave side of the macronucleus a minute *micronucleus*.

The natural habitat of *Balantidium coli* is the cecal level of the large intestine but the parasite also occurs at all lower levels. It feeds on host cells, bacteria and other nutritious substances in the tissues or lumen of the large bowel.

Asexual reproduction consists of transverse binary fission, in which the micronucleus first divides, then the macronucleus followed by the cytoplasm, resulting in two daughter organisms. Although conjugation has been observed in *B. coli*, this is not a common occurrence and apparently is not essential for its propagation.

The cyst (Fig. 15 *B*) is the resting and transfer stage. Encystation takes place with dehydration of the feces, either before or following evacuation from the large intestine.

Pathogenicity and Symptomatology.—In the hog, there is little if any evidence that *Balantidium coli* produces deep invasion of the intestinal wall, although there may be superficial erosion of the mucosa. In monkeys, the mucosal layer may be penetrated, with extensive submucosal destruction, and in man similar tissue damage occurs. Since *Balantidium coli* is a much larger, sturdier organism than *Endamœba histolytica*, it produces a bigger opening in the intestinal mucosa as it enters the wall. Moreover, its penetration seems to be accomplished more by boring action than by lysis, although definite evidence is lacking. Once *B. coli* establishes itself in the tissues it usually has no difficulty in penetrating through the muscularis mucosæ into the submucosa, where it spreads out radially, causing rapid destruction of the tissues (Fig. 17); but unlike *E. histolytica* it rarely invades the muscular coats and it has never been found in extra-intestinal tissues. Because of the relatively extensive lesion resulting from entry of *B. coli* into the intestinal wall, the ulcer is rapidly invaded by bacteria, and soon resembles the chronic ulcer of *E. histolytica*. While balantidial lesions may develop at any level of the large intestine, they most commonly occur in the cecal and sigmoid-rectal regions.

The symptoms in balantidiasis vary from fulminating, frequently fatal dysentery or profuse diarrhea to an essentially asymptomatic carrier state. In this respect they parallel the broad spectrum of symptoms in amebic colitis.

Diagnosis and Treatment.—Diagnosis is made on recovery of the characteristic trophozoites or cysts of *Balantidium coli* in the stool. (See Figs. 15 and 16.) Care must be taken that the stool and the water or physiologic saline solution employed in making fecal films for microscopic diagnosis of this infection are not contaminated with free-living infusoria, otherwise these ciliates may be mistaken for *B. coli*.

Relatively little attention has been paid to specific treatment of balantidiasis. Clinical and experimental tests with carbarsone, Aureomycin and Terramycin have demonstrated that these drugs are effective in relieving the symptoms, and in some cases they produce eradication of the organism. (See Table 5, page 64.)

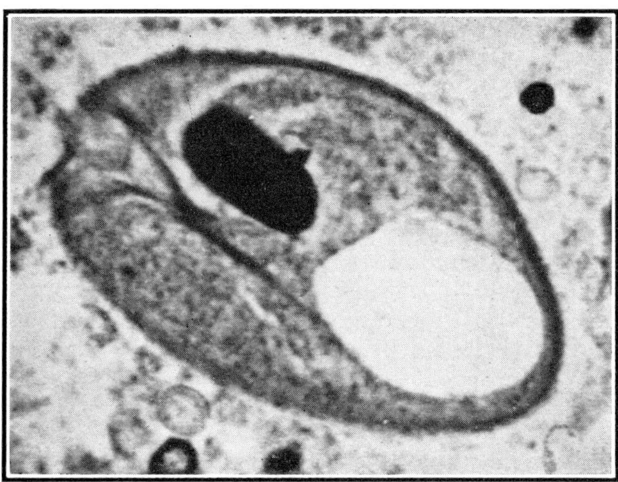

FIG. 16.—*Balantidium coli.* Trophozoite in a diarrheic stool. × 600. (Photomicrograph by Drs. James and Getz, in Medical Museum Collection, Armed Forces Institute of Pathology; from Craig and Faust's *Clinical Parasitology*, Lea & Febiger, Philadelphia.)

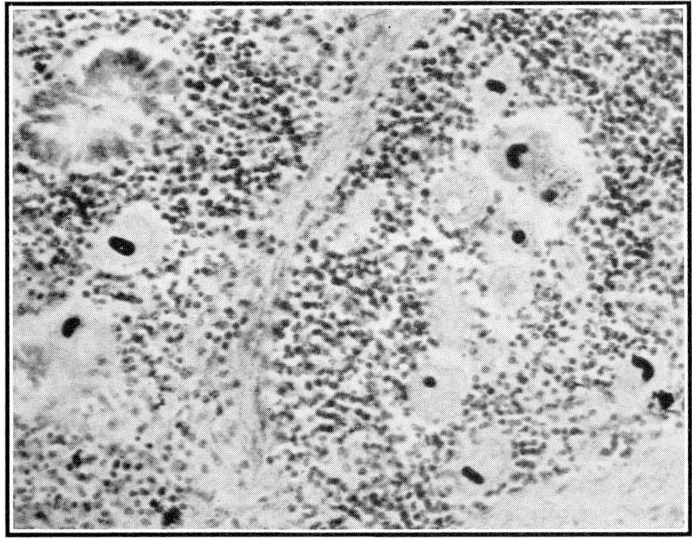

FIG. 17.—Balantidiasis of the colon, with several trophozoites of *Balantidium coli*, in the submucosa. Note extensive inflammatory reaction around the organisms. (Photomicrograph by Drs. James and Getz, in Medical Museum Collection, Armed Forces Institute of Pathology; from Craig and Faust's *Clinical Parasitology*, Lea & Febiger, Philadelphia.)

Control.—Since balantidiasis is very common in hogs and human infection from this source is so infrequent, control of this potential source of exposure is not primarily indicated. In contrast, exposure from human sources requires attention. Possibly the most practical method of attack is to discover all human cases in foci of moderate to heavy endemicity and treat all infected persons simultaneously with effective drugs.

THE FLAGELLATE PROTOZOA

These protozoa are distinguished by possessing in their trophozoite stage one to several long, thread-like extensions of the ectoplasm, the *flagella* (singular, *flagellum*), each of which arises from an *axoneme,* which is associated with a *kinetoplast.* Flagella, axonemes and kinetoplast constitute the *neuromotor apparatus,* of which the former two are the motor component and the latter, consisting of *blepharoplast* and *parabasal body,* the energizing portion.

Many flagellates are free-living; others are parasitic in certain plants; several live in the intestines of arthropods, many in the digestive tract of vertebrate hosts, a few in the genital tract of certain vertebrates, and several have become parasites in the blood and tissues of vertebrate hosts. A synoptic classification of the flagellate protozoa (the MASTIGOPHORA) is provided in Chapter 3, page 25. Species to be described in this chapter are parasitic in the digestive and genital tracts of man.

Giardia lamblia Stiles, 1915.—This flagellate parasite is probably restricted to the human small intestine. It has a cosmopolitan distribution but is common only in warm climates.

Epidemiology.—Infection with *Giardia lamblia* results from ingestion of viable cysts of this organism from previous human sources, *i. e.,* evacuated human stools. Giardiasis is most common in warm moist climates throughout the world and particularly in children who are closely associated with one another, as in children's asylums and large families. Exposure is probably most frequent from finger contact with perianal skin and soiled underpants. In heavily infected groups infection begins in early infancy and is built up to a peak incidence during the years of adolescence. Thereafter it rapidly declines to about one-third or one-fourth of the maximum, which tends to be maintained in later years.

Morphology, Biology and Life Cycle.—*G. lamblia* has a trophozoite and a cystic stage. The *trophozoite* (Fig. 18 *A, B*) is a delicate but very active organism, measuring 9.5 to 21 microns in length by 5 to 15 microns in width and only about 2 to 5 microns thick. When seen from the ventral aspect the trophozoite appears broadly rounded anteriorly and tapering to a point posteriorly; when viewed in profile it is relatively thin and in its anterior half is curved ventrally, forming an adhesive disc. There are *4 pairs of long flagella,* all arising from a complex system of *axonemes* connected with *paired blepharoplasts.* Approximately in the center of the trophozoite there is a deeply staining, short, rod-shaped organelle which is believed to be the *parabasal body.* In the anterior portion of the body there are *two ovoidal nuclei,* each with a central *karyosome,* one nucleus lying on each side of the mid-line. By means of the 8 flagella *Giardia* is able to move very actively, and by applying its cup-shaped anterior ventral disc it becomes firmly attached to epithelial surfaces. Multiplication is by longitudinal binary fission.

The *cyst* (Fig. 18 *C*) is ovoidal, measuring 8 to 12 microns in length by 7 to 10 microns in breadth. In preparation for encystment the flagella are retracted into their respective axonemal components which now appear as stiffly curved fibrils situated in parallel pairs. Meanwhile the protoplasm is condensed into an ovoidal mass and a thin hyaline membrane is secreted around the organism. At first the cyst contains only one pair of nuclei but in the ripe cyst four nuclei are present.

The primary habitat of the trophozoites is the intestinal crypts at the duodenal level, where myriads of the active organisms may be present. Smaller numbers are found at lower levels of the intestine, and at times likewise in the common duct and gall bladder. The stage commonly recovered in the feces is the cyst; trophozoites are seen in the stool only when it is frankly diarrheic or following saline catharsis.

Pathogenicity and Symptomatology.—A great majority of persons harboring *G. lamblia* are asymptomatic but some have symptoms referable to the duodenum and a few to the gall bladder, in which the only plausible etiology is the infection with *Giardia.* Although this flagellate does not invade tissues, it apparently occasionally produces irritation of the duodenal wall as a result of the activity of the flagella and

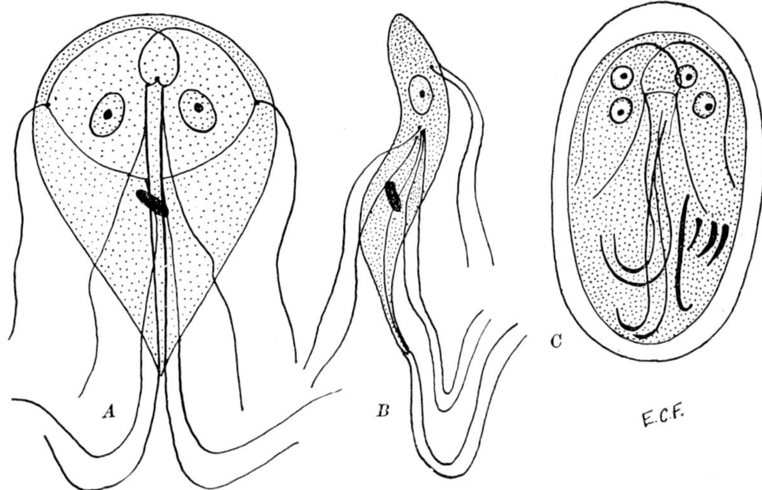

Fig. 18.—*Giardia lamblia.* *A*, trophozoite ventral view and *B*, profile view; *C*, cyst. × 4800. (After Faust, J. Lab. & Clin. Med., in Craig and Faust's *Clinical Parasitology*, Lea & Febiger, Philadelphia.)

attachment of uncountable numbers to the mucosal surface of the intestine. The most common symptoms in these cases are pain in "the pit of the stomach" and a persistent mucous diarrhea in which the stools have a thin gruelly consistency. The patient loses weight and frequently becomes dehydrated. If the gall bladder is involved there is evidence of catarrhal inflammation of this organ.

Diagnosis and Treatment.—Diagnosis is usually based on recovery of typical cysts, less frequently trophozoites in the stools. The cysts are easily concentrated by the zinc sulfate flotation technic (see Technical Aids, page 583). Trophozoites may also be obtained by duodenal aspiration and, if the infection involves the gall bladder, from bile aspirate. In at least 90 per cent of cases the infection is eradicated following quinacrine (Atabrine) therapy. (See Table 5, page 64.) Only symptomatic cases require treatment.

Control.—This can be accomplished only by training children and adults to develop cleaner habits of personal and group hygiene.

Chilomastix mesnili (Wenyon, 1910) Alexeieff, 1912.—This is a common protozoön of the human intestinal tract; it has a cosmopolitan distribution but is more prevalent in warm than in cool climates. It has both a trophozoite and a cystic stage. Infection is acquired from swallowing viable cysts contaminating food, drink or fingers introduced into the mouth.

The actively moving trophozoite (Fig. 19 *A*) is rounded anteriorly and is spirally twisted posteriorly to a tapering end. It measures up to 20 microns in length when in progressive forward movement but only about 6 microns when it is relatively quiescent and the posterior end is contracted and rounded; its greatest breadth is about 5 to 7 microns. In the anterior rounded portion there is a distinct longitudinal

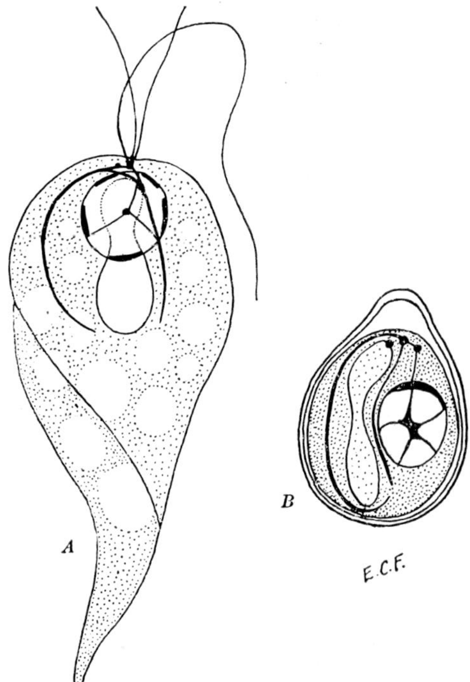

Fig. 19.—*Chilomastix mesnili.* *A*, trophozoite; *B*, cyst. × 3200. (After Faust, J. Lab. & Clin. Med., in Craig and Faust's *Clinical Parasitology*, Lea & Febiger, Philadelphia.)

cleft, the *cytostome.* Arising from a small group of *blepharoplasts* just within the anterior pole there are *2 short and 1 long flagella,* likewise *a delicate flagellum* which lies within the cytostome and 2 stiffer *curved fibrils*; one on each side of the cytostome. The conspicuous spherical *nucleus,* situated in the mid-line immediately behind the blepharoplasts, has a small central *karyosome* and chromatin plaques lining the nuclear membrane. *Chilomastix mesnili* moves forward with a jerky movement in a spiralled path. Multiplication is by longitudinal binary fission.

The *cyst* (Fig. 19 *B*) is lemon-shaped, measures 7 to 10 microns in length by 4.5 to 6 microns in breadth, has a relatively thick hyaline wall and the characteristic internal features of the trophozoite, *viz.*, cytostome, curved fibrils and nucleus. The fully mature cyst has 2 nuclei.

The natural habitat of *C. mesnili* is the lumen of the anterior portion of the large intestine of man. In unformed stools a majority of the evacuated organism are motile trophozoites, which, however, may encyst in a semi-liquid medium. Usually only cysts are seen in formed stools.

C. mesnili is not pathogenic, hence the only significance attached to its presence in the intestine is that ingested material has been polluted with human excreta.

Species of Trichomonas.—These flagellates have the following common characteristics in their trophozoite stage (Fig. 20): a rounded anterior and a somewhat pointed posterior end; a semi-rigid translucent rod-like *axostyle* which arises near the median anterior pole and extends through the entire body, protruding as a rather sharp spike through the posterior tip of protoplasm; a small *cytostome* on one side of the anterior end; a spherical or subspherical *nucleus* in the mid-line near the

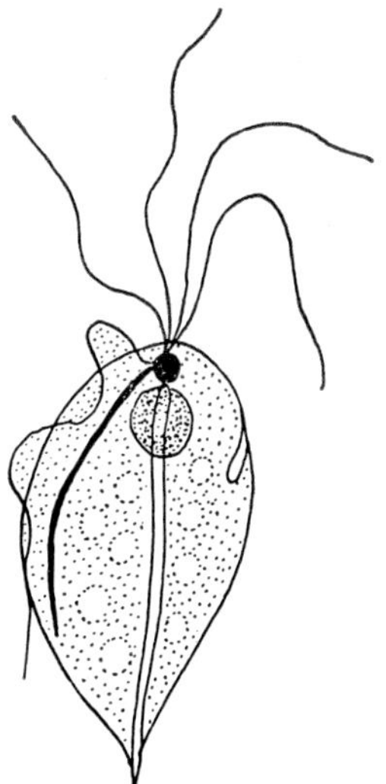

Fig. 20.—*Trichomonas hominis* from a diarrheic stool. This trophozoite at times has an additional anterior flagellum. × 1600. (After Faust, J. Lab. & Clin. Med., in Craig and Faust's *Clinical Parasitology*, Lea & Febiger, Philadelphia.)

anterior pole, a *blepharoplast* between the nucleus and the anterior margin of the organism, from which arise 3 to 5 *free flagella* and an additional *marginal flagellum* on an *undulating membrane*, which spirals down the side of the body. Multiplication is by longitudinal binary fission. Only trophozoites are described for those species that parasitize man.

Three distinct species of *Trichomonas* are adapted to the human host and none of these has been demonstrated as a normal parasite of other hosts except perhaps certain monkeys. The species which occur in man are: *T. hominis*, *T. tenax* and *T. vaginalis*. Although they closely resemble one another they are morphologically different, develop in different locations and are reciprocally not transplantable.

Trichomonas hominis (Davaine, 1860) Leuckart, 1879.—This trichomonad has a cosmopolitan distribution. It inhabits the lumen of the cecum. It is small, pear-shaped (Fig. 20), and measures 7 to 15 microns in length and about 4 to 7 microns in breadth. There are 3 to 5 *free flagella* (usually 4). Its *undulating membrane* has a characteristic movement which arises at the anterior attachment end and proceeds as successive waves to the posterior end of the membrane. The distal end of the flagellum on the margin of the undulating membrane extends a short distance behind the posterior termination of the membrane. There is a spherical *nucleus* near the anterior pole. At times the organism exhibits pseudopodial prolongations of its cytoplasm, and might be mistaken for a very active ameba were it not for the undulations of its membrane and the *axostyle* which protrudes a short distance through the posterior extremity. It feeds on mucus, bacteria and red blood cells if they are present in the lumen of the large intestine.

There is no proof that *T. hominis* is pathogenic. Since it has only a trophozoite stage, it is presumably acquired in a rounded-up unencysted stage and is probably able to survive passage through the stomach and anterior portion of the small intestine only if it is ingested in a menstruum of buffered semi-liquid food, or when there is no free hydrochloric acid in the gastric secretions. In formed stools this organism is extremely difficult to identify, although it may be present as an inactive rounded object. It is most commonly diagnosed in warm weather, particularly if the stools are unformed and contain considerable mucus. It is not clinically important. Furthermore, there is no evidence that active *T. hominis* escaping from the anus is able to colonize in the female genital tract.

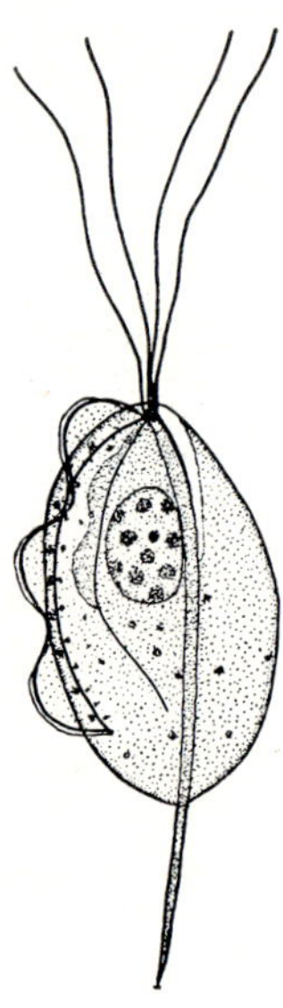

FIG. 21.—*Trichomonas tenax* in gingival scrapings × 1600. (After Wenrich, Am. J. Trop Med., in Craig and Faust's *Clinical Parasitology*, Lea & Febiger, Philadelphia.).

Trichomonas tenax (O. F. Müller, 1773) Dobell, 1939.—This trichomonad is probably a cosmopolitan parasite of man although relatively few surveys have been conducted to determine its geographic distribution. The active organism (Fig. 21) has 4 anterior *free flagella* of equal length, a relatively short *undulating membrane*, a slender *axostyle* which protrudes a considerable distance beyond the posterior end of the body, and a subspherical *nucleus*. On the average *T. tenax* is smaller than *T. hominis*. The normal habitat is the mouth, particularly in diseased gums, in tartar around the teeth and in carious teeth. It is not pathogenic but its presence indicates very poor dental and oral hygiene.

Trichomonas vaginalis Donné, 1837.—This trichomonad is a cosmopolitan parasite of man. The active organism (Fig. 22) is frequently but not always considerably larger than *T. hominis* and *T. tenax*, reaching maximum measurements of 27 microns in length and 18 microns in breadth. There are 4 anterior *free flagella* of equal length, a fifth flagellum on the margin of the relatively short *undulating membrane* but not extending beyond the posterior limit of the membrane, a long delicate *axostyle* protruding a considerable distance beyond the posterior tip of the organism, a large ovoidal *nucleus* and a large sausage-shaped *parabasal body*. This flagellate is found only in the trophozoite stage and multiplies by longitudinal binary fission.

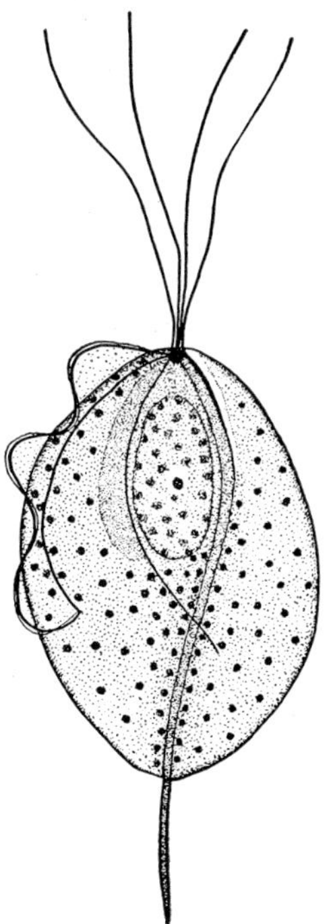

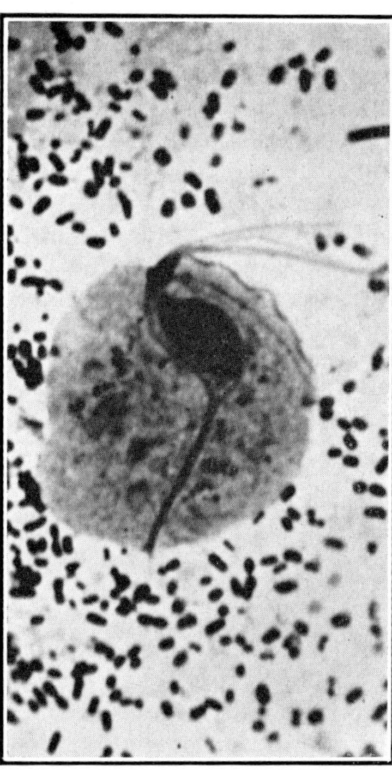

FIG. 22.—*Trichomonas vaginalis*. (Left, × ca. 1600, after Wenrich, Am. J. Trop. Med.; right, × 2000, after Prof. O. Jírovec, Charles Univ., Prague, courtesy of Melantrich, publisher; both in Craig and Faust's *Clinical Parasitology*, Lea & Febiger, Philadelphia.)

T. vaginalis is a normal inhabitant of the human vagina and of the male genital tract (probably localized in the prostate gland), and is frequently found in the urine of infected subjects. It is likely that the trichomonas described by several investigators from the vagina of monkeys is the same species. Transmission of the infection is accomplished principally through sexual intercourse, although there is the possibility that it may at times be transferred from female to female through a contaminated toilet seat, a common vaginal douche or from grossly contaminated clothing.

T. vaginalis infection in the male is essentially asymptomatic although at times it is associated with a nonspecific urethritis. In the female the propagation of this organism in the vagina may be symptomless, it may produce a characteristic type of vaginitis or it may be complicated by bacterial, fungous or spirochetal infection.

There is definite evidence that at times *T. vaginalis* is at least an important contributor to a distinct type of vaginitis characterized by leukorrhea, pruritus vaginæ and vulvæ, burning of the vagina and vulva, and chafing of the vulva. The *p*H of the vaginal discharge in these symptomatic infections is typically alkaline as distinguished from the slightly acid condition of the normal vagina. The symptoms vary from mild to almost intolerable but the disease is more annoying than disabling (Trussell, 1947).

Diagnosis of *T. vaginalis* infection is based on recovery of the organism in the urine, prostatic, or urethral discharges in the male, the urine and vaginal discharge or mucosal scrapings of the vagina in the female. This infection in the male is frequently terminated by oral administration of hydroxyquinolines, while symptomatic infection in the female requires both oral and topical therapy. For recommended therapy the reader is referred to Table 5, page 64. Control of *Trichomonas* vaginitis is a difficult problem but at least all married males found infected during urologic examination should be advised of the hazard of transmitting the infection to their wives during sexual intercourse and should be given specific treatment (Young, 1949).

Occasional Flagellate Parasites of the Human Intestine.—From time to time other species of harmless flagellate parasites of the large intestine of man are found in uncontaminated stools. These include *Embadomonas intestinalis* Wenyon and O'Connor, 1917; *E. sinensis* Faust and Wassell, 1921; *Enteromonas hominis* da Fonseca, 1951; *E. hervei* Lamy, Marshal and Chevrier, 1948, and possible other species. Moreover, coprozoic flagellates such as *Bodo caudatus* (Dujardin, 1841) Stein, 1878 and *Spiromonas angusta* (Dujardin, 1841) Kent, 1880 may at times be ingested and pass through the intestinal tract uninjured, or may be present in contaminated specimen containers or in water employed to make fecal films.

THE INTESTINAL SPOROZOA

The Sporozoa constitute a large group of the Protozoa, all of which are exclusively parasitic. Their life cycle involves an alternation of asexual and sexual generations. In the Coccidia only a single host is required; in the Hæmosporidea, which includes the malaria parasites, there is a required alternation of two hosts to complete the cycle. Two species of the Coccidia are parasites of the human intestinal tract, *viz., Isospora hominis* and *Isospora belli.*

Isospora hominis (Rivolta, 1878) Dobell, 1919 and *Isospora belli* Wenyon, 1923 have not been clearly distinguished from one another, so that it is difficult to differentiate these two species from descriptions in the literature. The only specific character thus far reported is the size of the oöcysts passed in the stool: those of *I. hominis* are smaller (16 by 10.5 microns) compared with *I. belli* (25 to 33 by 13 to 17 microns). It seems likely that the majority of diagnoses of *I. hominis* are actually *I. belli* and that the less common species, *I. hominis,* has seldom been seen. However, both species have been studied by Meira and Corrêa (1950) in southern Brazil and both have been seen by Elsdon-Dew and Freedman (1953) in Durban, Natal.

Epidemiology.—Until recent years very few cases of *Isospora* infection have been reported from man, usually as single infections in widely scattered areas of the world. Gradually data have been accumulated which indicate that a rather extensive endemic area of *Isospora* infection exists in the Southwest Pacific, from New Caledonia and the New Hebrides westward through Indonesia and northward through the Philippines to China. More recently centers of endemicity have been found in São Paulo State, southern Brazil (Meira and Corrêa, *l.c.*), Natal, Union of

South Africa (Elsdon-Dew and Freedman, *l.c.*) and Chile (Balmaceda, 1953). In most instances, but not all, the species has been *I. belli.*

Isospora is naturally acquired from ripe oöcysts in human excreta, which pollute food and drink, or which get into the mouth and are swallowed by direct person-to-person contact. This is confirmed by experimental infection of two human volunteers in Japan (Matsubayashi and Nozawa, 1948). The incubation period was 10 days in the Japanese cases (presumably inoculated with *I. belli*).

Morphology, Biology and *Life Cycle.*—*Isospora hominis* and *I. belli* are parasites of the human intestinal mucosa at the levels of the ileum, and possibly also of the duodenum (Elsdon-Dew *et al.*, 1953) and cecum. In related species of *Isospora* in dogs and cats the trophozoite develops in the epithelial cells of the distal segment of the ileum and the cecum and as a schizont produces numerous daughter merozoites. The merozoites escape from their parent, break out of the damaged host cell and invade other epithelial cells, in which they grow into mature trophozoites

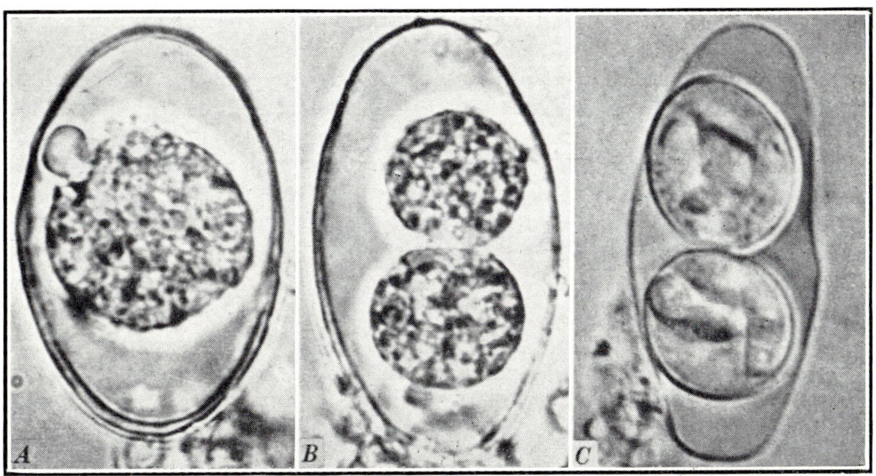

Fig. 23.—*Isospora belli.* A, cysts from freshly passed diarrheic stool; B, maturing oöcyst with two sporoblasts; C, mature oöcyst, having four vermiculate sporozoites within each sporoblast. × ca. 2000. (Photographed by Mr. J. E. Gullberg from material collected by Dr. E. K. Markell in the Southwest Pacific; in Craig and Faust's *Clinical Parasitology,* Lea & Febiger, Philadelphia.)

and, in turn, produce a new generation of merozoites. Eventually some of the merozoites become differentiated into mother sex cells (gametocytes). Each male gametocyte produces several motile male gametes, while each female gametocyte produces a single female gamete. One male gamete then fertilizes a female gamete which now becomes a spherical zygote. This fertilized egg now secretes a tough ovoidal wall around itself and is known as the oöcyst, which is the stage evacuated in the stool (Fig. 23 *A*). Within one or two days the spherical mass within the cyst wall divides to form two spherical bodies, the sporocysts. A few days later each sporocyst is found to contain four curved sausage-shaped objects, the sporozoites. Thus, the ripened oöcyst of *Isospora* contains 8 sporozoites, 4 in each of 2 sporocysts. The viable ripe oöcysts of *I. belli* and *I. hominis* are infective for man when taken into the mouth and swallowed. On arrival in the ileum they probably disintegrate and set the sporozoites free. When these reach the appropriate level of the intestine they enter epithelial cells and develop into trophozoites, thus initiating the asexual cycle.

Pathogenicity and Symptomatology.—Invasion of the mucosa of the ileum or cecum by sporozoites of *Isospora*, their development into trophozoites and repeated asexual multiplication in epithelial cells are believed to cause their destruction and at times considerable mucosal denudation. Probably many persons in endemic areas have asymptomatic infections or at least only mild symptoms. On the other hand, most cases which have been diagnosed have moderate to profuse diarrhea, or occasionally frank dysentery, but it is not certain that *Isospora* is always responsible for these manifestations. The Japanese experimental patients experienced diarrhea, abdominal tenderness and distension, nausea and a fever, lasting 10 days (Matsubayashi and Nozawa, 1948).

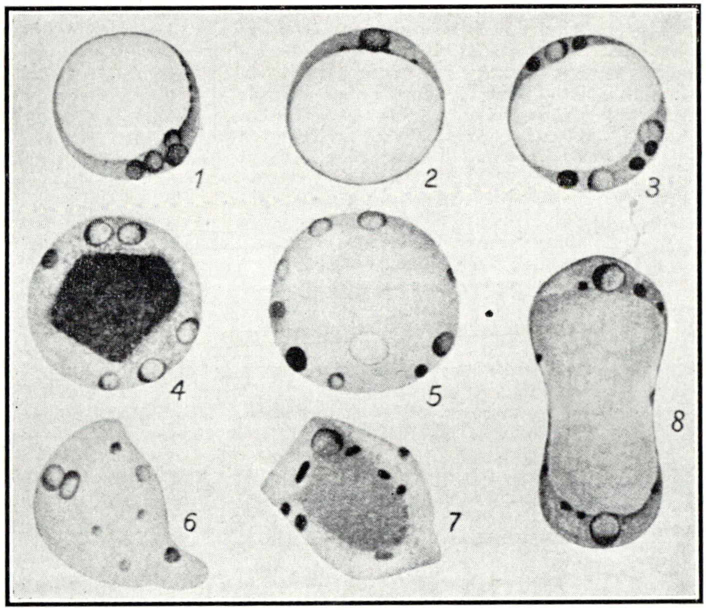

FIG. 24.—Various forms of the fungus *Blastocystis hominis* observed in human feces. (From Wenyon's *Protozoölogy*, courtesy of Baillière, Tindall & Cox, London, in Craig and Faust's *Clinical Parasitology*, Lea & Febiger, Philadelphia.)

Diagnosis and Treatment.—The stage of the organisms passed in the patient's fresh stool is the unripe oöcyst (Fig. 23 *A*). If the stool stands for a day or more before examination maturing stages will be seen (Fig. 23, *B*, *C*). These oöcysts are small, very transparent and are likely to be overlooked even with the high-dry objective of the microscope unless light coming through the substage condenser is greatly reduced. *Isospora* cysts concentrate well with the zinc sulfate flotation technic. (See TECHNICAL AIDS, p. 583)

Treatment is exclusively symptomatic. In early infections the patient should be placed on complete bed rest and a bland non-residue diet. In the author's experience with a few cases in China and that of Matsubayashi and Nozawa (1948), this management resulted in cessation of symptoms within a week, the stools became formed and the organisms were spontaneously lost. Failure to observe this regimen is possibly responsible for chronic infection which is difficult to terminate.

Control.—Until the epidemiology is better elucidated control measures can not be satisfactorily planned. Yet it seems most likely that improved group sanitation and personal hygiene are involved.

Occasionally species of *Eimeria* have been diagnosed from human stools. Critical examination has revealed that these coccidia are spurious parasites of man, since they have been ingested in a non-viable condition in sardines and other fish which are their natural hosts.

Blastocystis hominis Brumpt, 1912.—This ubiquitous fungus is at times present in scant or large numbers in the stools of human beings, both sick and well. Brumpt (1949, Vol. II, page 2006) states that "Blastocystis is a cause of daily errors in diagnosis," because it is mistaken for cysts of protozoa, especially amebas. This organism (Fig. 24) is rounded, varies in diameter from 2 to 15 microns, is surrounded by a thin colorless mucilaginous capsule, has a large central vacuole, and one or more nuclei in the peripheral rim of cytoplasm. From time to time dumb-bell-shaped dividing forms of *Blastocystis* are present in the medium. In unstained preparations *Blastocystis* is semi-opaque and is easily mistaken for cysts of *Endamœba histolytica*. However in iodine- or hematoxylin-stained films differentiation is readily made. Moreover, *Blastocystis* seldom floats in the zinc sulfate concentrate.

Blastocystis hominis is frequently acquired from consuming the skins of fresh fruits such as apples, peaches and grapes. Although its presence in the intestinal tract in large numbers may produce moderate flatus, it is essentially harmless and requires no therapeutic attention.

SUMMARY

The Protozoa parasitic in the digestive tract and at times in extra-intestinal organs and tissues of man belong to four main groups, namely, amebas, ciliates, flagellates and coccidia.

A. Amebic Infections

1. All amebas have an active trophozoite stage. The trophozoite multiplies by binary fission. Many amebas also have a cystic stage, which in some species provides survival. In parasitic amebas the cyst serves principally as a transfer stage to a new host. When viable amebic cysts are taken into the mouth and swallowed by susceptible hosts, opportunity is provided for the amebas to establish a new infection.
2. Man is parasitized by: *Endamœba histolytica* (large intestine); *E. gingivalis* (mouth); *E. coli* (cecum); *E. polecki*, a rare human parasite (probably the cecum); *Endolimax nana* (cecum); *Iodamœba bütschlii* (cecum), and *Dientamœba fragilis* (large intestine). All of these species except *E. gingivalis* and *D. fragilis* have a cystic stage.
3. The only tissue-invading ameba of man is *Endamœba histolytica*. It is world-wide in its distribution but is more prevalent in warm than in cold climates. All carefully tested strains manifest capacity to invade the wall of the large intestine, first and most frequently at the cecal level, secondly in the sigmoido-rectal area. The principal mechanism of invasion is lytic necrosis. The lesions are characterized by minute points of entry into the mucosa, colonization in this layer and extensive enlargement after penetration into the submucosa. *E. histolytica* may also invade and pro-

duce lesions in extra-intestinal foci. All extra-intestinal amebic lesions are secondary to earlier ones established in the large intestine.

4. The symptoms in amebiasis are remarkably variable, including, on the one hand, acute fulminating dysentery, exhausting diarrhea, appendicitis syndrome, and abscess of the liver, lungs or brain and, on the other hand, asymptomic infection.
5. Diagnosis of amebiasis by clinical procedures is tentative and requires laboratory confirmation. Accurate laboratory diagnosis is the basis for therapeutic procedures.
6. Treatment of amebiasis may usually be satisfactorily carried out with several relatively specific anti-amebic drugs. Yet no single drug or combination of drugs can be guaranteed to produce etiologic cure.
7. Control of amebiasis requires correction of the factors responsible for endemicity or epidemicity of the infection.

B. Infection with the Ciliate *Balantidium Coli*

Infection with this parasite of the large intestine of hogs, monkeys and man is acquired from ingesting the cysts. Man appears to be relatively refractory to infection from animal reservoirs but once *B. coli* becomes established as a human parasite it may produce extensive ulcers in the mucosa and submucosa of the large intestine. *B. coli* does not produce lesions in extra-intestinal locations. The symptoms in human balantidiasis range from fulminating dysentery and prostrating diarrhea to an essentially asymptomatic condition. Very little study has been given to specific treatment. Treatment of all diagnosed human infections in a community should serve as an effective control measure.

C. Flagellate Infections

1. The common flagellate parasites of man are: *Giardia lamblia* (duodenum and jejunum), *Trichomonas tenax* (mouth), *T. hominis* and *Chilomastix mesnili* (cecum) and *T. vaginalis* (male and female genital organs). *T. tenax*, *T. hominis* and *Chilomastix mesnili* are non-pathogenic.
2. *Giardia lamblia* has world-wide distribution but is more prevalent in warm climates, particularly in children. Cysts passed in the feces constitute the transfer stage. Usually giardiasis is asymptomatic but occasionally it may cause duodenitis with production of excess mucus and persistent diarrhea, or rarely catarrhal inflammation of the gall bladder. Patients may be freed of their infection with quinacrine. Control requires improvement in personal and group hygiene.
3. *Trichomonas vaginalis* is cosmopolitan. It is usually transmitted by sexual intercourse. In the male, infection is essentially symptomless; in the female, it may produce vaginitis with a characteristic discharge. Oral administration of iodo-hydroxyquinolines usually terminates infection in the male. Both oral and topical therapy are indicated for vaginal infection.

D. Infection with the Coccidia

Two species of this group of Sporozoa, *Isospora belli* and *I. hominis*, produce infection in man. These coccidia are widely distributed in the Southwest Pacific region, and both are endemic in southern Brazil, Natal (Africa) and Chile. Elsewhere they occur sporadically. Only the oöcyst stage passed in the stool has been described. Symptomatic cases suffer from moderate to severe diarrhea. No specific treatment is known. Epidemiology and control of these infections have not been studied.

REFERENCES

The Amebas

Anderson, H. H. 1952. The Use of Fumagillin in Amebiasis. New York Acad. Sci., *55*, 1118–1124.

Anderson, H. H., and Hansen, E. L. 1950. The Chemotherapy of Amebiasis. J. Pharm. & Exp. Therap., Pt. II, *2*, 399–434.

Anderson, H. H., and Reed, A. C. 1931. Amebiasis; Comments on Various Amebacides. Calif. & Wn. Med., *35*, 439–443.

Anderson, H. H., *et al.* 1949. Thioarsenites in Amebiasis. A Clinical Appraisal of New Amebacides. J. Am. Med. Assn., *140*, 1251–1256.

Berberian, D. A., Dennis, E. W., and Korns, R. F. 1952. Drug Prophylaxis of Amebiasis. J. Am. Med. Assn., *148*, 700–704.

Bozicevich, J. 1950. Discussion of "The Complement Fixation Test for Amebiasis," by K. L. Hussey and H. W. Brown. Am. J. Trop. Med., *30*, 154–157.

Buxton, P. A. 1920. The Importance of the House-fly as a Carrier of *E. Histolytica*. Brit. Med. J., *i*, 142–144.

Carrera, G. M. 1950. Pathology of Early Amebic Hepatitis. Arch. Path., *50*, 440–449.

Conan, N. H. 1948. Chloroquine in Amebiasis. Am. J. Trop. Med., *28*, 107–110.

Councilman, W. T., and Lafleur, H. A. 1891. Amœbic Dysentery. Johns Hopkins Hosp. Rept., *2*, 395–548.

Craig, C. F. 1917. The Occurrence of Endamœbic Dysentery in the Troops Serving in the El Paso District from July, 1916 to December, 1916. Military Surg., *40*, 286-302, 423–434.

————1937. Observations upon the Practical Value of the Complement Fixation Test in the Diagnosis of Amebiasis. Am. J. Pub. Health, *27*, 689–693.

————1944. *The Etiology, Diagnosis and Treatment of Amebiasis.* 332 pp. Williams & Wilkins Co., Baltimore.

David, N. A., Johnstone, H. G., Reed, A. C., and Leake, C. D. 1933. Treatment of Amebiasis with Iodochlorhydroxyquinoline (vioform NNR). J. Pharm. & Exp. Therap., *48*, 271.

Dennis, E. W., *et al.* 1949. Amœbicidal Activity of Bismuthoxy-*p*-N-glycolyl-arsanilate and 7-iodo-4-(1-methyl-4-diethylamino-butylamino) quinoline diphosphate. Am. J. Trop. Med., *29*, 683–689.

Deschiens, R. E. A. 1937. Rôle de la Flore Microbienne Associée à l'Amibe Dysentèrique dans l'Ètiologie de l'Amibiase Expérimentale. C. R. Soc. Biol., *125*, 1017–1020.

Elsdon-Dew, R. 1949. Endemic Fulminating Amebic Dysentery. Am. J. Trop. Med., *29*, 337–340.

Eyles, D. E., Jones, F. E., and Smith, C. S. 1953. A Study of *Endamœba Histolytica* and Other Intestinal Parasites in a Rural West Tennessee Community. Am. J. Trop. Med. & Hyg., *2*, 173–190.

Faust, E. C. 1930. A Study of the Intestinal Protozoa of a Representative Sampling of the Population of Wise County, Southwestern Virginia. Am. J. Hyg., *11*, 371–384.

————1954. *Amebiasis.* 154 pp. Charles C Thomas, Springfield, Ill.

Faust, E. C., and Swartzwelder, J. C. 1935. Effect of Continuous Passage of *Endamœba Histolytica* Through Experimental Dogs. Proc. Soc. Exp. Biol. & Med., *32*, 954–958.

Frye, W. W., Brooke, M. M., and Weinstein, P. 1952. Antibiotics in the Treatment of Acute Amebic Dysentery. Ann. New York Acad. Sci., *55*, 1104–1113.

Frye, W. W., and Meleney, H. E. 1932. *Endamœba Histolytica* and Other Intestinal Protozoa of Tennessee. IV. A Study of Filth Flies, Rats, Mice and Some Domestic Animals as Possible Carriers of the Intestinal Protozoa of Man in a Rural Community. Am. J. Hyg., *16*, 729–749.

———1936. The Viability of *Endamœba Histolytica* after Passage Through the Cockroach. J. Parasitol., *22*, 221–222.

Hakansson, E. G. 1936. *Dientamœba Fragilis*, A Cause of Illness. Am. J. Trop. Med., *16*, 175–183.

Hardy, A. V. 1935. The Occurrence of Infestations with *E. Histolytica* Associated with Water-borne Diseases. Pub. Health Repts., *50*, 323–334.

Hoare, C. 1950. Amœbiasis in Great Britain with Special Reference to Carriers. Brit. Med. J., *ii*, 238–241.

Hoekenga, M. 1952. The Prophylaxis of Malaria and Amebiasis with Milibis-Aralen. J. Lab. & Clin. Med., *39*, 267–270.

Hussey, K. L., and Brown, H. W. 1950. The Complement Fixation Test for Hepatic Amebiasis. Am. J. Trop. Med., *30*, 147–154.

Ivanhoe, G. L. 1943. Studies on the Transmission of Amebiasis in a Children's Home in New Orleans. Am. J. Trop. Med., *23*, 401–419.

Kaplan, B., Williamson, C. S., and Geiger, J. C. 1927. Amebic Dysentery in Chicago. Preliminary Report of a Survey of Food Handlers Following a Small Outbreak. J. Am. Med. Assn., *88*, 977–980.

Kessel, J. F., and Johnstone, H. G. 1949. The Occurrence of *Endamœba polecki*, Prowazek, 1912, in *Macaca Mulatta* and Man. Am. J. Trop. Med., *29*, 311–317.

Knoll, E. W., and Howell, K. M. 1945. Studies on *Dientamœba Fragilis;* Its Incidence and Possible Pathogenicity. Am. J. Clin. Med., *15*, 178–183.

Leidy, J. 1879. On *Amœba Blattæ*. Proc. Acad. Nat. Sci., Phila., *31*, 204–205.

McCoy, G. W., *et al.* 1936. Epidemic Amebic Dysentery. Nat'l Inst. Health Bull. No. 166. 187 pp. Washington, D. C.

McVay, L. V., Jr., and Sprunt, D. H. 1952. A Long-term Evaluation of Aureomycin in the Treatment of Amebaisis. South. Med. J., *45*, 183–190.

Milam, D. F., and Meleney, H. E. 1931. Investigations of *Endamœba Histolytica* and Other Intestinal Protozoa in Tennessee. Am. J. Hyg., *14*, 325–336.

Miller, M. J., and Choquette, L. P. E. 1947. Studies on Amœbiasis in Canada. Canad. J. Research, *E*, *25*, 1–4.

Miyagawa, M., Wykoff, D. E., and Ritchie, L. S. 1953. Mass Treatment of *Endamœba Histolytica* Carriers. U. S. Armed Forces Med. J., *4*, 1776–1777.

Morton, T. C., Stamm, W. P., and Seidelin, R. 1952. Indigenous Amœbiasis: A Recent Outbreak in England. Brit. Med. J., *ii*, 114–116.

Most, H., and Van Assendelft, F. 1951. Laboratory and Clinical Observations on the Effect of Terramycin in the Treatment of Amebiasis. Am. J. Trop. Med., *31*, 284–285.

———1952. Treatment of Amebiasis with Terramycin. Ann. New York Acad. Sci., *55*, 1114–1117.

Mühlens, P., and Menk, W. 1921. Ueber Behandlungsversuche der Chronischen Amöbenruhr mit Yatren. Muench. Med. Wchnschr., *68*, 802.

Newton, W. L. 1950. Water Treatment Measures in Control of Amebaisis. Am. J. Trop. Med., *30*, 135–138.

Ochsner, A., and DeBakey, M. 1939. Surgical Considerations of Amebiasis. Internat'l Abstr. Surg., *69*, 392–403.

Pipkin, A. C. 1949. Experimental Studies on the Rôle of Filth Flies in the Transmission of *Endamœba Histolytica.* Am. J. Hyg., *49*, 255–275.

Reardon, L. V. 1941. Incidence of *Endamœba Histolytica* and Intestinal Nematodes in a Georgia State Institution. J. Parasitol., *27*, 89–90.

Reardon, L. V., Verder, E., and Rees, C. W. 1952. The Cultural Requirements of *Endamœba Coli* and the Comparative Effects of Drying on the Cysts of *E. Coli* and *E. Histolytica.* Am. J. Trop. Med. & Hyg., *1*, 155–161.

Ritchie, L. S., and Davis, C. 1948. Parasitological Findings and Epidemiological Aspects of Epidemic Amebiasis Occurring in Occupants of the Mantetsu Apartment Buildings, Tokyo, Japan. Am. J. Trop. Med., *28*, 803–816.

Rogers, L. 1912. The Rapid Cure of Amœbic Dysentery and Hepatitis by Hypodermic Injections of Soluble Salts of Emetine. Brit. Med. J., *i*, 1924.

Schoenleber, A. W. 1941. The Food Handler as a Transmitter of Amebiasis. J. Trop. Med. & Hyg., *44*, 41–43.

Silverman, D. N. 1937. Treatment of Amebic Colitis with Diiodohydroxyquinoline (Diodoquin). Am. J. Dig. Diseases, *4*, 281–282.

Sodeman, W. A., and Beaver, P. C. 1952. A Study of the Therapeutic Effects of Some Amebacidal Drugs. Am. J. Med., *12*, 440–446.

Strong, R. P. 1901. The Etiology of the Dysenteries of the Philippine Islands. Circ. Trop. Dis., Manila, 54 pp.

Swartzwelder, J. R. 1937. Studies on the Infection of Dogs with Trophozoites of *Endamœba Histolytica* by the Oral Route. Pub. Health Repts., *52*, 1447–1451.

Tobie, J. E., *et al.* 1951. Laboratory Results on the Efficacy of Terramycin, Aureomycin and Bacitracin in the Treatment of Asymptomatic Amebiasis. Am. J. Trop. Med., *31*, 414–419.

Walker, E. L., and Sellards, A. W. 1913. Experimental Entamœbic Dysentery. Philippine J. Sci. (B), *8*, 253–331.

Wright, W. H. 1950. The Public Health Status of Amebiasis in the United States as Revealed by Available Statistics. Am. J. Trop. Med., *30*, 123–133.

Balantidium Coli

Burrows, R. C., and Jahnes, W. G. 1952. The Effect of Aureomycin on Balantidiasis. Am. J. Trop. Med. & Hyg., *1*, 626–630.

Hoekenga, M. T. 1953. Treatment of Balantidiasis in Honduras. Am. J. Trop. Med. & Hyg., *2*, 271–272.

Young, M. D., and Burrows, R. 1943. Carbarsone Treatment for *Balantidium Coli* Infection. Pub. Health Repts., *58*, 1272–1273.

The Flagellates

Feo, L. G. 1944. The Incidence and Significance of *Trichomonas Vaginalis* Infestation in the Male. Am. J. Trop. Med., *24*, 195–198.

Kessel, J. F. 1939. The Pathology of *Trichomonas* Vaginitis. Abstracts, 3rd Internat'l Congr. Microbiol., p. 161.

Kofoid, C. A., and Sweezy, O. 1920. On the Morphology and Mitosis of *Chilomastix Mesnili* (Wenyon), a Common Flagellate of the Human Intestine. Univ. Calif. Publ. Zoöl., *20*, 117–144.

Stabler, R. M., Feo, L. G., and Rakoff, A. E. 1941. Implantation of Intestinal Trichomonads (*T. hominis*) into the Human Vagina. Am. J. Hyg., *34*, C, 114–118.

Trussell, R. E. 1947. *Trichomonas Vaginalis and Trichomoniasis.* 277 pp. Charles C Thomas, Springfield, Ill.

Wenrich, D. H. 1944. Comparative Morphology of the Trichomonad Flagellates of Man. Am. J. Trop. Med., *24*, 39–51.

Young, R. V. 1949. Trichomoniasis in the Male. Rocky Mt. Med. J., *46*, 928–931.

The Coccidia

Dobell, C., and O'Connor, F. W. 1921. *The Intestinal Protozoa of Man.* 211 pp. Wm. Wood & Co., New York.

Elsdon-Dew, R., and Freedman, L. 1952. Intestinal Parasites in the Natal Bantu. S. Afr. J. Clin. Sci., *3*, 59–65.

————1953. Coccidiosis in Man: Experiences in Natal. Trans. R. Soc. Trop. Med. & Hyg., *47*, 209–214.

Elsdon-Dew, R., Roach, G. G., and Freedman, L. 1953. *Isospora Belli* (Wenyon) from Duodenal Intubation. Lancet, *i*, 348.

Matsubayashi, H., and Nozawa, T. 1948. Experimental Infection of *Isospora Hominis* in Man. Am. J. Trop. Med., *28*, 633–637.

Meira, J. A., and Correa, M. O. A. 1950. Isosporose Humana. Consideraçoes sobre 28 casos. Abstracts of Papers, V. Internat'l Congr. Mircobiol., page 154. Rio de Janeiro.

————1950. Isosporose Humana; Consideraçoes sobre 28 casos. Rev. Inst. Adolfo Lutz, *10*, 117–139.

Mukherjee, N. N. 1947. Incidence of Coccidiosis in the Arakan. Indian Med. Gaz. *82*, 735–736.

Thomson, J. G., and Robertson, A. 1926. Fish as the Source of Certain Coccidia Recently Described as Intestinal Parasites of Man. Brit. Med. J., *i*, 282–283.

Chapter 8

The Malaria Parasites

THE HEMOSPORIDIA

THE malaria parasites belong to the Class **Sporozoa,** Order **Hæmosporidea.** The life cycle of the *hemosporidia,* like that of the coccidia (see Chapter 7, pages 112–115), includes an asexual phase (*schizogony*) alternating with a sexual one (*gametogony* followed by *sporogony*). However, the coccidia utilize only one host to complete a cycle, while the hemosporidia require two hosts, an intermediate one in which the asexual phase develops and mother sex cells (*gametocytes*) are produced, and a definitive one in which the sex cells become mature *gametes.* Following maturation the male (*microgamete*) unites with the female (*macrogamete*) to form a *zygote,* which then becomes encysted (*oöcyst*) and produces a considerable number of sexual spores (*sporozoites*). The sporozoites, when introduced into the intermediate host, develop into the asexual stage. In this type of life cycle there are two separate transfer stages, the gametocyte and the sporozoite. The asexual phase of the cycle (*schizogony*) is found only in vertebrate hosts, while maturation and union of sex cells (*i. e.,* completion of *gametogony*) followed by production of spores (*sporogony*) takes place only in blood-sucking invertebrates, which are mostly arthropods and predominantly mosquitoes.

There are considerable differences in the way the asexual stages of different genera and species of hemosporidia develop in the tissues of the vertebrate host. In the genus *Leucocytozoön,* asexual multiplication occurs in fixed non-erythrocytic cells and only the gametocytes appear in circulating blood. In many species of malaria parasites of birds the earliest asexual stages occur in the fixed cells of the reticulo-endothelial system and the endothelial lining cells of the blood capillaries. After these primary exo-erythrocytic foci have become established, some of the asexual daughter cells (*merozoites*) invade red blood cells and initiate erythrocytic infection (Huff and Bloom, 1935; Manwell and Goldstein, 1939; Porter, 1942; Brumpt, 1936; James and Tate, 1938). The malaria parasites in monkeys and man have been demonstrated to establish their first (at least substantial) foci exclusively in the non-phagocytic parenchyma cells of the liver, after which the parasites are released into the circulating blood and begin to parasitize red blood cells (Shortt and Garnham, 1948; Shortt *et al.,* 1951; Garnham, 1951; Jeffery *et al,,* 1952). Thus, the malaria parasites and other hemosporidia, while following a general pattern in their development in the vertebrate hosts, have a wide spectrum of individual differences.

Sporozoites of the malaria parasites inoculated into man by an infected *Anopheles* mosquito disappear from circulating blood within approximately

30 minutes and no parasites can be found in red blood cells for several days. Thereafter they appear in increasing numbers in circulating red cells (*parasitemia*). Pre-erythrocytic development corresponds approximately to the clinical incubation period. Schaudinn's description (1902) of sporozoites directly entering red blood cells was erroneous: Sporozoites are carried to exo-erythrocytic foci, where they develop and multiply in fixed tissue cells, and only after a period of several days in those cells do some of their progeny enter the blood stream and initiate erythrocytic infection. In vivax malaria the pre-erythrocytic foci do not disappear with the eradication of the erythrocytic parasites but tend to remain, and following a longer or shorter symptomless, parasite-free period, release new broods into the blood stream to produce renewed parasitemia and symptoms (*i. e., relapse*). Finally, it seems probable that the mother sex cells (gametocytes) originate in exo-erythrocytic foci, from which they get into the circulation.

THE MALARIA PARASITES OF MAN

The Genus Plasmodium.—All malaria parasites belong to the genus *Plasmodium,* in which much of the asexual development takes place in red blood cells, with the production of so-called "malaria pigment," which is deposited within the body of the parasite. The growing asexual parasite (*trophozoite*) utilizes the globin part of the hemoglobin and retains the iron component as hematin (Morrison and Anderson, 1942). Increased destruction of the substance of the red blood corpuscles by an increasing numbers of parasites produces the anemia. Setting free into the blood plasma of the by-products of the parasites and the dead host cells causes a sensitization reaction characteristically resulting in malaria chills and fever. The plasmodia which are normal human parasites are not known to be the natural parasites of any other vertebrate host.

Historical Notes.—The clinical manifestations of the disease were recorded in ancient Chinese and Indian medical classics, and the ravages of malaria probably constituted a major cause for the decline and fall of the Roman Empire. Yet it was not until 1880 that Alphonse Laveran, a young French medical officer in Algeria, first demonstrated the parasites within red blood corpuscles in fresh wet microscopic films.

By 1894 Patrick Manson was firmly convinced that malaria was mosquito-transmitted and persuaded Surgeon Ronald Ross of the Indian Medical Service to test this theory experimentally. He first completed the mosquito phase of the cycle by employing the parasites of avian malaria in "grey mosquitos," *viz., Culex fatigans* (1898). Sometime later in West Africa he was able to demonstrate similar development of the human parasites in *Anopheles gambiæ* and *A. funestus.* During 1898–1899 Bignami, Bastianelli and Grassi in Italy also worked out the complete mosquito phase of human plasmodia in *Anopheles maculipennis.* A field test by British investigators demonstrated conclusively that malaria is contracted through the bites of infected mosquitoes (Manson, 1900).

Meanwhile Golgi (1886) first accurately described the tertian parasite and Grassi and Feletti (1890) assigned the names *vivax* to this species and *malariæ* to the quartan parasite, while Welch (1897), in Baltimore, named the species with crescent-shaped gametocytes *falciparum*. Although Craig (1900) was probably the first to study the remaining recognized malaria parasite of man (*P. ovale*), it remained for Stephens (1922) to give it the specific name *ovale*.

The full life cycle of human malaria parasites is illustrated in the accompanying diagram (Fig. 25).

Malaria Parasites in the Human Host.—This includes asexual development in fixed tissue cells and in the erythrocytes, and early gametogony.

Pre-erythrocytic Development.—Inoculation of the human subject occurs when an infected female *Anopheles* mosquito injects a droplet of saliva containing sporozoites of human plasmodia into cutaneous blood vessels preparatory to taking a blood meal. For a few minutes these sporozoites circulate in the blood stream but within a half hour they have disappeared (Fairley, 1945). The first colonization takes place in fixed tissue cells.

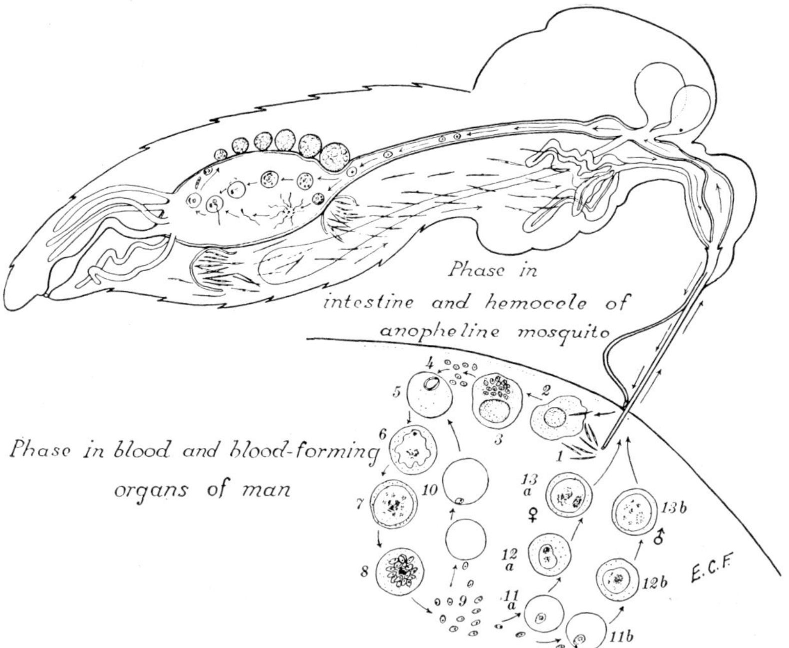

FIG. 25.—The full life cycle of the *vivax* malaria parasite of man, showing both the human and mosquito phases of the cycle. 1, sporozoites injected by infected *Anopheles* mosquito into the peripheral blood of man; 2, entry of the parasite into a tissue cell to initiate pre-erythrocytic schizogony; 3, multiplication in fixed tissue cell; 4, escape of pre-erythrocytic daughter organisms (merozoites) into visceral blood to initiate parasitemia; 5, early trophozoite in red blood cell; 6, maturing trophozoite; 7, early schizont; 8, mature schizont; 9, merozoites which have escaped from destroyed erythrocyte ready to undertake new erythrocytic schizogony; 10, early invasion of a new red blood cell; 11a, 12a, 13a and 11b, 12b and 13b, development respectively of female and male mother sex cells (gametocytes). Ripe gametocytes, when taken up by the *Anopheles* mosquito, complete maturation in the mosquito's stomach, unite in pairs and initiate sporogony, with eventual production of sporozoites, the terminal stage of the sexual phase of the cycle. (After Faust, in Craig and Faust's *Clinical Parasitology*, Lea & Febiger, Philadelphia.)

In human volunteers inoculated in England and the United States with large inocula of sporozoites of *Plasmodium vivax* (Shortt and Garnham, 1948) and *P. falciparum* (Shortt *et al.*, 1951; Jeffrey *et al.*, 1952), and monkeys similarly inoculated with the simian *P. cynomolgi* and *P. inui* (Shortt and Garnham, 1948; Garnham, 1951; Shortt *et al.*, 1953), the first evidence of a "take" has been 48 hours to 7 days later in the parenchyma cells of the liver, where young schizonts in active nuclear division have been observed. The schizonts grow remarkably in size with increase in the number of their nuclei and corresponding division of the cytoplasm of the parasite, to produce a large number of merozoites by the seventh or eighth day after inoculation (Shortt, 1951).

Following sporozoite-induced infection the minimum period of incubation (prepatency) for *P. vivax* as determined by subinoculation of the blood into a new subject is 8 days (Boyd and Stratman-Thomas, 1934), while the parasites are first detected microscopically in red blood cells on the tenth day. Comparable figures for *P. falciparum* are 7 and 10 days respectively (Boyd and Mathews, 1939). In *P. malariæ*, 27 to 37 days elapse between inoculation of sporozoites and the first detection of the parasites in the blood (Brumpt, 1949). If a recipient is inoculated with infected blood rather than sporozoites, the prepatent period is much less, and the parasites can be demonstrated in red cells from one to several days before clinical onset. In transfusion inoculation pre-erythrocytic development does not take place.

Period of Asexual Development in the Red Blood Cells.—When merozoites which have developed in pre-erythrocytic foci enter the red cells they transform into trophozoites, which grow and develop into schizonts, each producing the number of merozoites characteristic of the species of plasmodium. When fully matured, the merozoites break out of the parasitized red cell and soon actively enter undamaged red cells to repeat the asexual cycle. Merozoites of *P. vivax* have an affinity for young erythrocytes (reticulocytes), *P. falciparum* invades both immature and mature cells and *P. malariæ* prefers older red cells (Eaton, 1934; Kitchen, 1939).

The time required to complete one asexual multiplication after erythrocytic infection has become well established varies with the different species: for *P. vivax* and *P. ovale* it is 48 hours, for *P. malariæ*, 72 hours, and for *P. falciparum*, 36 to 48 hours, but with much less regular rhythm or synchronization than in the other species. Moreover, in *P. falciparum* only the young trophozoites are typically seen in circulating erythrocytes, while the more mature trophozoites and schizonts tend to develop only in visceral blood.

Early Gametogony in the Human Host.—In individuals who have acquired malaria through the bites of infected *Anopheles* mosquitoes, immature sexual cells of the plasmodia typically begin to appear in circulating erythrocytes after a few to several asexual erythrocytic multiplications have occurred. These cells do not multiply in the human body, remain viable for a relatively short time, possibly a week or less, and are phagocytosed soon thereafter.

Mosquito Phase of the Life Cycle.—Once ripe gametocytes of human malaria parasites are ingested by a female *Anopheles* in a blood meal and reach the "stomach" (midgut), they transform into mature sex cells. One *macrogametocyte* develops a single *macrogamete* (*oöcyte* or unfertilized egg) and one *microgametocyte* produces a few flagellated male cells (*microgametes*). A microgamete then enters a macrogamete, resulting in a fertilized egg (*zygote*), which becomes motile (*oökinete*), migrates through the cells of the stomach wall and becomes encysted (*oöcyst*) just under the hemocelic membrane of the stomach.

The oöcyst grows rapidly and develops a considerable number of internal nuclear centers. Each center then produces a large number of delicate spindle-shaped bodies (*sporozoites*). By the time the sporozoites become mature the wall of the greatly enlarged oöcyst bursts, releasing the ripened sporozoites into the "body cavity" (hemocele) of the mosquito. Many of these sporozoites eventually migrate to the salivary glands which they enter, then pass down through the salivary ducts into the median tube (hypopharyngeal tube) of the mosquito's proboscis. When the mosquito next punctures human skin to take a blood meal, sporozoites are injected into the cutaneous blood vessels and initiate a new human infection.

The optimal temperature and corresponding time for complete development of the sexual phases in the mosquito vary considerably in the three common species of human malaria parasites: for *Plasmodium vivax*, 25° C. (77° F.) and about 11 days; for *P. falciparum*, 30° C. (86° F.) and 10 to 11 days, and for *P. malariæ*, 22° C. (71.6° F.) and 18 to 21 days respectively (Siddons, 1944; Brumpt, 1949).

Humidity of the atmosphere is critically important for the life of the adult mosquito and consequently of its malaria parasites. The nearer the environmental moisture is to saturation at the optimal temperatures for the respective species of *Plasmodium*, the more likely is development to be normal.

Epidemiology

The epidemiology of human malaria comprehends basic information on the etiologic agents and their development both in man and the mosquito. For practical purposes the cycle concerns only the human host on the one hand and *Anopheles* mosquitoes on the other. Man is infected in nature from the bites of infected mosquitoes but he may also be accidentally infected by transfusion of whole blood from a donor who may have no symptoms, negative blood films and no history of malaria or of exposure to malaria for as long as 20 years or more. Occasionally malaria is transmitted from one drug addict to another through use of a common hypodermic needle.

The Etiologic Agents.—Different strains of the same species differ in virulence and in their relationship to relapse. Tropical strains of *Plasmodium vivax* are likely to relapse much earlier than those originating in temperate regions; they also have a tendency to produce more relapses. *P. malariæ* is much slower in development and usually milder in its manifestations but is even more difficult to eradicate, In contrast, *P. falciparum*, the most dangerous of all the malaria parasites of man because of its rapid multiplication and because of its pronounced proclivity to block capillaries in the brain, lungs, kidneys and other organs and to cause congestion in visceral blood sinuses, has only a moderate tendency to relapse and is eradicable by use of modern drugs which destroy only the erythrocytic parasites of *P. vivax* and *P. malariæ*.

All of the three common species of human malaria parasites are capable of producing infection in all species of *Anopheles* mosquitoes which are satisfactory hosts of any of these plasmodia (Young *et al.*, 1945, *et seq*).

Factors Relating to the Human Host.—These factors include race, age, sex, occupation, locality and immunity.

Race.—No race of mankind is naturally immune to infection with any of the four species of malaria parasites but races develop considerable tolerance to the species and particular strains of the parasite to which they have been exposed. In contrast, exposed individuals from areas of non-endemicity are almost always highly susceptible.

Age.—Infants and other young children in highly endemic areas are highly susceptible.

Sex.—There is no difference in susceptibility with respect to sex.

Occupation.—Persons whose occupation brings them in contact with infected mosquitoes are more liable to infection than those whose work does not provide this exposure hazard.

Locality.—Malaria is more commonly hyperendemic in tropical than in temperate climates, yet within each area there may be zones of hyper-endemicity and non-malariousness, even near one another. The malariousness of any area must be determined by carefully planned surveys of the incidence of malaria in the human population and in the *Anopheles* of the region.

Immunity.—Rarely persons have been found who appeared to be refractory to malaria following bites of infected mosquitoes. Yet there is no demonstrated proof of natural immunity. Whatever immunity exists results from previous exposure. Previous infection provides considerable immunity to subsequent exposure. This is relatively fast to the homologous strain of the same species of *Plasmodium,* much less so to heterologous strains of the same species and is essentially lacking to other species of malaria parasites (Boyd and Kitchen, 1936; Boyd, Stratman-Thomas and Kitchen, 1936). Yet immunity to homologous strains probably exists only as long as the original infection persists in the patients.

Other Factors in the Human Host.—Two additional considerations are most important in the transmission of the infection to the mosquito. These are the stages of the parasite in the patient's circulating blood and the number of infected individuals in a community. Transmission will not be accomplished unless there are gametocytes in the proper stage of ripeness in the circulating blood, and in sufficient numbers so that at least one female and one male gametocyte are taken up by the mosquito in a blood meal. The vitality of the gametocytes is also critical and this will vary from individual to individual patient, at different times during the infection and probably also with the virulence of the strain of plasmodium.

Persons in whom gametocytes are commonly circulating in peripheral blood over a considerable period of time are *carriers* who constitute a continuing danger to the community. In cases of malaria contracted through blood transfusion gametocytes are frequently lacking.

Malaria is frequently introduced into a non-malarious community by one or more gametocyte carriers who have acquired the infection in an endemic area. *Anopheles* mosquitoes biting the carrier acquire the infection and pass it on to uninfected human beings. In this way small epidemics have developed within recent years in a number of non-malarious localities in the United States as a result of this kind of epidemiologic relationship.

Factors Relating to the Mosquito Host.—The breeding habits of different species of *Anopheles* mosquitoes differ widely: Some select quiet pools, some slowly moving irrigation ditches, others backwaters or seepage channels of mountain streams, still others brackish water along coastal plains, and at least one species (*A. bellator*), bromeliads in tropical jungles. Yet all of these locations are relatively clean, clear and constant in supply compared with the places where domestic species of *Culex* and *Aëdes* may deposit their eggs. The site chosen by an *Anopheles* for oviposition may be densely shaded or sunny, and it may be related to particular types of aquatic vegetation or plankton.

It is not uncommon for several species of *Anopheles* to occur in the same area. In a tropical area one species may breed in brackish water, another in irrigated rice fields and a third in nearby jungle. Only one is usually the dangerous transmitter, the others are of secondary importance. Nor is it possible to determine their relative importance on the basis of their abundance.

A much more valid index is their preference for human blood over that of lower animals. A few species are avid for human blood (*i. e.*, they are *anthropophilous*) while most species are less selective (*i. e.*, they are *zoöphilous*). The former are characteristically the human malaria transmitters and usually breed near human habitations, since zoöphilous species lessen the chances of transmitting the infection back to the human host. The most notorious malaria transmitter is *Anopheles gambiæ*, a native of tropical Africa. Other examples of anthopophilous species are *A. darlingi* of tropical America and *A. culicifacies* of India, which always cause particular concern when they become established in new areas.

Eradication of all *Anopheles* mosquitoes in a malarious area will result in prevention of new human infections in that area. Fairly satisfactory control can sometimes be achieved by removal of the breeding grounds of the anthropophilous species.

Geographical Distribution of Human Malaria.—The potential distribution of human malaria is anywhere on the face of the earth where *Anopheles* mosquitoes breed in relative abundance and human gametocyte carriers are present. The natural distribution of the disease includes all tropical areas and adjacent temperate regions as far north and south of the Equator as an isothermal line where the mean temperature for the warmest month of the year is less than 24° C. (72° F.). Exceptions to this general statement consist of certain desert areas and altitudes above 9,000 feet, where *Anopheles* mosquitoes can not breed, although oases in deserts may constitute a favorable environment for small hotbeds of malaria. Another area of non-endemicity is the extensive group of islands in the Central and South Pacific where malaria-transmitting mosquitoes are not presently indigenous.

The known world distribution of malaria as of 1944 is shown in the accompanying map (Fig. 26). Since 1944 remarkable reduction in incidence and distribution of malaria has taken place in the United States, Puerto Rico, El Salvador, Venezuela, British Guiana, the Amazon Valley in Brazil, Portugal, Sardinia, Italy, Sicily, Jugoslavia, Greece, northern Turkey and Ceylon, as a result of intensive control measures directed

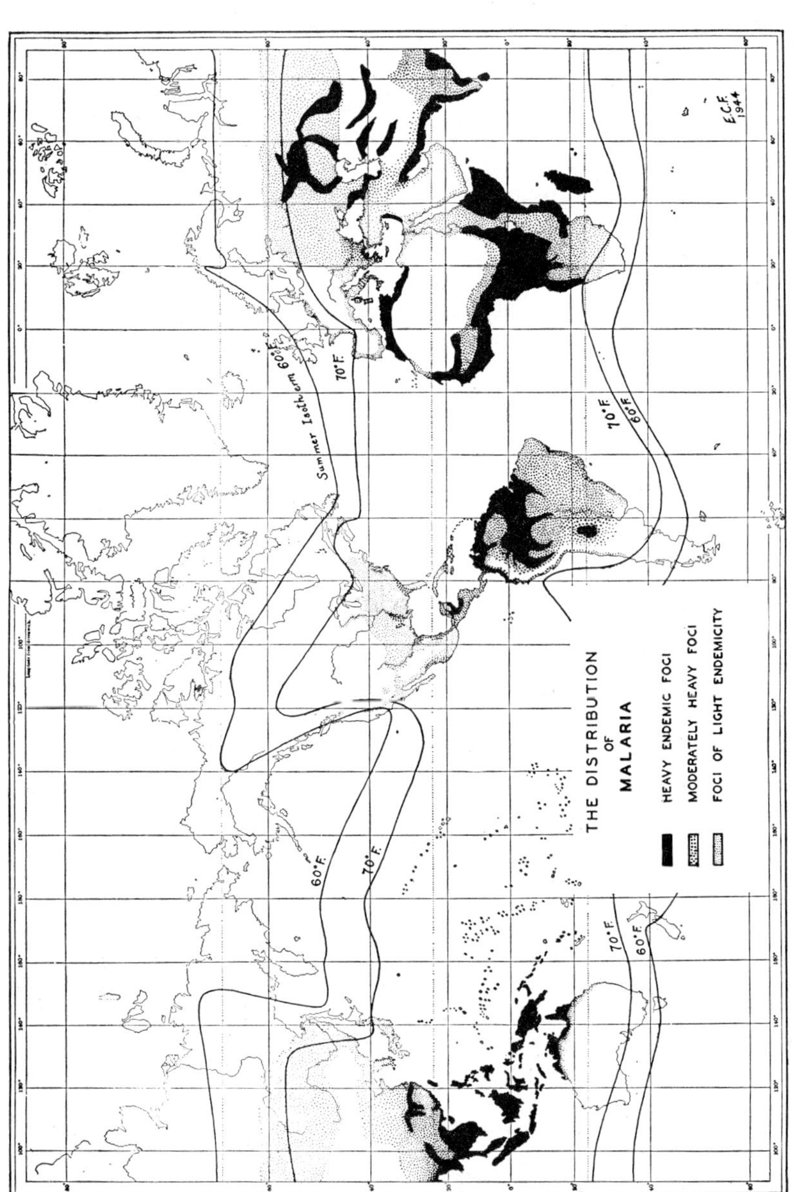

Fig. 26.—Map showing the distribution of malaria in 1944. The black areas indicate intense infection; the heavier dots, moderately heavy incidence; the lighter dots, milder (and marginal) endemicity subject to most satisfactory control. Since this map was prepared control has been effected in the United States, Puerto Rico, El Salvador, Venezuela, British Guiana, extensive areas in Brazil, Portugal, Sardinia, Italy, Sicily, Greece and Turkey. (After Faust, in Craig and Faust's *Clinical Parasitology*, Lea & Febiger, Philadelphia.)

primarily against *Anopheles* mosquitoes. Nevertheless, all of the recently controlled areas are subject to reactivation of malaria if the mosquito vector should again become abundant and human carriers from outside the country furnish the opportunity for local *Anopheles* to develop and transmit the infection to human subjects.

The four species of plasmodia infecting man are not equally extensive in their distribution. *Falciparum infection* is essentially confined to tropical and subtropical regions and has never become established in areas where there are long cold seasons.

Vivax infection is as prevalent as falciparum infection in warm climates but develops epidemically in cooler areas where there is an average temperature of 25° C. for at least three months of the year. Although *P. vivax* may survive cold months in the mosquito in protected sites, over-wintering of this parasite occurs mainly in the human host, with reactivation of parasitemia and clinical relapse when warmer weather develops.

Quartan malaria is almost invariably tropical or subtropical in its distribution in spite of its optimal temperature requirement of 22° C. Moreover, it has a comparatively low incidence in most warm countries where vivax and falciparum infections are highly endemic. But in parts of tropical Africa, Ceylon and Federated Malaya quartan malaria is prevalent and is at times the dominant type.

Ovale malaria has been reported sporadically from widely scattered tropical and subtropical regions, *viz.*, Philippines, New Guinea, U. S. S. R., Iran, Greece, Palestine, India, China, Mauritius and several foci in South America and tropical Africa. Ovale malaria is well established in central eastern Africa, although even there it is not the dominant type.

THE SPECIES OF PLASMODIA PRODUCING HUMAN MALARIA

Plasmodium Vivax (Grassi and Feletti, 1890) Labbé, 1899 (causing vivax or tertian malaria)

Plasmodium vivax is the most widely distributed of all the malaria parasites of man and in cooler climates is the only indigenous species.

Stages of P. Vivax in the Human Host.—These consist of (1) the sporozoite introduced into the skin by the bite of the injected mosquito, (2) pre-erythrocytic schizogony, (3) asexual forms in the red blood cells and (4) gametocytes in the red corpuscles.

The Sporozoite.—This stage is a minute, motile, spindle-shaped object with rather blunt ends, measuring approximately 15 microns long by 1 micron in mid-diameter. Near the center there is a nucleus which may have divided into two chromatin masses (Boyd, 1935). It is injected by the mosquito into the cutaneous blood vessels and remains in the circulation not longer than 30 minutes.

Pre-erythrocytic Development.—The earliest evidence thus far provided consists of moderately advanced, multinucleate schizonts in parenchyma cells of the liver on the seventh day following sporozoite inoculation of a human volunteer (Shortt and Garnham, 1948). These pre-erythrocytic merozoites are believed to be the stage which first invades the red blood cells.

Asexual Infection in the Red Blood Cells (Plate IV).—Once a merozoite has penetrated through the pellicle into the substance of a red blood corpuscle it transforms from a minute, solid, oval organism with a small central nucleus into the young trophozoite, a hyaline ring containing a large vacuole and a distinct nuclear mass on one margin. This is the so-called "signet ring" stage of the *vivax* parasite. The ring rapidly enlarges, its cytoplasm develops ameboid movement and increases as it grows in size at the expense of the hemoglobin of the red host cell. The undigestible iron component of the hemoglobin is deposited within the cytoplasm of the parasite as hematin ("malaria pigment"), in the form of delicate granules having a yellowish sheen resembling "fool's gold." Meanwhile the red cell swells and becomes paler and in Giemsa-stained or other Romanowsky-stained thin blood films minute dots are detected within the uninfected stroma of the red cells. These are the Schüffner's granules peculiar to *vivax* and *ovale* parasites, and may represent residual portions of the reticulum of the young red cell (reticulocyte), for which *vivax* merozoites have a predilection. Soon the ameboid outline of the growing parasite becomes its most conspicuous feature.

By the 36th hour practically all of the swollen host cell is occupied by the parasite, which loses its ameboid movement, becomes irregularly rounded and proceeds to segment into 12 to 24 rounded chromatin masses, each of which is then provided with an envelope of cytoplasm. This is the mature schizont and each of the internal bodies is a merozoite. The merozoites tend to be arranged rather irregularly in rosetted pattern around a central mass of hematin.

Shortly before the 48th hour the asexual process is complete, the merozoites break out of the destroyed host cell and are temporarily free in the plasma. Soon they actively enter uninfected red blood cells and initiate a replication of the asexual process. Repeated asexual production of the parasites builds up the parasitemia approximately 16-fold every 48 hours, with corresponding reduction of circulating red blood cells. Typically, however, there is host response to parasite activity: Circulating macrophages and leukocytes in increasing numbers engulf and destroy many of the free merozoites and even some of the parasitized red cells, so that decreased destruction of erythrocytes now results, and after several asexual cycles the primary parasitemia is temporarily terminated. After a period of weeks in tropical-strain infections or months in infections due to temperate-zone strains, parasitemia again develops, although usually it is not as intense or as persistent as in the primary attack.

Gametocyte Production (Plate IV).—The source of gametocytes is obscure but many malariologists believed they originate from merozoites produced in exo-erythrocytic fixed-tissue cells. They first appear in the circulation as solid rounded parasites within swollen, pale red cells. Schüffner's granules are already present in the unparasitized stroma of the red cell. At this early stage their sex can not be distinguished. As they grow they retain a rounded contour and do not exhibit ameboid activity. When fully developed, the male (microgametocyte) has a diffuse cytoplasm and a

PLATE IV

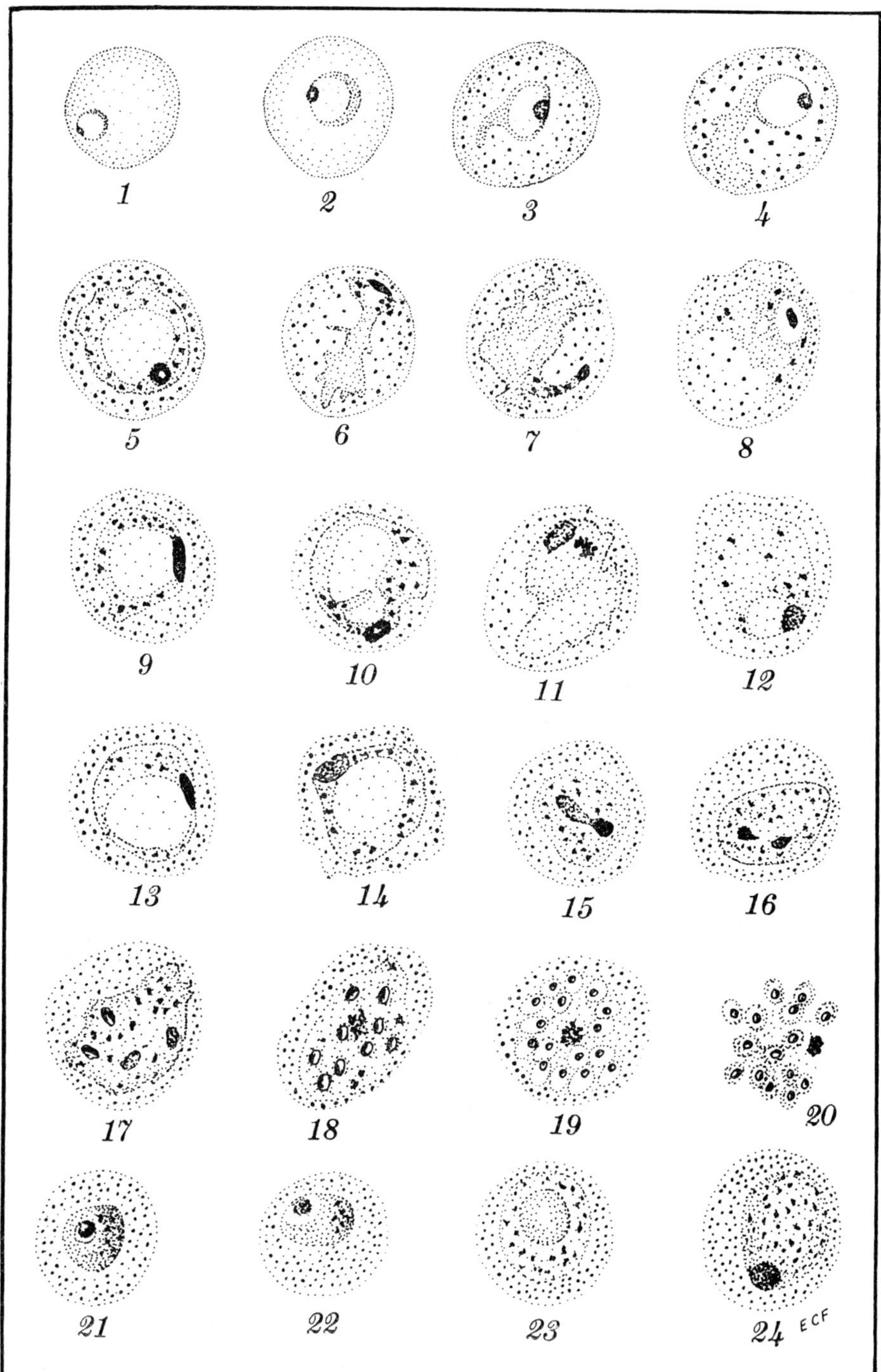

Plasmodium vivax, thin-blood films, all from peripheral blood, stained by Giesma or Wright technic. *1–10*, stages in development of the trophozoite; *11–14*, mature trophozoites; *15–18*, early and maturing schizonts; *19*, *20*, mature schizonts with fully developed merozoites; *21*, *22*, developing gametocytes; *23*, mature male gameotcyte; *24*, mature female gametocyte. × 2000. (Original.)

PLATE V

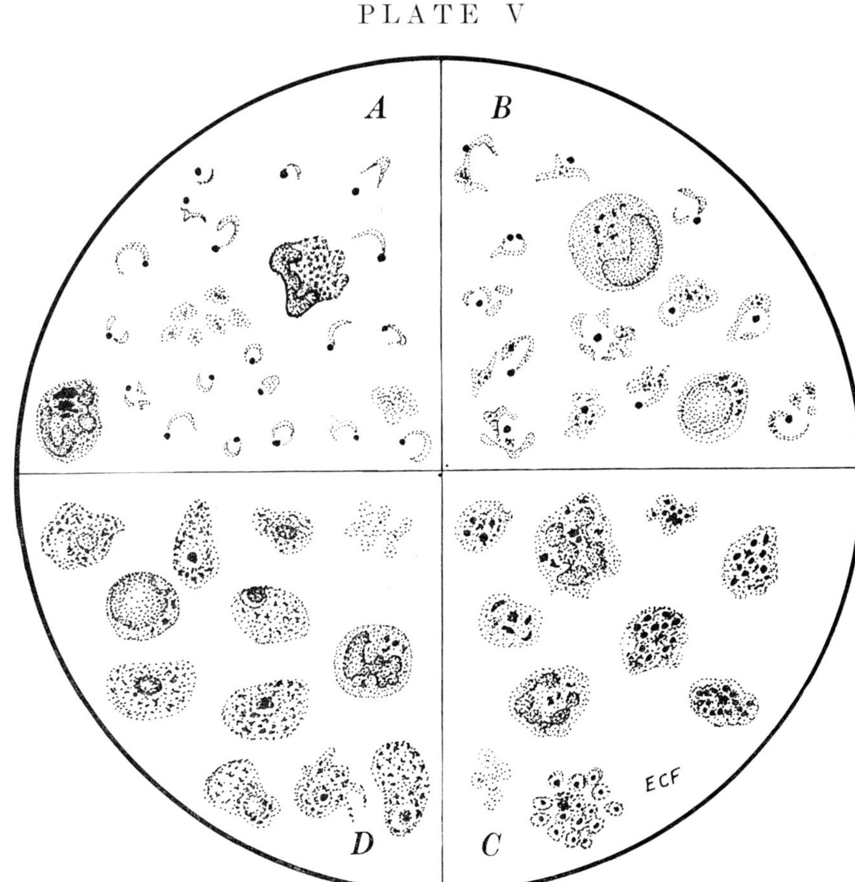

Plasmodium vivax, thick-blood films, stained by Field technic. *A*, young trophozoites; *B*, maturing and mature trophozoites; *C*, maturing and mature schizonts; *D*, maturing and mature gametocytes; all from peripheral blood. White blood cells and platelets are included for comparison. × 2000. (Original.)

rather loose skein of nuclear chromatin typically lying within a hyaline vacuole; and the hematin pigment is scattered throughout the cytoplasm. The mature female (macrogametocyte) has denser cytoplasm, a solid nucleus and little if any hyaline area around it. The hematin pigment is arranged in small agglomerations or in a wreath-like configuration near the margin of the cytoplasm. These mature gametocytes constitute the stage of transfer to the mosquito host.

Thick Blood Films.—In well-stained, thick films prepared by Giemsa's, Field's or Walker's technic (see TECHNICAL AIDS, pages 588–590), malaria parasites are not flattened and therefore appear condensed or shrunken. Likewise, the films have been dehemoglobinized so that red-cell boundaries are not apparent (Plate V). Special training is therefore required for thick-blood film diagnosis (Field and LeFleming, 1939–1941).

Young trophozoites (ring forms) of *Plasmodium vivax* may appear as "normal" unbroken rings, although they are considerably smaller than in thin films. More usually, however, they are much less recognizable and look like interrupted partial rings, with a distinct chromatin dot but with the cytoplasm broken into several fragments; or with the cytoplasm as a solid mass, so that it, together with the chromatin mass, looks like a broad exclamation mark or a question mark; or with the chromatin mass in the center and the cytoplasm a single mass on either side, so that the entire plasmodium may suggest a bird in flight. More mature trophozoites have a larger chromatin body, a more substantial mass of cytoplasm and, of course, the characteristic hematin pigment of *P. vivax*. The *schizonts* likewise in their early segmentation have substantial cytoplasm and hematin pigment and two to several deeply red chromatin masses. More mature schizonts have numerous chromatin bodies which come to be arranged around the hematin pigment center, and in the ripe schizont each chromatin mass will have a small bit of cytoplasm surrounding it.

The young *gametocytes* are more difficult to distinguish but are usually as large as late trophozoites, have a more continuous cytoplasm and more hematin pigment. Older gametocytes may be very irregular in outline, with dispersed cytoplasm, but have a wealth of characteristic hematin pigment.

Since the hemoglobin of the red blood cells has been dissolved, there will be no Schüffner's granules to help confirm the diagnosis and no opportunity to compare the size or color index of parasitized and uninfected cells.

Plasmodium Falciparum (Welch, 1897) Schaudinn, 1902

(Causing falciparum, tropical, malignant tertian, estivo-autumnal malaria)

Plasmodium falciparum is essentially limited to warm climates. While the term "tropical" is an appropriate designation for the disease produced by this plasmodium, it can be misleading because *vivax* infection is equally prevalent in the Tropics. The designation "estivo-autumnal," referring to the more frequent appearance of this infection during the latter part of the summer and early fall, is applicable only in the falciparum belt of the northern subtropical regions.

In 1881, Laveran described the distinctive crescentic character of the gametocytes of this plasmodium, although it was Golgi (1885) who first attributed species distinctiveness to this character. William H. Welch gave the name "*falciparum*" to this species.

The Sporozoite.—This stage of *P. falciparum* resembles the sporozoite of *P. vivax*. However, the *falciparum* sporozoites tend to be more slender, more pointed at their ends and appear to be more swollen in the center around the nuclear mass (Boyd, 1935).

Pre-erythrocytic Development.—As in *P. vivax* infection, the first few days of *P. falciparum* development in the human host have not been elucidated. In approximately 30 minutes the sporozoites disappear from circulating blood which remains parasite-free for several days (Fairley, 1945). The first fixed-tissue infection discovered in human volunteers submitted to sporozoite inoculations has been on the fourth day (Shortt *et al.*, 1951) or third to sixth day (Jeffery *et al.*, 1952), in the parenchyma cells of the liver lying within the hepatic cords. The smallest parasite found (Jeffery *et al.*, 1952) was a partially developed schizont with about 40 nuclei, and the most mature schizonts had several hundred well-formed merozoites beginning to escape from the schizont's limiting membrane and from the greatly distended host cell. Except for the somewhat shorter time required for development and ripening of the schizont, pre-erythrocytic development in *falciparum* infection closely parallels that of *P. vivax*. However, there is suggestive evidence that only one brood of merozoites is discharged by exoerythrocytic schizonts, after which residual infection is maintained by visceral erythrocytic parasites (Garnham, 1951).

Asexual Infection in Red Blood Cells (Plate VI).—The first appearance of *P. falciparum* in circulating blood is on the seventh day following sporozoite inoculation (Boyd and Mathews, 1939; Shortt *et al.*, 1951; Jeffery *et al.*, 1952). The earliest stage of the red-cell parasite is a very minute oval or circular ring with a distinct nuclear dot on one side and a very delicate rim of cytoplasm surrounding the vacuole. Much more frequently than in *vivax* infection the young *falciparum* parasite is found as a flattened blister (appliqué form) on the margin of the red cell just under the cell membrane, with the nuclear dot producing a minute median bulge on the external aspect. Likewise, rather frequently one can observe various stages of binary nuclear division in the ring stage of the trophozoite, followed by binary fission of the cytoplasm to form two ring-stage parasites. As the rings enlarge they develop a small cytoplasmic bib. There is typically no ameboid movement of the cytoplasm in the falciparum ring.

Although later stages of the *falciparum* trophozoite and the stages of schizogony may be found occasionally in peripheral blood, these stages typically develop only in visceral blood (capillaries, blood sinuses and in placental blood). The trophozoite continues to grow as an oval or rounded body, with relative decrease in size of the vacuole. Yet the growing parasite never occupies a major portion of the area of the red host cell, nor does it cause a swelling or appreciable reduction in the color value of the residual stroma. Moreover, there is no granular staining reaction of the uninfected portion of the parasitized red cell such as Schüffner's granules of *vivax* and *ovale* infections.

PLATE VI

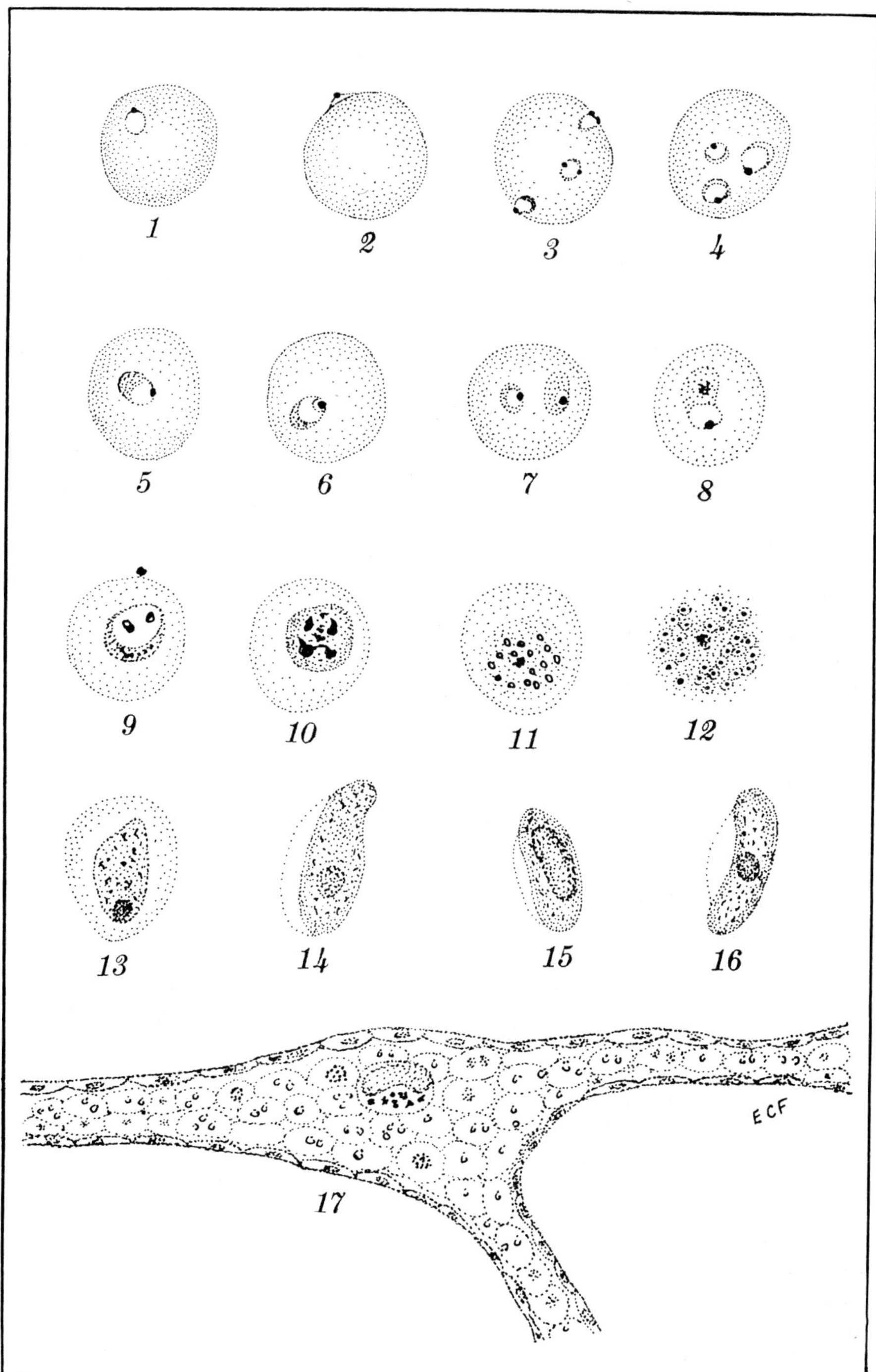

Plasmodium falciparum, thin-blood films, stained by Giemsa or Wright technic. *1–4*, young trophozoites from peripheral blood; *5–8*, maturing and mature trophozoites, usually found only in visceral blood; *9*, *10*, young schizonts, usually found only in visceral blood; *11*, *12*, mature schizonts, from peripheral blood; *13*, *14*, immature gametocytes, more often found in visceral than in peripheral blood; *15*, mature male gametocyte and *16*, mature female gametocyte, from peripheral blood; *17*, cerebral capillary crowded with parasitized red blood cells and one macrophage having ingested malaria pigment. × 2000. (Original.)

PLATE VII

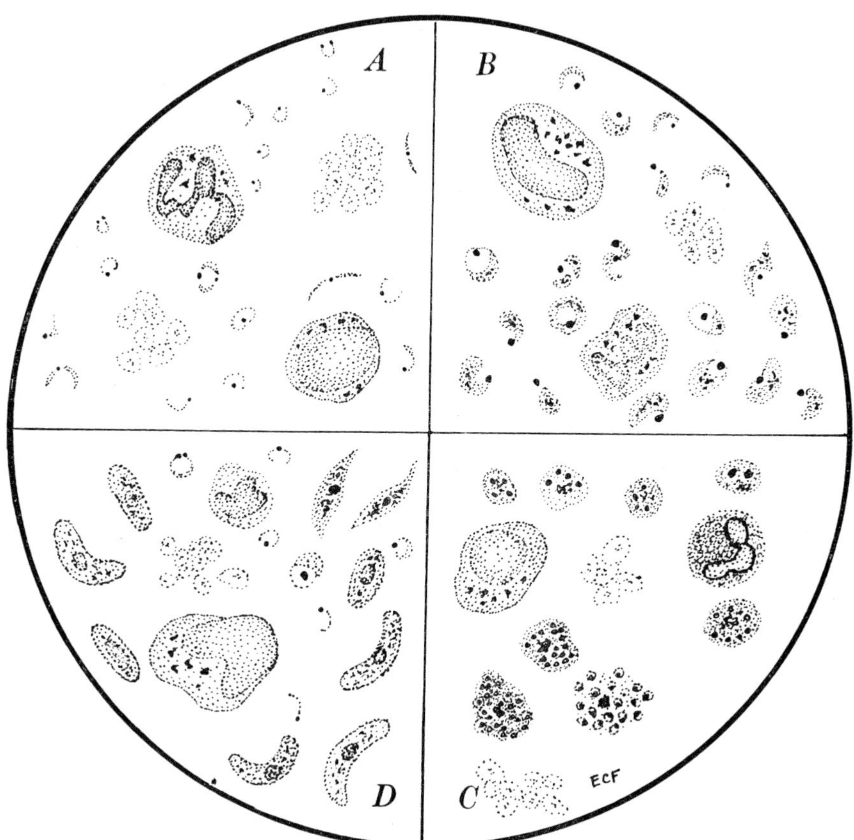

Plasmodium falciparum, thick-blood films, stained by Field technic. *A*, young trophozoites from peripheral blood; *B*, maturing and mature trophozoites, usually found only in visceral blood; *C*, young schizonts (above), from visceral blood, maturing and mature schizonts (below), from peripheral blood; *D*, young gametocytes (above, right) from visceral blood, maturing and mature gametocytes from peripheral blood. White blood cells and platelets, as well as several young and one mature trophozoites are included for comparison. × 2000. (Original.)

Schizogony usually begins about 24 hours after infection of the red cell and continues during the next 12 to 24 hours, with a total production of 8 to 36 (average 18 to 24) minute merozoites arranged in a rosetted pattern around a hematin pigment center. The smaller number of merozoites is usually associated with multiple infection of a red cell. Each merozoite has a dense nuclear dot and a small envelope of cytoplasm.

Escape of the merozoites from a ruptured cell, their short existence free in the blood plasma and their entry into uninfected red cells typically occur in visceral blood. The time for one asexual erythrocytic development may require only 24 hours in some strains of *P. falciparum* but the more common time span is 36 to 48 hours. There is much less synchronization in this than in *P. vivax* development, so that different asexual parasites and their progeny may at times "get out of step" and completely upset the rhythmic periodicity of asexual multiplication.

Gametocyte Production (Plate VI).—The immature gametocytes are seldom seen in peripheral blood. They are rounded or oval, with distinct cell membranes. Somewhat later when they appear in the circulation they are jelly-bean-shaped, then as they mature they become crescentic, tending to occupy one side of a considerably distended red cell. Finally the red cell membrane becomes only a thin, almost transparent veil which can be observed clearly on the concave side of the parasite, and when fully ripe the gametocyte may slip out of this envelope.

Immature gametocytes of *P. falciparum* are sexually indistinguishable, but by the time they have elongated and become partially ripe one can readily determine their sex. The male forms (microgametocytes) have delicate diffuse nuclear chromatin and diffuse hematin, and the females (macrogametocytes) a more condensed nucleus and compact mass of hematin. Moreover, in the fully ripened forms the female is typically longer, with more narrowly rounded ends, and the male, shorter, more reniform. These are the forms which carry on the life cycle when taken up by the female *Anopheles* mosquito in a blood meal.

Thick Blood Films.—Although the asexual stages of *Plasmodium falciparum* are the smallest of the three common species of malaria parasites, they are the most readily recognized and diagnosed in thick films. (Plate VII.) With Giemsa's, Field's or Walker's staining technic it is observed that the young trophozoite is a completed or partial azure-stained ring and that the chromatin dot takes an intensely deep-red stain. The more mature trophozoites and the schizonts are usually not found in peripheral blood. In placental blood the mature trophozoites tend to become an irregular solid mass with obliteration of the vacuole, and a moderately large deep-red dot of chromatin which is eccentric in position. The schizonts consist of dense masses of purplish-red chromatin surrounded by one common or individual cytoplasmic envelopes. The hematin pigment is readily recognized as a few grains or one small mass of dark metallic material. The mature gametocytes ("crescents") are frequently as characteristic as in thin films, but they may be falciform, ovoidal or irregular in contour. All have a wealth of hematin pigment, which is either dispersed (male gametocytes) or clumped together (female gametocytes).

The hemoglobin of the parasitized cell has been dissolved, so that the outline of the erythrocyte is indistinct and can not be used as a guide in orienting the parasites.

Plasmodium Malariæ (Laveran, 1881) Grassi and Feletti, 1890 (causing quartan malaria)

Plasmodium malariæ is probably the species which Laveran first observed and studied. It is much less frequently seen than *P. vivax* and *P. falciparum* and is rarely dominant in a malarious region.

The Sporozoite.—This resembles the sporozoite of *P. vivax* and *P. falciparum* but is somewhat coarser in appearance (Boyd, 1935).

Pre-erythrocytic Development.—There are no direct observations concerning the development of *P. malariæ* from the time the sporozoites are injected into peripheral blood vessels until the parasites first appear in circulating red blood corpuscles, a period varying from 27 to 37 days (Boyd and Stratman-Thomas, 1936).

Asexual Infection in Red Blood Cells (Plate VIII).—The erythrocytic asexual development of *P. malariæ* is exactly synchronized and repeats this phase of the cycle every 72 hours, hence the designation "quartan" or every fourth day in the old Roman sense. In addition, the number of merozoites produced each time is only about one-third that of *P. falciparum* and one-half that of *P. vivax*. These two factors in combination are responsible for the more gradual development of the parasitemia to clinical level.

As first seen in red cells the asexual quartan parasite is a small ovoidal or ring-like trophozoite, which exhibits very little ameboid activity. It is invariably smaller, more compact and utilizes less hemoglobin than *P. vivax*. As it enlarges, it presents a range in morphology from broadly oval to delicate or broad band-form extending across the entire diameter of the parasitized red cell, or occasionally it may be very irregular in outline. The fully developed trophozoite almost, but never quite fills the red cell, which is not enlarged or otherwise distorted but may manifest a slightly dusky or slatey hue. The hematin pigment is dark, usually coarse and gradually accumulates in a dark greenish-black mass in the center of the trophozoite. In the young ring stage the nuclear chromatin is concentrated in a single round mass. During growth of the trophozoite it is much more dispersed throughout the cytoplasm. But as the time for segmentation approaches it again becomes condensed.

Schizogony is accomplished in three or four successive binary divisions of the nucleus, usually resulting in 8 or 9 (6 to 12) centers, around each of which there is a small oval envelope of cytoplasm. These daughter units, the merozoites, are arranged fairly symmetrically around a center of hematin granules. On maturity the merozoites break out of the parasitized red cells and after a short, free interval in the blood plasma invade other red cells.

Gametocyte Production (Plate VIII).—The immature mother sex cells of *P. malariæ* bear a general resemblance to those of *P. vivax* but are smaller and are more compact. When they reach maturity their size is never as

PLATE VIII

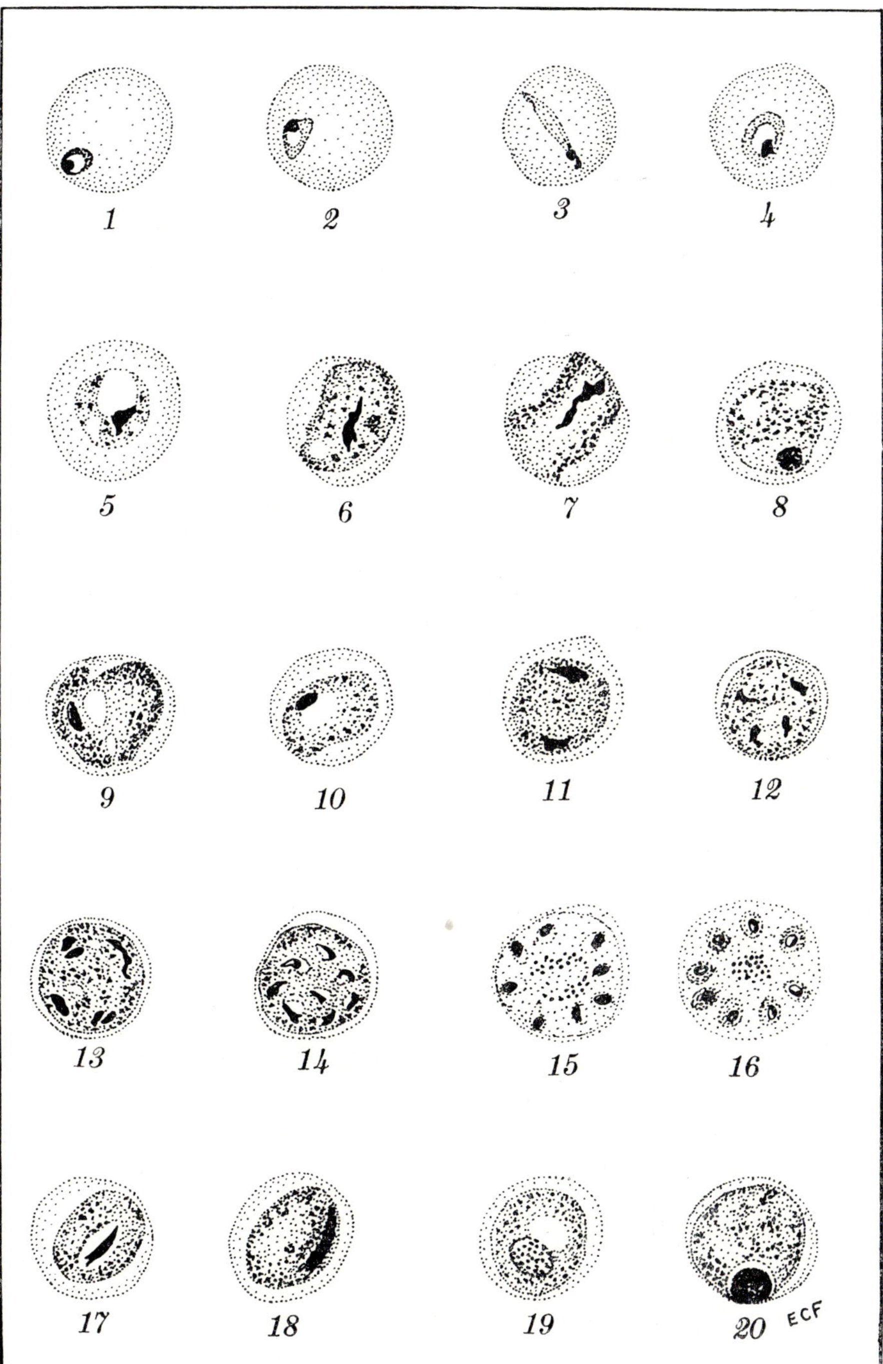

Plasmodium malariæ, thin-blood films, stained by Giemsa or Wright technic, all from peripheral blood. *1–4*, young trophozoites; *5–10*, maturing and mature trophozoites; *11–14*, young and maturing schizonts; *15*, *16*, mature schizonts; *17*, *18*, young gametocytes; *19*, mature male gametocyte; *20*, mature female gametocyte. × 2000. (Original.)

PLATE IX

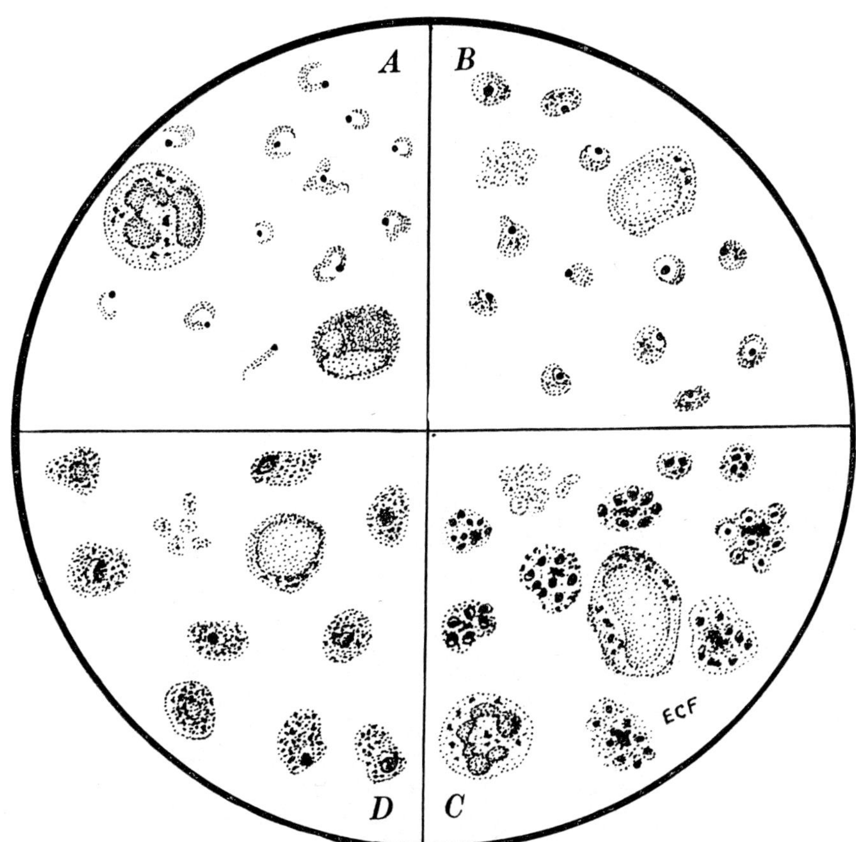

Plasmodium malariæ, thick-blood films, all from peripheral blood, stained by Field technic. *A*, young trophozoites; *B*, maturing and mature trophozoites; *C*, young schizonts (above), maturing and mature schizonts (below); *D*, maturing and mature gametocytes. White blood cells and platelets are included for comparison. × 2000. (Original.)

great as the normal red blood corpuscle and the parasitized cell is not enlarged. The ripe male cell (microgametocyte) is rounded, has relatively pale cytoplasm, diffuse hematin granules, and an oval aggregation of nuclear chromatin dots. The female cell (macrogametocyte) has denser cytoplasm, frequently more concentrated coarse hematin granules, and a dense subspherical nucleus in the midst of a vacuole.

Thick Blood Films.—On the whole, thick films of *Plasmodium malariæ* are more readily diagnosed than are those of *P. vivax* because the plasmodia have more continuous cytoplasm and appear less shrunken. (Plate IX.) Early *trophozoites* may have the outline of a question mark or a thick exclamation mark, with the chromatin centered between two fragments of cytoplasm, but they usually have a relatively regular subspherical cytoplasm in which the chromatin mass lies to one side. More mature trophozoites are solid, rather regular masses, with a few distinct dots of hematin pigment and an identifiable eccentric chromatin mass. Young *schizonts* are difficult to identify as such because their chromatin masses are poorly defined, and their cytoplasm is rather irregular in contour although not dispersed as in *P. vivax*. The ripe schizonts almost always consist of distinct daughter cells (merozoites) massed around a hematin pigment center, with apparently no residual cytoplasm to bind the organism together. The *gametocytes* are characterized by their mature size, undivided chromatin masses in the female, granular dispersed chromatin in the male, and always a wealth of characteristic hematin pigment. Since the hemoglobin of the parasitized cell has been dissolved, there are no distinct outlines of the erythrocytes to guide the diagnostician.

Plasmodium Ovale Stephens, 1922

Careful study of this organism was first made by Stephens (1922), who gave the plasmodium species identity on the basis of the enlarged, irregularly oval distortion of many of the parasitized red cells.

Sporozoite and Pre-erythrocytic Stages.—Although James, Nicol and Shute (1933) provided an account of the life cycle of *P. ovale* through the mosquito and four human volunteers, there is no information concerning the pre-erythrocytic period except that parasitemia developed on the 14th or 15th day following inoculation of sporozoites by the infected mosquito. However, Garnham *et al.* (1954) have demonstrated pre-erythrocytic schizonts in the parenchyma cells of the liver of a human volunteer 9 days after *P. ovale*-infected mosquitoes fed on the subject.

Asexual Infection in Red Blood Cells.—In certain respects this phase of the cycle of *P. ovale* resembles *P. vivax*; in other characters it is more like *P. malariæ*, and in at least one feature it is unique. The asexual erythrocytic cycle requires 48 hours, with more exact synchronization than occurs in *P. vivax*. Likewise, the unparasitized portion of the infected red blood corpuscle (Fig. 27) exhibits Schüffner's stippling to an even more marked degree than it does in *P. vivax*. The young trophozoite is ring-formed, with a condensed nuclear mass but cytoplasm which is more compact than that of *P. vivax*. The vacuole is frequently less conspicuous and there is lack of

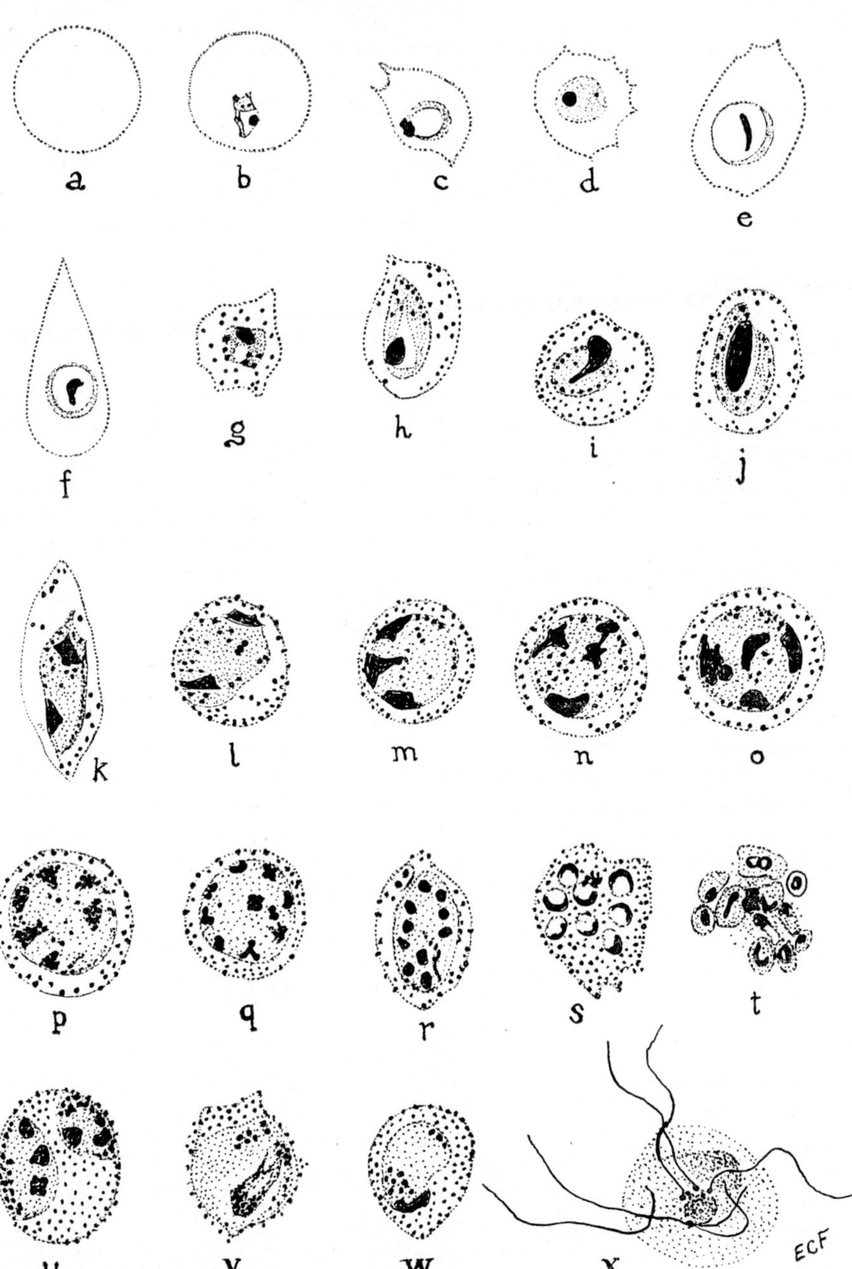

FIG. 27.—*Plasmodium ovale* in thin-blood films. *a*, uninfected red blood cell for comparison with *ovale*-infected cells; *b-j*, stages in development of the trophozoite, showing oval and irregular contours of many parasitized cells; *k-s*, developing schizont; *t*, merozoites which have escaped from exhausted red blood cell; *u*, 2 developing schizonts in one red cell; *v*, mature male gametocyte (microgametocyte); *w*, mature female gametocyte (macrogametocyte); *x*, exflagellation (maturation) of the microgametocyte, with production of about six microgametes. *g* through *w* show Schüffner's granules in the unparasitized stroma of the parasitized red cell. (Original adaptations; *b-r* and *t*, after Stephens and Owen, *s* and *u-x*, after James, Nicol and Shute.)

ameboid movement. Occasionally two plasmodia develop in the same red cell.

As the trophozoite grows it continues to be relatively condensed like *P. malariæ*; it is frequently rounded, at times distinctly oval or elongated but not typically band-form. Meanwhile many of the parasitized red cells become oval in contour, or even tear-drop-shaped, and at times have one to several sharp projections. The red cell may be normal in size or somewhat swollen but is not appreciably paler than normal. The hematin pigment is relatively scant and of a light brown color. When schizogony is initiated the nucleus divides first into two irregular chromatin masses, which, in turn, divide two or three times, until a relatively small number of chromatin masses (6 to 12, usually 8) are produced, as in *P. malariæ*. The mature schizont is rounded or oval and nearly fills the infected red cell. The hematin granules are concentrated in a single central mass, around which the maturing and mature merozoites are irregularly arranged. As the ripe merozoites break out of the degenerate red host cell they are observed to be irregularly oval, relatively large, and their nuclei have a tendency to be lenticular or vacuolated.

Gametocyte Production.—The gametocytes in the red blood corpuscles (Fig. 27) are very much like those of *P. malariæ*, are rounded in outline, are compact, and have similar staining reaction; but they can readily be differentiated in thin blood films by the presence of Schüffner's granules in the host cell. Differentiation from the same stage of *P. vivax* has to be made on the smaller, more compact character of *P. ovale*.

Thick Blood Films.—Although these films effectively concentrate *P. ovale*, by employing thick films it is practically impossible to differentiate these organisms from *P. malariæ*, since the enveloping host cell is rendered invisible by dehemoglobinization, hence the shape of the parasitized cell and Schüffner's granules are not available to orient the diagnostician.

PATHOGENESIS, PATHOLOGY AND SYMPTOMATOLOGY

During the development of malaria parasites in exo-erythrocytic foci, both preceding and subsequent to their invasion of the red blood cells, the relatively small amount of tissue destruction is apparently insufficient to provoke systemic reaction or to evoke symptoms (Russell, 1952). In contrast, invasion of the red cells initiates a train of events leading to overt malaria, conspicuous among which are the paroxysms of chills and fever, and anemia.

Pathogenesis.—The plasmodia which invade the red blood cells grow and segment at the expense of these host cells. As the number of parasites increases the number of erythrocytes is decreased with each successive schizogony. The rapidity with which this pathologic process develops depends on the species of plasmodium and on the host's immunologic reaction to the invader. *Vivax* infection builds up rapidly, *ovale* about one half as fast and *malariæ* only about one-third as rapidly as *vivax*.

Falciparum infection differs from the other types both quantitatively and qualitatively. The schizogonic cycle in the blood stream requires not more than 48 hours but is frequently less synchronized. Moreover, in *P.*

falciparum there is a tendency for more than one parasite, frequently several, to develop in a single red cell, either by one or more binary divisions of one invader or by multiple invasion. These combined mechanisms rapidly build up a high disease-producing potential, so that in two or three asexual cycles the number of infected red cells frequently reaches a dangerous threshold. Furthermore, the *falciparum* parasites have the unique property among plasmodia in man of producing agglutination of red cells, causing blockage of blood capillaries in the brain, lungs, kidneys and other viscera and hemostasis in the sinuses of the spleen, liver and bone marrow (Clark and Tomlinson, 1949).

With each successive escape of merozoites from ruptured red cells and discharge of necrotic red-cell débris into the plasma, there is new stimulus to humoral and cellular systemic reaction, and the more synchronized this event is, the greater is the activity of phagocytic cells in engulfing and destroying free merozoites, trophozoites and schizonts within red cells, free malaria pigment, and red-cell débris. This phagocytosis is most conspicuously carried out by the wandering histiocytes and particularly the fixed macrophages in the spleen, liver and bone marrow. This serves to prevent the infection from overwhelming the patient. It guards against exhaustion of red cells and fatal sensitization phenomena. It likewise builds up tolerance to the infection.

Pathology.—The lesions in malaria are relatively characteristic. Destruction of the red blood corpuscles by the plasmodia produces a microcytic, hypochromic type of anemia. In severe infections the number of erythrocytes may be reduced to one-fifth of normal, and in these patients it may be difficult to make satisfactory blood films. Except at the time of the paroxysms there is typically a leukopenia but with relative monocytosis (Kitchen, 1949). Moreover, agglutination of the parasitized red cells in falciparum infection and loss of plasma within the blood vessels in all types of malaria are responsible for so-called "sludging" of the corpuscular elements in the vessels. Thus, there is (1) a progressive decrease in the number and quality of circulating erythrocytes, with corresponding reduction in oxygen conveyance, hence oxygen starvation of the tissues, (2) multiple thrombosis in the smaller blood vessels, and (3) progressive decrease in circulating blood volume (Maegraith, Jones and Andrews, 1951).

Added to the changes which have just been mentioned is the pathologic background for the malaria paroxysms, namely, hypersensitization at the moment of the cyclic discharge of merozoites and necrotic remains of destroyed red cells, amounting at times to serum anaphylaxis.

The *brain* in falciparum malaria is congested, the capillaries are increased in number, swollen as a result of hemostasis and embolic blocking, and frequently there are multiple petechial hemorrhages into the perivascular tissues. The cortex appears dusky gray or even brown in macroscopic section (Clark and Tomlinson, 1949). Hemorrhage from the retinal vessels is relatively common.

The infected red cells accumulate in the sinuses of the spleen, liver and bone marrow. The *spleen* is typically enlarged, congested, soft and hemorrhagic in the acute primary stage, hard in the chronic stage (the "ague cake" of older medical textbooks). Its color darkens as the amount of hematin increases. This is particularly evident as the hyperemia subsides. Yet the organ remains hypertrophic in the chronic cases due to increase in the number of fixed macrophages in Billroth's cords. In chronic *vivax infection* the organ may weigh as much as a kilogram, and in chronic *falciparum* infection between 300 and 700 grams (Ash and Spitz, 1945). The *liver* is hypertropic and congested in acute malaria and its color index is greater than normal. As the infection becomes chronic the organ becomes firmer in consistency but not cirrhotic. The *bone marrow* undergoes the same changes as the spleen but to a lesser degree. In addition, there is reduced production of granulocytes and increased erythropoiesis in an attempt to meet the deficit in functioning red blood cells.

The *kidneys* are congested, the glomerular capillaries become thrombotic with accumulation of parasitized red cells, free hematin and wandering macrophages, and may rupture to produce multiple extravasations. The appearance is that of an acute or subacute glomerular nephritis. The *adrenals* may also be damaged by hemorrhage or affected by the general toxemia, and may, in turn, be responsible for a hypertensive heart. The *pulmonary capillaries* partake of the same congestive process. All *mucous membranes* may exhibit petechial hemorrhage; this is conspicuous in the case of the gastric mucosa. The *heart* also suffers from the embolic blockage of the coronary vessels, and is embarrassed by oxygen want (Ash and Spitz, 1945).

The *placenta* in *falciparum malaria* manifests a remarkable concentration of plasmodia in all stages of their development in the red cells of the relatively slow-moving blood in the maternal blood sinuses. In many cases the peripheral blood is essentially free of parasites until *post-partum*, when reactivation of the infection characteristically takes place. Although the abortion rate is high in falciparum malaria, there is no histologic evidence that transplacental infection occurs (Clark and Tomlinson, 1949).

Symptomatology.—The *biological incubation period* for each of the four species of plasmodia which are natural parasites of man has been provided earlier in this Chapter (p. 124). (Consult p. 129 for *Plasmodium vivax*; p. 135 for *P. falciparum*; p. 142 for *P. malariæ*, and p. 147 for *P. ovale*.) As soon as the plasmodia can be detected in thick films of peripheral blood, patent infection (*viz.*, parasitemia) is initiated. For one to several days thereafter, during which one or more asexual erythrocytic multiplications have taken place and synchronization of schizogony is being accomplished, there are no distinctive manifestations of the disease, although during the latter part of this *prodromal period* there is usually a slight elevation of temperature and the patient may appear somewhat toxic. When the individual's allergic threshold is exceeded a definite febrile episode ensues.

The Malaria Paroxysm.—Primary overt malaria characteristically develops suddenly with a shaking chill (and rigor in vivax infection), followed by a fever of 40° to 40.6° C. (104° to 105° F.), and accompanied by evidences of an acute febrile disease, such as headache, muscular pains, malaise, nausea and vomiting, abdominal pain, and increased pulse and respiration rates. After continuing for several hours the fever terminates by crisis and there is a drenching sweat. Thereafter the patient is exhausted but feels marked relief. This is the picture in vivax, ovale and quartan malaria. In falciparum infection the chill is usually less pronounced and the fever more prolonged, characterized by an initial rise, a pseudo-crisis, a second rise, then a true crisis. Much more frequently than in the other types, falciparum malaria is accompanied by pernicious manifestations, which may consist of coma, convulsions or cardiac failure, and there may be no remarkable rise in temperature. These are the symptoms characteristic of the primary paroxysm in malaria.

Following an essentially symptomless remission which varies with the species, there is a second paroxysm of essentially equal intensity, followed by several additional ones of somewhat lesser magnitude extending over a period up to 3 weeks or more before the symptoms are terminated. *This series of paroxysms constitutes the primary attack.*

Relapse.—After a series of paroxysms has terminated the primary attack it is characteristic for one to several relapses to occur, each simulating the primary series of paroxysms but usually less intense and fewer in number. During the weeks or months intervening between the primary attack and the first relapse, the parasites of vivax, quartan and ovale infections are probably latent in exo-erythrocytic fixed-tissue foci, and those of falciparum infection are quiescent in visceral blood sinuses. There is no really satisfactory explanation for the exacerbation but it seems probable that it is associated in some way with a lowered threshold of immunity on the part of the patient.

Many relapsing attacks may occur over a period up to two years before the disease becomes clinically silent. However, this does not necessarily mean that it has been eradicated. From time to time persons living in non-malarious regions who have been free of symptoms for 20 to 40 years have been demonstrated to have latent infection. Furthermore, malaria of subclinical grade may become activated following severe accidents, major surgery, or attacks of enteric, respiratory, renal or other supervening disease.

"Atypical Manifestations" and Complications in Malaria.—In cerebral malaria due to falciparum infection there may be a sudden primary onset with hyperpyrexia, convulsions, deepening coma, and often death resulting from shock and anoxia; or, if the patient survives the crisis, there may be paralysis, manifestations of bulbar involvement, psychotic disturbances, neurasthenia or other symptoms, depending on the location of the lesions in the central nervous system. The symptoms in malaria may cover a vast variety of manifestations, including evidences of disease in practically every organ and tissue of the body.

Malaria in Hyperendemic Areas.—In populations living in highly malarious areas and subject to periodic reëxposure throughout life, typical overt manifestations are observed only in the young; they are the subjects from whom the true malaria index of the community should be obtained on the basis of parasitemia and the degree of splenic enlargement. Older children and adults who have survived earlier attacks have developed considerable tolerance to the disease. They are the ones with the hardened, enlarged spleen.

Blackwater Fever (Hemoglobinuric Fever).—This is an acute clinical episode complicating *falciparum* malaria. Although it frequently occurs only after repeated exposure to this parasite, it may be precipitated within a few weeks following a primary paroxysm (Ash and Spitz, 1945). Typically within a few days of onset there are severe chills, with rigor, high fever, jaundice, vomiting, rapidly progressive anemia, and the passage of dark-red or black urine. Hemoglobinuria occurs more frequently in non-immune Caucasians than in native populations, but only in persons who have lived in areas where *falciparum* infection abounds; likewise this disease is most common during the *falciparum* season. It develops in untreated cases but is more prevalent, and at times epidemic, in those who have been inadequately treated. Finally, it tends to develop in malaria patients who have been subject to unusual amounts of fatigue, privation, exposure, exhaustion, shock or injury, intercurrent infection, childbirth or alcoholic excess (Salisbury, 1949).

The most conspicuous feature of this disease is the massive hemolysis and the release of hemoglobin by the glomeruli into the urine. This apparently takes place when the plasma concentration exceeds 100 mgm. per cent. The exact mechanism precipitating the hemolysis is not known. The most tenable explanation of blackwater fever is an immune reaction with uncontrolled production of hemolysin, the exact mechanism of which is still inadequately understood.

DIAGNOSIS, TREATMENT AND PROGNOSIS

Diagnosis.—In no other group of parasitic infections have there been as many unsupported clinical diagnoses and missed diagnoses as in malaria. The latter is probably due not so much to failure to recognize the typical febrile paroxysms of this disease with its periodic replications as to the multiplicity of atypical manifestations.

Clinical Diagnosis.—After a typical primary or relapsed attack has gotten under way and two or three regularly spaced paroxysms have been experienced by the patient there is some justification for making a presumptive diagnosis of malaria. In *bona fide* malaria, blood-film examination at the time of the first paroxysm will confirm the diagnosis by demonstration of parasites, will save the patient several days of suffering and in the case of pernicious falciparum infection may prevent fatal outcome. However, it is the vaguer, frequently unreliable history of "chills and fever" which is likely to lead to a clinical misdiagnosis of malaria and to antimalarial therapy, whereas a considerable number of infectious agents may produce a similar picture. Only if laboratory diagnosis is not available or the condition of the patient is critical, is there a reasonable excuse for undertaking a therapeutic test.

Malaria may be confused with many diseases. In many instances one or more of these diseases may coëxist with malaria or may be superimposed on chronic malaria, so that the symptoms are complex.

Laboratory Diagnosis.—Since the malaria paroxysms are due to the release of plasmodial merozoites at the end of each period of schizogony, blood films taken just before, or at the height of the malarial paroxysm

Table 8.—The Differential Characters of the Malaria Parasites of Man (Giemsa Stain)

(From Craig and Faust's *Clinical Parasitology*, 1951.

	Plasmodium vivax	*Plasmodium malariæ*	*Plasmodium falciparum*	*Plasmodium ovale*
Duration of schizogony	48 hours	72 hours	36 to 48 hours	48 hours
Motility	Active ameboid until about half-grown	Slightly ameboid during trophozoite stage	Seldom ameboid during trophozoite stage	Slightly ameboid during trophozoite stage
Pigment (Hematin)	Yellowish-brown, in fine grains and minute rodlets	Dark brown or almost black in coarse grains, rods, or irregular small clumps	Very dark brown or black in coarse granules or small masses	Dark brown in coarse granules or irregular masses
Infected red blood corpuscle	Much enlarged, pale with eosinophilic stippling (Schüffner's dots)	Not enlarged. Normal color. No granular stippling	Not enlarged or smaller than normal. Darker green (brassy). Basophilic dots and brick-red clefts in cytoplasm (Maurer's clefts or dots)	Somewhat enlarged, oval or irregular in shape, with eosinophilic stippling (Schüffner's dots)
Stages of development seen in peripheral blood	Trophozoites, schizonts and gametocytes	Trophozoites, schizonts and gametocytes	Usually only trophozoites and gametoyctes. In pernicious infections rarely schizonts may be seen	Trophozoites, schizonts and gametocytes
Multiple infection of red blood corpuscle	Quite common	Very rare	Very common	Rare

Area of red blood corpuscle occupied by fully developed schizont	Entire red blood corpuscle which is enlarged	Almost entire red blood corpuscle which is not enlarged	From two-thirds to three-quarters of red blood corpuscle which is not enlarged	About three-quarters of red blood corpuscle which is enlarged
Trophozoites (ring-forms)	Small and large rings with vacuole and usually one chromatin dot. Ameboid	Small and large rings with vacuole and usually one chromatin dot; or early "band" forms	Very small and larger rings with vacuole and frequently with 2 chromatin dots. Peripheral forms common. (Forms appliqué.)	Small and large rings with vacuole.
Segmenting schizonts	Irregular, bizarre forms. Vacuole present in early stage. Chromatin in fine grains or small irregular clumps	Oval or round, with vacuole in early stage. Chromatin in coarse granules or irregular clumps. Band forms often seen	Not usually seen in peripheral blood. Oval or round with chromatin in large granules and in small clumps	Round and oval with vacuole in early stage. Chromatin in irregular clumps or filamentous masses
Segmented schizonts	Fill greatly enlarged red blood corpuscle. 12 to 24 merozoites (usually 18 to 20) irregularly arranged about a mass of pigment	Almost fill a normal sized red blood corpuscle. 6 to 12 merozoites (usually 8 to 10) arranged like the petals of a flower surrounding a central pigment mass	Not usually seen in peripheral blood. Fill two-thirds to three-quarters of red blood corpuscle. 8 to 36 merozoites (usually 18 to 24) arranged about a central pigment mass	Fill about three-quarters of red blood corpuscle. 6 to 12 merozoites arranged about a central or eccentric pigment mass
Gametocytes	Round and fill the enlarged red blood corpuscle. Chromatin undistributed in cytoplasm	Round and fill the normal sized red blood corpuscle. Chromatin undistributed in cytoplasm	Crescentic or kidney-bean in shape. Usually appear free in blood. Chromatin undistributed in cytoplasm	Round and fill about three-quarters of the enlarged red blood corpuscle. Chromatin undistributed in cytoplasm

will contain the asexual stages of the parasite. If the films are made during afebrile intervals there will be fewer or no parasites in the red cells. However, once the infection becomes chronic, both trophozoites and gametocytes, especially in falciparum infection, may at times be found in considerable concentration in the blood of persons presenting no particular symptoms. Parasites are not likely to be circulating in the blood during suppressive therapy, immediately following curative treatment, or soon after self-medication with anti-malarial drugs for "chills and fever."

While thin-blood films are valuable for studying the morphologic characters of different asexual and gametocyte stages of the different species of plasmodia, thick-blood films are almost invariably employed for diagnosis. In a smaller area on the microscopic slide the thick film allows rapid examination of a much larger volume of blood, thus saving valuable time in diagnosis.

Staining of thick-blood films is carried out according to the Giemsa, Field or Walker technic. (See TECHNICAL AIDS, pages 588–590.) Description of the three common malaria parasites and illustrations indicating their appearance in thick-blood films have been included in a preceding section of this chapter (for *Plasmodium vivax*, page 133, Plate V; for *P. falciparum*, page 139, Plate VII, and for *P. malariæ,* page 145, Plate IX). Thick films of *P. ovale* provide comparable concentration of the parasites, but without Schüffner's granules and the bizarre outlines of infected red cells it is difficult to distinguish this species from *P. malariæ*.

Comparative information on the differential diagnostic characters of the four malaria parasites of man is found in the accompanying table (Table 8).

Treatment.—For nearly 300 years the only effective anti-malarials available were the cinchona bark and its refined product *quinine*. In 1924 Schulemann and associates (Schulemann and Memmi, 1927) synthesized an 8-aminoquinoline, *pamaquin* (Plasmochin). This was found to be lethal for gametocytes of *Plasmodium falciparum* but in doses sufficient to kill the asexual parasites it produced cyanosis and cramps. However, in very small amounts in combination with quinine ("Plasmochin compound") it was employed extensively in treating the disease. In 1933 Mietzch and Mauss synthesized an acridine compound, *quinacrine* (Atabrine), which was found to be more effective than quinine both as a suppressant and in clinical treatment. It eradicated *falciparum* infection and rapidly eliminated the erythrocytic asexual stages of *P. vivax* and *P. malariæ,* although in both of these latter species of plasmodia overt infection appeared after treatment was discontinued.

During the 1940's American chemists developed two 4-aminoquinolines, *chloroquine* (Aralen), and *amodiaquin* (Camoquin). These anti-malarials have all of the advantages and none of the disadvantages of quinacrine, but they provide no guarantee that vivax and quartan parasites will not produce clinical malaria after therapy is discontinued. Likewise, British chemists have synthesized *chlorguanide* (Paludrine) which has pronounced anti-malarial properties in well-tolerated doses. Three additional 8-aminoquinolines, *pentaquine, isopentaquine* and *primaquine* have been synthesized in the United States, all of which are less toxic than pamaquin and are effective in preventing development of overt vivax infection when administered in association with chloroquine. In 1952 British workers (Goodwin, 1952) announced successful clinical trials of *Daraprim*, a newly prepared pyrimidine compound.

Each of the presently known types of anti-malarial drugs will be briefly described and evaluated. Recommendations for treatment have been considered in Table 5, page 65.

Modern Anti-malarial Drugs

I. Cinchona Products

1. Quinine.—*Quinine sulfate* U.S.P. (83% base) is employed for oral administration; *quinine dihydrochloride* U.S.P. (82% base) is given intravenously, very slowly and in large fluid volume. Quinine destroys the asexual parasites in circulating erythrocytes, rapidly terminating clinical attacks, but relapses soon occur after full therapeutic treatment of vivax infection. This drug has no effect on fixed-tissue stages, and in suppressive doses is not dependable (Cooper, 1949).
2. Totaquine.—This standardized mixture of cinchona alkaloids is more economical than quinine since use is made of all the active fractions of cinchona bark. It is administered only by the oral route.

II. Acridine Compounds

1. Quinacrine.—*Proprietary names:* Atabrine, Atebrin, *et al.*

   Quinacrine hydrochloride U.S.P., containing 79% base, is rapidly concentrated in the tissues, including the skin, to which it imparts a saffron-yellow discoloration. Plasma concentration remains high for at least a week after completion of treatment. It is as effective in rapidly terminating clinical attacks as quinine, destroying the asexual plasmodia in circulating red cells. It cures falciparum infection but will not prevent vivax relapses. In suppressive doses it cures falciparum malaria and usually prevents overt infection in vivax and quartan malaria during the period of medication (Young and Eyles, 1948; Cooper, 1949).

III. 4-Aminoquinolines

1. Chloroquine.—*Proprietary names:* Aralen, *et al.*

   Chloroquine diphosphate dihydrate U.S.P. (62% base) is employed for oral administration; *chloroquine hydrochloride* (89% base), for parenteral use. Like quinacrine, this anti-malarial becomes rapidly concentrated in the tissues and is slowly degraded and excreted; unlike quinacrine, it produces no discoloration of the skin. Chloroquine is lethal to the asexual stages of the plasmodia in circulating red cells, but it does not reach fixed-tissue stages. As a suppressant it prevents overt infection during the period of infection, and terminates falciparum infection, but does not eradicate vivax malaria, which produces a primary clinical attack at variable times after suppressive treatment has been discontinued.

2. AMODIAQUIN.—*Proprietary names:* Camoquin, *et al.*

The *dihydrochloride dihydrate* (77% base), when administered orally, is rapidly taken up by the tissues, its degradation products are very active and its elimination from the body is relatively slow. It is well tolerated in recommended doses, and is very effective against the asexual stages of plasmodia in circulating red cells but has no effect on the tissue phase or on gametocytes. Its suppressive action is similar to that of chloroquine (Payne, 1951; Villarejos, 1951).

IV. Aryl Biguanides

1. CHLORGUANIDE.—*Proprietary names:* Paludrine, *et al.*

Chlorguanide acts upon the asexual erythrocytic stages of all types of malaria similar to the 4-amino-quinolines and likewise in alleviating clinical symptoms, but the action is slower. It sterilizes the gametocytes in falciparum infection and has valuable suppressive action, but vivax relapses are frequent (Fairley *et al.*, 1946). *P. vivax* and *P. falciparum* rapidly develop resistance to this drug (Wilson *et al.*, 1952).

V. 8-Aminoquinolines

1. PAMAQUINE.—*Proprietary names:* Plasmochin, Plasmoquine, *et al.*

In conjunction with sulfonamides, quinacrine or chlorguanide, pamaquine causes methemoglobinemia, not infrequently cyanosis, abdominal cramps, and at times acute intravascular hemolysis, particularly in Negroes (Cooper, 1949). In low dosage the gametocytes of falciparum malaria are sterilized and in conjunction with therapeutic doses of quinine ("Plasmochin compound"), chloroquine or amodiaquin the relapse rate of vivax infection is reduced.

2. PENTAQUINE.—Tissue concentration and metabolism of this drug closely resemble those of pamaquine. It may produce methemoglobinemia, and potentially may precipitate acute intravascular hemolysis. Its real usefulness consists in reduction in the relapse rate of vivax infections when this drug is administered in low dosage together with therapeutic amounts of quinine or chloroquine (Loeb *et al.*, 1946).

3. ISOPENTAQUINE.

This drug has been tested clinically and found to have antimalarial properties similar to pentaquine but with less danger of severe hemoglobinemia and cyanosis. It is not commercially available (Alving *et al.*, 1948).

4. PRIMAQUINE.

This 8-aminoquinoline is taken orally. Its toxicity is much less than that of the other members of this series. Its action is primarily against the fixed-tissue stages of vivax plasmodia. In amounts of 15 mgm. base daily for 14 days, administered orally in combination with therapeutic or suppressive doses of chloroquine, primaquine has been demonstrated to produce a high percentage of cures, with no toxic effects in light-skinned individuals. Dark-skinned persons have less tolerance but are not endangered by the standard dosage (Edgecomb *et al.*, 1950; Alving *et al.*, 1952).

VI. Pyrimidine Compounds

1. Daraprim.

When administered orally in a single dose of 100 mgm., Daraprim reaches a maximum blood serum concentration in 2 hours and by 8 hours falls to a low level, but its antagonistic activity to folic acid is maintained for at least 48 hours. As suppressant Coatney *et al.* (1952) found that single weekly doses of Daraprim as low as 0.78 mgm. protected against a tropical strain of *Plasmodium vivax*, and Goodwin (1952), taking 5 mgm. daily during exposure in an area of hyperendemicity for *P. falciparum*, did not acquire the infection. In primary attacks and relapses of *P. vivax* a single treatment dose of 25 mgm. has proved as satisfactory as 600 mgm. chloroquine base, although it acted somewhat more slowly and all cases later relapsed (Coatney *et al.*, 1952). Daraprim, like chlorguanide, when administered in suppressive doses, has caused drug fastness in all species of malaria parasites on which it has been tried.

Recommended Anti-malarial Therapy

There are four potential uses for anti-malarial drugs, *viz.*, (1) causal prophylaxis, (2) suppression of parasitemia and overt infection, (3) treatment of clinical cases, and (4) treatment of relapsing infections. To these should be added the management of blackwater fever.

The primary goal in malaria therapy is the destruction of the sporozoite stage of the plasmodia at the time of its injection into the skin by the *Anopheles* mosquito. No present-day drug produces this result. Recommendations for suppressive medication, treatment of clinical cases and management of relapsing infections are provided in Table 5 (page 65).

Blackwater Fever.—Whenever blackwater fever supervenes in malaria, quinine, quinacrine and the 8-aminoquinolines should be carefully avoided, since they serve to accentuate rather than to diminish or terminate the underlying hemolysis. If blood films are positive for parasites (almost invariably *Plasmodium falciparum*) or there are overt symptoms due to the infection *per se*, full therapeutic amounts of chloroquine, amodiaquin or chlorguanide may be safely administered. Supportive treatment should be instituted to combat cardiac failure, to maintain an equilibrium between fluid intake and output, and to prevent acidosis. Blood transfusion is contraindicated in toxic anuria, although it may be helpful in polyuric and asthenic patients. Persons subject to blackwater fever should leave the endemic area and avoid subsequent exposure (Salisbury, 1949).

Control

Control of malaria has as its objective the reduction of Anopheles below the transmission level (Boyd, 1949). The most dangerous species are those which prefer human blood, since they are most apt to transmit the infection to man.

Treatment of Human Infections.—As pointed out earlier in this chapter, page 126, the gametocytes are the stage for continuation of the cycle when ingested by the *Anopheles*. Thus, the dangerous patients are the gametocyte carriers.

Quinacrine and chloroquine, even in suppressive doses, prevent the development of all erythrocytic stages of the *falciparum parasites* and probably effect their eradication in exo-erythrocytic foci, thus eliminating the source from which falciparum gametocytes are derived. In *vivax*, and probably also in *quartan* and *ovale malaria*, none of the drugs valuable in terminating erythrocytic schizogony are particularly satisfactory against the exo-erythrocytic foci, hence against their gametocyte production (Sapero, 1949). In contrast, the 8-aminoquinolines are very effective in terminating exo-erythrocytic infection and hence gametocyte production. Primaquine is the most valuable member of this group.

Protecting Gametocyte Carriers from Mosquitoes.—If this program were meticulously carried out, very marked reduction would be achieved in the transmission of malaria. This includes the use of repellents on the uncovered areas of the skin, adequate screening of dwellings, bed nets, face nets and mosquito boots, all of which serve to keep the mosquito from direct contact with the skin (Watson, 1949).

Measures Directed against Adult Anopheles.—Adequate screening of homes and bed nets will protect human beings from some, but not all exposures. Similarly, repellents such as Rutgers 612 will prevent these mosquitoes from alighting on the skin for a few hours. Spraying of pyrethrum-DDT emulsion on the inside walls and in and around doors and windows of homes and adjacent buildings has many advantages over screening and repellent measures alone. Pyrethrum produces rapid "knockdown" of mosquitoes with which it comes in contact; DDT, acting more slowly, is lethal to the mosquito (Bishopp, 1949). Use of these insecticides has been found to be both practical and effective in killing the adult *Anopheles* and is a much simpler procedure and usually more economical than larvicidal control (Fig. 28). However, *Anopheles* mosquitoes tend to develop an awareness-sensitivity to residual DDT particles on walls and may not remain in contact with the surface long enough to produce lethal effects.

Measures Directed against Anopheles Breeding.—Malaria mosquitoes breed in quiet streams, pools, impounded bodies of water, irrigation canals, borrow pits, seepage channels, residual water from temporarily flooded plains, and swampy areas. Drainage, naturalistic technics and larvicidal measures have been employed to prevent such breeding. In all of these drainage programs it is essential to eliminate or keep to a minimum the aquatic vegetation in which the female *Anopheles* lays her eggs, and in which the hatched young develop through successive larval stages and pupate (Magoon and Knipe, 1949).

In small areas where drainage is not feasible, such as ponds or borrow pits, introduction of the minnow *Gambusia* may at times keep breeding controlled by consuming the larvas as they hatch. To be effective predators, the fishes must be able to reach the larvas and not be hindered by dense aquatic vegetation.

Naturalistic control refers to the development of natural conditions which are unfavorable for the breeding of a particular species of malaria vector

(Williamson, 1949). Thus, development of shade where the *Anopheles* requires sunshine, or removing dense vegetation in which the larvas develop, are considered to be particularly useful naturalistic methods. Russell (1952) has found this to be very effective against *Anopheles culicifacies* in India.

Larvicidal control is the most universally applicable technic to reduce mosquito breeding. The first larvicides employed were crude petroleum oils; when sprayed on the surface of aquatic breeding grounds, the oil killed practically all types of mosquito larvas. DDT made up as a 5% concen-

FIG. 28.—A few seconds use of a pyrethrum-DDT aërosol "bomb" will kill all mosquitoes in an average-sized room. (U. S. D. A. photograph, in Boyd's *Malariology*, courtesy of W. B. Saunders Co., Philadelphia.)

trate in oil solvents with a detergent which serves as an emulsifier acts as a contact and a stomach poison and is sprayed periodically on breeding sites by hand-compressor sprayer, by power sprayer or by airplane application over extensive areas such as swamps and tidal flats which can not be reached on foot or by land conveyance. DDT is the most effective and economical of all larvicides thus far developed (Bishopp, 1949).

Control of malaria can not be effectively carried out without accurate epidemiologic information concerning the amount and kind of malaria in the community, use of approved methods to determine the index of the infection in the community and in the mosquito (*viz.*, malariometry), the dangerous *Anopheles* vectors, the habitats and habits of their larval stages and of the adults. Coöperation of the native population should be developed by educational propaganda demonstrating the value of malaria control. For clear, concise information on field programs in malaria control, the reader is referred to Russell's "*Malaria, Basic Principles Briefly Stated*" (1952).

SUMMARY

1. The malaria parasites are protozoa which have become adapted to life in the fixed tissues of the body and the circulating red blood cells. Like other sporozoa they have an alternation of asexual and sexual generations but unlike the coccidia they require two hosts, one for asexual multiplication (schizogony) and early gametogony, and the other for completion of gametogony and sexual multiplication (sporogony).
2. The four species of malaria parasites which parasitize man (*Plasmodium vivax*, *P. falciparum*, *P. malariæ* and *P. ovale*) have no other natural hosts for the asexual phase of their life cycle and are adapted exclusively to *Anopheles* mosquitoes for the sexual phase.
3. In man erythrocytic schizogony occurs typically every 48 hours in *Plasmodium vivax* and *P. ovale*, every 72 hours in *P. malariæ*, and about every 36 to 48 hours in *P. falciparum*.
4. Development of these plasmodia in the *Anopheles* mosquito is dependent primarily on the environment. High atmospheric humidity is necessary for optimal survival of the mosquito and the sexual development of the parasite. Optimal temperature in the mosquito varies with the different species of plasmodia.
5. Malaria may be endemic, hyperendemic, epidemic or sporadic. In order to be maintained in a community there must be persons in whom gametocytes are present in the circulating red cells, the source of infection for the mosquito. The extrinsic cycle requires adequate breeding of *Anopheles* mosquitoes close to human habitations. Malaria tends to be hyperendemic in regions where there are numerous gametocyte carriers and anthropophilous *Anopheles*. Epidemics occur most frequently when a new strain of plasmodium is introduced into a malarious area or a non-immune population is exposed to infection.
6. *Falciparum* malaria is indigenous in the tropical and subtropical regions of the world wherever *Anopheles* mosquitoes breed. *Vivax* infection prevails not only in warm climates but in temperate regions where there is a warm period of the year. *Quartan* malaria (*P. malariæ* infection) is confined to tropical areas having consistently high atmospheric humidity. *Ovale* malaria is commonly endemic only in certain regions of tropical Africa.
7. The development of plasmodia in exo-erythrocytic foci, both preceding and subsequent to the infection of red blood cells, produces only incidental tissue pathology. The *essential pathogenesis* of the disease is associated with invasion and destruction of red blood corpuscles, and the release of increasing numbers of asexual daughter cells (merozoites) and red cell detritus into the blood plasma. These events produce

anemia and sensitization which become clinically evident as soon as a sufficient amount of foreign body substance and necrotic débris is set free into the plasma.

8. *Pathologic changes* due to malaria involve not only the blood cells but the spleen and other visceral organs. In falciparum malaria hemostasis in the blood sinuses and capillaries, particularly in the brain, lungs, coronary vessels and kidneys, produces acute conditions which may be rapidly fatal. Anemia, sensitization reactions and localized lesions are all characteristic of malaria.
9. The notable *symptoms* produced in malaria first develop with the synchronized release of considerable numbers of parasites and necrotic red cell detritus into the blood plasma, resulting in the malarial paroxysms, which consist of a shaking chill, then burning fever followed by sweating. Several of these paroxysms succeeding one another more or less at regular intervals constitute an attack. After one attack there is a remission from a few weeks to several months, then a relapsed attack. Relapse is an erythrocytic reactivation from latent exo-erythrocytic infection.
10. In *falciparum* malaria the manifestations may be atypical, the paroxysms are frequently less marked, and the fever less intense but extending over a longer period. Yet acute development of cerebral symptoms may suddenly supervene. Moreover, in this type of malaria blackwater (hemoglobinuric) fever may be precipitated as a result of sudden hemolysis within the blood stream.
11. Except in emergencies or when laboratory facilities are unavailable, *diagnosis* of malaria should always be checked by microscopic examination of the patient's blood. Dehemoglobinized and appropriately stained thick-blood films should be employed, since more positive diagnoses are made with thick films than with thin films.
12. *Treatment* of malaria has been remarkably advanced in recent years. In addition to quinine the following are now available: the acridine dye quinacrine, the 4-aminoquinolines chloroquine and amodiaquin, the aryl biguanide chlorguanide, the pyrimidine derivative Daraprim, and several 8-aminoquinolines, *viz.*, pamaquin, pentaquine, isopentaquine and primaquine. None of these are true causal prophylactics. However, chloroquine and amodiaquin are excellent suppressants, are rapidly effective in curative doses in eradicating erythrocytic asexual parasites, and terminate *falciparum* malaria. Primaquine has proved very satisfactory in eradicating *vivax* infection.
13. *Control* of malaria must consider both the human source of infection, *i. e.*, the gametocyte carrier, and the *Anopheles* mosquito. Reduction in malaria may be temporarily obtained by treating patients with antimalarial drugs and screening human carriers from the *Anopheles* vectors. A more effective procedure is to kill adult *Anopheles* mosquitoes by use of residual insecticidal sprays on the inside and outside of habitations. A more lasting attack on the mosquito consists in a continued program to reduce *Anopheles* breeding.

REFERENCES

ALVING, A. S., ARNOLD, J., and ROBINSON, D. H. 1952. Mass Therapy of Subclinical Vivax Malaria with Primaquine. J. Am. Med. Assn., *129*, 1558–1562.

ALVING, A. S., *et al.* 1948. Pentaquine (SN 13,276) and Isopentaquine (SN 13,274), Therapeutic Agents Effective in Reducing Relapse Rate in Vivax Malaria. Proc. IV Internat'l Congresses on Trop. Med. & Hygiene, U. S. Dept. State, Washington, D. C., *I*, 734–741.

BISHOPP, F. C. 1949a. Imagocides, pp. 1203–1220, in Boyd's *Malariology*, W. B. Saunders Co., Philadelphia.

———1949b. Larvicides, pp. 1339–1359, in Boyd's *Malariology*. W. B. Saunders Co., Philadelphia.

BOYD, M. F. 1938. The Threshold of Parasite Density in Relation to Clinical Activity in Primary Infections with *Plasmodium Vivax*. Am. J. Trop. Med., *18*, 497–503.

———(Editor). 1949. *Malariology*. 2 vols., 1643 pp. W. B. Saunders Co., Philadelphia.

BOYD, M. F., and KITCHEN, S. F. 1936. On the Efficiency of the Homologous Properties of Acquired Immunity to *Plasmodium Vivax*. Am. J. Trop. Med., *16*, 447–457.

BOYD, M. F., and MATHEWS, C. B. 1939. An Observation on the Incubation Period of *Plasmodium Falciparum*. Am. J. Trop. Med., *19*, 69–71.

BOYD, M. F., and STRATMAN-THOMAS, W. K. 1934. Studies on Benign Tertian Malaria. 6. On Heterologous Tolerance. Am. J. Hyg., *20*, 482–487.

BOYD, M. F., STRATMAN-THOMAS, W. K., and KITCHEN, S. F. 1936. On Acquired Immunity to *Plasmodium Falciparum*. Am. J. Trop. Med., *16*, 139–145.

BRAY, R. S., COOPER, W., LAINSON, R., AWAD, F. I., and WILLIAMSON, J. 1954. Pre-erythrocytic Stages of Human Malaria: Plasmodium Ovale. A Preliminary Note. Brit. Med. J., *i*, 257.

CLARK, H. C., and TOMLINSON, W. J. 1949. The Pathologic Anatomy of Malaria, in Boyd's *Malariology*, pp. 874–903. W. B. Saunders Co., Philadelphia.

COOPER, W. A. 1949. Summary of Antimalarial Drugs, Pub. Health Repts., *64*, 717–732.

FAIRLEY, N. H. 1945. Chemotherapeutic Suppression and Prophylaxis in Malaria. Trans. R. Soc. Trop. Med. & Hyg., *38*, 311–365.

FAIRLEY, N. H., *et al.* 1946. Researches on Paludrine (M 4888) in Malaria, Trans. R. Soc. Trop. Med. & Hyg., *40*, 105–151.

FIELD, J. W. 1948. *The Microscopic Diagnosis of Human Malaria.* Pt. I. A Short Descriptive Atlas of Thick-film Diagnosis. 116 pp. Kuala Lumpur, Inst. for Med. Research, Federation of Malaya.

FIELD, J. W., and LEFLEMING, H. 1939–1941. The Morphology of Malarial Parasites in Thick Blood Films. Trans. R. Soc. Trop. Med. & Hyg., *32*, 467–480; *33*, 507–520; *34*, 297–304.

GARNHAM, P. C. C. 1951. The Mosquito Transmission of *Plasmodium Inui* Halberstaedter and Prowazek, and Its Pre-erythrocytic Development in the Liver of the Rhesus Monkey. Trans. R. Soc. Trop. Med. & Hyg., *45*, 45–52.

GOODWIN, L. G. 1952. Daraprim—Clinical Trials and Pharmacology. Trans. R. Soc. Trop. Med. & Hyg., *46*, 485–495.

GREEN, R. 1929. Observations on Some Factors Influencing the Infectivity of Malarial Gamete Carriers, etc. Bull. Inst. Med. Research, Federated Malay States, No. 5, pp. 1–41. Kuala Lumpur, F. M. S.

HUFF, C. G., and BLOOM, W. 1935. A Malarial Parasite Infecting All Blood and Blood-forming Cells of Birds. J. Infec. Dis., *57*, 315–336.

JAMES, S. P., NICOL, W. D., and SHUTE, P. G. 1933. *Plasmodium Ovale* Stephens, 1922. Parasitol., *25*, 87–95.

JEFFERY, G. M., WOLCOTT, G. B., YOUNG, M. C., and WILLIAMS, D., JR. 1952. Exo-erythrocytic Stages of *Plasmodium Falciparum*. Am. J. Trop. Med. & Hyg., *1*, 917–926.

KITCHEN, S. F. 1949. Symptomatology: General Considerations: Falciparum Malaria; Quartan Malaria; Vivax Malaria; Ovale Malaria, pp. 966–1052, in Boyd's *Malariology*, W. B. Saunders Co., Philadelphia.

LAVERAN, A. 1880. Note sur un Nouveau Parasite Trouvé dans le Sang de Plusieurs Malades Atteints de Fièvre Palustre. Bull. de l'Acad. de Méd., Paris, *9*, 1235, 1268, 1346.

MAEGRAITH, B., JONES, E. S., and ANDREWS, W. H. H. 1951. Pathological Processes in Malaria. Trans. R. Soc. Trop. Med. & Hyg., *45*, 15–42.

MAGOON, E. H., and KNIPE, F. W. 1949. Water in Relation to the Problem of Drainage, pp. 1232–1251, in Boyd's *Malariology*. W. B. Saunders Co., Philadelphia.

MANSON, P. 1894. On the Nature and Significance of the Crescentic and Flagellated Bodies in Malarial Blood. Brit. Med. J., *ii*, 1306–1308.

———1900. Experimental Proof of the Mosquito-Malaria Theory. Brit. Med. J., *ii*, 949–951.

MIETZCH, F., and MAUSS, H. 1933. Atebrin, Ein Neuss Heilmittel gegen Malaria. Klin. Wochenschr., *12*, 1276.

MORRISON, D. B., and ANDERSON, W. A. D. 1942. On the Rôle of Parasite Pigment in the Malaria Paroxysm. Pub. Health Repts., *57*, 161–174.

MOST, H., *et al.* 1946. Chloroquine for Treatment of Acute Attacks of Vivax Malaria, J. Am. Med. Assn., *131*, 963–967.

PAYNE, E. H., *et al.* 1951. Intravenous Amodiaquin (Camoquin) in Naturally Acquired and Induced Malaria. Am. J. Trop. Med., *31*, 698–702.

ROSS, R. 1898. Report on the Cultivation of Proteosoma Labbé, in Grey Mosquitos. Indian Med. Gaz., *33*, 401–408, 448–451.

SALISBURY, E. I. 1949. Blackwater Fever, pp. 1053–1070, in Boyd's *Malariology*, W. B. Saunders Co., Philadelphia.

SCHULEMANN, W., and MEMMI, G. 1927. Plasmochin, ein Synthetisches, gegen die Malariainfektion Chinolinderivat, Beih. 1, Arch. f. Schiffs- u. Tropen-Hyg., *31*, 59–88.

SHORTT, H. E. 1951. History of Recent Researches on Tissue Phases of the Malaria Parasite at the London School of Hygiene and Tropical Medicine. Trans. R. Soc. Trop. Med. & Hyg., *45*, 175–188.

SHORTT, H. E., and GARNHAM, P. C. C. 1948. The Pre-erythrocytic Development of *Plasmodium Cynomolgi* and *Plasmodium Vivax*. Trans. R. Soc. Trop. Med. & Hyg., *41*, 785–795.

STEPHENS, J. W. W. 1922. A New Malaria Parasite of Man. Ann. Trop. Med. & Parasitol., *16*, 383–396.

VILLAREJOS, M., V. M. 1951. Experiences with Amodiaquin (Camoquin), a New Synthetic Antimalarial. Am. J. Trop. Med., *31*, 703–706.

WATSON, R. B. 1949. Personal Protection; Location and Mosquito-proofing of Dwellings, pp. 1181–1202, in Boyd's *Malariology*. W. B. Saunders Co., Philadelphia.

WENYON, C. M. 1926. *Protozoölogy*. 2 vols. pp. 1563. Baillière, Tindall & Cox, London.

WILCOX, A. 1950. *Manual for the Microscopical Diagnosis of Malaria in Man.* 2nd ed. pp. 29. Nat'l Inst. Health Bull. No. 180. Washington, D. C.

WILLIAMSON, K. B. 1949. Naturalistic Methods of Anopheline Control. pp. 1360–1384, in Boyd's *Malariology*, W. B. Saunders Co., Philadelphia.

WILSON, T., MUNRO, D. S., and RICHARD, D. R. 1952. Resistance of *Plasmodium Falciparum* and *P. Vivax* to Suppressive (and Curative) Doses of Proguanil Noted in 1951 in Malaya. Brit. Med. J., *i*, 564.

YOUNG, M. D., *et al.* 1945. Studies on Imported Malarias. I. Ability of Domestic Mosquitoes to Transmit Vivax Malaria of Foreign Origin. J. Nat. Malaria Soc., *4*, 127–131.

Chapter 9

Blood and Tissue Protozoa Other Than Malaria Parasites

In addition to the malaria parasites and related species of hemosporidia, other protozoa including certain flagellates (Mastigophora) and *Toxoplasma* which are adapted to life in the circulating blood and fixed tissues are considered in this chapter. A brief description of *Sarcocystis lindemanni* is likewise provided.

FLAGELLATE PROTOZOA OF THE BLOOD AND TISSUES

All species of Mastigophora multiply exclusively by longitudinal binary fission. Most of the parasitic forms reside in the digestive tract of their host and complete their life cycle in a single host. On the other hand, some species which parasitize the extra-intestinal tissues of man and other vertebrates have a 2-host cycle, in which there is an alternation between a vertebrate and a blood-sucking invertebrate.

Six species of flagellate protozoa inhabit the blood stream and tissues of man, *viz.*, *Leishmania tropica*, *L. brasiliensis*, *L. donovani*, *Trypanosoma rhodesiense*, *T. gambiense* and *T. cruzi*. For all of these organisms the invertebrate host is a blood-sucking insect: for the species of *Leishmania* it is a sandfly (*Phlebotomus*); for *T. rhodesiense* and *T. gambiense*, a tsetse fly (*Glossina*), and for *T. cruzi*, a triatomid bug.

In the insect host these organisms are typical flagellates with a single anterior flagellum. They live in the lumen of the insect's midgut, where they multiply. In species of *Leishmania* this stage is a simple, spindle-shaped organism called "leptomonas." In the trypanosomes the fundamental insect stage is somewhat more complex, since the flagellum does not originate in the anterior tip of the body as it does in the leishmanias but is reflected posteriad along the margin of an undulating membrane, ending somewhat anterior to the nucleus. This is the "crithidia" stage of the trypanosome.

In infections with species of *Leishmania* as well as *T. gambiense* and *T. rhodesiense* the flagellates multiply in the midgut of the insect, then migrate forward to the hypopharyngeal tube in the insect's proboscis, through which the *Leishmania* organisms are directly injected into the skin of the vertebrate host when the insect takes its next blood meal. For *T. rhodesiense* and *T. gambiense* the flagellates migrate from the hypopharyngeal tube up into the salivary glands where another multiplication occurs. Thereafter

Table 9.—Characteristic Stages of Species of Leishmania and Trypanosoma in Man and in the Insect Host

Stage of the Parasite	*Leishmania*	*Leptomonas*	*Crithidia*	*Trypanosome*
	A 	*B* 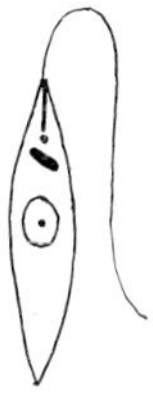	*C* 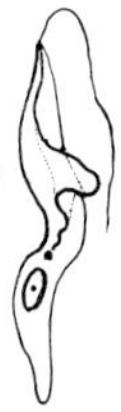	*D* 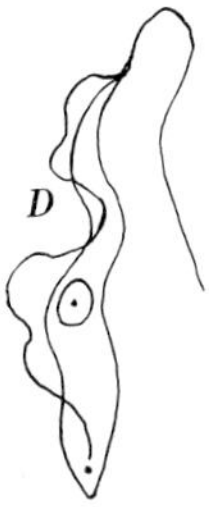
Name of Parasite				
Leishmania tropica	*Intracellular* in macrophages of skin and subcutaneous tissue	In midgut and later in proboscis of sand-fly (*Phlebotomus*); *transfer stage* to man	Lacking	Lacking
Leishmania brasiliensis	*Intracellular* in macrophages of skin; carried to mucocutaneous junctions	In midgut and later in proboscis of sand-fly (*Phlebotomus*); *transfer stage* to man	Lacking	Lacking
Leishmania donovani	*Intracellular* in macrophages; predominantly in liver, spleen, bone marrow and lymph nodes	In midgut and later in proboscis of sand-fly (*Phlebotomus*); *transfer stage* to man	Lacking	Lacking
Trypanosoma rhodesiense	Lacking	Lacking	In midgut of tsetse-fly (*Glossina*)	In proboscis of tsetse-fly; *transfer stage* to man; first in blood stream, then in lymph nodes
Trypanosoma gambiense	Lacking	Lacking	In midgut of tsetse-fly (*Glossina*)	In proboscis of tsetse-fly; *transfer stage* to man; first in blood stream, then in lymph nodes, later in central nervous system
Trypanosoma cruzi	*Intracellular* in macrophages, especially in skin, lymph nodes, liver and spleen; also in myocardium, brain and endocrine glands	Transitional stage only	In midgut of triatomid bug	In feces of triatomid bug; *transfer stage* to man; present in blood stream only during acute attacks

they return in increased numbers into the hypopharynx, now as infective trypanosomes. In *T. cruzi* a more primitive condition exists: The parasites pass through the posterior part of the digestive tract and are evacuated in liquid feces at the time the bug feeds. They then enter the skin or mucous membrane at or near the site where the bug punctures the host's epithelium.

In man and other suitable mammalian hosts the *Leishmania* organisms become ovoidal (*i. e.*, characteristically leishmania-form) and proceed to multiply within the cytoplasm of the host cell.

Trypanosoma rhodesiense and *T. gambiense* never invade host cells; they occur free in the blood stream or interstitially in the tissues.

T. cruzi likewise transforms from a crithidia to a metacyclic trypanosome before entry into its mammalian host. At the site of penetration it is almost immediately engulfed by wandering macrophages, in which it rapidly transforms into a leishmania stage and then multiplies. Some of the progeny then get into the blood stream and temporarily transform into a trypanosome form, but never multiply as trypanosomes. When these organisms reach fixed tissues, they enter the cells, again become leishmania-form and proceed to multiply and destroy the parasitized cells.

The essential features in the life cycle of the three species of *Leishmania* and three species of *Trypanosoma* which infect man are compared in Table 9.

THE LEISHMANIA PARASITES OF MAN

The genus *Leishmania* is named in honor of William Leishman, who discovered the species (*L. donovani*) which causes kala-azar. In man and reservoir hosts (dogs, rodents, etc.) the organism is a parasite in the cytoplasm of a macrophage cell in which it obtains nourishment and multiplies by binary division, soon causing the death of the host cell.

When a sand-fly "bites" an infected person or reservoir hosts, it sucks up parasitized macrophages or temporarily free parasites circulating in the peripheral blood or tissue juices. Soon after the leishmanias reach the midgut of the fly they transform into the flagellated leptomonas form, which then proceeds to divide rapidly. If conditions are favorable, the number of leptomonads is increased tremendously and in 3 to 5 days many of them have migrated up through the esophagus and pharynx into the delicate hypopharyngeal tube in the sand-fly's proboscis. They are now in a position to be injected into the skin of the next individual when the sand-fly prepares to take another blood meal.

The life cycle of species of *Leishmania* is illustrated in Figure 29.

Smith, Halder and Ahmed (1940) in India were able to transmit *L. donovani* to hamsters and mice by repeated "bites" of *Phlebotomus argentipes* in which enormous numbers of leptomonad forms had developed in the mid-gut. The same year Swaminath, Shortt and Anderson (1942), in the same laboratory, infected 5 of 5 human volunteers with *L. donovani*. They concluded that their success depended on keeping the sand-flies from taking a second blood meal during the critical incubation period when the flagellated organisms are migrating forward through the pharynx into the buccal cavity.

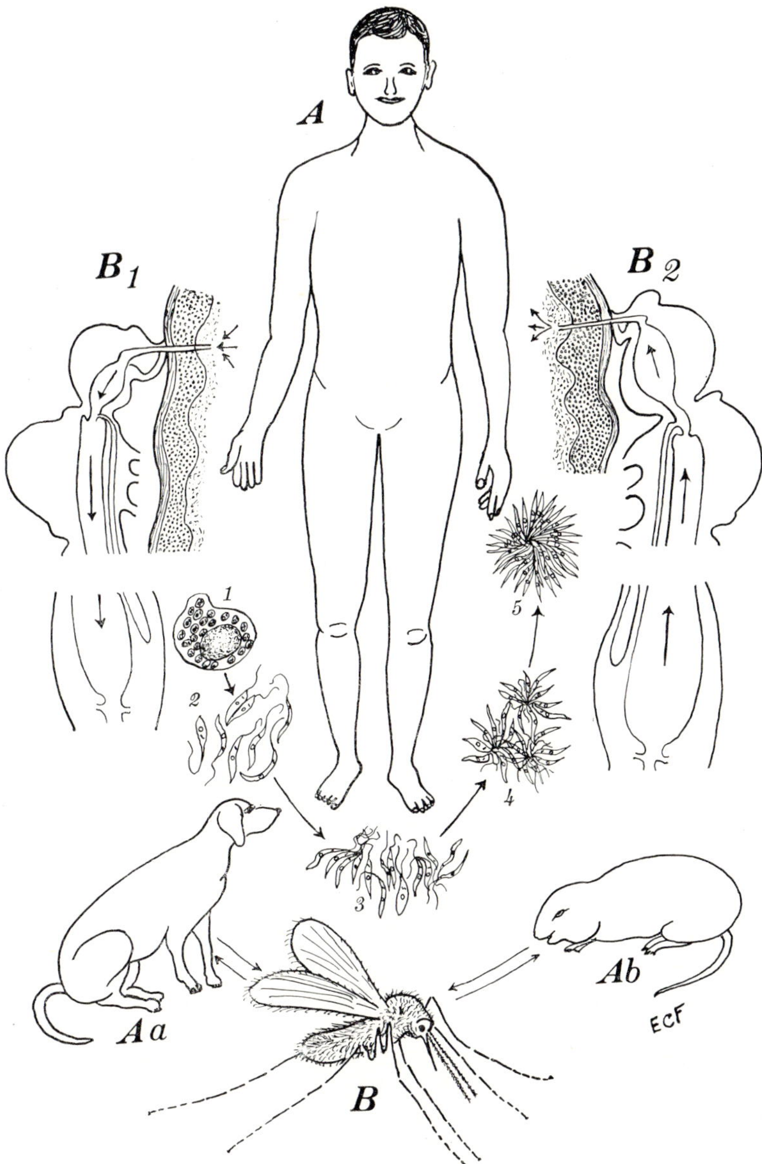

FIG. 29.—Life cycle of species of *Leishmania* which parasitize man. *A*, *Aa*, *Ab*, intrinsic phase of cycle, in which the parasites live and multiply in the leishmania stage within the cytoplasm of wandering and fixed macrophages of man (*A*), dog (*Aa*) or wild rodent (*Ab*); *B*, the sand-fly (*Phlebotomus*), intermediate host, in which the parasites live and multiply in the leptomonas stage in the lumen of the digestive tract; B_1, the parasites in macrophages (*1*) are sucked up from the skin and pass through the pharynx and esophagus into the sand-fly's midgut. Here they are set free and rapidly transform into the flagellated leptomonas stage (*2*). The leptomonads multiply by binary division (*3*, *4*, *5*) and begin to migrate back through the esophagus and pharynx into the sand-fly's proboscis, ready to be injected into the skin of the next human or reservoir host (B_2). (Original.)

Feng (1951), in North China, has provided evidence that the behavior of the chitinous peritrophic membrane, which forms around a blood meal in the midgut of the sand-fly, is of vital concern for the survival and growth of the parasites. In *Phlebotomus chinensis*, the transmitter of *L. donovani* in that area, this membrane begins to disintegrate on the third day, allowing the organisms to multiply and then move forward; but in *P. mongolensis*, a relatively unsatisfactory host, the membrane remains intact, gradually shrinks and prevents normal development and forward migration of the parasites.

Leishmania Tropica (Wright, 1903) Lühe, 1906

(Causing cutaneous leishmaniasis, locally known as Oriental sore, Delhi boil, Bagdad boil, Aleppo button, Jericho boil, etc.)

Historical Notes.—This organism was probably seen by Cunningham in 1885 and was the organism named *sporozoa furunculosa* by Firth in 1891. It was accurately described by Borovsky in 1898, and was redescribed and named by Wright in 1903, who studied the infection in an Armenian patient in Boston. French workers in North Africa (Sergent *et al.*, 1921) and Adler and Theodor (1926) in Palestine provided experimental evidence that *Phlebotomus papatasii* is the important transmitter of *L. tropica* in the Mediterranean area, while Adler and Ber (1941) produced 28 typical "sores" in 5 human volunteers bitten by infected *P. papatasii*.

Epidemiology.—Cutaneous leishmaniasis (see map, Fig. 30) has an extensive distribution from western and northwestern India and Pakistan, Central Asia, Turkestan and the Transcaucasus, through Iran, Iraq and other countries of the Middle East and Near East into the countries bordering on the Mediterranean Sea. It also occurs in several foci in tropical Africa. Cutaneous leishmaniasis is found in relatively barren, sandy, arid regions where there is considerable moisture at the time the sand-fly vectors are breeding.

Like the other species of *Leishmania*, *L. tropica* requires two hosts to complete its life cycle, *viz.*, man or other suitable mammalian host and an appropriate species of sand-fly. In Iraq and some other areas in the Middle East and Near East dogs are common reservoirs of the infection, but in Central Asia and Turkestan gerbils and other rodents are important natural hosts. The sand-fly obtains the parasite either from the human or reservoir host and after incubation of several days is able to inoculate the leishmanias into new hosts.

The vectors most widely distributed in the endemic-enzoötic zones are *P. papatasii* and *P. sergenti*. The stable-fly (*Stomoxys calcitrans*) may transmit the organism from an open ulcer to clean skin by mechanical transfer (Berberian, 1938), and there is evidence that close contact provides opportunity for direct person-to-person transmission.

Morphology and Biology of L. Tropica.—In the mammalian host *Leishmania tropica* lives within the cytoplasm of the large phagocytic monocytes. Here it multiplies by binary fission and soon destroys the host cell. It is a small ovoidal body (Fig. 31) about 2 to 3 microns in length and 1.0 to 1.5 microns in breadth. When sections or smears of the ulcer are stained by

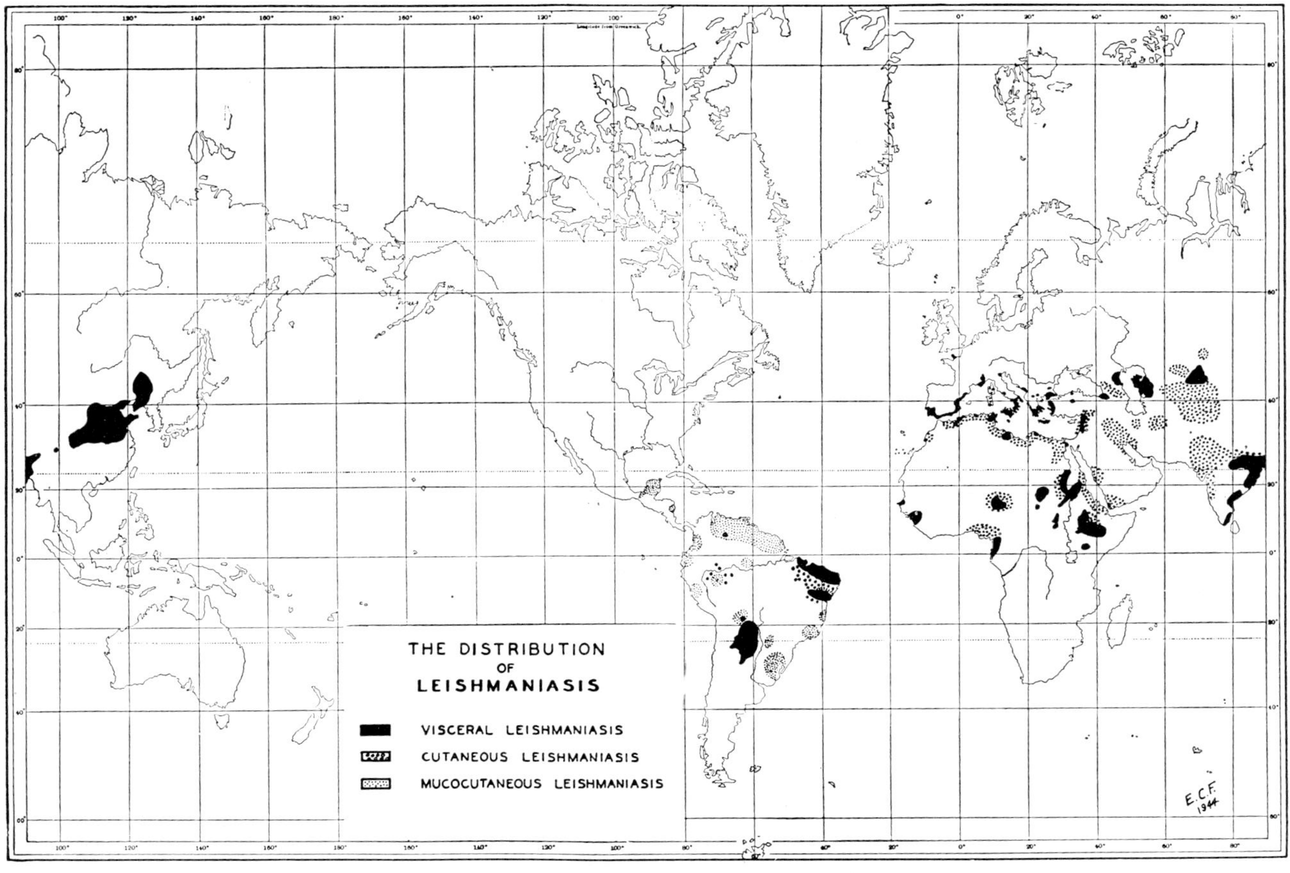

FIG. 30.—Map of the world showing the distribution of infections produced by the three different species of *Leishmania* (*L. tropica*, *L. brasiliensis* and *L. donovani*). (After Faust, in Craig and Faust's *Clinical Parasitology*, Lea & Febiger, Philadelphia.)

Giemsa's or Wright's technic, the cytoplasm of the leishmania stains light azure-blue, the subspherical nucleus a madder red and the short rod-shaped parabasal body, which characteristically lies at an oblique angle to the longer axis of the cell, a deep reddish violet. Nearby there is a minute, densely staining granule, the kinetoplast, which is at the inner end of the axoneme. There is no free flagellum. In the sand-fly the leptomonad stage (Fig. 32) is narrowly to broadly spindle-shaped, has an ovoidal nucleus near the equatorial plane, a short rod-shaped parabasal body near the anterior end, and a free flagellum which is usually somewhat longer than the body of the organism.

Pathogenesis and Symptomatology.—Tissue reaction is initiated with the introduction of the leptomonas stage of the parasite into the dermis. A wandering histiocyte in the vicinity picks up the parasite, which rapidly transforms into the leishmania stage, multiplies, and destroys the macrophage. Soon there is a dense concentration of macrophages in the invaded area, all of which are liable to infection and destruction. The center of the lesion then becomes necrotic and the margins containing parasitized macrophages may become infiltrated with giant and plasma cells.

The lesion appears first as a macule, then a papule with a slightly raised center covered by a thin blister-like layer of epidermis. The lesion now breaks down with discharge of a small amount of clear or purulent exudate. At its crater-like base in the dermis a granulating layer is formed and the margin becomes indurated by infiltration of fibroblasts (Fig. 33). If bacterially uncomplicated, the ulcer tends to dry up and the leishmanias slowly disappear, so that within about 9 months or less there is only a slightly raised, depigmented scar at the site. However, in endemic areas the lesion is commonly invaded by bacteria, so that an open, frequently verrucous, disfiguring ulcer develops (Fig. 34).

Characteristically there is one ulcer for each infected sand-fly "bite," developing at or near the point of inoculation on the exposed skin. Multiple new sores may result from accidental auto-inoculation at the time the ulcers are open.

According to Napier (1946), the *incubation period* may be as short as 2 weeks or as long as 3 years and usually fluctuates between 2 and 6 months. In uncomplicated cases, there are no systemic manifestations and since the infection is typically self-limiting the patients seldom seek medical assistance. However, the common occurrence of pyogenic complications causes not only painful, disfiguring, local ulcers but neutrophilic leukocytosis and fever, at times a bacterial septicemia.

Diagnosis.—Clinically the uncomplicated lesion may be mistaken for a variety of infections of the skin, hence demonstration of the parasite is essential. As soon as the ulcer opens, material scraped from the margin of the crater may be smeared onto a clean microscopic slide and stained by Giemsa's or Wright's technic. The leishmania stage of the parasite will be found within macrophages or spread out from ruptured macrophages. Scrapings from the ulcer may be placed on a blood-agar culture medium and incubated at room temperature for several days, with the expectation of recovering the leptomonas stage of the parasite.

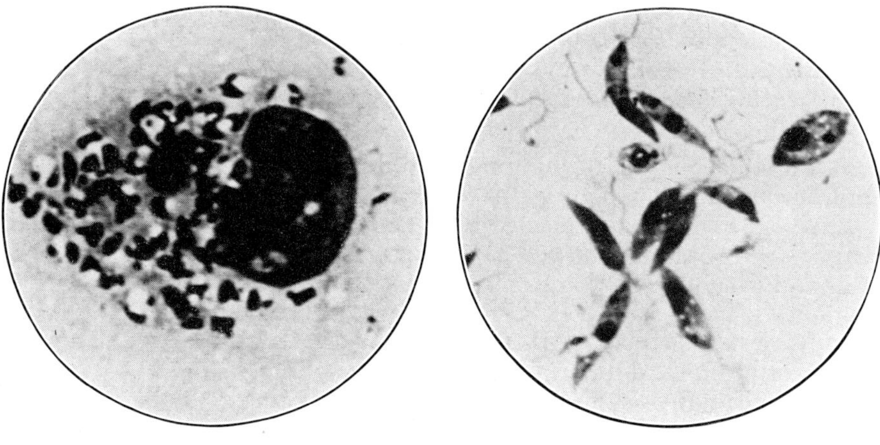

FIG. 31 FIG. 32

FIG. 31.—*Leishmania tropica.* Smear from cutaneous lesion of Armenian patient with Oriental sore diagnosed by Dr. J. H. Wright in Boston, 1903. On right, large mononuclear cell, with nucleus and many leishmanias on left about to burst out of the cell membrane. The cytoplasm of the parasites is lightly stained, the nucleus and adjacent parabasal body are densely stained. × 1800. (Photomicrograph from collection of Armed Forces Institute of Pathology, in Craig and Faust's *Clinical Parasitology,* Lea & Febiger, Philadelphia.)

FIG. 32.—*Leishmania tropica.* Leptomonas form of the parasite from blood-agar culture. This same morphologic form occurs in the midgut of the sand-fly. × 1800. (Photomicrograph of preparation by Craig from collection of Armed Forces Institute of Pathology, in Craig and Faust's *Clinical Parasitology,* Lea & Febiger, Philadelphia.)

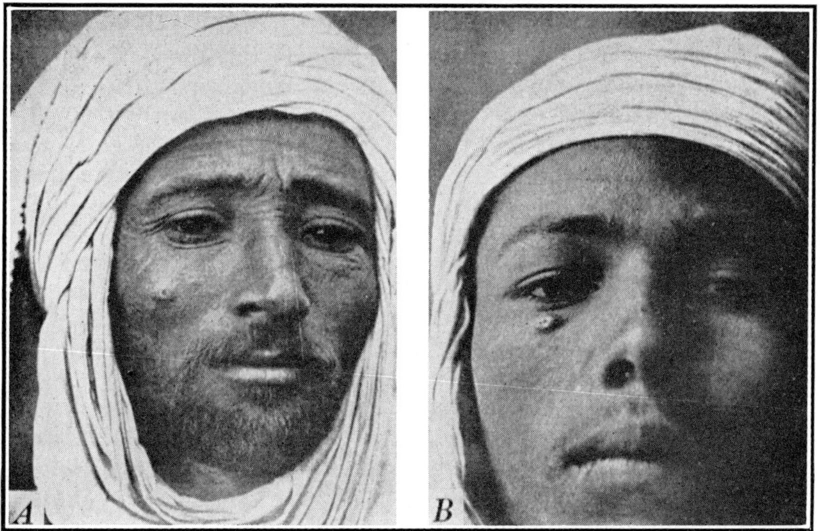

FIG. 33.—Lesions of cutaneous leishmaniasis. *A*, early stage following breaking down of the papule; *B*, slightly more advanced stage when the margin has become more raised and indurated and a granulating floor has developed in the center. (After Sergent *et al.*, in Arch. Inst. Pasteur d'Algerie, from Craig and Faust's *Clinical Parasitology,* Lea & Febiger, Philadelphia.)

Treatment.—One or a small number of clean ulcers may be treated with injections of stibophen (Fuadin) at the site of each lesion. For multiple ulcers this drug should be administered intramuscularly twice weekly for 8 weeks. (See specific recommendation, Table 5, page 64.) In case of bacterial invasion of the ulcer, it will be advisable to administer penicillin, bacitracin or other antibiotics to clear up the contamination before employing the specific leishmanicidal drug.

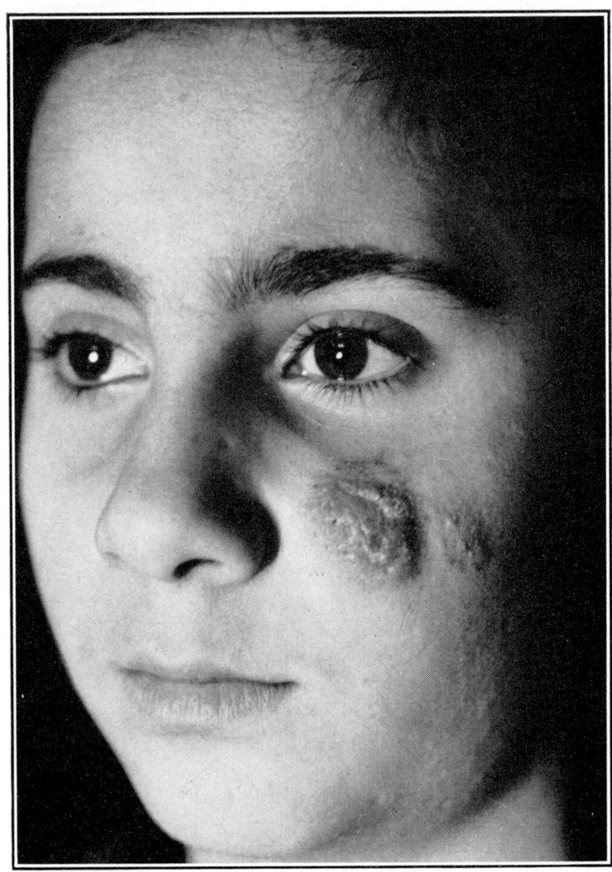

FIG. 34.—Untreated Oriental sore with verrucous surface in young Armenian woman. There are two lesions on the cheek, one of which is considerably more extensive than the other. (Photograph generously furnished by Dr. D. A. Berberian.)

Control.—Chemotherapy is not practical for mass control but immunization by injection of a pure culture of *L. tropica* into a covered area of the skin will provide lasting immunity (Berberian, 1939). The resulting ulcer should not be terminated chemotherapeutically for a period of about 30 days after inoculation, otherwise immunization will not be satisfactory. Dog reservoirs should be destroyed since they constitute a constant source for infection of the sand-fly. Residual DDT sprayed around the doors, windows and on the inside walls of human habitations and adjacent buildings is very effective in killing the adults and thus preventing extension of the infection (Hertig and Fisher, 1945).

Leishmania Brasiliensis Vianna, 1911

(Causing American leishmaniasis, espúndia, uta, úlcera de los chicleros, or muco-cutaneous leishmaniasis)

Historical Notes.—This mutilating type of leishmaniasis was prevalent among natives in the high Andean valleys of Peru at the time the first Spanish explorers entered the country (Weiss, 1943). In 1909 Lindenberg, in São Paulo, Brazil, isolated the organisms from cutaneous ulcers and two years later Carini (1911) recovered typical leishmania forms from cutaneous and naso-pharyngeal tissues in Brazil. Vianna (1911) gave the organism a specific name because of its proclivity to attack mucous membranes as well as the skin.

Epidemiology.—Infection with *Leishmania brasiliensis* extends from northeastern Argentina through the countries of Continental America as far north as Yucatan. (See map, Fig. 30.) In practically all of these regions of endemicity the disease is restricted to sylvatic areas. The highest prevalence is characteristically among young adult males, although all ages and both sexes on first exposure are equally susceptible.

Man is the common definitive host, but natural infection occurs in dogs, especially in Peru, where Herrer (1948) found 40 of 138 dogs infected, frequently without evident skin lesions.

Several species of *Phlebotomus* have been incriminated as likely transmitters, *viz.*, on the basis of natural infection and their common association with infected human cases; yet complete life cycle transmission of *L. brasiliensis* has apparently never been accomplished under carefully controlled conditions.

Morphology and Biology of Leishmania Brasiliensis.—The size and other morphologic characters of this organism within macrophages of man or reservoir hosts and in the sand-fly are indistinguishable from those of *L. tropica* and *L. donovani* (Figs, 31, 32). However, in a considerable proportion of human cases the organisms migrate from their primary location in the skin to develop in secondary sites in mucous membranes near cutaneous junctions.

Pathogenesis and Symptomatology.—The primary lesion is initiated in the mammalian host when the infected sand-fly injects the leptomonad stage of *L. brasiliensis* into the outer dermis. The organisms are engulfed by wandering histiocytes, in which the parasites rapidly become leishmaniaform, multiply by binary division and soon destroy the cytoplasm of the host cell. When the histiocyte ruptures and sets the leishmanias free, they are picked up by other macrophages in the vicinity, in which they continue to multiply.

The first macroscopic evidence of the lesion is a macule, which transforms into a slightly elevated pustule (Fig. 35), then opens at the center to discharge semi-liquid necrotic material. At times the base of the crater may become covered with a granulating layer and the ulcer gradually dry up. More frequently the ulcer remains open, with an oozing, glistening surface (Fig. 36). If the inoculation by the sand-fly is on the margin of the ear or the ear lobe, the parasites usually erode the skin and underlying cartilage

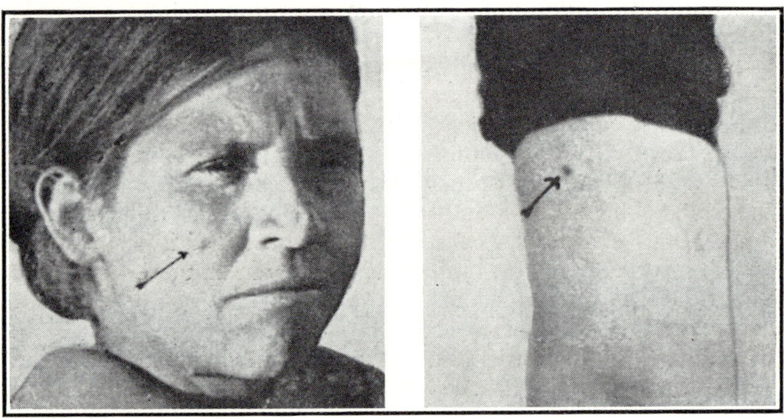

Fig. 35.—Initial primary lesions of muco-cutaneous leishmaniasis. (Photographs courtesy of Drs. Pessôa and Barretto, from *Leishmaniose Tegumentar Americana*, in Craig and Faust's *Clinical Parasitology*, Lea & Febiger, Philadelphia.)

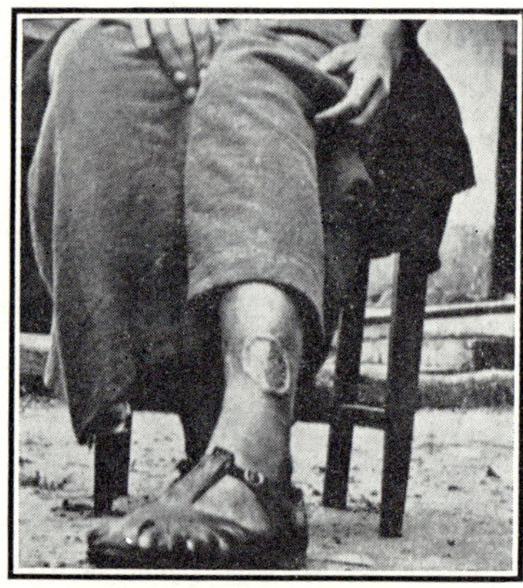

Fig. 36.—Primary lesion of muco-cutaneous leishmaniasis following breakdown of the central necrotic tissues, showing saucer-like enlargement with raised edges and raw weeping surface, without extensive bacterial invasion. (Photograph of a Paraguayan by Dr. Henry Hansen, in Craig and Faust's *Clinical Parasitology*, Lea & Febiger, Philadelphia.)

(Fig. 37), leaving a mutilated auricle which may have a smooth or granulomatous surface.

The relatively unique feature of *L. brasiliensis* infection is a tendency for the organisms to migrate to secondary foci at or near muco-cutaneous junctions. The most frequent site is the nasal septum. These lesions may be ulcerative, indurative or granulomatous. Blocking of lymphatic capillaries leads to necrosis and extensive destruction of soft and underlying hard tissues, producing extensive erosive mutilation of the nares, and at times of the nasa-pharynx, larynx and palatine bones (Fig. 38). Granulomatous disfigurement of the nose, lips and cheeks (Fig. 39) is common in

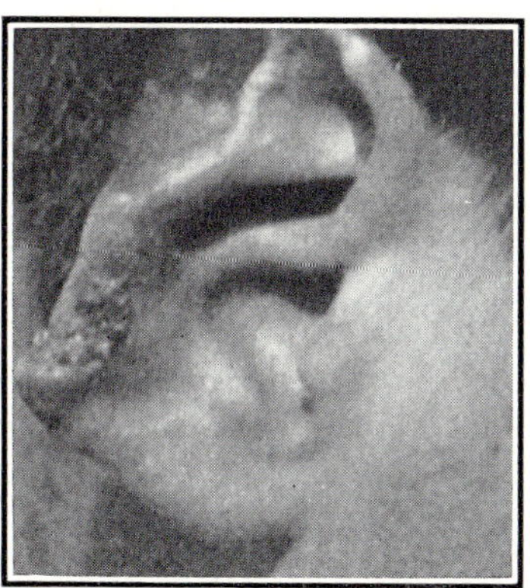

Fig. 37.—Erosion of the cartilage of the ear, with relatively clean healing in a native of Yucatan exposed to chiclero's disease. (Photograph, courtesy of Dr. Chavarria, Mexico, D. F., in Craig and Faust's *Clinical Parasitology*, Lea & Febiger, Philadelphia.)

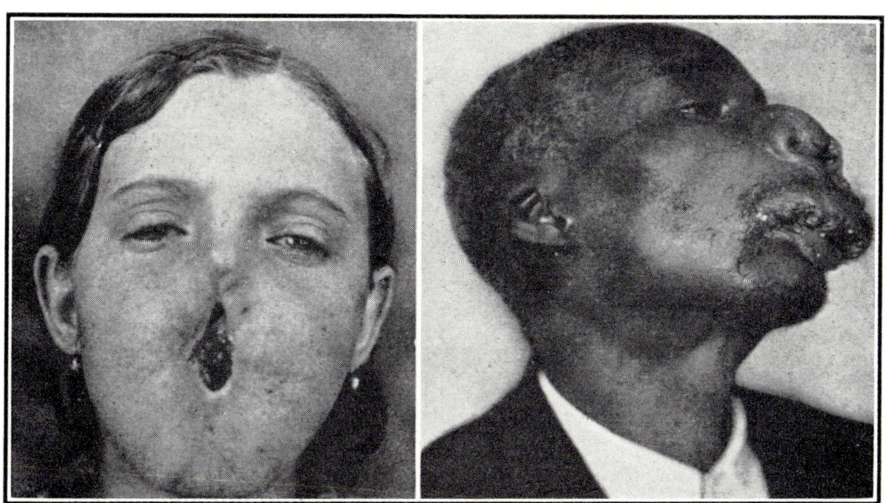

Fig. 38. Fig. 39.

Fig. 38.—Extensive erosion of hard and soft tissues of upper jaw, hard palate and nares, with partial healing, resulting from secondary implantation of *Leishmania brasiliensis* in the nasal septum. (Photograph, courtesy of Dr. M. Barretto, São Paulo, Brazil, in Craig & Faust's *Clinical Parasitology*, Lea & Febiger, Philadelphia.)

Fig. 39.—Granulomatous lesions of nares, lips and underlying tissues in secondary *L. brasiliensis* infection. (Photograph, courtesy of Dr. M. Barretto, São Paulo, Brazil, in Craig and Faust's *Clinical Parasitology*, Lea & Febiger, Philadelphia.)

persons with negroid blood. These secondary lesions are typically complicated by bacterial invasion.

The *symptoms* in muco-cutaneous leishmaniasis result from the primary lesion in the skin and from the secondary lesions. The *incubation period* until the primary lesion develops varies from a few days to several weeks. The early stage of the primary sore is essentially symptomless but following the opening of the ulcer and its enlargement the raw surface is tender and is easily contaminated. Bacterial invasion of the sore produces systemic reaction, with fever and neutrophilic leukocytosis. With muco-cutaneous involvement there are moderate to intense pain in the involved areas, anemia, relative monocytosis and malaise. The condition may persist for years.

Diagnosis.—As in other types of leishmaniasis, accurate diagnosis requires demonstration of the organism in smears or biopsied specimens from the lesion. As soon as bacteria invade the lesion they tend to overgrow the leishmanias so that the latter are difficult to discover. Culture of the organisms on the blood-agar medium and serologic tests are at times diagnostically useful.

Treatment.—The treatment of the uncomplicated primary lesion is similar to that for cutaneous leishmaniasis (page 174). The open sore and the secondary lesions are much more difficult to manage and require months or years of persistent treatment with antibiotics in association with antimonial preparations. Even though the leishmanias temporarily disappear, Pessôa and Barretto (1948) have found that the condition tends to relapse in a few months.

Control.—Since the disease is not contracted in the villages, residual DDT-spraying of homes is not a major weapon. However, area power spraying with DDT, along with residual spraying of dwellings, has been shown to be successful in destroying the adult flies.

Leishmania Donovani (Laveran and Mesnil, 1903) Ross, 1903

(Causing visceral leishmaniasis, commonly referred to as kala-azar)

Historical Notes.—In 1900, William Leishman first demonstrated the agent of kala-azar in smears from the spleen of an English soldier who died of a fever near Calcutta, India. In 1903, Charles Donovan found the same organism in smears from splenic puncture of a living case of the disease in Madras, India. Ross created the genus *Leishmania* in honor of the original discoverer. Leonard Rogers (1904) first cultured the leishmania and demonstrated that it had a flagellate stage. It was not until 1931–1934 that the Indian Kala-azar Commission proved that the sand-fly *Phlebotomus argentipes* was the probable transmitter in India, and a decade later that Swaminath, Shortt and Anderson (1942) were able to demonstrate natural transmission to 5 of 5 human volunteers by "bites" of infected *P. argentipes*.

Epidemiology.—Kala-azar is endemic in many regions of Asia, Africa, Europe, South America and Central America. (See map, Fig. 53, p. 171.) In China its distribution includes the northern, northeastern and northwestern parts of the country. In India the disease is hyperendemic in

Assam, Bengal, Bihar, and further south in the eastern part of the subcontinent, and is indigenous as far to the northwest as the Punjab. It has endemic foci in Turkistan, the Trans-Caspian region and between the Caspian and Black Seas, and in practically all of the Mediterranean countries. It is found in Ethiopia and in the Egyptian Sudan. In the Western Hemisphere kala-azar has been found in northern Argentina, Paraguay, Bolivia, several centers in Brazil, Venezuela, Colombia, Guatemala, El Salvador and recently in Mexico (Villaseñor *et al.*, 1953).

In most of these areas, the infection is endemic or hyperendemic but on occasion it may become epidemic. In Mediterranean countries and China it is primarily a disease of infants and young children. In India and South America, young adults are most frequently infected. In the Egyptian Sudan, a particularly fulminating type is observed, commonly in young adults.

In north China and the Mediterranean areas of endemicity dogs are common reservoir hosts and have likewise been found naturally infected in Brazil. Occasionally the disease may be transmitted by blood transfusion (Chung, Chow and Lu, 1948). The danger of dogs as reservoirs of kala-azar lies in the fact that the lesions caused by *L. donovani* in this host are primarily cutaneous, so that the sand-fly has direct access to infected macrophages.

Kala-azar is essentially a domestic disease in villages and communities near urban centers, where moisture is temporarily abundant for growth of rank vegetation in which the sand-flies breed. A new crop of human kala-azar cases may be anticipated about 3 months after the breeding season of the sand-fly transmitters.

Transmission of kala-azar in nature is accomplished by certain species of sand-flies. In India the transmission cycle is probably exclusively from man to sand-fly to man; in China and the Mediterranean countries it is basically from dog to sand-fly to dog and secondarily from dog to sand-fly to man, or at times from man to sand-fly to man.

Morphology and Biology of Leishmania Donovani.—In its leishmania and leptomonas forms *L. donovani* is indistinguishable in size or other morphologic characters from *L. tropica* (Figs. 31, 32) and *L. brasiliensis.* In its host tissue relations in man and most susceptible laboratory animals, however, *L. donovani* has a predilection for the reticulo-endothelial cells of the liver, spleen, bone marrow and visceral lymph nodes, and its primary colonization in the skin is usually inapparent. In the dog the conspicuous lesions are in the skin, so that in this reservoir host cutaneous leishmaniasis due to infection with *L. tropica* and kala-azar caused by *L. donovani* are difficult to distinguish.

Pathogenesis and Symptomatology.—The leptomonad stage of the parasite is introduced into the outer dermis by an infected sand-fly. In China, India, the Egyptian Sudan and the Mediterranean endemic area no evidence of a macule or papule has been found which can be definitely associated with exposure to the infection. The primary lesion is therefore inapparent. However, in an endemic area in the U. S. S. R., Mirzorian (1941) found that one or more minute papules the size of a pinhead appear on the exposed skin some time before *Leishmania donovani* infection can be otherwise demonstrated in infants. The first colonization of *L. donovani* in the human host is probably in the dermis, where the organisms multiply slowly and may remain quiescent for weeks or months. Eventually some of the increasing progeny gain access to the blood stream or lymphatics and are transported to the viscera, where they are trapped by fixed tissue macrophages and begin to multiply rapidly. Their greatest activity occurs in the liver, spleen, bone marrow and visceral lymph nodes.

As the number of leishmanias becomes greatly augmented, there is intense phagocytic activity and a remarkable increase in the number of macrophages. There is first a relative and then an absolute monocytosis and neutropenia. Meanwhile the unusual demand for macrophages gradually retards erythropoiesis. The decrease in neutrophils provides greatly reduced defense against pathogenic bacteria and the increasing anemia reduces the threshold of resistance to intercurrent diseases.

Although the leishmanias are found in all soft tissues of the body, they are particularly abundant in those rich in reticulo-endothelial cells (Napier, 1946). Hence the fundamental histopathology results from this parasite-host cell relationship.

The *liver* is enlarged and firm but somewhat friable. The most noteworthy change is the increase in size of the Kupffer cells and their increase in number, especially in the portal spaces. The *spleen* is likewise enlarged, so that it may extend ventrally well into the right lower quadrant, and dorsally to the right of the midline. The *bone marrow* exhibits pathologic activity in production of macrophages, many of which are parasitized, and in decreased erythropoietic function.

As a result of the neutropenia, bacteria and other potentially pathogenic microörganisms in the mouth, intestine and respiratory tract are enabled to enter the mucous membranes, or to penetrate more deeply into the tissues. Moreover, congestion in the smaller blood vessels results in multiple hemorrhages, particularly from mucous membranes.

The *incubation period* varies from as short a time as 10 to 14 days to many months, occasionally as long as a year and a half (Napier, 1946). The *onset* may be sudden, with acute manifestations, but the usual case develops insidiously, on the average about 90 days following exposure.

A typical acute case has fever of an undulant type fluctuating daily from 36.7 to 40° C. (90 to 104° F.), and may exhibit a double rise of temperature every 24 hours. Yet there is no pronounced headache or mental lethargy which characterize most febrile infections. The appetite is usually good. Loss of weight may be partly masked by edema of the face, trunk and feet, with emaciated legs over which the skin is tightly stretched and glistening (Napier, 1946). The abdomen is protuberant and both the liver and spleen can be palpated far below the costal margin. In spite of the engorged liver there is no periportal cirrhosis, hence no ascites (Fig. 40). The patient complains of the weight of these organs. There are marked palpitation, visible pulsation of the carotid arteries, and dyspnea on slight exertion. Bleeding typically occurs from the gums, lips and nares, and hemorrhage from the intestinal mucosa.

The blood picture is that of a moderate erythropenia (averaging about 3,000,000 r.b.c./cmm.), an absolute monocytosis and neutropenia, occasionally complete agranulocytosis.

Complications usually observed in kala-azar are principally those of the digestive and respiratory tracts. Napier (1946) regards diarrhea or dysentery as intercurrent in origin. A much more important complication is the respiratory syndrome. Children with kala-azar are usually hospitalized primarily because of bronchopneumonia rather than for kala-azar. Cancrum oris or noma is a complication at times observed in young patients.

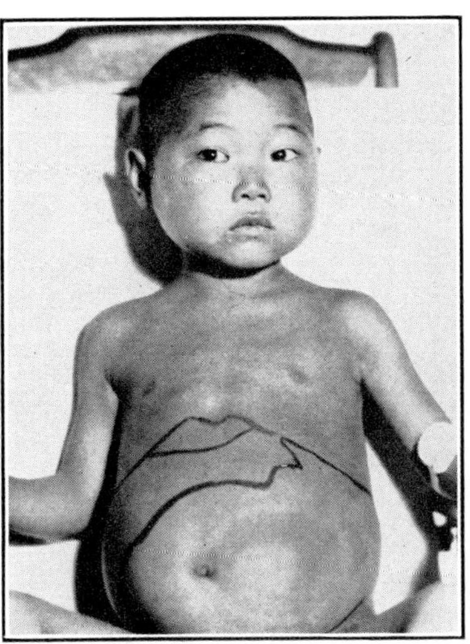

FIG. 40.—Chinese child acutely ill with kala-azar. Note enlarged liver, tremendously enlarged spleen and edema of face. (Photo, Peking Union Medical College Hospital.)

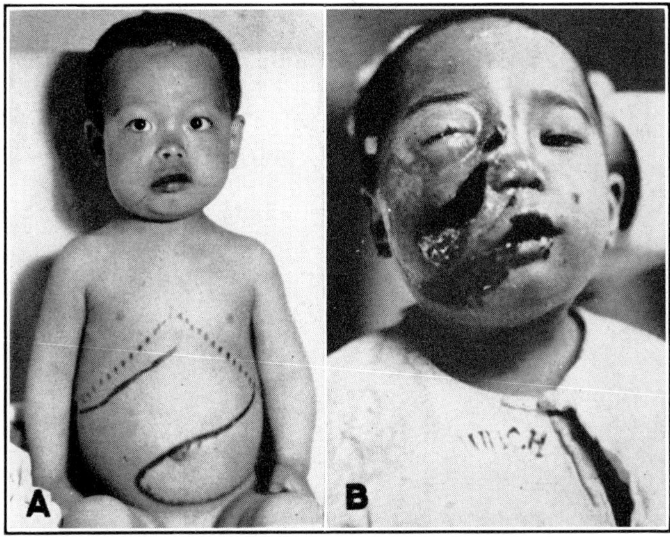

FIG. 41.—Cancrum oris complication in kala-azar. *Left*, early appearance; *right*, after the necrotic process is well advanced. (Photos, Peking Union Medical College Hospital.)

The lesion is usually located in the deep tissues of the cheek and first has the appearance of acute parotitis or cellulitis (Fig. 41, left). It soon breaks down through the surface and extends as a rapidly fulminating, necrotizing ulcer which terminates fatally (Fig. 41, right).

Diagnosis.—In an endemic area typical cases may be diagnosed on clinical grounds with a fair degree of assurance that their diagnosis is correct. However, since the patient who is seriously ill usually requires hospitalization for complications, there is ample time to obtain laboratory help during this interval between admission and the institution of specific treatment.

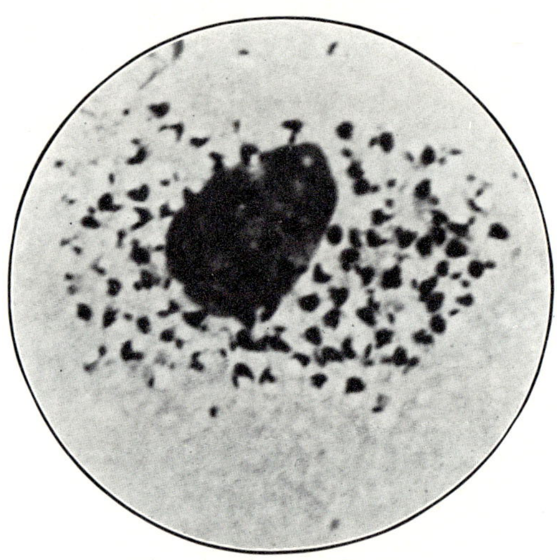

FIG. 42.—*Leishmania donovani* in macrophage, smear preparation, Wright's stain. Note that the parasites are spread out due to rupture of the host cell membrane in making the preparation. Compare with Figure 31, page 173. (Photomicrograph from preparation by Craig in Collection, Armed Forces Institute of Pathology, from Craig and Faust's *Clinical Parasitology*, Lea & Febiger, Philadelphia.)

The most suggestive laboratory evidence short of specific demonstration of the etiologic agent consists in a positive aldehyde test. (See TECHNICAL AIDS, page 611.) This indicates an excess of serum globulin. Sen Gupta (1944, 1952) prefers a nonspecific complement-fixation test which he has found to be positive in early infections or those of short duration when the aldehyde test is still negative.

For complete assurance that the patient is suffering from kala-azar the organism itself must be demonstrated. The usual procedure is to obtain a biopsy specimen of spleen, liver, lymph node or bone marrow by puncture technic. Most workers today prefer to obtain a bone marrow specimen from the iliac crest, employing the van den Bergh technic. (See "TECHNICAL AIDS," page 591.) A portion of the biopsy sample should be made into microscope slide smears stained by the Giemsa method. In these smears (Fig. 42) the leishmania bodies which have developed within the macrophages can be identified by their size, shape, azure-blue cytoplasm, medium-red nucleus and densely reddish-purple parabasal body. A portion of each sample handled aseptically should be cultured on blood-agar medium at room temperature for a week to 10 days, for demonstration of the leptomonad stage of the organism.

Treatment.—Supportive treatment and good nursing care are needed in most cases, particularly those with a complication of bronchopenumonia, severe diarrhea, dysentery, or cancrum oris. The advent of the sulfa drugs and especially the antibiotics has greatly reduced the hazards of these complications. Even cancrum oris in its earlier stage may be successfully terminated by adequate use of penicillin.

Specific Treatment.—Two types of drugs are employed in the treatment of kala-azar, antimonials and diamidines.

Antimonials.—Dating from 1915, tartar emetic was employed with considerable success. The sodium and potassium antimony tartrates have been superseded by pentavalent antimonials, of which ethyl stibamine (*Neostibosan*), *Urea stibamine* and sodium antimony gluconate (*Solustibosan*) have been the most useful (Napier, 1946). All of these are better tolerated than the older antimonials. Neostibosan and sodium antimony gluconate may be administered intramuscularly, which is a distinct advantage in mass treatment in clinics. With the latter drug, however, relapses are common. (See Table 5, p. 64.)

The Diamidines.—These drugs are employed routinely in the Sudan in the treatment of kala-azar, since this particular strain of *L. donovani* does not respond satisfactorily to antimony therapy. Likewise, in India, China and in the Mediterranean endemic area cases refractory to antimony are usually benefitted by diamidine therapy. Some of these, particularly in India, may develop a post-diamidine facial neuropathy which persists up to two years. (See Table 5, page 64.)

In India, a sequela to antimony treatment is known as post-treatment kala-azar dermal leishmaniasis, in which a verrucous condition develops in the skin. Histologically these excrescences contain leishmanias in focal concentrations of macrophages. This post-treatment phenomenon is interpreted as an indication of inadequate antimony treatment of the visceral lesions, with a residuum of leishmanias which have been driven to the skin where they continue to propagate.

Control.—With the demonstration that residual spraying of DDT in and around human habitations is both highly efficacious and economical in sand-fly control (Hertig, 1949), this measure has replaced all others as the main weapon of attack on kala-azar.

In areas where dogs constitute a constant source of infection for the sand-flies, campaigns to destroy all street dogs and others with obvious skin lesions will effectively reduce this reservoir of the disease.

TRYPANOSOME PARASITES OF MAN

Many species of trypanosomes parasitize fishes, amphibians, reptiles, birds and mammals. Leeches serve as intermediate hosts and biological vectors for the trypanosomes of aquatic vertebrates, and arthropods as the transmitters of the trypanosomes of non-aquatic hosts. Blood-sucking flies are the vectors for most species of this latter group but there are a few notable exceptions. *Trypanosoma lewisi* utilizes rat fleas (*Nosopsyllus fasciatus et al.*) *T. cruzi* is transmitted by triatomid bugs, and the species causing dourine in horses and mules, *T. equiperdum*, has become adapted to direct transmission from vertebrate to vertebrate through coitus. Blood-sucking arthropods may also mechanically transmit several species of trypanosomes through contamination of their proboscis with the organisms at the time of an interrupted blood meal.

The primitive method of trypanosome transmission by the blood-sucking vector consists of voiding the parasites in liquid feces at the time of feeding. This mechanism is employed by various trypanosomes which infect rodents, bats, anteaters, some species parasitic in cattle, sheep and antelopes, and by *T. cruzi.*

In a large number of instances the trypanosomes which have multiplied in the intestine of the vector migrate anteriorwards into the labial cavity and are introduced directly into the puncture wound made by the vector in the vertebrate host preparatory to taking a blood meal. This refinement in the mechanism of transmission is similar to that of sand-flies in the transmission of species of *Leishmania* (see above, pages 168–183).

Some species of trypanosomes apparently live in their natural vertebrate hosts without causing evident tissue damage. Others cause variable degrees of tissue pathology. The three species of trypanosomes which commonly parasitize man, *viz.*, *Trypanosoma rhodesiense, T. gambiense* and *T. cruzi,* are all pathogenic for the human host and not infrequently their infection has a fatal outcome.

Since *T. rhodesiense* and *T. gambiense* differ from *T. cruzi* in their life cycle, method of transmission and tissue relationship to the mammalian host, the former two will be considered separately from *T. cruzi.*

Trypanosome Parasites of Man Having Proboscis Emergence from the Vector

Trypanosoma rhodesiense, T. gambiense and certain other trypanosomes which infect game and domestic animals utilize *Glossina* (tsetse flies) as biological vectors. Multiplication of all of these trypanosomes occurs within the digestive tract of the tsetse fly and emergence of the organisms takes place through the hypopharyngeal tube within the proboscis; but the sites and morphologic stages of development vary depending on the species of trypanosome.

In *T. brucei, T. rhodesiense* and *T. gambiense* the trypanosome forms which are sucked into the labial cavity from the mammalian host pass directly through the proventriculus into the midgut, where multiplication occurs in an elongated trypanosome stage. Thereafter the organisms migrate back through the proventriculus and buccal cavity up the hypopharynx into the salivary glands, where a second multiplication occurs. These forms are crithidial, with a posterior nucleus, but they later transform into infective-stage trypanosomes, which accumulate in the salivary-gland ducts. In these species the hypopharynx is utilized only for transit and not for multiplication or metamorphosis of the parasites (Wenyon, 1926, pp. 514–515, Figs. 217–219). The developmental cycles of *T. brucei*, *T. rhodesiense* and *T. gambiense* in the tsetse fly are the most highly evolved among the trypanosomes.

In the mammalian host *T. brucei*, *T. rhodesiense* and *T. gambiense* are trypanosome forms (Fig. 43) circulating primarily in the blood stream, where they multiply by longitudinal binary division. In case the host-parasite adaptation is good, they produce no extensive humoral or tissue damage. This is illustrated by *T. brucei* in African game animals. *T. rhodesiense* is a strain of *T. brucei* which has recently become adapted to man. Here the adjustment is extremely poor, and the parasite typically produces an overwhelming infection with fatal consequences to the victim.

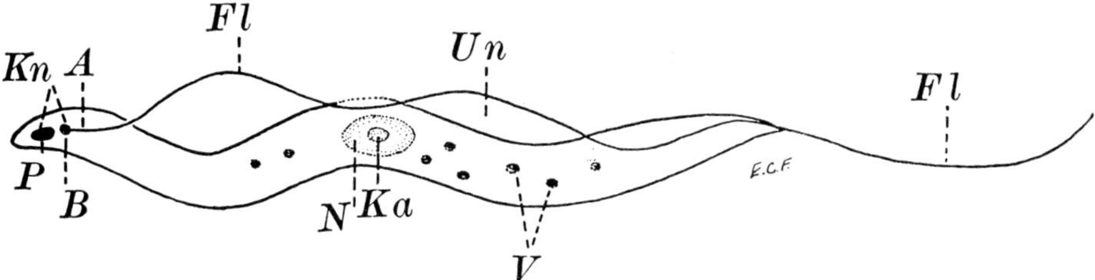

FIG. 43.—Diagram illustrating the morphology of a typical trypanosome. *Kn*, kinetoplast; *P*, parabasal body; *B*, blepharoplast; *A*, axoneme; *Fl*, flagellum; *Un*, undulating membrane; *N*, nucleus; *Ka*, karyosome; *V*, volutin granules. (From Craig and Faust's *Clinical Parasitology*, Lea & Febiger, Philadelphia.)

It is also likely that *T. gambiense* was originally derived from a parent stock of *T. brucei* but at a much earlier period than *T. rhodesiense*, so that the adjustment to the human host has been somewhat more satisfactory and the disease process is usually less fulminating than in *T. rhodesiense* infection.

The life cycle of the *T. brucei-rhodesiense-gambiense* complex is diagrammatically shown in Figure 44.

Trypanosoma Rhodesiense Stephens and Fantham, 1910

(Causing Rhodesian trypanosomiasis)

Historical Notes.—This hemoflagellate was discovered by Stephens and Fantham in 1909 (1910) in the blood of a patient in Rhodesia who had symptoms suggestive of a fulminating early stage of African "sleeping sickness." Three years later Kinghorn and Yorke (1912) demonstrated that it is transmitted to man by the tsetse fly, *Glossina morsitans*.

Epidemiology.—*T. rhodesiense* has a geographic distribution limited to the upland savannas of East Africa, including the northeastern part of Portuguese East Africa (Mozambique), Southern Rhodesia, Northern Rhodesia, Tanganyika and the lake district of eastern Uganda. (See map, Figure 45.)

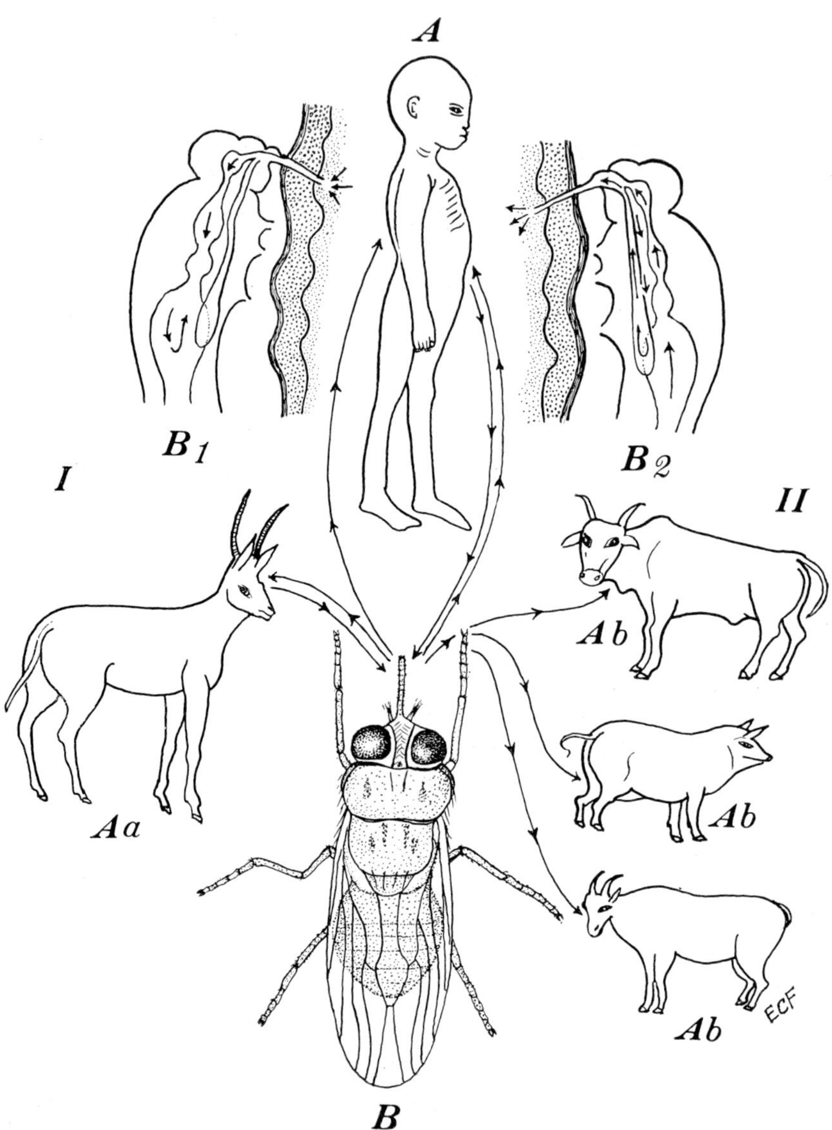

Fig. 44.—Diagram illustrating the life cycle of the *Trypanosoma brucei-rhodesiense-gambiense* complex in the vector (*Glossina* spp., tsetse fly), in wild game mammals, domestic mammals and man. *A*, *Aa*, *Ab*, susceptible mammalian hosts; *B*, the insect intermediate host and transmitter (tsetse-fly). *A*, human host of *T. rhodesiense* and *T. gambiense; Aa*, wild game animal, host of *T. brucei* and reservoir of *T. rhodesiense; Ab*, domestic animals, subsidiary hosts of *T. gambiense;* B_1, early phase, and B_2, later phase, of development in the tsetse-fly. (Original.)

Rhodesian trypanosomiasis is not related to age, sex, race or socio-economic status except as these are concerned with exposure to the transmitting agent, which is usually *Glossina morsitans*, both sexes of which are blood suckers and transmitters. Less commonly *G. swynnertoni* and rarely *G. palpalis*, *G. pallidipes* and *G. brevipalpis* serve as vectors. These flies breed in relatively dry habitats, preferring warm to cold environmental temperatures. Occasionally the tsetse fly may transmit the infection directly from person-to-person through a soiled proboscis at the time of an interrupted blood meal.

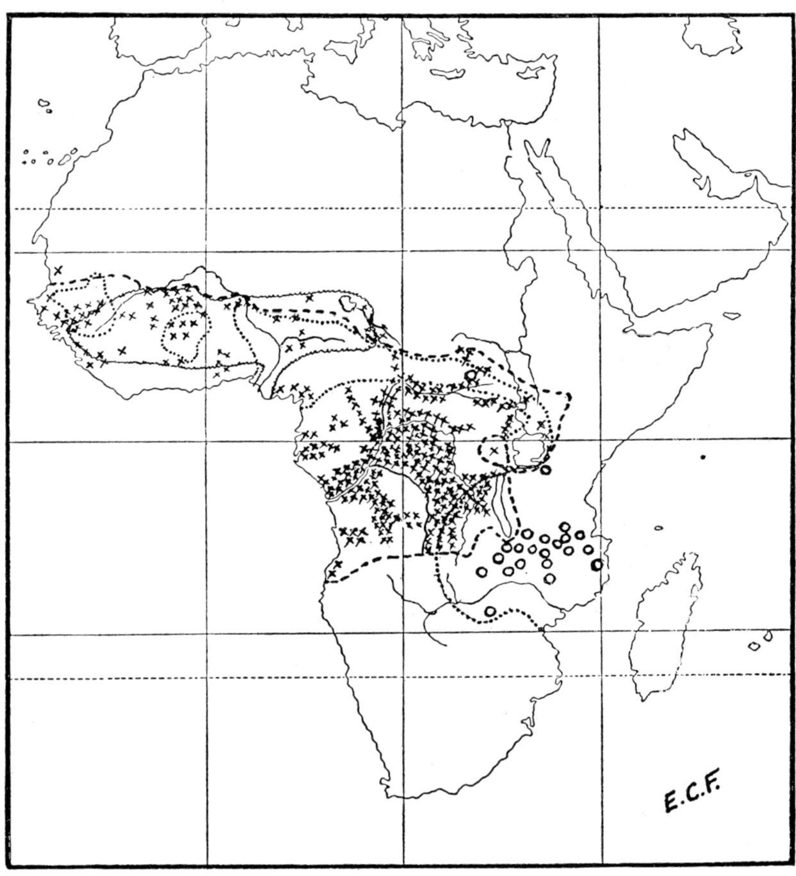

Gambian Trypanosomiasis

Rhodesian Trypanosomiasis

Limit of *Glossina palpalis* Belt

Limit of *Glossina morsitans* Belt

Limit of *Glossina tachinoides*Belt

FIG. 45.—Map of Africa showing the distribution of Rhodesian and Gambian trypanosomiasis and of the tsetse-fly vectors. (From Craig and Faust's *Clinical Parasitology*, Lea & Febiger, Philadelphia.)

Small numbers of persons are infected with *T. rhodesiense* compared with *T. gambiense* but the usually fatal course of the Rhodesian disease serves to emphasize its importance. It occurs typically in sporadic form but small epidemics at times develop.

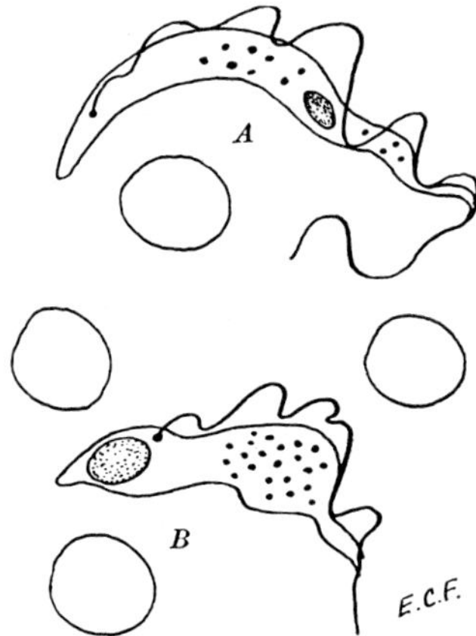

FIG. 46.—*Trypanosoma rhodesiense.* Stages seen in peripheral blood of the mammalian host. *A*, usual trypanosome form, the only stage found in peripheral human blood; *B*, crithidial form, occasionally seen in experimental rodent hosts. × 1600. (After Faust, courtesy, C. V. Mosby Co., in Craig and Faust's *Clinical Parasitology*, Lea & Febiger, Philadelphia.)

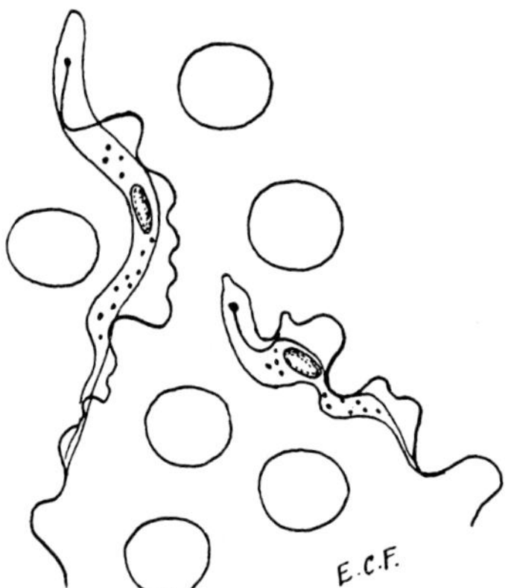

FIG. 47.—*Trypanosoma gambiense.* Trypanosome stage seen in peripheral human blood, morphologically indistinguishable from *T. rhodesiense.* × 1600. (After Faust, courtesy, C. V. Mosby Co., in Craig and Faust's *Clinical Parasitology*, Lea & Febiger, Philadelphia.)

Morphology, Biology and Life Cycle.—Wenyon (1926) refers to *T. rhodesiense* as "the human strain of *Trypanosoma brucei*," and all subsequent work is consistent with this view. Morphologically the infective trypanosome stage of these two species can not be distinguished, nor can it be differentiated from this stage of *T. gambiense* (see page 189).

When a tsetse fly takes a blood meal containing *T. rhodesiense* from animal reservoirs or man, the trypanosomes may be digested with the blood meal, may survive and multiply but be destroyed following a second blood meal, or may survive and multiply through both blood meals, then migrate to the salivary glands and reach the infective stage (Wenyon, 1926). The whole development within the fly averages approximately 14 days. When the infective-stage trypanosomes are introduced into the human host, they survive and multiply only in case they belong to the strain adapted to man.

Pathogenesis and Symptomatology.—On introduction into the human skin from the proboscis of an infected tsetse fly, *T. rhodesiense* first lodges in the local tissues where the trypanosomes set up an interstitial inflammatory reaction. This usually subsides within a week or two as the trypanosomes gain entry to the circulating blood, where they multiply. Then they enter the lymph nodes, where a second focus of inflammation occurs, with hyperplasia of the endothelial lining of the blood sinuses and perivascular infiltration of leukocytes, due to toxic metabolites of the trypanosomes. This process is rapid, fulminating and usually causes death of the patient in a few months. Only rarely does the patient survive long enough for the trypanosomes to invade the central nervous system and produce lesions characteristic of the third stage of *T. gambiense* infection (so-called "sleeping sickness").

Following an incubation period of 1 to 2 weeks, the patient suffers from febrile paroxysms, which frequently recur, with edema, extreme weakness, rapid loss of weight and myocarditis as the cardinal symptoms. Death supervenes within a year in untreated cases.

Diagnosis.—During febrile episodes the trypanosomes appear in circulating blood; at other times specific diagnosis must be based on recovery of the organisms from lymph node aspirates.

Treatment.—The only drug which has been found to be effective in Rhodesian trypanosomiasis is *Naphuride Na*, or *suramin* (Bayer 205) and this is valuable only during the early stage of the disease. It is administered intravenously in the amount of 1 Gm. once or twice weekly until 7 to 10 Gm. has been given. (See Table 5, page 65.)

Control.—This involves primarily setting up a barrier between human beings and infected tsetse flies. Fairburn (1943) recommended the following procedures: (1) remove people from forested or heavy bush regions (especially around lakes) to open country; (2) clear out brush between settlements, and (3) settle individual families in uninfected territory. Attempts to eradicate the disease by destruction of infected game animals have not succeeded.

Trypanosoma Gambiense Dutton, 1902

(Causing Gambian trypanosomiasis or African "sleeping sickness")

Historical Notes.—In 1901 Forde saw a trypanosome in the blood of a European in Gambia, West Africa. The next year Dutton proposed the name by which this organism has since been designated. In 1903 Castellani found trypanosomes in the cerebro-spinal fluid of patients in Uganda suffering from "sleeping sickness." The same year Bruce and Nabarro (1903) discovered that the organism was transmitted from man to man by a tsetse fly, *Glossina palpalis*.

Epidemiology.—Gambian trypanosomiasis is widely distributed through the central half of Africa, *viz.*, from Senegal to Angola on the west coast through extensive areas of French West Africa and French Equatorial Africa, the countries bordering on the Gulf of Guinea, the Belgian Congo as far east as the southwestern region of the Egyptian Sudan, and Uganda north and west of Lake Victoria (Fig. 45). In some of these countries the infection rate is low, in other areas extremely high.

The amount of infection is determined by the number of *Glossina palpalis* (or at times other species of tsetse flies) which have an opportunity to "bite" patients infected with *T. gambiense*. All of the endemic territory is in relatively low-lying regions of rain-forests, where there are luxuriant vegetation and moist ground in which the flies breed. Except in its extreme northeastern boundary *T. gambiense* does not overlap *T. rhodesiense* infection.

Age, sex, race and occupation have no relation to susceptibility to Gambian trypanosomiasis, although they may favor exposure. *Glossina palpalis* is the most common vector, although *G. tachinoides* is more frequently infected in some endemic areas or is the only tsetse fly present. Direct mechanical transmission may occur through a trypanosome-soiled fly's proboscis. Infection may also be transmitted by sexual intercourse.

The principal mammalian host of *T. gambiense* is man himself. However, domestic animals are highly susceptible to infection. There is no proof that wild game animals serve as reservoirs.

Morphology, Biology and Life Cycle.—Like *T. brucei* and *T. rhodesiense*, *T. gambiense* varies remarkably in size and shape in its trypanosome stage from delicate spindle-shaped with a free flagellum to broad and stumpy forms with or without a free flagellum (range of measurements: 14–33 microns long by 1.5–3.5 microns in breadth).

In the tsetse fly the organisms multiply in the midgut as delicate, elongated trypanosomes. After the 15th day they migrate back through the esophagus, pharynx and labial cavity, then up to the salivary glands. Here they transform into broad crithidial forms, divide many times and revert to the slender trypanosome type. They pass down the salivary ducts about the 20th day and are ready to be introduced into the next victim when the tsetse fly takes a blood meal. The migration and developmental stages within the fly are diagrammatically illustrated in Figure 44.

Pathogenesis and Symptomatology.—At the site of inoculation in the skin the trypanosomes provoke an interstitial inflammation which gradually subsides in 1 to 2 weeks. Meanwhile they gain access to the blood stream and initiate a rather heavy parasitemia. Although they never invade the cytoplasm of cells, their toxic metabolites produce proliferative and necrotic damage to all cells with which they come in contact, including particularly the endothelial lining of the smaller blood vessels. The parasites come more and more to lodge in lymph nodes, and later the arachnoid spaces of the central nervous system and then the brain substance. Thus, following the initial lesion in the skin, three progressive stages of tissue relationship occur, *viz.*, parasitemia, lymphadenitis and central nervous system involvement.

Symptoms.—The primary dermal lesion is seen in European patients, rarely if ever in native Africans. Within 6 to 14 days (the *incubation period*) the trypanosomes appear in circulating blood. In natives, this is characteristically a symptomless stage. But as soon as the parasites invade lymph nodes, causing painful enlargement, there is a febrile attack of about a week's duration, then an apyrectic period, typically followed by one or more bouts of fever. The trypanosomes are found in the blood only during the febrile episodes. The most pronounced lymphadenitis occurs in the posterior cervical triangle (Winterbottom's sign, see Fig. 48), but the

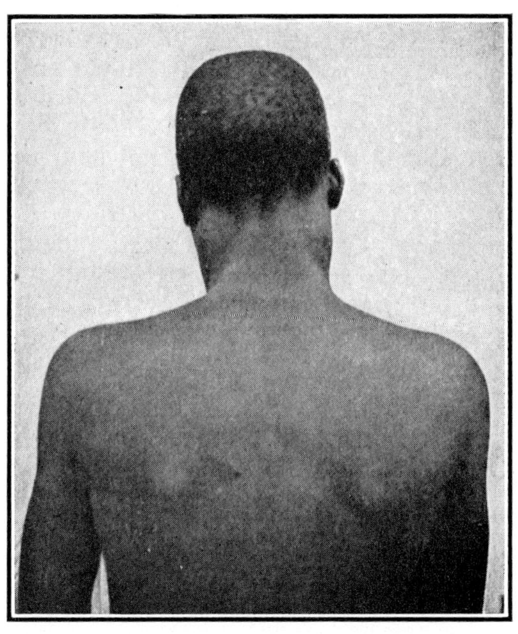

Fig. 48.—Enlargement of the lymph nodes of the posterior cervical triangle (Winterbottom's sign) during the active fulminating stage of Rhodesian and Gambian trypanosomiasis. (After Koch, from *Stitt's Diagnosis, Prevention and Treatment of Tropical Diseases*, courtesy, The Blakiston Co., in Craig and Faust's *Clinical Parasitology*, Lea & Febiger, Philadelphia.)

axillary lymph nodes and those of the groin are also frequently enlarged, as well as the spleen and liver. At this stage, the patient complains of headache, arthritic pain, weakness of the legs and cramps. Later dyspnea, precordial pain, disturbed vision, delayed sensation to pain, anemia and extreme weakness are apt to appear. At times, there is spontaneous improvement in the symptoms followed by another acute febrile attack. Again, the patient may die during this stage of the disease from fulminating toxemia as in Rhodesian trypanosomiasis.

The syndrome resulting from invasion of the central nervous systems is commonly referred to as "sleeping sickness" but this designation suggests only one of the more advanced neurological symptoms. Sleepiness occurs and becomes so pronounced that the patient falls asleep while eating or even standing (Fig. 49). In the more advanced stage the patient sleeps continuously, emaciation becomes extreme, convulsions occur, then profound coma and finally death, which frequently results from intercurrent infection.

Diagnosis.—A presumptive diagnosis should always be supplemented by demonstration of the trypanosome in blood, tissue juice aspirated from enlarged lymph nodes, bone marrow biopsy or spinal fluid. Since the trypanosomes rapidly disintegrate following their removal from the tissues, it

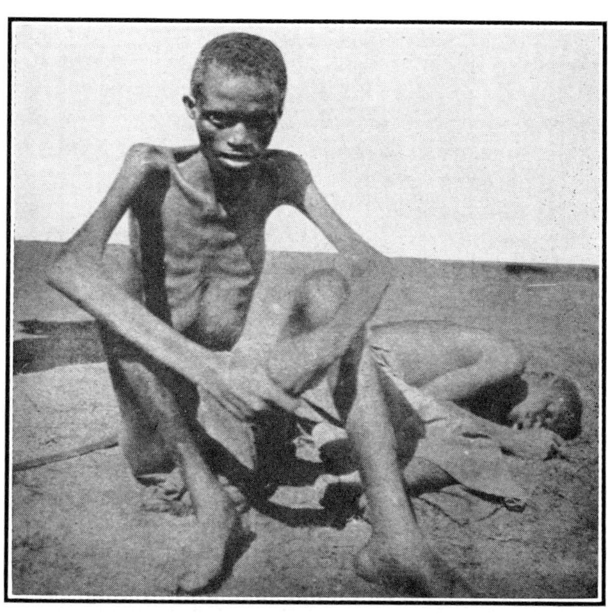

Fig. 49.—Sleeping sickness (terminal) stage of Gambian trypanosomiasis. The patient sitting on the ground illustrates the extreme emaciation and mental apathy, while the patient lying down typifies the tendency to fall asleep. (Photograph of patients from the Belgian Congo, courtesy of Dr. E. R. Kellersberger, in Craig and Faust's *Clinical Parasitology*, Lea & Febiger, Philadelphia.)

is necessary that the microscopic preparation be fixed and stained immediately. (See "Technical Aids," page 596.)

Treatment.—This should be undertaken at the earliest possible moment following proof that the disease is Gambian trypanosomiasis, since delay reduces the chances of recovery. The drugs most valuable in treatment are tryparsamide and certain other arsenicals, suramin sodium, and diamidine compounds.

Tryparsamide has been the most widely used and helpful drug in Gambian trypanosomiasis. It must be administered by vein, once or twice weekly, until 24 to 80 Gm. has been given, depending on the stage of the disease, with the larger dosage for the more advanced condition. When optic neuritis develops, treatment with this, or any other arsenical must be terminated immediately. Although *p*-arsenophenylbutyric acid (Eagle, 1946) and an arsenoxide derivative designated as Mel-B (Friedheim, 1949) appear to be valuable trypanocides, they have not been tested long enough for long-time comparison with tryparsamide.

Suramin (Bayer 205) is very effective in the febrile-lymphadenitis stage but valueless after the parasites have invaded the central nervous system. It is administered by vein, once weekly in 1-Gm. doses for 10 weeks.

Diamidines, particularly *pentamidine* and *propamidine*, are specifically valuable during the earlier stage of the infection and may be substituted for tryparsamide if optic neuritis develops.

Recommendations for treatment of trypanosomiasis will be found in Table 5, page 65.

Control.—The following measures have been found practical in reducing the incidence of Gambian trypanosomiasis in endemic areas: (1) discovery, isolation and specific treatment of all human cases, including mildly symptomatic and asymptomic carriers in the area; (2) protection of persons from *Glossina* "bite"; (3) quarantine of persons coming from infected into uninfected territory; (4) campaigns to destroy the breeding and resting places of the tsetse flies; (5) at times the removal of inhabitants from hyperendemic areas, and (6) administration of prophylactic doses of *suramin*, 1 Gm. intravenously every 3 months, or *propamidine*, 5 mgm./kilo body weight intramuscularly once every 5 or 6 months, to individuals liable to exposure. No satisfactory prophylactic measure has been developed to protect domestic animals from acquiring this disease.

Remarkable reduction in the incidence of Gambian trypanosomiasis has been obtained since mass diagnosis and treatment of the human population in endemic areas was undertaken on an extensive scale.

Trypanosome Parasites of Man Having Posterior Emergence from the Vector

Trypanosoma Cruzi Chagas, 1909

(Causing Chagas' disease or American trypanosomiasis)

Historical Notes.—In 1909 Carlos Chagas discovered a flagellate in the hindgut of a blood-sucking bug, *Panstrongylus megistus*. He allowed infected bugs to feed on a *Callithrix* monkey free of blood parasites and some days later found a trypanosome in the animal's circulating blood. Because of the unique morphology of the flagellate, Chagas named it *Trypanosoma cruzi*. Chagas then searched for the natural host. In bug-infested homes in the area he discovered the trypanosome first in the blood of a cat, then in that of a child with facial edema who was suffering from fever, anemia, splenomegaly and lymphadenitis. Soon many chronic cases with the same clinical manifestations were found to be due to infection with this parasite. On the erroneous conclusion that the agent multiplied by schizogony, Chagas, also in 1909, created a new genus *Schizotrypanum* for it, but in 1912 he realized his mistake and returned the flagellate to the genus *Trypanosoma*. Many workers, including Brumpt (1912), have studied the consecutive stages of the parasite in the insect and vertebrate host.

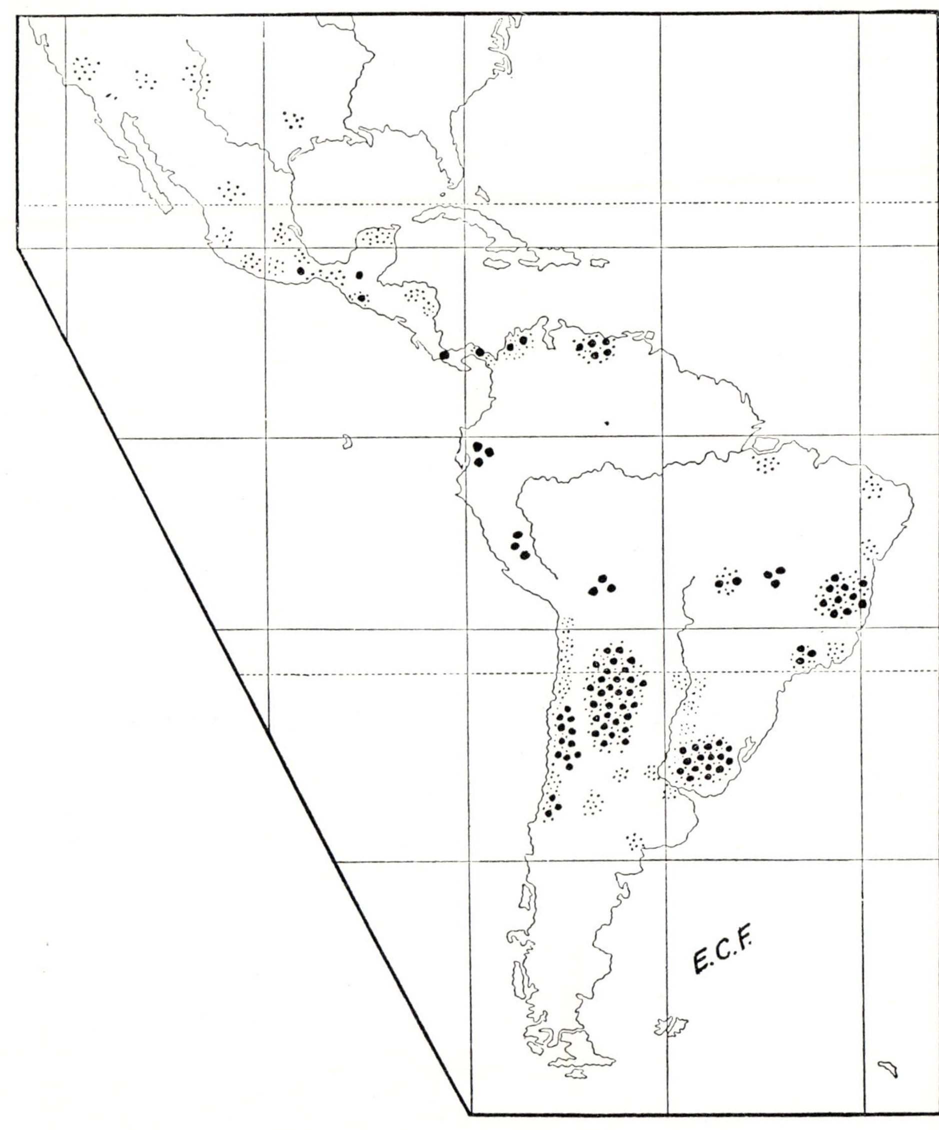

Chagas' Disease in Man.

Chagas' Disease in Reservoir Host.

Fig. 50.—Map showing the distribution of *Trypanosoma cruzi* infection (Chagas' disease). The heavy dots indicate foci of human infection, the lighter dots show the areas in which reservoir mammals and triatomid bugs have been found infected. Additional human cases have been reported from Michoacán and Jalisco States, Mexico and in reservoir hosts in northern Mexico, states of Nuevo León, Tamaulipas and Coahuila (1947). (From Craig and Faust's *Clinical Parasitology*, Lea & Febiger, Philadelphia.)

Epidemiology.—*Trypanosoma cruzi* is probably confined to the Western Hemisphere. In blood-sucking (triatomid) bugs and in reservoir hosts this trypanosome is found from central Chile, northern Argentina and Uruguay on the south to the southwestern part of the United States on the north, but in man it has not been demonstrated as a natural infection north of the southern half of Mexico. (See map, Fig. 50.) It is prevalent in the human

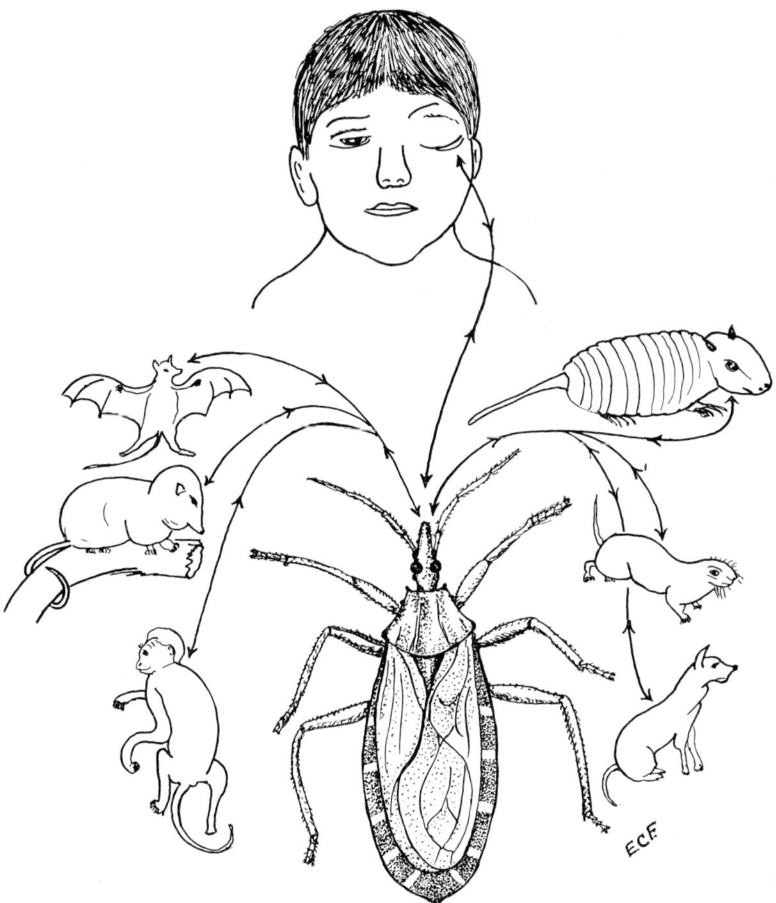

FIG. 51.—Diagram illustrating the life cycle of *Trypanosoma cruzi* in the vector (triatomid bug), in wild and domestic mammals and in man. (Original.)

population principally in dry areas of marginal agriculture, where the homes built of adobe and usually with thatched roofs provide abundant opportunity for the bugs to breed in cracks and crevices of the walls and for them to sally forth from their hiding places to feed on their victims. In some localities 40 to 50% or more of the inhabitants are infected.

Many species of triatomid bugs have been found naturally infected with *T. cruzi*. In addition to *Panstrongylus megistus* the most common of these are *Triatoma infestans* in the southern part of the infected area and *Rhodnius prolixus* in northern South America. At times, the percentage of infected bugs in an endemic area may be as high as 75 to 95%.

Many domestic and wild mammals are reservoirs of this infection. These include dogs, cats, pigs, armadillos, bats, ferrets, foxes, opossums, wild rodents, anteaters, squirrels and monkeys. Human beings constitute only one of a multitude of mammalian host species susceptible to the infection. (See diagram, Figure 51.)

T. cruzi is occasionally transmitted by blood transfusion.

Morphology, Biology and Life Cycle.—Two stages of *T. cruzi*, *viz.*, trypanosome and leishmania, are found in the mammalian host, and two, *viz.*, crithidia and trypanosome, in the insect host. (See Table 9, page 167.)

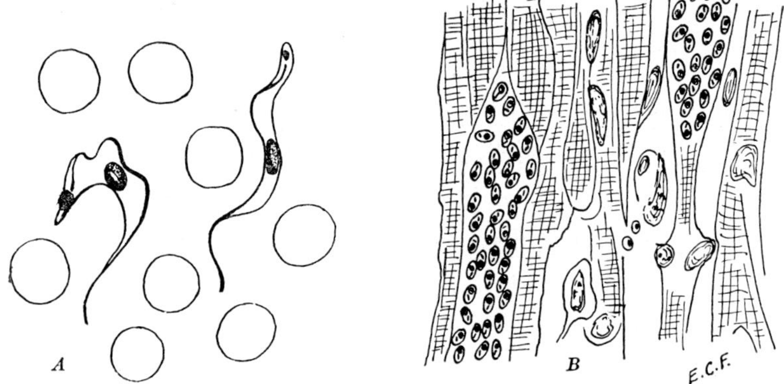

FIG. 52.—Stages of *Trypanosoma cruzi* in the mammalian host. *A*, typical trypanosome form in peripheral blood during febrile episodes; *B*, intracellular leishmania form in heart muscle. This latter form is also found in cells of the reticulo-endothelium, in the brain and other tissues. × 1600. (After Faust, courtesy C. V. Mosby Co., in Craig and Faust's *Clinical Parasitology*, Lea & Febiger, Philadelphia.)

While the infected bug is taking a blood meal it discharges drops of liquid feces on the skin or mucous membrane of the host. This excrement contains the metacyclic trypanosome stage of the parasite, which is rubbed into the site, or possibly at times actively invades mucous membranes. Almost immediately the trypanosomes are engulfed by nearby macrophages, in which the organisms rapidly transform into a leishmania stage, multiply by binary fission, cause disintegration of the macrophage and then invade and multiply within other macrophages. After 4 or 5 days some of the parasites from the primary focus get into the blood stream, in which they are transformed into a trypanosome stage, but in this stage they never divide. *Via* the circulating blood *T. cruzi* is carried to the viscera, where the organisms lodge and invade the cytoplasm of the cells, transforming again into leishmanias and multiplying. Thus, within the mammalian host the extra-cellular trypanosome stage is a very temporary one, found only in the blood stream, while the intra-cellular leishmania stage is the essential one. In this respect *T. cruzi* differs fundamentally from *T. brucei, T. rhodesiense, T. gambiense* and most other trypanosomes.

In the blood of man and reservoir hosts or susceptible laboratory animals *T. cruzi* is a typical trypanosome (Fig. 52 *A*, Fig. 53 *A*), delicately spindle-shaped, about 20 microns in length, with relatively few curves to its narrow undulating membrane and a short free flagellum, or considerably shorter, broader, more or less C-shaped, with or without a free flagellum (Fig. 53 *B*). The former morphologic type is the typical trypanosome, the latter indicative of transformation into or from a leishmania form (Wood, 1953). In its intra-cellular phase *T. cruzi* is a typical leishmania, ovoidal in shape, 1.5 to 5 microns in longer diameter, with a large nucleus and a deeply staining parabasal body (Fig. 52 *B*). In reticulo-endothelial cells *T. cruzi* can not be easily distinguished from species of *Leishmania*; but only *T. cruzi* invades myocardial and neuroglia cells as a leishmania-type organism.

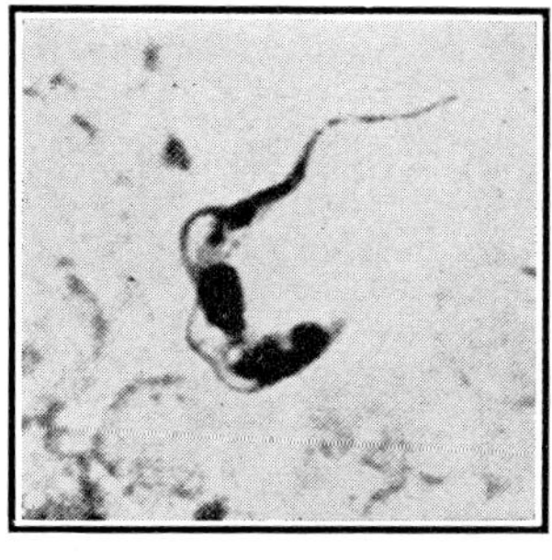

A

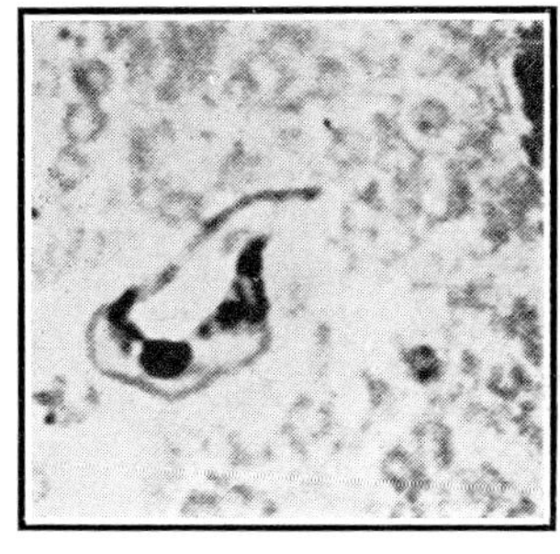

B

FIG. 53.—Photomicrographs of trypanosome forms of *T. cruzi* in peripheral blood of man during febrile episodes. *A*, specimen with large kinetoplast, *B*, relatively common C-shaped specimen. × 1600. (After Mazza, in Craig and Faust's *Clinical Parasitology*, Lea & Febiger, Philadelphia.)

The organism is sucked up by the triatomid bug as a free flagellate or as an intra-cellular leishmania within a macrophage. In the midgut of the bug the organism becomes flagellated and binary multiplication occurs. It does not migrate forward but proceeds to the hindgut, where it transforms into the metacyclic trypanosome form infective again for the vertebrate host. Once a triatomid bug has become parasitized with *T. cruzi*, it will retain the infection for months or years.

Pathogenesis and Symptomatology.—The site of inoculation of *T. cruzi* into the mammalian host may be anywhere on exposed skin or on a mucous membrane. The most common location is at the outer canthus of the eye. Multiplication of the organisms which have been engulfed by nearby macrophages and their entry into other macrophages produce a small granuloma (*chagoma*) which obstructs lymph flow. This is the primary, usually apparent lesion.

Four or five days later progeny get into the blood stream and circulate as typical trypanosomes. During this first period of parasitemia, lasting about 30 days, the organisms cause systemic toxemia. Meanwhile some of them become lodged in visceral organs, including not only reticulo-endothelial tissues but myocardium, endocrine glands and the glia cells of the brain. Here they multiply as leishmania forms, destroying the host cells. Reticulo-endothelial activity and increase in the number of fixed macrophage cells cause splenomegaly, hepatomegaly, adenopathy and engorgement of bone marrow, reminiscent of kala-azar (page 180). Colonies of the parasites which develop in myocardium produce insidious destruction of heart muscle and those which are located in the brain cells cause extensive neuropathologic changes.

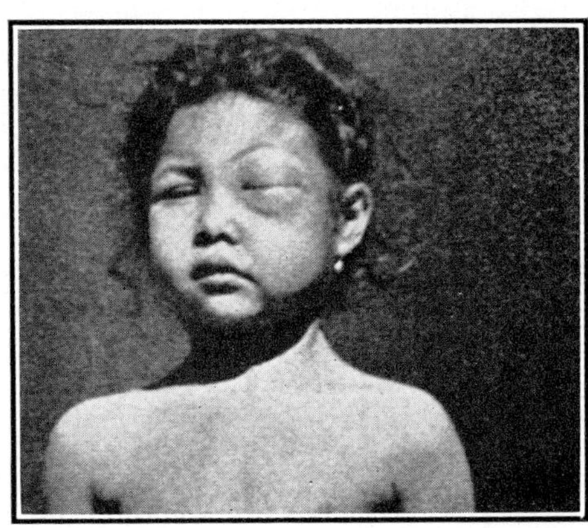

FIG. 54.—Photograph of Brazilian child suffering from acute stage of Chagas' disease. Note the unilateral palpebral edema (Romaña's sign) which is relatively characteristic of this disease. (Photograph by Dr. C. Romaña, in Craig and Faust's *Clinical Parasitology*, Lea & Febiger, Philadelphia.)

Symptoms in Chagas' disease are associated in sequence with the primary lesion, the parasitemia and the more chronic pathology due to development of the protozoön in the several visceral organs. Frequently the primary site is at the outer canthus of one eye, with unilateral palpebral edema (*Romaña's* sign), at times causing a swelling of the entire side of the face (Fig. 54). During the primary parasitemia of about 12 to 30 days, there is fever, a marked toxic condition suggesting typhoid fever, tachycardia and in children at times fatal termination. If the patient survives this acute stage, or if it is by-passed, the symptoms of the chronic disease depend on the localization of the parasites, *viz.*, cardiac, meningo-encephalitic, suprarenal, etc. This stage may last for years with gradual increase in the chronic manifestations, but with febrile exacerbations and parasitemia supervening from time to time.

Diagnosis.—During febrile periods diagnosis may be made by demonstrating the typical trypanosome stage of *T. cruzi* in blood films. Aspiration of spleen, liver, lymph nodes or bone marrow will frequently reveal the leishmania form of the organism in fixed macrophages. Aspirates may be planted on blood agar, and cultured at room temperature for demonstration of the crithidia stage of the parasite. Likewise, complement fixation of patient's blood serum, employing pure antigen obtained from cultured organisms, is a very satisfactory method. However, the procedure most commonly employed in endemic areas is *xeno-diagnosis*. A clean triatomid bug is allowed to "bite" the suspected Chagas'-disease patient. If the patient has Chagas' disease, the bug's fecal discharge 10 days later should contain active stages of the parasite.

Treatment.—Symptomatic relief is all that is available.

Control.—The task of control is a formidable one. This is particularly true for human beings since there is no drug which serves as a therapeutic agent either for curative or prophylactic purposes. However, residual spraying of the inside walls and roofs with a kerosene-detergent emulsion of Gammexane (gamma isomer of benzene hexachloride) once yearly will keep the habitation free of the bugs and thus minimize human exposure. Concerted anti-vector programs throughout endemic areas will greatly reduce the infection as a human disease.

Other Species of Trypanosomes Related to Trypanosoma Cruzi

Trypanosoma Rangeli Téjera, 1920

In 1920, Téjera found unusual crithidial and trypanosome stages of a flagellate in the gut of *Rhodnius prolixus*, the principal vector of *T. cruzi* in Venezuela. The organisms differed from similar stages of *T. cruzi*, so that Téjera gave it the name *T. rangeli*. In 1942, Medina obtained this same organism by xeno-diagnosis from two patients in Venezuela. The next year DeLeón and Montenegro, in Guatemala (DeLeón, 1949), apparently found the same trypanosome in triatomid bugs and in the peripheral blood of four children. More recently Pifano *et al.* (1949) found a high incidence of *T. rangeli* in *R. prolixus* in the Yaracuy River Valley, Venezuela. Forty-one human infections with *T. rangeli* (31 pure and 10 associated with *T. cruzi*) were demonstrated from the area by xeno-diagnostic technic. Pifano and Mayer (1949) believe that transmission to the vertebrate host probably occurs through the proboscis and not through the feces.

Trypanosoma Ariarii Groot, Renjifo and Uribe, 1951

This trypanosome occurs in the Ariari River Valley, Colombia. In human blood films the flagellate is trypanosome in form, averages 31 microns in length, with a relatively broad undulating membrane and a free flagellum rarely more than half the length of the body. The ovoidal nucleus is situated somewhat anterior to the equatorial plane and the small, round blepharoplast is subterminal. Human infection with this trypanosome, either alone or associated with *T. cruzi*, is relatively high in the Ariari Valley, where *Cebus fatuellus* and dogs are also naturally infected. The organism shows trypanosome division stages in mammalian blood. No intracellular leishmania stage has been demonstrated, and no clinical manifestations developed in two human volunteers in whom the course of the infection was carefully followed. Groot (1952) has demonstrated that in experimentally infected *Rhodnius prolixus* there is first a developmental phase in the midgut. Later, some of the organisms migrate into the hemolymph and forward to the salivary glands, where they complete their development and then descend into the proboscis, through which they are introduced into the mammalian host.

Until more information is available concerning *T. rangeli* and *T. ariarii* it is not possible to pass judgment on the validity of these species.

Blood and Tissue Protozoön of Uncertain Relationship

Toxoplasma Gondii Nicolle and Manceaux, 1908
(Causing toxoplasmosis)

This organism was discovered by Nicolle and Manceaux is a small North African rodent, *Ctenodactylus gundi*, and since that time has been found frequently in a large number of birds and mammals including man (Jacobs, 1953). Human infection has been demonstrated in many foci in the United States, South America, Europe, the Egyptian Sudan, Central Africa, Iran, Ceylon and possibly other areas. It is now known to be cosmopolitan both in lower animals and in man.

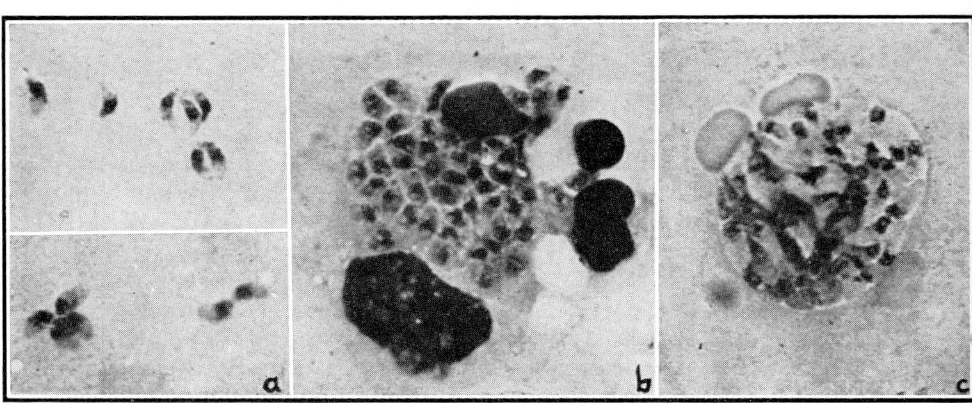

Fig. 55.—Photomicrographs of microscopic smear of *Toxoplasma gondii*, stained by Wright's technic. × 1000. (After Sabin, Brennemann's *Practice of Pediatrics*, courtesy W. F. Prior Co., in Craig and Faust's *Clinical Parasitology*, Lea & Febiger, Philadelphia.)

Epidemiology.—There is no conclusive evidence as to how this infection is propagated in nature. Experimentally in animals it may be induced by inoculating material containing the parasites by the oral, intranasal, intravenous, intracutaneous, subcutaneous, intraperitoneal or intracerebral route. An intermediate arthropod vector may sometimes be involved (Woke *et al.*, 1953). Both in human cases and experimental mammals the disease is transmitted from mother to offspring, and in lactating mice it has been acquired from mother's milk. Moreover, the large number of persons with toxoplasmin-positive tests but without symptoms suggests that there may be many inapparent cases for each symptomatic one.

Morphology.—*Toxoplasma gondii* is a delicate, ovoidal, pyriform or crescentic body measuring 4 to 6 microns long by 2 to 3 microns in breadth. At times, one or both extremities may be somewhat pointed, or they may be rounded. Employing Giemsa stain, one sees a delicate azure coloration of the cytoplasm and a reddish ovoidal nucleus, which lies somewhat towards the blunter end of the body. This organism is not directly related to any other group of the Protozoa.

Pathogenesis.—*Toxoplasma gondii* is primarily if not exclusively a parasite in fixed cells of the reticulo-endothelial system (Figs. 55 and 56) but frequently it has been found within wandering macrophages in peritoneal, pleural or cerebral exudates and in circulating blood. It does not grow free of host cells; to obtain the organism for diagnostic tests it must be inoculated into suitable laboratory animals (Frenkel, 1953).

Once *Toxoplasma* becomes implanted it develops within wandering or fixed macrophages comparable to *Leishmania donovani* (page 179). It tends to produce clear serous fluids in body cavities, necrosis of invaded tissues and centers of granulomata, frequently becoming calcified in cerebral foci. The degree of injury to organs varies remarkably from essentially insignificant, microscopic changes to profound, extensive, irreversible damage. The organs commonly attacked are the brain, eye and lungs.

Symptomatology.—The most seriously affected human cases are those of the newborn, with infection acquired *in utero* during the second or third trimester of fetal development, usually from a symptomless mother (Sabin, 1950). These infants at birth or during the first week or two *post-partum* commonly have evidences of

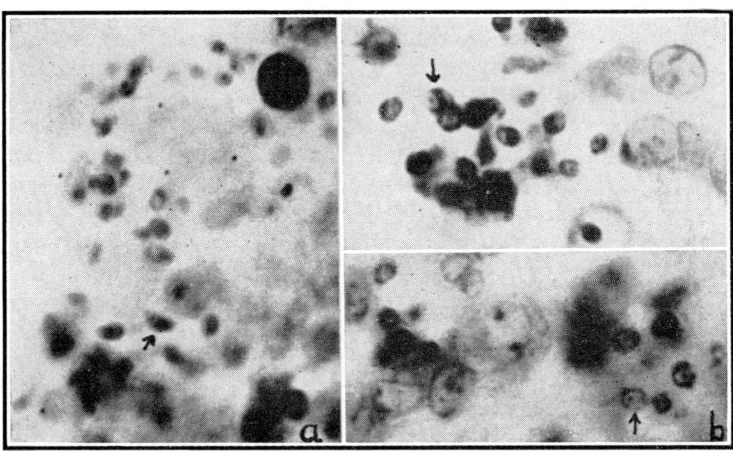

Fig. 56.—Photomicrographs of *Toxoplasma gondii* in fixed, stained tissue sections; *a*, following fixation in formalin and staining with hematoxylin-eosin, *b*, following fixation in Zenker-acetic acid and staining by Giemsa's technic. × 1400. (After Sabin, Brennemann's *Practice of Pediatrics*, courtesy W. F. Prior Co., in Craig and Faust's *Clinical Parasitology*, Lea & Febiger, Philadelphia.)

cerebral calcification and chorioretinitis, at times with hydrocephalus or microcephaly and psychomotor disturbances. In other cases, there may be rather indefinite symptoms produced by microscopic granulomas and necrotic areas in which the parasites occur. In the pulmonary type, the lungs are congested and the bronchioles infiltrated with macrophages packed with toxoplasmas. At times, the myocardium is invaded by the parasitized macrophages. Still another variety is one with maculo-papular eruption, high fever, mental stupor and atypical pneumonia (Pinkerton and Henderson, 1941).

Infection may be acquired *in utero*, with the probability of fatal termination soon after birth or irreversible changes leaving the child a helpless invalid; or it may be acquired at any period after birth (Wilder, 1952). Apparently the prognosis depends on the amount and virulence of the inoculum and the threshold of resistance of the host. A symptomless mother who gives birth to a *Toxoplasma*-infected infant may rest assured that her future offspring will not have this stigma (Sabin, *l.c.*).

Diagnosis may be made clinically on the basis of cerebral calcification, as demonstrated by the ventriculogram, and chorioretinitis, especially in the region of the macula, but this should be confirmed by demonstration of *Toxoplasma* in smear preparations, inoculation of laboratory mice with blood or suspected tissues, by immunologic tests, and *post-mortem* by demonstration of the parasites in the tissues. The complement fixation test (Warren and Sabin, 1943) and the neutralization test (Sabin and Ruckman, 1943) have been largely supplanted by the microchemical dye test (Sabin and Feldman, 1948; Feldman, 1953). (See "TECHNICAL AIDS," page 612.)

Treatment.—There is no effective treatment in toxoplasmosis. Aureomycin temporarily retards the progress of the disease in experimental animals but does not terminate the infection. (See Eyles and Coleman, 1953).

Control.—Until the epidemiology of toxoplasmosis is better understood it is impossible to plan effective control.

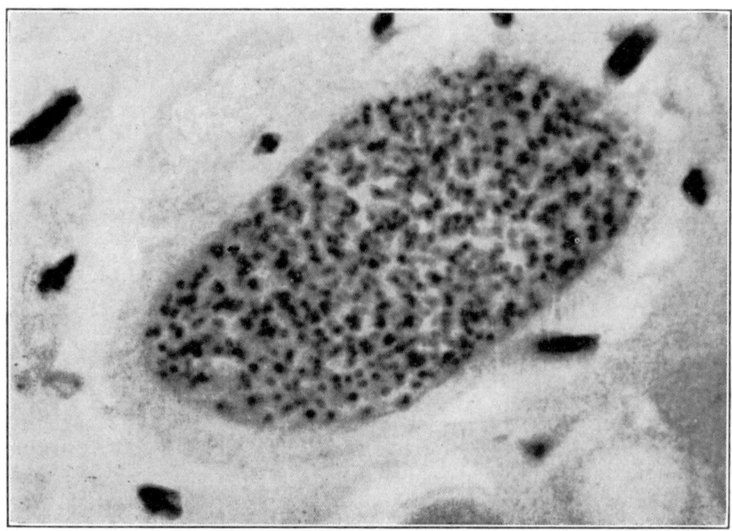

FIG. 57.—Photomicrograph of *Sarcocystis lindemanni* in left ventricular wall of a Panamanian child. The cyst contained about 170 spores. Except for enlargement and slight hyaline degeneration of the muscle fibers there were no myocardial lesions. × 1500. (After Gilmore, Kean and Posey, Am. J. Trop. Med., courtesy Williams & Wilkins, Baltimore.)

Sarcocystis Lindemanni Rivolta 1878

Although this organism and other species of the Sarcosporidia have for many years been classed as protozoa, their exact position is still unknown. Spindler and Zimmerman (1945) have found suggestive evidence that they may belong to the fungi, but this report has not been confirmed. *S. lindemanni* and related organisms are common parasites of the muscle fibers of various species of mammals, birds and reptiles. Sporadic human infection with *S. lindemanni* has been recorded incidentally in *post-mortem* examination of cases which died of other causes. It is not known how man acquires the infection but mice have been experimentally infected with *S. muris* by feeding them contaminated feces of infected mice.

The organisms (Fig. 57) are cylindrical, elongated or fusiform objects ("Miescher's tubes"), ranging in length from microscopic to 5 cm., lying in the parasitized muscle fibers, most commonly those of the tongue, larynx, esophagus, diaphragm, chest, abdomen and myocardium. They are hyaline and are surrounded by an outer envelope which may be somewhat radially striated. Within this outer layer the cyst is divided into compartments, the inner ones of which contain rounded, ovoidal, elongated or sickle-shaped spores ("Rainey's corpuscles"), measuring 12 to 16 microns in length by 4 to 9 microns in breadth. Each spore contains a nucleus near its rounded end. Thousands of these spores are developed in one cyst. When such a cyst containing ripe spores is ingested, the cyst membrane is dissolved in the small intestine and the spores each digest a path into the intestinal mucosa. Here they multiply, migrate to striated muscle and develop into new cysts.

Although *Sarcocystis* is pathogenic and frequently fatal to sheep and other animals, it has not produced detectable symptoms in man (Gilmore, Kean and Posey, 1942.)

SUMMARY

1. In addition to the malaria parasites, species of protozoa which produce systemic infection in man include flagellates of the blood and tissues, *Toxoplasma gondii* and *Sarcocystis lindemanni.*
2. Flagellate protozoa (Mastigophora) of the blood and tissues of vertebrate hosts typically have a developmental phase in a blood-sucking invertebrate which transmits the infection to the vertebrate. An overwhelming majority of these vectors are arthropods. The species of blood and tissue flagellates which parasitize man and other mammals belong to *Leishmania, viz., L. tropica, L. brasiliensis* and *L. donovani,* and *Trypanosoma, viz., T. rhodesiense, T. gambiense* and *T. cruzi.*
3. All species of *Leishmania* utilize sand-flies (*Phlebotomus*) as intermediate hosts. They are injected into the skin of the definitive host at the time the sand-fly takes a blood meal. The flagellates are engulfed by wandering macrophages, in which they transform into the leishmania stage, propagate by binary fission, destroy the host cell and are engulfed by other macrophages in which they continue to develop.
4. *Leishmania tropica,* which has a geographic distribution in the more arid regions of the Eastern Hemisphere, causes cutaneous leishmaniasis, in which a relatively small ulcer is produced at the site of each inoculation. The uncontaminated lesion heals in a period of months, leaving only a slight surface scar. Infection confers permanent immunity. Man, dogs and at times rodents constitute the susceptible vertebrate hosts.
5. *Leishmania brasiliensis,* which has an extensive distribution in the sylvatic regions of tropical America, causes muco-cutaneous leishmaniasis. The primary lesion resembles that of cutaneous leishmaniasis but has less of a tendency to heal. The essential characteristic of *L. brasiliensis* infection is its proclivity to extend to mucocutaneous junctions, particularly in the vicinity of the nares. Here a deep, disfiguring, erosive process develops, which may be weeping or granulomatous. Dogs are reservoir hosts in some endemic areas.
6. *Leishmania donovani,* with large areas of endemicity in northern China, eastern India, the Mediterranean countries, the Egyptian Sudan and several foci in continental Latin America, produces visceral leishmaniasis (kala-azar). This involves the entire reticulo-endothelium, especially spleen, liver, bone marrow and visceral lymph nodes. The

disease process consists of a vast increase in macrophages with comparable reduction in neutrophils and red blood cells, providing a picture of absolute monocytosis, neutropenia and anemia. The spleen and liver are greatly enlarged, and the bone marrow engorged. Intercurrent infections produce pathologic changes in the tissues of the respiratory and digestive tracts, and in the cheek (cancrum oris) in children. In China, the Mediterranean countries and tropical America dogs are important reservoirs.

7. Diagnosis of all types of leishmaniasis is most satisfactorily made by demonstration of the parasite within infected macrophages. Except for the Sudanese variety of kala-azar, all types of leishmaniasis are usually amenable to antimony therapy. Modern control is concerned with death of the adult sand-fly transmitter by use of residual DDT sprayed on the walls of human habitations, likewise destruction of infected dogs or other reservoirs.
8. *Trypanosoma rhodesiense* and *T. gambiense* are African in their distribution (*T. rhodesiense* in upland savannas of east Africa, *T. gambiense* in the rain-forest areas of west and central Africa. These species utilize tsetse flies (*Glossina*) as intermediate hosts and transmitters. Infection is through the "bite" of the fly. These organisms get into circulating blood and multiply. In lymph nodes they set up interstitial inflammation and necrosis. In *T. rhodesiense* infection the disease is so fulminating that patients characteristically die, but in *T. gambiense* infection the parasites invade the central nervous system, where necrotic damage causes a wide variety of nervous disorders, including "sleeping sickness."
9. African trypanosomiasis is diagnosed by recovery of the trypanosomes in the blood during periods of parasitemia, later in tissue juice aspirated from lymph nodes, and, in *T. gambiense* infection, from the spinal fluid after invasion of the central nervous system. Treatment of Rhodesian trypanosomiasis is effective only during the early stage. Gambian infection is treated with tryparsamide or other arsenicals, suramin and diamidines. Control consists in clearing extensive areas around human habitations to prevent transmission to man by tsetse fly bites, or removing the human population to non-infected areas.
10. *Trypanosoma cruzi* occurs in the tropics and subtropics of continental America. It utilizes triatomid bugs as transmitters. The parasites are discharged in small drops of liquid feces at the time the bug is taking a blood meal. When *T. cruzi* gets into the skin or mucous membrane of the definitive host, primary colonization is frequently at the outer canthus of the eye. Some of the organisms get into the blood stream, in which they are morphologically typical trypanosomes, although they do not divide in this stage. Later they lodge in liver, spleen, lymph nodes, myocardium, central nervous tissue or other organs, where they invade the fixed cells and multiply as leishmanias, with destruction of the parasitized cells.
11. *Trypanosoma cruzi* infection (Chagas' disease) is diagnosed by recovery of the trypanosome from blood during febrile episodes, or the leishmania stage from invaded cells, likewise by complement fixation or

xeno-diagnosis. There is no specific treatment. Human exposure can be greatly diminished by residual spraying of benzene hexachloride (Gammexane) inside homes, to kill the bugs which infest the dwellings.

12. *Toxoplasma gondii,* which has a cosmopolitan distribution in man, mammals and birds, is not related to any other one-celled organisms. It is an intra-cytoplasmic parasite, principally in reticulo-endothelial cells, in which it divides by longitudinal binary fission. The method by which infection is acquired has not been elucidated. In man this infection (toxoplasmosis) appears in all age groups; symptomatic disease is most common in infants, who may acquire the disease from a symptomless mother during fetal development. The pathologic process frequently causes cerebral calcification, chorioretinitis, pneumonitis and myocarditis, and there may be exanthematous lesions. Diagnosis consists in demonstrating the organism in the tissues, in inoculating experimental mice with material from suspected cases, or by immunologic technics. There is no satisfactory therapy. No effective control program has been developed.
13. *Sarcocystis lindemanni* is a relatively rare parasite of man, but is common in sheep and other mammals. It develops as an elongated microscopic or macroscopic cyst within striated muscle. It is probably acquired from contaminated food or drink. In man it is essentially asymptomatic.

REFERENCES

Adler, S., and Ber, M. 1941. The Transmission of *Leishmania Tropica* by the Bite of *Phlebotomus Papatasii.* Indian J. Med. Res., *29*, 803–809.

Berberian, D. A. 1938. Successful Transmission of Cutaneous Leishmaniasis by the Bites of *Stomoxys Calcitrans.* Proc. Soc. Exp. Biol. & Med., *38*, 254–256.

————1939. Vaccination and Immunity against Oriental Sore. Trans. R. Soc. Trop. Med. & Hyg., *33*, 87–94.

Bruce, D., and Nabarro, D. 1903. Progress Report on Sleeping Sickness in Uganda. Rept. Sleeping Sickness Comm. Roy. Soc., *1*, 11–88.

Brumpt, E. 1912. Le *Trypanosoma Cruzi* Évolue chez *Conorhinus Megistus, Cimex Lectularius, Cimex Boueti* et *Ornithodorus Moubata.* Bull. Soc. Path. Exot., *5*, 360–364.

Castellani, A. 1903. Trypanosoma in Sleeping Sickness. Brit. Med. J., *i*, 1218.

Chagas, C. 1909a. Nova Especie Morbida do Homem, Produzida por um Trypanozoma (*Trypanozoma Cruzi*). Nota Previa. Brazil Med., *23*, 161.

————1909b. Nova Tripanozomiaze Humana. Estudos sobre a Morfolojia e o Ciclo Evolutivo do *Schizotrypanum Cruzi,* n. gen., n. sp. Mem. Inst. Oswaldo Cruz, *1*, 159–218.

Chung, H. L., and Feng, L. C. 1951. Observations Concerning the Successful Transmission of Kala-azar in North China by Bites of Naturally Infected *Phlebotomus Chinensis.* Peking Nat. Hist. Bull., *19*, 302–326.

Cunningham, D. D. 1885. On the Presence of Peculiar Parasitic Organisms in the Tissue of a Specimen of Delhi Boil. Sci. Mem. Med. Off. Army India, Pt. I, 1884, p. 21.

Donovan, C. 1903. The Aetiology of One of the Heterogeneous Fevers of India. Brit. Med. J., *ii*, 1401.

Dutton, J. E. 1902. Preliminary Note upon a Trypanosome Occurring in the Blood of Man. Thompson Yates Lab. Rept. *4*, 455–468.

Eagle, H. 1946. The Treatment of Trypanosomiasis with *p*-Arsenosophenyl-butyric acid. Pub. Health Repts., *61*, 1019–1033.

Eyles, D. E., and Coleman, N. 1953. Antibiotics in the Treatment of Toxoplasmosis. Am. J. Trop. Med. & Hyg., *2*, 64–69.

FAIRBAIRN, H., and BURTT, E. 1946. The Infectivity to Man of a Strain of *Trypanosoma Rhodesiense.* Ann. Trop. Med. & Parasitol., *40*, 270–313.

FELDMAN, H. A. 1953. The Clinical Manifestations and Laboratory Diagnosis of Toxoplasmosis. Am. J. Trop. Med. & Hyg., *2*, 420–428.

FRENKEL, J. K. 1953. Host, Strain and Treatment Variation as Factors in the Pathogenesis of Toxoplasmosis. Am. J. Trop. Med. & Hyg., *2*, 390–411.

FRIEDHEIM, E. A. H. 1949. Mel B in the Treatment of Trypanosomiasis. Am. J. Trop. Med., *29*, 173–180.

GILMORE, H. R., KEAN, B. H., and POSEY, F. M. 1942. Sarcosporidiosis with Parasites Found in the Heart. Am. J. Trop. Med., *22*, 121–125.

GROOT, H. 1952. Further Observations on *Trypanosoma Ariarii* of Colombia, South America. Am. J. Trop. Med. & Hyg., *1*, 585–592.

HERRER, A. 1948. Nota Preliminar sobre Leishmaniosis Natural en Perros. Rev. Med. Exp., Lima, *7*, 62–69.

HERTIG, M. 1949. Phlebotomus and Residual DDT in Greece and Italy. Am. J. Trop. Med., *29*, 773–800.

———and FISHER, R. A. 1945. Control of Sandflies with DDT. Bull. U. S. Army Med. Dept., No. 88, 97–101.

JACOBS, L. 1953. The Biology of *Toxoplasma.* Am. J. Trop. Med. & Hyg., *2*, 365–386.

KINGHORN, A., and YORKE, W. 1912. On the Transmission of Human Trypanosomes by *Glossina Morsitans,* etc. Ann. Trop. Med. & Parasitol., *6*, 1–23.

KLEINE, F. K. 1909. Positive Infektionsversuche mit *Trypanosome Brucei* durch *Glossina Palpalis.* Deutsch. med. Wchnschr., *35*, 467–470.

KLIGLER, I. J. 1926. The Cultural and Serological Relationship of Leishmania. Trans. R. Soc. Trop. Med. & Hyg., *19*, 330–335.

LATYSHEV, N. J., and KRYNKOVA. 1941. On the Epidemiology of the Cutaneous Leishmaniases. Acad. Med. Armée Rouge, Moscow, *25*, 229–242. (Russian text.)

LAVERAN, A., and MESNIL, F. 1903. Sur un Protozoaire Nouveau (*Piroplasma Donovani* Laveran et Mesnil). Parasite d'une Fievre de l'Inde. Compt. Rend. Acad. d. Sc. Paris, *137*, 957–961.

LEISHMAN, W. 1903. On the Possibility of the Occurrence of Trypanosomiasis in India. Brit. Med. J., *i*, 1252–1254.

LINDENBERG, A. 1909. L'Ulcère de Bauru ou le Bouton d'Orient au Brésil. Communication Preliminaire. Bull. Soc. Path. Exot., *2*, 252–254.

NAPIER, L. E. 1946. *The Principles and Practice of Tropical Medicine.* Chapter on Kala-Azar, pp. 135–177. Macmillan Co., New York.

NICOLLE, C., and MANCEAUX, L. 1908. Sur une Infection a Corps de Leishman (ou Organismes Voisins) du Gondi. Compt. rend. Acad. Aci., *147*, 763–765.

NOGUCHI, H. 1926. Comparative Studies on Herpetomonads and Leishmanias. II. Differentiation of the Organisms by Serological Reactions and Fermentation Tests. J. Exp. Med., *44*, 327–337.

PESSÔA, S. B., and BARRETTO, M. O. 1948. *Leishmaniose Tegumentar Americana.* Rio de Janeiro. 527 pp.

PESSÔA, S. B., and PESTANA, B. R. 1940. A Introdermo-reacção de Montenegro nas Campanhas Sanitarias contra a Leishmaniose. São Paulo Med., *13*, 133–151.

PIFANO, F. 1949. Estado Actual de las Investigaciones en Venezuela sobre Una Nueva Trypanosomiasis Humana en la Region Neotrópica Producida por el *Trypanosoma Rangeli.* Arch. Venez. Path. Trop., y Parasitol., *1*, 135–152.

PINKERTON, H., and HENDERSON, R. G. 1941. Adult Toxoplasmosis. J. Am. Med. Assn., *116*, 807–814.

ROGERS, L. 1904. Preliminary Note on the Development of *Trypanosoma* in Cultures of the Cunningham-Leishman-Donovan Bodies of Cachexial Fever and Kala-azar. Lancet, *ii*, 215–216.

ROMAÑA, C., and MEYER, H. 1942. Estudo do Ciclo Evolutivo de "*Schizotrypanum Cruzi*" em Cultura de Tecidos de Embriãs de Galinha. Mem. Inst. Oswaldo Cruz. *37*, 19–27.

SABIN, A. B. 1950. Toxoplasmosis. Am. J. Ophthalm., *33*, 1255–1268.

———1953. Toxoplasmosis: Current Status and Unsolved Problems. Am. J. Trop. Med. & Hyg., *2*, 360–364.

SABIN, A. B., and FELDMAN, H. A. 1949. Dyes as Microchemical Indicators of a New Immunity Phenomenon Affecting a Protozoon Parasite (Toxoplasma). Science, *108*, 660–663.

SABIN, A. B., and RUCKMAN, I. 1943. Characteristics of the Toxoplasma Neutralizing Antibody. Proc. Soc. Exp. Biol. & Med., *51*, 1–6.

SEN GUPTA, P. S., and ADHIKARI, S. L. 1952. Observations on the Complement Fixation Test for Kala-azar. J. Indian Med. Assn., *23*, 89–93.

SERGENT, ED., SERGENT, ET., PARROT, L., DONATIEN, A., and BEQUET, M. 1921. Transmission du Clou de Biskra par le Phlebotome (*Phlebotomus Papatasii* Scop). Compt. Rend. Acad. Sci., *173*, 1030–1032.

SMITH, R. O. A., HALDER, E. C., and AHMED, I. 1941. Further Investigations on Transmission of Kala-azar; Second Series of Transmission of *L. Donovani* by *P. Argentipes.* Indian J. Med. Res., *29*, 799–802.

SPINDLER, L. A., and ZIMMERMAN, H. E., JR. 1945. The Biological Status of *Sarcocystis.* J. Parasitol., *31*, Suppl., page 13.

STEPHENS, J. W. W., and FANTHAM, H. B. 1910. On the Peculiar Morphology of a Trypanosome from a Case of Sleeping Sickness and the Possibility of Its Being a New Species (*T. Rhodesiense*). Proc. Roy. Soc., London, Ser. B, *83*, 28–33.

SWAMINATH, C. S., SHORTT, H. E., and ANDERSON, L. A. P. 1942. Transmission of Indian Kala-azar to Man by the Bites of *Phlebotomus Argentipes* Ann. and Brun. Indian J. Med. Res., *30*, 473–477.

VIANNA, G. 1911. Contribução para o Estudo da Anatomia Patológica da Moléstia de Carlos Chagas. Mem. Inst. Oswaldo Cruz. *3*, 276–294.

WARREN, J., and SABIN, A. B. 1943. The Complement-fixation Reaction in Toxoplasmosis. Proc. Soc. Exp. Biol. & Med., *51*, 11–14.

WEISS, P. 1943. Epidemiologia y Clínica de las Leishmaniosis Tegumentarias en el Perú. Rev. Med. Exp., Lima, *2*, 209–248.

WENYON, C. M. 1926. *Protozoology.* Vol. I. Baillière, Tindall & Cox, London.

WILDER, H. C. 1952. Toxoplasma Chorioretinitis in Adults. Arch. Ophthalm., *48*, 127–136.

WOKE, A., JACOBS, L., JONES, F. E., and MELTON, M. L. 1953. Experimental Results on Possible Arthropod Transmission of Toxoplasmosis. J. Parasitol., *39*, 523–532.

WRIGHT, J. H. 1903. Protozoa in a Case of Tropical Ulcer ("Delhi Sore"). J. Med. Res., *10*, 472–482.

Section III

ROUNDWORMS (Nematodes)

Chapter 10

Roundworms of the Digestive Tract and Related Species

INTRODUCTION

ALL true roundworms (nematodes) are characterized by certain morphologic features and by stages in their development which distinguish them as a phylum from the Nematomorpha, Acanthocephala, Trematoda, Cestoidea and Hirudinea. Before taking up the roundworms of the digestive tract and other species of parasitic nematodes adapted to extra-intestinal habitats it will be desirable to consider briefly the structural and life-cycle characteristics common to the nematode group.

Structure of Roundworms.—Nematodes are invertebrate animals lacking segmentation. They are typically elongate, cylindrical, with a fundamentally bilateral symmetry and in most species a superimposed secondary radial symmetry. They have a complete digestive tract and a body cavity which is not lined with mesothelium. With relatively few exceptions they have separate sexes, *i. e.*, they are *diecious*. They range remarkably in size, depending on the species, from forms too small to be readily seen by the unaided eye to others which are many centimeters in length and are several millimeters in diameter (Fig. 58).

Roundworms are covered with a cuticle, a secretion believed to be scleroprotein. Underlying this are the hypodermis and a basal dermomuscular layer. Arising from the hypodermis and projecting into the body cavity there are four longitudinal "lines" or cords, one median dorsal, one median ventral and two median lateral in position. These cords separate the somatic musculature into distinct quadrants. The simplest type of these muscle units consists of only two cells for each of the four quadrants. A somewhat more complex muscle structure consists of numerous cells, with their protoplasmic processes extending into the body cavity. In other species large numbers of muscle cells are crowded together to make a continuous band.

Specialized structures at the anterior extremity of the roundworm serve for attachment, penetration and for sensory purposes. The cuticle over the body as a whole may also be provided with scales or setæ, which are usually

Fig. 58.—Outline drawings of important nematode parasites of man, drawn to scale. *a*, *Trichocephalus trichiurus*, female (*left*), male (*right*); *b*, *Necator americanus*, female (*left*), male (*right*); *c*, *Ancylostoma duodenale*, female (*left*), male (*right*); *d*, *Trichostrongylus orientalis*, female (*left*), male (*right*); *e*, female parasitic *Strongyloides stercoralis; f*, *Enterobius vermicularis*, female (*left*), male (*right*); *g*, *Trichinella spiralis*, female (*left*), male (*right*); *h*, *Ascaris lumbricoides*, female (*left*), male (*right*); *i*, *Loa loa*, female (*left*), male (*right*); *j*, *Acanthocheilonema perstans*, female (*left*), male (*right*); *k*, female *Mansonella ozzardi; l*, *Wuchereria malayi*, female (*left*), male (*right*); *m*, *Wuchereria bancrofti*, female (*left*), male (*right*); *n*, *Onchocerca vulvulus*, female (*left*), male (*right*). (Original.)

more conspicuous in the anterior portion than more posteriorly; or the cuticle may be bossed or entirely smooth.

The *alimentary tract* (Fig. 59 *A*) is divided into three main portions: (1) an interior part consisting of oral cavity and esophagus (muscular except in the Trichinelloidea), both covered with an internal extension of the cuticle, (2) a midgut with a single layer of columnar epithelial cells, without cuticle, and (3) a hindgut or rectum, which is covered with cuticle.

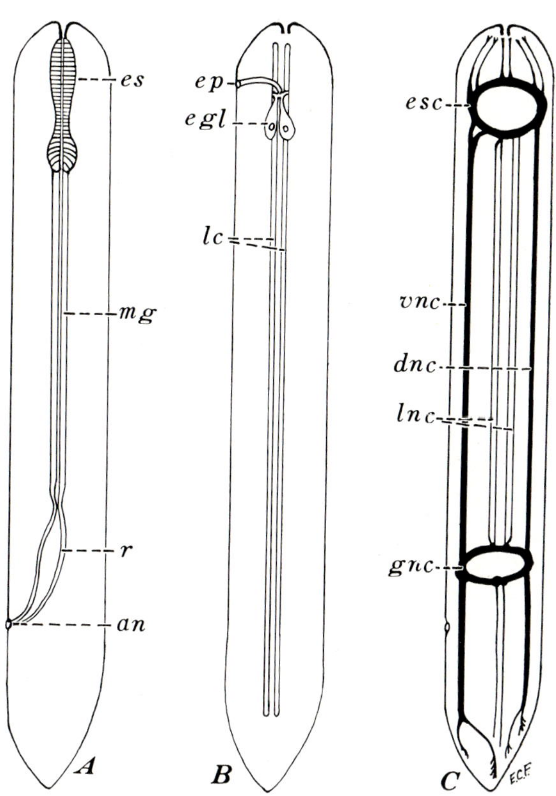

FIG. 59.—Diagrammatic representations of *A*, digestive system, *B*, excretory system and *C*, nervous system of nematodes, viewed from the left side. *an*, anal pore; *dnc*, dorsal nerve cord; *egl*, paired subventral excretory gland; *ep*, excretory pore; *es*, esophagus; *esc*, circum-esophageal nerve commissure; *gnc*, genital nerve commissure; *lc*, paired lateral excretory canal; *lnc*, lateral nerve cords; *mg*, midgut; *r*, rectum; *vnc*, ventral nerve cord. (Original adaptations.)

The *excretory system* (Fig. 59 *B*) consists fundamentally of two longitudinal tubules embedded in the lateral longitudinal cords. These tubules end blindly at their posterior ends; anteriorly they have a transverse ventral connection with a single mid-ventral opening close behind the mouth.

The *nervous system* (Fig. 59 *C*) is composed of a central circum-esophageal commissure (the "brain"), six short anterior trunks and six long posterior trunks which unite near the caudal extremity. There are numerous transverse commissures.

Cuticular organs of peculiar importance in the nematodes are the amphids and the phasmids. The *amphids*, regarded as sensory receptors, consist of a pair of minute, lateral bodies at the anterior end of the worm, each with an external chamber which may be a simple pore, or a circular, spiral, helical or elongate tubule. One large group of nematodes (the Phasmidia) possess a pair of caudal organs called *phasmids*, which are post-anal in position.

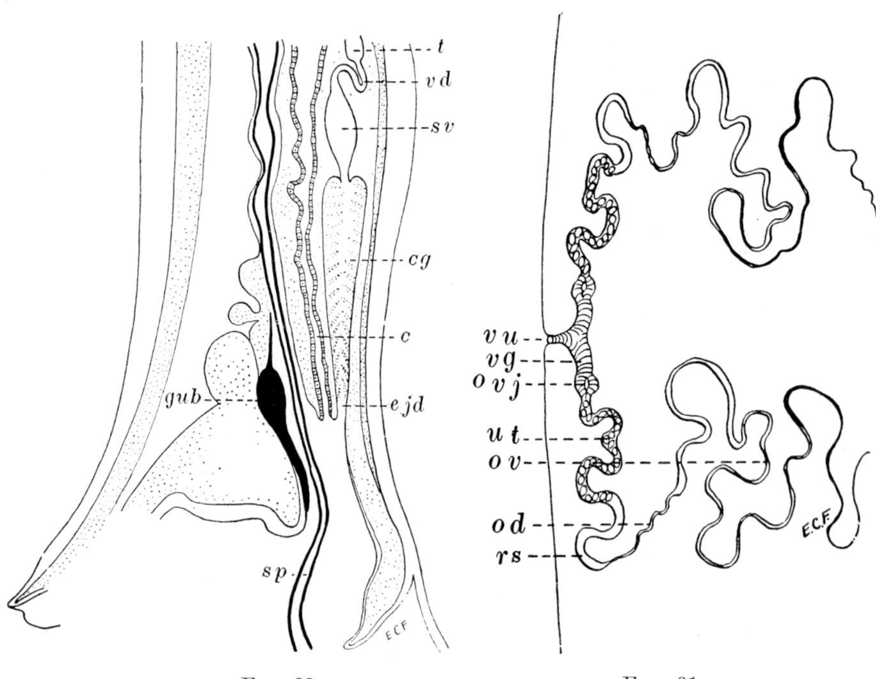

FIG. 60. FIG. 61.

FIG. 60.—Lateral view through the posterior end of male hookworm (*Ancylostoma duodenale*). *c*, posterior terminus of intestine (rectum); *cg*, prostate gland; *ejd*, ejaculatory duct; *gub*, gubernaculum; *sp*, copulatory spicules, *sv*, seminal vesicle; *t*, testis; *vd*, vas deferens. (Original adaptation from Looss, in Faust's *Human Helminthology*, Lea & Febiger, Philadelphia.)

FIG. 61.—Lateral view of the female genitalia of the hookworm (*Ancylostoma duodenale*). *od*, oviduct; *ov*, ovary; *ovj*, ovejector; *rs*, seminal receptacle; *ut*, uterus; *vg*, vagina; *vu*, vulva. (Original adaptation from Looss, in Faust's *Human Helminthology*, Lea & Febiger, Philadelphia.)

The *reproductive organs* of nematodes are usually found in separate male and female individuals. However, in a few instances the male or the primary male organ is parasitic in the body of the female (*syngonic*), or the female may be *parthenogenetic*. In rare instances, *viz.*, *Syngamus* spp., male and female worms are joined in permanent coitus. Males are almost invariably somewhat smaller than females and may be very much smaller, as in *Dracunculus*.

The *male reproductive system* (Fig. 60) consists typically of a single tubule, beginning at its inner end as a testis (*t*), then a vas deferens (*vd*), a seminal vesicle (*sv*), and an ejaculatory duct (*ejd*). This duct is lined with cement (prostate) glands (*cg*) and opens into the cloaca, which also receives the wastes from the rectum (c). Accessory copulatory structures consist of one, or more frequently a pair of copulatory spicules (*sp*), which may be of equal length and bristle-like or unequal and lancet-shaped, and commonly a regulatory structure, the gubernaculum (*gub*). In some species the cloaca is guarded by a genital cone. In hookworms and their relatives the posterior end of the male is extended into an umbrella-like structure of cuticle supported by fleshy rays (*bursa copulatrix*), which is applied around the vulva of the female at the time of insemination.

The *female reproductive system* (Fig. 61) may be composed of a single reproductive set (*viz.*, *Trichocephalus*) but in most nematodes it is bicornuate. It is tubular and is frequently coiled back and forth several times within the body cavity, so that its total length may be considerably longer than that of the worm. The following regions can usually be recognized: ovary (*ov*), oviduct (*od*), seminal receptacle (*rs*), uterus (*ut*), ovejector (*oj*) and vagina (*va*), all usually paired, and a single vulva (*vu*), which is midventral in position at, or anterior to the equatorial plane.

The *ovum* (unfertilized egg) originates from a multinucleate mass of protoplasm at the inner end of the delicate ovarian tubule. It is characteristically provided with yolk material. After passing down the oviduct the ovum is fertilized in the seminal receptacle. Immediately thereafter the essential shell layers are secreted by the egg itself, an inner, very resistant, thin vitelline membrane of sterol substance, and a somewhat thicker chorionic layer composed of chitin. In some roundworms such as *Ascaris* an additional albuminoid outer layer is laid on as a secretion from the uterine wall.

The daily production of eggs per female is approximately related to the size of the worm and the length of the uterus. The stage of development at the time of discharge from the vulva varies considerably. Eggs of *Ascaris* and *Trichocephalus* are completely unembryonated; those of hookworms are in the early stage of cell cleavage, and those of *Strongyloides* are frequently in the morula stage. *Trichinella* and *Dracunculus* discharge living young, *i. e.*, they are *larviparous*. Filaria worms give birth to microfilarias, prelarval snake-like embryos.

Life Cycle of Roundworms.—Nematodes are by no means all parasitic in their mode of life. The fundamental stages are the adult worm, the egg and larval stages.

Several groups of parasitic nematodes require two hosts. In the case of *Trichinella spiralis* all stages in the life cycle are completed in one host but infection of a new host is dependent on consumption of the larvas encapsulated in the striated muscles of the first host. *Dracunculus* infection in the definitive host results from ingesting water fleas (Cyclops) which harbor the larval stage. Blood-sucking arthropods are the required intermediate hosts of the filaria worms.

When entry into the definitive host takes place by the cutaneous route, the larva is a delicate, post-feeding, thread-like object, the *filariform stage*, which is adapted to skin penetration; when it is by the oral route the infective larva, the *rhabditoid stage*, is usually more robust, has a functional digestive tract, and is still within the egg shell, has previously hatched on the ground, or, in the case of *Trichinella*, is encapsulated in muscle tissue.

The order in which the intestinal roundworms will be considered is that presented in Table 1 (pages 17 to 18). For etiologic classification the reader is referred to Chapter 3, pages 29 to 31.

Enterobius Vermicularis (Linnaeus, 1758) Leach, 1853

(The human pinworm or seatworm, causing enterobiasis or oxyuriasis.)

Historical and Geographical Notes

This worm has been known since ancient times. It has a cosmopolitan distribution but is more common in persons living in cool or temperate zones than in strictly tropical areas.

Epidemiology

Pinworm infection is more prevalent in large family groups, in schools, asylums and mental institutions than it is in the population at large. Eggs containing almost mature larvas are deposited by the female worms after they migrate out the anus onto the perianal and perineal skin. Within 6 hours or less these eggs are fully infective. Exposure may occur in any of four ways: (1) The person harboring the infection may scratch the contaminated skin in an attempt to relieve itching of the area, and transfer the eggs on finger tips to the mouth; (2) individuals sleeping in the same bed or bedroom, or using the same toilet, may be exposed from fomites contaminated by the patient; (3) eggs which get into air currents from soiled undergarments in a dormitory or school room may be breathed into the mouths of a large number of persons, who usually acquire light infection, and (4) eggs may occasionally hatch in moist perianal folds and the emerging larvas crawl into the rectum and up to the cecal area, where they develop into mature worms. The theory of internal autoinfection has been discarded (Madsen, 1945).

Cool, moist atmosphere with little or no ventilation is optimal for survival of the eggs on fomites, while dry heat and good ventilation produce rapid death of the enclosed larvas (Jacobs, 1942; Heller, 1944).

Enterobius vermicularis infection is much commoner in children than in adults, and is particularly prevalent where several small children sleep together. High incidence is likewise invariably found in mental hospitals. In any population in which feces-soiled underclothing is worn day after day, where bathing is infrequent and where there are one or more carriers of the infection, a large percentage of the group will be found infected. The incidence of oxyuriasis ranges from saturation to a relatively incidental figure, depending on the environmental conditions and the level of personal and group hygiene.

Morphology, Biology and Life Cycle

The oral tip of the adult *E. vermicularis* is provided with three lips which are retractable into the minute oral vestibule. Likewise at the anterior end of the worm there are a dorsal and a ventral bladder-like inflation of the cuticle (Beaver, 1952).

The male worm (Fig. 62 *A*) measures 2 to 5 mm. long and has a maximum width of 0.1 to 0.2 mm. With its strongly curved posterior end, the lateral view of the worm forms an inverted question mark. The female worm (Fig. 62 *B*) is considerably larger than the male, having a length of 8 to

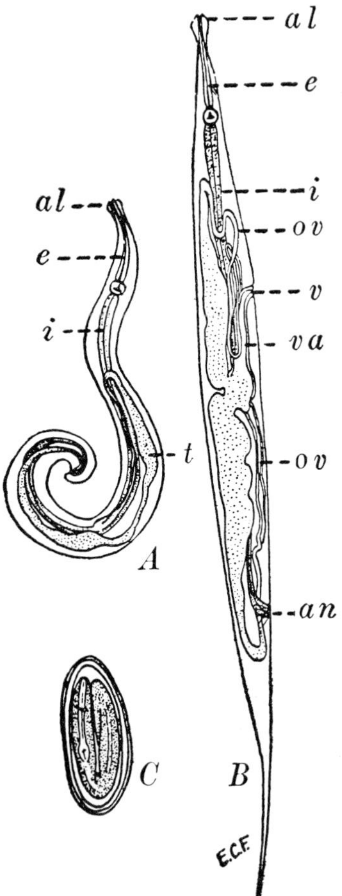

FIG. 62.—*Enterobius vermicularis* (pinworm or seatworm). *A*, male, *B*, female, showing digestive and reproductive system; *C*, embryonated egg. *al*, anterior dorsal and ventral cuticular swellings; *an*, anus; *e*, esophagus; *i*, midgut; *ov*, ovary; *t*, testis; *v*, vulva; *va*, vagina. The distended bicornuate enlargement in the female genitalia is the uterus. *A*, *B* × 16; *C*, × 280. (*A*, *B* adapted from Leuckart, in Faust's *Human Helminthology*, Lea & Febiger, Philadelphia.)

13 mm. and a maximum width of 0.3 to 0.5 mm. The sharply pointed post-anal portion occupies nearly one-third of the total length.

The characteristic habitat of these worms is at the cecal level of the intestine, where they are rather insecurely attached to the mucosa. If only a few worms are present they are most likely to be in the appendix; if there is a larger number they may extend into the cecum and ascending colon. Gravid females migrate down the bowel and out of the anus onto the perianal and perineal skin; in female subjects they may reach the vulva and wander up the genital tract, at times reaching the inner end of the tubules and the peritoneal cavity.

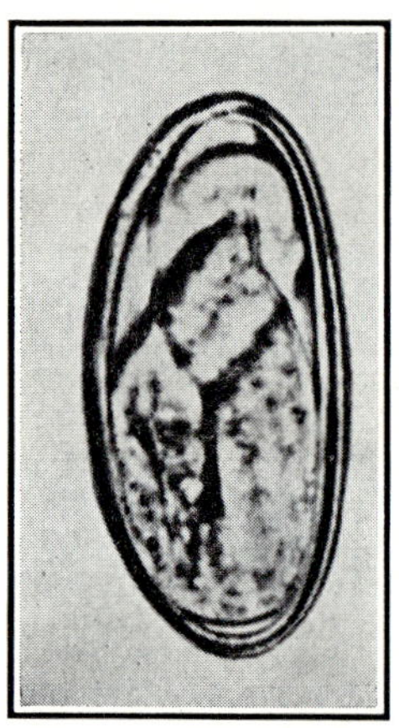

Fig. 63.—Photomicrograph of fully embryonated egg of *Enterobius vermicularis* lateral view, obtained by perianal swabbing. × 800. (From Cram, *Introduction to Nematology,* in Craig and Faust's *Clinical Parasitology,* Lea & Febiger, Philadelphia.)

The eggs *in utero* are unembryonated until the female worms arrive at the lower levels of the colon. Hence the occasional batches of eggs which are laid within the bowel are relatively immature (Heller, 1946). Fully developed eggs are characteristically deposited on the perianal skin. Each female has been found to discharge an average of about 11,000 eggs (Reardon, 1938).

The eggs discharged on the skin (Fig. 63) are essentially mature and contain a fully developed first-stage larva. They are flattened on the ventral side and convex dorsally. They measure 50 to 60 by 20 to 30 microns, and are provided with a double shell, an inner embryonic membrane and an outer albuminous one which causes them to stick together. The tickling or itching produced by ovipositing pinworms crawling on the skin almost inevitably provokes scratching, so that the eggs become attached to the finger tips or get under the nails, become temporarily stuck to soiled clothing and bed linen, or get in air currents and settle on tops of objects in the room. Thus, some of the eggs almost invariably reach the mouth of persons in the contaminated environment and are swallowed. In the duodenum the eggs hatch and from each there emerges a stout rhabditoid larva which measures 140 to 150 by 10 microns. It slowly passes down the small intestine, meanwhile undergoing two moults. On reaching the cecal level the adolescent worms mate, become attached to the mucosa and develop to maturity. One complete life cycle may require as short a period as 15 to 28 days (Cram, 1943), although Schüffner and Swellengrebel (1949) consider 43 days to be the expected prepatent period.

Pathogenesis and Symptomatology

At the sites of attachment to the wall of the appendix or elsewhere in the cecal area the worms may cause multiple focal inflammation of an acute or chronic catarrhal nature, or by necrosis of the cecal mucosa and exposure of sympathetic nerve endings be responsible for reflex nervous symptoms. Commonly the first recognizable symptom is an almost intolerable pruritus as the worms emerge from the rectum and crawl over the perianal and perineal skin. The itching is followed by scratching which adds to the irritation, with scarification or weeping eczema of the area, and allows bacteria to enter the lesion. At times in female subjects worms enter the genital tract and become encapsulated within the Fallopian tubules, or wander into the peritoneal cavity and become encapsulated on the peritoneum.

The common symptoms in children consist of insomnia or restless sleep, tiredness during the daytime, nymphomania in girls and nycturia in boys. In addition, nervous symptoms may occur.

The blood picture in pinworm infection is not remarkably altered. There may be a slight anemia and a low-grade eosinophilia.

Diagnosis

Specific diagnosis may be made on recovery of the worms from the perianal area or following an enema, more frequently on demonstration of the eggs (Fig. 63). Only occasionally are they found in the stool.

The Scotch-tape "swab" technic for recovery of pinworm eggs has been demonstrated to be the most satisfactory (Beaver, 1949). (See "TECHNICAL AIDS," page 586.) These preparations are more likely to be positive when the "swabs" are taken before the morning stool has been passed and before the bath.

Treatment

Since oxyuriasis is a familial and environmental infection, satisfactory results with chemotherapeutics can be obtained only in case all infected individuals in the household are discovered and treated simultaneously.

Soap-saline or quassia-chips infusion enemas may evacuate some of the worms but are only temporarily helpful. Various anthelmintics effective in other intestinal roundworm infections are likewise not particularly helpful in eradicating pinworms.

The standard treatment consists in the administration of *gentian violet medicinal* in 4-hour Seal-Ins or Enseals coating. The usual adult course is 65 mgm. (1 grain) taken three times daily with meals for 8 days, followed by 1 week's rest, then administration of the drug for another 8 days. For children the daily dosage is 1 cgm. for each year of apparent, not chronologic age. The enteric tablets are available in the following sizes: 1 cgm. ($\frac{3}{20}$ grain), 1.2 cgm. ($\frac{1}{5}$ grain), and 3 cgm. ($\frac{1}{2}$ grain). If all infected members of a group take the full course of treatment, 90 to 92% cures may be expected (Wright, Brady and Bozicevich, 1938; D'Antoni and Sawitz, 1940; Chanco, 1943). Peterson and Fahey (1945) who employed this drug for three successive 8-day courses in treating 1,100 pinworm patients among 1,871 inmates in a Minnesota mental hospital, reported 9% positive after the first course, 1% after the second and only 0.2% after the third. Difficulties in obtaining optimal results are twofold: (1) Some infected individuals fail to coöperate, and (2) some are unable to complete treatment because of side effects such as nausea and vomiting, abdominal cramps, diarrhea or constipation.

The first 8-day course with gentian violet is usually adequate to kill the worm in the intestine. The week of rest between the first and second 8-day periods of treatment allows any residual viable eggs in the environment to be ingested and hatch, so that the second course will then kill the new invaders.

Recently Brown and associates (Brown, 1952) have demonstrated that oxytetracycline (*Terramycin*) is as effective as gentian violet for eradicating pinworms, with a cure rate approaching 100% if all infected persons take the full course.

For small children unable to swallow capsules, powdered Terramycin may be spread on bread.

Piperazine hexahydrate, administered to children in the amount of 250 mgm. per day per year of life in a flavored syrup, for 7 days, then repeated after one week, was found by White and Standen (1953) to be as effective as gentian violet in curing oxyuriasis, and is essentially nontoxic.

Phenothiazine is also highly effective in eliminating pinworms but should not be administered to children, since it produces a rapidly developing hemolytic anemia (Kuitunen-Ekbaum, 1946; Deschiens and Lamy, 1947).

Diphenan and *Egressin* are essentially nontoxic but are ineffective in eradicating the worms.

Scarification and inflammation of the perianal and perineal skin should be treated with mild antiseptic ointments. Acute or subacute appendicitis due to pinworms may require surgical intervention.

Prognosis

This is invariably good provided the infection can be eradicated from the individual and his environment.

Control

The infection can be controlled by a twofold method of attack, *viz.*, personal and group hygiene on the one hand and mass chemotherapy on the other.

Infection in a family group can be appreciably reduced by developing habits of personal hygiene in the children; by providing small children with closed sleeping garments so that their fingers will not come directly in contact with the perianal skin; by keeping the finger nails short and by insisting that children scrub their hands thoroughly after each visit to the toilet and before meals.

Chemotherapy as outlined above under "Treatment" will provide relatively effective control if all infected persons are treated simultaneously and if all in the group take a complete course of the anthelmintic.

Syphacia Obvelata (Rudolphi, 1802) Seurat, 1916

This pinworm of rats and mice is an occasional human parasite. The adult worms somewhat resemble *Enterobius vermicularis* but are considerably smaller. Moreover, males as well as females have a long attenuated tail and the post-anal region of the male is coiled ventrally about 360 degrees. The worms live in the cecal and colonic levels of the large intestine. The eggs are shed in the perianal region in a fully embryonated state. They resemble those of *E. vermicularis* but are much larger (125 by 40 microns). Human infection probably results from contamination with rat or mouse droppings containing the eggs. Measures to eradicate rats or mice from the home provide control.

Trichocephalus Trichiurus (Linnæus, 1771) Blanchard, 1891 or **Trichuris Trichiura** (Linnæus, 1771) Stiles, 1901

(The human whipworm, causing trichocephaliasis or trichuriasis)

Historical and Geographical Notes

The human whipworm was first specifically described and named by Linnæus in 1771. Its life cycle was studied by Grassi (1887) and later by Fülleborn (1923) and Hasegawa (1924), and that of the related species (*T. vulpis*) in the dog by Miller (1941).

T. trichiurus is cosmopolitan in its distribution but is prevalent only in warm or temperate moist climates.

Epidemiology

Eggs of the whipworm are evacuated in the stool in an unembryonated condition and require a period of development on the ground to reach the infective stage. Conditions favorable for development of the egg consist of a moist, shaded, warm soil. A period of about 21 days is required until an active first-stage larva is coiled inside the egg shell. The egg is now infective when introduced into the mouth as a contamination of food or drink, adhering to play objects or candy dropped on the egg-infested ground and later taken into the mouth, or as a result of dirt eating.

In highly endemic foci small children develop heavy infection (Jung and Beaver, 1952), yet the greatest prevalence and heaviest worm burden characteristically occur in children of school age who contaminate the soil with their feces and later pick up the inoculum from the same or similar polluted sites. In countries where trichocephaliasis is endemic adults with primitive personal hygiene also have high incidence and heavy infection.

Human infection probably results exclusively from exposure to infective-stage eggs derived from human sources.

Morphology, Biology and Life Cycle

The adult whipworms (Fig. 64) have a capillary anterior three-fifths and a more fleshy posterior portion of the body. The anterior end is securely threaded into the intestinal mucosa, typically of the cecum and appendix, but if there are a large number of worms they are distributed posteriorwards through the colon and even the rectum. Typically *Trichocephalus* has a life expectation of several years in the intestine.

The male (Fig. 64 *A*) measures 30 to 45 mm. in length. Its more fleshy posterior end is curved ventrally into a watch-spring coil of 360 degrees or more. The female (Fig. 64 *B*) measure 35 to 50 mm. in length. Its more fleshy posterior portion is club-shaped.

The daily egg output of the ovipositing female is not definitely known but the average probably lies between 3,000 and 6,000. Reduced production may be expected in infections where the worms are close together and the parasitized intestinal mucosa is badly damaged.

The barrel-shaped eggs (Fig. 64 *C*) are laid in the one-celled stage. They possess a transparent inner shell, a golden-brownish outer shell and have a transparent blister-like prominence at each pole. When the fertilized eggs are evacuated in the stool on moist, shaded, sandy humus, they proceed normally with embryonation. The period of survival of these eggs on the soil is relatively short.

When viable infective-stage eggs are taken into the mouth and swallowed, hatching occurs in the duodenum. The delicately muscular larva temporarily enters the nearby intestinal crypts and secures harborage and nourishment by penetrating into the glands and stroma (Miller, 1941). For about 10 days, young worms are found in these locations at successively lower levels of the small intestine, and soon thereafter begin to appear in the cecum and appendix where they become attached. Approximately 90 days after the eggs are ingested the worms have matured, have copulated and a new cycle has begun.

Pathogenesis and Symptomatology

At each site where the worm's head is basted into the intestinal mucosa there is a small focus of tissue damage, and a petechial hemorrhage if the head of the worm has penetrated into a blood capillary. Moreover, there is some evidence that a digestive enzyme is secreted by the worm and that blood-sucking at times occurs. A few discrete lesions are relatively unimportant and produce no appreciable symptoms unless the patient is highly sensitive to systemic absorption of the worm's metabolites.

As the number of attached worms increases there is a corresponding amount of intestinal damage. In heavy infections the mucosa of the entire large bowel is typically covered with the squirming wiry organisms, matted together in slimy, bloody feces. The mucosa itself is hyperemic, at times

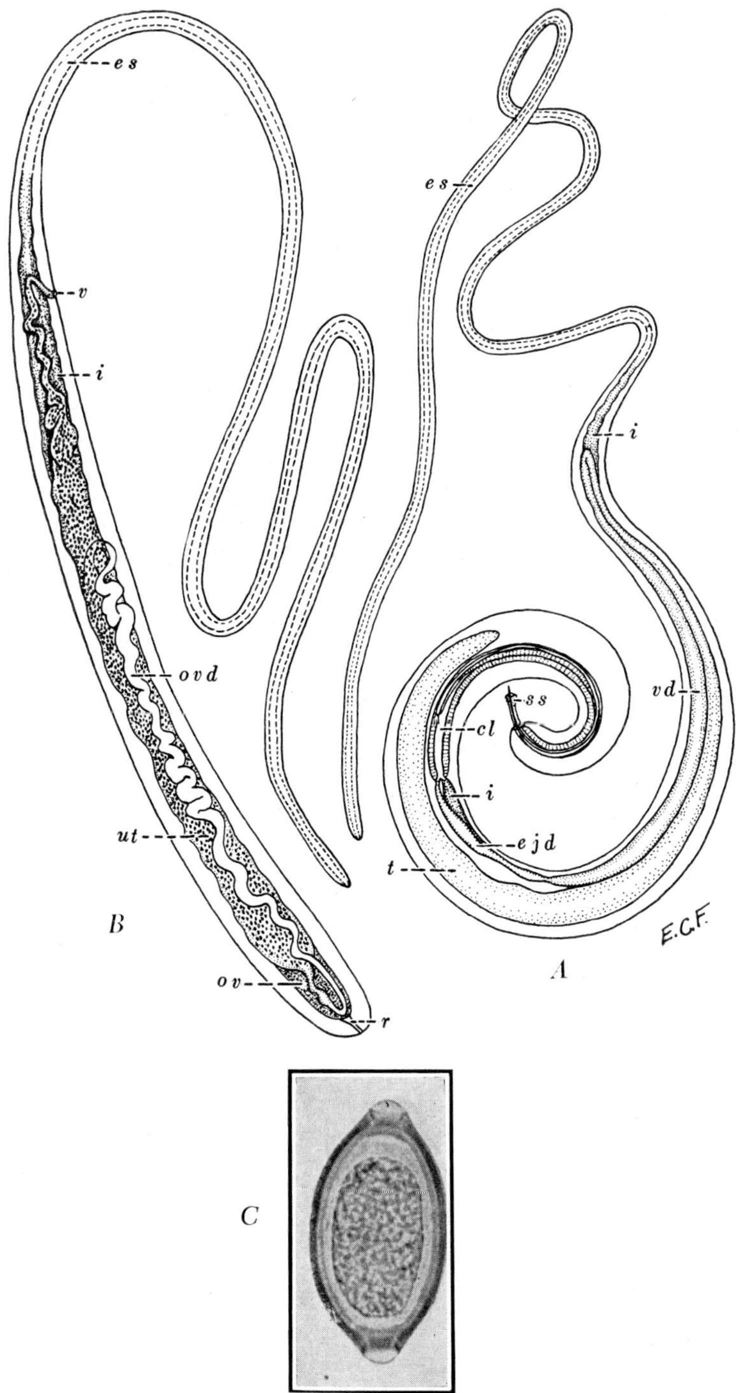

Fig. 64.—*Trichocephalus trichiurus* (whipworm). *A*, male, *B*, female, showing digestive and reproductive systems; *C*, photomicrograph of unembryonated egg evacuated in the stool. *cl*, cloaca; *ejd*, ejaculatory duct; *es*, esophagus; *i*, midgut; *ov*, ovary; *ovd*, oviduct; *r*, rectum; *ss*, copulatory spicules and sheath; *t*, testis; *ut*, uterus; *v*, vulva; *vd*, vas deferens. *A*, *B*, × 12; *C*, × 666. (In Faust's *Human Helminthology*, Lea & Febiger, Philadelphia; *C*, after Faust, courtesy, W. F. Prior Co.)

bleeding and superficially eroded, and may bear evidence of extensive inflammation. Irritation produced by these worms in the wall of the lower colon and rectum will eventually provoke prolapse of the rectum (Fig. 65).

Symptoms attributed to *Trichocephalus* infection include abdominal or epigastric discomfort, abdominal distension, flatulence, loss of appetite and weight, emaciation, anorexia, nausea, vomiting, appendicitis syndrome, mucous diarrhea, dysentery, anemia, leukocytosis and evidences of allergy such as eosinophilia and urticarial fever (Pallister, 1933; Corrêa and Melloné, 1938; Swartzwelder, 1939; Ross, 1942; Plessen, 1945; Whittier *et al.*, 1945). Basic malnutrition or amebic colitis not infrequently complicates the clinical picture.

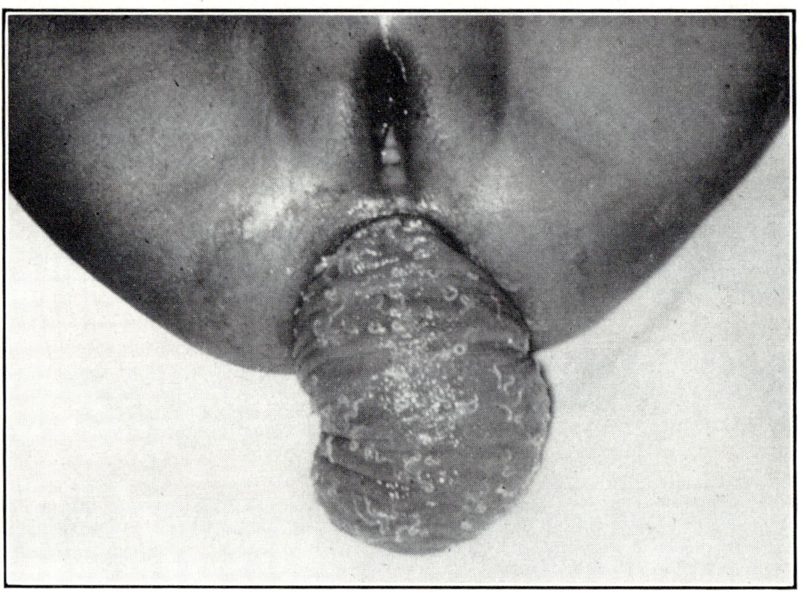

Fig. 65.—Prolapse of rectum in a Louisiana child, due to heavy infection with *Trichocephalus trichiurus*. (Courtesy of Dr. J. C. Swartzwelder.)

Jung and Beaver (1952) studied whipworm infection in 352 children 1 to 11 years of age in the Charity Hospital of Louisiana in New Orleans; these patients constituted 18% of 2,000 hospitalized children whose stools were currently being examined for parasites. The heavily infected individuals, with more than 30,000 eggs per cc. of stool and a calculated number of worms in excess of 200, suffered from chronic diarrhea or dysentery, and several had prolapse of the rectum.

Clinical trichocephaliasis is by no means rare in the warm humid coastal areas of the Southern United States, and at times is as severe as it is in tropical countries.

Diagnosis

Diagnosis of whipworm infection is made on demonstration of the characteristic eggs (Fig. 64 *C*) recovered from the stool.

Treatment

Most orally administered anthelmintics for the treatment of whipworm infection fail to reach the large intestine in sufficient concentration to be lethal to whipworms, which are frequently covered with slimy feces. To lessen this difficulty the author has recommended good saline purgation the night before treatment and in the morning a high retention enema to clear out residual mucus from around the worms. Then on an empty stomach the following anthelmintic mixture is administered: 9 parts of tetrachlorethylene and 1 part of oil of chenopodium, in the amount of 3 minims per year of age up to 15 years, when the adult dose of 3 cc. is given (Table 5, page 66). Two hours later a follow-up saline purge is recommended. No food or carbonated drink is permitted until good evacuation of the bowels has been produced. This treatment may be safely repeated in 1 week.

In case there is heavy whipworm infection, the following emulsion, administered as a high retention enema, will probably be more satisfactory: 1 Gm. of hexylresorcinol crystoids in 300 cc. of a 10% mucilage of acacia, to which 30 Gm. of fine kaolin may be added to minimize colonic cramps. (Table 5, page 66.) If the patient weighs more than 100 pounds, 600 cc. is recommended (Basnuevo, 1951, 1952). Several of these enemas may be required to remove all of the worms.

For debilitated patients or those suffering from malnutrition, a diet rich in animal proteins and vitamins is advised. Anemic persons may require iron supplements and at times transfusions of whole blood.

Prognosis

This is good to fair for lightly infected persons but is at times poor unless the worms are removed; in most cases the outcome is excellent following satisfactory anthelmintic medication.

Control

Whipworm infection is controllable. Reduction in exposure can be accomplished by providing clean toilet facilities for small children as well as adults, and educating all age groups to use these facilities consistently.

Capillaria Hepatica (Bancroft, 1893) Travassos, 1915
(The capillary liver worm)

This relative of the whipworm is a tissue parasite in the liver of domestic and wild mammals. The adult worms are considerably more delicate than *Trichocephalus trichiurus*. The eggs, measuring 51 to 67.5 microns by 30 to 35 microns, resemble those of *T. trichiurus* but have an outer shell perforated by minute pores. They are deposited in the hepatic parenchyma, where they embryonate. Subsequently another host becomes infected from consuming the carcass or through food or drink contaminated with decomposed viscera of an infected animal. The larva hatched from the egg in the duodenum of the new host enters the intestinal wall and migrates *via* mesenteric-portal blood to the liver, penetrates into periportal tissues and matures in 27 to 28 days.

From time to time eggs of this parasite have been found in specimens of human feces. Foster and Johnson (1939) believe that such spurious infection results from eating cooked livers of infected animals such as the peccary and monkeys.

Two genuine human infections with liver involvement have been reported in the medical literature, one in a British soldier in India (MacArthur, 1924), the other in a native of Louisiana (McQuown, 1950). The pathologic picture is that of an acute or subacute hepatitis, suggesting viral or amebic etiology. Diagnosis is postmortem. There is no known therapy. Prevention consists in avoiding consumption of raw livers of reservoir hosts.

Ascaris Lumbricoides Linnæus, 1758

(The giant intestinal roundworm, causing ascariasis)

Historical and Geographical Notes

Ascaris lumbricoides has been known to physicians since the dawn of history, partly because of its size and partly because of the extensive distribution of the infection. Davaine (1863) first discovered that fully mature *Ascaris* eggs hatch in the small intestine and Stewart (1916) showed that the hatched larvas require a migration to the lungs before they complete their development in the intestine. Ransom and Foster (1917) and Ransom and Cram (1921) demonstrated that the entire life cycle for the porcine variety takes place in a single natural host and Koino (1922) provided similar information for the human variety.

Ascaris lumbricoides is the most widely prevalent of all human roundworm infections and occurs endemically in all parts of the world except in cold, dry climates. Although the highest frequency of ascariasis is found in tropical areas, at times approaching saturation, it is also common in many temperate regions of the world, including rural and urban groups in the southeastern United States.

Epidemiology

Ascariasis is a disease due to human filth. In most hyperendemic areas infected small children in and around the home provide the major source for the infection by their promiscuous defecation in the dooryard, under the verandas and on the floor of the house (Cort, 1931; Otto, 1932; Headlee, 1936). These excreta contain the eggs, which are relatively resistant to desiccation and putrefaction. Embryonation takes place on hard clay soil as well as on loam. Infective-stage eggs remain viable for weeks or months, even surviving short periods of freezing (Headlee, 1936); only the direct heat of the sun is detrimental to them. When viable, fully embryonated eggs are picked up on fingers, candy or play objects dropped on polluted ground, or as a result of dirt-eating, and get into the mouth; they initiate infection as soon as they reach the small intestine.

An important additional source of exposure exists in regions of the world where human nightsoil is used to fertilize garden and field crops. Both the persons who handle the excreta and others who consume unprocessed green vegetables and fruits such as strawberries are liable to infection.

Hogs infected with *Ascaris* probably constitute a negligible source for human infection.

Morphology, Biology and Life Cycle

The adult *Ascaris* is the largest roundworm parasitizing the human intestinal tract (Fig. 58). It is elongated, cylindrical and tapers both

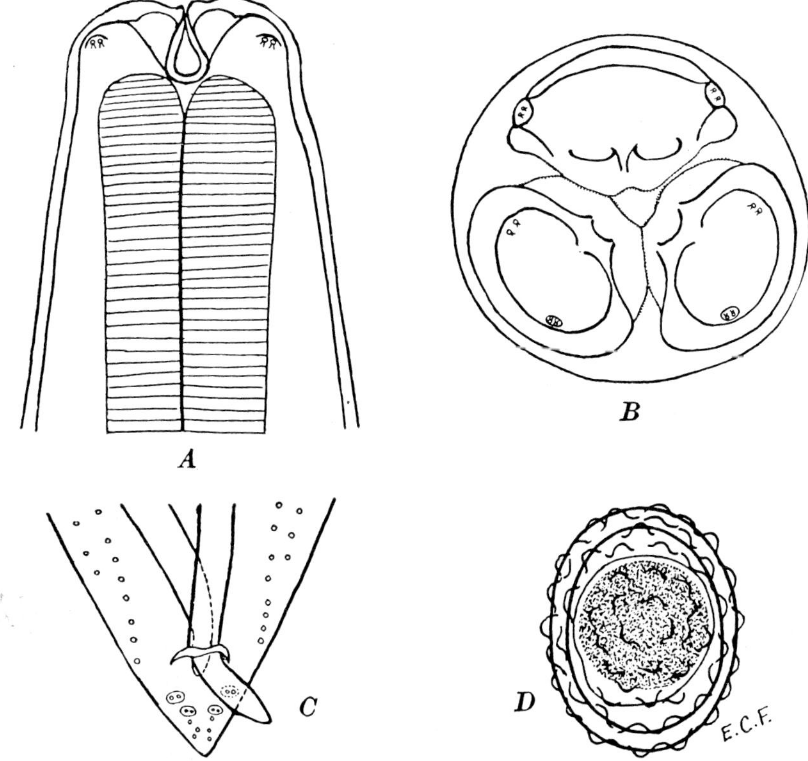

Fig. 66.—Diagnostic features of *Ascaris lumbricoides*. *A*, anterior extremity, ventral view; *B*, head-on view showing the 3 lips; *C*, posterior end of male, ventral view; showing the two copulatory spicules and the caudal papillæ; *D*, fertile egg, typical one-cell stage at time of evacuation in the stool. *A*, × 46; *B*, × 56; *C*, × 45; *D*, × 500. (After Yorke and Maplestone, in Faust's *Human Helminthology*, Lea & Febiger, Philadelphia.)

anteriorly and posteriorly to relatively blunt conical ends. The head (Fig. 66 *B*) is provided with three fleshy lips.

The male worm measures 15 to 31 cm. in length by 2 to 4 mm. in greatest diameter. Its posterior end is curved somewhat ventrally. The female worm measures 20 to 35 cm. in length by 3 to 6 mm. in greatest diameter, but specimens up to 40 cm. are occasionally observed. The daily egg production per female averages about 200,000.

The fertilized egg of *A. lumbricoides* (Figs. 66 *D*, 67, *1*) at the time of oviposition is broadly ovoidal, measures 45 to 75 microns by 35 to 50 microns, and consists of the following structures: (1) a coarsely granular, spherical egg cell which is separated from the shell at its two ends by a semi-lunar space; (2) a thin, innermost, lipoidal fertilization membrane, which is highly impermeable; (3) a relatively thick, transparent middle layer, which serves as a supporting structure and is believed to consist of chitin, and (4) an outermost, coarsely mammillated, albuminoid layer, laid down *in utero*, serving as an auxiliary barrier to permeable substances (Jaskoski, 1952).

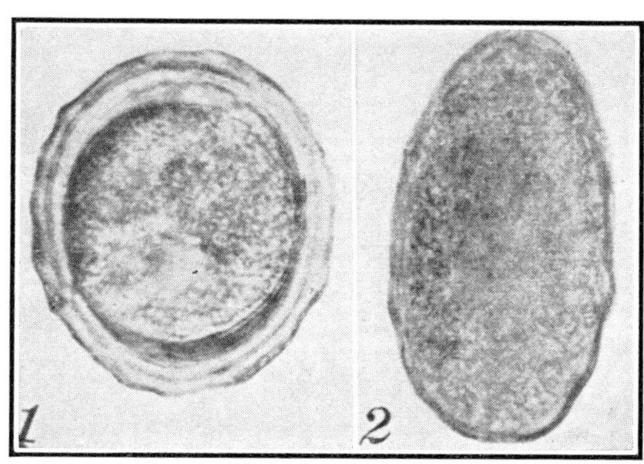

Fig. 67.—Photomicrographs of eggs of *Ascaris lumbricoides*. *1*, fertilized; *2*, infertile. × 600. (After Faust, courtesy of W. F. Prior Co., in Faust's *Human Helminthology*, Lea & Febiger, Philadelphia.)

Female worms without males, and at times young fertilized females, produce infertile eggs (Fig. 67, *2*), which are typically narrower and more elliptical (88 to 93.5 microns by 38.5 to 44 microns) than fertilized eggs. Internally they contain a mass of disorganized granules and globules which completely fill the shell.

Both fertile and infertile eggs are usually bile-stained by the time they are evacuated in the feces. The fertile eggs of *A. lumbricoides* are passed in the one-cell stage. They survive putrefaction and can withstand considerable desiccation and cold. In a cold dry climate they are dormant. At temperatures of 40° C. and above the embryos are soon killed, but at 22° C. to 33° C. complete development to the first-stage rhabditoid larva occurs in 9 to 13 days. During this period the outer shell layer is lost. Another week is required for the first moult, after which the eggs are infective and contain motile second-stage rhabditoid larvas. These eggs may remain viable on the soil for months and even years.

Exposure to *Ascaris* infection results from ingestion of the viable mature eggs. On reaching the duodenum the eggs hatch and the emerging robust larvas penetrate into the nearby intestinal wall, enter mesenteric venules or lymphatics and *via* the inferior vena cava or thoracic duct reach the chambers of the right heart and pass through the pulmonary vessels to the capillaries, where they are filtered out. In a few days, they perforate into the alveoli and after about 10 days, during which growth and two additional ecdyses take place, stout fourth-stage rhabditoid larvas migrate up the respiratory tree to the epiglottis, crawl over into the esophagus and are swallowed. On reaching the small intestine a final ecdysis occurs and the worms develop into adult males and females. The period from exposure to maturity in the appropriate host requires 8 to 12 weeks (Vogel and Minning, 1942).

Pathogenesis and Symptomatology

Stage of Larval Migration.—The passage from the intestine to the lungs provokes no remarkable pathologic changes, although at times there may be a transient hepatitis while the larvas are passing through the hepatic capillaries. As each larva breaks out of the pulmonary capillaries into the air sacs a minute hemorrhage is produced. In case many young worms are migrating simultaneously through the lungs the traumatic damage is considerable. More significant is the intense local cellular reaction around the larvas in the air sacs, with infiltration of eosinophils, epithelioid cells and macrophages, and the production of a distinctive type of pulmonary pathology, *viz.*, *Ascaris* pneumonitis. Although the larvas are seldom permanently trapped in the alveoli, their metabolites in intimate contact with the tissues initiate a generalized *Ascaris* sensitization.

The cardinal symptoms associated with larval *Ascaris* pneumonitis consist of dyspnea, usually of the asthmatic type; a dry or productive cough; râles, frequently musical and wheezing, or coarse, rarely crepitant; fever, moderate to 40° C.; usually a long-lasting, significant eosinophilia, and x-ray findings showing scattered mottling of the lungs, suggesting a possible diagnosis of pulmonary tuberculosis or viral pneumonia (Jung, 1953). This picture differs from Loeffler's syndrome in which the pathologic changes of the lungs are milder, are of shorter duration (3 to 8 days) and the subjective symptoms are less conspicuous; from tropical pulmonary eosinophilia, particularly with respect to the therapeutic response to arsenicals, and from visceral larva migrans (see pages 277–279) in which there are associated eosinophilic granulomas in the liver and hyperglobulinemia, as well as pulmonary infiltration, cough, fever and peripheral eosinophilia.

The Adult Worms.—The maturing and adult worms live typically in the small intestine, deriving nourishment from semi-digested food, at times from mucosal tags and from blood which they occasionally suck out of the villi. The detrimental effect on the host's nutrition is approximately proportional to the number of worms. In light infections there may be no apparent pathologic changes, although even a single worm may produce intestinal disturbances. In the average infection in children there is intermittent intestinal colic, loss of appetite and weight, insomnia or disturbed sleep, fretfulness, and at times severe nervous symptoms. The abdomen in these patients is characteristically protuberant.

From time to time adult or immature *Ascaris* pass down the bowel and out of the anus, or up into the stomach to be vomited or emerge through the nares. During these excursions the worms may become lodged in the appendiceal lumen or perforate the intestinal wall (Fig. 68), may enter the ampulla of Vater and block the common bile duct, or penetrate into the parenchyma of the liver or the pancreas. On reaching the posterior pharynx a worm may be sucked into the respiratory tract and obstruct the larynx,

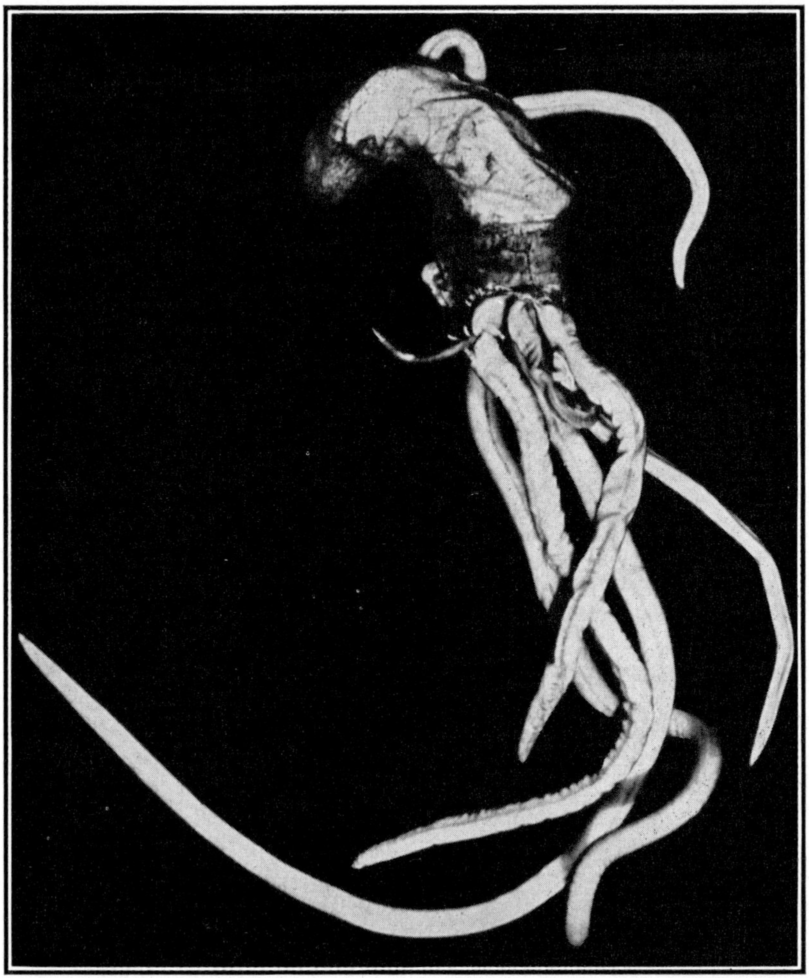

Fig. 68.—*Ascaris lumbricoides* in fatal case of acute abdomen of 6-year-old child. In addition to worms crowded into the greatly distended appendiceal lumen, 9 worms had migrated into the peritoneal cavity after perforation of the adjacent portion of the ileum. (From Faust's *Human Helminthology*, Lea & Febiger, Philadelphia.)

block a bronchus or penetrate into the pulmonary parenchyma and even the pleural cavity. *Ascaris* has also been found in the female genital tract and once in the heart. More frequently in small children a writhing mass of tangled worms produces an acute obstruction in the small bowel, which may be paralytic, spastic, intussusceptive or volvular in nature (Milwidsky, 1945).

These complications of intestinal ascariasis give rise to a variety of symptoms depending on the organs and tissues involved.

Rarely larvas which have migrated through the lungs may pass into the systemic circulation and reach ectopic sites, as in the vitreous or anterior chamber of the eye, and possibly the cerebral or renal blood vessels, with hemorrhage into adjacent tissues. More frequently referred symptoms are attributable to the toxic and allergenic metabolites absorbed from worms residing in the intestine.

The survival time of mature *A. lumbricoides* in the human intestine is relatively short, rarely exceeding a year. Yet in hyperendemic communities almost daily reëxposure is usual, so that new broods of larvas are migrating through the lungs and reaching the intestine to replace the previous mature one as soon as it is lost. Thus, there is a continuing intestinal infection in these patients, while sensitization phenomena are maintained potentially at a high clinical level.

The changes in the blood in cases of ascariasis consist in a prolonged moderate increase in eosinophils and possibly a low-grade anemia.

Ascariasis is frequently associated with whipworm and hookworm infection, and at times with amebiasis, as well as diseases due to other causes. These complicate the clinical picture and frequently prevent careful appraisal of the rôle played by the ascarids.

Diagnosis

During the biological incubation period specific diagnosis is not possible, although clinically the syndrome of larval *Ascaris* pneumonitis is relatively pathognomonic (Jung, 1953). Unfortunately this stage of the disease precedes the intestinal one by so many weeks that clinicians unaware of the relationship are apt to consider the pulmonary syndrome as an atypical pneumonia and treat it accordingly.

Once mature female worms are present in the intestine, the daily egg output of a single female, about 200,000, is suficient to reveal several characteristic eggs (Fig. 67) in an average unconcentrated cover-glass preparation of stool. In case only males are present (less than 5 per cent of infections) it is impossible to make specific identification preceding a therapeutic test. Mature *Ascaris* in extra-intestinal sites are rarely suspected as causal agents antecedent to exploratory surgery, even though a diagnosis of intestinal ascariasis has previously been made.

Treatment

Chemotherapy.—There is no conclusive evidence that any anthelmintic presently employed in intestinal ascariasis is lethal to the larval worms migrating through the lungs.

The standard treatment for intestinal ascariasis consists in the oral administration of *hexylresorcinol crystoids* in hard gelatin capsules. (See Table 5, page 66.) For satisfactory results the small intestine should be relatively free of food and feces, hence it is desirable to administer a saline purgative the night before treatment unless the patient is suffering from diarrhea or is severely dehydrated. The drug, in hard gelatin capsules, is administered on an empty stomach in the morning. Care must be taken that the capsules are not cracked open before they are swallowed, else there will be a painless superficial erosion of the buccal mucosa. The capsules may be placed on the back of the tongue of small children or in a small portion of fruit jelly, followed immediately by a drink of water. Two hours after the drug has been given, a follow-up saline purge is advised to hasten evacuation of the bowels and to prevent absorption of the worm's metabolites. Thereafter the patient may take a full meal. The therapeutic dose is 0.4 Gm. for children of pre-school age, 0.6 to 0.8 Gm. for school children up to 10 years of age, and 1.0 Gm. for older children and adults. One treatment has an average worm-removal rate of 84 to 92% and a cure rate of 75 to 80% (Lamson, Brown, Robbins and Ward, 1931). The treatment may be repeated safely any time subsequently to remove worms still present.

Several workers have employed diethyl carbamazine (*Hetrazan*) in the treatment of intestinal ascariasis. Etteldorf and Crawford (1950) in Memphis, Tennessee treated 15 lightly infected children, by administering 3 to 6 mgm. per kilo body weight orally three times daily for 7 to 11 days. Eleven patients were cured and the remaining four passed some worms. Hoekenga (1952) incorporated Hetrazan powder in syrup in a concentration of 30 mgm. per cc., and administered it to small Honduranian children in the amount of 26.4 mgm. per kilo body weight daily for 4 days. He reported 80% cures. This drug has the advantage that neither pre-treatment nor post-treatment purgation is required. It may also be useful in destroying larval ascarids migrating through the tissues.

Brown and Sterman (1954) have found *piperazine citrate* in syrup to be very effective in eliminating *Ascaris*. They state that "the preparation is highly acceptable to children, easily administered, and requires no fasting period."

Santonin, *Diphenan* and *Egressin* are all relatively safe chemotherapeutics but their *Ascaris*-removal rating is very low compared with hexylresorcinol crystoids. *Oil of chenopodium* is very effective but is highly toxic in therapeutic dosages (Jelliffe, 1951) and should not be administered for ascariasis.

Surgical Intervention.—In case there are symptoms of acute intestinal obstruction or perforation, appendicitis, gall bladder disease or other serious complication, anthelmintic medication and purgation are strictly contraindicated. The patient should be hospitalized and an attempt made to relieve the symptoms by conservative medical care. If the situation does not improve rapidly surgical intervention should be promptly undertaken.

Prognosis

This is usually excellent following appropriate treatment, but at times it is grave when surgical complications develop.

Control

Anthelmintic medication constitutes only a temporary measure for the great majority of infected individuals, since with relatively few exceptions persons living in *Ascaris* environments are subject to repeated exposure. The problem of control is therefore concerned directly with health education in the home and in the elementary school. Mothers must learn that ascariasis results from pollution of the soil with human excreta, primarily the promiscuous stools deposited by small children immediately around the door. There must therefore be clean, convenient places for the children to defecate and the child must be taught to use these toilet facilities regularly.

Soil in and around the dooryard which is contaminated with *Ascaris* eggs can be rendered safe by the following methods: (1) It can be treated with boiling water to kill the eggs; or (2) the top 2 inches can be spaded up and turned under. Jettmar (1950) states that *Ascaris* eggs are highly sensitive to heat above 40° C., to anoxia and to 0.1% pyrethrum.

An additional control problem is presented in countries where human feces constitute the essential fertilizer for field crops or truck gardens. Winfield (1937) has demonstrated that storage of fresh excreta with straw in compost pits soon raises the temperature above 50° C., so that *Ascaris* eggs in all stages of development are killed, yet the nitrogen value of the compost is not reduced. This method of prophylaxis is equally effective in certain other widespread helminthic infections, including hookworm disease, trichocephaliasis and schistosomiasis.

Toxocara canis (Werner, 1782) Johnston, 1916 (dog ascarid), and **Toxocara cati** (Schrank, 1788) Brumpt, 1927 (cat ascarid)

Toxocara canis, the cosmopolitan ascarid of dogs, was once reported from man in Egypt (Leiper, 1907) but the species diagnosis is questioned. The males have a length of 4 to 6 cm. and the females, 6.5 to 10 cm. There are a pair of lateral spear-like, cervical alæ or wings which are much longer than broad and extend distally an appreciable distance from the anterior end. The eggs are subglobose to ovoidal, densely granular internally, superficially pitted, and measure 85 by 75 microns. Infection results from ingesting eggs containing motile, second-stage rhabditoid larvas. A migration route to the lungs is required before the worms mature in the lumen of the small intestine. Although adult dogs suffer little harm from this infection, the migrating larvas in pregnant bitches are transmitted to their young, which frequently die of the infection. If young dogs survive this period, frequently the worms are spontaneously eliminated and a solid immunity is established.

Toxocara cati, the common ascarid of the cat, has been reported 18 times as a human intestinal infection (Mendheim, Scheid and Schmidt, 1952), although some of these cases may be examples of spurious parasitism, due to ingestion by young children of *T. cati* eggs in dirt and later the evacuation of these eggs in the child's feces. The males have a length of 4 to 6 cm. and the females, 4 to 12 cm. There are a pair of lateral heart-shaped cervical alæ, which are not more than three times as long as broad. The eggs are subglobose, densely granular internally, thin-shelled, more delicately pitted than those of *T. canis*, and are somewhat smaller (75 by 65 microns). They are very resistant to desiccation. After embryonation on the soil to the motile second rhabditoid larval stage, the eggs are infective. Upon being swallowed they hatch in the duodenum and after a migration route to the lungs mature in the lumen of the small intestine. The adult worms produce no notable symptoms. Congenital transmission has not been reported.

Extra-intestinal infection with larval *Toxocara canis* and *T. cati* are considered under the heading "Larva Migrans," page 277.

Lagochilascaris Minor Leiper, 1909

This small ascarid is a normal parasite of the small intestine of the cloudy leopard (*Felis nebulosa*), but sexually mature specimens have been recovered 5 times from extra-intestinal tissues of man (Faust, 1949). The male has a length of only 9 mm. and a maximum breadth of 0.4 mm.; the female, of 15 mm. and 0.5 mm. respectively. *L. minor* lacks cervical alæ but possesses a keel-like ledge which extends practically the entire length of each lateral line. There is a hare-lipped vertical cleft in the heavy cuticular covering of each of the three conspicuous lips (hence the generic name "hare-lipped ascaris"), while the entire labial structure is set off from the cervical region by a deep circumscribing furrow. The eggs are spherical, relatively transparent internally, thick-shelled with pittings resembling those of *Toxocara cati*, and measures 65 microns in diameter. The life cycle of *L. minor* has not been elucidated.

HOOKWORMS AND RELATED ROUNDWORMS

This group consists of many species which have in common the following morphologic characteristics: They lack distinct lips such as characterize ascarid nematodes; the posterior end of the males is extended into an umbrella-like copulatory bursa which is typically supported by 6 paired and 1 unpaired ribs; the ovaries, oviducts and uteri of the female are twinned, and the thin-shelled, transparent eggs are in an early stage of embryonation when oviposited.

With few exceptions the adult worms live in the digestive tract of their host. Eggs discharged in the feces complete their development on the soil and give birth to rhabditoid larvas, which feed, grow and after two moults are infective. In some species the third-stage larva is semi-rhabditoid and is infective for the host by the oral route; in other species the third-stage larva is filariform and infection is typically percutaneous. Many of these worms are economically important parasites of domestic animals, particularly herbivores, and only incidentally infect man, but two species of hookworms are among the most extensive disease-producing agents of mankind. Human hookworms belong to two genera, *viz.*, *Necator*, in which the buccal capsule is provided with semi-lunar cutting plates, and *Ancylostoma*, in which the capsule contains paired tooth-like processes.

Necator Americanus (Stiles, 1902) Stiles, 1903

(The "American murderer," causing human hookworm infection of warm climates)

Historical and Geographical Notes

The clinical manifestations of heavy hookworm infection were described from the West Indies as early as 1742 and from the southern United States

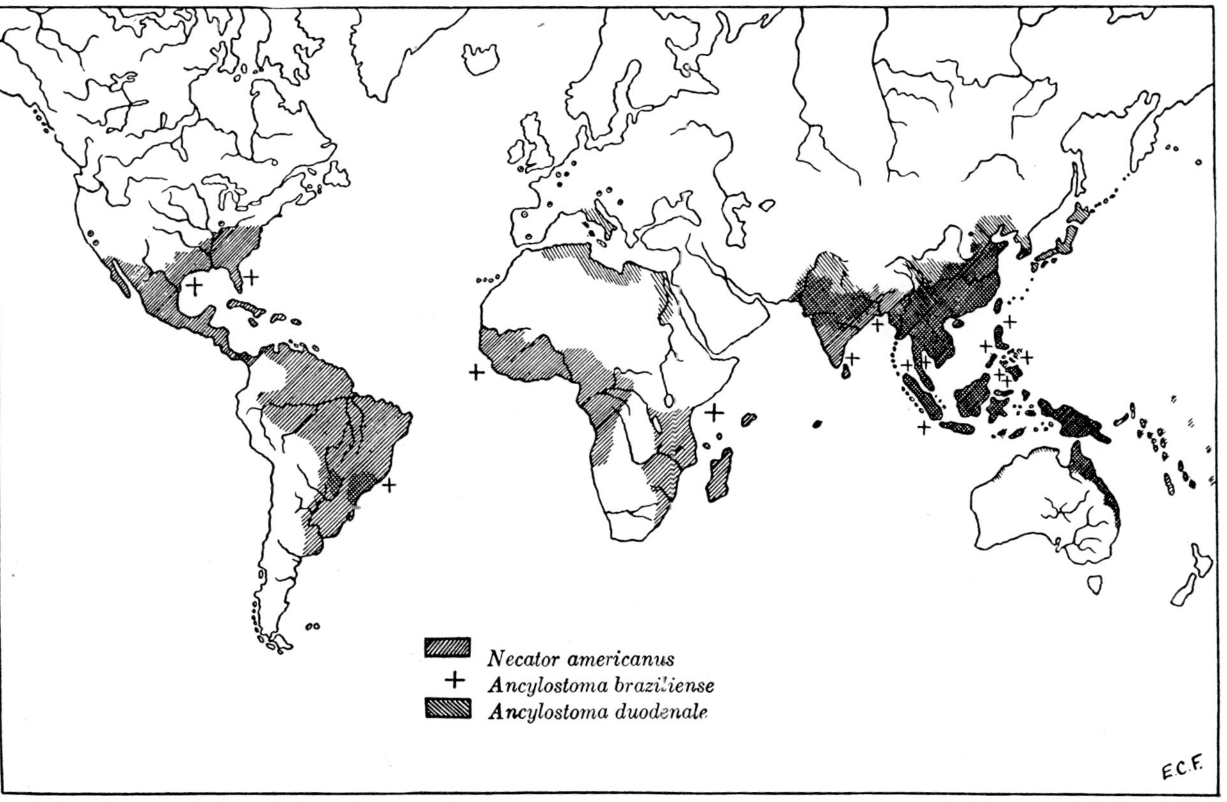

FIG. 69.—Map showing world distribution of the important species of hookworms producing infection in man. *Ancylostoma duodenale* is the prevalent (or only) hookworm on the west coast of South America (not shown on the map). (From Faust's *Human Helminthology*, Lea & Febiger, Philadelphia.)

by the middle of the 19th Century. The hookworms recovered from patients in the Americas were first regarded as *Ancylostoma duodenale*, which had been described by Dubini from Italy, in 1843, but Maréchal (1868) and Lutz (1888) considered them to be different. Stiles (1902) recognized that they belonged to a new species which he designated *Uncinaria americana*, and a year later placed in a new genus, *Necator* (the "killer" or "murderer"). Soon the "American hookworm" was found to be the prevailing species throughout the hookworm belt of the Southern

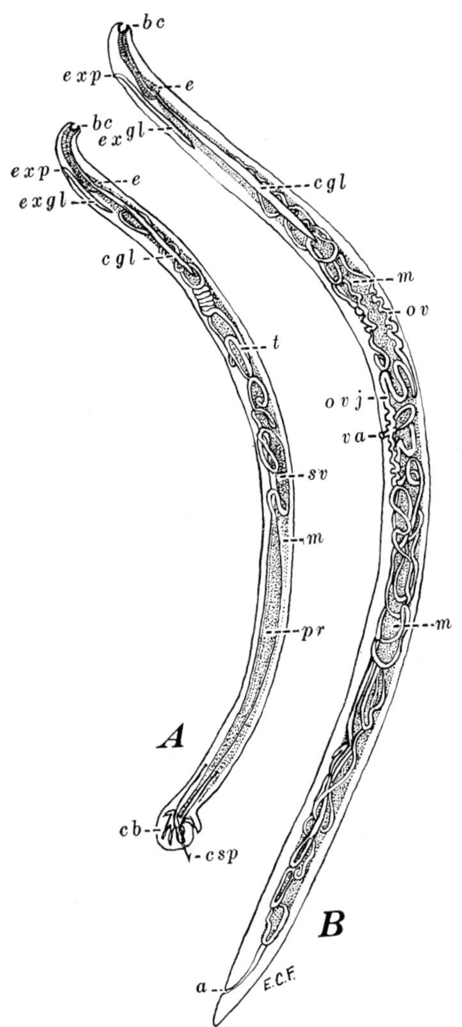

FIG. 70.—*Necator americanus* adults, lateral view. *A*, male; *B*, female. *a*, anal pore; *bc*, buccal capsule; *cb*, copulatory bursa; *c gl*, paired cephalic gland; *c sp*, copulatory spicules; *e*, esophagus; *ex gl*, excretory gland; *ex p*, excretory pore; *m*, midgut; *ov*, ovary; *ovj*, ovejector; *pr*, prostate gland; *sv*, seminal vesicle; *t*, testis; *vu*, vulva. × 18. (Original adaptation from Lane.)

United States, Mexico, Central America, the West Indies and South America east of the Andes. Some years later *Necator americanus* was discovered to be the important autochthonous species in the Eastern Hemisphere south of 20° N. latitude. (See map, Fig. 69.) This hookworm was probably introduced into the Western Hemisphere with the importation of African slaves (Scott, 1943).

Epidemiology

(See below under "Epidemiology of Hookworm Infections," pages 242–243.)

Morphology, Biology and Life Cycle

Necator americanus (Fig. 70) is a cylindrical worm, dirty grayish-yellow in color, at times with a reddish tinge due to blood in its intestinal tract.

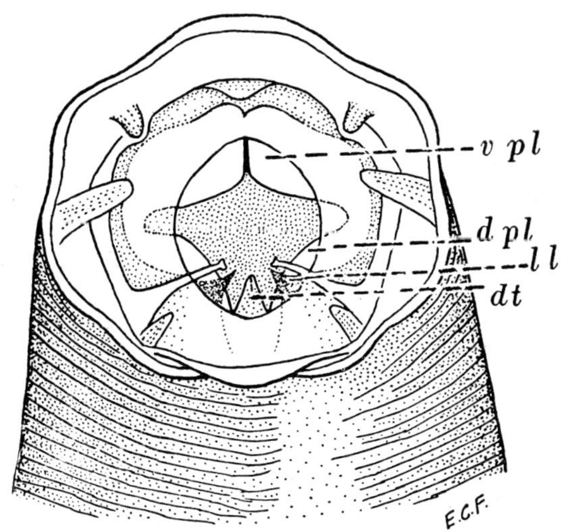

FIG. 71.—Anterior end of *Necator americanus*, looking into the buccal cavity. *dpl*, dorsal cutting plate; *dt*, dorsal tooth; *ll*, lateral lancet; *vpl*, ventral cutting plate. × 400. (From Faust's *Human Helminthology*, Lea & Febiger, Philadelphia.)

The anterior end is strongly reflexed dorsally. The small buccal capsule (Fig. 71) is provided with two upper (ventral) semilunar cutting plates (*vpl*), two poorly developed dorsal plates (*dpl*), a median dorsal tooth (*dt*), and in the depth of the mouth cavity a pair of short triangular lancets (*ll*). Opening from within into the depth of the buccal capsule are a pair of very long cephalic glands (*cgl*), the secretions of which may serve to digest the tips of intestinal villi to which the head is attached or possibly to secrete an anticoagulant for extravasated blood. Immediately internal to the buccal cavity there is a powerful, muscular esophagus, having a length about one-sixth that of the entire worm. Within its wall there are a dorsal gland and paired ventrolateral glands. Contraction of the esophageal musculature serves to anchor the head securely to the intestinal wall of the host, while dilatation followed by contraction sucks blood from the host's intestinal capillaries into the worm's own digestive tract.

The male measures 7 to 9 mm. in length by 0.3 mm. in breadth. The copulatory bursa (Fig. 70 *A*) is bilaterally symmetrical. The supporting ribs for each half consist of a small dorsal pair, bifurcated at the tip; a slender, unbranched externo-dorsal ray; a large fleshy, trifurcated lateral; a cleft ventral pair, and an inconspicuous short pre-bursal ray. The two copulatory spicules are long delicate bristles which are fused at their outer ends, terminating in a fish-hook barb. The female (Fig. 70 *B*) measures 9 to 11 mm. in length by 0.4 mm. in breadth. The posterior tip is rather sharply conical. The vulvar opening is mid-ventral, somewhat anterior to the equatorial plane.

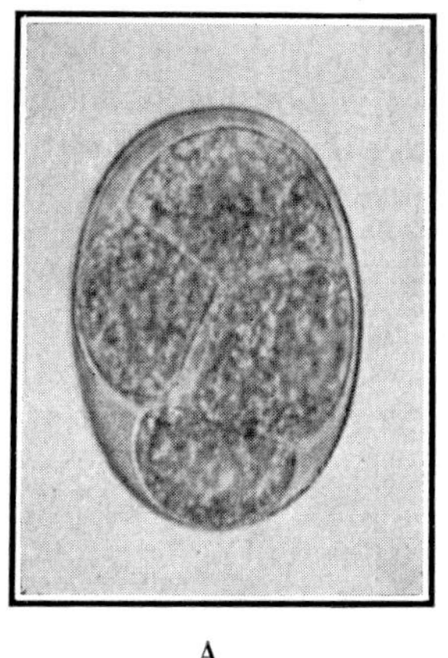

A

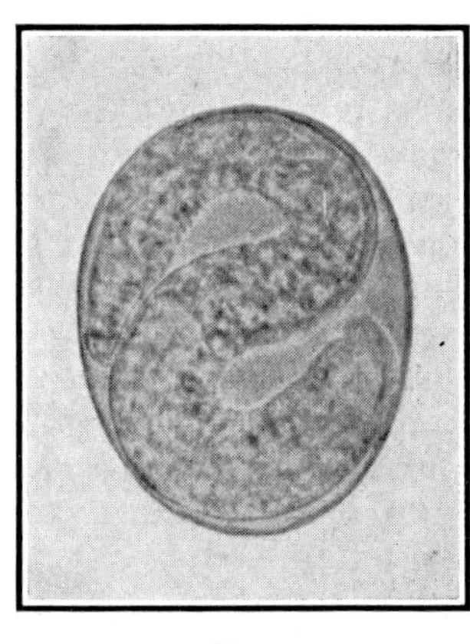

B

FIG. 72.—Photomicrographs of eggs of human hookworm. *A*, 4-cell stage; *B*, egg with slightly immature rhabditoid larva. × 666. (From Faust's *Human Helminthology*, Lea & Febiger, Philadelphia.)

The eggs (Fig. 72 *A*) are thin-shelled, transparent, broadly ovoidal, and measure 64 to 76 microns by 36 to 40 microns. They are in an early stage of cleavage when laid by the mother worm in the lumen of the small intestine. In a normally passed stool they range in development from 4-celled to a morula stage; in a constipated stool they may reach the early larval stage (Fig. 72 *B*).

Necator americanus is attached to the upper levels of the small intestine, from the mid-duodenum through the jejunum; but heavy infections may extend far down into the ileum and occasionally into the cecum. In addition to man, the common host, this species has been occasionally reported from African monkeys, the pangolin (*Manis javanicus*) in Indonesia, an African rodent (*Cœndu villosus*), the rhinoceros and the dog.

Larval Development.—When the host's feces are deposited on moist, sandy loam, in a warm, shaded location, or when diluted fresh human excreta are spread on the land as fertilizer, embryonation of viable hookworm eggs usually proceeds rapidly and hatching takes place in 24 to 48 hours. Optimal conditions include good aeration of the top soil, which must be moist but not saturated with water, protection from direct rays of the sun, and a temperature of 31° to 34.5° C. (Svensson, 1925). The larva emerging from the egg shell is typically *rhabditoid* (Fig. 73 *B*), and measures 0.25 to 0.3 mm. in length by about 17 microns in maximum di-

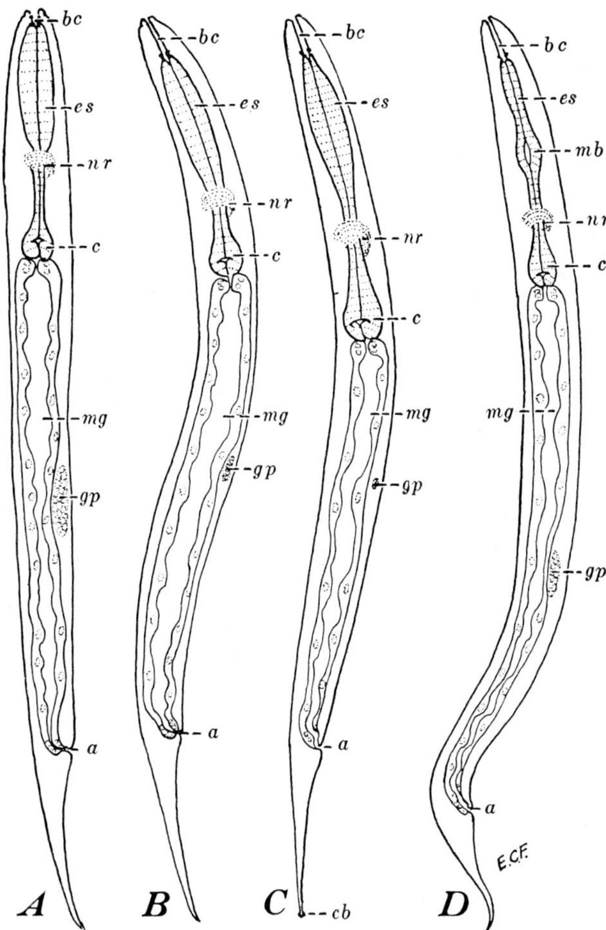

FIG. 73.—Diagrams of the rhabditoid larvas of *A*, *Strongyloides*, *B*, hookworms, *C*, *Trichostrongylus* and *D*, *Rhabditis*. × ca. 400. *a*, anus; *bc*, buccal chamber; *c*, cardiac bulb of esophagus; *cb*, bead-like knob of caudal tip; *es*, esophagus; *gp*, germinal primordium; *mb*, mid-esophageal bulb; *mg*, midgut; *nr*, nerve ring. (From Craig and Faust's *Clinical Parasitology*, Lea & Febiger, Philadelphia.)

ameter. It feeds actively on bacteria and organic débris, grows, sheds its cuticle and continues to feed and increase in size up to 0.5–0.6 mm. in length, while retaining its rhabditoid form. Between the fifth and eighth day it stops feeding, becomes relatively inactive and transforms within the old cuticle into the more delicate *filariform* larva (Fig. 74 *C*), which has a closed mouth, an elongated esophagus and a sharply pointed tail. Maximum survival of most of these larvas probably does not exceed two weeks. As soon as they escape from the old cuticle (second moult) they become reactivated, wriggling about in the top soil, and on contact with exposed human skin penetrate under epidermal scales or into hair follicles. The most common area of invasion in persons who step barefooted on the infested ground is the tender skin between the toes, but farmers in contact

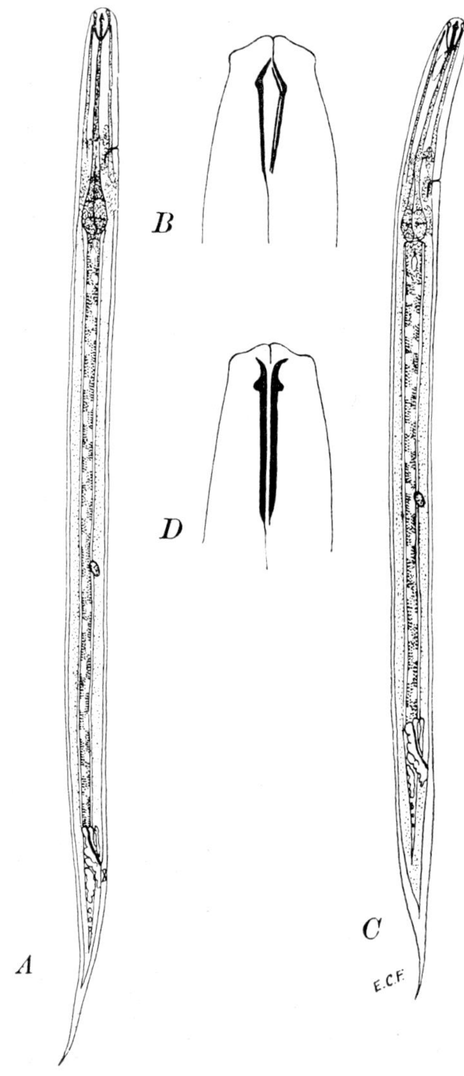

Fig. 74.—Filariform larvas of human hookworms. *A*, *Ancylostoma duodenale; B*, head of *A. duodenale* showing buccal spears; *C*, *Necator americanus; D*, head of *N. americanus* showing buccal spears. *A*, *C*, × 160; *B*, *D*, greatly enlarged. (*A*, *C*, adapted from Looss, *B*, *D*, after Heydon; in Faust's *Human Helminthology*, Lea & Febiger, Philadelphia.)

with soil fertilized with infested human excreta also are exposed on the hands, and miners on any area of the skin which touches infested earth. While infection may be acquired by swallowing dirt containing the filariform larvas, this route of entry into the body is probably an infrequent one.

Migration in the Host and Development to the Adult Stage.—The filariform larvas penetrate down through the epidermis, enter the cutaneous blood vessels and within 24 hours or less after skin contact are carried through the right heart to the lungs. In 2 or 3 days they break out of the pulmonary capillaries into the air sacs, ascend the respiratory tree to the epiglottis, and descend to the upper levels of the small intestine; meanwhile they have undergone a third moult of cuticle and acquired a temporary buccal capsule. The young worms now become attached to the villi of the duodenum and jejunum, grow, shed the fourth cuticle including the temporary buccal capsule, and develop into adult worms. A minimum of 5 weeks is required from the time filariform larvas enter the skin until the worms have matured in the intestine, have copulated and females begin to lay eggs. Under favorable conditions each female *Necator americanus* produces 5,000 to 10,000 eggs daily. Although these worms may occasionally remain in the human intestine for 9 or 10 years, a majority die or are evacuated in one to two years.

For pathologic and clinical aspects of infection with *Necator americanus*, see "Hookworm Infection and Hookworm Disease," pages 243–246, also "Larva Migrans," pages 277–279.

Ancylostoma Duodenale (Dubini, 1843) Creplin, 1845

(The "Old World hookworm," causing human hookworm infection of temperate climates in the Eastern Hemisphere)

Historical and Geographical Notes

Although this species of hookworm was probably referred to in the Eber's papyrus (1600 B.C.), the first description was provided by Dubini (1843), based on autopsy study of a Milanese woman in 1838. Grassi and Parona (1878) demonstrated that the presence of hookworms in the bowel could be diagnosed from their eggs in the stool, and Perroncito (1880) hatched the eggs and studied the free-living stages in the soil. Looss (1896–1897) found that the infective-stage filariform larvas enter the body by the skin route and that they migrate *via* the blood vessels to the lungs, then make their way into the alveoli, travel up to the epiglottis, are swallowed and pass down the digestive tract to the small intestine, where they develop into adults.

The original distribution of *A. duodenale* was probably limited to the subtropical and temperate regions of the Eastern Hemisphere north of the Equator. Extensive migrations of Asian peoples carried this infection to more tropical climates, so that today it is mixed with *Necator americanus* in southeastern Asia, the South Pacific and Southwest Pacific islands and Indonesia (Darling, 1920). (See Fig. 69, p. 233.) *A. duodenale* is the only important hookworm of man on the west coast of South America, where it was possibly introduced by the early Spanish explorers and

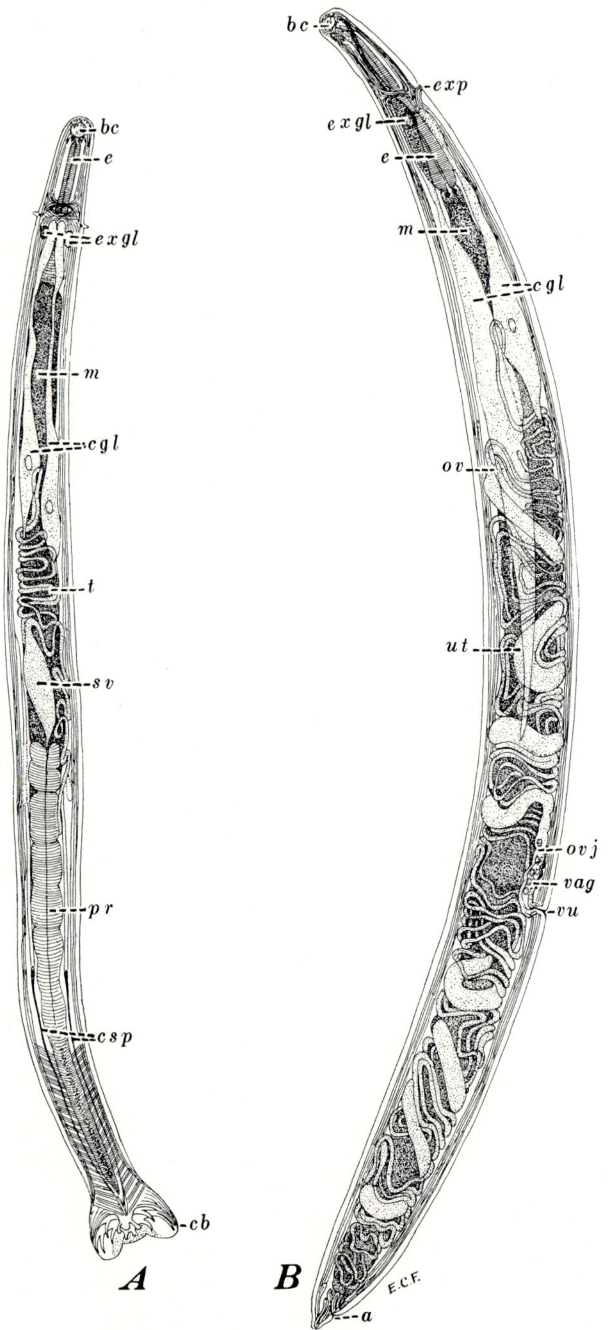

FIG. 75.—*Ancylostoma duodenale* adults, lateral view. *A*, male; *B*, female. *a*, anal pore; *bc*, buccal capsule; *cb*, copulatory bursa; *c gl*, paired cephalic gland; *c sp*, copulatory spicules; *e*, esophagus; *ex gl*, excretory gland; *ex p*, excretory pore; *m*, midgut; *ov*, ovary; *ovj*, ovejector; *pr*, prostate gland; *sv*, seminal vesicle; *t*, testis; *vag*, vagina; *vu*, vulva. × 20. (Adapted from Looss, in Faust's *Human Helminthology*, Lea & Febiger, Philadelphia.)

colonizers. Stoll (1947) has estimated that the total hookworm-infected population of the world is 456.8 millions, of which 359 millions live in Asia, 49 millions in Africa, 42 millions in tropical America and 1.8 millions in North America.

Epidemiology

(See below under "Epidemiology of Hookworm Infections," pages 242–243.)

Morphology, Biology and Life Cycle

The adults of *A. duodenale* are cylindrical in shape, pinkish or ivory-gray in color, narrowed anteriorly and have their head curved somewhat dorsally (Fig. 75). Their cup-shaped mouth capsule is heavily reinforced and is provided on the upper (ventral) side with 4 conspicuous, slightly curved,

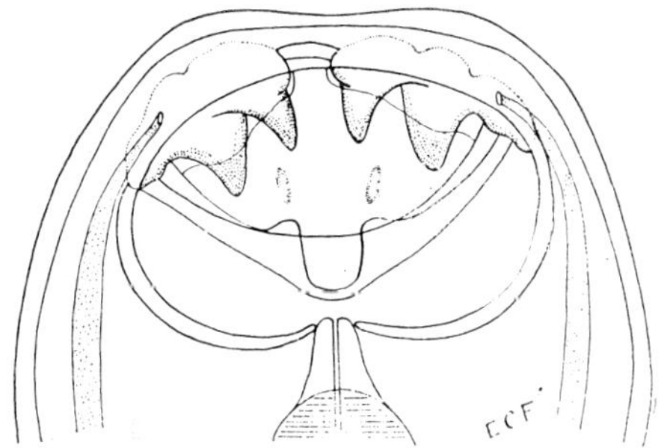

Fig. 76.—Anterior extremity of *Ancylostoma duodenale*, showing buccal capsule and tooth pattern. × 240. (From Faust's *Human Helminthology*, Lea & Febiger, Philadelphia.)

subequal teeth, one pair on either side of the median ventral line. In the depth of the capsule there are a pair of small teeth. Dorsally there is a plate with a median cleft (Fig. 76).

The male (Fig. 75 *A*) measures 8 to 11 mm. in length by 0.4 to 0.5 mm. in breadth. It is provided with a bell-shaped copulatory bursa which is considerably broader than long and is supported by fleshy ribs having the following pattern for each half of the bursa: dorsal, single at its root but bifurcated at the tip; externo-dorsal, arising from the root of the dorsal; three laterals, outwardly well separated from one another, and two ventrals, close to one another. The female (Fig. 75 *B*) measures 10 to 13 mm. in length by 0.6 mm. in breadth and tapers rather bluntly at the posterior end. The anal pore lies ventrally near the caudal tip and the vulvar opening mid-ventrally at the beginning of the posterior third of the body. Each female lays 10,000 to 20,000 eggs daily.

Man is probably the only normal host of *A. duodenale*.

The broadly ovoidal eggs (Fig. 72 *A*) average 60 by 40 microns, have a thin, tough, transparent shell and are in the 2- to 8-cell stage of cleavage when evacuated in the normally formed stool. Embryonation to the first rhabditoid larval stage takes place in 24 to 48 hours on moist sandy loam in a shaded environment at an optimum temperature of about 25° C. (Svensson, 1925).

Hatching and free-living larval stages on the soil are similar to those of *Necator americanus* (see page 236).

Rhabditoid larvas of hookworms (Fig. 73 *B*) have a long buccal chamber and an inconspicuous genital primordium; those of *Strongyloides* have a short inconspicuous buccal chamber (Fig. 73 *A*) and a distinct genital primordium. Filariform larvas of hookworms have a sharply pointed tail; those of *Strongyloides* have a notched caudal termination. (See page 254, Fig. 82 *B*, *D*.)

Infection with filariform larvas of *A. duodenale*, their migration through the lungs and their development to the mature male and female worms in the intestine parallel these phases of the life cycle of *Necator* (pages 236–239).

Ancylostoma braziliense Gomez de Faria, 1910

This species was first described from the intestine of dogs and cats in Brazil and subsequently from these hosts from many warm areas of the world. Human intestinal infection with *A. braziliense* is relatively uncommon.

A. braziliense is about 30% smaller than *A. duodenale* (males 7.75 to 8.5 mm. long, females 9 to 10.5 mm. long). The most easily recognized morphologic difference between these two species is the buccal capsule: that of *A. braziliense* has a smaller aperture and the dental plate on each side of the mid-ventral line is provided with a very small inner tooth and a large outer one. Eggs of this species are indistinguishable from those of *A. duodenale*. The stages of larval development are also similar, although the oral route of invasion for filariform larvas of *A. braziliense* is apparently more frequent than the percutaneous route in canine and feline hosts (Kirby-Smith, Dove and White, 1926).

Clinical interest in *A. braziliense* is concerned primarily with human skin exposure to filariform larvas of this species derived from canine and feline hosts, causing a dermatitis referred to as "cutaneous larva migrans" or "creeping eruption." This topic is considered under "*Larva Migrans*." (See pages 277–279.)

Ancylostoma caninum (Ercolani, 1859) Hall, 1913

This is the common hookworm of dogs and cats in temperate climates. It has been reported on four occasions as an incidental intestinal parasite of man (Deane, 1950). *A. caninum* is appreciably larger than *A. duodenale* (males 10 mm. long by 0.4 mm. broad, females 14 mm. long by 0.6 mm. broad). The buccal capsule is wide and has a large orifice. Each of the two upper (ventral) dental plates is provided with 3 teeth, of which the innermost is the smallest and the outermost the most fully developed. The eggs resemble those of *A. duodenale* but are slightly larger (63.8 by 40.4 microns). The life cycle is similar to that of *A. duodenale* but the free-living stages develop best in a somewhat cooler climate.

A. caninum has been employed experimentally for many years in the dog in studying the biological, immunologic and clinical aspects of hookworm infection and their application to hookworm disease in man. Occasionally creeping eruption of the human skin is caused by *A. caninum*. (See under "*Larva Migrans*," pages 277–279.)

Epidemiology of Hookworm Infection

Hookworm infection constitutes one of the most prevalent of all helminthic parasitoses of man in warm climates. For practical purposes only two causal agents of intestinal infection need to be considered, namely, *Necator americanus* and *Ancylostoma duodenale*. *N. americanus* is typically adapted to a warmer climate, although *A. duodenale* likewise thrives in the hookworm belt of the Tropics.

N. americanus and *A. duodenale* are parasites almost exclusively of man, so that wherever these infections are endemic they result from unsanitary methods of disposal of human feces containing the eggs of these two hookworms. Defecation on favorable soil or the spreading of the infested feces in the form of liquid manure on the land provides opportunity for the eggs to complete embryonation, to hatch, and for the larvas which emerge from the egg shells to feed, grow and transform into the infective filariform stage. These larvas remain near the surface close to the sites where defecation occurs or where feces are spread on the ground.

An essential to the continued propagation of human hookworm infections is the custom of natives in warm climates to walk barefooted. When they step on polluted soil, the skin of their feet comes in contact with infective-stage larvas, which enter the epidermis and initiate infection. Persons working in fields which have been recently fertilized with unripened human nightsoil are exposed wherever the hands or feet touch infested soil containing hookworm filariform larvas, while miners in unsanitated underground tunnels may become infected on practically any area of the skin.

Data on the prevalence of hookworms in an area must be supplemented by a relatively accurate estimate of the intensity of the infection in each infected individual, *i. e.*, the worm burden. Darling (1922) employed mass treatment in heavily infected hookworm communities to obtain evacuation of the worms, which were collected from the stools and counted. Cort and his associates carried out a comprehensive study of hookworm epidemiology (1921–1925) and developed the Stoll technic (1923) for counting hookworm eggs passed in the stool. Recently Beaver (1949, 1950) has devised a standardized direct fecal-film egg-count procedure. The hemoglobin and serum protein levels of each person surveyed are useful in evaluating the clinical importance of the infection at different intensities of infection. It is equally necessary to consider associated disease processes in assessing the rôle of the hookworms in the over-all clinical picture.

Another measure for studying hookworm epidemiology is related to the sites on the soil polluted with human excreta and the degree of soil infestation with hookworm larvas. Separation of these and other nematode larvas from the soil is accomplished with the Baermann apparatus (see "Technical Aids," page 596).

Clinical Aspects of Hookworm Infection and Hookworm Disease

The Skin Lesion.—At each site on the feet, arms or other surface area where the filariform larva of *Necator americanus* or *Ancylostoma duodenale* enters the skin it produces a minute wound (Fig. 77). In 96% of 19,000 *N. americanus* patients Ashford and Gutiérrez Igaravidez (1911) obtained a history of penetration dermatitis, consisting typically of an initial intense itching and burning, followed by edema and erythema, then a papule which transformed into a vesicle. This is the uncomplicated "ground itch" of hookworm infection. Fülleborn (1930) states that hookworm dermatitis is relatively uncommon following exposure to *A. duodenale*.

Occasionally *Necator* and *A. duodenale*, as well as *A. caninum* and *Bunostomum phlebotomum*, produce "creeping eruption" in the skin similar to *A. braziliense*.

Larval Migration through the Lungs.—Characteristically the migrating larvas of *Necator americanus* and *A. duodenale* reach the pulmonary capillaries almost immediately after entry into the cutaneous venules. As they penetrate into the air sacs, they produce minute focal hemorrhages, but only in case of massive migration of larvas simultaneously is a bronchial pneumonitis of clinical grade usually produced. Another item of clinical interest is that hookworm larvas during transit through the lungs do not typically produce the degree of sensitization characteristic of *Ascaris* (page 227) or *Strongyloides* (page 257).

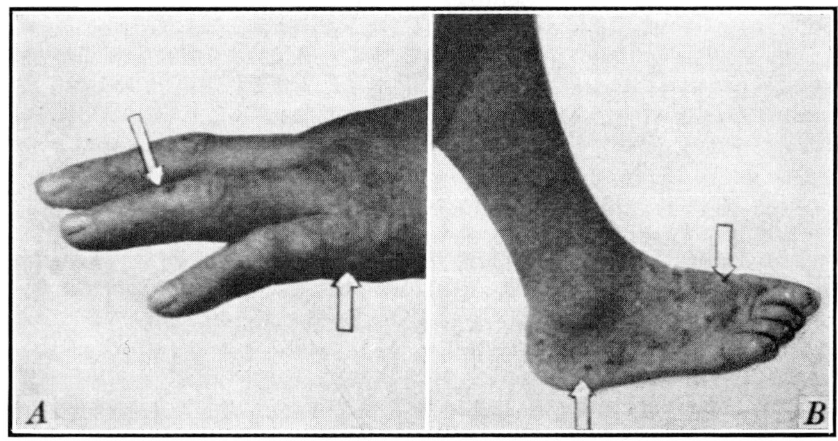

FIG. 77.—Cutaneous lesions ("ground itch") following exposure to hookworm larvas in the soil. (After Chang *et al.*, courtesy of Johns Hopkins Press, in Craig and Faust's *Clinical Parasitology*, Lea & Febiger, Philadelphia.)

Intestinal Infection.—Once the adolescent hookworms have migrated to the upper levels of the small intestine, they soon acquire a temporary mouth capsule, become attached to the wall, and by suction and lysis produce necrosis of the tips of the villi (Fig. 78). Blood is sucked out of the villi at each site of attachment and passes through the digestive tract of the worm. This extraction of blood begins before the worms have matured and continues as long as they remain attached. Early in the intestinal infection each hookworm is capable of removing as much as 0.67 cc. of blood daily, but in older infections one worm may cause the loss of not more than 0.1 cc. daily.

Etiology of Hookworm Disease.—The essential damage produced in hookworm infection is hemorrhage from the intestinal wall. In general, this is proportional to the number of attached worms. Thus, counts of less than 2100 eggs per cc. of feces (representing about 50 worms) are seldom of clinical grade (Scott, 1946), between 2100 and 5000 eggs per cc. are in the borderline class with respect to hemoglobin level (Beaver, 1951), while those with counts of more than 11,000 eggs per cc. almost invariably have a significant hookworm anemia (Scott, 1945).

The type of anemia produced by hookworms is typically microcytic and hypochromic (Foster and Landsberg, 1934; Rhoads, Castle, Payne and Lawson, 1934). In light infections, the blood loss can be completely compensated and in moderately heavy infections compensated by an adequate, well-balanced diet containing iron, other minerals, rich animal proteins and vitamin A. In severe hookworm disease, however, even with a highly fortified diet, the hematopoietic mechanism is unable to produce new

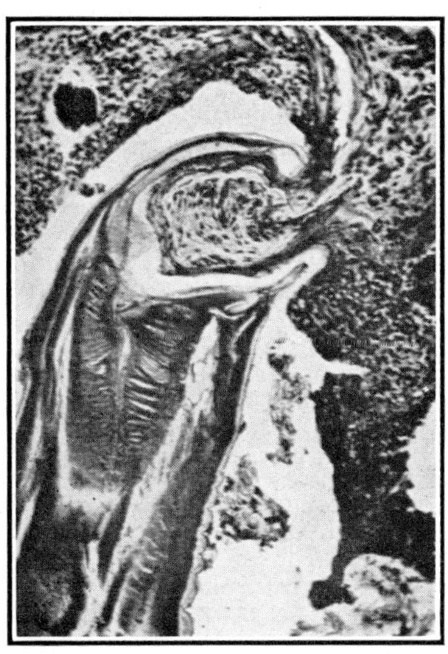

Fig. 78.—Photomicrograph showing method of attachment of *Necator americanus* to the human jejunum. The tip of a villus has been sucked into the mouth of the worm but erosion and hemorrhage have not yet occurred. (From collection, Armed Forces Institute of Pathology, in Craig and Faust's Clinical Parasitology, Lea & Febiger, Philadelphia.)

supplies of normal red blood cells as rapidly as they are lost. In chronic infections, this may exhaust the red bone marrow and result in an aplastic anemia (Stransky and Dauis-Lawas, 1950). Moreover, underlying protein deficiency in the diet, even with adequate absorbable iron intake, may contribute measurably to the anemia of hookworm patients, a majority of whom subsist essentially on carbohydrates.

In hookworm areas exposure begins fairly early in childhood and is repeated again and again throughout life.

Symptomatology.—In *acute cases* resulting from single heavy exposure there is characteristically a prodromal syndrome of nausea, headache, irritating cough (during lung migration of the larvas) and a worn out feeling. This is followed by severe colicky pains in the pit of the stomach, flatulence, diarrhea, or dysentery in which the stools are viscous and frequently reddish black, loss of weight and strength, dyspnea, dizziness and marked pallor. During this period there is an eosinophilic leukocytosis; later a significant anemia develops.

In *chronic hookworm disease* the patient may complain of dyspepsia, epigastric burning, flatulence, hunger pains, gastralgia, and dyspnea on slight exertion. His abdomen is tender, his skin is sallow, he is nervous, irritable, "run down" and not able to perform heavy labor. He may have persistent enteralgia, alternating diarrhea and constipation, dyspnea, precordial pain, tachycardia, arterial hypertension, and low systolic pressure due to lack of "circulatory compensation for reduced oxygen-carrying capacity of the blood" (Porter, 1931). He is listless, has a sad, puffy, pallid facies, flabby muscles and is weak-kneed. His feet and hands tinge, burn and "go to sleep" easily. His skin becomes dry and harsh. He is mentally dull, has blurred vision and is physically not fit for any kind of work. In children there is characteristically both physical and sexual stunting. In childbirth there is a heavy toll both in mothers and offspring (Wickramasuriya, 1935).

In severe chronic hookworm disease the symptoms are greatly exaggerated. The patient is persistently cold even in a hot climate. He craves clay or any bulky material to fill his intestinal tract (*i. e.*, syndrome of *geophagia*). He frequently succumbs to "famine diarrhea" or heart failure.

Diagnosis

Experienced clinicians state that they are unable by physical examination alone to distinguish between the anemia and edema of malnutrition and hookworm disease, and blood chemistry studies indicating a hypoproteinemia will fail to provide a differential diagnosis. On the other hand, direct fecal film examination employing the Beaver standard egg-count technic (page 584), makes it possible to obtain a relatively accurate estimate of the number of worms in the infection.

Treatment

Supportive Therapy.—In light to moderate hookworm infections in which the anemia is not severe, specific treatment can usually be undertaken without a preliminary period of supportive treatment. For individuals with low hemoglobin levels it is desirable to precede specific chemotherapy for a week to ten days with a diet rich in animal proteins and vitamin A, to build up the serum protein deficit and relieve the edema. Iron must also be administered to replace that lost through intestinal hemorrhage caused by the worms. One or more whole blood transfusions may be needed. Liver should not be prescribed unless the blood picture indicates that there is a primary anemia.

Specific Therapy.—In hookworm infection uncomplicated with ascariasis the drug of choice is *tetrachlorethylene* (C_2Cl_4) (See Table 5, page 66). It is available in 0.5 cc. and 1 cc. soft gelatin globules; in order to be effective it should be fresh and should be kept in a cool, dark place. In the absence of alcohol and absorbable oil in the intestine this drug is essentially non-toxic, since it is almost insoluble in gastric and intestinal juices, does not irritate mucous membranes, and produces no appreciable damage to liver or kidneys (Lamson, Brown and Ward, 1932). A full therapeutic dose has a worm-removal value of approximately 90 per cent.

Tetrachlorethylene should be taken on an empty stomach, preceded the night before by a saline purgative, preferably Glauber salts (sodium sulfate), in the amount of 15 Gm. (½ ounce) for adults, dissolved in a glass of water. For persons 15 years of age and older the therapeutic dose of tetrachlorethylene is 3 cc., taken at one time; for children, 3 minims for each apparent year of age. If children are too small to swallow 0.5 cc. capsules, the drug may be placed on a teaspoon with sugar or syrup. No food or carbonated drinks should be permitted until a post-treatment saline purge administered 2 hours following the drug has emptied the bowels.

A week following specific therapy a follow-up stool examination should be made to determine the efficacy of the treatment. Re-treatment with tetrachlorethylene may be undertaken in a week to remove remaining hookworms.

If hookworm infection is complicated with whipworm infection it may be desirable to administer 3 cc. (adult dose) of tetrachlorethylene and oil of chenopodium combined in the proportion of 9:1. (See page 223, also Table 5, page 66.)

In combined hookworm and *Ascaris* infections, especially in children, hexylresorcinol crystoids is the drug of choice, just as it is in uncomplicated ascariasis. (See page 229, also Table 5, page 66.)

Prognosis

Prognosis is good to excellent in all uncomplicated light to moderate hookworm infections following removal of the worms and relief of the anemia and hypoproteinemia. In severe cases careful management may be equally satisfactory, but in heavy chronic infections there may be residual, irreversible cardiac damage.

Control

Two major lines of attack are indicated, namely, (1) anthelmintic treatment of all infected individuals to reduce to a minimum the sources of soil infestation and (2) sanitary disposal of human excreta. Recent programs confine specific medication to the infected individuals, particularly those with a heavy worm burden. Equally important is the sanitary disposal or sterilization of human feces, to prevent contamination of the ground.

Control also embodies improvement in the diet of hookworm communities to reduce the effects of malnutrition. Thus, it is evident that hookworm control must be made an integral part of comprehensive health projects, including medical care, sanitary engineering, health education, nutrition and improved agricultural methods.

OTHER BURSATE NEMATODES

Two species of nematodes belonging to the family Strongylidæ and found normally as intestinal parasites of simian hosts have been reported from man. They are *Ternidens deminutus* and *Œsophagostomum apiostomum*.

Ternidens deminutus (Railliet and Henry, 1905) Railliet and Henry, 1909

This worm has been diagnosed from man in natives of Southern Rhodesia (50 to 65 per cent incidence, according to Sandground, 1931), Nyasaland and Mozambique. In size and shape it resembles human hookworms but is distinguished from the latter species by a terminal buccal capsule which is subglobose and is guarded internally by a double crown of stout bristles. The eggs are also like those of hookworms but are larger, averaging 84 by 51 microns. The third-stage larva is semi-rhabditoid rather than filariform and is not capable of penetrating the skin, hence it probably enters the body by the oral route (Sandground, 1931).

T. deminutus is found throughout the intestinal tract, with its head inserted into the wall. It produces cystic nodules (Sandground, 1931) or small circumscribed, craterous ulcers, and at times causes perforation with peritonitis. The worms are hemophagous and heavy infections result in anemia (Amberson and Swarz, 1952). Anthelmintics employed in treating hookworm infection (page 246) are only moderately effective in eliminating *T. deminutus*.

Œsophagostomum apiostomum (Willach, 1891) Railliet and Henry, 1905

This worm, a common parasite of monkeys in West Africa and the Philippines and China, has been reported from man in Northern Nigeria and in the vicinity of Lake Omo, East Africa. Although *Œ. apiostomum* is approximately the size of hookworms, like *T. deminutus* it has a terminal buccal capsule, beset with a crown of 12 pyramidal setæ. Infection probably results from swallowing third-stage semi-rhabditoid larvas, which pass down to the cecum, invade the wall and become encapsulated in a fibrous nodule, within which the worms grow. Then they break out of the capsule into the cecal canal, where they become attached to the mucosa and mature. The eggs measure 60 to 63 by 27 to 40 microns and are indistinguishable from those of hookworms.

The development of the tumors in the submucous and muscular coats of the cecum may be responsible for hypermotility in the area but the essential damage occurs when the emerging adolescent worms rupture the tissue capsule, with hemorrhage of nearby blood vessels and occasional perforation into the peritoneal cavity. During development within the nodule chemotherapy is unavailing but as soon as the worms emerge into the cecal canal they may be eliminated by administration of tetrachlorethylene as in hookworm infection (page 246).

A subspecies, *Œ. stephanostomum thomasi*, was once recovered from the human intestine in Manãos, Brazil.

Syngamus laryngeus Railliet, 1899

Species of the genus *Syngamus* are relatively small-sized nematodes, in which the male and female worms are typically joined in permanent copula. They possess a thick-walled, cavernous buccal capsule, armed at its base with a number of small teeth. The male is only about one-third as long as the female. The outer shell of the ovoidal eggs consists of a large number of truncated prisms cemented together. Eggs of species parasitizing birds have a pair of polar caps; eggs of those parasitizing mammals lack these caps.

Several species of *Syngamus* have been described from mammals. Human infection, probably for the most part with *S. laryngeus*, but possibly also with *S. nasicola*, has been reported 3 times from Puerto Rico, 5 times from Brazil, 4 times from Martinique, and once each from St. Lucia (W. Indies), Trinidad and the Philippines (Andrade Lima and Simoes Barbosa, 1951).

These worms reside as adults in the upper respiratory tract of their hosts, causing asthma, hemoptysis, and paroxysms of coughing and sneezing, during which the worms may be expelled from their attachment to the respiratory mucosa. Life history data have not been reported for species of *Syngamus* parasitizing mammals. Human infection is incidental; since the worms are probably always expelled during paroxysms of coughing no special therapeutic measures are indicated.

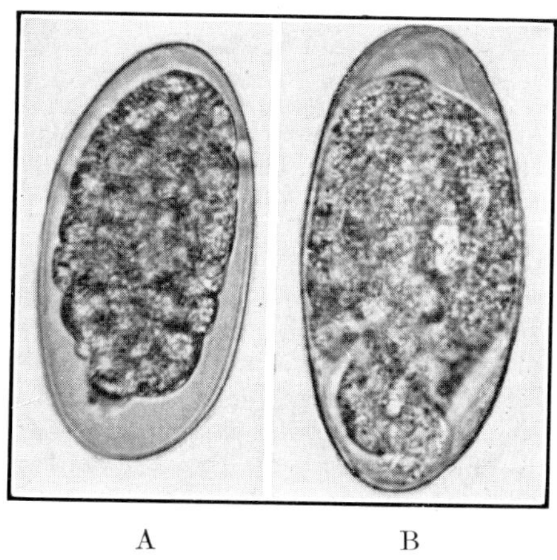

A B

FIG. 79.—Eggs of *Trichostrongylus orientalis*. A, in freshly evacuated stools; *B*, with slightly immature, motile first-stage larva. × 500. (Photomicrographs by Dr. T. B. Magath, in Craig and Faust's *Clinical Parasitology*, Lea & Febiger, Philadelphia.)

Species of **Trichostrongylus**

Species of *Trichostrongylus* are delicate thread-like nematodes lacking a buccal capsule and dental apparatus and possessing a relatively large copulatory bursa in the male. They are typically attached to the small intestine of ruminants and are incidental parasites of man, but *Trichostrongylus orientalis* is more commonly found in man than in other mammals. Eggs of these worms (Fig. 79) are oval-elliptical, measure from 70 to 90 microns by 40 to 50 microns depending on the species, and are usually in the morula stage of development when evacuated in the stool. Under favorable conditions the eggs become fully embryonated and hatch in about 24 hours. The first and second stage larvas are rhabditoid in type like those of hookworms but can be readily distinguished by a minute bead-like knob at the tip of the tail. (Fig. 73.) Transformation to the infective pseudo-filariform larva occurs between the 60th and 96th hour. This stage is very resistant to desiccation, is unable to penetrate skin but when ingested with grass burrows into the intestinal wall. About 4 days later it emerges and without a migration to the lungs inserts its anterior end deeply into the wall and develops into an adult. The incubation period is about 3 weeks (Lie Kian Joe, 1947).

Generic diagnosis is made on the characteristic eggs (Fig. 79) recovered from the stools and their differentiation from hookworm eggs (Fig. 72, page 236). Specific diagnosis depends on study of the differential features of the copulatory bursa and spicules in the male (Fig. 80).

Stoll (1947) has estimated human infection with *Trichostrongylus* to be 5.5 millions, almost all of which occur in Asia.

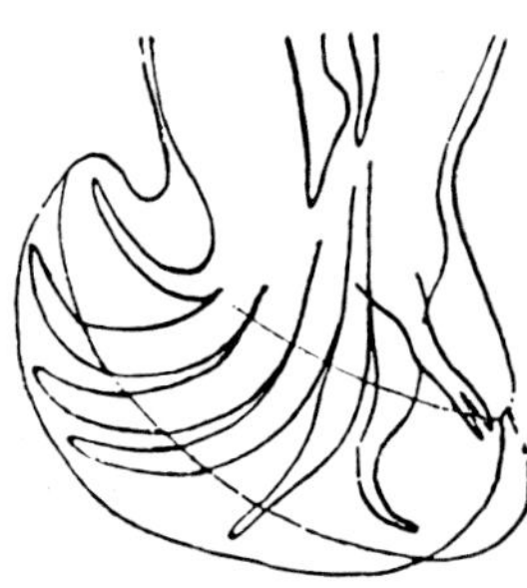

FIG. 80.—Copulatory bursa of male *Trichostrongylus orientalis*. × 250. (From Faust's *Human Helminthology*, Lea & Febiger, Philadelphia.)

Trichostrongylus Colubriformis (Giles, 1892) Ransom, 1911.—This cosmopolitan trichostrongyle has been recovered from sheep, goats, gazelles, antelopes, deer, camels, baboons, apes, squirrels and rabbits, and from man in Egypt, Iran, India, Armenia, Indonesia, Australia and once in a surgical appendix in New Orleans, U. S. A. Lie Kian Joe (1947) reported high incidence but light worm burden among inhabitants of Indonesia, but in one insane patient who came to autopsy he recovered more than 5000 specimens together with many hookworms.

Trichostrongylus Probolurus (Railliet, 1896) Looss, 1905.—This cosmopolitan species is a common parasite of sheep, gazelles and camels and has been reported from man in Egypt, Armenia and Siberia.

Trichostrongylus Vitrinus Looss, 1905.—This cosmopolitan species is a parasite of oxen, sheep, goats and camels, and has been reported from man in Egypt, Armenia and Siberia.

Trichostrongylus Orientalis Jimbo, 1914.—This species is a common parasite of man in Japan and Korea and has also been found in man and herbivorous animals in China, Formosa and Armenia. In man the commonly parasitized level of the digestive tract is the duodenum but worms have been found attached to the pyloric wall of the stomach and to the jejunum. The adults are grayish-white. The males measure 3.8 to 4.8 mm. in length and the females 4.9 to 6.7 mm.; the delicate heads measure only 7 and 9 microns in diameter respectively. The posterior end of the male is shown in Fig. 80. The eggs of *T. orientalis* (Fig. 79) measure 75 to 91 microns by 39 to 47 microns.

Other species of *Trichostrongylus* reported incidentally from man include: *T. instabilis* (Armenia, Siberia), *T. axei* (Armenia, Siberia, Mauritius, Java), *T. skrjabini* (Armenia) and unidentified species from Tunisia, Belgian Congo, Southern Rhodesia, Iran, Chile, Hawaii and Fiji, and a Greek resident in United States. Human infection with *Trichostrongylus* sp. also occurs in Georgia (U. S. A.). Eggs of these several species have been frequently mis-diagnosed as those of hookworms.

Clinical Notes on Trichostrongyles in Man.—Light infections usually produce no symptoms but large numbers of worms cause a secondary anemia due to their blood-sucking habits and possibly to their toxic metabolites secreted into the intestinal wall. Only a transient eosinophilia has been observed (Lie Kian Joe, 1947). Treatment to eradicate trichostrongyles is not satisfactory.

On a single occasion each of the following species of related bursate worms has been reported as an intestinal parasite from man: *Ostertagia ostertagi* and *O. circumcincta* (U. S. S. R.); *Hæmonchus contortus*, the sheep wireworm (Brazil), and possibly *Mecistocirrus digitatus* (Hongkong). In addition, *Metastrongylus elongatus*, the lung worm of hogs, has been found twice in the human respiratory tract and once in the human digestive tract of European subjects.

Strongyloides Stercoralis (Bavay, 1876) Stiles and Hassall, 1902
(The human threadworm, causing strongyloidiasis)

Historical and Geographical Notes

The human *Strongyloides* was first observed in the diarrheic stools of French troops who had served in Cochin-China. At necropsy of 5 of these men minute nematodes were recovered from the wall of the ileum and from the biliary and pancreatic ducts. Bavay (1876) named those organisms recovered from the feces *stercoralis* and those from the intestine *intestinalis*, but the studies of Grassi (1879), Perroncito (1880) and Leuckart (1882) demonstrated the two were different stages in the life cycle of the same species. Askanazy (1900) provided evidence that the parasitic females inhabited and oviposited in the intestinal mucosa. Several investigators including Looss (1905) and Fülleborn (1914) proved that infective-stage filariform larvas in the soil enter the skin and carry out a migration through the lungs similar to hookworms. Fülleborn (1926) demonstrated further that rhabditoid larvas in the feces may at times transform to the infective stage on moist perianal skin and be capable of producing autoinfection without leaving the human body, while Nishigori (1928), Faust (1932–1940), Hartz (1946) and other investigators found that internal autoinfection may occur.

Leichtenstern (1899) observed that under certain conditions, particularly in the Tropics, there are one or more free-living generations of *Strongyloides* which develop on the soil before infective filariform larvas appear, while in other cases there is direct development to the filariform stage.

Strongyloides stercoralis is primarily a parasite of warm climates but it has been found sporadically in temperate and even cold regions. In parts of Brazil and Panamá the incidence is much higher than in other countries in which careful parasitologic surveys have been conducted. Several hundred European prisoners of war contracted strongyloidiasis in Burma, Siam and Malaya during World War II (Caplan, 1949; Napier, 1949; Sandosham, 1952).

Epidemiology

In some respects *S. stercoralis* behaves like human hookworms; in other ways it is quite different. Eggs laid by the parasitic females in the intestinal mucosa hatch before they escape into the intestinal canal, so that only rhabditoid larvas are found free in the intestinal contents. The larvas feed in transit down the bowel and have usually transformed into the second rhabditoid stage by the time they are evacuated in the stool. Under favorable conditions on the soil they mature into the infective filariform stage within 24 to 48 hours. They have a greater affinity for water than hookworm larvas; however, on contact with human skin they burrow under epidermal scales or into hair follicles, enter cutaneous blood vessels and migrate through the lungs to the intestinal tract much like the hookworms. This *direct mode of development* is probably the most frequent type of life cycle of *Strongyloides*.

In warm climates with abundant rainfall rhabditoid larvas evacuated in the stool onto favorable soil may develop into free-living rhabditoid males and females, which mate and produce eggs that hatch and give birth to a second generation of rhabditoid larvas. Under optimal environmental conditions these larvas may likewise grow into rhabditoid adults. Usually after a single generation of free-living adults the rhabditoid larvas transform into the infective filariform stage. This is the *indirect mode of development.*

Another type of exposure to *Strongyloides stercoralis* is *autoinfection*, due to maturing of the larvas to the filariform stage on perianal skin, or before leaving the intestine, enabling them to enter the intestinal wall, penetrate into mesenteric venules and by portal-hepatic venous blood reach the right side of the heart and be carried to the lungs. Autoinfection probably explains the persistence of strongyloidiasis long after individuals have been removed from contact with infested soil.

Strongyloides infection is more common in adults than in young children, and is particularly prevalent in mental hospitals and prisons in warm, moist climates.

Dogs are occasionally found infected with strains of *Strongyloides* indistinguishable from *S. stercoralis*, yet all reliable evidence indicates that man almost invariably begets his own *Strongyloides* infection, as a result of his careless personal hygiene.

Morphology, Biology and Life Cycle

The Adult Worms of the Parasitic Generation.—The adult parasitic *Strongyloides stercoralis* are dimorphic: The males are rhabditoid and the females are filiform (Fig. 81).

Parasitic males (Fig. 81 *B*) have been found in experimentally infected dogs (Kreis, 1932; Faust, 1933) but have not been described in natural human infections, probably due to the fact that they do not invade the intestinal wall and are eliminated from the bowel shortly before or soon after the females begin to oviposit. The parasitic females (Fig. 81 *A*) are slender filiform worms, measuring up to 2.2 mm. in length by 30 to 75 microns in diameter.

While adolescent parasitic female *Strongyloides stercoralis* may be inseminated by males, a majority of them are probably parthenogenetic. Upon maturing, 28 days or less following cutaneous exposure of the human host, each parasitic female *S. stercoralis* lays several dozen eggs daily during the first few months of maximum fecundity.

Larvas of the Parasitic Generation.—The eggs laid by the parasitic females are thin-shelled, ovoidal, and measure 50 to 58 microns by 30 to 34 microns. As they filter through the mucosa towards the intestinal lumen

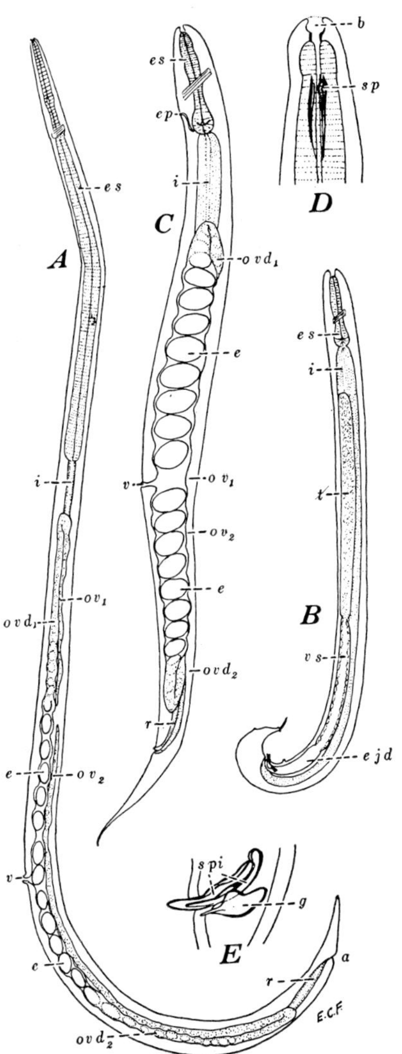

Fig. 81.—*Strongyloides stercoralis.* *A*, parasitic female, × 75; *B*, free-living male, × 160; *C*, free-living female, × 160; *D*, anterior end of free-living male, × 500; *E*, copulatory spicules and gubernaculum of male, greatly enlarged. *a*, anus; *b*, buccal chamber; *e*, uterine egg; *ejd*, ejaculatory duct; *ep*, excretory pore; *es*, esophagus; *g*, gubernaculum; *i*, midgut; ov_1 and ov_2, anterior and posterior ovaries; ovd_1 and ovd_2, anterior and posterior oviducts; *r*, rectum; *sp*, buccal spears; *spi*, copulatory spicules; *t*, testis, *v*, vulva; *vs*, seminal vesicle. (*A*, *B*, *C*, after Faust; *D*, *E*, adapted from Kreis; from Faust's *Human Helminthology*, Lea & Febiger, Philadelphia.)

they complete their development and hatch, setting free the fully developed first-stage rhabditoid larvas. As the larvas descend through the intestinal canal, they feed, grow, and in most infections probably moult once, so that the stage evacuated in the stool is the second rhabditoid larva (Fig. 73 *A*, 82 *A*).

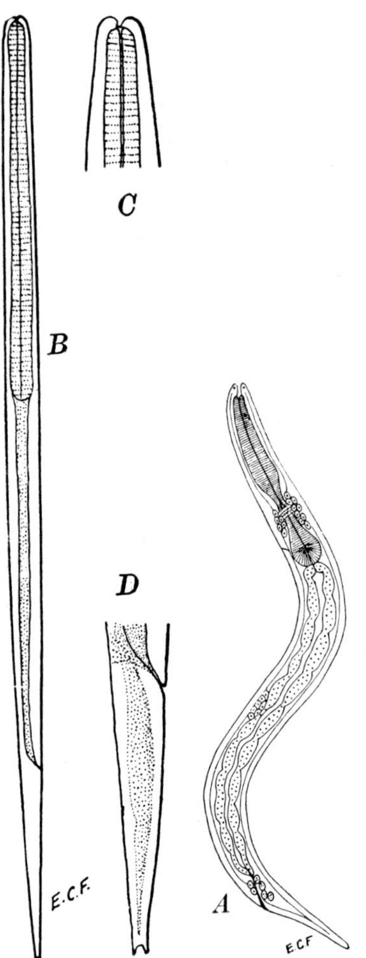

Fig. 82.—Larval stages of *Strongyloides stercoralis*. *A*, rhabditoid larva, × 310; *B*, filariform larva, × 120; *D*, *C*, anterior and posterior ends of filariform larva, × 540. (*A*, after Looss; from Faust's *Human Helminthology*, Lea & Febiger, Philadelphia.)

A day or two after the feces containing rhabditoid larvas are deposited on warm, moist, clayey soil in a shaded site metamorphosis to the filariform stage (Fig. 82 *B*) takes place. The larvas enter exposed human skin and initiate a new infection.

Autoinfection.—This is an abbreviated type of the direct mode of development, in which metamorphosis to the infective (filariform) larval stage occurs within the intestinal canal or on the perianal skin, and reinfection of the individual takes place without the organisms leaving the host's body.

Free-living Generations.—The interpolation of one or more free-living generations undoubtedly represents the original and only mode of development of species of *Strongyloides* before they acquired an adaptation to parasitism. It is not common in *S. stercoralis* outside of the Tropics. In a particular infection it may occur as the exclusive type or be associated with the more common, direct cycle type.

Both males and females of the free-living generation are rhabditoid forms. The male (Fig. 81 *B*) is broadly cylindrical, with a rounded anterior end and a pointed caudal extremity curved conspicuously to the ventral side. It measures about 0.7 mm. long by 40 to 50 microns in diameter. The female (Fig. 81 *C*) more closely resembles the rhabditoid larval stage with an attenuated posterior extremity beginning just behind the vulva and terminating in a sharply pointed tail. Free-living females require insemination before they lay fertile eggs.

The eggs of the free-living generation are laid in an early stage of embryonation, develop rapidly in well-aërated, warm, wet ground, and hatch. In 2 or 3 days, free-living rhabditoid larvas have either developed into rhabditoid adults or have transformed into filariform larvas.

Larval Migration from the Skin to the Intestine.—On contact with the skin (and occasionally the buccal mucosa) filariform larvas of *S. stercoralis* (either direct or indirect mode of development) bore their way through the epidermis down to the small blood vessels, penetrate into the venules and are carried through the right side of the heart to the lungs. When they reach the pulmonary capillaries they break out into the alveoli, where they moult twice and transform into post-filariform and then adolescent worms (Faust, 1933). In case a large number of filariform larvas are migrating through the lungs simultaneously, some of them may pass into the arterial circulation, to be trapped in various tissues and occasionally to be evacuated in the urine (Whitehall and Miller, 1944).

In some individuals, the presence of the worms in the terminal respiratory passages provokes a remarkable cellular infiltration. This may result in female worms entering the bronchial epithelium and developing to maturity in this location, but a majority ascend the respiratory tree to the epiglottis, and pass through the stomach to the small intestine, where the females burrow into the mucosa, mature and begin to oviposit.

The life cycle of *Strongyloides stercoralis* is synoptically illustrated in Figure 83.

Location of Parasitic Females in the Intestine.—The most common level of the intestine parasitized by *S. stercoralis* is the duodenum, next is the jejunum. However, all levels of the digestive tract from the pyloric wall of the stomach to the anus have been found invaded in both human and experimental hosts.

Almost without exception the parasitic females live among the epithelial and gland cells, or in the tunica propria, and under normal conditions do not penetrate the muscularis mucosæ into the deeper layers of the intestinal wall.

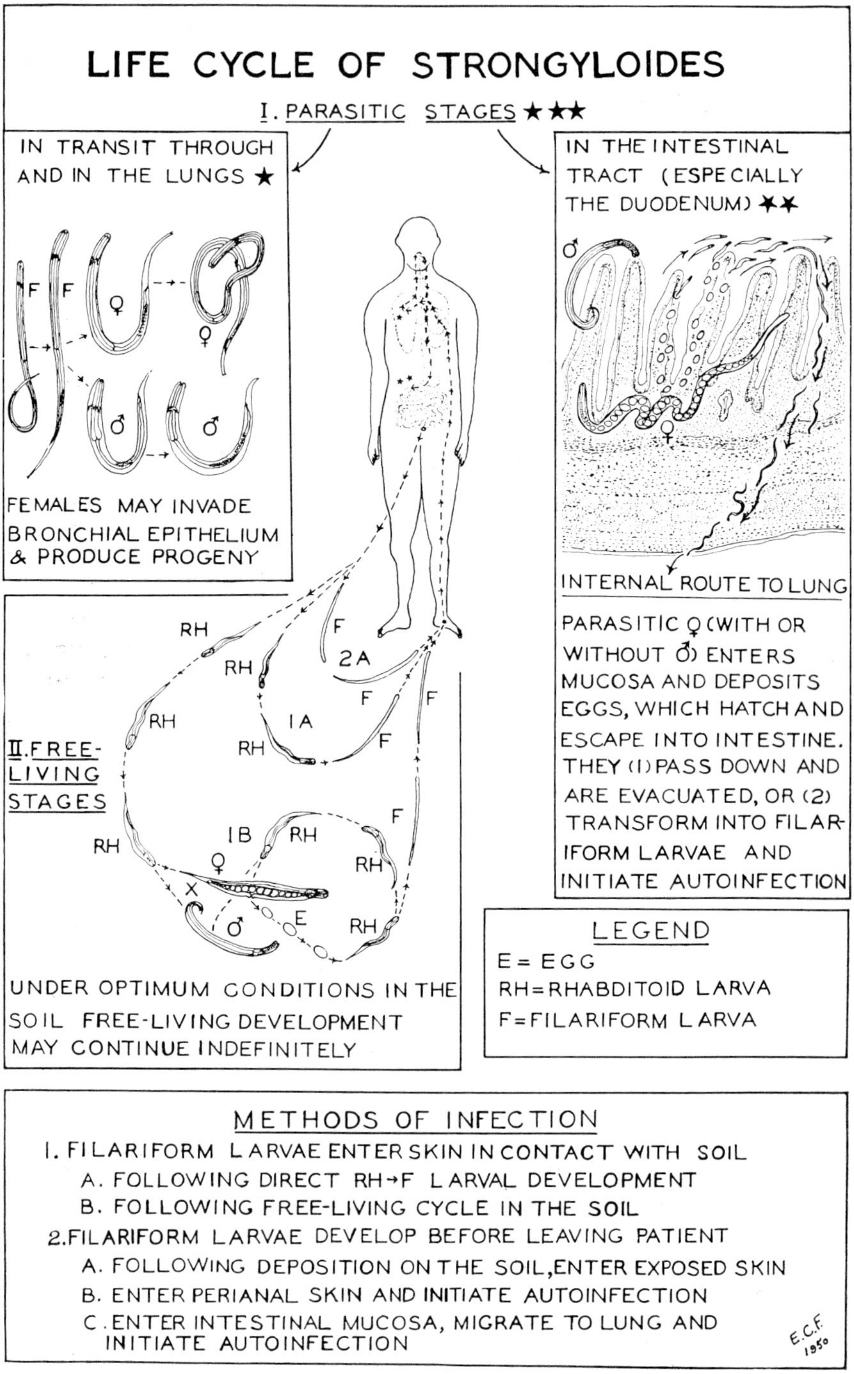

LIFE CYCLE OF STRONGYLOIDES

I. PARASITIC STAGES ★★★

IN TRANSIT THROUGH AND IN THE LUNGS ★

F F ♀ ♀ ♂ ♂

FEMALES MAY INVADE BRONCHIAL EPITHELIUM & PRODUCE PROGENY

IN THE INTESTINAL TRACT (ESPECIALLY THE DUODENUM) ★★

♂ ♀

INTERNAL ROUTE TO LUNG

PARASITIC ♀ (WITH OR WITHOUT ♂) ENTERS MUCOSA AND DEPOSITS EGGS, WHICH HATCH AND ESCAPE INTO INTESTINE. THEY (1) PASS DOWN AND ARE EVACUATED, OR (2) TRANSFORM INTO FILARIFORM LARVAE AND INITIATE AUTOINFECTION

II. FREE-LIVING STAGES

RH F RH 2A RH F F RH 1A F RH F 1B RH RH RH ♀ X ♂ E RH

UNDER OPTIMUM CONDITIONS IN THE SOIL FREE-LIVING DEVELOPMENT MAY CONTINUE INDEFINITELY

LEGEND

E = EGG

RH = RHABDITOID LARVA

F = FILARIFORM LARVA

METHODS OF INFECTION

1. FILARIFORM LARVAE ENTER SKIN IN CONTACT WITH SOIL
   - A. FOLLOWING DIRECT RH→F LARVAL DEVELOPMENT
   - B. FOLLOWING FREE-LIVING CYCLE IN THE SOIL
2. FILARIFORM LARVAE DEVELOP BEFORE LEAVING PATIENT
   - A. FOLLOWING DEPOSITION ON THE SOIL, ENTER EXPOSED SKIN
   - B. ENTER PERIANAL SKIN AND INITIATE AUTOINFECTION
   - C. ENTER INTESTINAL MUCOSA, MIGRATE TO LUNG AND INITIATE AUTOINFECTION

FIG. 83.—Life cycle of *Strongyloides stercoralis*. (From Craig and Faust's *Clinical Parasitology*, Lea & Febiger, Philadelphia.)

Pathogenesis and Symptomatology

The Skin Lesion.—No lesion has been described comparable to the "ground itch" of hookworm infection. Usually *Strongyloides* larvas proceed rather rapidly from the sites of entry to the cutaneous blood vessels but some of them may temporarily become trapped in the dermis and possibly never reach their destination.

Larval Migration through the Lungs.—On arrival in the pulmonary capillaries the larvas produce hemorrhage at each site of escape into the alveoli, followed by a pronounced cellular infiltration into the invaded respiratory passages. Conspicuous among these cells are eosinophils, lymphocytes and epithelioid cells. Occasionally this results in young female worms invading the bronchial epithelium, where they develop into adults and oviposit. If many larvas are in transit through the lungs there will be small areas of consolidation in the terminal bronchioles, resulting in a *Strongyloides* pneumonitis.

The Adult Worms in the Intestine.—Not more than 28 days following invasion of the skin, a majority of the young worms will have arrived in the intestine, the females will have entered the mucosa, matured, begun to oviposit, the eggs will have hatched and active rhabditoid larvas are for the first time present in the stools. The male worms which may have reached the intestinal tract do not enter the mucosa, produce no detectable damage and therefore do not contribute to the pathologic picture.

Unless large numbers of females are simultaneously entering the mucosa they cause relatively little irritation as they penetrate between epithelial cells to the base of the glands or into the tunica propria of the villi (Hartz, 1946). Damage to the invaded intestinal mucosa is cumulative, due to continued movements of the females within the tissues, the deposition and hatching of the eggs, and the active escape of first-stage rhabditoid larvas out of the mucosa into the intestinal canal. There is an infiltration of eosinophils, epithelioid cells, occasionally giant cells, and fibroblasts. The affected tissue becomes increasingly non-functional and areas of 0.5 to 1.0 cm. diameter are at times sloughed off down to the muscularis mucosæ.

Systemic damage to the intestinal infection consists of sensitization and probably toxic reactions, varying in degree in different individuals and in different stages of the infection. As in ascariasis (page 229), these effects are potentially enhanced or reactivated by reinoculation or by auto-infection.

Symptoms.—Entry of the filariform larvas of *S. stercoralis* from the surface of the skin to the cutaneous blood vessels produces a relatively mild needling sensation at each site of penetration and often is not specially noted by the patient. In transit through the lungs the young worms may cause symptoms suggesting bronchopneumonia, at times with consolidation of one or more lobules. In case female worms develop to maturity in the bronchial epithelium they may be responsible for chronic bronchial disease (Kyle, McKay and Sparling, 1948).

In a voluntary self-infection, Desportes (1944–1945) developed prodromal abdominal symptoms 26 days after skin inoculation, consisting initially of hunger pains, followed in a few days by profound lassitude and diffuse abdominal pain which increased in frequency and intensity up to 6 weeks, after which time it became less acute. Jones (1950) found that the most common complaint is abdominal pain which is rather sharply localized.

The blood picture at the beginning of the intestinal phase is typically one of leukocytosis, with a ratio of eosinophils to total white cells ranging from 5.0 to 68 or even 75%. In the chronic stage neutropenia, monocytosis and a considerably smaller percentage of eosinophils are characteristic.

In internal autoinfection the invasion of filariform (or rhabditoid) larvas into the deeper layers of the intestinal wall and their migration by internal blood routes to the lungs may produce paralytic ileus (Nolasco and Africa, 1926), hepatitis, cholecystitis, myocarditis, pneumonia or tracheitis, with symptoms of abdominal pain, diarrhea alternating with constipation, tender liver, dyspnea, cough, hemoptysis and low-grade fever (Kyle, McKay and Sparling, 1948). Whitehall and Miller (1944) reported genito-urinary complication of intestinal infection in a male patient who gave a history of abdominal discomfort, nocturia, urinary incontinence and diurnal urgency to urinate, with the stools negative and the urine positive for *Strongyloides* larvas. Redewill (1949) studied genito-urinary strongyloidiasis in a man and his wife, in whom there was severe urticaria of the preputia.

For the relationship of *S. stercoralis* to "creeping eruption" see "*Larva Migrans*," page 277.

Diagnosis

Since there is no well-defined clinical syndrome which is pathognomonic of strongyloidiasis, proof of the infection depends on demonstration of the organism. Routine diagnosis is made by recovery of active rhabditoid larvas (Fig. 73 *A*) in fecal films examined microscopically, but occasionally filariform larvas (Fig. 82 *B*) are found in such preparations, particularly if the feces have stood at laboratory temperature for a day or more before examination is made.

Many times an exhaustive examination of the stools of *Strongyloides* patients will be negative when duodenal aspiration will provide a positive diagnosis. Jones (1950) demonstrated active larvas in 91% of 71 *Strongyloides* patients on whom duodenal aspiration was performed, in contrast to 27.4% positives of 952 stools and 80% of patients diagnosed by multiple stool examination. However, stools are sometimes positive when duodenal aspirates are negative. Occasionally larvas of *S. stercoralis* are recovered from the sputum, urine or aspirates from body cavities.

Treatment

Many drugs have been employed in attempts to cure *Strongyloides stercoralis* infection; the only one which has been conclusively demonstrated to have moderate efficacy is *gentian violet medicinal.* It was introduced into the United States by the author in 1930 (Faust, 1936). For routine treatment it is administered orally in the form of $1\frac{1}{2}$-hour Seal-Ins enteric-coated tablets. The standard course of treatment for adults consists of 2×0.032 Gm. ($\frac{1}{2}$ grain) tablets 3 times daily with meals for a period of 16 days (total, 3.2 Gm. or 48 grains). For children, the daily dose is 1 centigram for each year of apparent age. (See Table 5, page 66.) Recently acquired infections are more likely to be cured than old chronic infections.

Some individuals are unable to take a full course of gentian violet tablets, due to nausea, vomiting and acute colicky pain in the pit of the stomach. Unless these manifestations of intolerance are severe and continue beyond the first few days, patients should be encouraged to complete the treatment. Other persons are able to take intensive gentian violet therapy and complete a full course in 5 to 7 days.

For cases which do not respond satisfactorily to the standard treatment the author (Faust, 1936) has recommended transduodenal intubation of 25 cc. of a 1% aqueous solution of gentian violet medicinal.

Another drug which may be useful in strongyloidiasis is *Hetrazan* (diethyl carbamazine). In preliminary clinical trials, it has been administered in the amount of 2 mgm. per kilo body weight 3 times daily for 20 days. In some instances, marked clinical improvement and disappearance of the larvas from the stools has occurred. (See Table 5, page 66.)

Prognosis

Strongyloidiasis at times produces exhaustion as a result of extreme dehydration, occasionally with fatal outcome. Otherwise the prognosis is good with respect to survival but chronic infections commonly cause disability. Treatment should be carried out on all cases in which there is clinical evidence that illness is due to the infection. This is particularly important when autoinfection is suspected. Absence of eosinophils in the peripheral blood of *Strongyloides* patients is a poor prognostic sign.

Control

Control of human strongyloidiasis is concerned primarily with reduction of the sources of exposure, both extrinsically and in the individual. Since ground contaminated with *Strongyloides*-positive human stools will frequently contain infective-stage larvas in one to two days, special precautions must be taken to prevent promiscuous defecation on the soil.

A second aspect of control is related to autoinfection in the infected individual. Today autoinfection is accepted as a comparatively common method of reinfection. Hence, ways must be found to reduce the chances of autoinfection: (1) by educating the patient to keep his anal area free of fecal soil and (2) by reducing the opportunities for internal autoinfection. The latter can be accomplished by keeping the bowels open, *i. e.*, avoiding constipation, and by periodic medication with gentian violet on possibly Hetrazan.

Rhabditoid Nematodes as Pseudoparasites of Man

Species of the genus *Rhabditis* and related free-living forms which are coprophagous in their mode of nutrition are from time to time seen in human stools and are diagnostically confused with the rhabditoid larvas and free-living adult stages of *Strongyloides*, although some have a long acuminate tail. These pseudoparasites can be readily distinguished from the rhabditoid stages of *Strongyloides*, hookworms and *Trichostrongylus* by an examination of the esophagus. The species of *Rhabditis* have a median esophageal swelling (Fig. 73, *D*, *mb*) which is lacking in *Strongyloides*, hookworms and *Trichostrongylus* (Fig. 73 *A–C*).

The recovery of *Rhabditis* in fecal smears usually indicates a contamination of the specimen after it has been passed, but occasionally these nematodes may be ingested and survive passage through the digestive tract (*Rhabditis hominis*, *R. donbass*, *R. schachtiella*). Other species (*R. pellio*, *R. axei*) have been sporadically reported from vaginal secretions and urine, while *R. niellyi* was once recovered from an itching cutaneous papule.

The vinegar eel (*Turbatrix aceti*), which grows in "mother of vinegar," has been diagnosed from the urine and vaginal secretions of women who used vinegar as a vaginal douche, and on one occasion from a contaminated (?) specimen of urine passed by a male patient.

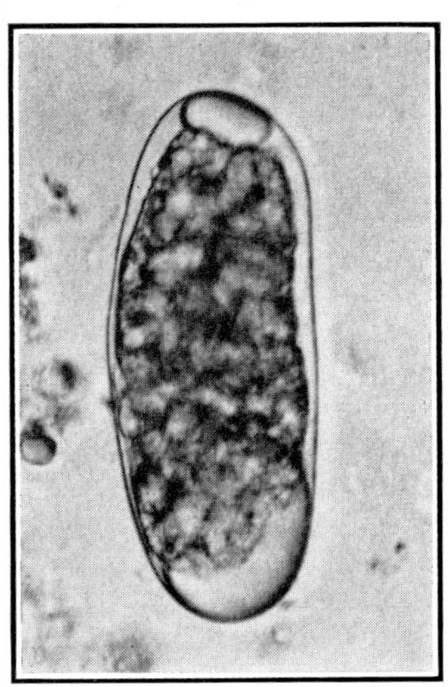

Fig. 84.—Photomicrograph of egg of *Meloidogne javanica* (syn. *Heterodera marioni*, *H. radicicola*) from human stool. × 500. (Courtesy of Dr. T. B. Magath, from Craig and Faust's *Clinical Parasitology*, Lea & Febiger, Philadelphia.)

Other nematodes which are natural parasites of plants are consumed as food. The enlarged underground roots of radishes, turnips, rutabagas and parsnips are particularly subject to infection with these nematodes. The species most frequently involved is *Meloidogne javanica* (syn. *Heterodera marioni* or *H. radicicola*). The stage recovered in the stool is commonly the partially embryonated egg, which is thin-shelled, hyaline, elongate-ovoidal with rounded ends, and measures 82 to 120 microns by 24 to 43 microns (Fig. 84). These eggs may be confused with infertile *Ascaris* or hookworm eggs and, if they are somewhat flattened on one side, with those of pinworms.

SPIRUROID NEMATODES

These roundworms vary remarkably in their appearance: Some are delicate filiform objects, others are wiry and still others are stout and relatively short. All have a moderately slender esophagus lacking a posterior swelling. In most species the males have caudal wings (alæ). In all species for which the life cycle has been elucidated there is an arthropod intermediate host.

Gongylonema Pulchrum Molin, 1857

This thread-like nematode is a cosmopolitan parasite of ruminants, and has also been found in pigs, bears, hedgehogs, monkeys, and occasionally in man, with the following diagnosed human cases in different countries: Italy, 2; Germany, 1; Bulgaria, 3; U. S. S. R., 1; Ceylon, 1, and the United States, 9.

In ruminants the male worms reach a length of 62 mm. and a diameter of 0.15 to 0.3 mm., and the female worms, 145 mm. and 0.2 to 0.5 mm. respectively. The anterior end of the worm is provided with 8 longitudinal series of cuticular blister-like bosses, which converge anteriorly towards the small buccal cavity. The caudal end of the male is provided with an asymmetrical pair of wings, median ventral to which are several pairs of pre-anal and post-anal papillæ. The female lays fully embryonated eggs which are transparent, thick-shelled, broadly ovoidal and measure 50 to 70 microns by 25 to 37 microns.

When ingested by various species of dung beetles and cockroaches they hatch, burrow into its hemal cavity and become encapsulated. The definitive host is infected by swallowing the infected insect (Ransom and Hall, 1915; Baylis, Sheather and Andrews, 1925), the larvas are freed and migrate up to the esophagus or mouth cavity, in the mucous and submucous membranes of which they develop into adult worms and in which the females oviposit.

In the reported human cases worms have been extracted from, or have spontaneously emerged from the lips, gums, hard and soft palate, tonsil and angle of the jaw, but never from the esophagus. The symptoms in human infection consist primarily of local irritation and nervousness, and in one case a pharyngitis and stomatitis. These manifestations disappear on removal of the worm. No chemotherapy is indicated. Care should be taken not to consume raw, unfiltered water.

Thelazia Callipæda Railliet and Henry, 1910, and

Thelazia Californiensis Kofoid and Williams, 1935

These nematodes most commonly reside in the conjunctival sac of the host. *T. callipæda* is Oriental in its geographic distribution and commonly parasitizes the dog, while *T. californiensis* has been reported only from California. Workers in California have reported the cat, sheep, black bear and two species of deer parasitized with *T. californiensis*. Human infection with the former species has been described six times from China, twice from Korea and once from India. Only a single human infection with *T. californiensis* has been published.

The adult worms are wiry, creamy-white threads which measure 4.5 to 13 mm. by 0.25 to 0.75 mm. (males) and 6.2 to 17 mm. by 0.3 to 0.85 mm. (females). The posterior end of the male is strongly curved towards the ventral side. The vulva in the female opens midventrally a considerable distance in front of the equatorial plane. The female lays hyaline, thin-shelled ovoidal eggs. The life cycle of species of *Thelazia* has not been elucidated. It seems possible that the ingestion of cockroaches or other insects harboring the encapsulated larval stage may be responsible for infection with mammalian species of *Thelazia*.

Thelazia causes considerable damage to the tissues of the eye, including inflammation of the conjunctival sac, excess lacrymation, and superficial scarification of the corneal conjunctiva as the worms migrate out of the conjunctival sac across the front of the eye and back again. They may be easily removed with eye forceps after the introduction of a few drops of procaine into the conjunctival sac.

Physaloptera Caucasica von Linstow, 1902

The reservoir hosts of this worm are African monkeys but the species has a considerably wider geographic range than tropical Africa. Infection of the human intestinal tract has been reported from the Caucasus, tropical Africa and Southern Rhodesia.

The worms are relatively large, stout, creamy-white objects, which measure 14 to 50 mm. long by 0.7 to 1.0 mm. in diameter (males) and 24 to 100 mm. long by 1.14 to 2.8 mm. in diameter (females). Although they have a superficial resemblance to young ascarids, they may be distinguished by a cuticular collarette, a pair, rather than three, fleshy lips surrounding the mouth, and distinctive dental processes and papillæ just inside the mouth. The smooth, hyaline thick-shelled eggs are broadly ovoidal, measure 44 to 65 microns by 32 to 45 microns and are fully embryonated when laid.

Mönnig (1934) has suggested that coprophagous beetles or cockroaches may be the required intermediate hosts of species of *Physaloptera*.

The adult worms live with their heads deeply buried in the wall of the digestive tract from the level of the esophagus to the mid-level of the ileum. Likewise the liver may at times be parasitized. Epidemiologic, clinical and preventive aspects of this infection have not been studied.

Gnathostoma Spinigerum Owen, 1938, and

Gnathostoma Hispidum Fedtschenko, 1872

Biological Data.—These nematodes are natural parasites of certain mammals which feed on fish or other cold-blooded vertebrates. Adults of *Gnathostoma spinigerum* are found in tumors of the digestive tract of the cat, wild cat, leopard, tiger, dog, and weasel, from Japan to Indonesia and India. Human infection with this species, almost invariably in an advanced larval stage in extra-intestinal sites, has been reported from Thailand, Malaya, Indo-China, China, Japan, Indonesia, India and Palestine. Adults of *G. hispidum* have been obtained from gastric tumors of hogs and wild hogs in Japan, China, India and other parts of Asia, Europe and Australia. Human infections with immature worms of this species in extra-intestinal sites have been described once each from Japan and China and twice from India.

The adult worms of both species are robust cylindroidal objects with rounded ends. In the tiger the adult males of *G. spinigerum* reach a length of 11 to 25 mm. and the females, 25 to 54 mm. They possess a subglobose cephalic swelling separated from the body proper by a distinct cervical constriction (Fig. 85 *B*). Both ends are curved ventrally and in the digestive tract the worms are tightly coiled within the tumor cavity. The head portion of the adults is provided with eight encircling rows of sharp curved hooklets (Fig. 85 *B*, *C*). The eggs deposited by the females in the tumor cavities are transparent, ovoidal, with a pitted outer shell and a mucoid plug at one end (Fig. 85 *G*). They measure 65 to 70 microns by 38 to 40 microns and are essentially unembryonated when evacuated in the feces of the cat, which is the natural domestic host.

The life cycle of *G. spinigerum* has been elucidated by Prommas and Daengsvang (1933, 1936, 1937) and Daengsvang and Tansurat (1938) in Thailand, Yoshida (1935) in Japan, and Africa, Refuerzo and Garcia (1936) in the Philippines. On dilution with water, eggs in the host's feces become fully embryonated within 1 week at temperatures of 27° to 31° C. and hatch. First-stage rhabditoid larvas reportedly actively enter water fleas (*Cyclops*), bore their way into the hemal cavity and in 10 to 14 days transform into second-stage larvas. When the infected *Cyclops* is ingested by fresh-water fishes, frogs or snakes, the larvas migrate into the flesh, become encapsulated and transform into the third stage. Consumption of the infected flesh by a mammal provides opportunity for completion of the cycle: The larva is dissolved out of the tissues, invades the gastric (or intestinal) wall and develops to maturity in the cavity of the tumor, which has an opening into the lumen of the digestive tract through which eggs of the worm escape into the intestinal canal.

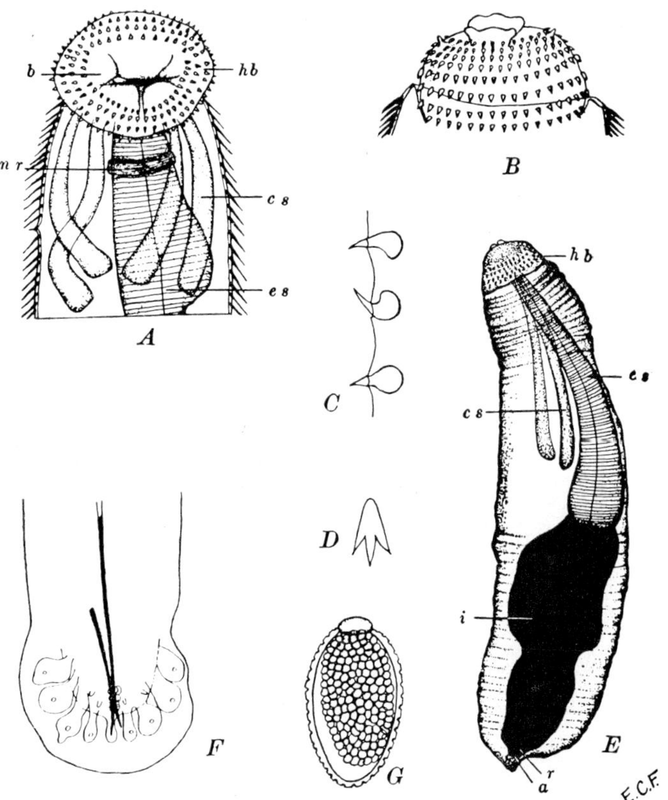

Fig. 85.—*Gnathostoma spinigerum.* *A*, anterior end of immature worm, ventral view, showing bulbous head (*hb*) with four rings of hooklets, two pairs of salivary glands (*cs*), nerve ring (*nr*) and esophagus (*es*), × 100; *B*, head of more mature worm, lateral view, with eight cephalic rings of hooklets, × 100; *C*, detail of head hooklets; *D*, detail of anterior body spine; *E*, immature worm, lateral view, showing head bulb (*hb*), esophagus (*es*), one pair of salivary glands (*cs*), midgut (*i*), rectum (*r*) and anus (*a*) × 40; *F*, posterior end of male, ventral view, showing peri-anal papillæ and copulatory spicules, × 40; *G*, egg from cat's feces, × 333. (*A-E*, after Morishita and Faust; *F*, after Baylis and Lane; from Faust's *Human Helminthology*, Lea & Febiger, Philadelphia.)

Epidemiology.—A majority of the human infections observed by Prommas and Daengsvang (1934) and Daengsvang (1949) in Thailand were in females, who had infected cats in their homes and consumed fermented uncooked flesh of the fish *Ophiocephalus striatus* which is a common host of the third larval stage of *G. spinigerum*.

Pathogenesis.—Species of *Gnathostoma* are not well adapted to man as the definitive host and hence, rarely if ever reach maturity within tumor cavities of the digestive tract. Instead, the excysted third-stage larva digested out of the flesh of the fish host migrates from the intestinal canal to the cutaneous or subcutaneous and somatic muscular tissues, where it produces a picture of "larva migrans," a granulomatous lesion or a stationary abscess. The worms have been observed in tissues from practically all surface areas, including the breast and occasionally the eye (Sen and Ghose, 1945; Chang, 1949; Daengsvang, 1949). Toumanoff and Le Van-Phung (1947) have called attention to the high eosinophilia which is characteristically associated with human gnathostomiasis. (See "*Larva Migrans*," page 277.)

Treatment.—This is concerned with removal of the larval or possibly the mature worms from the superficial tissues and is usually accomplished by excision.

Control.—Thorough cooking of fish or other second intermediate hosts intended for human consumption will prevent infection in man.

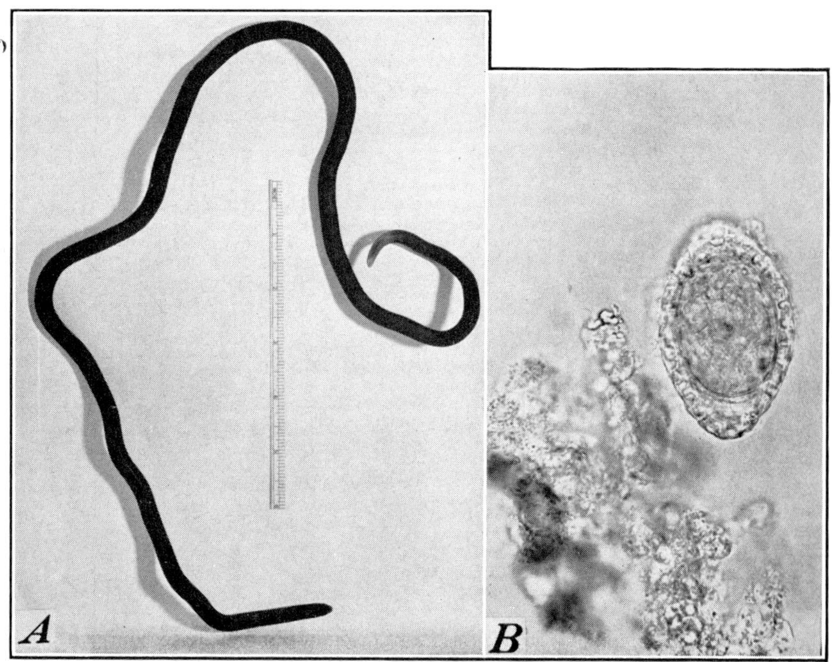

Fig. 86.—*Dioctophyma renale*. *A*, Mature female from kidney of a naturally infected dog; *B*, photomicrograph of egg, × 500. (Original, courtesy, Dr. T. B. Magath, Mayo Clinic.)

Dioctophyma Renale (Goeze, 1782) Stiles, 1901

(Giant kidney worm)

This large roundworm is rather widely distributed throughout the world in fish-eating mammals, including the dog, wolf, *Canis jubatus*, cat, puma, glutton, raccoon, coati, mink, marten, skunk, weasel, otter and seal, and has also been reported from the ox and horse. Ten authentic human infections are on record.

The adult worms (Fig. 86 *A*) are large cylindrical nematodes which are blood-red in color. The males measure 14 to 20 mm. in length by 4 to 6 mm. in diameter and at their posterior extremity have a bell-shaped copulatory bursa which is not supported by rays, as in the hookworms and their relatives, but on its inner aspect is covered with papillæ. The females measure up to 100 cm. in length by 5 to 12 mm. in diameter. The eggs (Fig. 86 *B*) are ellipsoidal, dirty brown in color, have deep pittings in the shell except at the poles, and measure 64 to 68 microns by 40 to 44 microns. The normal habitat of the adults is in the parenchyma of the kidney, but they may be found in the peritoneal and thoracic cavities.

The life cycle of *D. renale* is remarkably complicated. As described by Woodhead (1950), eggs which escape in the urine to the outside world require 6 months for complete embryonation and remain viable for at least 5 years. When ripe eggs are ingested by branchiobdellid annelids which are parasitic on fresh-water fishes, the eggs hatch and the emerging larvas migrate from the annelid's foregut into its tissues, transform into Gordius-like second-stage larvas and become encapsulated. If a fish consumes the infected annelids, the larvas migrate to the mesenteries of the fish, encyst and metamorphose into the third larval stage, then grow and transform into the fourth stage. Mammals which eat raw infected fish become the definitive hosts. The complete cycle from egg to adult worm requires a minimum of two years.

One to as many as eight adult *D. renale* have been recovered from infected mammals. In the kidney the worms gradually consume the parenchyma, finally leaving only the renal capsule. Animals or patients having the kidney infection discharge blood and pus in their urine, and suffer from acute renal colic. At times a worm migrates into the ureters and may escape through the urethra, but blockage of the urinary passages for any considerable time produces uremic poisoning with fatal outcome. All of the human infections have involved the kidneys. Diagnosis is made on microscopic demonstration of the typical eggs passed in the urine or on the spontaneous discharge of a worm *per urethram*. No chemotherapy has been developed for this disease. Control consists in thorough heating of all fresh-water fish before using it as food.

Trichinella Spiralis (Owen, 1835) Railliet, 1895

(Trichina worm, causing trichinosis)

Historical and Geographical Notes

This minute nematode was first observed in its coiled larval stage encapsulated in striated muscle of necropsy cases in London, in 1828 and 1833. Two years later Paget (1835) found the same stage of the parasite post-mortem in a tuberculosis patient and referred the material to Richard Owen, who described the organism and gave it the specific name *spiralis*. Von Siebold (1844) and Dujardin (1845) suggested that the form which had been observed was the undeveloped larval stage of a roundworm; in 1860 Leuckart and Virchow proved experimentally that this hypothesis was correct. Meanwhile pathologists in other European countries found trichina cysts in human muscle tissue, while Joseph Leidy (1846), in Philadelphia, first demonstrated their presence in domestic swine.

In 1860, Zenker provided evidence that this infection in man was responsible for serious and at times fatal symptoms. This stimulated unusual clinical interest throughout Europe and resulted in intensive study of the epidemiology and pathogenesis of trichinosis in man, together with the institution in Germany of microscopic examination of diaphragms of all slaughtered hogs to determine if the pork was safe for human consumption (Stäubli, 1909).

Until recent decades, human infection with *Trichinella spiralis* was an important clinical and public health problem in the pork-eating populations of Europe; today the infection is still widely distributed in Germany, Spain, Hungary and the lower Danube countries, but with relatively light incidence, and occasional epidemics (Roth, 1946). In contrast, it has come to be recognized as a widely disseminated, clinically important disease in the United States and parts of Latin America, with epidemic outbreaks in small or moderate-sized groups of the population.

Epidemiology

In nature trichinosis is an enzoötic disease, for the most part propagated between the black rat and the brown rat which are cannibalistic. Although all stages in the life cycle of *Trichinella spiralis* are developed in a single host, in order that the parasite may survive it is necessary that the infected flesh of one host be consumed by another. Almost all mammals are susceptible to infection.

Human trichinosis results for the most part from consumption of inadequately processed pork, but at times from eating bear meat (northwestern United States, Alaska) or walrus flesh (Greenland). In the United States during 1949–1952 hogs fed on grain or forage were found to have considerably less than 1% infection, with an average of only 5 and a maximum of 7 or 8 viable trichina cysts per gram of muscle tissue as determined by artificial digestion technic, whereas hogs fattened on uncooked municipal garbage from Boston, New York and Philadelphia had an incidence of 11.21 per cent with recovery of 100 to 2,741 larvas per gram by the same technic (Schwartz, 1952). Intensive infections in the United States, including epidemic outbreaks, are almost invariably traceable to garbage-fed hogs, both those raised in considerable numbers for the large slaughter houses and those butchered on the farm for very limited consumption.

The common methods of exposure to trichinosis in the United States are diagrammatically illustrated in Figure. 87.

On the basis of autopsy surveys of more than 10,000 persons in the United States it has been calculated that the average incidence of trichinosis is 16% (Sawitz, 1938), but Gould (1952) believes that more thorough examination would reveal about 30%. Of the 350,000 estimated new cases developing in the United States each year, 16,000 may be expected to have symptoms of clinical grade (Link, 1952). The incidence of trichinosis varies within wide limits in different parts of the United States (Craig and Faust, 1951). Although human trichinosis has been found to occur in all Latin American countries surveyed except Panamá and Puerto Rico, moderately high incidence has been reported only from Mexico and Chile. Alicata (1938), in Hawaii, found 15% of wild hogs infected with *Trichinella spiralis* and 7.4% of a random sampling of human diaphragms positive. Epidemics have occurred in recent years in the eastern, northern, western and southwestern parts of the United States, Sweden (Roth, 1946), Greenland (Roth, 1948) and Syria (Brumpt, 1949). Stoll (1947) has estimated that 27.8 million persons throughout the world have trichinosis and that three-fourths of these live in North America. The total figure appears to err considerably on the conservative side.

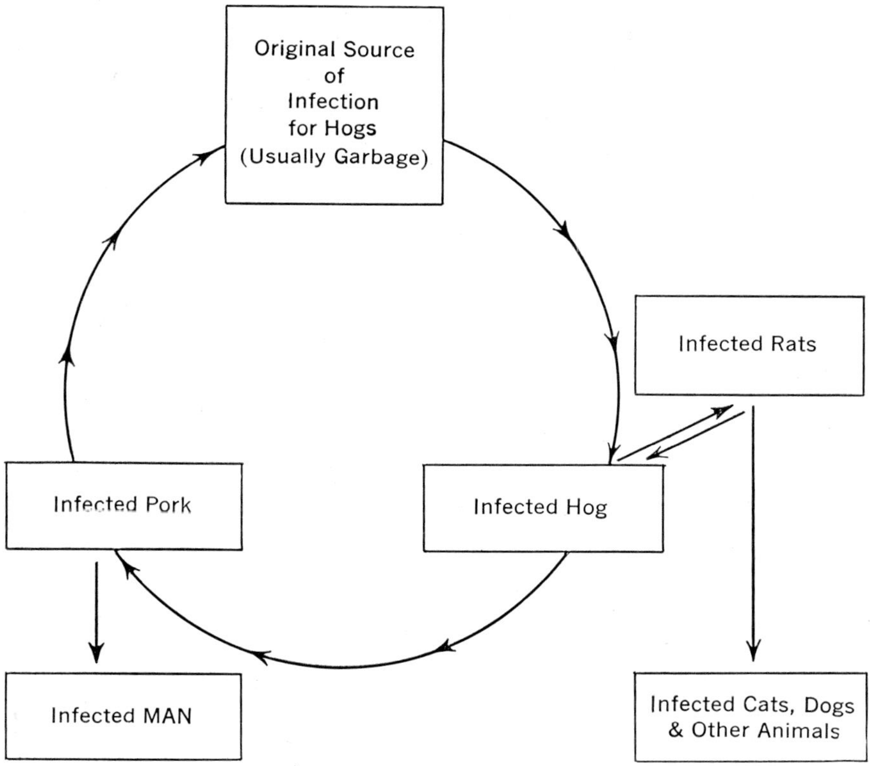

FIG. 87.—Diagram illustrating the common methods of exposure to trichinosis in the continental United States. (From Faust's *Human Helminthology*, Lea & Febiger, Philadelphia.)

Morphology, Biology and Life Cycle

The adult *Trichinella spiralis* is a delicate thread-like nematode (Fig. 88) hardly visible to the unaided eye. The male (Fig. 88 *A*) measures 1.4 to 1.6 mm. in length by 40 to 50 microns in diameter; it is very slender anteriorly but somewhat more robust in its posterior half. The cloacal opening is terminal and is guarded by a pair of conspicuous conical papillæ. The female (Fig. 88 *B*) is somewhat more than twice as long as the male and about one and a half times as large in diameter. The vulvar opening lies midventrally approximately one-fifth the body length from the anterior end.

When the excysted larvas first invade the intestinal mucosa, typically at the level of the duodenum and adjacent segment of the jejunum, they enter the glandular crypts where they develop to maturity, copulate and

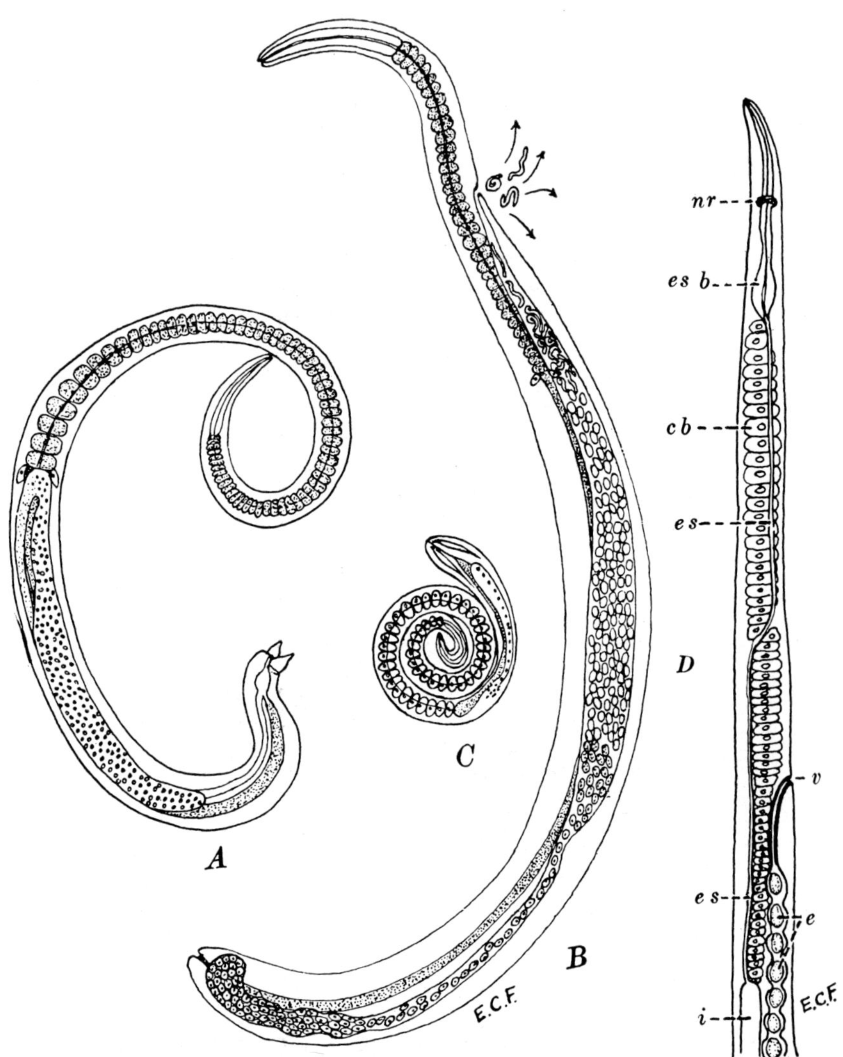

FIG. 88.—*Trichinella spiralis.* *A*, adult male, with tubular testis originating in the posterior region of the body, ascending anteriorwards to the equatorial plane, then bending abruptly and proceeding posteriorwards as the dilated vas deferens, which joins the delicate ejaculatory tubules that empties into the cloaca at the posterior end of the body; *B*, adult female with club-shaped ovary in the posterior part of the body, constricted oviduct and distended uterus which opens through the vulva in the anterior fifth of the body; *C*, larva recently deposited by female; *D*, anterior end of female, showing esophagus (*es*) with its cell bodies (*cb*) and pseudo-bulb (*es b*), uterine egg (*e*), midgut (*i*), nerve ring (*nr*) and vulva (*v*). *A*, *B*, × 90; *C*, × 660; *D*, greatly enlarged. (*A*, *B*, after Yorke and Maplestone; *C*, adapted from Staübli; *D*, after Chitwood, from Faust's *Human Helminthology*, Lea & Febiger, Philadelphia.)

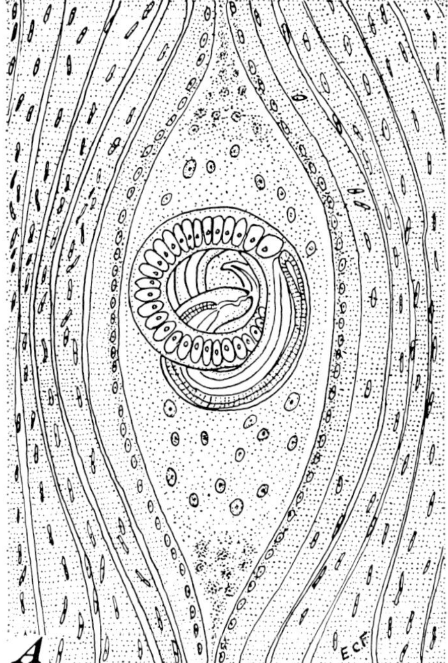

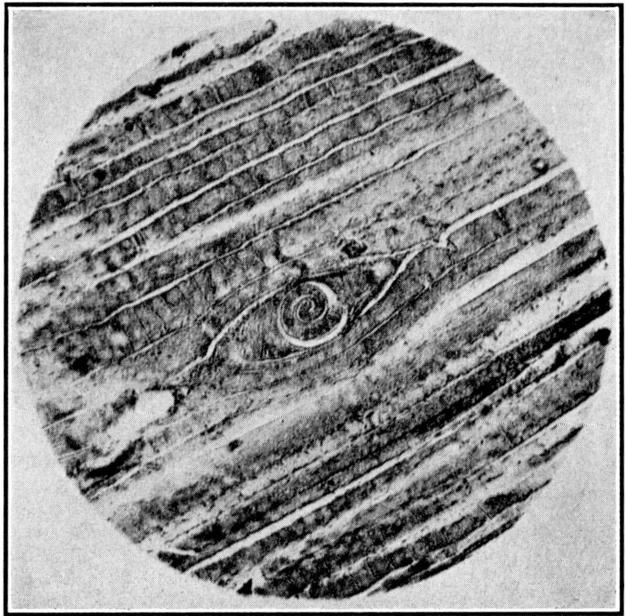

B

FIG. 89.—Encapsulated larvas of *Trichinella spiralis*. *A*, Young cyst about three weeks old, greatly enlarged; *B*, photomicrograph of mature viable cyst. (*A*, adapted from Tang; *B*, after Aldridge; from Craig and Faust's *Clinical Parasitology*, Lea & Febiger, Philadelphia.)

the female proceeds to produce uterine eggs in not more than 5 days. The males are rather rapidly dislodged from the mucosa, are swept down the bowel and are eliminated, but the females burrow more deeply into the mucosal cells, the interglandular stroma, the muscularis mucosæ and even the mesenteric lymph nodes. Soon they begin to larviposit (Fig. 88 *B*). The little larvas measure about 100 by 6 microns. At first many of them (Fig. 88 *C*) escape into the intestinal canal but as the mother worms become more deeply buried in the intestinal wall an increasing number of the larvas reach the mesenteric venules or lymphatics and become distributed throughout the body. The females continue to produce progeny in limited numbers for 4 to 16 weeks or more, with a total output of about 1500.

Between the 7th and 14th day after exposure most of the larvas have entered the blood stream and have been filtered out in striated muscle.

Encapsulation begins about the 21st day, with the production of an ellipsoidal sheath around the tightly coiled larva (Fig. 89 *A*, *B*). These cysts have their long axis parallel to that of the muscle fibers. Muscles most heavily parasitized are the diaphragm, larynx, base of the tongue, abdomen, intercostals, biceps, psoas, pectoral, gastrocnemius and deltoid. Encapsulation does not take place in the myocardium. As the larva grows to a length of 0.8 to 1.0 mm. within the cyst capsule, it provokes inflammation and degeneration of adjacent muscle fibers, with the formation of a double-walled adventitious capsule. Although some encapsulated larvas remain viable for many years, many of them become calcified between the sixth and twelfth month.

Fig. 90 provides a synoptic diagram of the consecutive stages in the life cycle and their time relationship to the lesions produced and the cardinal symptoms.

Pathogenesis and Symptomatology

Pathogenesis.—The entry of the young excysted worms into the intestinal mucosa causes catarrhal inflammation and at times profuse hemorrhage due to irritative damage to host cells and acute eosinophilic cellular reaction around the invaders.

Once larviposition has begun and the larvas are in migration through the tissues, their temporary lodgment in capillaries or perivascular sites provokes the same type of cellular response. This is particularly notable in the myocardium through which the larvas migrate but in which they do not encyst, with necrosis and fragmentation of the muscle fibers followed by fibrocytic repair. Similarly, if they become temporarily trapped in the capillaries of the brain, eyes, lungs or other organs, an acute inflammatory reaction occurs around the invaders.

On invasion of striated muscle fibers from the adjacent capillaries, the larvas become tightly coiled on themselves and produce an immediate tissue change consisting of inflammation of the sarcolemma of the involved muscle fibers, fragmentation of the fibers and deposition of a primary (inner) capsular membrane, then formation of a thicker (outer) adventitious coat from the endomysium. The completed capsule is ellipsoidal with blunt ends (Fig. 89). As soon as complete encapsulation has been accomplished the larva is effectively isolated. Eventually the entire cyst becomes calcified as a result of the invasion of fat cells at the two poles of the capsule.

In addition to the intense focal infiltration of eosinophils around adults and larvas of *T. spiralis* in the tissues there is a characteristic hypereosinophilia in the circulating blood.

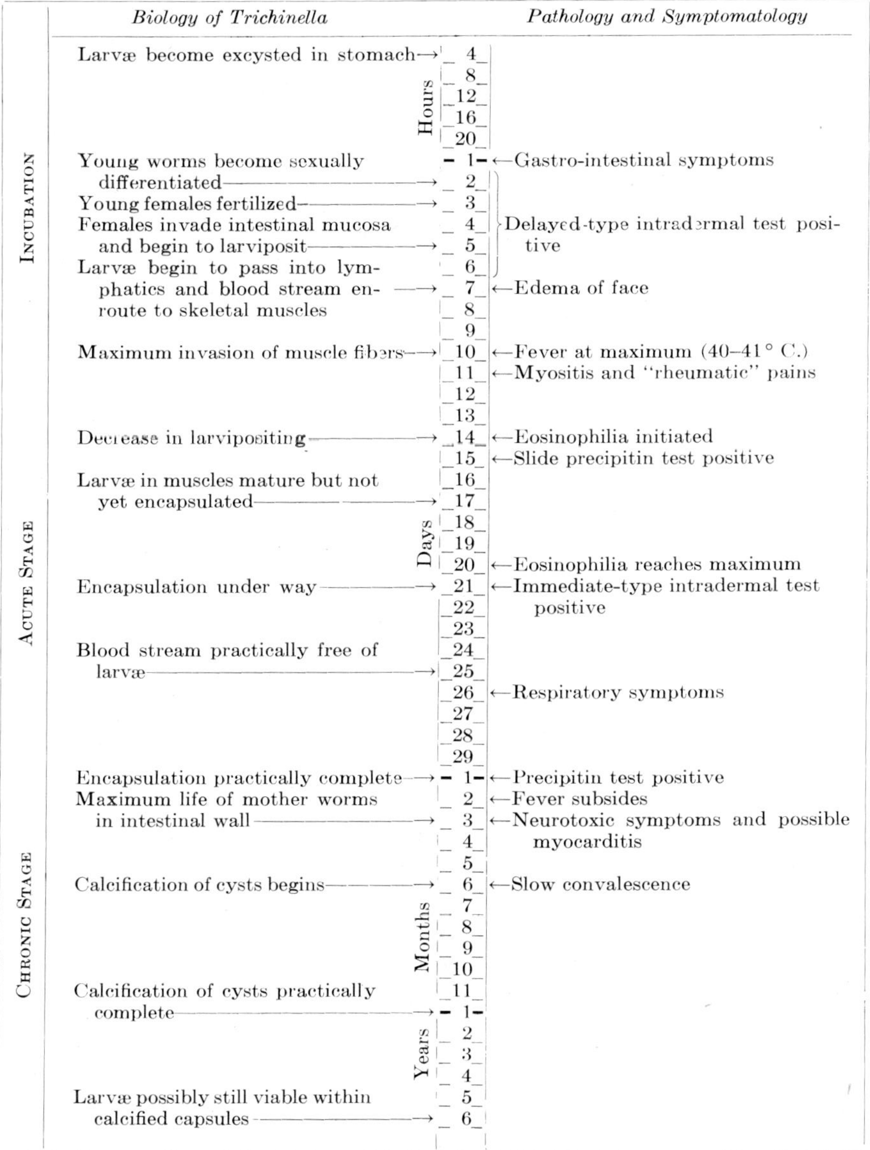

Fig. 90.—Synoptic diagram illustrating (*on left*) the progressive biological stages of *Trichinella spiralis* and (*on right*) the parallel clinical picture. (After Cameron, from Faust's *Human Helminthology*, Lea & Febiger, Philadelphia.)

Symptomatology.—During the invasion of the duodenal and jejunal mucosa by a large number of excysted trichina larvas the symptoms mimic those of salmonellosis ("acute food poisoning"). This syndrome lasts through the 7th day. Meanwhile larval migration is responsible for severe, and at times completely incapacitating myositis ("muscular rheumatism"), producing difficulty in breathing, mastication, speech and use of the extremities. Dyspnea may be intense and edema, particularly of the face, is characteristic. There is fever of 39° to 40° C., occasionally 41° C., remittent in type. At times there are petechial hemorrhages of the skin and mucous membranes, in the conjunctivæ and in the retinal vessels. These symptoms are most prominent during the 2nd week but continue throughout the period of larviposition (1 to 3 months). An eosinophilic leukocytosis of 15 to 50% or higher develops during this period.

The third clinical stage is a culmination of the traumatic and toxic effects of the infection. The edema persists, especially around the eyes, sides of the nose, temples, hands, feet and conjunctivæ. There may be profound cachexia. If extensive migration of the larvas takes place through the cerebral capillaries, grave motor and psychic disturbances may occur, while the lesions in the myocardium may be responsible for a syndrome of congestive heart failure (Blumer, 1936; McNaught, 1938). Fatal outcome or chronic invalidism is not infrequent in these heavy infections.

The average case of trichinosis is not severe and frequently does not produce detectable symptoms, although a history of digestive upset following consumption of infected meat and succeeded by muscular pains can at times be elicited in relatively asymptomatic cases.

Diagnosis

Unless the physician obtains a clear picture of the typical symptoms in his patient, he must depend on laboratory evidence to support a clinical diagnosis of trichinosis. This can not usually be obtained until the larvas produced by the female worms have migrated into striated muscles and have begun to encyst, about 21 days after exposure. Meanwhile severe illness and irreversible pathologic changes may have occurred.

There are two available methods of clinical laboratory diagnosis, namely, (1) biopsy of a small piece of gastrocnemius, deltoid or biceps muscle from the vicinity of its tendinous attachment and its microscopic examination, either under compression for evidences of encysting or encysted larvas, or after artificial digestion in gastric juice and demonstration of excysted larvas, and (2) immunologic tests. The common immunologic test is the intradermal reaction developed by Bachman (1928). (See "TECHNICAL AIDS," page 612.)

Treatment

There is no specific therapy for trichinosis, hence palliative and supportive treatment must be relied upon to carry the patient through the critical period. However, if the disease is suspected during the early intestinal phase the repeated administration of Glauber salts (sodium sulfate) may dislodge many of the female worms before they become deeply embedded in the intestinal mucosa, measurably reducing the number of larvas produced, hence the damage resulting from their migration and encapsulation.

Prognosis

In heavy infections this is poor to grave, in lighter infections it is fair to good. In persons who are only incidentally exposed the prognosis is excellent. In severe epidemics 0.5 to 30% of the patients succumb, with an average of about 3.0%.

Control

Preventing Infection in Swine.—Although occasional human infection results from consumption of inadequately processed flesh of infected bears, whales and walruses, these sources are relatively incidental compared to domestic pork. In the United States within recent years high endemicity and at times epidemic outbreaks of trichinosis have occurred mostly in areas where raw municipal garbage constitutes a considerable part of hog food (Schwartz, 1952). Hence legislation in each state to require that all such garbage be thoroughly heated before it is fed constitutes a practical goal which has not been attained. This measure, consistently carried out throughout the entire country, would probably protect many consumers by providing trichina-free pork.

Condemning Infected Carcasses.—To be effective this requires not only gross inspection of pork for detection of trichina lesions but laborious microscopic examination of samples from the diaphragm and other infected muscles of each slaughtered hog. This is impracticable.

Sterilizing the Meat.—This can be accomplished by two practical methods, freezing and thorough cooking. Augustine (1933) demonstrated that refrigeration at minus 18° C. (minus 0.4° F.) for 24 hours provides essentially safe pork. Gould (1945) recommends storage of pork in deep-freeze units as a modern method which is simple, effective and is particularly applicable to rural areas. Thorough cooking of pork is always a safeguard but the danger lies in failure to heat the inside of the meat sufficiently to kill the trichina cysts even though the outside may be golden brown.

There is the possibility that irradiation with cobalt may eventually provide a means of devitalizing trichina cysts in carcasses.

Larva Migrans

Definition and General Remarks.—*Larva migrans* is a term applied to the migration of larval nematodes in unsuitable hosts. Unable to complete their normal migration, the young worms wander for a time in the host's tissues but are eventually trapped by a granulomatous infiltration of host cells.

There are four different biological types among roundworms which favor larva migrans in man as an inappropriate or poorly adapted host, *viz.*, those in which (1) infective-stage larvas actively enter the skin from the soil; (2) infective-stage larvas are deposited on or in the skin by a blood-sucking insect vector; (3) infective-stage eggs are ingested and hatch in the duodenum, and (4) larvas encapsulated in animal tissue are ingested, with excystation of the larvas in the small intestine.

Migration of larval stages of metazoan parasites in unsuitable hosts is not peculiar to roundworms. This condition occurs in the trematodes, as, for example, when the cercarias of non-human blood flukes enter the human skin and produce schistosome dermatitis (see page 427). It is found in relatives of the fish tapeworm when the larval stage accidentally gets into the tissues of man and causes sparganosis (see page 360). Likewise it results when certain species of fly larvas (maggots) get into the skin or mucous membranes and produce myiasis (see pages 505–512).

Location of the Larva Migrans Lesion.—The site of invasion is determined to a considerable extent by the structural form of the larva. The type of nematode adapted to skin penetration is the filariform larva. On the other hand, the rhabditoid larva can not penetrate skin and must be introduced perorally. In the latter case it may still be within the egg shell, or encapsulated in the tissues of an intermediate or alternate host, or it may be a resistant, free-living larva. The rhabditoid larva hatched from the egg or digested out of its adventitious capsule in the inappropriate host may be carried through the intestinal canal and evacuated in the stool without opportunity for actual tissue-invasion. Occasionally, it may penetrate into the intestinal wall and develop into an adult worm, either near the site of invasion or after migration to a more suitable location. Finally, the larva may enter the intestinal wall and undertake tissue migration.

Larval nematodes which have developed in the soil to the filariform stage and employ the cutaneous mode of entry into the body (*i. e.*, hookworms) are responsible primarily for *cutaneous larva migrans* in the poorly adapted host. Those which are introduced onto the skin by blood-sucking insect intermediate hosts (*i. e.*, the filaria worms) at times cause creeping somatic lesions, at other times, visceral lesions. Those hatched from eggs in the small intestine and normally requiring a migration to the lungs (*i. e.*, ascarids) are responsible primarily for *visceral larva migrans*. The fourth type, ingested in an advanced larval stage in host tissues (*i. e.*, spiruroid nematodes) may migrate through the viscera or the subcutaneous tissues.

Cutaneous Larva Migrans

Historical Notes.—The clinical manifestations of this infectious process have been known since 1874, when Lee described a linear cutaneous eruption with an advancing end, but the etiology was not definitely demonstrated until 1926, when Kirby-Smith, Dove and White proved experimentally that the common causative agent in the southern United States is the canine or feline strain of the hookworm *Ancylostoma braziliense*.

Geographical Distribution.—Cutaneous larva migrans resulting from exposure to non-human strains of *A. braziliense* has a widespread distribution throughout the sandy coastal areas of the United States from southern New Jersey to the Florida Keys on the Atlantic Coast and along the entire littoral of the Gulf of Mexico, extending inland in Texas as far as a line drawn north and south through Dallas and San Antonio. However, the largest number of cases is found in the vicinity of Jacksonville, Florida. Creeping eruption due to *A. braziliense* has also been reported from many other subtropical and tropical coastal regions, including southern Brazil, Uruguay and Argentina, Spain, southern France, South Africa, India, the Philippines and Australia.

Other species of hookworms are also capable of producing cutaneous larva migrans in man, *viz.*, the cosmopolitan hookworm of dogs, *Ancylostoma caninum* (Heydon, 1929; Maplestone, 1933; Meillon and Lavoipierre, 1944; Hunter and Worth, 1945; Shelmire, 1947); the European dog hookworm *Uncinaria stenocephala* (Fülleborn, 1927); the human hookworms, *Necator americanus* and *A. duodenale* (Maplestone, 1933; Beaver, 1945, and unpublished data), and the hookworm of cattle, *Bunostomum phlebotomum*

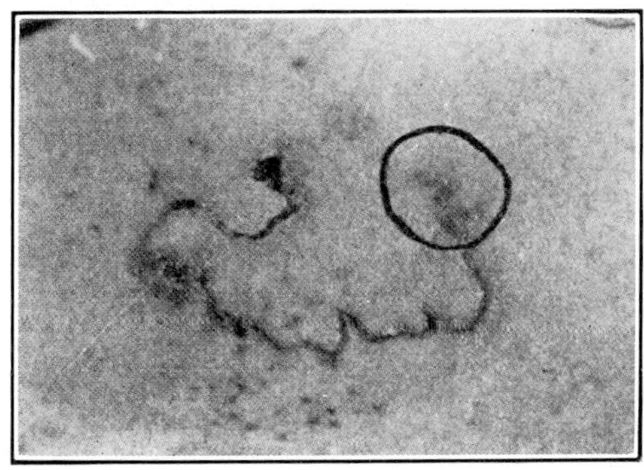

FIG. 91.—The early lesion of larva migrans due to the cutaneous migration of an *Ancylostoma braziliense* filariform larva. The circle indicates the location of the worm at the blind, inner end of the tunnel. (After Kirby-Smith, from Faust's *Human Helminthology*, Lea & Febiger, Philadelphia.)

(Mayhew, 1947). However, cases resulting from natural exposure to the infective stage of these worms other than *A. caninum* are very few compared to *A. braziliense.*

Epidemiology.—Exposure results from contact of the human skin with warm, moist sandy soil, containing filariform larvas of hookworms originating from the excreta of dogs and cats. The sites of exposure to *A. braziliense* of non-human origin are found (1) on bathing beaches where temporary residents are stretched out on the infested ground sunning themselves and (2) under houses where workers temporarily lie prone on the ground repairing exposed plumbing fixtures. In both of these epidemiologic situations extensive body surfaces are liable to exposure. Knox (1953) has stated that one of every 2000 persons who visit the Mississippi Gulf Coast annually develop creeping eruption, while Wilson (1952) found 7000 reported cases for Florida in 1950 and estimated that probably 14,000 additional cases were not reported.

Pathogenesis and Symptomatology.—At each point where the filariform larva of *A. braziliense* invades the skin it produces an itching, reddish papule. In two or three days the larva has developed a serpiginous tunnel between the stratum germinativum as a roof and the corium as a floor. The lesion is at first erythematous and soon becomes elevated and vesicular (Fig. 91). As the larva proceeds through the skin at a rate of several millimeters a day, the older portion of the tunnel becomes dry and crusty. The progressive movement of the worm and the tissue irritation which it produces are responsible for an intense pruritus which almost invariably leads to scratching. This opens the lesion to pyogenic organisms. Activity of the larva may continue for several weeks or months, resulting in extensive skin involvement (Fig. 92) and at times serious systemic illness.

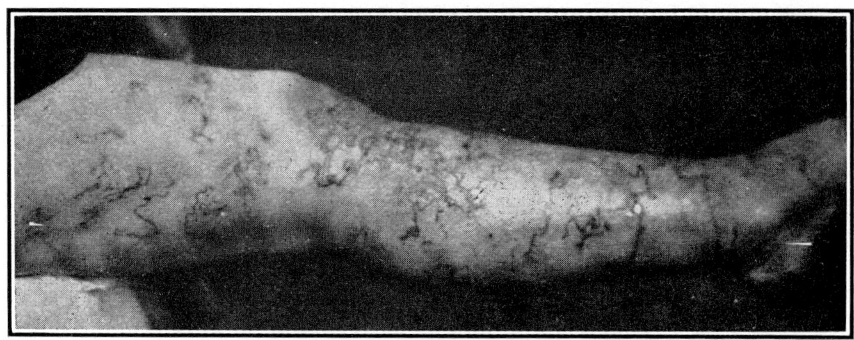

FIG. 92.—Late stage of multiple larva migrans of *Ancylostoma braziliense* origin. (After Kirby-Smith, in Stitt's Diagnostics, courtesy, P. Blakiston's Son & Co., from Faust's *Human Helminthology*, Lea & Febiger, Philadelphia.)

Diagnosis.—Dermatologists and general practitioners in endemic areas have come to recognize the classical picture of an advancing serpiginous tunnel in the skin with an associated intense pruritus as pathognomonic of cutaneous larva migrans, but the lesion may be atypical (Knox, 1953). Furthermore, creeping eruption of hookworm origin must be differentiated from that produced by fly larvas (*Hypoderma* spp., *Gasterophilus* spp., *et al.*, see pages 509 and 510), and, in Oriental regions, from that due to *Gnathostoma* spp. (see page 262).

Treatment.—Knox (1953) believes that freezing with ethyl chloride spray is still the method of choice. Hitch (1947) employed several antimonials and Mapharsen (oxophenarsine hydrochloride) and concluded that the arsenical was the best tolerated and most successful. Horton (1950) reported success with Hetrazan (diethyl carbamazine). Wilson (1952) found that frequently no treatment was necessary except topical application of ethyl acetate collodion over the advancing part of the tunnel to deprive the larva of oxygen. For multiple lesions, he treated 53 patients intramuscularly with Stibanose (sodium antimony gluconate).

Control.—Unlike intestinal hookworm infection in man due to *Necator americanus* and *Ancylostoma duodenale*, in which man is solely responsible for pollution of the soil, with few exceptions the hookworms concerned in cutaneous larva migrans are intestinal parasites of domestic animals, almost exclusively dogs and cats. Control of the sources of exposure must therefore be directed towards reduction of hookworms in dogs and cats, including periodic de-worming of these animals and destruction of all vagrant dogs and cats.

Cutaneous Larva Migrans of Strongyloides Origin.—The studies of Napier (1949) Caplan (1949) and Sandosham (1952) on a type of creeping eruption associated with strongyloidiasis in non-native ex-prisoners-of-war in Siam and Burma, and the reported existence of the same clinical type of dermatitis in Indo-China (Galliard and Chabaud, 1952), Iraq and on the Mediterranean Coast, provide suggestive evidence that cutaneous larva migrans may result from perianal autoinfection in persons harboring *Strongyloides stercoralis*. (See page 254.)

Clinically the creeping cutaneous lesion in strongyloidiasis advances more rapidly than that following exposure to *Ancylostoma braziliense*, and the duration of the eruption is much shorter. Sandosham (*l.c.*) states that indigenous populations in tropical Southeast Asia are not subject to constipation, do not use a commode type of latrine, cleanse the anal region with water instead of toilet paper and bathe frequently, hence are not liable to perianal autoinfection with *Strongyloides*. Moreover, their probable tolerance to the local strains of the parasite would result in less damage and correspondingly less clinical evidence of the infection.

Cutaneous Larval Filariasis

This subject has been given almost no consideration as a type of larva migrans. It will be mentioned briefly here but is presented somewhat more adequately in Chapter 11 (Filaria Worms), page 312. Immature and larval filarias, possibly all belonging to the species *Dirofilaria conjunctivæ*, have been removed on several occasions from cutaneous and palpebral nodules of persons in Mediterranean countries, Thailand, Argentina and Florida, U. S. A. It seems probable that mosquitoes are the intermediate hosts and vectors, and that human infection is only incidental to that of an as-yet-unknown reservoir. It is possible that *D. conjunctivæ* in man (an obviously suboptimal host) is actually the dog heart worm (*Dirofilaria immitis*).

Visceral Larva Migrans

Compared with cutaneous larva migrans, the visceral type has been recognized clinically for only a short time, while its nematode etiology has been demonstrated very recently (Wilder, 1950; Beaver *et al.*, 1952). As in the cutaneous type, "the invading larvæ generally are of species naturally adapted to hosts other than man, remain immature and eventually perish in the tissues" (Smith and Beaver, 1953). These lesions have been reported from the liver (Perlingiero and György, 1947; Zuelzer and Apt, 1949; Mercer *et al.*, 1950; Behrer, 1951; Beaver *et al.*, 1952; Milburn and Ernst, 1953), the brain (Beatyman and Woolf, 1951), and the eye (Wilder, 1950). (Fig. 93.) Careful study of biopsied liver specimens by Beaver *et al.* (1952) and of experimentally infected mice by Smith and Beaver

(1953) has lead to the conclusion that the larvas involved are those of *Toxocara,* in most instances *T. canis,* but at times perhaps *T. cati* or even species or strains of the genus *Ascaris* not adapted to the human host.

Because *Ascaris lumbricoides* has at times been found as an intestinal infection in association with granulomatous lesions of the viscera, it has commonly been assumed that the latter are necessarily the result of visceral migration of human *Ascaris* larvas. Aside from the morphologic differences between infective-stage *Ascaris* and *Toxocara* larvas, several of the cases

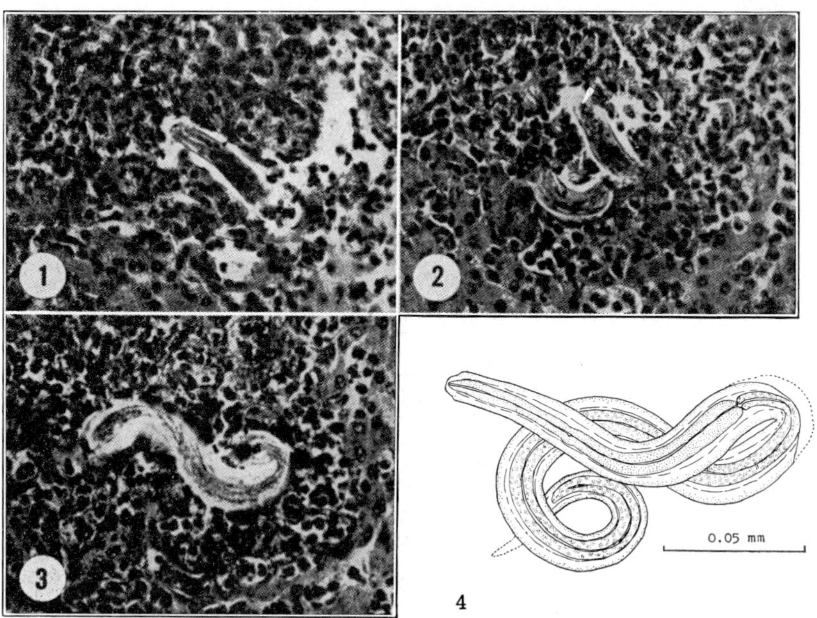

Fig. 93.—Visceral larva migrans of *Toxocara* (*canis*) origin in liver of a $2\frac{1}{2}$-year-old white female, New Orleans, La. *1, 2, 3,* photomicrographs through different levels of the larva, × 286; *4,* graphic reconstruction from camera lucida drawings through five serial sections of this larva. (After Beaver *et al.*, from Pediatrics, 1952.)

studied have been children who provided a history of eating dirt, which is as commonly seeded with eggs of *Toxocara* as with those of human *Ascaris* (Headlee, 1936), and some patients lived in areas where human ascariasis is not endemic.

The Clinical Picture.—In visceral larva migrans this varies from an asymptomatic condition, except for a persistent eosinophilia (Smith and Beaver, 1953), to symptoms of chronic hypereosinophilia, hepatomegaly, moderate pulmonary infiltration, fever, cough, and hyperglobulinemia (Beaver *et al.*, 1952). Beatyman and Woolf (1951) found an ascarid larva in a cerebral lesion in association with acute poliomyelitis and Wilder (1950) had a considerable series of pseudotuberculous eye lesions each with a nematode larva in the center.

Diagnosis of Visceral Larva Migrans.—This requires demonstration of the parasite in specimens obtained by biopsy or necropsy. In cases with liver involvement, biopsy of a small subcapsular nodule will usually provide the necessary evidence.

Treatment.—There is no specific therapy. In a majority of cases the prognosis is excellent, with complete recovery.

Control.—Smith and Beaver (1953) emphasize the "need for ridding household pets of their intestinal parasites" at frequent intervals in order to safeguard young children from contracting roundworm infections normally occurring in these animals.

Spiruroid Larva Migrans

Species of *Gnathostoma* (*G. spinigerum* and *G. hispidum*) have been recovered in an advanced larval stage from subcutaneous tissues. In Thailand, where *G. spinigerum* has been found on many occasions in the human host, exposure results from consuming uncooked fermented fish which contains the encapsulated third larval stage of the worm. Unable to develop into the adult worm in the wall of the human stomach, the larva undertakes an extra-intestinal migration and is discovered in serpiginous tunnels in the skin, in abscess pockets in subcutaneous tissues, or occasionally in the eye.

SUMMARY

1. Roundworms (nematodes) are unsegmented Metazoa that are typically elongated, cylindrical, and possess bilateral symmetry. They are covered with a cuticle secreted by a hypodermis, have a dermomuscular layer, a body cavity not lined with mesothelium and a complete digestive tract. With few exceptions they are diecious.
2. Although a majority of roundworms are free-living, a very large number have become adapted to parasitism. All species have the same fundamental stages in their life cycle, *viz.*, the parent worms, the egg and several successive larval stages.
3. The pinworm (*Enterobius vermicularis*) represents the simplest type of obligate parasitism among the nematodes. It is a cosmopolitan human parasite, which is particularly prevalent among children. The adult worms live superficially attached to the appendiceal and cecal mucosa. The gravid female migrates down the intestine and out the anus, depositing almost fully embryonated eggs on the perianal and perineal skin. *Via* fingertips or in air currents they get into the mouth and are swallowed. On arrival in the small intestine they hatch and develop into adult worms in 45 days or less.

   The commonest symptom of pinworm infection is an itching of the perianal skin, resulting in scratching and scarification of the area, and at times serious nervous disorders. The infection is most satisfactorily diagnosed by use of the Scotch-tape anal "swab" to collect the characteristic eggs. Gentian violet tablets, and possibly Terramycin and Hetrazan or Piperazine, are satisfactory for eradicating this infection, provided all positive individuals in a community are diagnosed and are given full treatment simultaneously. Control includes careful habits of personal and group hygiene.

4. The whipworm (*Trichocephalus trichiurus*) is prevalent in warm moist climates. The adult worms live with their delicate anterior ends securely threaded into the cecal mucosa. The females lay a few thousand eggs daily. These become infective in about 3 weeks on warm, moist, shaded soil. When taken into the mouth and swallowed the eggs hatch and in about 90 days develop into adult worms.

   The lesion produced may be inconsequential if only a few worms are present, or extensive if there is a heavy worm burden. It consists of damage to the intestinal mucosa and systemic absorption of the worm's toxic metabolites. Diagnosis is based on recovery of the typical eggs in the feces. No single safe drug is eminently satisfactory in whipworm infection. Control consists in sanitary disposal of human excreta.

5. The giant intestinal roundworm (*Ascaris lumbricoides*) is cosmopolitan and is particularly common in small children in the Tropics and warmer temperate climates. The adult worms typically live unattached in the small intestine. Each female lays about 200,000 eggs daily. When deposited on the ground, the eggs become infective within 2 to 3 weeks. When they get into the mouth and are swallowed they hatch in the small intestine. The larvas migrate *via* blood or lymphatic vessels to the lungs, then break out into the alveoli, climb up the air passages, and are swallowed. On reaching the small intestine they develop into adults in about 8 to 12 weeks following exposure.

   During larval migration through the lungs the larvas produce pneumonitis and systemic sensitization. Later, in the intestine, the infection may be relatively benign, although it is commonly accompanied by colicky pains, indigestion and evidences of malnutrition. The worms may cause intestinal obstruction, or they may perforate the bowel wall, block the appendiceal lumen or the common bile duct, or enter the parenchyma of the liver. Diagnosis is made on recovery of the typical eggs in the feces. The worms may be evacuated by oral administration of hexylresorcinol crystoids. Control consists of sanitary disposal of human excreta.

6. The two common human hookworms are widely distributed in the moist temperate and tropical regions of the world. *Necator americanus* is more abundant in warm climates, including the southeastern United States, and *Ancylostoma duodenale* more frequent in the north temperate zones of the Eastern Hemisphere. The adult worms are attached by their heads to the mucosa at the upper levels of the small intestine. Each female lays daily a few thousand eggs. When the eggs are deposited on warm, moist, sandy loam in a shaded location, they soon hatch and the escaping larvas feed, grow, moult, then feed again and in 5 or more days transform into the infective stage. On contact with human skin they penetrate to the cutaneous blood vessels, are carried to the lungs, escape into the air passages, climb up to the epiglottis, crawl over into the esophagus and then pass down to the

duodenum or jejunum, where they become attached and in 5 weeks or more develop into adults.

Hookworm disease results primarily from the loss of blood which the worms suck out of the intestinal capillaries. This is responsible for the anemia and hypoproteinemia, and indirectly for stunted physical and sexual growth, lethargy, and physical and mental degradation in hookworm-infected populations. Diagnosis is made on recovery of the typical hookworm eggs in the feces. Treatment consists in oral administration of tetrachlorethylene in soft gelatin capsules to remove the worms, soluble iron to relieve the anemia and diets rich in protein to compensate for the hypoproteinemia. Control of human hookworms requires anthelmintic treatment of all infected persons, together with provision for sanitary disposal of human excreta.

7. In certain countries man is exposed to infection with hookworms and related nematodes of domestic animals, including *Ancylostoma braziliense, A. caninum, Ternidens deminutus, Œsophagostomum apiostomum, Syngamus laryngeus,* and several species of *Trichostrongylus.*

8. The human threadworm (*Strongyloides stercoralis*) is prevalent in warm, moist climates and occurs sporadically in temperate regions. The infection is more frequently found in adults than in children, and results from pollution of warm, wet, shaded soil with human excreta. The parasitic females live embedded in the mucosa of the intestine, usually at the duodenal level. Here they lay eggs which hatch, releasing a first-stage larva, which feeds as it passes down through the intestine. On favorable ground it becomes infective in 24 to 48 hours, or may pass through one or more complete free-living cycles before producing the infective filariform stage. On contact with human skin the filariform larva enters the cutaneous blood vessels and migrates through the lungs before reaching the intestinal tract. The biological incubation period is 28 days or less. At times filariform larvas developing in transit down the intestine or on soiled perianal skin produce autoinfection.

   The most frequent symptoms of strongyloidiasis are profuse diarrhea and pains in the pit of the stomach. Diagnosis is based on demonstration of rhabditoid larvas in the stool or duodenal aspirate. Treatment with gentian violet is clinically helpful but is not always curative. Control in a community requires sanitary disposal of human excreta; in the individual non-constipating foods and clean toilet habits are recommended to reduce the chances of autoinfection.

9. Spiruroid nematodes are normal parasites of domestic and wild mammals and occur infrequently in man. Ingestion of the encysted larva provides the means of exposure for the definitive host. Species reported from man include *Gongylonema pulchrum, Thelazia callipæda* and *T. californiensis, Physaloptera caucasica, Gnathostoma spinigerum* and *G. hispidum.*

10. The giant kidney worm (*Dioctophyma renale*) has a cosmopolitan distribution in fish-eating mammals. Ten human cases have been reported.

11. The trichina worm (*Trichinella spiralis*) is found in most countries of the world except in the Tropics. All stages in the life cycle are completed in one host but two hosts are required for continuation of the

infection. Trichinosis is enzoötic among brown and black rats. Human infection results from consumption of uncooked or undercooked pork, occasionally bear or walrus meat, containing the encysted larvas.

There are three clinical stages in the infection, *viz.*, (1) a food-poisoning syndrome during the biological incubation period; (2) symptoms of severe muscular rheumatism during larval migration, and (3) following encystation of the larvas in muscle fibers, symptoms developing from cumulative traumatic, inflammatory and toxic damage. A majority of cases are essentially asymptomatic. Specific diagnosis is made on recovery of the encysted larvas in biopsied muscle or on immunologic tests, none of which is positive until 21 days after exposure. There is no specific therapy. Control may be effected by cooking all garbage fed to hogs, condemning all infected meat, subjecting pork to freezing for 24 hours or more, and thorough cooking of the meat.

12. "Larva migrans" is the migration of larval nematodes in inappropriate hosts, in which the young worms are unable to mature and are sooner or later destroyed by host tissue reaction. There are four principal categories, *viz.*, (1) cutaneous larva migrans produced by filariform larvas of non-human hookworms; (2) cutaneous (and visceral) larva migrans due to filariform larvas of non-human filaria worms; (3) visceral larva migrans produced by larvas of *Toxocara canis* hatched from eggs in the small intestine and migrating into liver, lungs, or other organs, and (4) visceral (or cutaneous) larva migrans due to immature spiruroid nematodes. Cutaneous larva migrans has also been reported as a sequela of perianal autoinfection in strongyloidiasis. Chemotherapy is relatively effective for hookworm-induced cutaneous larva migrans. Control of larva migrans requires periodic de-worming of dogs and cats.

REFERENCES

Africa, C. M., Refuerzo, P. G., and Garcia, E. Y. 1936. Observations on the Life Cycle of *Gnathostoma Spinigerum*. Philippine J. Sci., *59*, 513–521; *61*, 221–225.

Amberson, J. M., and Swarz, E. 1952. *Ternidens Deminutus* Railliet and Henry, a Nematode Parasite of Man and Primates. Ann. Trop. Med. & Parasitol., *46*, 227–237.

de Andrade Lima, L. I., and Simoes Barbosa, F. 1951. Consideraçoes em Tarno de um Caso de Singamose Humana. Publ. Avulsas do Inst. Aggeu Magalhães, Brasil, *1*, 27–34.

Ashford, B. K., and Gutiérrez Igaravidez, P. 1911. Uncinariasis (Hookworm Disease) in Porto Rico. A Medical and Economic Problem. Senate Doc. No. 808, Washington. 335 pp.

Askanazy, M. 1900. Ueber Art und Zweck der Invasion der *Anguillula intestinalis* in die Darmwand. Centralbl. Bakt., *27*, 569–578.

Augustine, D. L. 1933. Effects of Low Temperatures upon Encysted *Trichinella Spiralis*. Am. J. Hyg., *17*, 697–710.

Bachman, G. W. 1928. A Precipitin Test in Experimental Trichiniasis. J. Prev. Med., *2*, 513–523.

Basnuevo, J. 1952. Recientes Adquisiciones en la Clínica y en la Terapéutica de la Tricocefaliasis Infantil. Rev. Kuba, *8*, 4–5.

Bavay, A. 1876. Sur l'Anguillule Stercorale. Compt. Rend. Acad. Sci., Paris, *83*, 694–696.

Beaver, P. C. 1949a. Methods of Pinworm Diagnosis. Am. J. Trop. Med., *29*, 577–587.

——1949b. Quantitative Hookworm Diagnosis by Direct Smear. J. Parasitol., *35*, 125–135.

——1950. The Standardization of Fecal Smears for Estimating Egg Production and Worm Burden. J. Parasitol., *36*, 451–456.

——1951. Hemoglobin Determination in Hookworm Disease Case-Finding. Am. J. Trop. Med., *31*, 90–97.

——1952. The Detection and Identification of Some Common Nematode Parasites of Man. Am. J. Clin. Path., *22*, 481–494.

Beaver, P. C., Snyder, C. H., Carrera, G. M., Dent, J. H., and Lafferty, J. W. 1952. Chronic Eosinophilia Due to Visceral Larva Migrans. Pediatrics, *9*, 7–19.

Blumer, G. 1936. Trichinosis, with Special Reference to Changed Conceptions of Pathology and Their Bearing on Symptomatology. New England J. Med., *214*, 1229–1235.

Bozicevich, J. 1938. Studies on Trichinosis. XII. The Preparation and Use of Trichina Antigen. Pub. Health. Repts., *53*, 2130–2138.

Brannon, M. J. C., and Faust, E. C. 1949. Preparation and Testing of a Specific Antigen for Diagnosis of Human Strongyloidiasis. Am. J. Trop. Med., *29*, 229–239.

Brown, H. W. 1952. Use of Antibiotics in the Treatment of Helminthic Infections. Ann. New York Acad. Sci., *55*, 1133–1138.

Caplan, J. P. 1949. Creeping Eruption and Intestinal Strongyloidiasis. Brit. Med. J., *i*, 396.

Chang, E. 1949. Uveitis of a Cantonese Caused by *Gnathostoma spinigerum* (Owen, 1836). Chinese Med. J., *67*, 166–168.

Cort, W. W. 1931. Recent Investigations on the Epidemiology of Human Ascariasis. J. Parasitol., *17*, 121–144.

Cort, W. W., *et al.* 1921–1925. Investigations on the Control of Hookworm Disease. Am. J. Hyg., Vols. *1* to *5*. (34 Separate Papers.)

Cram, E. B. 1943. Studies on Oxyuriasis. XXVIII. Summary and Conclusions. Am. J. Diseases Children, *65*, 46–59.

Cruz, W. O. 1948. Hookworm Anemia, a Deficiency Disease. Proc. 4th Internat'l Congr. Trop. Med & Malaria, Washington, pp. 1045–1054.

D'Antoni, J. S., and Sawitz, W. 1940. The Treatment of Oxyuriasis. Am. J. Trop. Med., *20*, 377–383.

Daengsvang, S. 1949. Human Gnathostomiasis in Siam with Reference to the Method of Prevention. J. Parasitol., *35*, 116–121.

Darling, S. T. 1922. The Hookworm Index and Mass Treatment. Am. J. Trop. Med., *2*, 397–447.

Deane, M. P. 1950. Helmintos Eliminados por um Grupo de Residentes da Amazonia, após um Tratamento pelo Hexilresorcinol. Rev. Serv. Especial Saúde Publica, *3*, 443–464.

Desportes, C. 1944–1945. Sur *Strongyloides Stercoralis* (Bavay, 1876) et sur les *Strongyloides* de Primates. Ann. de Parasitol., *20*, 160–190.

Dubini, A. 1843. Nuovo Verme Intestinale Umano (*Agchylostoma Duodenale*), Constitutente un Sesto Genere dei Nematoidei Proprii dell' Uomo. Ann. Univ. di Med., Milano, *106*, 5–13.

Etteldorf, J., and Crawford, L. 1950. Treatment of Ascariasis in Children. Use of 1-diethylcarbamyl-4-methyl piperazine dihydrogen citrate (Hetrazan). J. Am. Med. Assn., *143*, 797–799.

Faust, E. C. 1931. Human Strongyloidiasis in Panama. Am. J. Hyg., *14*, 203–211.

——1933. The Development of *Strongyloides* in the Experimental Host. Am. J. Hyg., *18*, 114–132.

——1935. The Pathology of *Strongyloides* Infection. Arch. Path., *19*, 769–806.

——1936. *Strongyloides* and Strongyloidiasis. Rev. de Parasitol. (Habana), *2*, 315–341.

——1949. *Human Helminthology*. 3rd ed., 744 pp. Lea & Febiger, Philadelphia.

Faust, E. C., and DeGroat, A. 1940. Internal Autoinfection in Strongyloidiasis. Am. J. Trop. Med., *20*, 350–375.

Foster, A. O., and Landsberg, J. W. 1934. The Nature and Cause of Hookworm Anemia. Am. J. Hyg., *20*, 259–290.

Frant, S. 1934. Five Years' Experience with Trichinosis in New York City. Pub. Health Repts., *49*, 869–875.

Fülleborn, F. 1914. Untersuchungen über den Infektionsweg bei *Strongyloides* und *Ankylostomum* und die Biologie dieser Parasiten. Arch. f. Schiffs u. Tropen-Hyg., Beih., *5*, 26–80.

———1926. Hautquaddeln und "Autoinfektion" bei *Strongyloides*-Trägern. Ibid., *30*, 721–732.

———1927. Durch Hakenwurmlarven des Hundes (*Uncinaria Stenocephala*) beim Menschen Erzeugte "Creeping Eruption." Hamburg Univ. Abhandl. Geb. Auslandsk., Bernhard Nocht Festschrift, *26*, 121–133.

Galliard, H., and Chabaud, A. G. 1952. Anomalies, d'Eteignant par Passage chez le Chien, d'une Souche de *Strongyloides Stercoralis*, Isolée d'un Cas d'Urticaire Migrant. Comparaison avec Différentes Souches Normales Étudiées au Tonkin. Ann. de Parasitol., *32*, 588–597.

Gould, S. E. 1952. Trichinosis in Man and Its Prevention. Proc. 1st Nat'l Conf. on Trichinosis, Chicago. p. 53.

Hartz, P. H. 1946. Human Strongyloidiasis with Internal Autoinfection. Arch. Path., *41*, 601–611.

Hasegawa, T. 1924. Beitrag zur Entwicklung von Trichozephalus im Wirte. Arch. f. Schiffs- u. Tropen-Hyg., *28*, 337–340.

Headlee, W. H. 1936. The Epidemiology of Human Ascariasis in the Metropolitan Area of New Orleans, Louisiana. Am. J. Hyg., *24*, 479–521.

Heller, E. R. 1944. The Epidemiology of Enterobiasis. Med. Parasit. & Par. Dis., Moscow, *13*, 16–23. (Russian text.)

Hitch, J. M. 1947. Systemic Treatment of Creeping Eruption. Arch. Derm. & Syphil., *55*, 664–673.

Hoekenga, M. T. 1952. Treatment of Ascariasis in Children with Hetrazan Syrup. Am. J. Trop. Med. & Hyg., *1*, 688–692.

Jacobs, A. H. 1942. Enterobiasis in Children; Incidence, Symptomatology, and Diagnosis, with a Simplified Scotch Cellulose Tape Technique. J. Pediatrics, *21*, 497–503.

Jaskoski, B. J. 1952. The Protein Coat in Development of *Ascaris Lumbricoides* Eggs. Exp. Parasitol., *1*, 291–302.

Jelliffe, D. B. 1951. Oil of Chenopodium in the Treatment of Ascariasis. J. Trop. Med. & Hyg., *54*, 143–146.

Jones, C. A. 1950. Clinical Studies in Human Strongyloidiasis. I. Semeiology. Gastroënterol., *16*, 743–756.

Jung, R. C. 1953. A Study of the Pneumonitis Due to Larval Ascaris Infection. Ph.D. Dissertation, Tulane Univ.

Jung, R. C., and Beaver, P. C. 1952. Clinical Observations on *Trichocephalus Trichiurus* (Whipworm) Infestation in Children. Pediatrics, *8*, 548–557.

Kirby-Smith, J. L., Dove, W. E., and White, G. F. 1926. Creeping Eruption. Arch. Derm., Syph., *13*, 137–173.

Knox, J. M. 1953. Creeping Eruption (Larva Migrans) at Keesler Field Air Force Base. J. La. State Med. Soc., *105*, 69–72.

Koino, S. 1922. Experimental Infection of the Human Body with Ascarides. Japan Med. World, *2*, 317–320.

Kuitunen-Ekbaum, E. 1946. Phenothiazine in the Treatment of Enterobiasis. II. Canad. J. Pub. Health, *37*, 103–113.

Kyle, L. H., McKay, D. G., and Sparling, H. J., Jr. 1948. Strongyloidiasis. Ann. Int. Med., *29*, 1014–1042.

Lamson, P. D., Brown, H. W., Robbins, B. H., and Ward, C. B. 1931. Field Treatments of Ascariasis, Ancylostomiasis and Trichuriasis with Hexylresorcinol. Am. J. Hyg., *13*, 803–822.

Leichtenstern, O. 1899. Zur Lebensgeschichte der *Anguillula intestinalis*. Centralbl. Bakt., *2*, 226–231.

Leidy, J. 1846. Entozoön in the Superficial Part of the Extensor Muscles of the Thigh of the Hog. Proc. Acad. Nat. Sci. Phila., *3*, 107–108.

Leuckart, R. 1860. Untersuchungen über *Trichina Spiralis*. 120 pp. Leipzig u. Heidelberg.

———1882. Ueber die Lebensgeschichte der Sogenannten *A. Stercoralis* und deren Beziehungen zu der Sogenannten *A. intestinalis*. Bericht. über d. Verhandl. d. Sächs. Gesellsch. d. Wissensch. Math.-Phys. Klasse. Leipzig, *34*, 85–107.

Lie Kian Joe. 1947. *Trichostrongylus* Infection in Man and Domestic Animals in Java. J. Parasitol., *33*, 359–362.

Link, V. B. 1952. Trichinosis: A National Problem. Proc. First Nat'l Conf. on Trichinosis, Chicago, 3–7.

Looss, A. 1896. Notizen zur Helminthologie Ægyptens. I. 3. Die Lebensgeschichte des *Ancylostomum Duodenale*. Centralbl. Bakt., *20*, 863–870.

———1897. II. Ibid., *21*, 913–926.

———1905. Die Wanderung der *Ancylostomum*- und *Strongyloides*-Larven von der Haut nach dem Darm. Compt. Rend. 6e Congrès Intern. de Zool., Berne, 1904, pp. 225–233.

MacArthur, W. P. 1924. A Case of Infestation of the Human Liver with *Hepaticola Hepatica* (Bancroft, 1893) Hall, 1916. Proc. R. Soc. Med. (Sec. Trop. Dis., Parasitol.), *17*, 83–84.

McNaught, J. B., Beard, R. B., and Myers, J. D. 1941. The Diagnosis of Trichinosis by Skin and Precipitin Tests. Am. J. Clin. Path., *11*, 195–209.

McQuown, A. L. 1950. *Capillaria Hepatica;* Report of Genuine and Spurious Cases. Am. J. Trop. Med., *30*, 761–767.

Madsen, H. 1945. Biological Observations upon *Enterobius Vermicularis* (Pinworm). Acta Path., *22*, 392–397.

Maplestone, P. A. 1933. Creeping Eruption Produced by Hookworm Larvæ. Indian Med. Gaz., *68*, 251–256.

Mayhew, R. L. 1947. Creeping Eruption Caused by Larvæ of Cattle Hookworm *Bunostomum Phlebotomum*. Proc. Soc. Exp. Biol. & Med., *66*, 12–14.

Mazzotti, L., and Quintanar, E. 1943. Examen de 1,551 Niños de la Ciudad de México, Utilizando el Método de Graham, par Investigar Oxyuriasis. Rev. Inst. Salub. y Enferm. Trop., México, *4*, 173–178.

Mendheim, H., Scheid, G., and Schmidt, J. 1952. Die Selteneren Spulwurminfektionen beim Menschen. Zeitschr. f. Tropenm. u. Parasitol., *3*, 368–371.

Milburn, C. L., and Ernst, K. F. 1953. Eosinophilia-Hepatomegaly Syndrome of Infants and Young Children. Pediatrics, *11*, 358–367.

Miller, M. J. 1941. Quantitative Studies on *Trichocephalus Vulpis* Infections in Dogs. Am. J. Hyg., *33* (Sec. D), 58–70.

Milwidsky, H. 1945. The Surgical Complications of Ascariasis. Acta Med. Orientalia, *4*, 370–384.

Napier, L. E. 1949. *Strongyloides Stercoralis* Infection. Part II. Strongyloidiasis Among Ex-Prisoners-of-War. J. Trop. Med. & Hyg., *52*, 46–48.

Nolasco, J. O., and Africa, C. M. 1936. A Fatal Case of Paralytic Ileus Associated with Severe *Strongyloides* Infestation Suggesting Internal Autoinfection. J. Philipp. Ids. Med. Assn., *16*, 275–283.

Otto, G. F. 1932. Ascaris and Trichuris in Southern United States. J. Parasitol., *18*, 200–208.

Pallister, R. A. 1933. Trichuriasis in Malaya. Malayan Med. J., *8*, 303–304.

Palmer, E. D. 1950. A Note on the Treatment of Strongyloidiasis with Gentian Violet. Am. J. Trop. Med., *30*, 91–92.

Parsons, H. E. 1952. Nematode Chorioretinitis. A.M.A. Arch. Ophthalm., *47*, 799–800.

Perroncito, E. 1880. Osservazioni Elmintologiche Relative alla Malattia Sviluppatasi Endemica negli Operai del Gothardo. Atti R. Accad. Lincei, Roma, Mem. Cl. Sc. Fis. Mat. e Nat., *7*, 381–433.

Peterson, M. C., and Fahey, J. 1945. Oxyuriasis: Simplified Method of Diagnosis with Glass Slide; Incidence in a Minnesota State Hospital; Result of Treatment with Gentian Violet. J. Lab. & Clin. Med., *30*, 259–261.

Porter, W. B. 1937. Heart Changes and Physiologic Adjustment in Hookworm Anemia. Am. Heart J., *13*, 550–579.

Ransom, B. H., and Cram, E. B. 1921. The Course of Migration of *Ascaris* Larvæ. J. Parasitol., *2*, 80–86.

Ransom, B. H., and Foster, W. D. 1917. Life History of *Ascaris Lumbricoides* and Related Forms. J. Agric. Research, U. S. Dept. Agr., *11*, 395–398.

Ransom, B. H., and Hall, M. C. 1915. The Life History of *Gongylonema Scutatum.* J. Parasitol., *2*, 80–86.

Rausch, R. 1953. Science and Public Health Research in Alaska. Animal-Borne Diseases. Pub. Health Repts., *68*, 533–534.

Reardon, L. 1938. Studies on Oxyuriasis. XVI. The Number of Eggs Produced by the Pinworm, *Enterobius Vermicularis,* and Its Bearing on Infection. Pub. Health Repts., *53*, 978–984.

Redewill, F. H. 1949. *Strongyloides Stercoralis* Involving the Genito-urinary Tract. Urol. and Cut. Rev., *53*, 609–614.

Rhoads, C. P., Castle, W. B., Payne, G. C., and Lawson, H. A. 1934. Hookworm Anemia: Etiology and Treatment, with Especial Reference to Iron. Am. J. Hyg., *20*, 291–306.

Sandground, J. H. 1926. Biological Studies on the Life Cycle in the Genus *Strongyloides* Grassi, 1879. Am. J. Hyg., *6*, 337–388.

————1931. Studies on the Life-History of *Ternidens Deminutus,* Nematode Parasite of Man, with Observations on Its Incidence in Certain Regions of South Africa. Ann. Trop. Med. & Parasitol., *25*, 147–184.

Sandosham, A. A. 1952. An Investigation into the Association of Creeping Eruption with *Strongyloides* Infection Contracted in the Far East. J. Helminthol., *26*, 1–24.

Sawitz, W. 1938. Prevalence of Trichinosis in the United States. Pub. Health Repts., *53*, 365–383.

Schüffner, W., and Swellengrebel, N. H. 1949. Retrofection in Oxyuriasis. A Newly Discovered Mode of Infection with *Enterobius Vermicularis.* J. Parasitol., *35*, 138–146.

Schwartz, B. 1952. Trichinæ in Swine. Proc. 1st Nat'l Conf. on Trichinosis, Chicago, pp. 26–30.

Scott, H. H. 1943. The Influence of the Slave Trade in the Spread of Tropical Disease. Trans. R. Soc. Trop. Med. & Hyg., *37*, 169–188.

Scott, J. A. 1945. Hookworm Disease in Texas. Tex. Repts. on Biol. & Med., *3*, 558–568.

Sen, K., and Ghose, N. 1945. Ocular Gnathostomiasis. Brit. J. Ophthalm., *29*, 618–626.

Stewart, F. H. 1916. On the Life History of *Ascaris Lumbricoides.* Brit. Med. J., *ii*, 5–7.

Stiles, C. W. 1902. A New Species of Hookworm (*Uncinaria Americana*) Parasitic in Man. Am. Med., *3*, 777–778.

Stoll, N. R. 1923. An Effective Method of Counting Hookworm Eggs in Feces. Am. J. Hyg., *3*, 59–70.

————1947. This Wormy World. J. Parasitol., *33*, 1–18.

Stryker, W. A. 1947. The Intestinal Phase of Human Trichinosis. Am. J. Path., *23*, 819–827.

Swartzwelder, J. C. 1941. *Toxocara Cati* (Cat Ascarid) Infection in Man. J. Trop. Med. & Hyg., *44*, 61–62.

Thorborg, N. C., Tulinius, S., and Roth, H. 1948. Trichinosis in Greenland. Acta Path., *25*, 778–794.

Toumanoff, C., and Le-Van Phung. 1947. Note au Sujet d'un Cas de Gnathostomose Humaine Observée en Indochine. Bull. Soc. Path. Exot., *40*, 168–174.

Virchow, R. 1865. Zur Trichinen-Lehre. Arch. Path. Anat., *32*, 332–371.

Vogel, H., and Minning, W. 1942. Beiträge zur Klinik der Lungen-Ascariasis und zur Frage der Flüchtigen Eosinophilen Lungen-Infiltrate. Beitr. zur Klinik der Tuberkulose, *98*, 620–654.

White, R. H. R., and Standen, O. D. 1953. Piperazine in the Treatment of Threadworms in Children. Brit. Med. J., *ii*, 755.

Whitehall, R., and Miller, M. H. 1944. Infestation of the Genito-Urinary Tract by *Strongyloides Stercoralis.* Bull. Johns Hopkins Hosp., *75*, 169–174.

Whittier, L., Einhorn, N. H., and Miller, J. F. 1945. Trichuriasis in Children. Am. J. Dis. Children, *70*, 289–292.

WICKRAMASURIYA, G. A. W. 1935. The Grave Risks of Hookworm Disease as a Complication of Pregnancy. J. Obst. & Gyn., *42*, 217–267.

WILDER, H. C. 1950. Nematode Endophthalmitis. Trans. Am. Acad. Ophthalm., *55*, 99–109.

WILSON, J. F. 1952. A Treatment of Larva Migrans with Stibanose. Sou. Med. J. *45*, 127–131.

WINFIELD, G. F. 1937. Studies on the Control of Fecal-borne Diseases in North China. I. Problems and Methods. Chinese Med. J., *51*, 217–236.

WOODHEAD, A. E. 1950. Life Cycle of the Giant Kidney Worm, *Dioctophyma Renale* (Nematoda), of Man and Many Other Mammals. Trans. Am. Micr. Soc., *69*, 21–46.

WRIGHT, W. H., BRADY, F. J., and BOZICEVICH, J. 1938. Studies on Oxyuriasis. VIII. A Preliminary Note on Therapy with Gentian Violet. Proc. Helm. Soc. Washington, *5*, 5–7.

WRIGHT, W. H., KERR, K. B., and JACOBS, L. 1943. Studies on Trichinosis. XV. Summary of the Findings of *Trichinella Spiralis* in Random Samplings of the Population of the United States. Pub. Health Repts., *58*, 1293–1313.

ZUELZER, W., and APT, L. 1949. Disseminated Visceral Lesions Associated with Extreme Eosinophilia. Am. J. Dis. Child., *78*, 153–181.

Chapter 11

The Filaria Worms

Introductory Remarks

THE true filarias (Filarioidea) have a unique stage in their life cycle, the *microfilaria*, which distinguishes them as a group. This embryo or prelarval form develops as a tightly coiled filiform object within the eggshell in the uterus of the mother worm. About the time of oviposition the embryo uncoils into a delicate snake-like form. In some species, the eggshell becomes correspondingly elongated to accommodate itself to the uncoiled embryo and the microfilaria is referred to as "sheathed." In other species, the shell splits, allowing the naked embryo to escape as an "unsheathed" microfilaria.

From the site where the microfilarias are deposited the embryos enter blood (or lymphatic) vessels and reach the skin. In order to proceed with their development they must be picked up by an appropriate blood-sucking arthropod, in which they transform first into rhabditoid larvas and then the infective filariform larva, which is discharged from the mouth parts of the arthropod at the time it is feeding on the skin of the definitive host. The young worm now enters the host's tissues and after a considerable period of migration settles down in a suitable location to develop into the adult worm.

Species of True Filaria Worms Parasitizing Man

There are six species of filarias for which man is the only proven definitive host, *viz.*, *Wuchereria bancrofti*, *W. malayi*, *Onchocerca volvulus*, *Loa loa*, *Acanthocheilonema perstans* and *Mansonella ozzardi*. In addition, *Acanthocheilonema streptocerca* is found both in man and chimpanzees, while immature specimens of *Dirofilaria conjunctivæ* and possibly other species of filarias have been described from human tissues.

Anatomical Sites of Human Filarias.—The anatomical locations of the adult filarias in the human body vary, depending on the species. *Wuchereria bancrofti* and *W. malayi* characteristically reside in lymphatic vessels. *Onchocerca volvulus* is imprisoned in fibrous tumors in the subcutaneous tissues. *Loa loa* adults migrate through subcutaneous tissues. *Acanthocheilonema streptocerca* is found in connective tissue of the skin. *A. perstans* and *Mansonella ozzardi* have been found only in body cavities. *Dirofilaria conjunctivæ* (only immature females) have been reported from cutaneous and visceral nodules.

Arthropod Intermediate Hosts.—The obligatory intermediate hosts of the human filarias are various blood-sucking flies, *viz.*, for species of

Wuchereria (and probably *Dirofilaria conjunctivæ*), domestic and semi-domestic mosquitoes; for *Onchocerca volvulus*, the coffee-fly *Simulium;* for *Loa loa*, the mango-fly *Chrysops*, and for species of *Acanthocheilonema* and *Mansonella ozzardi*, the biting midge *Culicoides*.

Geographical Distribution of the Human Filarias.—*Wuchereria bancrofti* and *Acanthocheilonema perstans* are established throughout practically the entire warm belt of the world. *W. malayi* is widely distributed in the countries of the China Sea area, in southeastern Asia, Indonesia, Ceylon and the eastern part of India. *Loa loa* and *A. streptocerca* are confined to tropical Africa. *Onchocerca volvulus* is widely disseminated in tropical Africa and has become established in at least four foci in the Western Hemisphere. *Mansonella ozzardi* is indigenous to tropical America.

Wuchereria Bancrofti (Cobbold, 1877) Seurat, 1921

(Bancroft's filaria, causing Bancroft's filariasis)

Historical Notes

This infection was known to the ancient Hindus (600 B.C.), and the Persian physicians Rhazes and Avicenna referred to its chronic manifestations as elephantiasis arabicum. In 1863 Demarquay, in Paris, first found microfilarias of this worm in hydrocele fluid of a patient from Cuba; in 1866 Wucherer, in Brazil, observed them in chylous urine, and in 1872 Timothy Lewis, in India, discovered them in peripheral blood. The adult females were first seen by Bancroft (1876–1877) and the adult males by Sibthorpe (1888), both recovered from lymphatic tissues in Australia. Patrick Manson, in Amoy, China demonstrated (1878) that the night-biting mosquito *Culex fatigans* (=*C. quinquefasciatus*), was an essential intermediate host and described (1879) noctural periodicity of the microfilarias in peripheral blood. Manson-Bahr (1912) and O'Connor (1923) showed that microfilarias of the strains of *W. bancrofti* in the South Pacific islands exhibited no periodicity.

Geographical Distribution

Bancroft's filariasis is widely distributed throughout the tropical areas of the world and in some regions extends well into subtropical areas. (See map, Fig. 94.) Until recent decades it was endemic in the southeastern United States. It seems probable that it did not occur in the Western Hemisphere until it was introduced from Africa with the slave trade.

In parts of India and the South Pacific islands the incidence of Bancroft's filariasis is high. In other tropical areas there is wide endemicity but relatively low prevalence in the population. Altogether approximately 200 million persons are afflicted.

Epidemiology

Man is the only known definitive host of *Wuchereria bancrofti* and female mosquitoes of the genera *Culex*, *Aëdes*, *Mansonia* and *Anopheles* are neces-

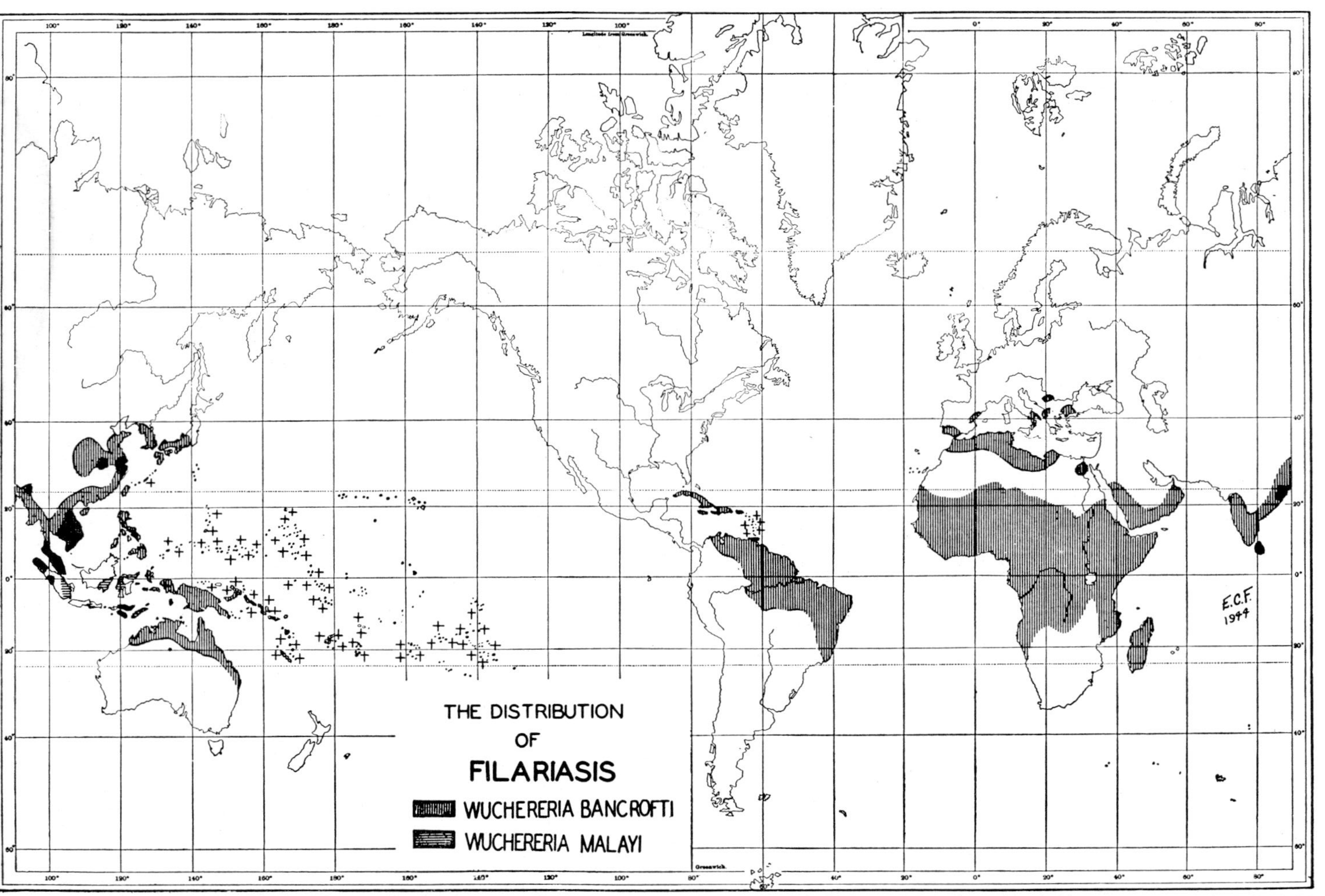
THE DISTRIBUTION
OF
FILARIASIS
WUCHERERIA BANCROFTI
WUCHERERIA MALAYI
E.C.F.
1947

sary intermediate hosts. The adult worms develop in the human lymphatic system and the microfilarias enter the blood stream and reach the peripheral circulation. When picked up by the appropriate mosquito the microfilarias transform into larvas in the thoracic muscles, migrate to the tip of the fly's proboscis and are transferred to a human host when the mosquito feeds. Under optimal conditions the mosquito phase of the cycle is completed in 10 or 11 days; in contrast, at least as many months are usually required from the time the infective-stage larva enters the skin until microfilarias of the next generation are recovered from peripheral blood.

All persons of all ages and racial groups are susceptible to infection with *W. bancrofti*. In areas of high endemicity children are exposed early in life. Conditions highly favorable for continued propagation of the infection consist of human carriers with many microfilarias in their blood and appropriate mosquitoes breeding near human habitations serving as vectors from infected to uninfected individuals.

Morphology, Biology and Life Cycle

The Adult Worms.—The adults of *W. bancrofti* (Fig. 58 *m*, page 210) are creamy white, elongated threads which taper at both ends and have a smooth cuticle. The head is slightly swollen and is unarmed. The male measures about 40 mm. in length by 0.1 mm. in cross section. Its caudal end is curved ventrally as much as 360 degrees. The female measures 80 to 100 mm. in length by 0.24 to 0.3 mm. in diameter. The vulva opens midventrally about 0.8 to 0.9 mm. from the anterior end.

The Microfilarias.—In the inner portion of the two uteri the elongated embryos are tightly coiled within thin, transparent, ovoidal egg membranes, which measure about 38 by 25 microns. As the embryos are pushed along towards the outer ends of the uteri they uncoil and the membranes are stretched into "sheaths" that are somewhat larger than the microfilarias.

On escape from the mother worm the microfilarias may remain for some time in the lymphatic vessels or they may soon enter the blood stream. In most strains of *W. bancrofti* they circulate periodically, passing through peripheral blood at night and congregating in visceral blood, particularly the pulmonary capillaries, during the daytime. In the South Pacific strains no particular periodicity is exhibited.

The microfilarias of *W. bancrofti* (Fig. 95) as they actively circulate in the blood stream or lymph measure 127 to 320 microns in length by 7.5 to 10 microns in cross section. They are bluntly rounded at the anterior tip and attenuated posteriorly. In a wet blood film they move about gracefully, pushing the red blood corpuscles to one side. Internally they possess no digestive tract but a relatively solid column of cells with densely staining nuclei, among which certain specific anatomical landmarks may be discovered when the organisms are stained by intravital or permanent dyes. (For staining technics, see "TECHNICAL AIDS," page 590.) For differential diagnostic purposes it may be noted that the embryo is "sheathed," its caudal extremity is free of cells, its movement is graceful, and it exhibits nocturnal periodicity in peripheral blood in all geographic areas where other human filarias are endemic.

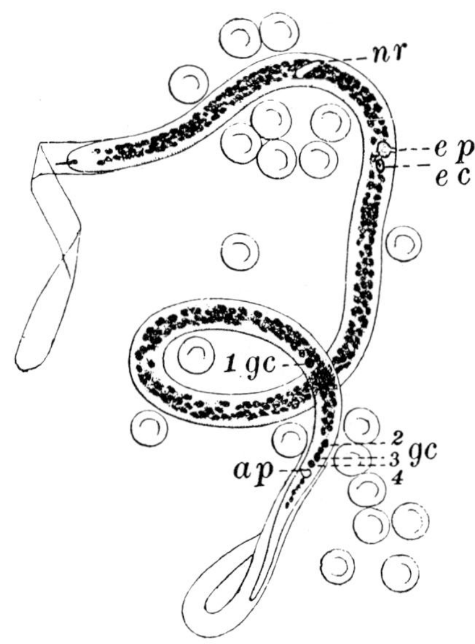

FIG. 95.—"Ensheathed" microfilaria of *Wuchereria bancrofti*. *nr*, nerve ring; *ep*, excretory pore; *ec*, excretory cell; 1, 2, 3, 4 *gc*, so-called "genital cells"; *ap*, anal pore. × 666. (From Faust's *Human Helminthology*, Lea & Febiger, Philadelphia.)

Table 10. Differential Characters Between the Microfilarias of Wuchereria Bancrofti, W. Malayi and Loa Loa

NOTE.—Percentages indicate proportion of total length from anterior tip.

Character	*Mf. bancrofti*	*Mf. malayi*	*Mf. loa*
1. Periodicity	Usually nocturnal	Nocturnal	Diurnal
2. Length in microns (thick films)	244 to 296	177 to 230	250 to 300
3. Excretory cell and excretory pore	Small (30.75%), near excretory pore (28.95%)	Large (37.07%), far behind excretory pore (30.09%)	Similar (36.6%) to *Mf. malayi;* (31.6%)
4. "G" cells	Small, of similar size; G_1 (70.14%) far ahead of G_2–G_4	Larger than in *Mf. bancrofti;* G_1 (68.33%) relatively near and larger than G_2–G_4	Similar to those of *Mf. malayi* G_1 (68.6%)
5. Anal pore	82.48%	82.28%	81.9%
6. Tail	Tapers to delicate point; no terminal nuclei	Swollen at levels of 2 terminal nuclei	Tapers gradually; caudal nuclei continuous with those of trunk
7. Appearance	Moves in graceful, sweeping curves	Stiff, with secondary kinks	Similar to *Mf. malayi*
8. Pathogenesis	Lymphangitis of genitalia and lower extremities; later elephantiasis or varicose lymphatics	Lymphangitis and elephantiasis confined mostly to the extremities	Fugitive inflammation of subcutaneous tissues
9. Insect hosts	*Culex, Aëdes,* occasionally *Mansonia, Anopheles*	*Mansonia, Anopheles*	*Chrysops*

The important diagnostic differences between the "sheathed" microfilarias of *W. bancrofti*, *W. malayi* and *Loa loa* are provided in Table 10, while the more easily recognized structural features of the "sheathed" and "unsheathed" microfilarias of man are illustrated in Figure 96.

The Mosquito Phase of the Cycle.—In the mosquito each microfilaria which has just been ingested is found in the midgut ("stomach") within a "sheath." Soon the embryos lose their "sheaths" and some pass out in the fecal dejecta. Others invade the stomach wall and within 24 hours in a suitable mosquito host they migrate to the thoracic muscles and become relatively quiescent. During the next 2 to 7 days they transform into a

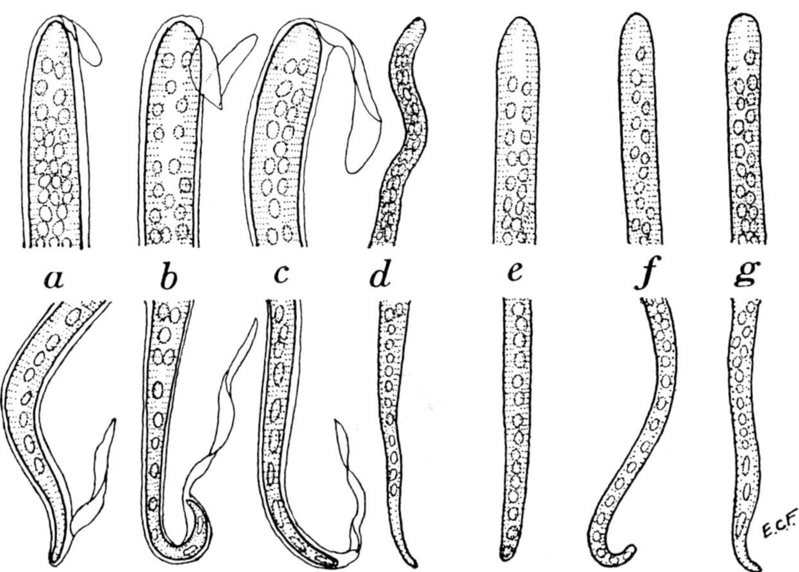

FIG. 96.—Differential characters of the head and tail ends of the microfilarias of man. *a*, *Wuchereria bancrofti; b*, *W. malayi; c*, *Loa loa; d*, *Onchocerca vulvulus; e*, *Acanthocheilonema perstans; f*, *A. streptocerca; g*, *Mansonella ozzardi.* Greatly enlarged, drawn to scale. (From Craig and Faust's *Clinical Parasitology*, Lea & Febiger, Philadelphia.)

sausage-shaped rhabditoid larval form (Fig. 97, Fig. 98 *A*). The larva now measures 225 to 300 microns in length by 15 to 30 microns in cross section. Soon the worm transforms into an active, elongated, filariform type (Fig. 98 *B*), which migrates out of the thoracic muscles into the head of the mosquito and then down to the tip of the proboscis sheath (labium), from which it enters the human host at the time of the next blood meal. The complete mosquito phase is accomplished in 10 to 40 days.

The Biological Incubation Period.—The route through which the infective larvas enter the skin and migrate to the sites where they later develop into adults is not completely known. Yokogawa (1938, 1939) found that they undertake invasion only if there is lymph exudate from the mosquito's puncture wound. Thereafter the successful individuals continue to migrate through lymphatic vessels, growing slowly and with increasing frequency becoming temporarily trapped in lymph nodes in various parts of the body. Unless they are destroyed elsewhere in the lymphatic system, the adolescent worms tend to congregate in the groin glands and in the epididymis of the male and labial glands of the female. However, they may settle down in lymphatic varices, in nodular dilatations of the lymphatic vessels in the lower extremities, or may complete their development in the thoracic duct. After maturing and mating they become coiled together and parturition is

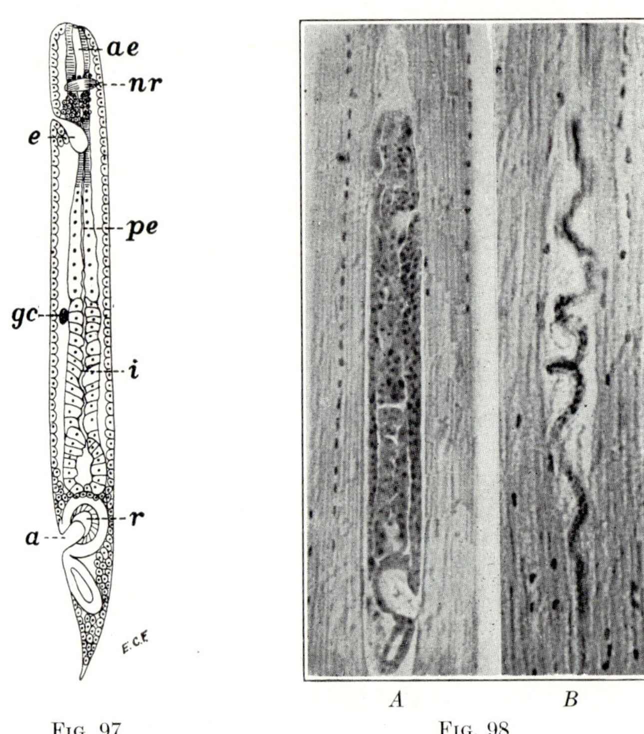

Fig. 97 Fig. 98

Fig. 97.—"Sausage-shaped" rhabditoid larva of *Wuchereria bancrofti* from thoracic muscles of *Culex pipiens*. *ae*, anterior esophagus; *nr*, nerve ring; *e*, excretory bladder; *pe*, posterior esophagus; *gc*, genital primordium; *i*, midgut; *r*, rectum; *a*, anus. × 300. (From Faust's *Human Helminthology*, Lea & Febiger, Philadelphia.)

Fig. 98.—Photomicrographs of *A*, rhabditoid larva and *B*, filariform larva of *Wuchereria bancrofti* in thoracic muscles of *Culex pipiens*. × 300. (After Dr. C. U. Lee, from Faust's *Human Helminthology*, Lea & Febiger, Philadelphia.)

begun. Approximately one year or more is required from invasion of the skin until the worms have completed their development, but there are instances of much shorter incubation (Jordan, 1952). The life cycle is diagrammatically illustrated in Figure 99.

Pathogenesis and Symptomatology

The Acute Stage.—The symptoms resulting from Bancroft's filariasis are due primarily to local and systemic sensitization and tissue reactions to the invader. The larval and adolescent forms of *W. bancrofti* and later the sexually mature worms are in intimate contact with the endothelial lining of the lymphatic vessels and at times the lymph nodes. As long as the immature worms are in active migration they produce relatively little local reaction; but when trapped they tend to produce an acute tissue response, consisting of an accumulation of histiocytes, epithelioid cells, lymphocytes, giant cells and eosinophils in the lumen of the vessel around the worms, hyperplasia of the endothelium and perilymphatic cellular infiltration. At times this is sufficient to strangulate the worms in migration months before

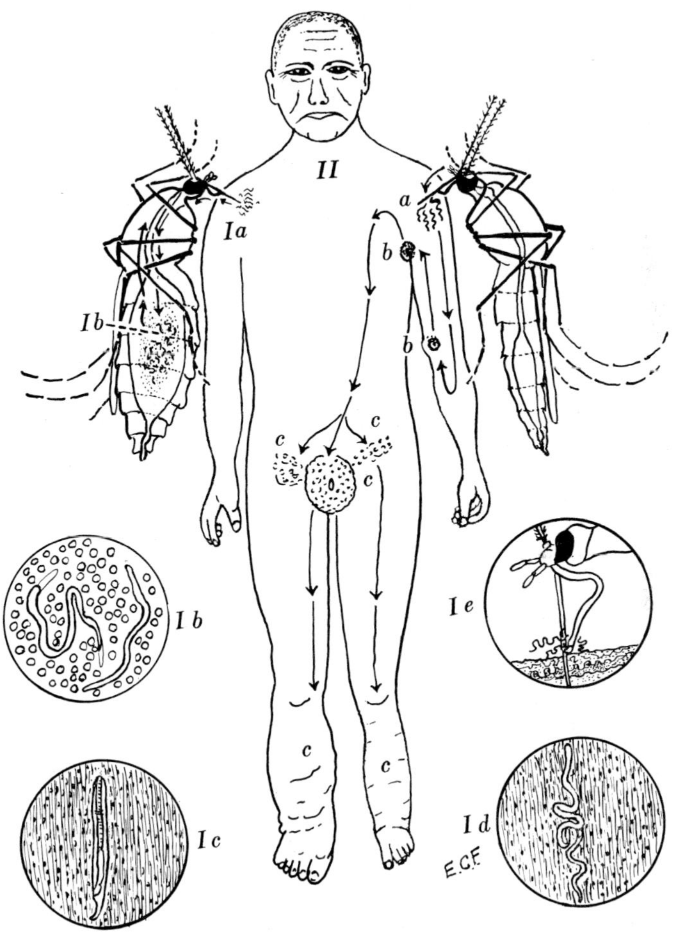

FIG. 99.—Diagrammatic representation of the life cycle of *Wuchereria bancrofti* in mosquito and man. I. Mosquito phase: *a*, microfilarias taken into stomach in blood meal from a human carrier; *b*, microfilarias exsheathing in stomach; *c*, development of rhabditoid larva in thoracic muscles; *d*, transformation to filariform larva in thoracic muscles; *e*, filariform larva escaping from tip of proboscis onto human skin. II. Human phase: *a*, filariform larvas entering peripheral lymphatics; *b*, *b*, development of acute lymphangitis and lymphadenitis in epitrochlear and axillary lymph nodes; *c*, *c*, *c*, *c*, development of chronic (fibrotic) lesion in groin, scrotum, and lower extremities. (Original.)

maturity (Michael, 1944). Later, when the worms settle down and develop into adults, parturient females and microfilarias produce acute tissue reactions. These tissue changes tend to constrict the wall of the vessel and obliterate its channel. (See Fig. 100.)

Wherever such acute inflammatory reaction takes place there is a reddened, swollen, raised lymphatic tract immediately around and retrograde to the site of blockage. It is exquisitely tender, painful and there is at times a febrile reaction. King (1944), states that the earliest symptoms in young adult males develop 3 to 16 months after exposure; that the cardinal manifestations are lymphangitis, usually with an associated lymphadenitis, and only in 20% with fever of mild type and short duration.

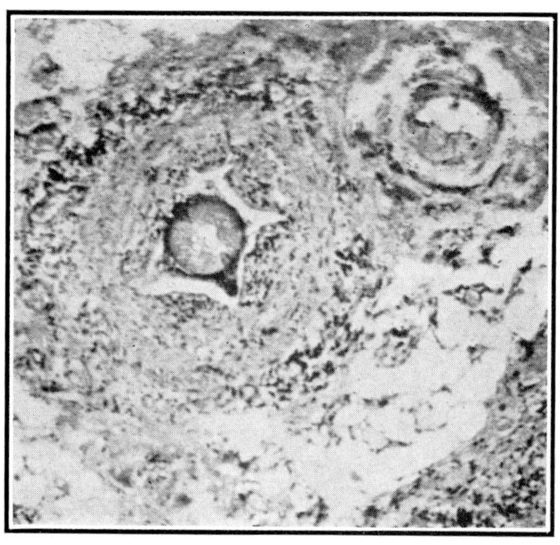

FIG. 100.—Section through a lymphatic vessel in the epididymis, showing early acute tissue reaction around *Wuchereria bancrofti*. × 100. (Photomicrograph from preparation of Dr. F. W. O'Connor, Collection, Armed Forces Institute of Pathology, from Faust's *Human Helminthology*, Lea & Febiger, Philadelphia.)

The lymphangitis may originate in an upper extremity, mostly epitrochlear, but eventually practically all of the lesions concentrate in the scrotum and consist of inflammatory involvement of the spermatic cord, epididymis, testis or entire scrotal organ. Relapses of the acute syndrome are frequent. In lightly exposed white immigrants in Samoa, Webster (1946) found that bouts of lymphangitis with fever occurred annually. In natives of endemic areas this stage of the infection may be symptomless. Since first exposure is likely to take place early in childhood, the severe early involvement of the genitalia is usually lacking. Living worms may be present for years in dilated lymphatic channels (Fig. 101) without remarkable symptoms. These persons characteristically have microfilarias circulating in their blood and constitute the usual source of infection for the mosquito.

The Chronic Stage.—The tissue changes shown in Figure 101 represent a mild form of the chronic stage. The advanced chronic stage may develop in highly sensitized reactors directly from the acute inflammatory condition of a lymphatic vessel containing the worms or may build up slowly from the milder fibrotic type. In either case reexposure hastens the reaction. As a result of obliterative changes in the vessels, thrombi, and proliferative changes, the worms die and are absorbed or become calcified. This chronic process may not mature until many years after initial exposure.

The organs and tissues in which these changes occur are the groin, with the development of nodular groin-gland varicosities; the lower extremities, one or both of which become elephantoid with redundant skin and a dense fibrous subcutaneous matrix filled with islands of lymph; the scrotum, which may reach tremendous size, the penis or the prepuce; the labia clitoridis; the tunica vaginalis, with resultant lymphocele or chylocele; the peritoneum, with production of chylous ascites, and the vesical or renal lymphatics, the rupture of which causes lymphuria or chyluria. With relatively rare exceptions all of these pathologic changes in Bancroft's filariasis occur in organs and tissue below the diaphragm.

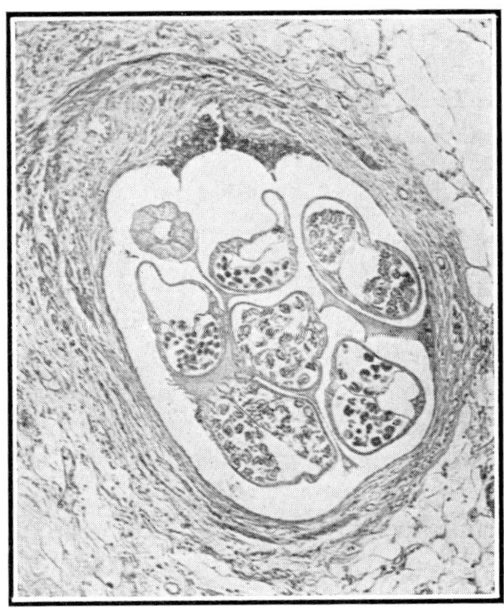

FIG. 101.—Mild fibrotic tissue reaction around a living parturient female *Wuchereria bancrofti* in an inguinal lymph node. × 66. (Photomicrograph by Faust from preparation by Conrad Bauer, from Faust's *Human Helminthology*, Lea & Febiger, Philadelphia.)

Once the parent worms have died, there is no further production of microfilarias, which soon cease to appear in the peripheral blood. However, in native populations in endemic areas the blood may be positive for microfilarias in spite of long-standing chronic lesions, due to new active infections which have been superimposed on the older ones.

Some workers (Anderson, 1924; Grace, 1932, 1934) claim that the pathogenesis of the lymphangitis and lymphadenitis in Bancroft's filariasis is not due to the worms themselves but to β hemolytic streptococcus which has entered the lesion, but McKinley (1931), Michael (1944) and Hartz

(1944) have found no evidence of bacteria in the actual centers of inflammation, and have concluded that the tissue reaction is due to the worms themselves. In the more chronic stage, when the indurated, thickened, poorly nourished skin of elephantoid members becomes cracked, abundant opportunity is provided for invasion by bacteria and fungi.

Undue emphasis is placed on the advanced chronic lesion in Bancroft's filariasis and little attention is devoted to the fundamental early pathogenesis of the lesion.

There are a few instances in which immature filarias, considered to be *W. bancrofti*, have been reported from unusual foci. Wright (1934), Fernando (1935) and McMullen and Cruickshank (1938) each reported a case of ophthalmofilariasis, while Faust *et al.* (1952) described precocious development of post-microfilarias and rhabditoid larvas in one patient and a single fertile female recovered from a small pulmonary artery at necropsy of a second patient. Mya (1928) has attributed right hemiplegia in a patient to the migration of microfilarias of *W. bancrofti* through cerebral capillaries.

Diagnosis

Routine surveys to determine the incidence of Bancroft's filariasis in an area are based on (1) demonstration of the microfilarias of *W. bancrofti* in blood films and (2) clinical evidence of the disease. In native populations in endemic regions these two types of information seldom coincide: a higher percentage of persons in the younger age groups have microfilaremia and a higher percentage in the older age groups have symptoms.

During the biological incubation period microfilarias have not yet been produced and therefore can not be demonstrated. Hence diagnosis must be based on history of exposure, lymphangitis and lymphadenitis compatible with Bancroft's filariasis and occasional demonstration of immature worms in an inflamed lymphatic focus (Michael, 1944). Moreover, in persons having a single exposure the worms may be destroyed by tissue reaction and never reach maturity, hence there is no production of embryos. Intradermal tests, employing *Dirofilaria* antigen, will be positive in 90% of these cases. (See "Technical Aids," page 613.)

Once microfilarias are being discharged they can be recovered in blood films. In all areas except the South Pacific islands they are present in appreciable numbers in peripheral blood only at night, usually with greatest frequency between 10 P.M. and 2 A.M. Diagnosis is more commonly made with thick films. For preparation of these films and their staining the reader is referred to "Technical Aids," pages 590–591.

After the parent worms die, microfilarias soon disappear from the blood, and diagnosis must be made on the epidemiologic and clinical history. Care should be exercised to distinguish filarial lymphangitis and its sequelæ from similar clinical pictures resulting from non-filarial disease.

Treatment

Before patent infection with Bancroft's filaria has developed, specific chemotherapy is not likely to be considered. After the worms have died, it is probably useless. At times symptomatic relief is successful in allaying pain and in case of bacterial complications the use of antibiotics may be helpful. Moreover tight bandaging of elephantoid extremities (Knott, 1938), and surgical removal of redundant tissues (Auchincloss, 1930) may aid in directing lymph flow into collateral channels and thus reduce the amount of accumulated lymph. In cases of acute lymphangitis resulting from recent primary exposure, the patient should be removed from the endemic area to a stimulating climate. At times psychologic therapy is necessary for young adult males with scrotal involvement.

Specific Chemotherapy.—Until recent years chemotherapy in Bancroft's filariasis has been unsatisfactory. Certain antimonials and arsenicals will kill the circulating microfilarias and after prolonged administration inhibit their production (Brown, 1944; Culbertson *et al.*, 1947; Otto and Maren, 1947; Otto *et al.*, 1952). More rapid filaricidal results can be obtained with suramin sodium (Bayer 205) but this drug like the antimonials and arsenicals requires administration by needle.

The advent of Hetrazan (diethyl carbamazine) has provided the first anthelmintic of practical usefulness in the treatment of Bancroft's filariasis (Santiago-Stevenson *et al.*, 1947; Hewitt *et al.*, 1950; Halawani *et al.*, 1949; Galliard and Mille, 1949; Hawking and Lourie, 1949; Nor el Din and El Tamini, 1952; von Schowingen, 1952). The advantages of this drug are its oral route of administration, the relatively good tolerance of the patient for the drug and its relatively rapid beneficial clinical effects. Most satisfactory results are obtained when Hetrazan is taken in the amount of 2 mgm. per kilo of body weight 3 times daily for 10 or more days. It rapidly destroys the microfilarias in circulating blood and with moderate speed kills the parent worms.

Control

Control of Bancroft's filariasis can be effected by (1) treatment of all microfilaria carriers in an endemic area and (2) elimination of the mosquito transmitters. Use of DDT as a larvicide and residual spray in and around habitations has been demonstrated to reduce infection in many communities, and when combined with Hetrazan therapy promises much in the control of the disease (Beye *et al.*, 1952).

Wuchereria Malayi (Brug, 1927) Rao and Maplestone, 1940
(Malayan filaria, causing Malayan filariasis)

Historical and Geographical Notes

The "sheathed" microfilaria of this species was first observed in blood films of natives of Celebes by Lichtstein (1927), who was unable to infect *Culex* mosquitoes with the living embryos. Brug (1927) designated the new organism *Filaria malayi*. Rao and Maplestone (1940), in India, and Bonne *et al.* (1941), in Indonesia, obtained and described the adult worms.

The geographical distribution of *W. malayi* is relatively extensive (Fig. 94, page 290), including Korea, Central and South China, Indo-China, the

Philippines, Malaya, Sumatra, Celebes, Borneo, Ceram, New Guinea. Ceylon, and at least four states of India. In some of these countries *W. malayi* is coextensive with *W. bancrofti,* and undoubtedly some of the earlier records incorrectly reported *W. bancrofti* when they should have been *W. malayi.*

Epidemiology

W. malayi is transmitted by mosquitoes of the genera *Mansonia* and *Anopheles.* Species of *Mansonia* are intermediate hosts almost exclusively of *W. malayi* while certain species of *Anopheles* are equally good transmitters of *W. malayi, W. bancrofti* and malaria parasites. In areas where *Mansonia* is the vector Malayan filariasis is typically rural (Field, 1951); where an anopheline is involved the disease is essentially urban or suburban (Feng, 1936).

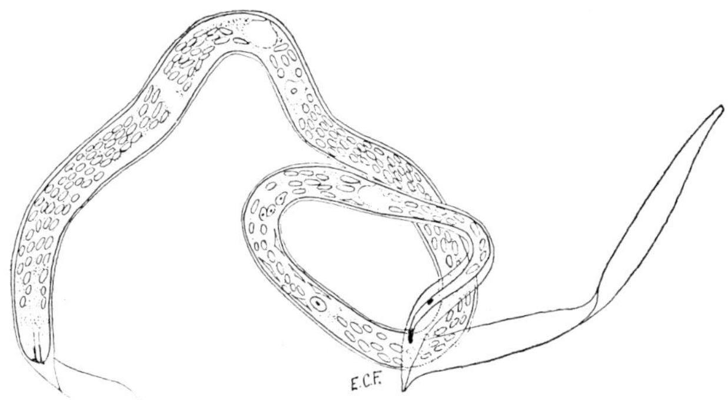

Fig. 102.—Microfilaria of *Wuchereria malayi.* × 666. (Original camera lucida drawing from blood film of Celebes carrier, Brug material, from Faust's *Human Helminthology,* Lea & Febiger, Philadelphia.)

Morphology, Biology and Life Cycle

The adults of *W. malayi* (Fig. 58 *l*, page 210) resemble those of *W. bancrofti* in most respects but are specifically distinguishable. The males measure 22 to 23 mm. in length by 88 microns in cross section. Their posterior end is tightly coiled. The female (only a single complete specimen has been described) measures 55 mm. long by 160 microns in cross section. The most distinctive morphologic character of *W. malayi* consists of the two cells in the tip of the tail of the microfilaria (Figs. 96 *b*, 102 and Table 10, p. 292).

Although the microfilaria of *W. malayi* exhibits nocturnal periodicity in its migration through cutaneous blood vessels, this is not as absolute as in the periodic strains of *W. bancrofti.* Feng (1936) has studied the intermediate stages of this species in *Anopheles hyrcanus* var. *sinensis* and has found that complete development requires a minimum of only 6 days.

Clinical Aspects

Relatively little study has been made of the pathogenesis and symptomatology of Malayan filariasis. It is known, however, that the lymphangitis and later the chronic manifestations of the disease are confined almost exclusively to the extremities, usually the arms (Rao, 1945). In northern Ceram Brug (1933) found a relatively close correlation between this infection and elephantiasis. On the other hand, Field (1951), in Malaya, found five times as many symptomless carriers of *W. malayi* as elephantoid cases.

Specific diagnosis of Malayan filaria is based on demonstration of the characteristic microfilaria in night-time blood. Wilson (1950) and Field (1951) have reported favorably on the value of *Hetrazan* (diethyl carbamazine) in the treatment of this disease.

Control

In endemic areas of Malayan filariasis where species of *Anopheles* are the vectors, anti-larval spraying and residual spraying of homes with DDT will provide effective control as it does in malaria. In countries where *Mansonia* species are involved and the infection is rural, the problem is more complicated, since the larvas of these mosquitoes obtain oxygen by inserting their breathing tubes into the hanging roots of water plants. Iyengar (1933), in Travancore (India), recommended periodic removal of these plants from the water as a practical control measure, and Sweet and Pillai (1937) found this procedure was effective in reducing the incidence of new infections. The use of 2-4-D (Weedone) has been effective in killing *Pistia* in Ceylon and has been accompanied by notable reduction in new cases of this disease. Field (1951) believes that treatment of carriers with Hetrazan will render the great majority free of microfilarias and the *Mansonia* vectors "non-infective for at least a year."

Onchocerca Volvulus (Leuckart, 1893) Railliet and Henry, 1910
(Convoluted filaria, causing onchocercosis)

Historical and Geographical Notes

This species was first described by Leuckart (1893) from material removed from a native of the Gold Coast, West Africa. In 1915, Robles found the same worm in a native worker on a coffee plantation in Guatemala, on the western slope of the Continental Divide, and demonstrated its causal relationship to blindness. In 1926, Blacklock proved that a blackfly, *Simulium damnosum*, was an essential intermediate host and transmitter of the disease in Africa.

O. volvulus is distributed throughout extensive areas of tropical Africa, including Senegal, Sierra Leone and Liberia on the West Coast, the Gold Coast, Nigeria, French Equatorial Africa, the Belgian Congo, the southern Sudan, Uganda, Tanganyika and possibly Kenya. In the Western Hemisphere, to which it was probably introduced from Africa (Ruiz Reyes,

1952), it is established on the Pacific Coast of Guatemala, the adjacent Mexican states of Chiapas and Oaxaca, and in the eastermost part of Venezuela and nearby Dutch Guiana.

Epidemiology

Man is the only definitive host of *O. volvulus*, and species of *Simulium* are the intermediate hosts and transmitters. The flies breed in fast-flowing mountain streams above the coastal plains and the adults usually bite man and other animals close to their breeding places, but the flies may be carried in air currents and thus pick up, incubate and transmit the infection many kilometers distant from where they breed. Persons bathing or washing clothes in the clean mountain streams or drawing water from this supply are frequently bitten by the flies. In many endemic zones the disease is associated with coffee planting; laborers on these plantations are more commonly infected than supervisory personnel because of greater exposure. The flies do not enter well-shaded homes.

Morphology, Biology and Life Cycle

Adult Worms.—The adults of *O. volvulus* (usually as a mated pair) are intricately coiled up in the midst of a dense, fibrous, subcutaneous tumor but occasionally females have been found free in connective tissue. The nodules may develop on any part of the body but are frequently located near the junction of long bones or on the scalp. In most instances they can be seen or palpated but there are cases in which microfilarias are present in the skin without evidence of nodules.

The worms themselves (Fig. 58 *n*, page 210) are wiry, creamy-white threads which are bluntly rounded at both ends. The males measure 19 to 42 mm. in length by 130 to 210 microns in cross section. They are tightly recurved ventrally at the posterior end. The females measure 33.5 to 50 cm. in length by 270 to 400 microns in cross section.

The Microfilarias.—The embryos are coiled within a broadly ovoidal egg membrane in the inner end of the uterus but become uncoiled and elongated as they reach the outer end. On delivery from the mother worm they escape from the eggshell, *i. e.*, they become "unsheathed." They are of two sizes, 150 to 287 by 5 to 7 microns and 285 to 368 by 6 to 9 microns. The anterior and posterior ends of this microfilaria are illustrated in Figure 96*d*, p. 293. The free microfilarias circulate in the superficial lymphatic vessels and connective tissue of the skin and rarely, if ever, get into the blood stream except accidentally.

The Insect Phase of the Life Cycle.—Although *Simulium* flies are blood suckers, they also imbibe tissue juices, otherwise they would not have an opportunity to pick up the microfilarias of *O. volvulus*. Vargas (1942), in Mexico, found that the microfilarias taken up by *Simulium* migrate from the dorsal food reservoir, rather than the midgut, directly to the thoracic muscles, where they are transformed into rhabditoid and then filariform larvas, with two moults of cuticle. This requires a minimum of 6 days. Thereafter the larvas proceed down to the tip of the fly's proboscis, ready to infect the next human host. The species of *Onchocerca* which parasitize horses and cattle are specifically distinguishable from *O. volvulus* in their microfilarial stage (Gibson, 1952).

The Biological Incubation Period.—There is almost no specific information concerning this filaria from the time it invades the skin until it reaches maturity in a subcutaneous nodule. The worms mature slowly and may require as long as a year to reach full size, but occasionally *Onchocerca* nodules have been detected in infants 3 to 10 months old. Some of the tumors appear on covered parts of the body not accessible to the fly, suggesting that the invading worms may have migrated some distance from the site of entry before they were trapped by host tissue infiltration. Yet an overwhelming majority are located on or near exposed areas of the skin.

Pathogenesis and Symptomatology

The Parent Nodules.—With relatively infrequent exceptions the presence of the maturing or adult *O. volvulus* causes a local cellular reaction of a fibrocytic nature; this results in encapsulation of the worms which lie tangled within the dense fibrous matrix (Fig. 103). Occasionally the tumor presents an abscessing center due to bacterial invasion and rarely the parasites escape encapsulation and migrate through the tissues like *Loa loa* (page 309). There may be only a single nodule or the lesions may be multiple. As many as 126 have been reported from 1 patient in Africa (Hisette, 1932) and 150 from another (Strong *et al.*, 1938), but usually the number in African patients is much smaller. In Guatemala and Mexico the number rarely exceeds 6 (Puig Solanes *et al.*, 1948). In Africans, most of whose entire skin area is exposed to *Simulium* bites, the nodules are more commonly found on the trunk, buttocks or elbows than on the head (Fig. 104). *S. damnosum* usually "bites" close to the ground. In native Americans, whose body is covered except for the head, forearms, ankles and feet, a majority of cases have nodules most commonly on the scalp (Fig. 105). The parent nodule is typically painless and is benign.

Sensitization Reaction.—Almost invariably *O. volvulus* infection provokes an acute sensitization reaction, particularly noted in the skin, which may reveal pigmentation dermatitis, licheniform, eczematoid or erysipelatoid lesions (Goldman and Ortiz, 1946), or extreme dermatoglyphia in fair-skinned patients. There is typically a high eosinophilic leukocytosis, while there may be a tissue concentration of eosinophils, plasma cells and at times giant cells near the nodules. Moreover, the migration of microfilarias through the connective tissue of the skin characteristically produces a severe pruritic dermatitis.

Ocular Lesions.—Beginning with Robles' original observations (1915) workers in Guatemala and Mexico, later in Africa (Hisette, 1932; Aplemans, 1935), and recently in the endemic area of Venezuela (Noble, 1952), have noted the causal relationship of onchocercosis to ophthalmitis and loss of vision. The microfilarias of *O. volvulus* invade all of the tissues of the eye, producing punctate, vascular or interstitial keratitis, iritis, chorioretinitis, congestion and punctate hemorrhage around the limbus of the eye, congestion and edema of the conjunctiva, exudation into the vitreous and later degenerative changes of the optic nerve. The patient first complains

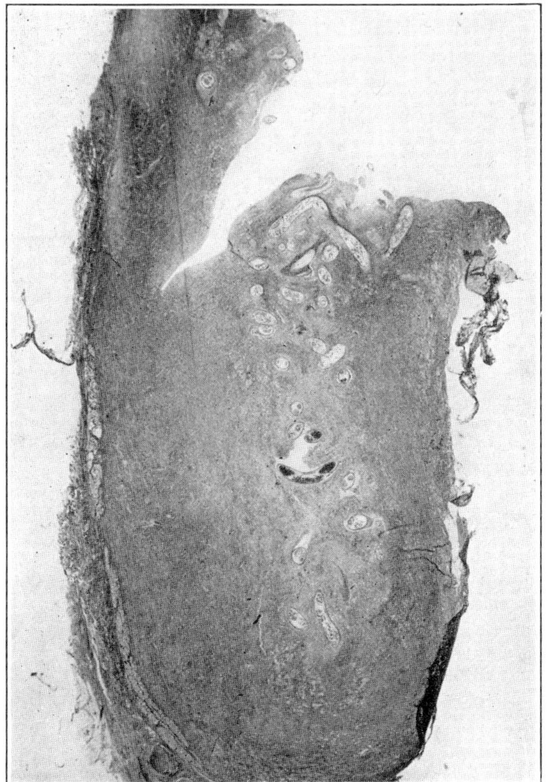

A

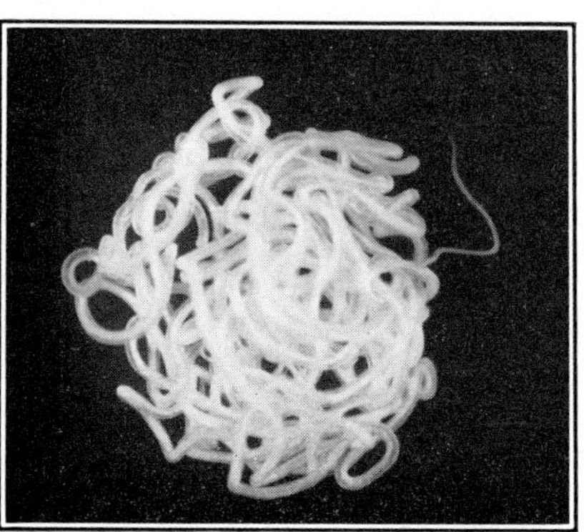

B

FIG. 103.—*A*, Section through *Onchocerca volvulus* tumor removed from the scalp of a Guatemalan patient, × 6, (Original photomicrograph, from Faust's *Human Helminthology*, Lea & Febiger, Philadelphia); *B*, tangled pair of parent worms (female stouter, male more filiform) digested out of nodule, × 3. (Original, courtesy of Dr. Luis Mazzotti, Mexico, D. F.)

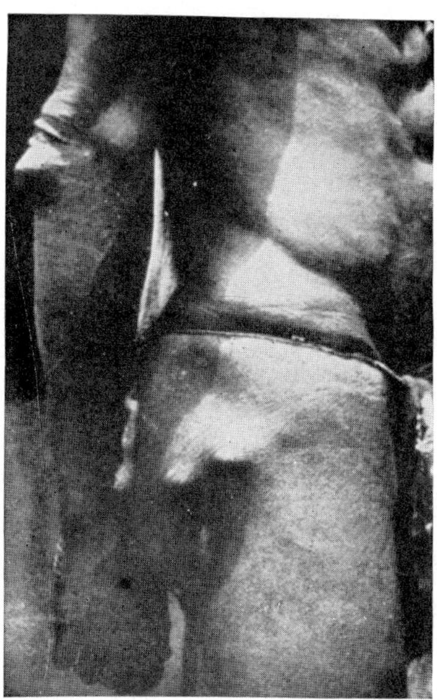

Fig. 104.—*Onchocerca volvulus* nodules in region of trochanter and at elbow of African patient. (After Blacklock, Ann. Trop. Med. & Parasitol., from Faust's *Human Helminthology*, Lea & Febiger, Philadelphia.)

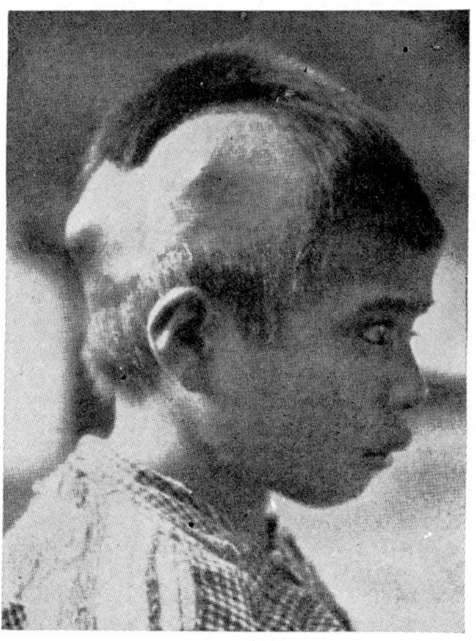

Fig. 105.—*Onchocerca volvulus* nodules on scalp of a Guatemalan boy. The right eye shows evidence of partial blindness. (After Strong, in Onchocerciasis, 1934, courtesy of Harvard Univ. Press, from Faust's *Human Helminthology*, Lea & Febiger, Philadelphia.)

of impaired vision, then intense photophobia, partial loss of vision, and finally, in many instances, suffers total blindness. Puig Solanes *et al.* (1948) have found that ocular damage is commoner in persons who have multiple *Onchocerca* tumors, and Noble (1952) has observed that in eastern Venezuela where the infection is relatively light the eye lesions are minimal.

Diagnosis

Diagnosis can not be made from blood films since the microfilarias of *O. volvulus* do not circulate through the blood stream. Routinely thin skin shavings about 0.5 cm. in diameter are removed with a sharp razor blade. If the microfilarias are abundant a single biopsy from the small of the back will suffice; if they are scant in number it may be desirable to obtain specimens from each shoulder blade, posterior cervical triangle, intercostal area and ileal crest. The specimen is placed in a drop of tepid physiologic salt solution on a microscopic slide and mounted with a cover-glass. Microfilarias will soon emerge from positive tissues and move about actively in the medium. Experienced clinicians working in endemic areas will also be able to demonstrate the organisms with the ophthalmic microscope.

While the intradermal test, employing filaria antigen, is diagnostically positive in about 90% of proven cases (Rodhain and Dubois, 1932), skin biopsy is a more practical procedure.

Treatment

As soon as a subcutaneous nodule has been demonstrated to be an *Onchocerca* tumor the first and most important therapeutic task is to excise the nodule. This has a twofold clinical purpose, *i. e.*, (1) to forestall further opportunity for microfilarias to damage the eye, and (2) to reduce the likelihood of hypersensitization when chemotherapy is instituted.

Suramin (Naphuride sodium, Bayer 205) is a very valuable drug in the treatment of onchocercosis, since it not only kills the circulating microfilarias but also, somewhat more slowly, destroys the parent worms (Burch and Ashburn, 1951). This drug is fairly well tolerated, but its practical disadvantage consists in the route of administration, namely, by vein, which poses a serious problem for ambulatory clinics in endemic areas.

Hetrazan (diethyl carbamazine) has the advantage of oral administration, and is probably as effective in killing the microfilarias in onchocercosis as it is in Bancroft's filariasis when full therapeutic dosage is attained, but difficulty is experienced with respect to allergic side reactions to a much greater degree in onchocercosis. Ruiz Reyes (1951) states that with a standard course of treatment, consisting of 2 mgm. per kilo body weight 2 or 3 times daily for 10 days, there are manifestations of intense pruritic dermatitis, edema, conjunctivitis, adenopathy, fever and intestinal colic for the first 4 days of treatment, after which these symptoms tend to subside. He recommends three or four courses of treatment during the first year and two courses during each of the following years. Hawking (1954) suggests preliminary treatment with Hetrazan to kill the microfilarias, and subsequent use of surinam sodium, which is more likely to be lethal to the adult worms.

Prognosis

In untreated infections, the prognosis is poor.

Control

In order to effect control of onchocercosis the attack should be carried out against (1) the human carrier and (2) the transmitter. Ruiz Reyes (1951) emphasizes the public health importance of periodic denodulization to prevent the development of new broods of microfilarias and adequate Hetrazan therapy to kill circulating microfilarias.

Vector control in onchocercosis is considerably more difficult than that presented in Bancroft's filariasis, because the transmitters breed in swiftly running mountain streams and do not ordinarily enter living quarters of the victims. Larvicides sprayed on the flowing water are rapidly dissipated and residual spraying of homes to kill the adult flies is ineffective since the flies seldom invade the living quarters. In the endemic areas of Mexico, it has been discovered (Vargas, 1952; Nettel, 1952) that the breeding places are much more circumscribed than the areas of human infection. Once the former have been mapped, the larvicidal application of DDT during the dry season when the streams are at pool stage, narrows the attack within practical limits.

The two methods outlined above, one concerned with the human carrier and the other with the vector, provide a satisfactory program for the control of onchocercosis.

Loa Loa (Cobbold, 1864) Castellani and Chalmers, 1913

(The "eye worm," causing loaiasis)

Historical and Geographical Notes

The first authentic record of this worm was provided in 1770, by Mongin, who reported the extraction of a female specimen from the front of the eye of a Negress in St. Domingo, West Indies. Other cases among African slaves in the American Tropics continued to be described until 1844. The first indigenous observation from Africa is attributed to Guyot (1778). The worm was not specifically described until 1864, and another long interval elapsed before Connal and Connal (1921, 1922) conclusively proved Manson's hypothesis (1895) that the mango-fly, *Chrysops dimidiata*, is a necessary intermediate host and transmitter.

The endemic zone of loaiasis is limited to West and Central Africa, where the infection is widely distributed. Snijders (1935) found high prevalence (90%) in some villages of the Belgian Congo, and Gordon *et al.* (1950) state that it is a common infection in the British Cameroons and Southern Nigeria. Caucasians as well as natives in these countries contract the infection.

Epidemiology

The distribution of *Loa loa* corresponds to that of the mango flies *Chrysops dimidiata* and *C. silacea.* They breed in relatively clear, flowing streams in high-canopied rain forests and come out to nearby clearings to bite man (Gordon *et al.*, 1950). In this way they pick up the microfilarias from human carriers and later, after a period of incubation, inoculate other persons with the infective-stage larvas.

Morphology, Biology and Life Cycle

The Adult Worms.—The adults (Fig. 58 *i*, page 210) inhabit the subcutaneous tissues, through which the worms are continually migrating. They are thread-like, whitish, have a bossed cuticle, and taper gradually towards both ends. The head is unarmed. The male measures 30 to 34

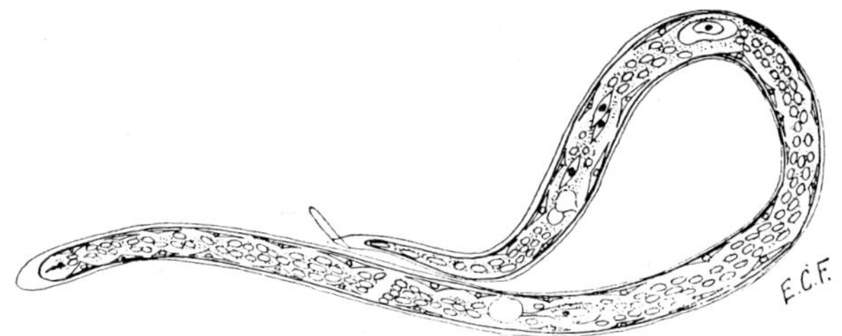

Fig. 106.—Microfilaria of *Loa loa.* × 666. (After Fülleborn, from Faust's *Human Helminthology*, Lea & Febiger, Philadelphia.)

mm. in length by 0.35 to 0.43 mm. in diameter. Its caudal end is curved ventrally. The female measures 50 to 70 mm. in length by 0.5 mm. in diameter. The embryos develop as tightly coiled objects within ovoidal thin shells in the inner end of the two uteri but become uncoiled and elongated in the outer portion of the uteri. They retain their "sheath" when deposited by the mother worms.

The Microfilarias.—The microfilarias of *Loa loa* exhibit day-time (diurnal) periodicity in peripheral blood, displaying stiff, ungraceful but rapid movements among the red blood cells. These "sheathed" microfilarias (Fig. 96, Fig. 106, p. 293) are relatively large, measuring 250 to 300 microns in length by 6 to 8.5 microns in mid-diameter, and have a core of nucleated cells which extend without interruption into the tip of the tail. The morphologic features which distinguish the microfilaria of this species from that of *Wuchereria bancrofti* and *W. malayi* are provided in Table 10 (page 292).

The Insect Phase of the Life Cycle.—When the microfilarias of *Loa loa* are ingested by the day-biting *Chrysops dimidiata* or *C. silacea* feeding on a human carrier, they soon become exsheathed in the midgut of the fly and migrate to muscular and connective tissues, undergo transformation to the filariform larva (Connal and Connal, 1922), then migrate down to the tip of the fly's proboscis, ready to be transferred to the next human host about the tenth day after the infective meal. Gordon and Crewe (1953) state that these larvas begin to leave the proboscis "as soon as, but not before, the labium of the insect begins to bend following the entrance of the fascicle into the host's tissues."

The Biological Incubation Period.—Very little is known concerning the development of *Loa loa* after it enters the human skin. Gordon and Crewe (*l.c.*) state that the invading larvas migrate down to the muscular tissue. As in other filaria infections of man, the incubation period may require as long as 12 months. During this period and after maturity the females (and males?) migrate through the subcutaneous tissues of the body and periodically reach the head, crossing in front of the eyes under the corneal conjunctiva during each excursion. The life expectancy of the adult worms is at least 4 and as much as 15 years.

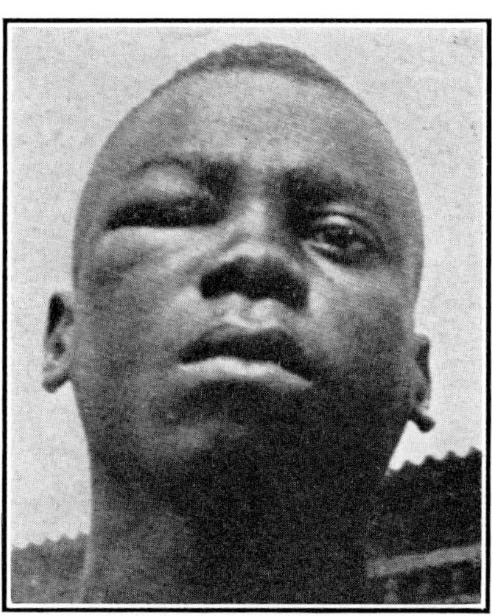

Fig. 107.—Unilateral palpebral edema in *Loa loa* infection at the time a female worm is migrating across the front of the right eye. In Dubois and van den Berghe's *Diseases of Warm Climates*, courtesy Grune & Stratton, from Craig and Faust's *Clinical Parasitology*, Lea & Febiger, Philadelphia.)

Pathogenesis and Symptomatology

In their migrations through various parts of the body the adult worms can be demonstrated in the extremities, trunk and head. The worms are more of a nuisance than a cause of severe local tissue reaction, although almost always there is a temporary inflamed tract ("fugitive swelling" or "Calabar swelling") in the wake of each worm. Moreover, migration through the bulbar conjunctivæ is always troublesome and is attended with considerable pain and edema (Fig. 107).

Dubois and van den Berghe (1948) recognize three clinical types of loaiasis, *viz.*, (1) essentially symptomless carriers; (2) patients with demonstrable adult worms and microfilarias who have allergic reactions, including edema, pruritus and eosinophilia, and (3) patients with allergic manifestations but without demonstrable adults or microfilarias, possibly due to death of the worms before they reach maturity.

Diagnosis

After the end of the biological incubation period the microfilarias of *Loa loa* can be found in day-time blood except in those cases in which the worms apparently fail to mature. For demonstration and differential diagnosis thick-blood films stained by the Giemsa technic are recommended. (See "TECHNICAL AIDS," page 590.) In case the organisms are not demonstrable but the patient's history and the clinical findings suggest loaiasis, intradermal testing with filaria antigen will almost always provide an immediate positive reaction in individuals who have the disease. (For this and other immunologic tests in loaiasis, see "TECHNICAL AIDS," pages 613–614.)

Treatment

The classical method of treatment consists of extracting the parent worm at the time it is migrating across the front of the eye. This requires experience and skill, to prevent damage to the corneal conjunctiva and the escape of the worm into the deeper tissues of the orbit or penetration into the eyeball.

Since the introduction of Hetrazan (diethyl carbamazine) in the treatment of loaiasis, with few exceptions the results with this drug have been consistently favorable, irrespective of the clinical type of the disease. A full course of treatment consists of the oral administration of 2 mgm. per kilo body weight 3 times daily for 10 to 20 days. Ordinarily the use of this anthelmintic produces no serious side effects. (Compare with onchocercosis, page 306.) Marked clinical improvement may be expected in symptomatic cases with Hetrazan therapy. Madell and Spingarn (1953) have reported success of suramin sodium and failure of Hetrazan in a case of thoracic loaiasis.

Prognosis

The prognosis is excellent with specific therapy.

Control

Reduction in the infection rate in native populations in endemic territories will depend on a two-pronged attack, *viz.*, (1) chemotherapeutic destruction of the microfilarias in the human host and (2) use of larvicides to kill the breeding stages of the mango-flies which transmit the infection from person to person. Bites by these flies may be avoided for short periods of time by application of dimethyl phthalate to exposed areas of the skin.

Acanthocheilonema Streptocerca (Macfie and Corson, 1922) Faust (in Craig and Faust, 1951) and Acanthocheilonema Perstans (Manson, 1891) Railliet, Henry and Langeron, 1912

A. streptocerca was first described by Macfie and Corson (1922) from the microfilarial stage seen in skin biopsies of 45% of natives of a Gold Coast village, during a survey to determine the incidence of *Onchocerca volvulus*, *A. perstans* and other human filarias. Sharp (1928) found 29.5% incidence of this filaria in the British Cameroons, and van den Berghe and Chardome (1952) have demonstrated that the parasite has a wide distribution in the western, central and northeastern parts of the Belgian Congo, with a particularly high incidence in the central area. In 1946, Peel and Chardome for the first time discovered adult worms (females only), in the cutaneous connective tissue of chimpanzees (*Pan paniscus* and *P. satyrus*). The microfilarias are "unsheathed," taper at both ends and have a crooked posterior end (Fig. 96 *f*, page 293). They are somewhat shorter (180 to 240 microns long) and more slender (3 microns in diameter) than the microfilarias of *Loa loa* and *Wuchereria* (Fig. 96 *a–c*). According to Chardome and Peel (1949) the biting gnat *Culicoides grahami* serves as intermediate host and vector. Most infected persons appear to be symptomless carriers but cutaneous edema and elephantiasis in some infected natives in the Congo may be due to this filaria. Diagnosis is made by skin biopsy deep enough to include dermal tissue, in which the microfilarias will be found in positive cases. Chemotherapy and control measures have not been developed.

Mature worms of *A. perstans* were first found by Daniels (1898) in aborigines of British Guiana. They were identified by Manson as the definitive stage of microfilarias which he had previously described from blood films of natives from the Congo, and for which he had proposed the species name "*perstans*" (1891). This worm has an extensive distribution on the east coast of South America from Panamá to Argentina, in western and central Africa and is mildly endemic in Algeria and Tunis. Man is the important and possibly the only definitive host. The intermediate hosts and transmitters in Africa are the biting gnat *Culicoides austeni* (Sharp, 1928; Hopkins and Nicholas, 1953) and possibly *C. grahami*. The adults (Fig. 58 *j*, page 210) live in body cavities. No pathogenicity has been demonstrated in persons who have this infection. Diagnosis is made on discovery in blood films of the "unsheathed" microfilarias, which measure about 200 microns in length by 4.5 microns in diameter, and their differentiation from this stage of *A. streptocerca*, *Loa loa* and *Wuchereria bancrofti* in Africa, and *Mansonella ozzardi* and *W. bancrofti* in South America. (See Fig. 96.) Chemotherapy and control measures have not been developed.

Mansonella Ozzardi (Manson, 1897) Faust, 1929

This filaria was first obtained by Ozzard as a microfilaria in a blood survey of Carib Indians who lived inland in British Guiana, and was described as a new species by Manson (1897). It is indigenous to Latin America from northern Argentina to Yucatan and in the West Indies (Puerto Rico, St. Vincent, Dominica). The adults (Fig. 58 *k*, p. 210) live in body cavities, threaded into mesenteries or embedded in visceral fat. The microfilarias are "unsheathed," delicate, graceful objects measuring 185 to 200 microns in length by 5 microns in diameter, and are non-periodic in their migration through peripheral blood. The biting gnat *Culicoides furens* has been found to be the intermediate host and transmitter in British Guiana (Buckley, 1934), and *C. paraënsis* is circumstantially suspected to be the vector in northern Argentina (Romaña and Wygodzinsky, 1950). No symptoms have been attributed to this infection. Chemotherapy and control have not been studied.

Dirofilaria Conjunctivæ (Addario, 1885) Desportes, 1939–1940

On a number of occasions immature filarias, all females except in one instance (Forbes, 1918), have been removed from tumors or abscess pockets in various anatomical locations of the human body. Desportes (1939–1940) has provided evidence that they are assignable to the genus *Dirofilaria*. Some of the cases involved the palpebral conjunctivæ and other tissues of the eye (Addario, 1885; Supino, 1900; Parodi and Bonavia, 1920; Coutelan, Joyeux and Artigues, 1933; Faust *et al.*, 1952); in one the filaria was obtained from the upper lip (Pace, 1866); in others from an arm (Forbes, 1918; Faust *et al.*, 1952), and in still others from the gastrosplenic ligament (Babes, 1879), the infra-mammary region (Desportes, *l.c.*), etc. The countries in which human infections have been discovered include France, Corsica, Italy, Sicily, Trieste, Hungary, Roumania, Macedonia, Turkey, India, Central Africa, Thailand, Argentina and Florida, U. S. A.

Man does not provide a suitable environment for these worms, since they are unable to reach maturity in the human host. Moreover, it is highly probable that this filaria is a relatively common parasite of some animal closely associated with man and that the infection has a cosmopolitan distribution. The species of *Dirofilaria* which meets all of these criteria is the dog heartworm, *D. immitis*. There is likewise the possibility that *Dirofilaria magalhaesi* (Blanchard, 1896), from Brazil, and *D. louisianensis* Faust, Thomas and Jones, 1941, from New Orleans, Louisiana, each of which have been reported once as an adult human parasite, are actually *D. immitis*.

Dracunculus Medinensis (Linnæus, 1758) Gallandant, 1773 (The dragon worm, Medina worm or Guinea worm, causing dracunculosis or dracontiasis)

Historical and Geographical Notes

This worm has been known since the days of antiquity. Priests of ancient Egypt, the Hebrews, Greeks and Romans were all familiar with it. Fedtschenko (1869) first provided evidence that the infection required a species of "water flea" (Cyclops) as an intermediate host.

Dracunculus medinensis has a distribution throughout tropical Africa, Arabia, Transjordania, Iraq, Iran, Afghanistan, Turkestan, southeastern U. S. S. R., Pakistan, western India, Madras Presidency of India and parts of Indonesia. It apparently no longer occurs endemically in the Western Hemisphere. In reservoir hosts, *D. medinensis* is found in fur-bearing mammals in North America, in the dog in China and has also been reported from horses, cattle, leopards, polecats and monkeys in endemic areas of the Old World. One autochthonous human case has been recorded for Korea (Kobayashi, 1928). Stoll (1947) has estimated that 48.3 million persons are infected, of whom 15 millions live in Africa and the remainder mostly in Asia.

Epidemiology

In all areas where man is involved the epidemiology is concerned solely or almost exclusively with the infection in the human host and species of Cyclops. *D. medinensis* is acquired from swallowing water containing the infected arthropod. Human customs of bathing, washing clothes and drawing water from open wells or ponds are responsible for propagation of this disease. Moreover, the incubation period in the human host corresponds to the annual visits of pilgrims, whose ablutions provide the inoculum for the Cyclops and at the same time new infection from drinking the infested water.

Morphology, Biology and Life Cycle

Dracunculus medinensis is commonly referred to as a filaria. While it grossly resembles the true filaria worms (Filarioidea), it lacks a microfilarial stage and employs as intermediate host a primitive aquatic arthropod rather than one specialized in piercing the host's skin. Furthermore, the adult worms are distinctly different from the filarias, *e. g.*, the females are very much larger than the males; in gravid females the vulva becomes atrophied, the vagina disintegrates and first-stage rhabditoid larvas are discharged from a prolapsed segment of the uterus through a rupture in the body wall near the mouth.

The adults of *D. medinensis* are elongated cylindrical threads (males) or cords (females), which are bluntly rounded at the anterior end and curved ventrally. In the females this serves to anchor the worm in position in its tunnel after it begins to migrate from the viscera to the surface of the host's body. The male measures from 12 to 20 mm. in length by 0.4 mm. in diameter. The female measures from 70 to 120 cm. in length (with an average somewhat less than one meter) by 0.9 to 1.7 mm. in diameter. The worms develop to maturity in body cavities and visceral connective tissues. As soon as the female becomes gravid it migrates to the subcutaneous tissues and produces a papule in the dermis. Within one to a few days this changes to a blister, which ruptures. On immersion in fresh water a loop of the uterus is prolapsed and on contact with the water bursts open, discharging a swarm of delicate, wiry rhabditoid larvas which have a long attenuated tail, a transversely striated cuticle and a pair of anal papillæ set into deep pockets.

The Extrinsic Phase of the Life Cycle.—The larva discharged into the water moves about stiffly, at times coiling on itself to produce the appearance of the Greek letter *alpha*. This apparently attracts Cyclops which ingest the larvas. On arrival in the arthropod's midgut, the larva penetrates into the hemocele and, following one moult of cuticle, becomes infective in about 10 days. If the Cyclops is ingested by man or other suitable hosts the infection is successfully transferred. A considerable number of species of Cyclops have been incriminated as natural hosts of *D. medinensis*.

The Biological Incubation Period.—On arrival in the duodenum of the definitive host, the larvas are digested out of the Cyclops and migrate through the intestinal wall to loose connective tissue, usually in a retroperitoneal location. Here they grow into adult worms over a period of 8 to 12 months.

Pathogenesis and Symptomatology

The biological incubation period is characteristically symptomless. Fairley and Liston (1925) state that a few hours preceding the appearance of the skin lesion there are pronounced systemic prodromata, consisting of erythema and urticarial rash, with intense pruritus, nausea, vomiting, diarrhea, severe dyspnea, giddiness and at times syncope, all resulting from the activation and migration of the gravid female. Then a reddish papule develops at the site where the head of the worm penetrates the dermis, with a vesicular center and indurated collar, and measuring 2 to 7 mm. in diameter. The lesion is most frequently found between the metatarsal bones (Fig. 108), or on the ankles or calf of the leg, but it may develop at a knee joint, on the hands, thighs, arms, trunk, buttocks, inguinal region, scrotum, shoulders, angle of the jaw, fronto-nasal area, or soft palate. If the worm fails to reach the body surface it dies and disintegrates, at times producing a sterile abscess (Jelliffe, 1950), or it may become calcified (Fig. 109).

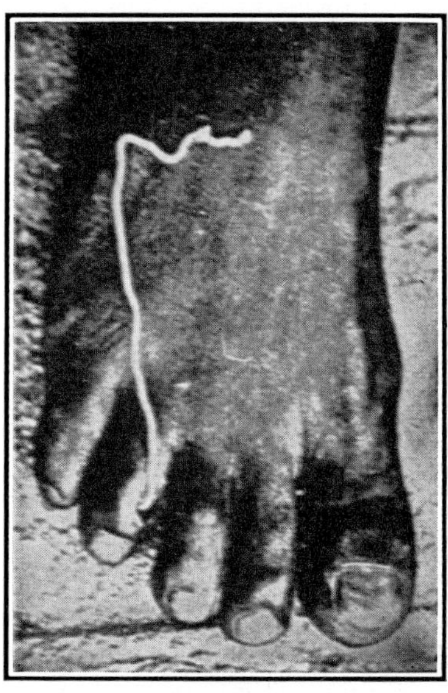

Fig. 108.—Female *Dracunculus medinensis* partially removed from a metatarsal lesion. (After Castellani and Chalmer's Tropical Medicine, from Faust's *Human Helminthology*, Lea & Febiger, Philadelphia.)

The blister is typically sterile before it bursts, and contains macrophages, eosinophils and neutrophils in a yellowish fluid. As soon as it ruptures, releasing the highly allergenic fluid, the patient's symptoms abate, but sepsis frequently develops in the worm's tunnel.

Although multiple *Dracunculus* infections are by no means rare (occasionally as many as 15 to 50), relatively few patients have more than 6 and the majority only 1. But reëxposure in highly endemic areas provides opportunity for reinfection, which is accepted fatalistically by native populations.

Diagnosis

There is no reliable means of diagnosing dracunculosis until the gravid female worm migrates to the skin and produces the typical blister, although in endemic regions the hypersensitization reaction which immediately precedes the patent infection can be regarded as a relatively certain prodrome of the fully developed infection. As soon as the worm projects its anterior extremity out of the skin, specific diagnosis can be made.

Treatment

Prompt administration of an anti-histaminic drug is indicated to relieve the prodromal symptoms and prevent possibly fatal anaphylatic shock.

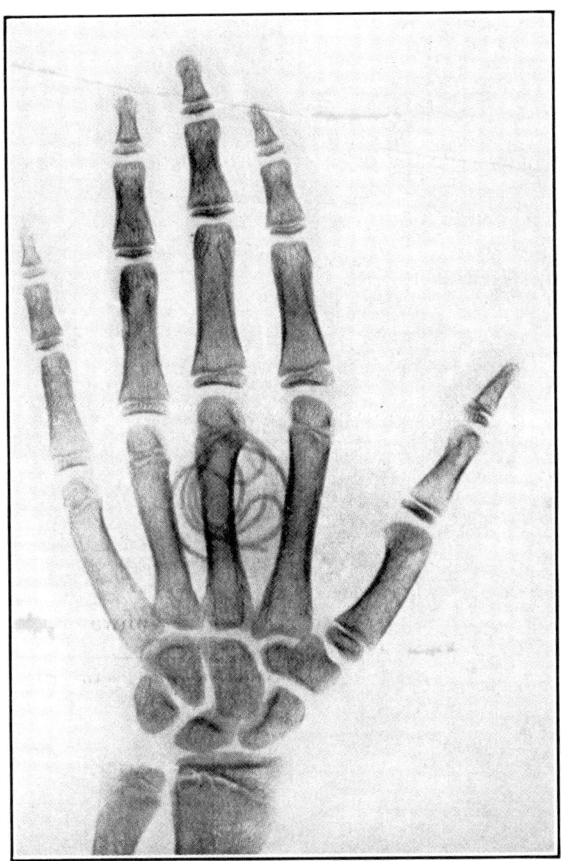

Fig. 109.—Photograph of calcified, somewhat immature female *Dracunculus medinensis* in the fleshy portion of the hand. (After Jelliffe, courtesy, J. Trop. Med. & Hyg.)

From ancient times natives have learned to wind the emerging end of the worm on a small stick, an inch or two a day, using gentle traction to prevent breaking the worm in two within the cutaneous tunnel. In this way the complete worm is eventually extracted. In 1942 Elliott employed anthelmintic medication in 23 of 59 cases which came under his care. It consisted of an emulsion of phenothiazine powder (2 Gm.) mixed with 0.35 Gm. lanolin and 15 cc. sterile olive oil, to which successively 5 cc. sterile water and 20 cc. sterile olive oil were added. The emulsion was autoclaved for 30 minutes at 115° C., then allowed to cool. The worm's tunnel was anesthetized with procaine, then 20 cc. of the emulsion injected into the central path of the worm, followed by 10 cc. on either side. After brisk massage of the track for 5 minutes the relaxed worm was withdrawn in an intact condition.

Prognosis

Dracunculosis is temporarily disabling and occasionally results in chronic invalidism, but the prognosis is usually good.

Control

Methods must be developed to prevent villagers from infesting wells and ponds with viable larvas of the worm, so that their drinking water will be protected. Furthermore, the introduction of plankton-feeding fish into all bodies of water in which Cyclops breed will appreciably reduce the number of these intermediate hosts.

SUMMARY

1. True filaria worms have a *microfilaria* which distinguishes them from all other groups of nematodes. This is deposited by the mother worm, either with the eggshell stretched out to accommodate itself to the uncoiled embryo, *i. e.*, "sheathed," or without the shell, *i. e.*, "unsheathed." The microfilarias migrate to the skin where they are found in blood-vessels, lymphatics or cutaneous connective tissue. When picked up by certain skin-piercing arthropods they transform into rhabditoid larvas and then the infective filariform larval stage. When the arthropod next punctures the skin of the definitive host, the larvas enter the skin and migrate to the site where they develop into mature worms.
2. Seven species of filarias are important natural parasites of man. *Wuchereria bancrofti* and *W. malayi* reside in lymphatic vessels; *Onchocerca volvulus* is found in subcutaneous nodules; *Loa loa* migrates through the subcutaneous tissues; *Acanthocheilonema perstans* and *Mansonella ozzardi* live in body cavities, and *A. streptocerca* is adapted to the connective tissues of the skin.
3. *Wuchereria bancrofti* inhabits lymphatic vessels and is most frequently found in the region of the groin and pelvic organs. The "sheathed" microfilarias get into the blood stream and migrate to the cutaneous circulation, in most geographical areas at night. Domestic and semi-domestic mosquitoes serve as intermediate hosts and transmitters. *W. bancrofti* has an extensive distribution in warm climates. The adolescent and mature worms provoke an acute lymphangitis and lymphadenitis around, and retrograde to the sites where the worms are trapped. Such reactions tend to recur and eventually kill the worms. Fibrosis of the lymph channels and surrounding tissues causes varicose groin gland and elephantiasis of the genitalia and lower extremities. Bacteria have not been demonstrated in the primary lesion. During the time of micro-

filaremia the embryos may be seen in peripheral blood at night. Hetrazan clears the blood of microfilarias and more slowly kills the parent worms. Control consists in administering Hetrazan to carriers to prevent infection of the mosquito vectors and use of DDT to kill the mosquitoes.

4. *Wuchereria malayi* likewise inhabits the lymphatic vessels, and in most respects is comparable to *W. bancrofti*. The lesions are confined to the extremities. Hetrazan is an effective therapeutic. *W. malayi* is widely distributed in countries bordering on the China Sea, in Indonesia, eastern India and Ceylon. The urban type, transmitted by anopheline mosquitoes, can be controlled by residual spraying of homes with DDT; the rural type, transmitted by *Mansonia* mosquitoes, is controlled by the application of 2-4-D (Weedone) to destroy the aquatic plants from the underwater parts of which the larvas obtain oxygen.
5. *Onchocerca volvulus* is confined in its maturing and adult stage to fibrous tumors in the subcutaneous tissues. The "unsheathed" microfilarias circulate through connective tissue, including that of the skin. They are transmitted by the coffee-fly *Simulium* which breeds in rapidly flowing mountain streams and bites in the open. The infection has extensive distribution in tropical Africa, on the Pacific slopes of Guatemala and adjacent states of Mexico, eastern Venezuela and Dutch Guiana. The worm nodules are benign but the infection produces systemic and dermal sensitization. The microfilarias migrate into the tissues of the eye and the optic nerve and are responsible for failing vision and eventual blindness. Specific diagnosis is made by recovering the microfilarias from superficial skin biopsies. Treatment consists in enucleation of the nodules as soon as they appear, administration of Hetrazan to kill the circulating microfilarias and suramin to kill the adults. Control of the insect vector requires application of DDT to the breeding sites during the dry season when the streams are at pool stage.
6. *Loa loa* is a filaria of West and Central Africa. The parent worms migrate through subcutaneous tissues and periodically cross the front of the eye. The "sheathed" microfilarias exhibit diurnal periodicity in the cutaneous blood vessels. The mango-fly *Chrysops*, which breeds in flowing streams, is the transmitter. There are (1) relatively symptomless microfilaria carriers; (2) persons with demonstrable worms who have symptoms of an allergic nature, and (3) those who have symptoms but in whom the causative agent can not be demonstrated. Hetrazan is usually vermicidal and symptomatically beneficial.
7. *Acanthocheilonema perstans*, which has an extensive distribution in tropical Africa, Atlantic coastal areas of South America, and some of the West Indies, and *Mansonella ozzardi*, which is indigenous to tropical America, live in body cavities. Their "unsheathed" microfilarias constantly circulate in peripheral blood. *A. streptocerca*, which inhabits the deeper cutaneous connective tissues, is endemic in parts of Central Africa. Its "unsheathed" microfilarias are found in the dermal layer of the skin. These three species are transmitted by the biting gnat *Culicoides*.

8. *Dirofilaria conjunctivæ* is the name applied to immature filarias, almost exclusively females, which have been recovered from nodules or abscess pockets of persons in Europe, Asian countries, Africa, Argentina and Florida (U. S. A.). Most of the lesions have involved the conjunctivæ and other tissues of the eye, the nares, lips and superficial tissues of the upper extremities. Man is regarded as an unfavorable host of this filaria, which is a natural parasite of some animal closely associated with man, conceivably the cosmopolitan dog heartworm, *D. immitis*.
9. *Dracunculus medinensis* is a common parasite of man throughout tropical Africa, the Middle East and India. The worms mature in visceral tissues, after which the gravid female migrates to the skin and produces a blister. On contact with fresh water active first-stage larvas are discharged from the lesion into the water. When ingested by the "water flea" Cyclops, the larvas mature and are ready for transfer to the human host. Intense allergic reactions characteristically develop during migration of the female to the skin. Natives extract the worm, a few inches each day, so as not to break it in two in the tissues and produce an abscess. Dracunculosis is propagated as a result of the unsanitary customs of native populations. Practical control measures are required (1) to prevent infected persons from entering water for bathing, washing their clothes and drawing water, (2) and to kill the Cyclops in the water.

REFERENCES

Beye, H. K., Edgar, S. A., Mille, R., Kessel, J. F., and Bambridge, B. 1952. Preliminary Observations on the Prevalence, Clinical Manifestations and Control of Filariasis in the Society Islands. Am. J. Trop. Med. & Hyg., *1*, 637–661.

Blacklock, D. B. 1926. The Development of *Onchocerca Volvulus* in *Simulium Damnosum*. Ann. Trop. Med. & Parasitol., *20*, 1–48, 203–218.

Brown, H. W. 1944. The Treatment of Filariasis (*Wuchereria Bancrofti*) with Lithium Antimony Thiomalate. J. Am. Med. Assn., *125*, 952–958.

Brug, S. L. 1927. Een Nieuwe Filaria-Soort (*Filaria Malayi*), Parasiterende bij den Mensch. (Voorloopige Mededeeling.) Geneesk. Tidjschr. Med.- Indië, *5*, 750–754.

Burch, T. A., and Ashburn, L. L. 1951. Experimental Therapy of Onchocerciasis with Suramin and Hetrazan. Am. J. Trop. Med., *31*, 617–623.

Connal, A., and Connal, S. 1922. The Development of *Loa Loa* (Guyot) in *Chrysops Dimidiata* (van der Wulp). Trans. R. Soc. Trop. Med. & Hyg., *16*, 64–89.

Desportes, C. 1939–1940. *Filaria Conjunctivæ* Addario, 1885, Parasite Accidental de l'Homme, Est un Dirofilaria. Ann. de Parasitol., *17*, 380–404, 515–532.

Dubois, A., and Van Den Berghe, L. 1948. *Diseases of the Warm Climates. Their Clinical Features, Diagnosis and Treatment.* 445 pp. Grune & Stratton, New York.

Elliott, M. 1942. A New Treatment for Dracontiasis. Trans. R. Soc. Trop. Med. & Hyg., *35*, 291–298.

Fairley, N. H., and Liston, W. G. 1925. Studies on Guinea-Worm Disease. Coll. Papers, Indian J. Med. Research and Indian Med. Gaz., 1924. 76 pp.

Faust, E. C., Agosin, M., Garcia-Laverde, A., Sayad, W. Y., Johnson, V. M., and Murray, N. A. 1952. Unusual Findings of Filarial Infections in Man. Am. J. Trop. Med. & Hyg., *1*, 239–249.

Feng, L. C. 1936. The Development of *Microfilaria Malayi* in *A. Hyrcanus* Var. *Sinensis* Wied. Chinese Med. J., Supp.. I, pp. 345–367.

Field, J. W. (Editor). 1951. *The Institute for Medical Research 1900–1950.* Studies from the Institute of Medical Research, Federation of Malaya, Jubilee Volume, No. 25, Kuala Lumpur, 389 pp.

Goldman, L., and Ortiz, L. F. 1946. Types of Dermatitis in American Onchocerciasis. Arch. Derm. & Syph., *53*, 79–93.

GORDON, R. M., and CREWE, W. 1953. The Entrance of *Loa Loa* into the Mammalian Host and the First Stage of Its Migration to the Deeper Tissues. Trans. R. Soc. Trop. Med. & Hyg., *47*, 6.

GRACE, A. W., GRACE, F. B., and WARREN, S. 1932. The Parallel Incidence of *Filaria Bancrofti* and the β hæmolytic Streptococcus in Certain Tropical Countries. Am. J. Trop. Med., *12*, 493–508.

HARTZ, P. H. 1944. Contribution to the Histopathology of Filariasis. Am. J. Clin. Path., *14*, 34–43.

HAWKING, F. 1950. Some Recent Work on Filariasis. Trans. R. Soc. Trop. Med. & Hyg., *44*, 153–192.

HAWKING, F., and THURSTON, J. P. 1951. The Periodicity of Microfilariæ. I. The Distribution of Microfilariæ in the Body. II. The Explanation of Its Production. Trans. R. Soc. Trop. Med. & Hyg., *45*, 307–340.

HEWITT, R., KENNEY, M., CHAN, A., and MOHAMED, H. 1950. Follow-up Observations on Treatment of Bancroftian Filariasis with Hetrazan in British Guiana. Am. J. Trop. Med., *30*, 217–237.

HOPKINS, C. A., and NICHOLAS, W. L. 1953. The Development to the Infective Stage of *Acanthocheilonema Perstans* in Bred *Culicoides Austeni*. Trans. R. Soc. Trop. Med. & Hyg., *47*, 6–7.

HUNTINGTON, R. W., JR., EICHOLD, S., and SCOTT, O. K. 1950. Acute Allergic Filarial Lymphangitis (Mumu) in American Troops in the Samoan Area in World War II. Am. J. Trop. Med., *30*, 873–880.

JELLIFFE, D. B. 1950. Calcification of a Guinea-Worm. J. Trop. Med. & Hyg., *53*, 210–211.

KING, B. G. 1944. Early Filariasis Diagnosis and Clinical Findings. Am. J. Trop. Med., *24*, 285–298.

KNOTT, J. 1938. The Treatment of Filarial Elephantiasis of the Leg by Bandaging. Trans. R. Soc. Trop. Med. & Hyg., *32*, 243–252.

MACFIE, J. W. S., and CORSON, J. F. 1922. A New Species of Filarial Larva Found in the Skin of Natives in the Gold Coast. Ann. Trop. Med. & Parasitol., *16*, 465–471.

MCKINLEY, E. B. 1931. The Rôle of Bacteria in Acute Filarial Lymphangitis. Puerto Rico J. Pub. Health & Trop. Med., *6*, 419–427.

MADELL, S. H., and SPINGARN, C. L. 1953. Unusual Thoracic Manifestations in Filariasis Due to *Loa Loa*. Am. J. Med., *15*, 272–280.

MANSON, P. 1878. Further Observations on *Filaria Sanguinis Hominis*. China Imp. Customs Med. Repts., *3*, No. 14, 1–26.

———1879. Additional Notes on *Filaria Sanguinis Hominis* and Filaria Disease. *Ibid.*, No. 18, 31–51.

MANSON-BAHR, P. H. 1912. Filariasis and Elephantiasis in Fiji. Being a Report to the London School of Tropical Medicine. 192 pp. London.

MICHAEL, P. 1944. Filariasis and Navy and Marine Personnel. Report of Laboratory Investigations. U. S. Naval Med. Bull., *42*, 1059–1074.

MOORTHY, V. N. 1938. A Redescription of *Dracunculus Medinensis* Velsch. J. Parasitol., *23*, 220–224.

NETTEL, F. R. 1952. Oncocercosis. Revisión del Problema Entomólogico de la Oncocercosis y Plan para Erradicación de *Simulium Ochraceum* Walker. Med. (Méx.), *32*, 438–441, 482–493.

NOBLE, B. R. 1952. Contribución al Estudio de la Oncocercosis en Venezuela. Lesiones Oculares. IV Congr. Panam. de Oftalmol., pp. 3–18.

O'CONNOR, F. W. 1923. Researches in the Western Pacific. Being a Report on the Results of the Expedition Sent from the London School of Tropical Medicine to the Ellice, Tokelau and Samoan Islands in 1921–1922. London Sch. Trop. Med. Research Mem. Ser. 6, *4*, 1–57.

OTTO, G. F., BROWN, H. W., BELL, S. D., JR., and THETFORD, N. D. 1952. Arsenamide in the Treatment of Infections with the Periodic Form of the Filaria, *Wuchereria Bancrofti*. Am. J. Trop. Med. & Hyg., *1*, 470–473.

PEEL, E., and CHARDOME, M. 1946. Note Préliminaire. Sur des Filaridés de Chimpanzés *Pan Paniscus* et *Pan Satyrus* au Congo Belge. Rev. Travaux Sci. Méd. Congo Belge, May, No. 5, 244–247.

Puig Solanes, M., Vargas, L., Mazzotti, L., Guevara Rojas, A., and Noble, B. 1948. Oncocercosis. Univ. Nac. de Méx., 129 pp.

Rao, S. S., and Maplestone, P. A. 1940. The Adult of *Microfilaria Malayi* Brug, 1927. Indian Med. Gaz., *75*, 159–160.

Ruiz Reyes, F. 1951. Tratamiento de la Oncocercosis con Dietilcarbamazine. Med. (Méx.), *31*, 495–504.

Santiago-Stevenson, D., Oliver González, J., and Maldonado, J. 1949. Treatment of Filariasis Bancrofti with Hetrazan. Follow-up Observations Fifteen Months after Treatment. J. Am. Med. Assn., *139*, 308–309.

Sharp, N. A. D. 1928. *Filaria Perstans;* Its Development in *Culicoides Austeni.* Trans. R. Soc. Trop. Med. & Hyg., *21*, 371–396.

Strong, R. P. 1934. *Onchocerciasis, with Special Reference to the Central American Form of the Disease.* 234 pp., Cambridge (Mass.).

————1938. *Onchocerciasis in Africa and Central America.* Am. J. Trop. Med., Suppl., *18*, 1–57.

Van Den Berghe, L., and Chardome, M. 1952. The Geographical Distribution of *Acanthocheilonema Streptocerca* in the Belgian Congo. Trans. R. Soc. Trop. Med. & Hyg., *46*, 99–102.

Vargas, L. 1952. Consideraciones sobre Una Campaña contra la Oncocerciasis. Med. (Méx.), *32*, 189–192.

Webster, E. H. 1946. Filariasis among White Immigrants in Samoa. U. S. Naval Med. Bull., *46*, 186–192.

Wilson, T. 1950. Hetrazan in the Treatment of Filariasis Due to *Wuchereria Malayi.* Trans. R. Soc. Trop. Med. & Hyg., *44*, 49–66.

Yokogawa, S. 1939. Investigations on the Mode of Infection of *Wuchereria Bancrofti.* Second Report. Japan. J. Med. Sci., Pt. V, Path., *4*, 197–204.

SECTION IV

Tapeworms and Flukes

Chapter 12

Intestinal Tapeworms (Cestodes)

Introduction

TAPEWORMS, or cestodes, constitute a Class of the flatworms (Phylum Platyhelminthes), a relatively large group of invertebrates, having certain morphologic features which distinguish it from other phyla of the Animal Kingdom. (See Chapter 3, page 26.) Its members are bilaterally symmetrical, have a longitudinal axis, lack true segmentation, and have no body cavity. They possess an excretory system provided with terminal flame cells (*solenocytes*), and primitively they are covered with a ciliated epithelium. Most species of flatworms are hermaphroditic.

There are three Classes of flatworms, *viz.*, the turbellarians (Turbellaria), the flukes or trematodes (Trematoda) and the tapeworms (Cestoidea). Most turbellarians are free-living forms which are found in moist habitats but a few species have become parasitic. All trematodes and tapeworms are obligatory parasites.

Tapeworms as a Group

The Adult Worm.—The sexually mature tapeworm is a parasite in the small intestine of its vertebrate host, securely anchored to the mucosa. A few species of primitive tapeworms (Cestodaria) have only a single reproductive unit containing both male and female genitalia, but all of the others (Cestoda) are strobilate, *i. e.*, they consist of a chain of units made up of the following parts: (1) a *scolex*, or attachment organ, the "head"; (2) a delicate "neck" immediately behind the scolex, the region of growth from which all of the more distal portion of the strobila is derived, and (3) a series of *proglottids*, commonly called "segments," beginning with *immature* units, arising directly from the "neck," then *mature* units which contain the fully developed sex organs, and distalmost the *gravid* units which are reservoirs for the eggs. All of the species of tapeworms which parasitize man and higher animals are of the strobilate type. The number of their proglottids varies from three or four in the hydatid worm (*Echinococcus granulosus*) to a thousand or more in the beef tapeworm (*Tænia saginata*) and three or four thousand in the fish tapeworm (*Diphyllobothrium latum*). (See Figs. 110 and 125, pp. 322 and 342.)

The strobila is typically dorso-ventrally flattened, creamy to chalky white in color, and is covered with a glistening, smooth cuticle, which is derived from the underlying layer, the hypodermis. Internal to the hypodermis are the longitudinal muscles and within this layer the transverse muscle fibers. Cuticle, hypodermis and muscular tissue engirdle the loose meshwork of undifferentiated parenchyma cells, within which are the nervous, excretory and genital systems. A digestive tract is lacking.

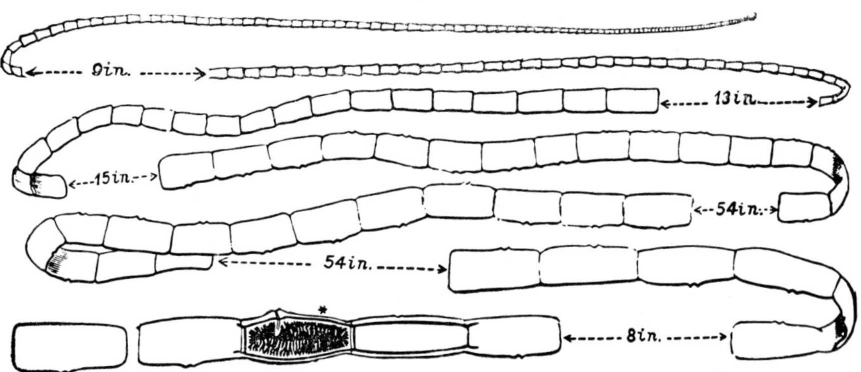

Fig. 110.—Strobila of *Tænia saginata*, the beef tapeworm of man, showing scolex, neck, immature, mature and gravid proglottids. * Uterine pattern of a gravid proglottid. Natural size. (After Leuckart, Parasiten des Menschen, from Faust's *Human Helminthology*, Lea & Febiger, Philadelphia.)

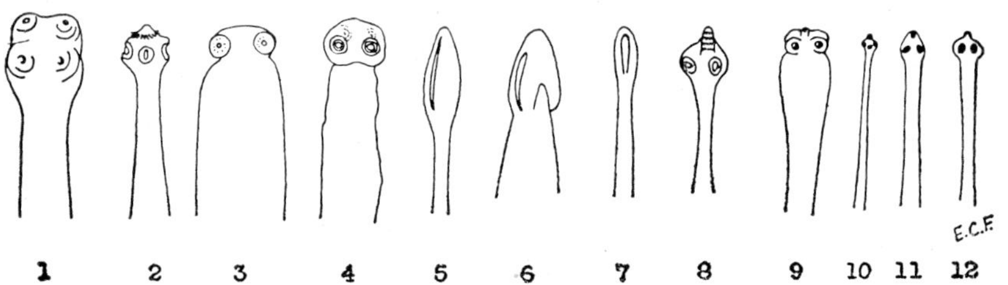

Fig. 111.—Attachment end of several human tapeworms. 1, *Tænia saginata;* 2, *T. solium;* 3, *T. africana;* 4, *T. confusa;* 5, *Diphyllobothrium latum;* 6, *D. cordatum;* 7, *D. houghtoni* or *D. mansoni;* 8, *Dipylidium caninum;* 9, *Raillietina madagascariensis;* 10, *Hymenolepis nana;* 11, *H. diminuta;* 12, *Bertiella studeri.* × 6. (From Faust's *Human Helminthology*, Lea & Febiger, Philadelphia.)

The *scolex* or attachment organ in most species of human tapeworms (Fig. 111) is more or less knob-like and is provided with four cupped suckers which lie in the same transverse plane equidistant from one another, two being situated ventrolaterally and two dorsolaterally. *Tænia saginata* and *Hymenolepis diminuta* are examples of species which lack hooklets arranged in circles anterior to the suckers. *Tænia solium, Echinococcus granulosus* and *Hymenolepis nana* possess rostellar hooklets and *Dipylidium caninum* has an apical proboscis armed with several (usually 6) circular rows of hooklets. In species of *Diphyllobothrium*, the scolex is spatulate and is provided with a long median ventral and a similar medium dorsal sucking groove.

The *nervous system* of tapeworms serves rather imperfectly to coördinate the movements of the entire strobila. Its center is situated in the scolex, and from this there arise three pairs of nerve trunks in the lateral positions, which extend through the distalmost proglottid. At the posterior end of each proglottid there is a transverse commissure which connects all six of the longitudinal trunks with one another.

The *excretory system* consists of two ventrolateral and two dorsolateral longitudinal canals joined with one another by anastomoses in the scolex and by a transverse anastomosis near the posterior margin of each proglottid. Opening into the longitudinal canals at frequent intervals there are numerous capillaries, each of which originates internally from a

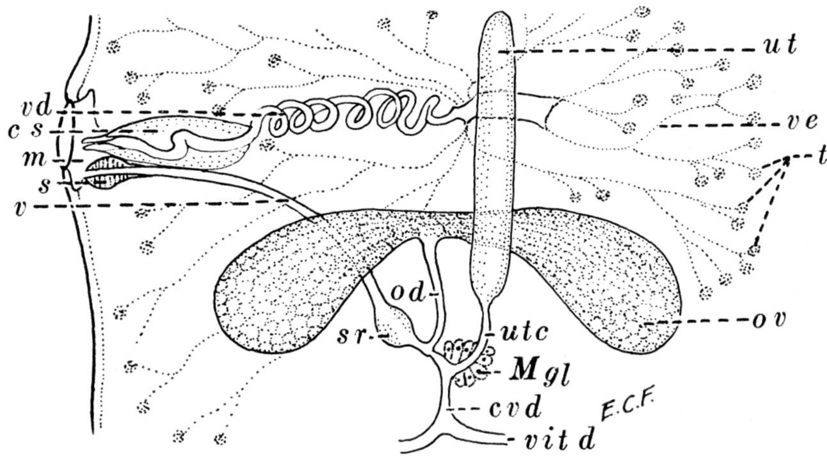

FIG. 112.—Diagram of the genital organs of *Tænia saginata*. *cs*, cirrus sac; *cvd*, common "vitelline" (*e. g.*, shell gland) duct; *m*, common genital atrium, or metraterm; *Mgl*, Mehlis' gland; *od*, oviduct; *ov*, ovary; *s*, sphincter at outer end of vagina; *sr*, seminal receptacle; *t*, testes; *ut*, uterus; *utc*, uterine canal; *v*, vagina; *vd*, vas deferens; *ve*, vas efferens; *vit d*, "vitelline" (*e. g.*, shell gland) duct. (From Faust's *Human Helminthology*, Lea & Febiger, Philadelphia.)

cell (the *solenocyte*) which has a number of delicate vibrating cilia extending into the lumen of the capillary and giving the impression of a flickering candle flame, hence the popular designation "flame cell."

The *genital organs* begin to develop in the more distal immature proglottids and reach full growth and function in the mature proglottids. In most species, there is one complete set of male and female organs for each proglottid, but in *Dipylidium caninum* and *Diplogonoporus grandis*, there are two complete sets. In *Tænia saginata* and other cyclophyllidean forms which parasitize man and higher animals, the genital openings are midlateral in position; however, in the Pseudophyllidea, the group to which species of *Diphyllobothrium* belong, these openings are midventral near the anterior end of the proglottid. For *Tænia saginata* the general arrangement of the genitalia is illustrated in Figure 112.

During the period of egg production the naked ovum is passed through the oviduct, is fertilized on its way into the oötype or soon thereafter, is provided with yolk material, then a thick shell is secreted. Another thin membrane (the embryonal envelope) is added and the fully formed shell is shuttled into the uterus, where the egg matures. The club-shaped uterine

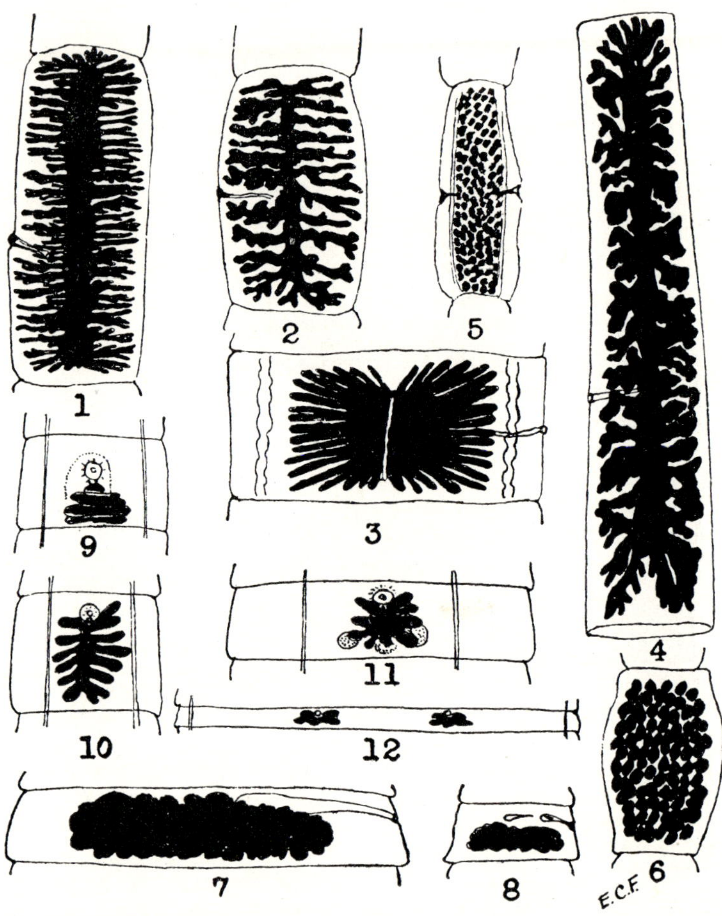

Fig. 113.—Uterine pattern of several human tapeworms. 1, *Tænia saginata;* 2, *T. solium;* 3, *T. africana;* 4, *T. confusa;* 5, *Dipylidium caninum;* 6, *Raillietina madagascariensis;* 7, *Hymenolepis diminuta;* 8, *H. nana;* 9, *Diphyllobothrium houghtoni* or *D. mansoni;* 10, *D. cordatum;* 11, *D. latum;* 12, *Diplogonoporus grandis.* 1–5 and 9–12, × 3; 6–8, × 15. (From Faust's *Human Helminthology*, Lea & Febiger, Philadelphia.)

pouch soon begins to expand by the production of a considerable number of main lateral branches, which, in turn, develop secondary and tertiary branches. Meanwhile all of the egg-producing organs characteristic of the mature proglottid atrophy. In this way the proglottid is transformed into a reservoir for the storage of ripening eggs, *e. g.*, it becomes gravid.

The essential difference between the genital system of *Tænia saginata* and species of *Diphyllobothrium* lies in the fact that the uterus of the latter group is provided with a pore, through which eggs are discharged before they have an opportunity to embryonate.

The fully developed uterine patterns of several of the human tapeworms are illustrated in Figure 113.

Although the strobila is attached by its scolex to the intestinal mucosa, the worm lives essentially free in the canal and under normal conditions of intestinal peristalsis is barely able to maintain its position. In case of hypermotility of the small bowel, the main portion of the strobila frequently breaks away from the scolex, is passed down the canal and is evacuated in the stool. However, as long as the scolex remains attached, a completely new strobila will usually be formed from the neck.

Lacking a digestive system, all nutriment must be absorbed in a predigested state through the body wall. Since tapeworms have a high ratio of glycogen and phospholipids to protein, it has been suggested that they obtain their oxygen supply from stored glycogen (Smyth, 1947; Read, 1949). Their large reserve of calcium carbonate throughout the parenchyma, in the form of numerous rounded granules, is believed to serve as a buffer against hyperacidity in the upper levels of the small intestine. Evidence has been provided to show that vitamins, particularly vitamin G, are essential for the normal development of tapeworms (Addis and Chandler, 1946; Read, 1951).

Developmental Stages of Tapeworms.—In the group to which *Diphyllobothrium* belongs, the eggs are discharged from the uterus and are evacuated in the stool in an unembryonated stage. In order to proceed with their development, they must reach cool, fresh water. All other tapeworms parasitizing man retain their eggs *in utero* until they are mature. In species of *Hymenolepis*, the distalmost gravid proglottids disintegrate while still attached to the strobila so that the fully developed eggs are recovered in the feces; but in species of *Tænia* and in *Dipylidium caninum* the gravid proglottids become detached from the strobila and pass out of the bowel without liberating their eggs. Irrespective of the mechanism involved, the mature egg contains an embryo which is provided with three pairs of hooklets, the *hexacanth embryo*. The eggs of tapeworms parasitizing man are illustrated in Plate III, *J–O* (page 57).

The mature embryos of species of *Diphyllobothrium* and their relatives have a ciliated epithelium. All other species of human tapeworms produce eggs in which the hexacanth embryo lacks a ciliated epithelium.

There are several morphological types of larvas characteristic of different species of tapeworms (Fig. 114). Species of *Diphyllobothrium* have two distinct stages in their larval development, the *procercoid* and the *plerocercoid*, both of which are solid structures lacking a bladder. In *Hymenolepis nana*, *H. diminuta* and *Dipylidium caninum* the single larval stage, *cysticercoid*, contains only a residual bladder in the caudal portion. In species of *Tænia* it is a *cysticercus*, which has a conspicuous bladder surrounding the invaginated head. In *Multiceps* there is a somewhat larger bladder, the *cenurus*, into which a number of heads (scolices) protrude. In *Echinococcus* the larval stage is a *hydatid*, a large bladder into which multiple scolices project and later may become freed from the germinal membrane to develop as daughter hydatids within the parent cyst.

When the mature larva surrounded by its host tissues is ingested by the definitive host and reaches the small intestine, the larva is digested out of the tissues, the head then evaginates, becomes attached to the intestinal mucosa and in the course of a few weeks or months develops into a complete strobila.

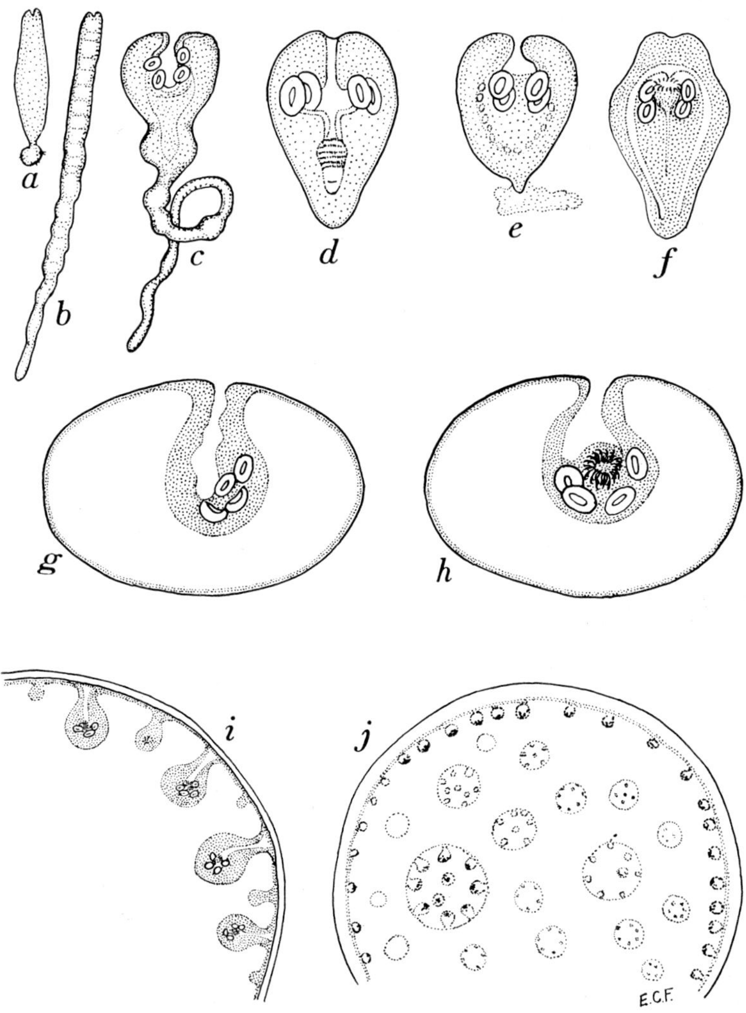

FIG. 114.—Types of tapeworm larvas. *a*, *procercoid* and *b*, *plerocercoid* (sparganum) larvas of a pseudophyllidean species (*Diphyllobothrium latum*); *c*, *tetrathyridium* larva of *Mesocestoides*; *d*, *cysticercoid* larva of *Dipylidium caninum*; *e*, *cysticercoid* larva of *Bertiella studeri*; *f*, *cysticercoid* larva of *Hymenolepis nana*; *g*, *cysticercus* larva of *Tænia saginata*; *h*, *cysticercus* larva of *T. solium*; *i*, cenurus larva of *Multiceps*; *j*, unilocular *hydatid* larva of *Echinococcus granulosus*. *a*, × 66; *b*, × 6; *c*, × 2; *d*, × 40; *e*, × 133; *f*, × 160; *g*, *h*, × 3; *i*, × 20; *j*, × ½. (Original.)

TÆNIA SAGINATA Goeze, 1782

(The beef tapeworm, causing beef tapeworm infection)

Historical and Geographical Notes

This tapeworm was widely known in ancient Egypt and Greece and was highly prevalent in Europe during the Middle Ages. The larva was apparently first reported from the muscles of cattle by Wepfer in 1675. Leuckart (1862) first demonstrated that human infection resulted from consumption of infected raw beef.

Beef tapeworm infection has a cosmopolitan distribution among beef-eating peoples, particularly in Ethiopia and Mohammedan countries. It occurs in about 1% of the population of Mexico, and is widely distributed in Australia, New Zealand, France, Switzerland, Denmark, Italy and the United States.

Epidemiology

Cattle acquire the larval stage of *T. saginata* by grazing on moist pasture land polluted by sewage containing the fully embryonated eggs of this tapeworm. Under suitable conditions of moisture and temperature the eggs may remain viable for 8 weeks or more (Penfold *et al.*, 1937; Newton *et al.*, 1949). Approximately 2 to 3 months after the cattle are exposed the larvas have matured and the meat is infective. Within a year, however, they have usually become calcified. In some populations human infection results from eating frankly raw beef. In most endemic areas, it is due to consumption of steaks or hamburgers which are browned on the surface but are still red in the center. While a majority of infections in the United States are contracted from heavily infected country-killed cattle, about three-tenths of 1% of inspected beef in the large slaughter houses has a minimal infection.

With rare exceptions man is the only definitive host of *T. saginata*.

Morphology, Biology and Life Cycle

The Adult Worm.—The adult worm develops typically in the middle third of the small intestine, attached by its scolex to the mucosa. The average length of the relaxed worm is approximately 5 meters, although there are records of specimens of 25-meters length or more. There are 1000 to 2000 proglottids, of which from one-third to one-half are gravid. Usually only a single specimen occurs in an infection, but there may be two or more (Fig. 115), in which case the size of each worm is correspondingly reduced. New proglottids produced from the neck serve to compensate for the daily loss of the distalmost gravid ones, which become separated from the strobila and pass out of the bowel.

The fully developed strobila is delicate anteriorly and more robust posteriorly (Fig. 110, page 322). The scolex (Fig. 115) is rhomboidal and is provided with 4 hemispherical suckers, which are the sole organs of attachment. Instead of hooklets on a rostellar prominence as in *T. solium* (see Fig. 120, page 333) there is a slight apical depression. Rather commonly there is melanotic pigmentation anterior to, and between each two suckers. Immediately behind the delicate unsegmented neck there is a region of immature proglottids in which the genital organs are not yet developed. Gradually the more distal of these proglottids increase in breadth and width until they reach a maximum width of 12 mm. These are the mature ones, each of which contains a full set of functioning male and

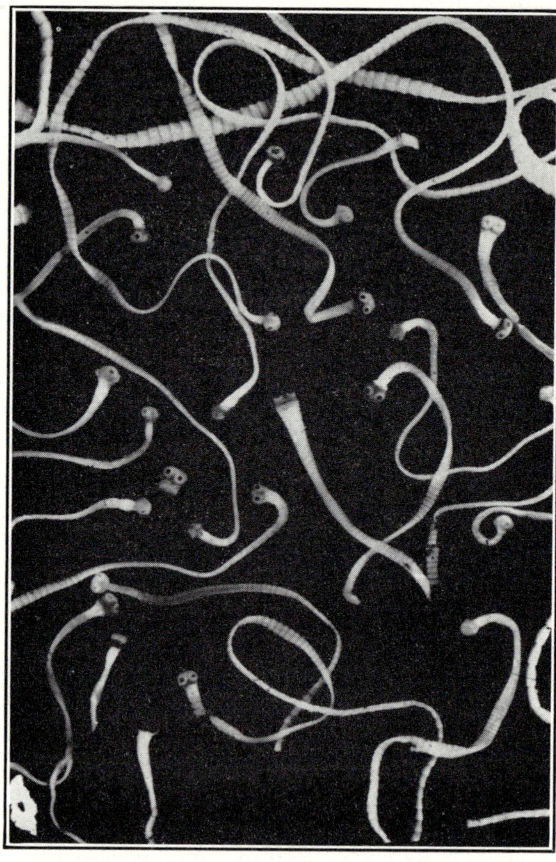

Fig. 115.—Multiple *Tænia saginata* infection, showing characteristic scolex, neck and adjacent immature proglottids. Twenty-eight worms (scolices) were recovered from this patient in Beirut, Lebanon. Note the melanotic pigmentation of several of the scolices. Natural size. (Courtesy, Dr. D. A. Berberian.)

female reproductive organs (Fig. 116). Still more distally the strobila shows a transformation of mature to gravid units, accompanied by marked elongation and slight narrowing of the proglottids. This is due to the development of the large number of branched lateral arms of the uterus (15 to 20) characteristic of *T. saginata* (Fig. 117). (Compare with this same stage of *T. solium*, Fig. 121, page 334.) The average uterus of a gravid proglottid of *T. saginata* contains about 80,000 eggs (Penfold *et al.*, 1937). The terminal proglottids become separated from the strobila and actively migrate

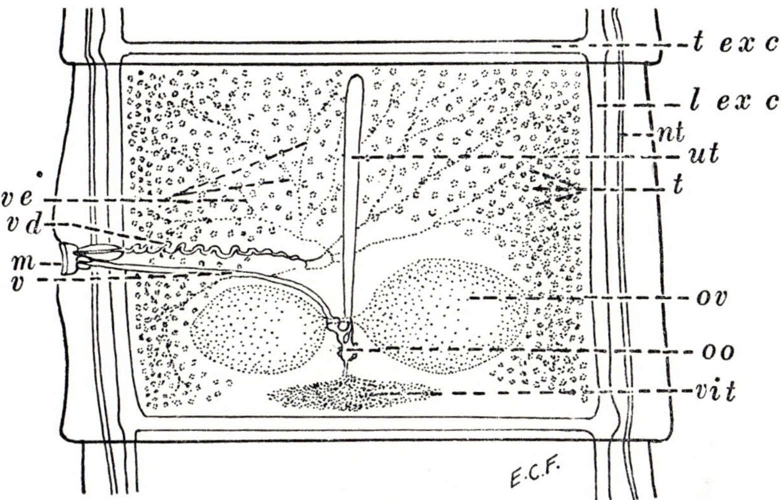

FIG. 116.—Mature proglottid of *Tænia saginata*, showing important organs. *l exc*, lateral excretory trunk; *m*, genital atrium, or metraterm; *nt*, lateral nerve trunk; *oo*, oötype; *ov*, ovary; *t*, testes; *t exc*, transverse excretory canal; *ut*, uterus; *v*, vagina; *vd*, vas deferens; *ve*, vasa efferentia; *vit*, so-called "vitellaria" (*e. g.*, shell gland follicles). × 10. (From Faust's *Human Helminthology*, Lea & Febiger, Philadelphia.)

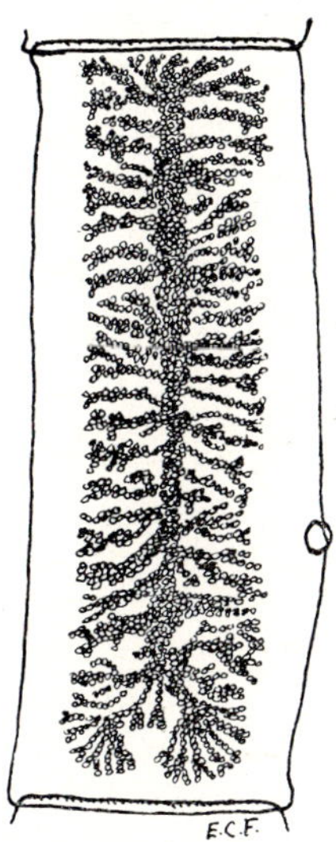

FIG. 117.—Gravid uterine pattern of *Tænia saginata*, showing main longitudinal stem and lateral arms, crowded with eggs. Note that 18 or more arms can be counted on either side of the longitudinal stem, a species-diagnostic character. × 4. (Adapted from original by the author.)

out of the bowel or are evacuated in the stool, usually in an intact condition without rupture of the uterus or liberation of the eggs.

The eggs of *T. saginata* are essentially spherical, measure 31 to 43 microns in diameter, have a thin, transparent outer embryonal envelope and a thick, sienna-brown shell composed of many truncated pyramids cemented together. Within this shell there is a hexacanth embryo which has delicate lancet-shaped hooklets (Fig. 118).

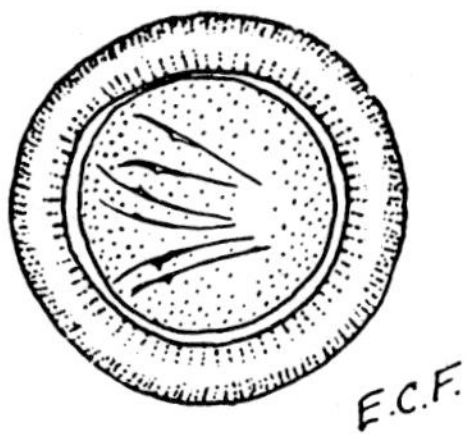

FIG. 118.—Fully embryonated egg of *Tænia saginata*, showing the thick outer shell and three pairs of hooklets within the embryo. × 666. (From Faust's *Human Helminthology*, Lea & Febiger, Philadelphia.)

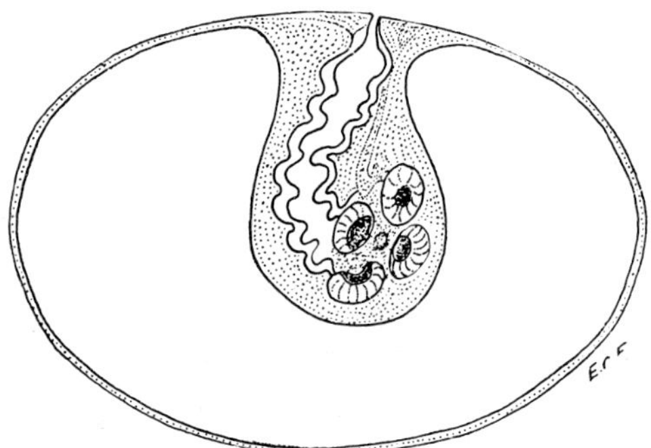

FIG. 119.—Optical view of the cysticercus stage of *Tænia saginata* (*Cysticercus bovis*) from striated muscle of beef. Note that the head is invaginated within the fluid-filled bladder. × 6. (From Faust's *Human Helminthology*, Lea & Febiger, Philadelphia.)

Developmental Stages.—Once the evacuated gravid segments disintegrate on moist earth or in sewage, the eggs are set free and are ready for development in the intermediate host. Cattle grazing on infested ground pick up the eggs, which hatch in their duodenum. The emerging embryos penetrate into the mesenteric venules or lymphatics and reach skeletal muscles or the heart, where they transform in 60 to 75 days into the typical cysticercus stage (*Cysticercus bovis*), which has a miniature head like that of the adult worm, invaginated into the fluid-filled bladder (Fig. 119). Thereafter for a period of several months persons who consume raw or inadequately processed infected beef are subject to infection. In three to six months after human exposure the complete strobila has been developed and gravid proglottids are being shed.

Pathogenicity and Symptomatology.—Infection with *T. saginata* may be symptomless except for the inconvenience resulting from gravid proglottids crawling out of the anus. However, towards the end of the incubation period there are typically a diarrhea, false hunger pains and moderate loss of weight. The blood picture at this time shows an eosinophilic leukocytosis but later there may be a slight leukopenia. At times liver damage may develop as a result of absorption of toxic metabolites of the worm (Vannfält, 1952). Occasionally chronic diarrhea may produce complete exhaustion with fatal termination unless specific therapy is instituted in time. Gravid proglottids may become lodged in the appendiceal lumen and cause appendicitis (Altenkamp, 1935; Upton, 1950). Rarely a mass of tangled strobila may cause acute intestinal obstruction (Minning, 1952).

Diagnosis

Eggs of *T. saginata* are only occasionally recovered from the feces. They are indistinguishable from those of *T. solium*. In all mature infections gravid proglottids (Fig. 117), are being evacuated. When the unpreserved proglottids are gently compressed between two slides and held in front of a bright light it is easy to count the number of main lateral arms of the uterus (15 to 20, usually 18) on each side of the main uterine stem. This constitutes specific diagnosis.

Treatment

Many anthelmintics have been employed in the treatment of *T. saginata* infection. Crude preparations of pumpkin seed and of areca nut are currently used in some countries, and both oleoresin of male fern and carbon tetrachloride has been found to be effective. Nevertheless, recent clinical studies have indicated that *quinacrine hydrochloride* (Atabrine) is probably more dependable and at the same time less toxic than these older preparations (Saccomanno, 1946; Neghme and Faiguenbaum, 1947; Hernández-Morales, 1949; Sodeman and Jung, 1952).

The standard method of administration of quinacrine is as follows. On the day before treatment the patient takes only a light, non-residue diet and towards evening a saline purge to clean out the bowel, since successful treatment depends on an empty intestine. The drug is given the following morning on an empty stomach, as a single dose in the amount of 0.5 to 1.0 Gm. (depending on the weight of the patient) together with an equal amount of sodium bicarbonate to counteract nausea and vomiting. Two hours later saline purgation is employed to evacuate the worm, which is characteristically passed intact, living but considerably contracted and stained a deep safranin yellow. Food may be taken as soon as the post-treatment purge has been effective. Failure to remove the worm results from inadequate preparation for treatment or lack of coöperation on the part of the patient. Under satisfactory management the cure rate is essentially 100 per cent.

Chloroquine diphosphate (Aralen) has also been successfully employed in the treatment of beef tapeworm infection. Arteaga Camero (1951) administered 2 Gm. in one dose to adult patients, and reported no toxic side effects.

Prognosis

This is usually excellent following specific therapy. In cases of appendicitis or obstruction due to this worm, anthelmintic medication or even saline purgation is contraindicated and surgical intervention is required. Systemic infection with the larval stage of *T. saginata, e. g., Cysticercus bovis,* need not be feared, since only three incidental infections have been reported from man.

Control

Basically the control of teniasis consists in the sanitary disposal of human feces, so that eggs of *T. saginata* in the excreta or community sewage do not reach swampy pastures where cattle graze. Newton, Bennett and Figgat (1949) have found that a 12-inch column of sand of $\frac{1}{2}$ mm. size is an effective filtering mechanism. Beef which has been kept 24 hours or longer in a deep freezer is sterilized. Likewise, heating the meat to 65° C. is a safeguard since the critical thermal death point (LD 100) for the cysticerci embedded in beef muscle is 56° C. (Allen, 1947).

Tænia confusa Ward, 1896, a close relative of *T. saginata*, has been recorded from man sporadically in Nebraska, Texas, Louisiana, Mississippi, Tennessee and Illinois, in Africa (Nigeria and East Africa) and Japan. Experimentally the author (Faust, 1930) found that the calf is an acceptable intermediate host. Two specimens of another unarmed Tænia, *T. africana* von Linstow, 1900, have been described from a native soldier near Nyasa Lake, East Africa.

TÆNIA SOLIUM Linnaeus, 1758

(The pork tapeworm, causing pork tapeworm infection)

Historical and Geographical Notes

The larval stage of this worm (*Cysticercus cellulosæ*) was described from swine by Greek naturalists. Gessner (1558) and Rumler (1588) first reported human infection with the cysticercus. Goeze (1782) first differentiated the adult *T. solium* from *T. saginata*, and Küchenmeister (1855) and Leuckart (1856) first conducted life cycle studies.

Pork tapeworm infection is cosmopolitan wherever raw or inadequately processed pork is consumed. It is much less prevalent in Germany than it was a century ago but is relatively common in the Balkan states and Slavic countries. It is found in North China and Manchuria and is present in the outcasts of India. There is widespread infection in continental Latin America, from Mexico to Chile, where it is as prevalent as *T. saginata* infection. It is not found in Mohammedan populations or among communities of orthodox Jews. Autochthonous cases of *T. solium* in the United States have declined since about 1925 and possibly have ceased to exist.

Epidemiology

Human infection with the adult *Tænia solium* results from the consumption of essentially raw pork containing viable *Cysticercus cellulosæ*. It may be fresh or smoked loin, shoulder, ham or sausage. The hog is the only known source from which man obtains the larval stage, and man is the only natural host of the adult worm. However, man is also a suitable host for the cysticercus, a subject which is considered in Chapter 13, pages 350–353.

Morphology, Biology and Life Cycle

The Adult Worm.—In most respects *Tænia solium* resembles *T. saginata*. Grossly *T. solium* is shorter, usually having a length of less than 3 meters, due to a smaller number of proglottids (fewer than 1000) and shorter gravid

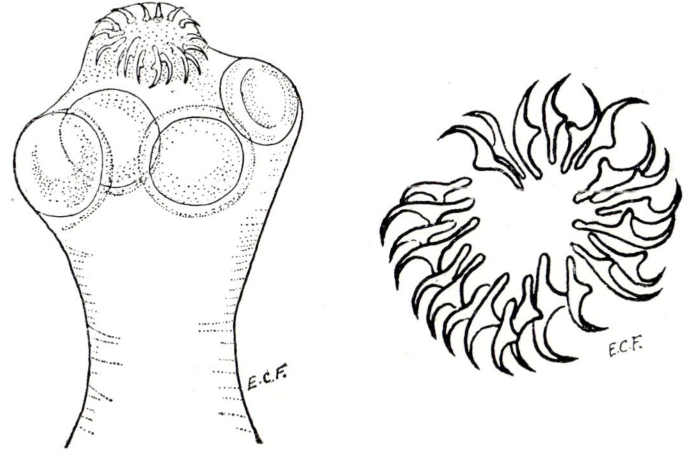

Fig. 120.—*Left*, scolex of *Tænia solium*, showing four suckers and rostellar crown of hooklets. × 40. (Adaptation of photomicrograph by Dr. L. Szidat, from Craig and Faust's *Clinical Parasitology*, Lea & Febiger, Philadelphia); *right*, head-on view of the rostellar hooklets of *T. solium*, showing two alternating rows of larger and smaller hooklets. × 120. (Original.)

proglottids. The neck region is also stouter and anterior to the four cup-shaped suckers on the scolex there is a double circle of alternating large and small hooklets, numbering from 22 to 32 and measuring 160 to 180 microns and 110 to 140 microns respectively (Fig. 120).

The mature proglottid of *T. solium* closely resembles that of *T. saginata* but can be distinguished when stained and mounted in a clearing medium due to the presence of a median accessory ovary in addition to the two lateral ovaries of *T. saginata* (Fig. 116). The gravid proglottid of *T. solium* (Fig. 121) is readily differentiated from that of *T. saginata* (Fig. 117) because it contains approximately one-half the number (7 to 13, usually 9) of main lateral uterine arms on each side of the longitudinal uterine stem.

The eggs of *T. solium* are indistinguishable from those of *T. saginata* (Fig. 118).

Developmental Stages.—Gravid proglottids passed in the stool or actively migrating out of the anus of the patient disintegrate when they are deposited on the ground. To proceed with their development the eggs must be ingested by hogs. The hexacanth embryos hatch in the duodenum and migrate from the intestinal wall through blood and lymphatic channels until they reach striated muscles, including skeletal muscle and myocar-

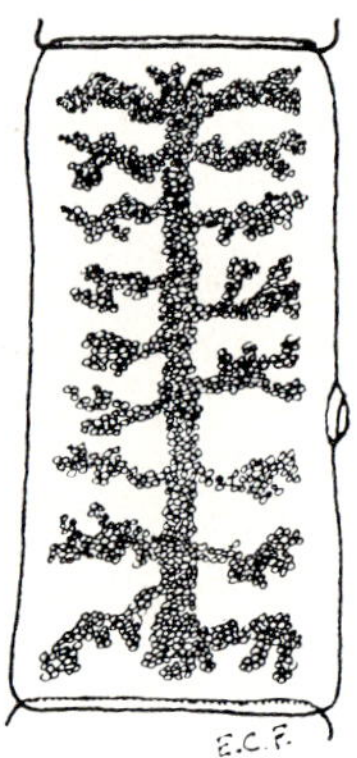

Fig. 121.—Gravid uterine pattern of *Tænia solium*, showing main longitudinal stem and lateral arms, crowded with eggs. Note that only about 9 arms can be counted on either side of the longitudinal stem, a species-diagnostic character. × 4. (Adapted from original by the author.)

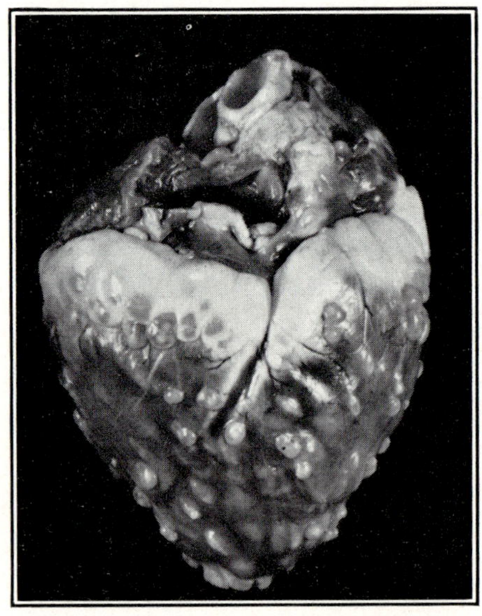

Fig. 122.—Numerous cysticerci of *Tænia solium* (*C. cellulosæ*) in wall of "measly" heart of a hog. × ⅔. (Photograph courtesy of Dr. D. A. Berberian.)

dium. Here the embryos transform in 2 to 3 months into the cysticercus-type of larva (*Cysticercus cellulosæ*), glistening pearly white objects (Fig. 122). These cysticerci measure about 5 mm. in length by 8 to 10 mm. in breadth. An optical section (Fig. 114 *h*, page 326) shows the head deeply invaginated into the fluid-filled bladder and provided with four suckers and an apical crown of hooklets. When human beings eat pork containing the viable cysticerci, the larvas are digested out of the meat, the heads evaginate from the bladder, become attached to the wall of the proximal portion of the ileum and in approximately three months each develops into a complete strobila.

Pathogenicity and Symptomatology

The adult *T. solium* in the human small intestine produces the same train of pathologic processes and clinical manifestations as *T. saginata* (see page 331). However, because of the shorter length of the strobila there is less likelihood that intestinal obstruction will develop. The extraintestinal development of cysticerci of *T. solium* in the human host and the serious clinical consequences of human cysticercosis are considered in Chapter 13 (pages 350–353).

Diagnosis

Although eggs of *T. solium* are occasionally found in the patient's stools or in anal swabs, specific diagnosis is based on demonstration of the relatively small number of main lateral arms of the uterus (7 to 13, usually about 9) in gravid proglottids compressed between two glass slides (Fig. 121).

Treatment

Specific treatment of intestinal *T. solium* infection is important not only to remove the adult worm but also to prevent autoinfection with the eggs which are responsible for extra-intestinal cysticercosis. *Quinacrine hydrochloride* (Atabrine) as administered for the removal of *T. saginata* (page 331) is the drug of choice in *T. solium* infection.

Prognosis

This is good to excellent with respect to intestinal infection, provided the adult worm is removed by specific chemotherapy.

Control

The serious, frequently disabling, and at times fatal consequences of human cysticercosis resulting from larval *T. solium* infection indicate the peculiar need for adequate control of this infection. In endemic areas human feces should not be deposited in locations where hogs have access to them. Pork should be adequately processed before it is eaten. This can be accomplished by thorough cooking, at least one-half hour for each pound of meat, or by freezing in deep-freezers for at least 24 hours. Persons harboring this worm should be freed of their infection.

Tænia tæniæformis (Batsch, 1786) Wolffhügel, 1911, a species with rostellar hooklets, commonly parasitic in the intestine of cats, has been recovered once from a 5-year-old child in Buenos Aires, Argentina.

For extra-intestinal infection with species of *Multiceps* and *Echinococcus granulosus* see Chapter 13, pages 353–360.

HYMENOLEPIS NANA (von Siebold, 1852) Blanchard, 1891

(The dwarf tapeworm, causing dwarf tapeworm infection)

Historical and Geographical Notes

Hymenolepis nana was discovered by Bilharz, in 1851, in the small intestine of a native boy in Cairo, Egypt, and its life cycle was first elucidated by Grassi (1887) and Grassi and Rovelli (1892), who demonstrated that no intermediate host is required.

Dwarf tapeworm infection in human beings is primarily limited to children in warm climates. It is prevalent throughout India, the U. S. S. R., the countries bordering on the Mediterranean, all of the countries of Latin America, Hawaii, and most of the islands of the South and Southwest Pacific. It is the common tapeworm in the southeastern United States.

Epidemiology

H. nana requires no extrinsic development and has only a single host in its life cycle; infection is essentially one of anus-to-mouth transmission. For this reason younger children are particularly favorable subjects. Moreover, although young children can be infected with *H. nana* eggs from rodent sources, this type of infection is relatively uncommon. Lack of personal cleanliness and particularly the soiling of underpants with egg-laden feces provide opportunity for repeated exposure of the small child and his playmates (Keller, Leathers and Bishop, 1932; Keller and Leathers, 1934; Bacigalupo, 1932).

Morphology, Biology and Life Cycle

The Adult Worm.— *H. nana* is the smallest of the tapeworms which parasitize the human intestine (Fig. 123). The entire worm has a length of only 25 to 40 mm. and a maximum breadth not usually exceeding 1 mm. The small head is provided with 4 cup-shaped suckers and a rostellar circle of 20 to 30 minute hooklets. The neck is long and slender, all of the approximately 200 proglottids are broader than long and the terminal gravid proglottids usually disintegrate before separation from the strobila, so that the eggs are thoroughly mixed with the feces. The average infection consists of a few to several worms, but infections with several hundred worms are encountered and at times a thousand or more may be demonstrated.

The eggs of *H. nana* (Fig. 123 *C*) are grayish hyaline, nearly spherical objects which measure 30 to 47 microns in diameter. There are two thin membranous shells, of which the inner one has two polar thickenings, each provided with 4 to 8 long thread-like filaments extending into the space between the two shells. Each worm produces only about one egg per 80 mgm. of formed stool (Beaver and Sodeman, 1952).

Developmental Stages.—When the eggs present in the feces or on soiled underpants are picked up on finger tips, get into the mouth and are swallowed, they hatch in the duodenum and the liberated embryos penetrate into the stroma of nearby villi, where they rapidly transform into cysticer-

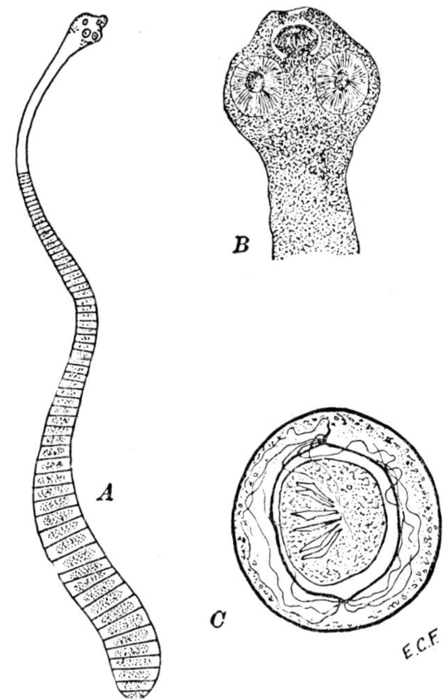

Fig. 123.—*Hymenolepis nana.* *A*, complete strobila, × 10; *B*, scolex, greatly enlarged, with rostellar hooklets invaginated into crown of the scolex; *C*, egg, × 466. (*A*, original; *B*, after Blanchard; *C*, after Brumpt; from Faust's *Human Helminthology*, Lea & Febiger, Philadelphia.)

coid larvas (Fig. 114 *f*, page 326). These then migrate out to the duodenal or jejunal canal, become attached to the mucosa, and in about 2 weeks develop into complete strobilæ. Thus, both the larval and mature stages are developed in the same individual. Moreover, in heavy infections it seems entirely probable that reinfection may occur by internal autoinfection due to hatching of eggs in the upper levels of the small bowel.

Bacigalupo (1931) and Bailey (1947) have demonstrated that certain strains of the murine variety of *H. nana* can utilize fleas and beetles for development of the cysticercoid larval stage.

Pathogenicity and Symptomatology

Infection with a few *Hymenolepis nana* may produce no detectable symptoms or it may be responsible for diarrhea, anorexia, vomiting, insomnia, loss of appetite and weight, irritability and peevishness, and rarely choreiform symptoms. Heavy infection invariably is pathogenic: There are moderate to profuse bloody-mucous diarrheic stools, abdominal pain, anorexia and exaggerated nervous disorders, or extreme apathy.

Diagnosis

This is based on recovery of the species-characteristic eggs (Fig. 123 *C*) in the stools.

Treatment

Hexylresorcinol crystoids will frequently produce evacuation of all the worms in a light infection. The drug is administered as a single dose in hard gelatine capsules on an empty stomach (preceded on the previous night by adequate saline [Glauber salts] purgation), and prescribed in the amount of 0.2 to 0.4 Gm. for children of preschool age, 0.6–0.8 Gm. for older children and 1.0 Gm. for adults. It should be followed in 2 hours by post-treatment saline purgation.

For heavier infections *quinacrine hydrochloride* (Atabrine) is the drug of choice (Hoekenga, 1951; Beaver and Sodeman, 1952). It is administered as for *Tænia saginata* infection (page 331). Most cases can be cured by two or three administrations at fortnightly intervals, provided reëxposure is prevented.

Prognosis

This is excellent for the average case with adequate specific therapy. In heavily infected persons the prognosis is unfavorable.

Control

Control of dwarf tapeworm infection will result only after cleanly personal habits have been developed in children.

Hymenolepis Diminuta (Rudolphi, 1819) Blanchard, 1891

(The rat tapeworm, causing rat tapeworm infection)

This is a cosmopolitan tapeworm of rats, mice and other rodents, and has been reported on more than 200 occasions from human hosts, usually children, from India, Indonesia, the U. S. S. R., Japan, the Philippine Islands, Belgium, Italy and other southern European countries, Latin American countries from Argentina to Mexico and Cuba, and from several parts of the United States, particularly Georgia (Sunkes and Sellers, 1937), Tennessee (Keller, 1931) and Texas (Chandler, 1922). The strain of *H. diminuta* recovered from man is identical to that found in rodents.

The strobila of *H. diminuta* is small compared with *T. saginata* and *T. solium* but is not dwarf like that of *H. nana*. It measures 20 to 60 cm. in length by 3.5 to 4.0 mm. in maximum width at its distal end and may consist of a thousand or more proglottids. The knob-like scolex is provided with four relatively small suckers and a deep apical suctorial pocket. Rostral hooklets are lacking. The neck is short and stout. The terminal gravid proglottids disintegrate while still attached to the strobila, liberating fully embryonated eggs (Fig. 124), which are broadly ovoidal to subspherical, hyaline with a straw-colored hue, and measure 72 to 86 microns by 60 to 79 microns in greater and lesser diameters. There is considerable space between the outer and inner egg membranes. The latter is provided with a pair of polar thickenings but lacks the polar filaments which are characteristic of *H. nana* eggs.

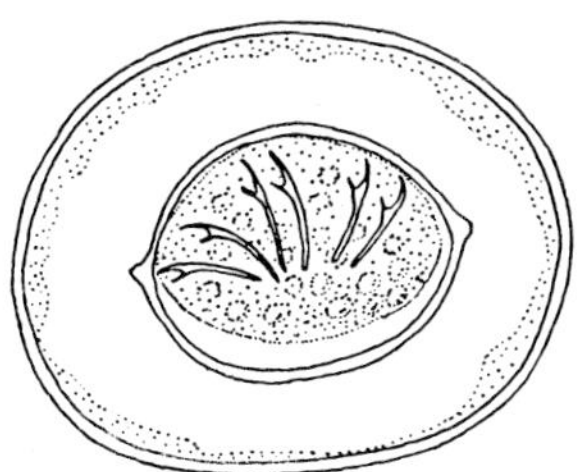

FIG. 124.—Egg of *Hymenolepis diminuta*. × 500. (From Faust's *Human Helminthology*, Lea & Febiger, Philadelphia.)

In order to proceed with their development, the eggs voided in the feces of the definitive host must be ingested by an arthropod, usually the larval stage of rodent fleas which breed in rat nests, but other fleas, many species of dung beetles, meal beetles, roaches, lepidopterans (meal moths), earwigs and diplopods have been found naturally or experimentally to be suitable intermediate hosts (Oldham, 1931). When the infected arthropod is ingested by the natural definitive host or by man and reaches the duodenum, the cysticercoid is digested out of its vector-host, the head becomes evaginated and attached to the duodenal or jejunal mucosa, and develops into the adult strobila in a few weeks. There is characteristically only a single worm in human infections, although as many as 19 have been recovered from 1 patient (Minning, 1952).

The symptoms resulting from *H. diminuta* infection usually consist of mild digestive upsets, pain in the pit of the stomach and loss of appetite, at times with associated nervous disorders due to absorption of the worm's metabolites. Diagnosis is made on the recovery of the typical eggs (Fig. 124) in the stool and their differentiation from those of *H. nana* (Fig. 123 *C*). Treatment is similar to that employed in *H. nana* infection. Prognosis is excellent following removal of the worm. Control consists fundamentally in measures to eradicate rats and mice around the home and in residual spraying of their nests and burrows with DDT to kill their ectoparasites.

Dipylidium Caninum (Linnæus, 1758) Railliet, 1892

(The dog tapeworm, causing dog tapeworm infection)

This cosmopolitan tapeworm of dogs and cats has been found a few hundred times in children who give a history of fondling infected dogs or cats. Human cases have been diagnosed from Europe, the Philippines, China, Japan, Southern Rhodesia, Argentina, Costa Rica, Puerto Rico, and the southern United States.

The adult worms are medium-sized, measuring from 10 to 50 cm. in length, and consist of several hundred proglottids. The mature proglottids contain twinned genitalia and a genital pore at each lateral margin. The distalmost gravid proglottids are more or less pumpkin-seed-shaped. The scolex is roughly rhomboidal in shape, measures about 0.3 to 0.4 mm. in diameter, has 4 conspicuous, deeply excavated suckers and an introversible apical club-shaped proboscis provided with 6 rows of minute hooklets. The neck is distinctly constricted. In dogs and cats the infection typically consists of several to many worms; in children it is almost invariably solitary. The intact gravid proglottids, containing polygonal-shaped masses of mother egg capsules, separate from the strobila, at times singly but more often in chains, and pass down the intestinal canal and out the anus.

Once the proglottids reach the ground they begin to disintegrate, setting free the mother capsules, each of which contains several fully embryonated eggs. (See Plate III, Fig. *O*, page 57). When the larva of the dog flea or the cat flea, the dog louse, and possibly other arthropods, ingests the egg capsules or individual eggs, hatching occurs in the midgut and the liberated embryo migrates into the arthropod's hemocele, where it transforms into a cysticercoid larva (Fig. 114 *d*). The definitive host becomes infected when the infected adult flea is accidently taken into the mouth and swallowed.

This infection in the child may produce profuse diarrhea and unrest. Occasionally there may be severe sensitization reactions, such as urticaria, fever, significant eosinophilia and rarely convulsions (Schaeppi, 1949). Diagnosis is made on recovery of the characteristic gravid proglottids evacuated in the stool or migrating out of the anus, and observing the polygonal pattern of the mother embryonic membranes within the uterus. Treatment is similar to that recommended for *Hymenolepis nana* (page 338). Prognosis is excellent with removal of the worms.

Control of dog tapeworm infection consists in periodic administration of arecoline hydrobromide to dogs and cats to remove their tapeworms (Batham, 1946) and disinfestation to get rid of their ectoparasites. For dogs dusting with DDT powder is very satisfactory but cats are highly sensitive to this insect toxicant and should be treated with benzene hexachloride (Gammexane) ointment rubbed into the skin and later washed out with soap and water.

OTHER (LESS COMMON) CYCLOPHYLLIDEAN TAPEWORMS

Bertiella studeri of simian hosts, has been reported on a few occasions from man (Island of Mauritius, India, Sumatra, the Philippines, and St. Kitts, West Indies). A related species, **B. mucronata,** also a simian parasite, has been found once in Cuba in an immigrant from the Canary Islands. The adult worms of *B. studeri* are medium-sized (20 to 30 cm. long), and are characterized by having a subspherical scolex with four suckers and a rudimentary apical proboscis lacking hooklets. The eggs of *B. studeri* have an irregular ovoidal outer shell measuring 49 to 50 microns by 45 to 46 microns and an inner shell which has a distinct bicornuate protrusion. Stunkard (1939, 1940) has demonstrated experimentally that certain species of oribatid mites (*Scheloribates lævigatus* and *Galumna* spp.) serve as suitable intermediate hosts, in which a cysticercoid-type of larva develops (Fig. 114 *e*).

Inermicapsifer cubensis has been found as a relatively common human parasite, mostly in children, on the island of Cuba and primarily in the vicinity of Habana (Calvo Fonseca, 1951). The strobila has a length of 27 to 42 cm., contains 310 to 368 proglottids and has a scolex with four prominent suckers and a very inconspicuous apical region lacking hooklets (Baer, Kourí and Sotolongo, 1949). Gravid proglottids are crowded with many mother egg capsules, each containing 6 to 11 spherical eggs measuring 49 to 55 microns in diameter. **I. arvicanthidis,** a rodent parasite of Africa, has been identified once from a 2-year-old white male in Kenya (Baylis, 1949) and once from a 6-year-old native of Ruanda-Urundi, Belgian Congo (Fain, 1950).

Mesocestoides variabilis, a mesocestoidean parasite of carnivorous mammals, has been reported once from a 13-months-old white child in Texas (Chandler, 1942) and once from Denmark in a native of Greenland (Chandler, 1949).

Raillietina madagascariensis, R. celebensis and **R. demerariensis** have been described from man in different parts of the world. Rodents are the known reservoirs of the first two species.

Drepanidotænia lanceolata, a cosmopolitan parasite of geese, has been recovered once from a German boy 12 years of age, who spontaneously passed two complete worms. The intermediate host is a species of *Cyclops* (Ruszkowski, 1932).

DIPHYLLOBOTHRIUM LATUM (Linnæus, 1758) Lühe, 1910
(Synonym: *Dibothriocephalus latus*)

(Fish tapeworm, causing fish tapeworm infection or diphyllobothriasis)

Historical and Geographical Notes

Diphyllobothrium latum was undoubtedly prevalent in the Baltic Sea area at an early period and became widely disseminated as the Germanic peoples overran Europe during the decline of the Roman Empire. With Scandinavian colonization of the lakes region of Michigan, Wisconsin and Minnesota (U. S. A.) and adjacent Canada, the infection became firmly established in North America. More recently it was introduced from Germany into the lake districts of Chile (Neghme and Bertín, 1951) and Argentina (Szidat and Fernando Soria, 1952), and from Ireland into New South Wales, Australia (Sanders, 1951).

Today *D. latum* is indigenous throughout many parts of the U. S. S. R., in the Baltic Sea countries, Switzerland, Spain, northern Italy, Ireland, Roumania and the Danube delta, northern Manchuria and Japan. In North America it is common in the lake region of northern Michigan and northern Minnesota, southeastern Manitoba and the Lake Nippigon district of Ontario (Cameron, 1945), northern Alberta (Saunders, 1949), in populations of Canadian eskimos (Brown *et al.*, 1948) and Alaskan eskimos (Hitchcock, 1950). There is a minor focus in Jefferson Co., Florida (Summers and Weinstein, 1943). It has recently been established in the lakes of southern Chile (Neghme and Bertín, *l. c.*), of Argentina (Szidat and Fernando Soria, *l. c.*), and Australia (Sanders, 1951). There are unconfirmed reports of endemic infection in Africa, Papua and the Philippines.

Epidemiology

A number of epidemiologic conditions must exist before the life cycle of *Diphyllobothrium latum* can be completed: (1) Eggs of the worm must be discharged into cool fresh water, where they embryonate and hatch; (2) the emerging ciliated embryos must be eaten by certain species of water "fleas" (*Diaptomus* or *Cyclops*), in which the embryos transform into procercoid larvas; (3) the infected water "fleas" must then be eaten by

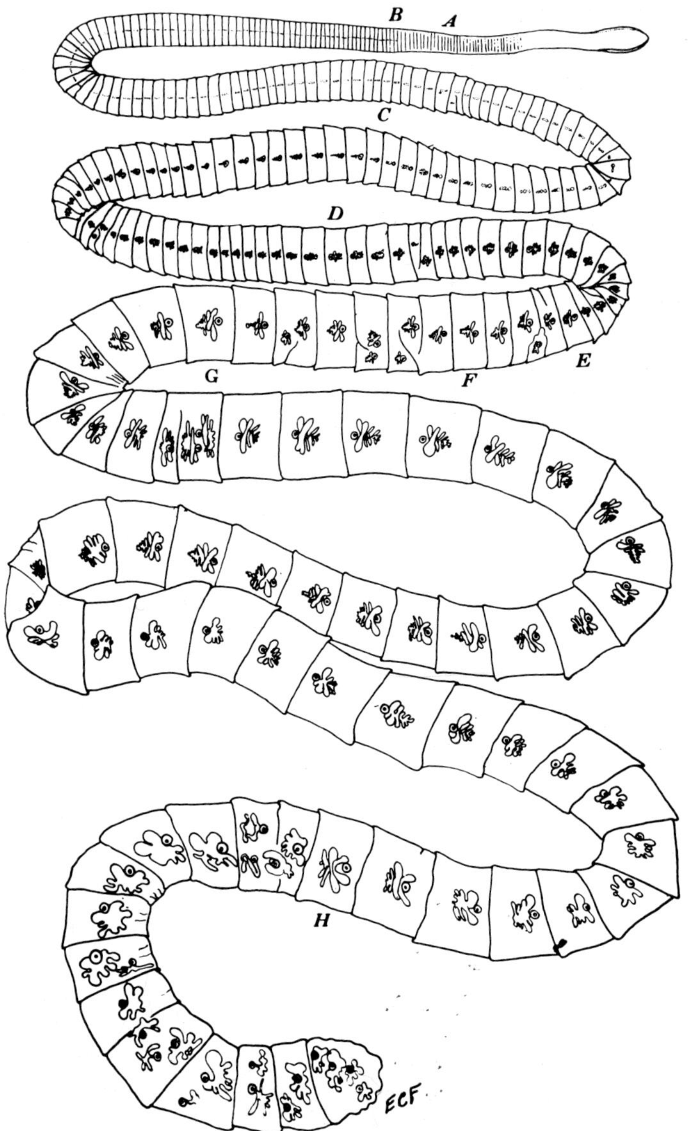

Fig. 125.—Complete strobila of *Diphyllobothrium latum*, with the original terminal proglottid still attached; obtained 24 days after experimental feeding of a dog with *Salmo irideus* containing sparganum larvas. *A*, immature proglottids of post-cervical region in which genital primordia have not yet developed; *B*, proglottids with earliest evidence of genital primordia; *C*, proglottids with developing but undifferentiated genitalia; *D*, proglottids with early differentiation of genital sucker and external vaginal pore; *E*, proglottids with male genital sucker, uterine coil with external pore, vagina and vaginal pore, oötype and shell-gland follicles (in lateral fields), but no evidence of ovaries, testes or vasa efferentia; *F*, proglottids containing uterine coils and imperfectly formed egg shells *in utero; G*, proglottids with uterus differentiated into inner and outer coils, shell-gland material consolidating into follicles, shell-gland ducts distinguishable, testes and ovaries forming, but only infertile eggs *in utero; H*, proglottids with all genital organs fully developed. Note the formation of accessory proglottids at different levels of the strobila. $\times 8\frac{1}{3}$. (After Faust, An. Inst. Med. Trop., Lisbôa.)

plankton-feeding fishes, in the flesh of which the procercoids transform into the sparganum larval stage, and (4) the infected fish must be consumed raw by the definitive host, in the intestine of which the spargana develop into adult worms.

Although dogs, and in some areas probably bears, are reservoirs of *D. latum*, man is primarily responsible for establishing and maintaining the life cycle in which he is involved. Moreover, fish caught in some endemic areas are shipped on ice to distant cities, where persons consuming the raw fish become infected. This is a relatively common occurrence among Jewish housewives and their small children in New York City, who become infected by tasting "gefüllte fisch" before it is thoroughly cooked.

Minning (1952) refers to the heavy incidence of *D. latum* infection in certain Baltic Sea areas, *viz.*, 36% of the children and 100% of adult male fisherfolk in Eastern Prussia, 50% of the inhabitants in the environs of Helsinki (Finland), and 78% of the population of northwestern U. S. S. R.

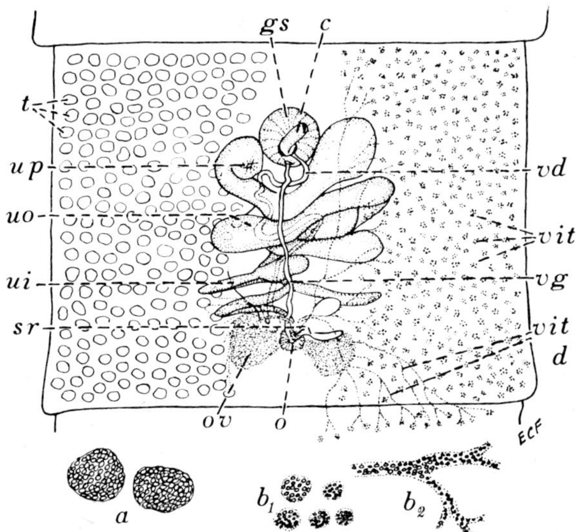

FIG. 126.—Mature proglottid of *Diphyllobothrium latum*, ventral view. *a*, two testes greatly enlarged to show internal structure; b_1, shell-gland follicle and b_2, portion of shell-gland duct, both greatly enlarged; *c*, cirrus organ; *gs*, male genital sucker; *oo*, oötype; *ov*, ovary; *sr*, seminal receptacle; *t*, testes, shown only in left field but symmetrically present also in right field; *ui*, inner uterine coils; *uo*, outer uterine coils; *up*, uterine pore; *vd*, vas deferens; *vg*, vagina; *vit*, shell-gland follicles, shown only in right field but symmetrically present in left field; *vit d*, shell-gland ducts. × 16⅔. (After Faust, An. Inst. Med. Trop., Lisbôa.)

Morphology, Biology and Life Cycle

The Adult Worm.—The fully developed strobila of *D. latum* (Fig. 125) is ivory colored and has a length of 10 meters or more, with as many as 4000 proglottids. The scolex is elliptical, or spatulate, measures about 2.5 mm. in length by one mm. in breadth, and is provided with a median ventral and a median dorsal grooved sucker in place of the four cup-shaped suckers of cyclophyllidean tapeworms. The adjacent portion of the neck is unusually delicate. Proglottid formation in *D. latum* occurs at the distal end of the neck as it does in other strobilate tapeworms, but accessory proglottids are produced at all levels of the worm (Fig. 125). The genitalia in a mature proglottid are shown in Figure 126.

The eggs within the fully developed uterus are continuously discharged through the uterine pore. The terminal proglottids gradually become non-productive and disintegrate. The egg of *D. latum* (Fig. 127) differs in several respects from that of the cyclophyllidean tapeworms. In addition to being unembryonated at the time it is evacuated in the host's stool, it is broadly ovoidal, has an operculum at one end and a small but distinct thickening of the shell at the opposite end. The size of the egg varies

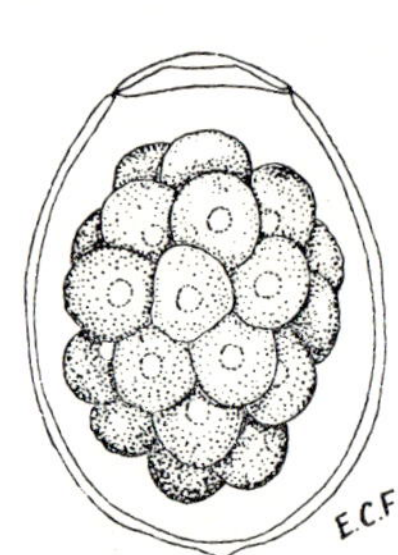

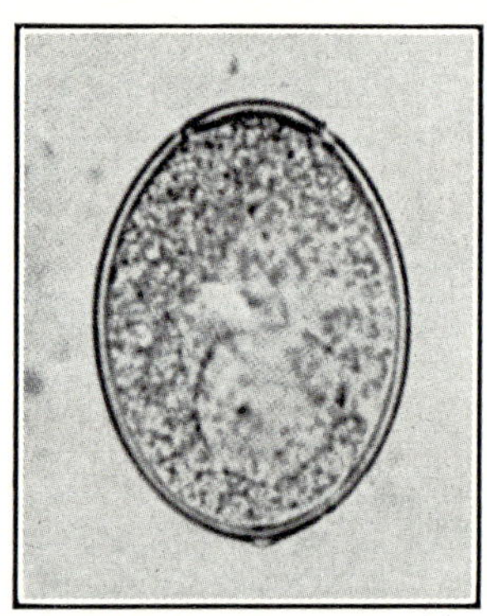

Fig. 127.—Egg of *Diphyllobothrium latum*. *Left,* camera lucida drawing, × 500 (after Faust); *right* photomicrograph, × 550 (after Fülleborn, in Vogel and Minning's Wurnkrankheiten, courtesy, Springer-Verlag, Berlin, Göttingen and Heidelberg).

considerable (56 to 76 by 40 to 51 microns), with an average of 59 to 71 by 42 to 49 microns (Faust, 1952).

Developmental Stages.—Embryonation of the eggs which reach cool fresh water (15 to 25° C.) requires 11 to 15 days. Then the embryo escapes through the opened operculum, casts off its embryonal envelope and by means of its ciliated covering swims about in the water. In order to proceed with its development it must be eaten within 12 hours by an appropriate species of water "flea" (*Cyclops* or *Diaptomus* in Europe, *Diaptomus* in North America). Once ingested by this copepod, the embryo burrows into the hemocele of the host, where it transforms into the procercoid larva (Fig. 114 *a*, p. 326). If the infected copepod is then consumed by a fish, the larva migrates into the flesh or connective tissue of this host and transforms into a sparganum larva (Fig. 114 *b*). The larger, edible fishes acquire the infection from eating infected smaller species or infected young of their own kind.

The fishes most frequently responsible for human infection are: in Europe, European pike, perch, salmon, lake trout, rainbow trout, ruff, "lawyer," grayling and eel; in Japan, trout, pink salmon, dog salmon, blueback salmon, *Hucho perryi* and *Salmo irideus;* in North America, barred pike, wall-eyed pike, sand pike, burbot and carp; in Chile, Argentina and Australia, *Salmo irideus*, *S. lacustris* or *S. fario* (all introduced species); and in Lake N'gami district of Africa, European barbel.

Consumption of infected fish flesh by man or other suitable definitive host completes the epidemiologic cycle. In approximately 3 to 5 weeks the worm develops to maturity and egg production is initiated. In addition to man, the dog, bear and many other fish-eating mammals have been reported to harbor the adult worm.

Pathogenicity and Symptomatology

D. latum may produce no symptoms, but in approximately 50% of the infections there are digestive disturbances, including diarrhea, heartburn, a sense of fullness in the epigastrium, hunger pains, or loss of appetite, anorexia, nausea and vomiting (Minning, 1952). Von Bonsdorff (1947) states that sudden vomiting of portions of the worm is characteristic, and is accompanied by symptoms suggesting peptic ulcer, cholelithiasis, ileus or appendicitis. The infection may be multiple: Grant (1930) reported 1 case with 106 worms and Tarassov (1936), 1 with 143 worms.

In certain instances, particularly noted in Finland, there is a macrocytic, hyperchromic anemia, the so-called "bothriocephalus anemia," although in these patients, unless there is an underlying aplastic anemia, the reticulocyte count is normal or only slightly elevated. Von Bonsdorff (*l. c.*) found that severe symptoms are associated with jejunal attachment, which this investigator believes to be responsible for an impairment of the interaction of the extrinsic and intrinsic factors of Castle. In the average case the only change in the blood picture is a moderate eosinophilia and slight leukocytosis.

Diagnosis

This is based on the recovery of the characteristic eggs (Fig. 127) in the stool or the occasionally vomited proglottids. A single worm at the height of productivity may produce up to 15,000 eggs per gram of formed stool (Szidat and Wigand, 1934), amounting to approximately 15 eggs per average fecal smear.

Treatment

This is similar to that recommended for *Tænia saginata* infection (page 331)

Prognosis

In the average case this is excellent following specific therapy. Even in patients with severe symptoms, including macrocytic anemia caused by the parasite, remission of symptoms is usually obtained following removal of the parasite.

Control

Control of fish tapeworm infection in endemic areas requires (1) sanitary disposal of human excreta so that viable eggs of *D. latum* do not reach bodies of fresh water in which the intermediate hosts breed, and (2) thorough cooking of all fish obtained from the area. Deep-freezing of the fish is not as certain a safeguard in this infection as it is in trichinosis, since the spargana in the fish survive prolonged low temperatures, although they are killed by a temperature of $-10°$ C. sustained for 48 hours (Magath and Essex, 1931). Some protection can be afforded persons living at a distance from endemic areas by prohibiting the shipment of fish during the warmer months when the fishes acquire the infection.

INFECTIONS OF MAN PRODUCED BY OTHER SPECIES OF PSEUDOPHYLLIDEA

Diphyllobothrium cordatum, a common intestinal parasite of the seal, the walrus and the dog in Greenland and Iceland, of the dog in Japan, and of the bear in Yellowstone National Park, Wyoming (U. S. A.), has incidentally been reported as a human parasite in Greenland (1860) and Japan (1929). The distinguishing external character of this species is the inverted heart-shaped scolex. The eggs are indistinguishable from those of *D. latum*.

Diphyllobothrium houghtoni, an intestinal parasite of the dog and cat in China, has been recovered twice from the human intestine in that country (Faust, Campbell and Kellogg, 1929). (See "Sparganosis," Chapter XIII, page 360.)

Diplogonoporus grandis, a common intestinal parasite of whales, has been reported 6 times in Japanese subjects. The proglottids are very broad compared with their length, and are provided with twinned genital organs, the external openings of which are situated ventrally, one on each side of the median line. The eggs are broadly ovoidal, dark brown in color and measure 63 to 68 microns in length by 50 microns in breadth.

Digramma brauni has been recovered twice from the intestine of Roumanian patients. The strobila, about 12 cm. long, has externally inconspicuous proglottid formation, slit-like dorsal and ventral suctorial grooves on the scolex, a very inconsipcuous neck and twinned genitalia. Birds are believed to be the normal hosts of this worm (Joyeux and Baer, 1929).

Ligula intestinalis has been obtained twice from man in Roumania and once fom, a French patient. The worm is ribbon-like, 18 to 20 cm. long by 8 to 12 mm. wirde has a triangular scolex, lacks a distinct neck region and has a middorsal and a midventral sucking groove extending the entire length of the strobila. The normal hosts are fish-eating birds.

SUMMARY

1. Tapeworms are flatworms (Platyhelminthes) which live as adults in the intestinal tract of vertebrate hosts, attached to the wall of the intestine. All tapeworms which parasitize man consist of a scolex or attachment organ, a neck or region of growth, and a number of proglottids, beginning just behind the neck with immature ones, which develop successively and almost imperceptably into mature and then into gravid proglottids.

The mature units contain male and female reproductive organs. Gravid proglottids are storehouses for embryonating eggs.

2. The stages in the life cycle of human tapeworms consist of the egg, within which there develops a hexacanth embryo, the larval stage (or stages), and finally the adult worm. For *Hymenolepis nana* (dwarf tapeworm) one individual serves as host for larval and adult stages.
3. *Tænia saginata* (beef tapeworm) has a distribution wherever beef is consumed. Man is its sole definitive host. The worm has a length of 5 meters or more and a scolex with 4 suckers but no rostellar hooklets. The gravid proglottids have a diagnostically specific uterine pattern. These proglottids break off from the strobila, ordinarily pass out of the bowel without liberating the stored eggs, and disintegrate on moist ground. Cattle grazing in sewage-polluted marshy meadows pick up the eggs. The hatched embryos migrate to striated muscle and transform in 2 to 3 months into cysticerci (*Cysticercus bovis*). Thereafter for several months when man consumes the infected beef he acquires the infection, which matures in about 3 months.

   Beef tapeworm infection frequently produces digestive and nervous symptoms, and occasionally obstruction or appendicitis requiring surgical intervention. Diagnosis is based on demonstration of the characteristic uterine pattern of gravid proglottids. Quinacrine hydrochloride (Atabrine) removes this worm. Control requires sanitary disposal of human excreta and consumption of beef only after it has been thoroughly cooked or frozen.
4. *Tænia solium* (pork tapeworm) has an extensive distribution among pork-eating populations, especially in Latin America, but it has gradually disappeared from the United States. Man is its sole definitive host and swine the usual intermediate host, but man may also serve as an efficient larval host. The adult *T. solium* is somewhat smaller than *T. saginata* (about 3 meters long), its scolex possesses a rostellar crown of hooklets anterior to the 4 suckers, the number of its proglottids is considerably less and the uterus in the gravid proglottids has a smaller number of main lateral uterine arms. The distalmost proglottids become separated from the worm, are evacuated in the excreta and disintegrate on the ground. Hogs ingest infested human excreta and in 2 to 3 months harbor cysticerci (*Cysticercus cellulosæ*) in their musculature. Man becomes infected from eating inadequately cooked or otherwise improperly processed pork.

   The symptoms of intestinal pork tapeworm infection are similar to those produced by *Tænia saginata*. Diagnosis is made on demonstration of the specific uterine pattern of the gravid proglottid. Quinacrine hydrochloride (Atabrine) is the drug of choice for treating this infection. Control requires sanitary disposal of human excreta and consumption of pork only after it has been thoroughly cooked or frozen.
5. *Hymenolepis nana* (dwarf tapeworm) is widely distributed in tropical and subtropical areas, including southeastern United States. Dwarf tapeworm is particularly prevalent in children. An infection consists of a few or many worms. The gravid proglottids disintegrate in the intestine so that eggs are present in the feces. They are immediately infective

when introduced from anus to mouth on finger tips. Complete development requires only 2 or 3 weeks.

Infection with dwarf tapeworm may be symptomless or it may produce severe gastro-intestinal and nervous disorders. Diagnosis is based on recovery of typical eggs in the stool. In small children hexylresorcinol crystoids is preferred, for older children and adults quinacrine hydrochloride (Atabrine). Control requires the development of habits of personal and group hygiene, particularly washing of hands after visiting the toilet and the frequent change of underpants.

6. *Hymenolepis diminuta* (rat tapeworm) and *Dipylidium caninum* (dog tapeworm) are medium-sized tapeworms each of which has been reported on a few hundred occasions from the human host, almost always in children. Human exposure results from accidental ingestion of the arthropod intermediate hosts. These infections may be symptomless or may provoke intestinal, allergic and nervous disorders. Control consists in eradication of domestic rodents, periodic deworming of dogs and cats, and use of insect toxicants to kill the arthropod vectors.
7. *Diphyllobothrium latum* (fish tapeworm) is a relatively common parasite of man, the dog, and other fish-eating mammals in the fresh-water lake regions throughout northern and central Europe and Asia and of north-central United States, Canada and Alaska. Other endemic foci have been discovered in Chile, Argentina and Australia. This tapeworm is endemic in cool moist climates, where the infected excreta reach water in which copepods (*Diaptomus* and *Cyclops*) and fishes serve respectively as primary and secondary larval hosts and man eats the essentially raw parasitized fish flesh. Additional infections develop in persons who eat fish shipped from endemic foci. The scolex is spatulate, has a median dorsal and a median ventral sucking groove and lacks hooklets. The eggs are discharged in an unembryonated stage through a patent uterine pore in the mature proglottids. The eggs develop in cool fresh water, and liberate ciliated embryos which are eaten by suitable species of copepods. Fishes consume the infected copepods and fish-eating mammals acquire the infection from the fish.

   In about 50% of human cases, there are severe gastro-intestinal symptoms, at times a macrocytic hypochromic anemia, all of which are relieved by removal of the parasite. Diagnosis is based on recovery of the typical eggs in the stool. Treatment consists in the administration of quinacrine hydrochloride (Atabrine). Control requires sanitary disposal of human excreta and abstinence from eating raw fish.

REFERENCES

Allen, R. W. 1947. Thermal Death Point of Cysticerci of *Tænia Saginata*. J. Parasitol., *33*, 331–338.

Altenkamp, T. 1935. Akute Appendicitis bei Bandwurm. Münch. Med. Wochenschr., *82*, 418–419.

Baer, J., Kouri, P., and Sotolongo, F. 1949. Anatomie, Position Systematique et Epidemiologie de *Inermicapsifer Cubensis* (Kourí, 1938) Kourí, 1940, Cestode Parasite de l'Homme a Cuba. Acta Trop., *6*, 120–130.

BEAVER, P. C., and SODEMAN, W. A. 1952. Treatment of *Hymenolepis Nana* (Dwarf Tapeworm) Infection with Quinacrine Hydrochloride (Atebrin). J. Trop. Med. & Hyg., *55*, 97–99.

VON BONSDORFF, B. 1947. *Diphyllobothrium Latum* and Pernicious Anemia. IX, X. Acta Med. Scandinav., *129*, 142–155, 213–233.

CHANDLER, A. C. 1942. First Record of a Case of Human Infection with Tapeworms of the Genus *Mesocestoides*. Am. J. Trop. Med., *22*, 493–496.

FAUST, E. C. 1952. Some Morphologic Characters of *Diphyllobothrium Latum*. An. do Inst. de Med. Trop. (Lisbôa), *9*, 1277–1300.

FAUST, E. C., CAMPBELL, H. E., and KELLOGG, C. R. 1929. Morphological and Biological Studies on the Species of Diphyllobothrium in China. Am. J. Hyg., *9*, 560–583.

GRANT, F. 1930. Ein Hundert und Sechs Bothriocephalusketten bei einem Kranken. Klin. Wochenschr., *9*, 502.

GRASSI, B. 1887. Entwicklungscyclus der *Tænia Nana*. Centralbl. f. Bakt., *2*, 305–312.

HERNÁNDEZ MORALES, F. 1949. The Treatment of *Tænia Saginata* with Atabrine. Puerto Rico J. Pub. Health & Trop. Med., *25*, 78–81.

JANICKI, C., and ROSEN, F. 1917. Le Cycle Évolutif du *Dibothriocephalus Latus* L. Bull. Soc. Neuchât., Sc. Nat., *42*, 19–53.

KÜCHENMEISTER, E. 1855. Experimenteller Nachweis, dass *Cysticercus Cellulosæ* Innerhalb des Menschlichen Darmkanales Sich in *Tænia Solium* Umwandeldt. Wien. Med. Wochenschr., *5*, 1–4.

LEUCKART, R. 1862. Ueber *Tænia Solium* und *T. Mediocanellata*. Nachr. K. Gesellsch. Wissensch. u. Georg-Aug. Univ., Göttingen, *1*, 15–21.

MÁGATH, T. B. 1937. Factors Influencing the Geographic Distribution of *Diphyllobothrium Latum*. pp. 366–380, Skrjabin Festschrift, Moscow.

MINNING, W. 1952. Cestoden-Infektionen, in Vogel and Minning's *Wurmkrankheiten, Handbuch der Inneren Medizin*, Vol. I, Pt. 2, pp. 935–971.

NEGHME, A., and FAIGUENBAUM, J. 1947. Nueva Modálidad de Tratamiento en las Teniasis. Rev. Med. Chile, *75*, 54–57.

NEWTON, W. L., BENNETT, H. J., and FIGGAT, W. B. 1949. Observations on the Effects of Various Sewage Treatment upon Eggs of *Tænia Saginata*. Am. J. Hyg., *49*, 166–175.

PENFOLD, W., PENFOLD, H. B., and PHILLIPS, M. 1937. *Tænia Saginata:* Its Growth and Propagation. J. Helminthol., *15*, 41–48.

READ, C. P. 1951. Studies on the Enzymes and Intermediate Products of Carbohydrate Degradation in the Cestode *Hymenolepis Diminuta*. Exp. Parasitol., *1*, 1–18.

SACCOMANNO, T. G. 1946. Nuevo Tratamiento de la Teniasis. Prensa Méd. Argent., *33*, 1657–1658.

SANDERS, D. F. 1951. *Diphyllobothrium Latum* in Australia. Med. J. Austral., *ii*, 533.

SAUNDERS, L. G. 1949. A Survey of Helminth and Protozoan Incidence in Man and Dogs at Fort Chipewyan, Alberta. J. Parasitol., *35*, 31–34.

SMYTH, J. D. 1947. The Physiology of Tapeworms. Biol. Rev., *22*, 214–238.

SODEMAN, W. A., and JUNG, R. C. 1952. Treatment of Teniasis with Quinacrine Hydrochloride. J. Am. Med. Assn., *148*, 285–286.

STUNKARD, H. W. 1940. The Morphology and Life History of the Cestode, *Bertiella Studeri*. Am. J. Trop. Med., *20*, 305–333.

SZIDAT, L., and FERNANDO SORIA, M. 1952. Difilobothriasis en Nuestro Pais. Prensa Méd. Argentina, *39*, 77–78.

TARASSOV, V. 1936. Expérience Acquise par Cinq Annees d'Études sur les Bothriocephalus dans la Partie Nord-est de l'Urss 1931–1935. Ann. de Parasitol., *14*, 472–484.

UPTON, A. C. 1950. Tænial Proglottides in the Appendix: Possible Association with Appendicitis. Am. J. Clin. Path., *20*, 1117–1120.

Chapter 13

Tapeworms in Extra-intestinal Foci

Introduction

While a majority of tapeworms which parasitize man reside in their definitive (strobilate) stage in the small intestine, it was noted in Chapter 12 that there are a few capable of producing human infection in their larval stage, always in extra-intestinal foci. These are the cysticercus of *Tænia solium*, the cenurus of *Multiceps* species, the hydatid cyst of *Echinococcus granulosus* and the sparganum (plerocercoid) of several species of *Diphyllobothrium*. The first three are larvas of cyclophyllidean tapeworms and the fourth of pseudophyllidean species. With the exception of the cenurus of *Multiceps* all of these larval forms are relatively common in the human host in certain geographical areas. All produce significant symptoms and all may have fatal termination.

Cysticercus of Tænia Solium

Biological and Epidemiologic Notes.—The larval stage of *Tænia solium* is referred to as *Cysticercus cellulosæ* and infection with this larva as cysticercosis cellulosæ. Except for two incidental findings of the cysticercus of the beef tapeworm (*C. bovis*) in human skeletal muscles and one from a lymph node of the meso-appendix (Niño, 1950), all known cases of human cysticercosis have resulted from infection with *C. cellulosæ*.

Man is the only proven host of the definitive stage of *T. solium* and the hog is the usual intermediate host in which the hexacanth embryo hatched from the egg in the intestinal tract migrates to striated muscle and transforms into the cysticercus, or bladder worm. (See Fig. 114 *h*, page 326.) However, man is also a satisfactory host for development of this larva.

Human exposure to cysticercosis, like that of the hog, results when the ripe eggs of *T. solium* are ingested and reach the duodenal canal. There are three possible ways in which this may occur, *viz.*, (1) Eggs which have been liberated from disintegrating gravid proglottids passed by a patient who has the intestinal infection get into the mouth of another person and are swallowed (hetero-infection); (2) eggs may be transferred from anus to mouth on unclean finger tips of an individual who has an intestinal infection with *T. solium* (external auto-infection), and (3) gravid proglottids in an individual harboring the adult *T. solium* may become detached from the main strobila, be regurgitated into the stomach and then return to the duodenal canal, where they disintegrate and liberate ripened eggs (internal auto-infection). Dixon and Hargreaves (1944) found that 26% of 284 cases of cerebral cysticercosis in British service troops who had been stationed in India were due to auto-infection, and Lech (1949), in Brazil, found that 23% of ophthalmic cases also harbored the adult *T. solium.* But Minning (1952) regards hetero-infection as the common method. Some of these cases are due to the custom of fertilizing gardens of green vegetables with human manure.

Pathogenicity and Symptomatology.—The lesions produced and the symptoms evoked by cysticercosis depend primarily on the tissues in which the embryos become established but also on the number of cysticerci which develop. Infection is more frequently multiple than solitary. MacArthur (1934) and other workers have found, that if there are many visible or palpable cysticerci in the subcutaneous tissues or superficial muscles, one or more will usually have matured in the brain or other internal organs. Austoni (1939) counted between 15,000 and 20,000 larvas in 1 patient.

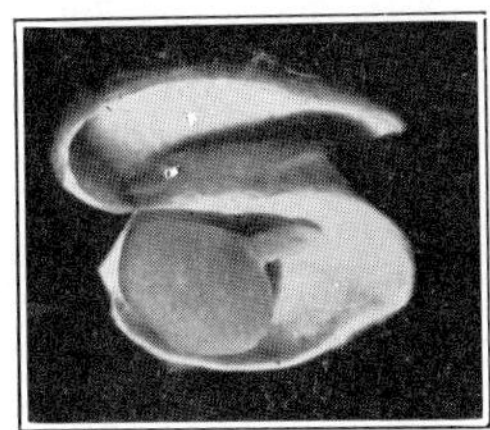

FIG. 128.—*Cysticercus cellulosæ* within outer adventitious capsule, removed from the biceps muscle of a patient with multiple cysticercosis without a history of intestinal *Tænia solium* infection. Natural size. (Photo by the author, from Faust's *Human Helminthology*, Lea & Febiger, Philadelphia.)

The cysticerci may remain viable in the human host up to 4 or 5 years (MacArthur, *l. c.*) but at times they die and become calcified much earlier. Except in the cysticercus racemosus type, or when present in the vitreous, pia mater or ventricles of the brain, these little bladder worms in human tissues are surrounded by a tough adventitious capsule, which may be infiltrated with eosinophilic leukocytes. The racemosus type is an unencapsulated larva which develops in the subarachnoid spaces at the base of the brain and occasionally in the choroid plexus. It grows to giant size, may reach an over-all length of 15 cm., and produces numerous aciniform branches, hence the designation "racemosus." (Unbranched, Fig. 128.)

Cysticerci which develop in the subcutaneous and muscle tissues cause essentially no pain unless they encroach on nerve endings, but when they become calcified they occasion considerable inconvenience. Likewise, during the life of the larvas in the meninges little if any evidence of their presence is usually provided, but if they develop as emboli in blood or lymphatic vessels acute symptoms will result.

Except for superficial tissues the most common location of *C. cellulosæ* is the eye (Andrade, 1940). In the vitreous and anterior chamber of the eye the living cysticerci are unencapsulated and are constantly changing shape, with periodic eversion and introversion of their scolex (Fig. 129). Usually the subjective symptoms are minimal except for discomfort caused by the shadows cast in front of the retina. However, the parasite may cause damage to any tissue of the eyeball or in the lacrymal sac. At times this results in uveitis, iritis, dislocation of the retina or atrophy of the choroid membrane. The larva may also invade the palpebral conjunctiva, the subconjunctiva or become encapsulated in the muscular funnel of the orbit.

Epilepsy is the most frequent symptom of cysticercosis of the meninges (Dixon and Hargreaves, 1944; Elsæsser, 1944; Obrador, 1948; Asenjo and Bustamente, 1950). Infection of the fourth ventricle is responsible for hydrocephalus, headache commonly at the base of the brain, diplopia and other manifestations of ophthalmic lesions (Ramírez and Verástegui, 1952), dizziness, nausea and vomiting (Minning, 1952).

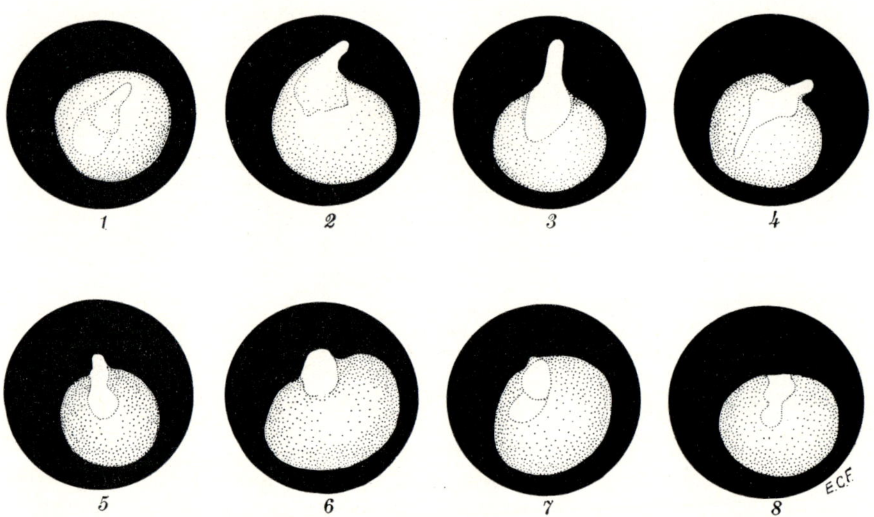

Fig. 129.—Successive stages (1–8) in the movements of an unencapsulated *Cysticercus cellulosæ* in a patient with subretinal cysticercosis. × $1\frac{1}{2}$. (Original adaptation of retinophotographs by de Penido Burnier, in Andrade's *Oftalmologia Tropical.*)

There is general agreement that significant host-tissue reaction and symptomatic cysticercosis are produced following the death of the larva and its discharge of foreign proteins. This stage may appear as early as 6 months after earliest possible infection (1 case studied by the author in China) or as late as 12 years (Edwards, 1946) or even 20 years afterward (Dixon and Hargreaves, 1944).

Diagnosis.—This may be made from biopsy of one or more of the little bladder-worm nodules appearing as slight elevations of the subcutaneous tissue or superficial muscles on any part of the body, compressed between two glass slides and examined under low power of the microscope. The presence of a single invaginated or evaginated scolex having four suckers and a crown of rostellar hooklets (Fig. 114 *h*) is specifically diagnostic. On the other hand, the first suggestion of cysticercosis may be obtained when the patient consults an ophthalmologist for visual difficulties or develops a series of epileptiform seizures without a history of epilepsy in early childhood. The ophthalmoscope will frequently visualize the motile organism in the eye (Fig. 129) with sufficient fidelity to provide the diagnosis, which can then be confirmed after surgical removal of the larva. If the symptoms are due to a brain lesion only a tentative diagnosis can be made of a space-occupying object which at times may be fairly accurately located topographically by encephalography (Asenjo and Bustamente, 1950) and, in infection of the fourth ventricle or at the base of the brain, by determining the exact pattern of visual impairment (Ramírez and Verástegui, 1952). Specific diagnosis of the causative agent can be made only after exploratory removal.

Treatment.—Surgery is the sole therapeutic procedure in cysticercosis. Removal of superficial nodules is a simple procedure but is not usually necessary except for diagnostic purposes, since the organisms provoke little tissue reaction and are not capable of migrating to vital centers. In reporting on 116 Brazilian cases involving the eye, Lech Junior (1949) recommends removal of the parasite as early as possible while it is still alive, to prevent total loss of sight in the effected organ if the cysticercus is allowed to die. Asenjo and Bustamente (1950) state that extirpation of a solitary cysticercus of the brain results in complete recovery (60%) or partial recovery (40%); but with generalized cerebral infection operative technics are inadequate.

Prognosis.—This is always excellent with respect to superficial lesions but the implication that there are additional cysticerci in the eye, brain or other foci modifies the prognosis. If surgical removal of a solitary larva from a vital organ is successful, complete or partial recovery may be expected.

Control.—The prevention of cysticercosis requires a twofold attack, namely, on the hog, which is the source of human intestinal infection with *Tænia solium*, and on the human carrier of the adult worm. Yet fundamentally control is a problem of personal and group hygiene in human communities, particularly in rural areas.

Cenurus of Multiceps Species

General Considerations.—A cenurus is the larval stage of tapeworms belonging to the genus *Multiceps*, the adults of which develop in the small intestine of dogs, cats and their wild relatives. Identification of the particular species of *Multiceps* is difficult and at times practically impossible (Nagaty and Ezzat, 1946). The mature eggs of *Multiceps* are indistinguishable from those of *Tænia* (Fig. 118, page 330); they hatch in the duodenum of herbivorous or omnivorous mammals and the liberated hexacanth embryos migrate to extra-intestinal sites in which they grow and transform into the cenurus-type of larva (Fig. 114 *i*, p. 326). The *cenurus* is a bladder filled with fluid, having multiple heads rather than a single one developing from the germinative membrane which lines the bladder cavity. The cenurus is usually considerably larger than the cysticercus. Infection with a cenurus larva is called cenurosis.

Multiceps Multiceps.—This is the commonest species and is cosmopolitan in sheep-raising areas. Dogs are the usual hosts of the adult worm. The larval hosts are principally sheep and goats, but other herbivores on grasslands polluted with the excreta of the infected dog hosts are also subject to infection. There are several records of human infection. The embryos that hatch from the egg in the duodenum of the intermediate host and migrate into extra-intestinal foci may become lodged in any soft tissue of the body but typically they develop in the brain or spinal cord (*Cœnurus cerebralis*), producing lesions which cause "blind staggers" or giddiness, hence the common English name for this parasite, the "gid" worm.

Human infections have been reported twice from France (Brumpt, 1913; Roger, Sautet and Paillas, 1942), once from South Africa (Cluver, 1941), twice from England (Chapham, 1941; Buckley, 1947) and once from Nevada, U. S. A. (Johnstone and Jones, 1950). The infected persons have ranged in age from early childhood to late middle life. This series of 5 cases probably represents only a small percentage of the actual number.

Depending on the location in which the growing cenurus is located, it may be rotund or produce finger-like ramifications between relatively dense nerve tissues. Depending on its exact anatomic relationship to the tissues, the patient may develop aphasia, epileptiform seizures, hemiplegia, paraplegia, transverse myelitis or other manifestations of neurologic lesions. In most cases only a single larva with multiple scolices has been recovered, but in at least one instance (Johnstone and Jones, 1950) 20 cenuri were obtained at exploratory operation and many others at necropsy.

Diagnosis can be made only tentatively on the basis of a space-occupying lesion in a particular focus in the central nervous system. This must be confirmed after recovery of the larva and study of its morphologic characters. Prognosis has been invariably grave. Control consists in meticulous care not to contaminate food, drink or finger tips with excreta of dogs in enzoötic areas.

Multiceps Serialis.—The adult worm of this species is found in the small intestine of dogs and their wild relatives, and the cenurus larva in the muscles of rabbits and other rodents, rarely monkeys. Two human infections have been reported from France (Bonnal, Joyeux and Bosch, 1933; Brumpt, Duvoir and Sainton, 1934) and one from rural California (Johnstone, personal communication, 1943).

Multiceps Glomeratus.—The adult worm of this tapeworm has not been discovered, so that the species description is limited to the cenurus stage, first reported from a small African rodent (gerbille) and diagnosed from human musculature in northern Nigeria (Turner and Leiper, 1919). Additional cenuri from human infections, one from the Belgian Congo (Taramelli and Dubois, 1931) and a second from northern Nigeria (Cannon, 1942) have been tentatively assigned to this species.

Hydatid Cysts of Echinococcus Species

General Considerations.—A hydatid (or hydatid cyst) is the larval stage of species of *Echinococcus*, the adults of which are parasites attached to the intestinal mucosa of dogs, wolves, foxes and related carnivorous mammals. Usually there are a few to several adult worms in an infection and at times there may be hundreds or thousands. The complete strobila (Fig. 130) is very small, rarely over a centimeter in length and consists of scolex, neck, one immature, one mature and one or two gravid proglottids. In addition to 4 minute suckers the scolex is provided with a double row of alternating rostellar hooklets. The gravid proglottids disintegrate in the small intestine of the definitive host, so that the eggs are evacuated in the feces. These eggs can not be distinguished from those of *Tænia* or *Multiceps* which are natural parasites of dogs or from those of *T. saginata* (Fig. 118, page 330) and *T. solium* of the human host,

Almost any mammal which picks up and swallows *Echinococcus* eggs is a suitable intermediate host for the larval or hydatid stage. The eggs hatch in the duodenal canal and the embryos work their way into the wall of the intestine, reach a mesenteric venule (or lymphatic vessel) and are distributed through extra-intestinal tissues, in which they become lodged in capillary filter beds (hepatic, pulmonary, etc.). The embryo then transforms slowly into a hydatid larva, which is characterized by having a mother cyst wall and many scolices, which are derived from the germinative membrane lining the fluid-filled bladder, become free in the bladder and many transform into daughter cysts (Fig. 114 *j*, page 326). Thus far only the species *Echinococcus granulosus* has been demonstrated to be capable of developing in the human host.

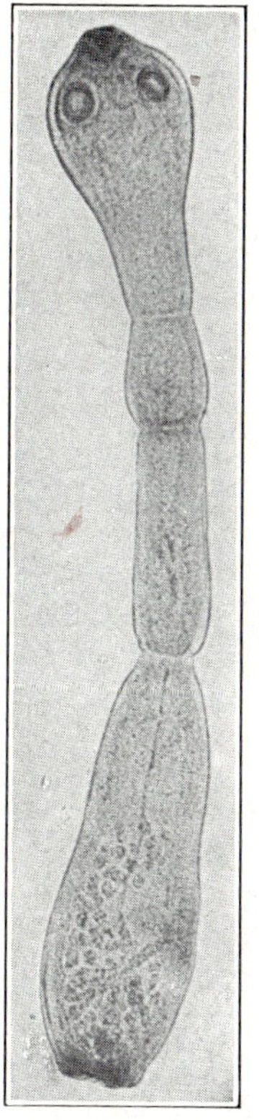

Fig. 130.—Complete strobila of *Echinococcus granulosus*, with scolex. neck, one immature, one maturing and one mature proglottid. The terminal gravid proglottid is lacking. × 40. (Original photograph, from Faust's *Human Helminthology*, Lea & Febiger, Philadelphia.)

ECHINOCOCCUS GRANULOSUS

(Batsch, 1786) Rudolphi, 1805

(The hydatid tapeworm, causing hydatid disease or echinococcosis)

Historical and Geographical Notes

Although hydatid cyst was known to ancient physicians and historians, the infection was frequently confused with other cystic tumors. Redi (1684), Hartmann (1685) and Tyson (1691) suspected the animal nature of the cyst, while Pallas (1766) considered that the hydatid of man was possibly the same as that of sheep, cattle and other domestic animals. Goeze (1782) demonstrated that the organism was a tapeworm. The adult worm in the dog's intestine was discovered by Hartmann (1695), and von Siebold (1852) first fed cysts from cattle to dogs and in three weeks recovered the minute strobilæ from the intestinal villi. Krabbe and Finsen in Iceland (1863) and Thomas in Australia (1888) obtained similar results by feeding cysts from human infections.

Hydatid cyst is widely distributed throughout the temperate and subtropical regions of the world, as well as in other areas where sheep, cattle or hogs are extensively raised. Autochthonous infection in man is limited to the enzoötic regions. (See map, Fig. 131.) Today human infection is

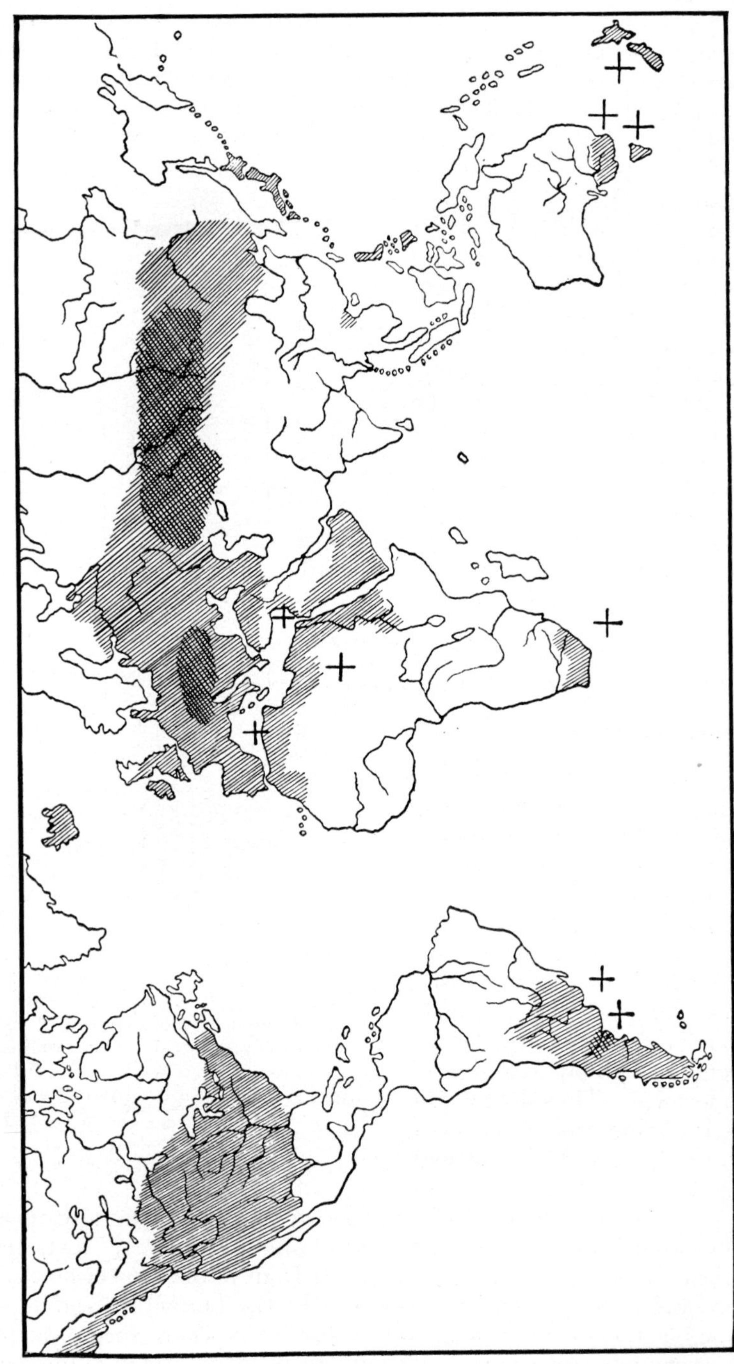

Fig. 131.—Map showing distribution of hydatid disease (larval *Echinococcus granulosus* infection) in reservoir hosts and man. + indicates heavy endemicity. The crosshatched lines in Europe, Asia and South America indicate areas in which human alveolar hydatid has been reported. (After Faust in Nelson's Loose-Leaf Medicine, from Faust's *Human Helminthology*, Lea & Febiger, Philadelphia.)

common in Argentina, Chile, Uruguay, Paraguay, southern Brazil, South Africa, Tanganyika, Palestine, Lebanon, and Algeria. It is also frequently encountered in southern Australia, New Zealand, in extensive areas of central Asia and in North China. In Europe, moderately high incidence is confined to the Balkans. A few genuine autochthonous cases are diagnosed each year from scattered foci in the United States and southern Canada. Studies among the Eskimos in northern Canada (Miller, 1953) and Alaska (Rausch and Schiller, 1951) indicate the disease to be highly endemic in parts of these subarctic areas.

Epidemiology

Human infection with hydatid cyst is apt to occur in any locality where dogs harbor the adult worms and sheep or hogs serve as common reservoirs of the larval stage. Cattle do not often constitute a reservoir hazard since the multiple cystic nodules (multilocular hydatid) in these animals are characteristically sterile. Exposure most commonly takes place in childhood, particularly among boys who play with infected dogs. Herders of infected sheep and swine are likewise frequently exposed. Unless the embryos of the worm filter out in tissues where the developing hydatids will embarrass vital processes, the hydatid may grow for 5 to 20 years before it causes serious concern to the patient. Hence, exposure usually occurs several to many years before diagnosis is made. In England Barrett and Thomas (1952) found that human infection may be acquired from urban scavenger dogs or greyhound and whippet-racing animals.

Pathogenesis and Symptomatology

The older statistics indicated that a majority (approximately 75%) of human hydatids develop in the liver, near the first capillary filter after the hexacanth embryos have burrowed into the intestinal wall and gotten into the mesenteric venules; that infection of the lungs is next in prevalence, and that if they pass the pulmonary filter the embryos may settle down in any organ or tissue of the body, including bone, and proceed to develop into hydatids. In heavily endemic areas in South America, the pulmonary location is stated to be more frequent than the hepatic one, suggesting that the mesenteric lymphatics rather than the portal blood may at times be the more common exit from the intestine.

Primary hydatid cysts are usually single but they may be multiple Moreover, Obrador *et al.* (1951) have reported on a Spanish case with multiple intradural hydatids associated with generalized cysticercosis of the somatic tissues, and Sorour *et al.* (1951), in Egypt, have described a peritoneal hydatid which had a granulomatous fibrous capsule infiltrated with *Schistosoma* eggs.

Types of Human Hydatids.—There are three distinct morphologic types in human tissues, *viz.*, unilocular, alveolar and osseous. The *unilocular cyst* (Fig. 114 *j*, page 326) is one in which there is a central, fluid-filled cavity lined with a germinative layer, surrounded by an intact but very friable laminated membrane covered with a host-tissue capsule. A large majority of human hydatids are unilocular, but occasionally the laminated membrane fails to develop and no fibrous capsule is formed, so that the parasite digests its way through the organ in which it has become implanted. This is the *alveolar hydatid.* It occurs most frequently in the liver. In case the hexacanth embryo is filtered out of blood vessels in bony tissues, no limiting membranes are produced and the organism proceeds to grow as a protoplasmic stream which erodes the cancellous structure, particularly of the long bones and pelvic arch. This is the *osseous hydatid.*

The size and contour of the unilocular hydatid are dependent on the site of implantation and on its age. If it is situated in relatively non-resistant tissues, the cyst will enlarge under Glisson's capsule into the peritoneal cavity. After 12 to 20 years it may be as large as a football and hold several liters of clear, sterile hydatid fluid, typically with a large number of scolices and daughter hydatids. If the cyst becomes bacteriologically contaminated, the fluid will be purulent and have no viable scolices, or the cyst may be completely filled with caseous material. If the embryo becomes embedded near resistant tissues such as tendons and large blood vessels, the cyst may develop digitate processes around the tissues. In the lungs, the cyst is always encapsulated.

The amount of systemic intoxication or sensitization resulting from a unilocular hydatid depends on how well it is insulated from the surrounding host tissues. This may be essentially complete, with little or no toxic or allergic evidence of the parasite. On the other hand, if the wall is highly vascularized there may be considerable leakage of sensitizing fluids, as indicated by marked eosinophilia and at times urticaria or angioneurotic edema. If a large intra-abdominal cyst bursts, either spontaneously or following a severe blow on the abdomen, anaphylaxis may be precipitated by the sudden liberation of hydatid fluid into the peritoneal cavity. Moreover, scolices spilled out of the cystic cavity will become implanted on the peritoneum and produce multiple secondary growths. Rupture of a pulmonary cyst into a bronchus results in coughing up the contents and possibly the spontaneous clearance of the infection. Hydatid of the brain produces increasing symptomatic evidence of an intra-cranial tumor, with neurological manifestations corresponding to the location and size of the foreign body.

Alveolar hydatid is always serious; it may be likened to a metastasizing neoplasm in its enlargement within an organ, although it is much less likely to spread to other locations. Osseous hydatid is an insidious process which gradually erodes the bone to a stage where fracture or crumbling suddenly occurs.

Diagnosis

If the unilocular cyst develops in a vital organ or location it may produce symptoms at an early stage, but if it is relatively unconfined it may reach considerable size before the patient consults a physician because of the physical inconvenience due to its presence. Thus, cysts resulting from exposure in childhood may not be diagnosed until middle life.

In endemic areas, experienced clinicians may obtain strong suspicion of hydatid disease from the patient's history, the symptoms presented and the x-ray picture. More specific diagnosis can be obtained by the intradermal test, employing a known amount of hydatid antigen. (See "TECHNICAL AIDS," page 616.) A positive reaction of the immediate type, *e. g.*, within 15 minutes, indicates that the patient has, or has had hydatid disease. If this is confirmed by a positive precipitin or complement-fixation test, the evidence is much stronger that the infection is presently active and that the reaction is not merely a sensitization reaction from a previously active hydatid. Such serologic confirmation is particularly important in case the symptoms suggest that secondary cysts may have developed from scolices which were accidentally spilled into a cavity during removal of a primary cyst, or that one or more residual cysts may not have been discovered at the earlier exploratory examination. Final diagnosis consists in the demonstration of free scolices or daughter cysts from aspirated hydatid fluid, or of the histologic structure of the cyst wall, with its laminated membrane, as seen in stained sections made from the excised cyst.

Treatment

Chemotherapy is of no avail in hydatid disease. The standard procedure is surgical removal of the cyst. Once clinical suspicion of a hydatid cyst has been supported by specific positive immunologic tests, the surgeon should be prepared to operate; or, in case hydatid cyst has been previously unsuspected and a fluid-filled mass is discovered at exploratory operation, he should proceed to excise the cyst wherever this is feasible, using meticulous care not to spill the contents into the operative cavity. The technics employed depend on the location of the cyst or cysts.

A wealth of information is available in the surgical literature concerning operative procedures for removal of hydatid cysts. Source information on Latin American experience for 1949–1950 is summarized in "Latin American Contribution to Scientific Progress. Parasitology (1949–1950)," pages 139–143, Unesco Science Coöperation Office for Latin America, Montevideo, 1953.

Biological therapy has been increasingly employed in types of hydatid disease in which the parasites are in inoperable locations, as in the bone, or in which multiple cysts have developed in several anatomical locations. Casiraghi (1949) has reported good results following the intradermal administration of sterile hydatid fluid in the amount 0.1 cc. every 5 to 7 days, plus a maximum of 3 cc. injected subcutaneously, depending on the patient's tolerance. Other clinical investigators have employed the protein component of the fluid, which they regard as the useful therapeutic fraction. Injections are continued for a period of years (Belleville, 1950). Improvement in subjective symptoms and in the general condition of the patient is usually noted, associated with gradual devitalization and atrophy of the cyst. Biological therapy probably has a valuable prophylactic rôle following operative removal of a hydatid cyst to prevent development of secondary cysts.

Prognosis

Without surgical intervention or biological therapy the eventual prognosis is poor. If the original cyst is treated early by one or the other, or preferably both of these methods, the chances of improvement and at times complete recovery are good to fair.

Control

Control must be directed against the dog, the carrier of the adult *Echinococcus granulosus,* and sheep and hogs, the common reservoirs of the viable hydatid. The dog becomes infected from devouring infected viscera of infected sheep and hogs. In some countries where these animals are condemned as unfit for human consumption their livers are fed to dogs. All infected carcasses should be deeply buried or incinerated. Man becomes infected from ingesting the eggs of *E. granulosus* evacuated in the dog's excreta. Stray dogs should be destroyed. This can be effectively carried out in connection with campaigns to reduce rabies. Domestic dogs should be periodically de-wormed. Personal hygiene in endemic areas includes care that children not contaminate their fingers with dog's excreta while playing with these animals.

Sparganum of Diphyllobothrium Species

Historical, Biological and Geographical Notes.—In 1882, while serving as medical officer of the Imperial Customs at Amoy, China, Patrick Manson performed a clandestine autopsy at night. In the kidney fat, he discovered a dozen glistening, ribbon-like worms, which Cobbold (1882) designated "*Ligula mansoni*," and which were later found (Joyeux *et al.*, 1928) to be the sparganum (plerocercus stage) of *Diphyllobothrium mansoni*, a common parasite of dogs and cats in the Orient and widely distributed in these hosts in other parts of the world.

Several related species of *Diphyllobothrium* belonging to the subgenus *Spirometra* (*D. houghtoni*, *D. decipiens*, *D. erinacei*, *D. ranarum*, *D. reptans*, *D. okumurai*, *D. mansonioides*, etc.) are also intestinal parasites of canine and feline hosts. These pseudophyllidean tapeworms utilize *Cyclops* as their first intermediate host. Various species of vertebrates other than fishes, *e. g.*, frogs, snakes, birds and mammals, are the hosts for the sparganum stage. Bonne (1942) and Gan (1949) have elucidated the complete life cycle of *D. ranarum* in Indonesia. More recently, in Korea, Weinstein, Krawzyk and Peers (1954) have found that in that country snakes constitute an important second intermediate host for the sparganum stage of an undesignated species of *Spirometra*.

A large majority of human infections with unbranched spargana (Fig. 132) occur in the China Sea area (Japan and Korea, southern China and Indochina), and in Indonesia. Other cases have also been reported from Africa, Holland, Australia and the Western Hemisphere, including Texas (4 cases), Louisiana (5 cases), Uruguay and British Guiana. A branching type, *S. proliferum*, has been diagnosed at least 6 times in Japan and once in Florida (U. S. A.).

Epidemiology.—Human infection with the sparganum stage of these species of *Diphyllobothrium* results from (1) drinking unfiltered raw water containing procercoid-infected *Cyclops;* (2) eating infected tadpoles or snake flesh as a "tonic," and (3) applying plerocercus-infected flesh of frogs, snakes or possibly warm-blooded animals as a poultice on an inflamed eye or finger. Usually only a single sparganum is found in the human host but there may be several, as in Manson's original finding. Rarely the infection is miliary. Likewise, a few human cases of infection have been reported in which many proliferating spargana have been recovered (*Sparganum proliferum*).

Pathogenesis and Symptomatology.—Infection with sparganum larvas is called sparganosis. While the infection is still young there is apt to be relatively little host tissue reaction but more prolonged residence of the parasite provokes an infiltration of eosinophils, epithelioid cells and lymphocytes. As the infection becomes chronic there develops an extremely tender, puffy area around the parasite, filled with a chylous fluid, in the midst of which the larvas are elongating and contracting. Later the parasite may die and the entire lesion become caseous.

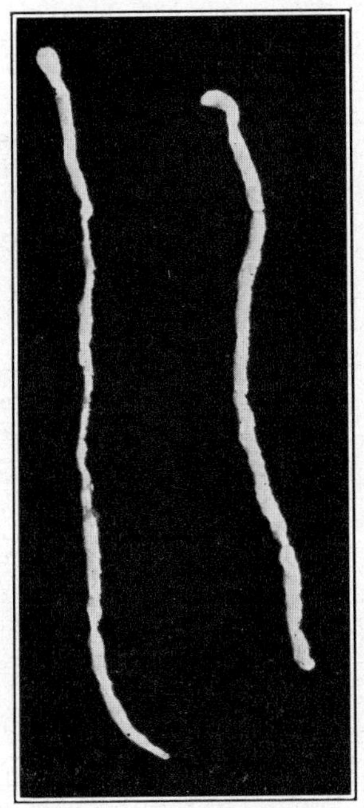

Fig. 132.—Mature spargana of *Diphyllobothrium mansoni* from muscle fascia of experimentally infected rabbits. × 2. (Original, from Faust's *Human Helminthology*, Lea & Febiger, Philadelphia.)

Ocular sparganosis is usually a very serious disease. It is characterized by intense pain, irritation and palpebral edema (Fig. 133), with excessive lacrymation. If the worm lodges under the conjunctiva it is likely to provoke nodule formation; if its position is retrobulbar, lagophthalmos and corneal ulceration are characteristic. In the *proliferating* type of *sparganosis* the parasitized tissues become honeycombed, filled with chylous fluid, elephantoid if lymph channels are involved, and are responsible for intense itching of the skin if the subcutaneous tissues are invaded.

Diagnosis.—Unless physicians live in endemic areas and have had experience with cases of sparganosis, the living, contracting and elongating larva removed from a superficial furuncle or nodule will be a distinct novelty. It can be diagnosed only as a sparganum of some species of *Diphyllobothrium*, subgenus *Spirometra*, unless recovered intact in the living condition, fed to a kitten or puppy and grown to the adult stage.

Treatment.—A single sparganum in superficial tissues is easily removed after incision under procaine anesthesia and withdrawal of the worm by gentle traction. Ocular sparganosis is a more serious matter and requires skill to remove the parasite thout additional damage to the tissues of the eye. Miliary infection, particularly of the proliferating type, is not amenable to known medical or surgical tretament.

Prognosis.—This is excellent with clean removal of solitary spargana from superficial tissues, fair to good in ocular sparganosis if the worm is extracted early. In miliary and proliferating infections, the prognosis is invariably grave.

Control.—Effective control of sparganosis requires a radical change in the habits of persons living in highly enzoötic areas. Drinking water must be boiled or satisfactorily filtered. The flesh of animals apt to harbor the sparganum stage should be thoroughly cooked before it is eaten, and under no circumstance should it be used as a poultice for an inflamed part of the body.

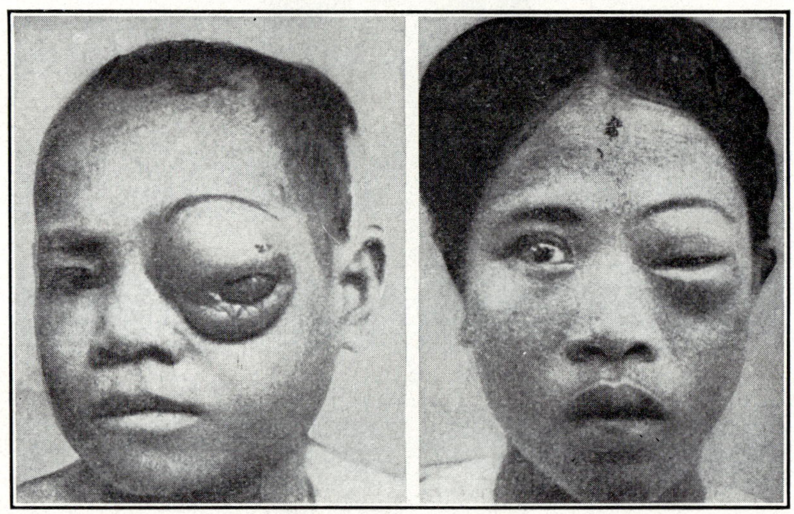

Fig. 133.—Ocular sparganosis, two cases from Indo-China. Note unilateral palpebral edema and in one case marked lagophthalmos. (After Keller, in Brumpt's *Précis de Parasitologie*, from Craig and Faust's *Clinical Parasitology*, Lea & Febiger, Philadelphia.)

SUMMARY

1. Human infection with tapeworms in extra-intestinal foci results from the implantation and growth of cysticercus ("bladder worm") of *Tænia*, almost exclusively the pork tapeworm, *T. solium;* cenurus of *Multiceps* species; hydatid cyst of *Echinococcus granulosus*, and sparganum (plerocercus) of species of *Diphyllobothrium*, subgenus *Spirometra*.
2. Although the hog is the usual host of the cysticercus of *Tænia solium*, man is also a frequent larval host. Human exposure to cysticercosis results either by auto-infection or hetero-infection. Many cysticerci become lodged in subcutaneous tissues and somatic muscles but at least a few almost always reach the central nervous system, the eye or other vital centers. In relatively dense tissues they provoke host encapsulation but in the meninges, ventricles of the brain or the eye they remain unencapsulated. At times they develop extensive ramifications through the tissues (racemosus type). When the cysticerci die in the

brain and the eye they are responsible for acute inflammatory tissue changes which occasion severe symptoms. Control in endemic areas consists in the sanitary disposal of all human excreta, prohibition of the use of unsterilized human nightsoil as fertilizer, treatment of human cases of *Tænia solium* in the intestinal tract and abstinence from eating inadequately cooked or unfrozen pork.

3. The cenurus larva of *Multiceps* develops in nature in herbivorous mammals but a few cases of human infection have been reported, including two from California (U. S. A.). Human exposure results from accidental ingestion of the eggs of the adult *Multiceps* evacuated in the feces of the dog, the usual definitive host. The most serious type of cenurosis is due to infection with *Cœnurus cerebralis,* with fatal termination.
4. The hydatid larva of *Echinococcus granulosus* develops in mammals grazing on ground contaminated with the feces of dogs infected with the adult worms. Man is frequently parasitized with this larva in heavily infected areas. The larvas grow slowly over a period of years. Occasionally the insulating wall of the cyst is lacking and the hydatid spreads as an unconfined malignancy, particularly in the liver (alveolar type). If the hexacanth embryo reaches bony structures, the organism proceeds to grow as an erosive protoplasmic stream (osseous type). Hydatid cyst in human infection occurs most commonly in the liver and lungs.

   Diagnosis of hydatid disease is obtained by use of the intradermal reaction supplemented by a precipitin or complement fixation test, employing hydatid antigen. Chemotherapy is ineffective. Surgical removal of the cyst is the usual therapeutic measure but biological therapy may be valuable. Control requires improvement in personal and group hygiene, to prevent oral contamination with dog's feces; the deep burying of animals which have died or been condemned for human consumption, destruction of all stray dogs in enzoötic areas, and periodic de-worming of pet and range dogs.
5. The sparganum (plerocercus) of species of *Diphyllobothrium* (subgenus *Spirometra*) develops in nature in the extra-intestinal tissues of frogs, snakes, birds and many mammals, including man. Human infections have been reported from Africa, Holland and the United States but most cases occur in the Orient. The adult worms are intestinal parasites of dogs and cats and their wild relatives. Human exposure results from drinking raw water containing infected *Cyclops,* from eating the uncooked infected flesh of tadpoles, snakes, or from applying infected flesh as a poultice to an inflamed eye, finger, etc. Infection may be single or multiple; occasionally it is miliary and rarely proliferating. The sparganum in the tissues provokes an infiltration of eosinophils, epithelioid cells and lymphocytes, and causes an elephantoid condition if lymphatic channels are blocked. Deeply implanted and miliary infections invariably have a poor prognosis. Control of human sparganosis requires boiling or filtering all drinking water, abstinence from eating raw flesh of infected hosts, and discontinuance of the habit of poulticing injured and inflamed body surfaces with sparganum-infected flesh.

REFERENCES

de Andrade, C. 1940. Oftalmologia Tropical (Sul-Americana). Rio de Janeiro, pp. 111–115.

Asenjo, A., and Bustamente, E. 1950. Die Neurochirurgische Behandlung der Cysticerkose. Deutsche Med. Wochenschr., *75*, 1180–1183.

Barrett, N. R., and Thomas, D. 1952. Pulmonary Hydatid Disease. Brit. J. Surg., *40*, 222–244.

Belleville, G. I. 1950. Terapéutica Biologica de la Hidatidosis. Bol. Acad. Argent. Ciruj., *34*, 244–245.

Bonnal, G., Joyeux, Ch., and Bosch, P. 1933. Un Cas de Cénurose Humaine dû à Multiceps Serialis (Gervais). Bull. Soc. Path. Exot., *26*, 1060–1071.

Bonne, C. 1942. Researches on Sparganosis in the Netherlands East Indies. Am. J. Trop. Med., *22*, 643–645.

Brumpt, E. 1913. *Précis de Parasitologie*, 2nd ed., p. 281, Paris, Masson et Cie.

Brumpt, E., Duvoir, M. E., and Sainton, J. 1934. Un Cas de Cénurose Humaine dû au *Cœnurus Serialis*. Ann. de Parasitol., *12*, 371–383.

Casiraghi, J. C. 1949. Terapéutica Biológica de la Hidatidosis. Bol. y Trab. Soc. Argent. de Ciruj., *10*, 229–239.

Clapham, P. A. 1941. An English Case of *Cœnurus Cerebralis* in the Human Brain. J. Helminth., *19*, 84–86.

Cruz, H. 1948. On an English Case of An Intermedullary Spinal Cœnurus in Man, with Some Remarks on the Identity of *Cœnurus* spp. Infesting Man. J. Helminth., *22*, 73–76.

Dixon, H. B. F., and Hargreaves, W. H. 1944. Cysticercosis (*Tænia Solium*). Quart. J. Med., *13*, 107–121.

Edwards, C. 1946. Cerebral Cysticercosis without Epilepsy. Lancet, *i*, 500–501.

Gan, K. H. 1949. Research on the Life Cycle of *Diphyllobothrium Ranarum*. Docum. Neerl. et Indones. Morbis Tropicis, *1*, 90–92.

Johnstone, H. G., and Jones, O. W., Jr. 1950. Cerebral Cœnurosis in an Infant. Am. J. Trop. Med., *30*, 431–441.

Lech Junior. 1949. Ocular Cysticercosis. Am. J. Ophthalm., *32*, 523–547.

MacArthur, W. P. 1934. Cysticercosis as Seen in the British Army, with Special Reference to the Production of Epilepsy. Trans. R. Soc. Trop. Med. & Hyg., *27*, 343–363.

Miller, M. J. 1953. Hydatid Infection in Canada. Canadian Med. Assn. J., *68*, 423–434.

Minning, W. 1952. Cysticercose, in Vogel and Minning's *Wurmkrankheiten, Handbuch der Inneren Medizin*, pp. 947–952. Berlin, Göttingen, Heidelberg.

Nino, F. L. 1950. Cisticercosis Humana en la República Argentina; Estudio de Una Nueva Observación. Prensa Méd. Argent., *37*, 3040–3044.

Obrador, S. 1948. Clinical Aspects of Cerebral Cysticercosis. Arch. Neur. and Psychiat., *59*, 457–468.

Pilotti, M., and Faiguenbaum, J. 1951. Sobre las Localizaciones del Quiste Hidático. Boll. de Inform. Parasitol. Chilenas, *6*, 55–57.

von Siebold, C. T. E. 1952. Expériences sur la Transformation des Vers Vésiculaires ou Cysticerques en Tænias. Ann. Sc. Nat. Zool., 3 ser., *17*, 377–381.

Sotomayór, M. 1947. (Hydatid Cyst in Peruvian Children.) Rev. Hosp. Niño, June, 1947, p. 127.

Turner, M., and Leiper, R. T. 1919. On the Occurrence of *Cœnurus Glomeratus* in Man in West Africa. Trans. Soc. Trop. Med., *13*, 23–24.

Weinstein, P. O., Krawzyk, H. J., and Peers, J. H. 1954. Sparganosis in Korea. Am. J. Trop. Med. & Hyg., *3*, 112–129.

Chapter 14

Intestinal, Hepatic and Pulmonary Flukes (Trematodes)

TREMATODES AS A GROUP

Introduction

FLUKES, or trematodes (Class Trematoda), constitute a major subdivision of the flatworms (Phylum Platyhelminthes). (See Chapter 3, pages 26 to 28.) Of the three recognized subclasses of the Trematoda, *viz.*, Monogenea, Aspidogastrea and Digenea, only the digenetic trematodes produce infection in man and higher animals.

Life Cycle.—Digenetic trematodes have a complicated life cycle, consisting of three (or more) consecutive generations. The definitive stage is usually hermaphroditic but in some species of schistosomes (blood flukes) it is diecious. In most Digenea the fertilized egg (Fig. 134, *Ia*), after its discharge from the definitive host, hatches in water, with the escape of a ciliated larva (*miracidium*), which swims about for a short time (Fig. 134, *Ib*), but in order to proceed with its development must penetrate the soft tissues of an appropriate mollusc, usually a snail. This is accomplished by the secretion of digestive enzymes elaborated in so-called "penetration glands" which discharge the secretion at the anterior end of the miracidium.

Within the lymph spaces of the molluscan host, the miracidium sheds its ciliated epithelium and transforms into a simple elongated sac, a *first-generation sporocyst* (Fig. 134, Ic_1), or in some species a slightly more elaborate form called a *redia* (Fig. 134, Ic_2). Germ cells developed from the inner wall of the sporocyst (or redia) give rise to a number of *second-generation sporocysts* (Fig. 134, II_1) or *redias* (Fig. 134, II_2). The investigations of Cort and his students (Brooks, 1930; Cort, 1944, etc.) provide convincing proof that the characteristic mechanism is one of polyembryony, *e. g.*, germ cell lineage. The second-generation organisms escape from their mothers, grow and produce internally third-generation larvas, which, when mature, break out of the mollusc and temporarily become free-living organisms in the water. This stage is the *cercaria*, or tailed larva (Fig. 134, $IIIa_{1-3}$).

The cercaria possesses certain uniquely larval organs, namely, cystogenous and penetration glands. Secretion of cystogenous material provides a temporary protective wall around the organism. Secretion of digestive enzymes elaborated in the penetration glands aids the larva to penetrate the tissues of its next host. Some groups of cercarias develop the one type of mechanism, some the other, and some have both types.

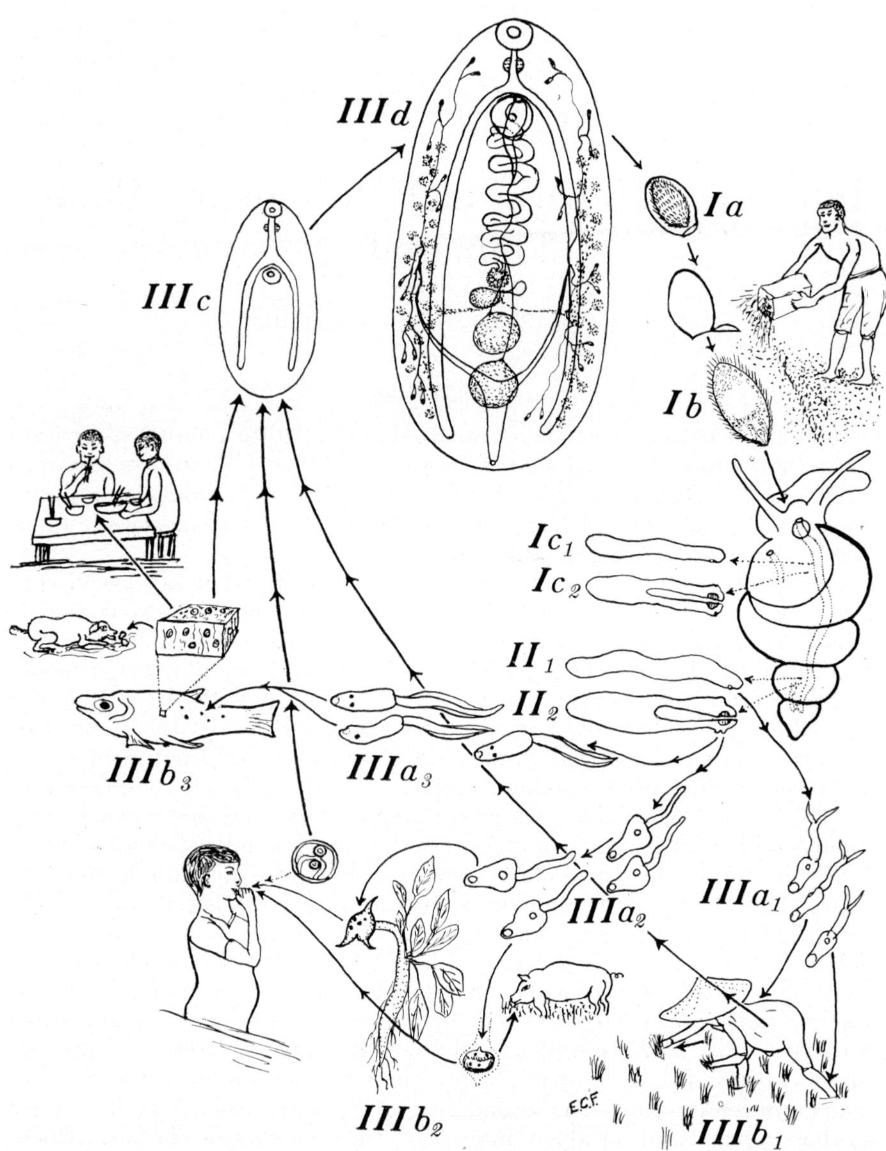

FIG. 134.—Diagrammatic life cycle of digenetic trematodes. *I*, first generation; *II*, second generation; *III*, definitive generation. *Ia*, fertilized egg; *Ib*, free-swimming miracidium hatched from egg; *Ic* , first-generation sporocyst, or *Ic*·, first-generation redia; II_1, second-generation sporocyst, or II_2, second-generation redia; $IIIa_{1-3}$, free-swimming cercaria; $IIIb_1$, cercaria penetrating directly into skin of definitive host (blood flukes); $IIIb_2$, cercaria crawls upon vegetation and encysts (*Fasciolopsis*, *Fasciola*); $IIIb_3$, cercaria enters tissues of aquatic animal and encysts (*Clonorchis*, *Opisthorchis*); *IIIc*, young trematode, and *IIId*, mature trematode in definitive host. (Original.)

Depending on the particular group of digenetic trematodes, the cercaria (1) becomes attached to the skin of a definitive vertebrate host, discards its tail, penetrates into the tissues (Fig. 134, $IIIb_1$), and after a period of migration and growth matures in this host (blood flukes); (2) crawls upon an aquatic plant (*Fasciolopsis buski, Fasciola hepatica*), drops its tail, rounds up and encysts (Fig. 134, $IIIb_2$); or (3) shedding its tail, penetrates into the tissues of an aquatic animal (*Clonorchis sinensis, Opisthorchis felineus, Paragonimus westermani*), or terrestrial animal (*Dicrocœlium dendriticum*), in which it becomes encysted (Fig. 134, $IIIb_3$). In the latter two types of development the definitive host becomes infected when it ingests the plant or animal tissues on which or in which the encysted stage occurs.

As soon as the cercaria becomes separated from its tail it is referred to as a *metacercaria*. In its definitive host the metacercaria (Fig. 134, *IIIc*) develops into the adult worm (Fig. 134, *IIId*). Cercaria, metacercaria and adult worm constitute the third generation in the life cycle.

The Mature Worm in its Definitive Host.—While a majority of digenetic trematodes are located in the digestive tract of their definitive hosts, several reside in the bile passages, a few in the parenchyma of the lungs, and the schistosomes in portal-caval venous blood. These worms vary in size and shape: Some (*Fasciola, Fasciolopsis*) are large and fleshy; others are as small as a mustard or turnip seed (heterophyid species); still others are thin and flabby (*Clonorchis, Opisthorchis, Dicrocœlium*), and the blood-inhabiting schistosomes are more or less delicately cylindrical.

The adult trematode is covered with a cuticle secreted by the hypodermis. This may be smooth or may have spines or plaque-like denticles. Species of echinostomes likewise have a cervical collarette of spines. In addition to a sucker which surrounds the mouth, in most families there is a median ventral, blind acetabulum, which may be close to the oral sucker, near the equatorial plane or at the posterior extremity. Under the hypodermis there are successively a transverse and a longitudinal muscle layer, oblique muscles and a loose parenchymatous matrix surrounding the internal organs.

The Digestive System.—This consists of a mouth (buccal cavity), then an esophagus which is provided with a spherical or pyriform, usually muscular pharynx, and finally a pair of ceca which in most species are simple and end blindly in the subdistal portion of the worm.

Typically the nutriment in which the trematode lies is taken into its digestive tract, where the digestible part is absorbed through the cecal wall, after which the wastes are expelled by regurgitation.

The Nervous System.—Relatively large saddle-like nerve commissures are located in the anterior portion of the worm dorsal to the pharynx. Connected with this central nerve mass are three pairs of nerve trunks, one pair each in the lateral, dorsolateral and ventrolateral positions, extending both anteriorwards and posteriorwards. Numerous transverse commissures are found in the region of the ventral acetabulum and the genital organs. Terminal sensory nerve endings are under all surface areas and are particularly numerous in the anterior part of the body.

The Excretory System.—This system consists of a median posterior bladder emptying dorsally through a posterior pore; primary and secondary collecting tubules which are bilaterally symmetrical, and capillaries with terminal "flame cells" (*solenocytes*). Similar groups of digenetic trematodes usually have the same fundamental type of excretory pattern in the miracidium, cercaria, metacercaria and mature worm.

Lymph-Vascular System.—Two or four main longitudinal lymphatic trunks with numerous collateral branches have been observed in several groups of trematodes, particularly those which have an encysted metacercarial stage.

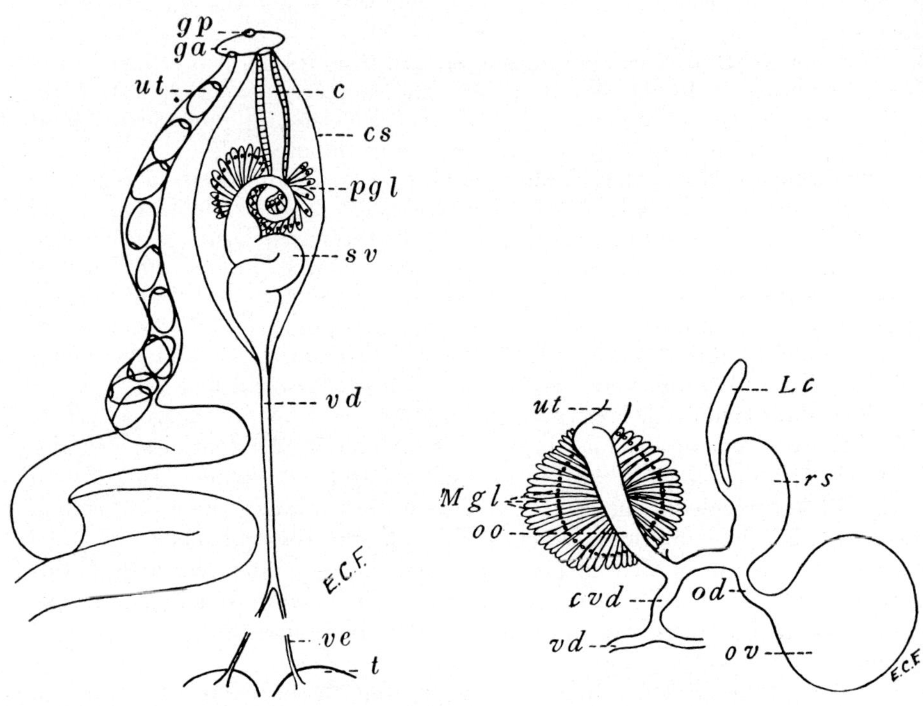

FIG. 135. Digenetic Trematodes FIG. 136.

FIG. 135.—Male and female reproductive organs leading to the genital pore. *c*, cirrus organ; *cs*, cirrus sac; *ga*, genital atrium; *gp*, genital pore; *pgl*, prostate gland; *sv*, seminal vesicle; *t*, testis; *u*, uterus; *vd*, vas deferens; *ve*, vas efferens. (Original, from Faust's *Human Helminthology*, Lea & Febiger, Philadelphia.)

FIG. 136.—Female reproductive organs in the vicinity of the oötype. *cvd*, common vitelline duct; *Lc*, Laurer's canal; *Mgl*, Mehlis' gland; *od*, oviduct; *oo*, oötype; *ov*, ovary; *rs*, seminal receptacle; *ut*, proximal end of uterus; *vd*, vitelline duct. (Original, from Faust's *Human Helminthology*, Lea & Febiger, Philadelphia.)

The Genital System.—All digenetic trematodes except the blood flukes are hermaphroditic. Each organism is typically self-fertilizing, so that an isolated worm is able to reproduce its kind.

The usual *male reproductive organs* (Fig. 135) are the *testes*, commonly two; for each testis a *vas efferens*, a common *vas deferens*, a swollen, *seminal vesicle*, *prostate glands*, and a muscular *cirrus* or penial *organ*. A sacculate *cirrus sac* surrounds these terminal male genitalia. The male system opens into the common *genital atrium* (*ga*), which is provided with a *genital pore*.

The *female genitalia* (Fig. 135, left; Fig. 136) consist of a single *ovary*, an *oviduct*, a *seminal receptacle*, *Laurer's canal*, the so-called "*vitellaria*" probably containing in part shell-gland material, paired and common collecting ducts, the *oötype*, surrounded by *Mehlis' gland*, and the coiled *uterus*, which originates on the anterior face of the oötype and proceeds in tortuous coils to the genital atrium.

Spermatozoa which reach the genital atrium from the male system proceed up the uterus and reach the seminal receptacle, where they are stored. The naked egg (the *ovum*), the spermatozoa and the vitelline-shell gland material pass into the oötype and then into the proximal segment of the uterus. Here the naked ovum is first surrounded by vitelline cells rich in glycogen, fertilization occurs and fused basophilic granules, containing orthodihydrophenol and protein, form the enveloping shell. As each egg is completed it is carried forward in the uterus to make way for other eggs about to be produced.

Eggs of *Fasciola*, *Fasciolopsis*, *Paragonimus*, echinostomes, amphistomes and monostomes are unembryonated when oviposition occurs, and require a period of development in the water before they hatch. Eggs of schistosomes are partially embryonated when oviposited but are usually mature when they are discharged in the excreta and soon hatch when they reach fresh water. Although eggs of *Clonorchis*, *Opisthorchis* and heterophyid species are mature when they are evacuated in the host's stool, they do not hatch in water but must be ingested by the appropriate snail before the miracidia are released.

The eggs of most digenetic trematodes are operculate; a few, particularly in the schistosomes, are non-operculate.

INTESTINAL FLUKES

FASCIOLOPSIS BUSKI (Lankester, 1857) Odhner, 1902

(The giant intestinal fluke, causing fasciolopsiasis)

Historical and Geographical Notes

Fasciolopsis buski was first observed by Busk in the duodenum of a Laskar sailor who was autopsied in London. Its natural geographical distribution is limited to Central and South China, Formosa, Indochina, Thailand, parts of Indonesia, Assam, Bengal and possibly other Oriental countries. The life cycle was elucidated by Nakagawa (1921) for the hog and by Barlow (1925) for man (auto-experiment).

Epidemiology

The natural definitive hosts of *Fasciolopsis buski* are man and the hog. Endemicity is associated with the cultivation of buffalo nuts (*Trapa natans* in China, *T. bicornis* in Thailand and Bengal), the "water chestnut"

(*Eliocharis tuberosa*), the lotus, water bamboo and other aquatic plants, portions of which are consumed raw by native populations. Use of human excreta containing the eggs of *F. buski* to fertilize fields of aquatic plants provides a major source of inoculum for the molluscan stages of the life cycle. Children are particularly apt to have heavy infections.

Morphology, Biology and Life Cycle

The Adult Worm.—The mature *F. buski* lives attached to the wall of the duodenum or jejunum. It is a large, fleshy worm, at times broadly ovate

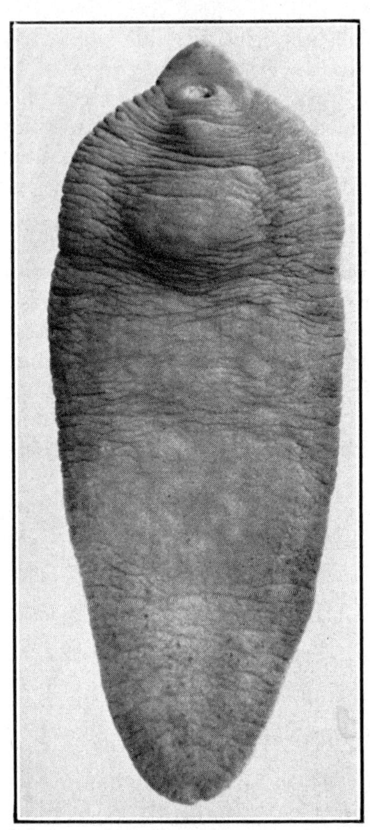

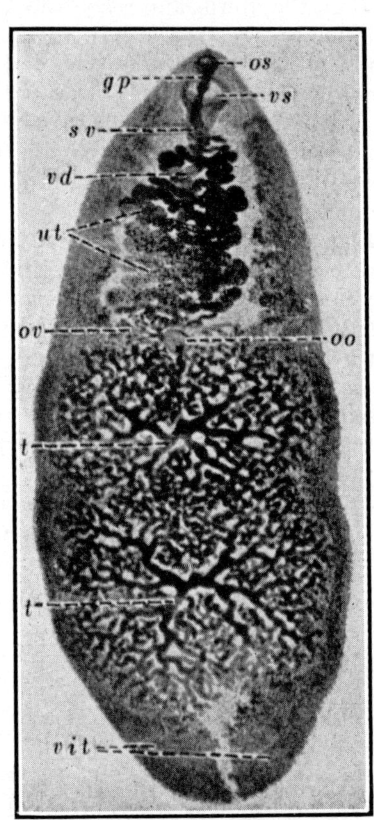

Fig. 137.—Adult *Fasciolopsis buski*. *Left*, photograph of living worm, ventral view. × 4. (Courtesy of Professor Doctor José G. Basnuevo, Habana); *right*, stained specimen, ventral view. × 4. *gp*, genital pore; *oo*, oötype; *os*, oral sucker; *ov*, ovary; *sv*, seminal vesicle; *t*, testis; *ut*, uterus; *vd*, vas deferens; *vit*, vitellaria; *vs*, ventral acetabulum. (Adapted by Faust from Roudabush, from Craig and Faust's *Clinical Parasitology*, Lea & Febiger, Philadelphia.)

but more often elongate ovoidal (Fig. 137), measuring 20 to 75 mm. in length, 8 to 20 mm. in breadth and 0.5 to 3.0 mm. in thickness. The integument is spinose. The oral sucker (*os*) is much smaller than the nearby ventral acetabulum (*vs*). Conspicuous features of the genitalia are the extensive, highly branched testes (*t*) which occupy much of the posterior three-fifths of the body, the small branched ovary (*ov*), and the relatively short, convoluted uterus (*ut*).

The eggs are large, hen's-egg-shaped, measure 130 to 140 microns by 80 to 85 microns, have a thin, transparent shell with a small, slightly convex operculum at one end, and are unembryonated when evacuated in the host's stool. They are very difficult to differentiate from eggs of *Fasciola hepatica*.

To proceed with their development the eggs of *F. buski* must reach quiet fresh water. Here they embryonate in 3 to 7 weeks at a temperature of 80° to 90° F. (26.7° to 32° C.), following which a miracidium with a pair of conspicuous eye spots breaks out of the shell through the opened operculum, then escapes from its embryonic membrane and swims about vigorously in the water. On contact with an appropriate small planorbid snail (species of *Segmentina, Hippeutis, Gyraulus,* etc.) the miracidium penetrates the soft tissues and transforms into a sporocyst. In this mother spore sac a generation of redias is produced, then within each redia a second brood of redias. Usually the second redial generation produces a number of vigorous cercarias, which erupt from the snail and, after swimming about, crawl onto aquatic vegetation and become encysted. Man commonly becomes infected while peeling off the hull of the seed pods of the water buffalo nut or the skin of the "water chestnut" between his teeth and lips, so that some of the encysted metacercarias are set free and are swallowed. After excystation in the duodenum, the larvas become attached to nearby mucosa and in about three months develop into mature worms (Barlow, 1925).

The life cycle of *Fasciolopsis buski* is illustrated diagrammatically in Figure 138.

Pathogenicity and Symptomatology

The damage produced by these large fleshy worms is traumatic, obstructive and toxic. At each site of attachment to the wall of the duodenum or jejunum, a mucosal ulcer is produced. A few worms cause no serious intestinal symptoms but frequently there are dozens to hundreds of worms in an infection. These embarrass digestion and at times cause acute obstruction. The toxic metabolites of the parasite are absorbed systemically and produce edema of the face, especially around the eyes, of the abdomen and lower extremities. There is characteristically a high-grade eosinophilia.

The early symptoms are diarrhea and hunger pains; those in heavy infections mimic peptic ulcer. Ascites and asthenia are notable characteristics, as well as generalized abdominal pain and the passage of unformed foul-smelling stools containing much undigested food. The appetite is at times capricious, but anorexia, nausea and vomiting typically occur. In heavy infections death results from anasarca.

Diagnosis

This is based on recovery of the characteristic eggs of *F. buski* in the stools. (Plate III, *P*, p. 57.)

Treatment

This consists in the oral administration of *hexylresorcinol crystoids* in a single dose, in the amount of 0.4 Gm. for children under 7 years of age and increasing to one Gm. for those 13 years or older. Treatment may be repeated at weekly intervals if required. This drug is both safe and relatively efficient (McCoy and Chu, 1937). Conservative measures are indicated in cases of profound toxemia or intestinal obstruction due to the worms.

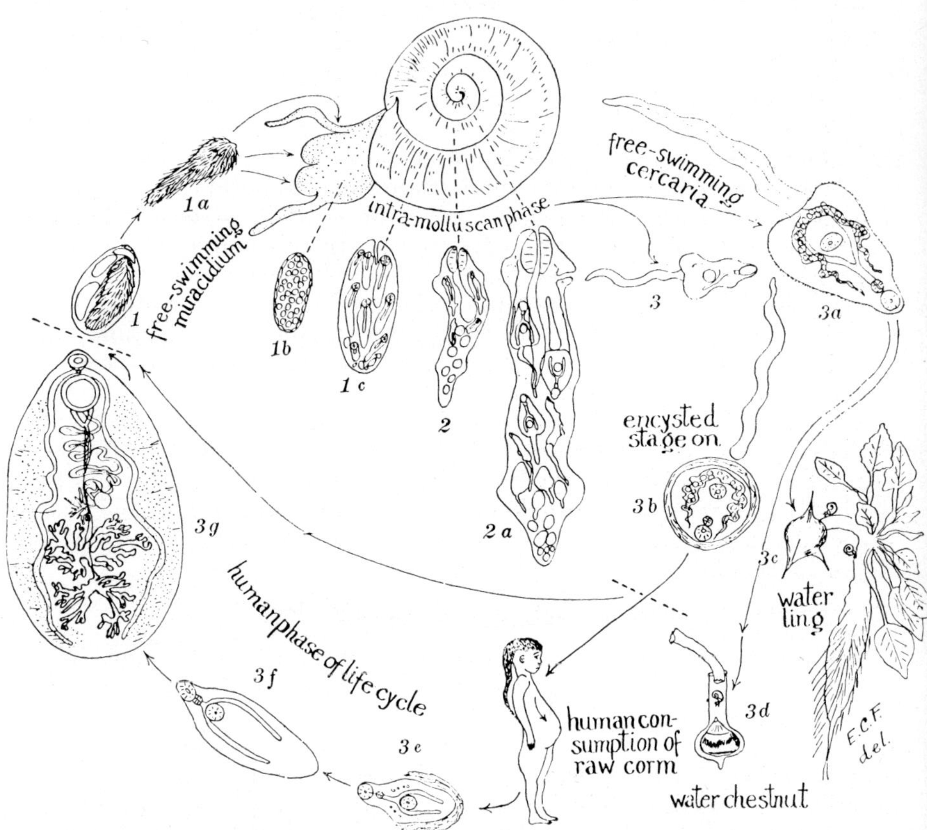

FIG. 138.—Diagram of the life cycle of *Fasciolopsis buski*. *1*, *1a-1c*, first generation (*e. g.*, egg → miracidium → sporocyst); *2*, *2a*, redia generations; *3*, *3a-3g*, definitive generation (*e. g.*, cercaria → encysted metacercaria → adult worm). (Original, from Faust's *Human Helminthology*, Lea & Febiger, Philadelphia.)

Prognosis

For the average patient the prognosis is good following hexylresorcinol treatment. In advanced cases with anasarca, death may result from cardiac failure unless extreme care is exercised.

Control

While individual patients may be freed of their infection by appropriate anthelmintic medication, persons in endemic areas, especially children, are periodically reëxposed by consuming raw plant products from the infested sites. To be effective, control requires that human excreta be sterilized before use as fertilizer and that hogs not be allowed to forage in the fields where these plants are grown so that these animals will not pollute the ground with their feces.

AMPHISTOMATE FLUKES

Two amphistomes have been reported as human parasites. These medium-sized fleshy worms have the following common characteristics: a large ventral sucker situated at the posterior end of the worm; large, operculate eggs which are unembryonated when evacuated in the stool, and metacercarias which encyst like those of *Fasciolopsis buski* on vegetation, so that exposure of the definitive host results from consumption of infested grass or other plant vectors. Herbivorous and omnivorous mammals are the usual definitive hosts.

Watsonius watsoni (Conyngham, 1904) Stiles and Goldberger, 1910 has been obtained only once from man, a West African Negro who died of a severe diarrhea. At necropsy many worms were found attached to the duodenal and jejunal mucosa and free in the large bowel. Monkeys are considered to be the natural reservoirs.

Gastrodiscoides hominis (Lewis and McConnell, 1876) Leiper, 1913 is a relatively common human parasite in Assam and has been reported as endemic in Cochin-China. Pigs in India and deer (*Tragulus napu*) in Malaya are known reservoirs. The parasite, which is attached to the human cecum and ascending colon, produces a mucous diarrhea. The eggs (Plate III, *W*, p. 57) are elongate spindle-shaped, with bluntly rounded ends, and measure 150 to 152 microns by 60 to 72 microns.

ECHINOSTOMATE FLUKES

Members of this group are characterized by a collarette of distinctive spinose processes mounted on a circumoral disc. The spines are interrupted on the ventral side and in the genus *Echinochasmus* also mid-dorsally. Frequently there is a distinct constriction at the posterior level of the collarette. A few echinostomes are natural human parasites in Oriental countries, while several others have been incidentally reported from man.

Echinostoma ilocanum (Garrison, 1908) Odhner, 1911.—This infection is relatively common among the Ilocano population of Luzon, occurs on Leyte and possibly on Mindanao and other Philippine islands. It has also been reported from man in Java. In the Philippines *Rattus norvegicus* is a reservoir host and in Canton, China the dog is commonly infected. Exposure results from eating raw snails containing the encysted metacercarial stage.

The mature worms (Fig. 139) are reddish-gray in color, measure 2.5 to 6.5 mm. in length by 1 to 1.35 mm. in breadth, are attenuate at both ends and are attached to the wall of the host's small intestine. The small circumoral disc is provided with 49 to 51 spines. The large, straw-colored, hen's-egg-shaped eggs measure 83 to 116 microns by 58 to 69 microns, have a small operculum at one end and are unembryonated when discharged in the feces. They mature in 6 to 15 days in fresh water, following which hatching occurs. The molluscan hosts are species of planorbid and lymneid snails, in which the miracidia transform into redias, which produce a second generation of redias, and these, in turn, cercarias which have the same number and characteristics of collarette spines as the adult worms. After the cercarias escape from the snail they enter the soft tissues of large edible snails such as *Pila conica* (Philippines)and *Viviparus javanicus* (Java) in which they encyst. Consumption of raw infected snails provides opportunity for infection of the definitive host.

The worms produce inflammatory reaction and ulceration at the sites of their attachment to the intestinal wall. In some patients there are likewise toxic manifestations. The usual symptoms are intestinal colic and diarrhea. Diagnosis is

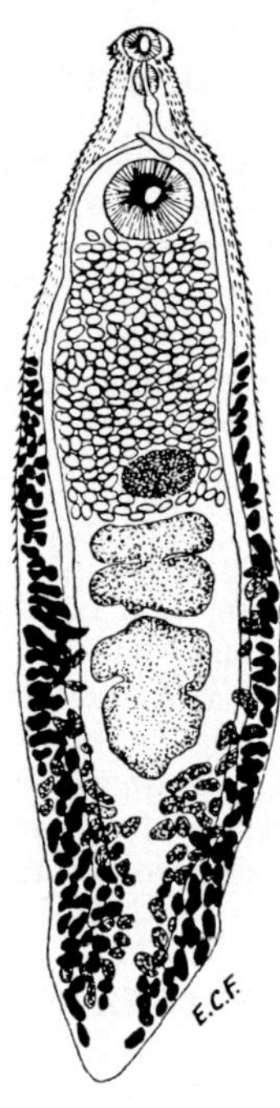

Fig. 139.—Adult *Echinostoma ilocanum*, ventral view. × 20. (After Odhner, from Faust's *Human Helminthology*, Lea & Febiger, Philadelphia.)

based on recovery of the eggs and their differentiation from those of other echinostomes, *Fasciolopsis buski* and *Fasciola hepatica*. Treatment consists in administration of tetrachlorethylene as in hookworm infection. (See page 246.) Control requires that all edible snails be thoroughly cooked before they are eaten.

Echinostoma lindoënsis Sandground and Bonne, 1940, described from the island of Celebes, is closely related to *E. ilocanum* but possesses only 37 collar spines. It utilizes a small planorbid snail as first intermediate host and large viviparous snail or bivalves (*Corbicula* spp.) as a second intermediate host.

Echinostoma malayanum Leiper, 1911, recovered from isolated human cases in Singapore, Kuala Lumpur (Malaya), Batang (on Sino-Tibetan border), and northern Sumatra, is provided with 43 circumoral spines. It utilizes *Lymnæa leuteola* as first intermediate host in India. The metacercarias may encyst in the same host, in *Indoplanorbis exustus* or in the fish, *Barbus stigma*.

Echinostoma melis (Schrank, 1788) Dietz, 1909 has been obtained from diarrheic stools of a Roumanian patient (León, 1816) and at necropsy of a Chinese patient (Hsü, 1940). The circumoral disc of this fluke is provided with 27 spines.

Echinostoma revolutum (Fröhlich, 1802) has been found in post-treatment stools of a native female Formosan (Anazawa, 1929) and is believed to be a relatively common human parasite on Formosa; it is likewise reported three times from man in Indonesia (Bonne, Bras and Lie Kian Joe, 1948). It has 37 circumoral spines. The first intermediate hosts are numerous species of non-operculate snails. Human exposure results from eating salted or essentially uncooked limpets (*Corbicula producta*) containing the encysted metacercarias.

Echinostoma cinetorchis Ando and Ozaki, 1923, the metacercarias of which encyst in the tissues of tadpoles and frogs, has been found occasionally as an incidental human infection in Japan, Formosa and Java.

Paryphostomum sufrartyfex (Lane, 1915) Bhalerao, 1931 is an echinostome diagnosed once from an 8-year-old girl on an Assam tea plantation and has also been reported from Indian pigs. The worm has a conspicuous reniform oral disc with a collarette of 39 to 42 spines. The infection in the patient produced edema and other toxic manifestations similar to those in *Fasciolopsis buski* infection.

Himasthla muehlensi Vogel, 1933 was recovered once from a German patient who believed he contracted the parasite from eating several raw clams (*Venus mercenaria*) in New York City. This worm is long and narrow and has a small oral disc surmounted with a collarette of 32 spines. For the related species, *Himasthla quissetensis* Stunkard (1937) found that the herring gull (*Larus argentatus*) probably constitutes the usual definitive host.

Echinoparyphium paraulum (Dietz, 1909), a natural parasite of a variety of avian hosts, has been reported once as a human infection in the U. S. S. R. (Skrjabin, 1938).

Echinochasmus perfoliatus (von Rátz, 1908) Dietz, 1910, a common intestinal parasite of dogs and cats in Eastern and Southern Europe, the U. S. S. R. and the Orient, has been diagnosed once in a Japanese patient who had eaten uncooked fresh-water fish (Tanabe, 1922). This small fluke has an oral disc surmounted with 24 spines which have a dorsal as well as a ventral interruption. Species of the snail *Parafossarulus* serve as the first intermediate host, and many fresh-water fishes as the second intermediate host in which the metacercarias become encysted.

PLAGIORCHID FLUKES

Species of this family group utilize grubs of certain insects as second intermediate hosts. The cercaria, after emerging from its molluscan host, invades these larval insects and encysts within them. Birds and mammals which eat the infected grubs acquire the definitive stage of the worm, which matures in the small intestine. Rodents, cats, dogs and on rare occasions man have been found to harbor species of *Plagiorchis*. *P. philippinensis* has been obtained once at necropsy of an Ilocano in Manila (Africa and Garcia, 1937); *P. javanensis* (Fig. 140) has been recovered from a native Javanese at post-mortem examination (Sandground, 1940), and *P. muris* has been developed as an experimental human infection from the Douglas Lake, Michigan area (McMullen, 1937).

TROGLOTREMA SALMINCOLA (Chapin, 1926) Witenberg, 1932

This minute fluke a distant relative of the lung flukes (*Paragonimus*), is a common parasite of the small intestine of the dog, coyote, fox, raccoon, mink and lynx on the Pacific Coast of North America and has been reported from the aborigines of Eastern Siberia. Infection is acquired in North America from eating raw salmon and trout caught in coastal streams. The flukes are small (0.8 to 1.1 mm. by 0.15 to 0.18 mm.), pyriform, are dorso-ventrally flattened and produce at one time only a few broadly ovoidal, yellowish, thick-shelled, operculate, unembryonated eggs, measuring 60 to 80 microns by 34 to 50 microns. After maturing in cool fresh water the eggs hatch and the miracidia penetrate snails belonging to the genus *Galba*. The cercarial progeny which emerge from the molluscan host have an oral stylet and a knob-like tail. They enter the fish and become encysted in the kidneys. Fish constitute the source of infection for the mammalian hosts.

The flukes themselves produce no appreciable damage in the intestine of the definitive host. However, an associated rickettsia (Corby and Gorham, 1950) is responsible for a severe, frequently fatal disease in dogs, coyotes and foxes, referred to as "salmon poisoning." This infection has not been reported for man.

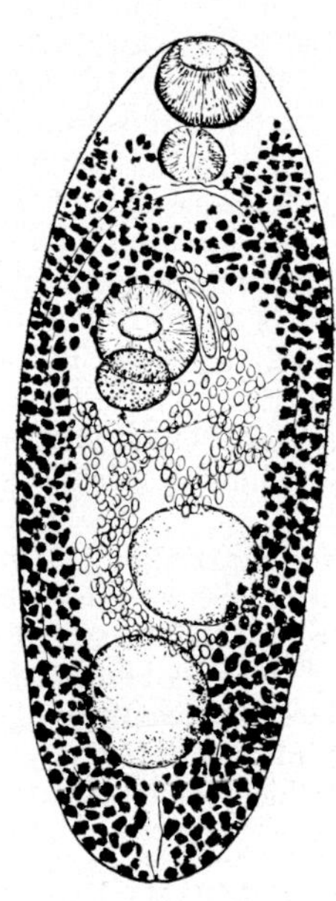

Fig. 140.—Adult *Plagiorchis javanensis* from human host. × 40. (After Sandground, from Faust's *Human Helminthology*, Lea & Febiger, Philadelphia.)

HETEROPHYID FLUKES

Members of this family group are very small, compact, ovoidal, pyriform or occasionally tongue-shaped organisms which live attached to the mucosa at the upper levels of the small intestine of birds and mammals. They are found at the base of the mucosal crypts and may be partially buried in the glands. In routine autopsies they are frequently overlooked, but if present are readily obtained by examining superficial scrapings of the mucosa after these have been shaken for 10 to 15 minutes in a 0.5% solution of sodium sulfate.

The small, ovoidal, operculate eggs each contain a fully mature miracidium at the time they are evacuated in the feces of the definitive host, but hatching occurs only after ingestion by an appropriate snail. Within the soft extra-intestinal tissues of the mollusc the miracidium transforms into a sporocyst. There are two generations of redias, which produce cercarias with a pair of pigmented "eye-spots" and a long tail which has a dorsal and a ventral fluted fin (*e. g.*, is lophocercous). The cercaria, after escape from the snail, becomes attached to the underside of the scales of fishes or penetrates into superficial tissues, where it discards its tail, rounds up and becomes encysted. Fish-eating birds and mammals which consume the infected fish in an uncooked condition become the hosts for the definitive stage.

Several species of heterophyid trematodes are common intestinal parasites of man.

HETEROPHYES HETEROPHYES (von Siebold, 1852) Stiles and Hassall, 1900

Historical and Geographical Notes.—This minute fluke was first found by Bilharz, in 1851, at the autopsy of a native of Cairo, Egypt (Bilharz, 1852). It is a common parasite in the lower Nile valley and occurs in Japan, Korea, Central and South China, Formosa and the Philippines.

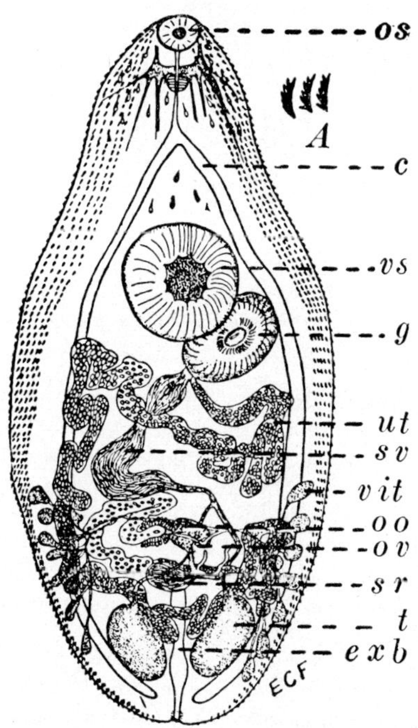

Fig. 141.—Adult *Heterophyes heterophyes*, ventral view. × 50. *c*, cecum; *exb*, excretory bladder; *g*, genital sucker (gonotyl); *oo*, oötype; *os*, oral sucker; *ov*, ovary; *sr*, seminal receptacle; *sv*, seminal vesicle; *t*, testis; *ut*, uterus; *vit*, vitellaria; *vs*, ventral acetabulum. (Adapted from Looss, in Faust's *Human Helminthology*, Lea & Febiger, Philadelphia.)

Epidemiology.—Infection is acquired from eating fresh- or brackish-water fish (frequently the mullet) in a raw, salted or dried condition. Fresh-water snails become infected when they ingest the eggs of the fluke discharged in the definitive host's excreta which reach the water.

Morphology, Biology and Life Cycle.—The mature *Heterophyes heterophyes* (Fig. 141) is a minute pyriform worm, broadly rounded posteriorly and somewhat narrower anteriorly. It measures 1 to 1.7 mm. in length by 0.3 to 0.4 mm. in breadth. It is covered with minute spines set close together. The oral sucker is very small (90 microns in diameter) and the ventral acetabulum considerably larger (230 microns in diameter). A conspicuous feature of this species is the genital sucker which lies on the lateral posterior border of the ventral acetabulum. The seminal vesicle lacks an enveloping cirrus sac and there is no cirrus organ.

The eggs (Fig. 142) are small (28 to 30 microns by 15 to 17 microns), have a conspicuous conical operculum, and contain a mature miracidium. When these eggs are ingested by *Pironella conica* (Egypt) or *Cerithidia cingula alata* (Japan), they hatch and proceed with their intra-molluscan stages of development. The cercarias which escape from the mollusc encyst superficially in fresh- or brackish-water fishes, which constitute the source of infection for man and other mammals.

H. katsuradai Ozaki and Asada, 1925 in Japan and *H. brevicæca* Africa and Garcia, 1935 in the Philippines are closely related species which have occasionally been recovered from the human host.

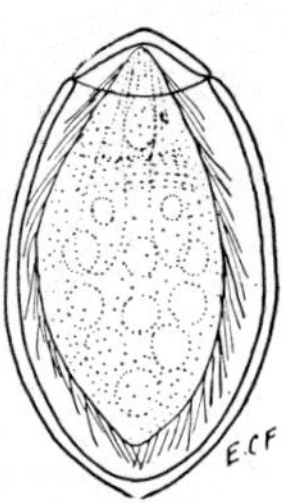

Fig. 142.—Egg of *Heterophyes heterophyes*. × 1120. (Original, from Faust's *Human Helminthology*, Lea & Febiger, Philadelphia.)

Pathogenicity and Symptomatology.—The presence of *Heterophyes* and related species in the mucosal crypts of the duodenum and jejunum produces superficial irritation of the glands, with excess secretion of mucus and superficial necrosis of the mucosa. In heavy infections this may be accompanied by colicky pains and a mucous diarrhea. More serious is the occasional deep penetration of the worms into the mucous coat of the intestine, so that their minute eggs get into mesenteric venules or lymphatics and are carried to distant sites, such as the heart, brain or spinal cord, where they may stimulate granulomatous reaction (Africa *et al.*, 1935, 1936) with symptoms related to these lesions.

Diagnosis.—Eggs of *H. heterophyes* (Fig. 142) and other heterophyid flukes can be diagnosed following their recovery in the stool. They must be differentiated from eggs of *Clonorchis sinensis* and species of *Opisthorchis* which are about the same size and general shape.

Treatment.—This consists in the administration of hexylresorcinol crystoids by mouth as recommended in ascariasis (page 229), or tetrachlorethylene by mouth as recommended in hookworm infection (page 246).

Prognosis.—This is usually good to excellent following appropriate chemotherapy.

Control.—Control can be effected by the thorough cooking of all fish intended for human consumption.

METAGONIMUS YOKOGAWAI Katsurada, 1912

Historical and Geographical Notes.—*Metagonimus yokogawai* was first described by Katsurada, in 1912, from material obtained by Yokogawa from man and dogs in Formosa. This is probably the most common heterophyid fluke in Japan, Korea, Formosa, the Philippines, Central and South China, the Maritime Provinces of the U. S. S. R., northern Siberia and the Balkans. It has also been reported from human cases in Spain (Lopez-Neyra and Pozo, 1932). In highly endemic areas in Japan a considerable percentage of the population is infected.

Epidemiology.—Man, other fish-eating mammals and the pelican are the natural hosts, which become infected from consuming the fresh-water trout (*Plectoglossus altivelis*), *Odontobutis obscurus* and *Salmo perryi*. Pollution of water with the egg-laden excreta of the definitive hosts provides the source of infection for the molluscan and fish hosts.

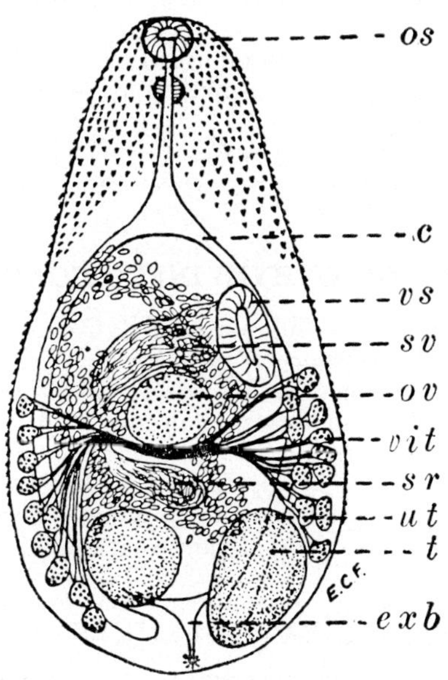

Fig. 143.—Adult *Metagonimus yokogawai*, ventral view. × 36. *c*, cecum; *exb*, excretory bladder; *os*, oral sucker; *ov*, ovary; *sr*, seminal receptacle; *sv*, seminal vesicle; *t*, testis; *ut*, uterus; *vit*, vitellaria; *vs*, ventral acetabulum. (Original, from Faust's *Human Helminthology*, Lea & Febiger, Philadelphia.)

Morphology, Biology and Life Cycle.—*Metagonimus yokogawai* (Fig. 143) resembles *H. heterophyes* in its habitat in the definitive host, its shape, size (1 to 2.5 mm. by 0.4 to 0.75 mm.) and its life cycle. The distinctive features concern the ventral acetabulum, which is deflected to one side of the midline, and the genital opening, which lacks an independent sucker but has its muscular rim fused with that of the ventral acetabulum.

The eggs of *M. yokogawai*, measuring 26.5 to 28 microns by 15.5 to 17 microns, closely resemble those of *H. heterophyes* (Fig. 142) and are also readily mistaken for those of *Clonorchis sinensis*. The snail hosts are species of *Melania*, *Semisulcospira*, etc., which ingest the eggs and in which the miracidia transform into sporocysts, with two successive generations of redias and finally the development of cercarias having a pair of pigmented "eye-spots," and a dorsal and a ventral fluted tail fin. The cercarias which escape from the snails become attached to fresh-water fishes and encyst under the skin. Consumption of the uncooked infected fish provides the opportunity for infection of the definitive hosts.

Pathogenicity and Symptomatology.—These minute worms are attached to the cells in the mucosal crypts, usually at the duodenal and jejunal levels of the small intestine, causing excess secretion of mucus, superficial erosion of the mucosa and granulomatous infiltration around eggs deposited in the stromal tissues. The worms have also been demonstrated deep in the mucosal layer, where they remain until they die (Africa, 1937) but without host-tissue encapsulation. The symptoms evoked depend on the number of worms in an infection, their depth of penetration and the patient's reaction to the infection. Characteristically, there is a mild to moderate mucous diarrhea of a persistent type.

Diagnosis.—This is based on recovery of the eggs in the stool and their differentiation from those of other heterophyid flukes, *Clonorchis sinensis* and species of *Opisthorchis*.

Treatment.—This consists in the administration of hexylresorcinol crystoids by mouth as recommended in ascariasis (page 229), or tetrachlorethylene by mouth as in hookworm infection (page 246).

Prognosis.—This is usually good to excellent following appropriate chemotherapy.

Control.—Thorough cooking of fresh-water fish will safeguard the human population.

OTHER HETEROPHYID INFECTIONS OF MAN

Other species of heterophyid flukes reported from the human host, include *Centrocestus armatus*, *C. formosanus*, *Haplorchis pumilio*, *H. microrchia*, *H. yokogawai*, *H. taichui*, *Diorchitrema formosanum*, *D. amplicæcale*, *D. pseudocirratum*, *Metagonimus minutus* and *Stellantchasmus falcatus*. Most of these species occur in the China Sea area but *S. falcatus* and *D. pseudocirratum* have also been diagnosed in Hawaiians, who have eaten locally caught mullet (Alicata, 1947, 1949). All of these species have the potential capacity to produce ectopic lesions in case their eggs get into the lymphatics or blood stream from the intestinal wall.

HEPATIC FLUKES

FASCIOLA HEPATICA Linnaeus, 1758

(The sheep liver fluke, causing fascioliasis hepatica)

Historical and Geographical Notes

Fasciola hepatica was the first trematode to be described (de Brie, 1379) and was likewise the one on which the first complete life cycle was elucidated, in Germany (Leuckart, 1882) and in Australia (Thomas, 1883). It has an extensive geographical distribution and is particularly prevalent in sheep-raising areas, in many of which the fluke was introduced with the importation of sheep from Europe. In many regions fascioliasis is economically an important disease. In several countries human infection is an increasing clinical and public health problem.

Epidemiology

Sheep liver fluke infection is contracted by ingesting vegetation on which the metacercarias of *F. hepatica* have encysted. In the case of sheep and many other herbivorous and omnivorous mammals exposure results from eating grass which has grown in marshy meadows or around ponds or streams where the infected snail hosts abound. Human infection is usually due to eating fresh water-cress (*Nasturtium officinale*) to which the metacercarial cysts are attached. Autochthonous human infections have been diagnosed in Mexico, Costa Rica, Cuba, Republica Dominicana, Puerto Rico, Chile, Argentina, Uruguay, Madeira, Spain, southern France, Italy, Corsica, the north coast of Africa, Greece, Hungary, Roumania, Lebanon, Syria, many areas in the U. S. S. R., China, Hawaii, French Somaliland and South Africa. In Cuba and other Latin-American countries, southern France and Algeria human infection is relatively frequent and clinically important. Epidemics have been reported from Cuba (Arenas *et al.*, 1948) and France. No native cases of human fascioliasis have been demonstrated for continental United States, although the disease is prevalent in sheep and cattle in the South and West, and has become established in the Middle West.

Morphology, Biology and Life Cycle

The Adult Fluke.—The mature *Fasciola hepatica* (Fig. 144) is a relatively large worm, measuring up to 30 mm. in length by 13 mm. in breadth. It is more or less flattened and leaf-like along the margins, fleshy throughout the middle. At the anterior end there is a distinct, conical projection, while the posterior end is broadly rounded. The most conspicuous morphologic features of *F. hepatica* and other species of this genus are the extensive branching of the intestinal ceca, as well as of the two testes and the vitelline follicles, and, in contrast, the small amount of space in which the relatively short, convoluted uterus is confined.

F. hepatica adults reside typically in the proximal bile passages and the gall bladder. Occasionally they fail to reach this location and are found ectopically in the peritoneal cavity or other anatomical sites.

The Life Cycle.—The eggs are produced in the proximal end of the uterus (Stephenson, 1947) and are unembryonated when expelled from the genital pore. They pass from the common bile duct into the duodenum and are carried through the intestinal tract, to be evacuated in the stools. These eggs are large (130 to 150 microns by 63 to 90 microns), regularly hen's-egg-shaped, grayish hyaline, relatively thin-shelled, and have a small flat operculum at one end. They require 9 to 15 days to mature in fresh water at an optimum temperature of 22° to 25° C. (72° to 77° F.). Upon hatching the miracidium, which is provided with a pair of pigmented "eye-spots," invades a lymneid snail and transforms into a sporocyst. Within 30 days, second and third generation redias and cercarias have been produced. Then the cercarias swarm out of the snail, and after crawling upon moist vegetation shed their tail, round up and encyst as minute white spherules. These cysts survive for a considerable time in a moist atmosphere but soon succumb to drying.

When the viable cysts ingested by mammals reach the duodenal level, they excyst and the metacercarias actively burrow through the intestinal wall, migrate across the peritoneal cavity to the liver, then burrow through Glisson's capsule and the hepatic parenchyma to the bile ducts, where they develop into adults in 3 to 4 months after exposure. Because of the circuitous route employed in reaching the bile passages, at times the young worms go astray and are recovered as immature forms or adults in ectopic locations.

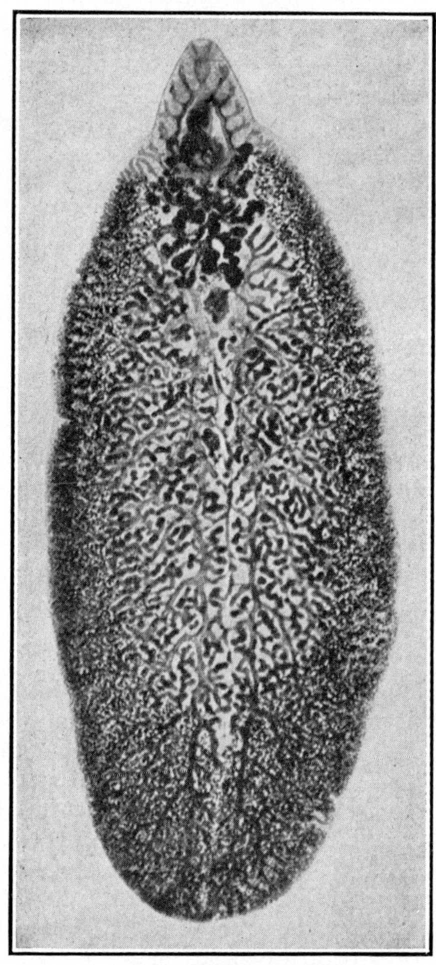

FIG. 144.—Adult *Fasciola hepatica*, ventral view. × 4 (Photograph by Professor H. J. Van Cleave, adapted from Faust in Brennemann's *Practice of Pediatrics*, W. F. Prior Co.)

Pathogenicity and Symptomatology

In the average human infection the first significant lesions produced by the migrating young *Fasciola hepatica* are after their penetration of Glisson's capsule *en route* through the hepatic parenchyma to the bile ducts, where they cause both traumatic damage and toxic irritation, with necrosis of tissues along the pathway, so that in multiple migrations they are responsible for extensive necrosis ("liver rot"). Once they reach the larger bile passages they cause hyperplasia of the biliary epithelium, with neutrophilic and eosinophilic infiltration and development of a fibrous capsule around the ducts. In heavy infections, early erosion of the epithelium allows the worms to wander back into the hepatic parenchyma, where they mature and lay their eggs in abscess pockets.

Symptoms in human infections are due mostly to the lesions produced in the bile passages and include biliary colic with coughing and vomiting; marked jaundice; generalized abdominal rigidity, with tenderness in the right hypochrondrium; diarrhea; irregular fever; profuse sweating; urticaria; significant eosinophilia (occasionally up to 60% of the total white blood cells); at times cholelithiasis; profound systemic intoxication; and occasionally macrocytic anemia comparable to that produced by *Diphyllobothrium latum* (page 345). In chronic infections there may be evidences of extensive hepatic cirrhosis with ascites. Chronic urticaria has been demonstrated in some patients (Prats *et al.*, 1953).

F. hepatica has been recovered from various abnormal locations, in which the mature or adolescent worms are characteristically found in abscess pockets. These sites include bloodvessels, the lungs, subcutaneous tissues, the ventricles of the brain and the orbit, at times in conjunction with mature worms in the bile passages (Diss, 1937; Neghme and Ossandon, 1943).

If livers of sheep or goats, parasitized with living *E. hepatica*, are consumed raw, the worms may become active and attach themselves to the soft palate, posterior pharynx or larynx; or they may crawl into the nasopharynx and even into the Eustachian tubes, producing endematous congestion.

False fascioliasis refers to the recovery of eggs of *Fasciola* in the stool following the ingestion of infected livers of sheep, goats or cattle, raw or cooked.

Diagnosis

Most cases of true fascioliasis hepatica are first apprehended by recovery of the eggs in the stool. These require differentiation from eggs of *Fasciolopsis buski*, which are almost identical in size. For safe diagnosis it is desirable to obtain samples of uncontaminated bile B. In case of false fascioliasis, eggs of *Fasciola* will no longer appear in the patient's stool after he has been placed on a liver-free diet.

Treatment

The usual treatment for fascioliasis consists in the administration of *emetine hydrochloride*. Arenas *et al.* (1948) state that 40 mgm. of this drug given subcutaneously once each day for 8 days is curative, producing symptomatic relief and permanent disappearance of the eggs in both the feces and the bile. *Carbon tetrachloride* is also effective against adult worms in the bile passages but is highly toxic, particularly when there is considerable liver damage. Fries (1946) combined these two drugs successfully in treating an infected French family.

Control

Fundamental control requires the institution of measures to eradicate the natural infection in sheep and other herbivorous animals. Since most human infections result from use of water-cress as salad greens, control of human fascioliasis hepatica will be obtained if this delicacy is omitted from the diet in enzoötic areas.

FASCIOLA GIGANTICA Cobbold, 1856

(The giant liver fluke, causing fascioliasis gigantica)

This fluke differs from *Fasciola hepatica* in its greater length, more attenuate shape, shorter anterior cone, slightly larger ventral acetabulum, the more anterior position of the testes and the larger size of the eggs (160 to 190 microns by 70 to 90 microns). The natural hosts are the camel, cattle, water buffalo and other herbivorous mammals. The life cycle parallels that of *F. hepatica*, including lymneid snails as first intermediate hosts. Human infections have been reported from Senegambia (De Govea, 1895), Indochina (Codville *et al.*, 1928), Tashkend (Pigoulewsky, 1927) and Hawaii (Alicata, 1953; Stemmermann, 1953). The clinical aspects of this infection are essentially the same as in fascioliasis hepatica. Control has not been studied.

DICROCŒLIUM DENDRITICUM (Rudolphi, 1818) Looss, 1899

(The lancet fluke, causing dicrocœliasis)

This delicate fluke is a common parasite of the bile passages of sheep and other herbivorous mammals in Europe, North Africa, northern Asia, parts of the Orient and to a lesser extent in North and South America. Numerous diagnoses of human infection have been reported from the U. S. S. R. and elsewhere: most of these are cases of false parasitosis resulting from consumption of infected livers, with the evacuation of eggs of *D. dentriticum* in the consumer's feces, but there are a number of genuine human cases which have originated from Germany, Switzerland, Czechoslovakia, France, Italy, Egypt, Lebanon, North Africa, Belgian Congo, Nigeria, Asiatic U. S. S. R., China and Java.

Morphologic and Biologic Aspects.—The adult worm (Fig. 145) resides in the smaller bile ducts. It is lancet-shaped, flat, thin and transparent. It is relatively small, measuring 5 to 15 mm. in length by 1.5 to 2.5 mm. in breadth, and has a smooth cuticle. The most conspicuous features of its internal anatomy are the position of the two testes anterior to the ovary in the anterior half of the body and the distribution of the major portion of the long uterine coils in the median field of the posterior half of the body. The eggs are asymmetrically ovoidal, thick-shelled, dark brown in color, have a broad convex operculum, measure 38 to 45 microns by 22 to 30 microns and typically contain a mature miracidium when evacuated in the feces of the definitive host.

In order to proceed with their development the eggs must be ingested by a land snail, in which the hatched miracidium transforms into a first generation sporocyst which produces a brood of second-generation sporocysts. Each of these, in turn, produces cercarias which are elongated-oval organisms having a delicate oral stylet and a long attenuated tail. The cercarias emerge from their molluscan host only when rains succeed a long dry period, and become massed in slime balls. Krull and Mapes (1952), working in an enzoötic region in central New York State, have demonstrated the need for a second intermediate host, which in their investigations is a foraging ant (*Formica fusca*), which eats the slime balls and in which the metacercarias become encysted. Infection is acquired accidentally by ingesting the infected ants.

Clinical Data.—The presence of *D. dendriticum* in the bile passages provokes hyperplasia of the biliary epithelium, fibrosis around the ducts and in heavy infections, pressure portal cirrhosis. In human cases the common symptoms consist of biliary colic, hepatitis, abdominal distress, flatulent dyspepsia, diarrhea, vomiting, chronic constipation and systemic intoxication. Diagnosis is based on the continued recovery of the characteristic eggs in the stool or from biliary drainage. (See Plate III *Q*, p. 57.) No dependable chemotherapy has been developed. Control measures have not been developed.

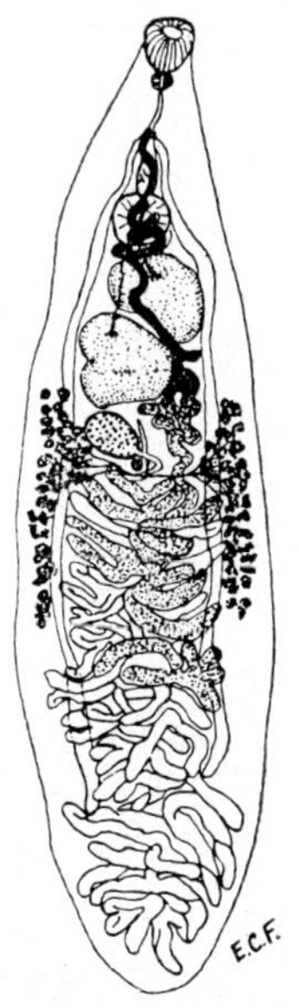

Fig. 145.—Adult *Dicrocœlium dendriticum*, ventral view. × 10. (Adapted from M. Braun, in Faust's *Human Helminthology*, Lea & Febiger, Philadelphia.)

CLONORCHIS SINENSIS (Cobbold, 1875) Looss, 1907

(The Chinese liver fluke, causing clonorchiasis)

Historical and Geographical Notes

This fluke was first reported by McConnell (1875) from the bile passages of a Chinese carpenter who came to autopsy in Calcutta. Although the infection had been found in Japan as early as 1875, it was first reported from that country by Baelz in 1883. The first local record for endemic South China was published by Heanley in 1908.

The endemic-enzoötic area of *C. sinensis* includes all of Japan, the southern half of Korea, Formosa, practically all of China except the western and northwestern provinces, and Indochina. Heavy centers of human infection are confined to the main island of Japan, Kwangtung Province in South China and the Red River Valley in northern Indochina. There is no evidence that the infection has become established outside the countries bordering on the China Sea.

Epidemiology

Infection is contracted by eating fresh-water fish containing the encysted metacercarial stage of *C. sinensis*, in a raw condition, pickled in brine or rice wine, smoked or dried (Faust and Khaw, 1927). In heavily endemic areas the use of human night soil as food for fishes greatly increases the opportunity for maintaining heavy infection in the mollusc and later the fish hosts.

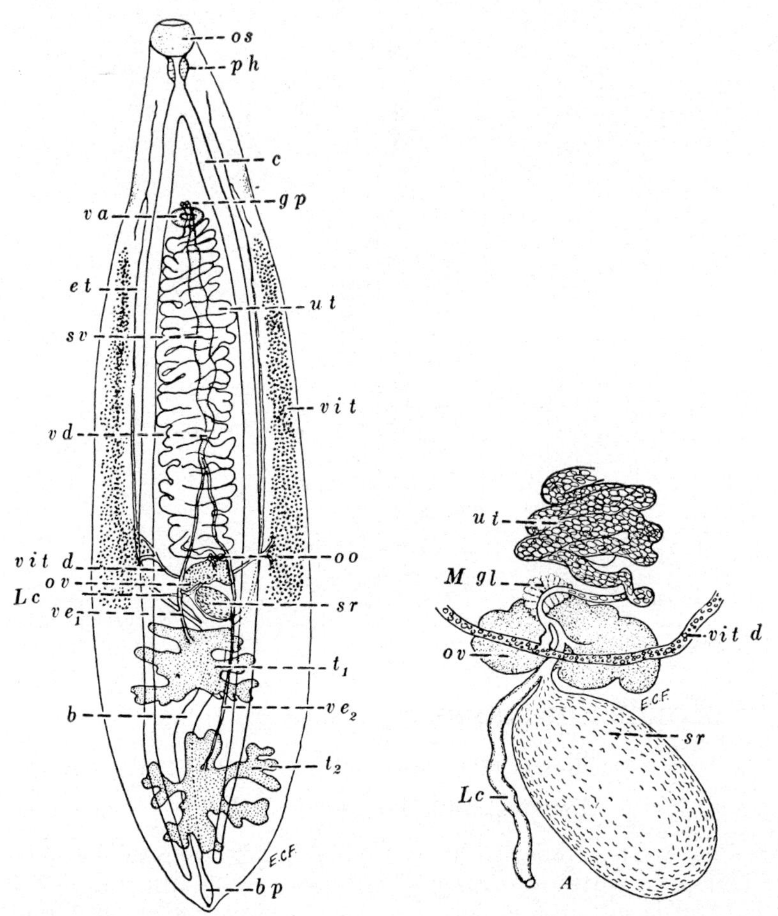

Fig. 146.—Adult *Clonorchis sinensis*, ventral view. × 8. *A*, detail of the region of the oötype, dorsal view, greatly enlarged. *b*, excretory bladder; *bp*, excretory pore; *c*, cecum; *et*, excretory tubule; *gp*, genital pore; *Lc*, Laurer's canal; *Mgl*, Mehlis' gland; *oo*, oötype; *ov*, ovary; *ph*, pharynx; *sr*, seminal receptacle; *sv*, seminal vesicle; t_1, t_2, testes. *ut*, uterus; *vd*, vas deferens; ve_1, ve_2, vasa efferentia; *vit*, vitellaria; *vit d*, vitelline duct. (Original, from Faust's *Human Helminthology*, Lea & Febiger, Philadelphia.)

Morphology, Biology and Life Cycle

The Adult Worm.—The mature *C. sinensis* lives typically in the bile passages, most frequently in the more distal tributaries under the surface of the liver; but in heavy infections after the smaller bile ducts have been occupied the worms collect in the larger passages, the gall bladder and occasionally even in the pancreatic duct. The worms (Fig. 146) are elongated, lanceolate, flat and flabby, transparent, golden brown to pinkish in the living condition and measure 10 to 25 mm. in length by 3 to 5 mm. in breadth. The cuticle is smooth and shiny. All of the important internal structures are visible in the unstained living worm. At the anterior tip there are a globose oral sucker and at about one-fifth the body length posteriorly, a smaller ventral acetabulum.

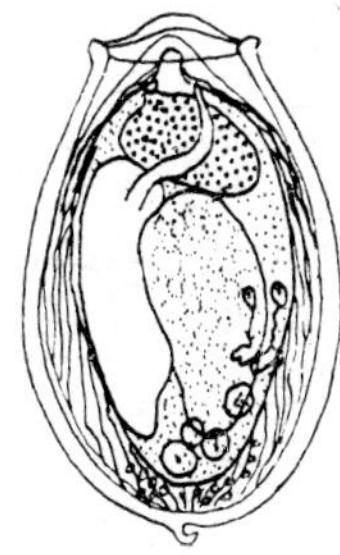

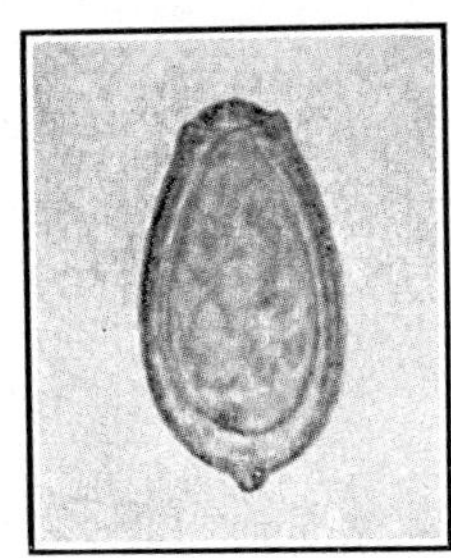

Fig. 147.—Eggs of *Clonorchis sinensis*. *Left*, showing asymmetrical internal structure of miracidium. × 1200 (after Faust and Khaw); *right*, × 830 (after Faust in Brennemann's *Practice of Pediatrics*).

The eggs (Fig. 147) are broadly ovoidal, have a moderately thick, light yellowish-brown shell with a distinct convex operculum which fits into a circular rim of the shell, and usually a small knob at the opposite end. They measure 27.3 to 35.1 microns in length by 11.7 to 19.5 microns in greatest diameter and are fully embryonated when discharged into the bile ducts and later evacuated in the host's feces. These eggs do not hatch when set free in fresh water, but if they are ingested by appropriate species of operculate snails (*Parafossarulus*, *Bulimus*, *Semisulcospira*, *Alocinma*, *Melanoides tuberculatus*, etc.) they hatch in the snail's mid-gut and the miracidia penetrate into the soft tissues surrounding the intestine, where they transform into first-generation sporocysts, in which second-generation redias are produced. The third-generation larvas, the cercarias (Fig. 148), escape from the snail and swim about for a short time in the water. In contact with fresh-water fishes the cercarias penetrate under the skin, discard their tails and after they have penetrated into the flesh round up and become encysted. Consumption of the infected fish flesh in an essentially raw condition provides the opportunity for infection of man and other definitive hosts. The metacercarias are digested out of the flesh and excyst in the duodenum, whereupon the larvas migrate through the ampulla of Vater to the smaller bile radicles, become attached and develop into adult worms.

Clonorchis infection in man is long-lived, surviving for at least 20 to 25 years. In endemic areas it develops in childhood and increases quantitatively at least past middle life as a result of repeated consumption of the raw infected fish (Faust and Khaw, 1927).

The life cycle is diagrammatically illustrated in Figure 149.

Pathogenicity and Symptomatology

Wherever the mature *Clonorchis sinensis* become located in the bile passages they provoke a marked hyperplasia of the biliary epithelium with subsequent dense fibrous encapsulation of the duct. As the number of

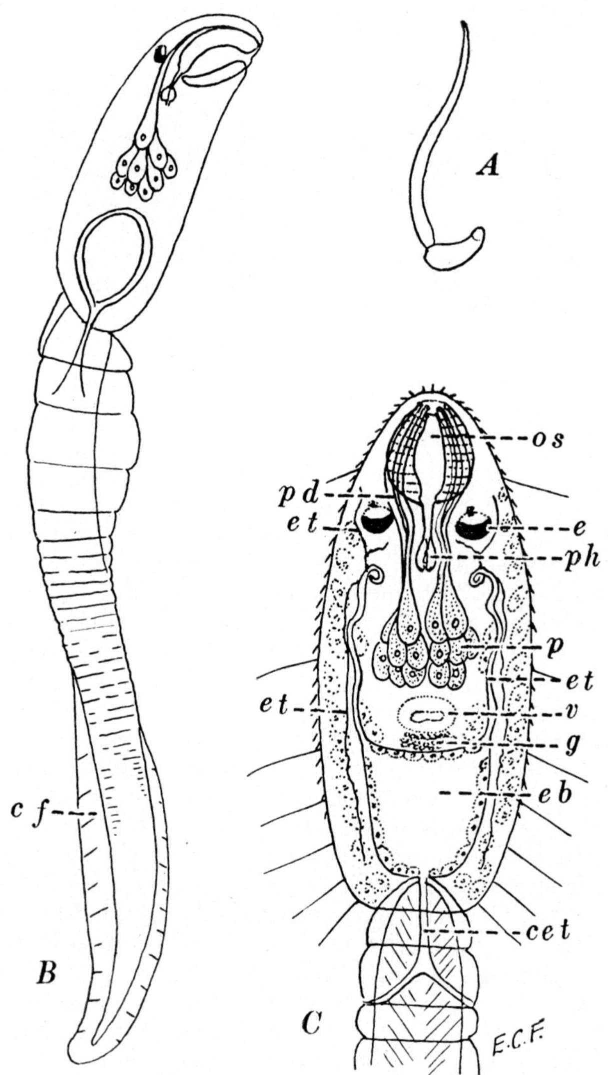

Fig. 148.—Cercaria of *Clonorchis sinensis*. *A*, × 75; *B*, × 300; *C*, body and adjacent portion of tail, × 616. *cet*, caudal excretory tubule; *cf*, tail fin; *e*, "eye-spot"; *eb*, excretory bladder; *et*, excretory tubule; *g*, genital primordium; *os*, oral sucker; *p*, penetration gland; *pd*, penetration gland duct; *ph*, pharynx; *v*, ventral acetabulum. (Adapted from Yamaguti, in Faust's *Human Helminthology*, Lea & Febiger, Philadelphia.)

worms gradually increases over a period of years, practically all of the terminal bile ducts become modified by reduction of their lumens, as well as by fibrous thickening of the walls and pressure necrosis of adjacent hepatic parenchyma. Occasionally, pressure cirrhosis with ascites results from involvement of practically all of the functional liver tissue.

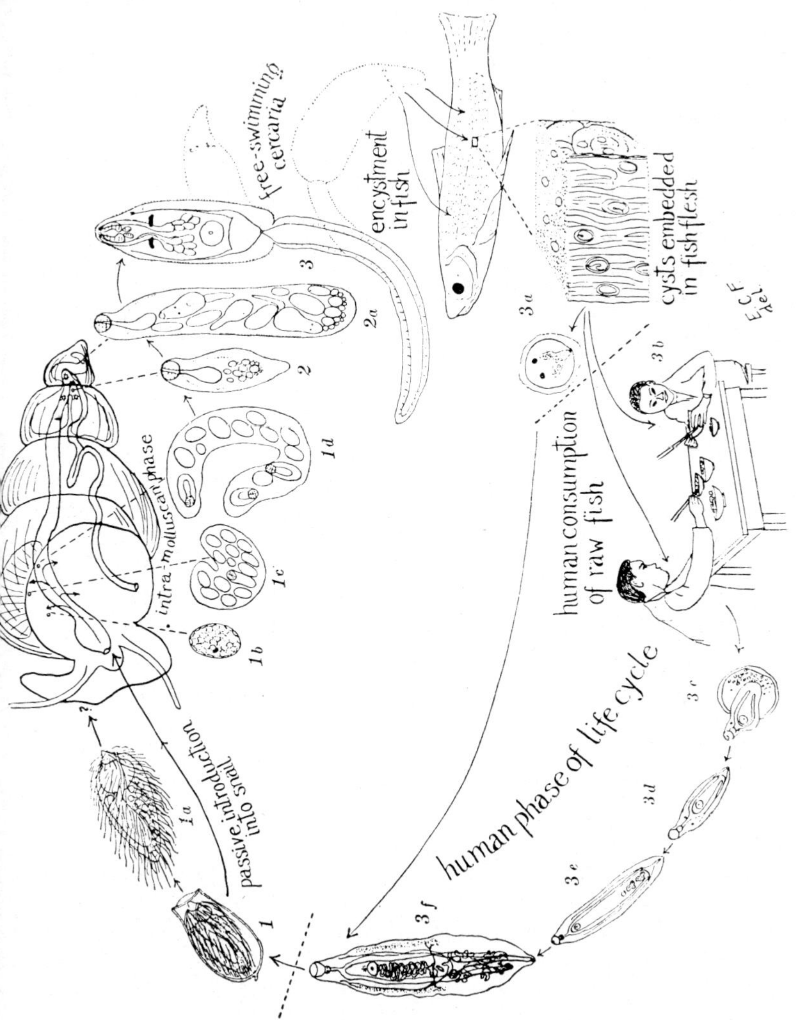

FIG. 149.—Diagram of the life cycle of *Clonorchis sinensis*. *1*, *1a-1d*, first generation (*e. g.*, egg → miracidium → sporocyst); *2*, *2a*, second generation (*e. g.*, redia); *3*, *3a-3f*, definitive generation (*e. g.*, cercaria → encysted metacercaria → excysted young worms → adult worm). (Original, from Faust's *Human Helminthology*, Lea & Febiger, Philadelphia.)

In human cases of light infection symptoms suggestive of very mild liver disturbances can be discovered. With involvement of more extensive areas, there is capricious appetite, a sense of fullness in the abdomen, hepatomegaly with nodular thickenings on the surface of the liver evident on palpation, diarrhea and toxic edema. There may be a syndrome of catarrhal cholangitis, palpitation of the heart with tachycardia, vertigo and central nervous system disorders attributed to impairment of the detoxifying properties of the liver (Otto, 1935).

In an extensive epidemic of clonorchiasis observed by Koenigstein in Shanghai (1949) prodromal symptoms were observed less than a month after exposure and before eggs were detected in the stools. The clinical onset was gradual or sudden, with chills and fever up to 40° C. The liver was large and tender and the scleræ were yellowish tinged. In some cases there was congestive splenomegaly. Eosinophil counts ranged from 10 to 40%. Some weeks later the picture was one of cholecystitis and hepatitis. Ling (1949) likewise emphasizes the gall-bladder syndrome, with radiating paroxysmal epigastric pain and jaundice.

Diagnosis

This is based on recovery of the characteristic eggs (Fig. 147) by direct fecal films, sedimentation of the stools, acid-ether technic (see "TECHNICAL AIDS," page 582), or by duodenal or biliary drainage.

Treatment

No satisfactory chemotherapy has been developed for chronic *Clonorchis* infections. In early infections, before fibrous encapsulation of the bile ducts has developed, gentian violet and tartar emetic have specific usefulness. *Fuadin* (neoantimosan), as administered in schistosomiasis (page 425), provides temporary improvement in symptoms but is not curative. Chloroquine diphosphate is also symptomatically useful (Basnuevo, 1949; Edelman and Spingarn, 1949; Koenigstein, 1949). Temporary disappearance of eggs in the feces or in aspirated bile can not be relied on as an index of cure.

Prognosis

In light infections, the prognosis is usually good even without treatment. In heavy chronic infections, it is unsatisfactory.

Control

Sterilization of human excreta in highly endemic areas will materially reduce opportunity for heavy exposure, although the excreta of infected dogs and cats will probably provide enough inoculum to maintain the infection in the snails and fishes. The thorough heating of all fish intended for consumption will safeguard the human population.

Opisthorchis Felineus (Rivolta, 1884) Blanchard, 1895

(The cat liver fluke, causing opisthorchiasis felinea)

This worm was originally described from the cat in Italy, and a few years later from man in Siberia (Winogradoff, 1892). It has a wide distribution in eastern and southeastern Europe and Asiatic U. S. S. R. It is reportedly common in Indochina and has been recovered from man in Japan and India, although it is probably not indigenous in these latter two countries.

The adult worm (Fig. 150) closely resembles *Clonorchis sinensis* (Fig. 146) in size and general appearance. One notable difference is the smaller size and lesser notching of the testes. The eggs of *O. felineus* are narrower (30 by 11 microns) than those of *Clonorchis* but otherwise bear a close resemblance. The only demonstrated molluscan host is the snail *Bulimus tentaculata* (Vogel, 1934). Several fresh-water fishes serve as secondary intermediate hosts. In addition to man, the dog, cat, fox, wolverine and seal have been found naturally infected.

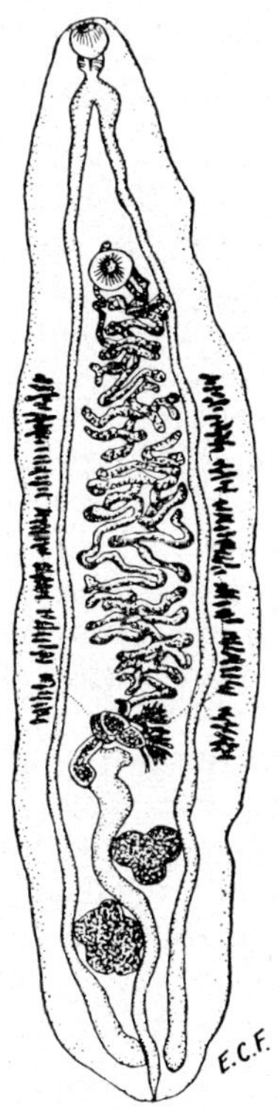

Fig. 150.—Adult *Opisthorchis felineus*, dorsal view, × 10. (After Stiles and Hassall, from Faust's *Human Helminthology*, Lea & Febiger, Philadelphia.)

The clinical aspects of *O. felineus* infection are similar to those due to clonorchiasis. Therapy is not particularly promising. Control measures have not been developed but thorough heating of fish consumed by man is indicated.

Opisthorchis Viverrini (Poirier, 1886) Stiles and Hassall, 1896

This worm, which is closely akin to *O. felineus*, is geographically endemic in Northern Thailand, where 25% of the population is infected. The eggs are smaller than those of *O. felineus* (26 by 13 microns). In addition to man, the civet cat and other fish-eating mammals are infected in the endemic area. The life cycle has not been elucidated but undoubtedly parallels that of *Clonorchis* and *O. felineus*. Clinical aspects of the infection have received little consideration.

Additional species of *Opisthorchis* reported from man are: *O. noverca* Braun, 1902, a common parasite of dogs, the wolverine and the pig in India, and *Opisthorchis* species Gomez and Rodriguez, 1949 in an isolated area near the Pacific Coast of Ecuador, found in 4 to 32% of the human population and 2% of the dogs.

PULMONARY FLUKES

PARAGONIMUS WESTERMANI (Kerbert, 1878) Braun, 1899

(The Oriental lung fluke, causing Oriental paragonimiasis, pulmonary distomiasis, or endemic hemoptysis)

Historical and Geographical Notes

This fluke was first discovered in the lungs of two Bengal tigers which died in Hamburg and Amsterdam (Kerbert, 1878). The next year a Portuguese resident of Formosa was found by Ringer to have a pulmonary worm, which Manson recognized to be a distomate fluke. In 1880 Manson found eggs of the same type in rusty-brown sputum of a Chinese patient. Cobbold (1880) named this human parasite *ringeri*. Simultaneously Baelz found similar eggs in bloody sputum of a native Japanese and three years later discovered the flukes in lungs of Japanese subjects. Yamagiwa (1892) in Japan and Musgrave (1907) in the Philippines recovered the same parasites respectively in the brain and abdominal viscera. The life cycle of the Oriental lung fluke has been elucidated as a result of the careful studies of Kobayashi (1918–1921) in Korea, and Yokogawa (1919) in Formosa. Present-day opinion favors the view that the human fluke *ringeri* is the same as *P. westermani*.

The heavily endemic region of Oriental paragonimiasis is confined to the China Sea areas, particularly Japan, Korea, Formosa and the Philippines. Additional infections have been reported from Central and South China, possibly Manchuria, Indochina, Thailand, Malaya, Bengal, Malabar, Madras, Assam, New Guinea, Samoa, Solomon Islands, Java, Sumatra, Belgian Congo, Nigeria, Tripoli, Peru, Ecuador, Colombia and Venezuela, but it is not known if all of these infections are indigenous, or if the parasites are identical with *P. westermani*.

Epidemiology

In all countries in which the epidemiology of Oriental paragonimiasis has been carefully studied the definitive host acquires the infection from eating the tissues of fresh-water crabs or, in Korea, also of the crayfishes *Astacus japonicus* and *A. similis*, raw or pickled in brine, vinegar or rice wine. Although these crustaceans may be caught in brackish water, they live typically in clear, fresh water, usually mountain streams, which are contaminated with the egg-laden excreta of human and reservoir hosts, which provide the inoculum for the molluscan hosts and subsequently the crustaceans.

In addition to man the following mammals have been found to be naturally infected: the tiger, wild cat, cat, leopard, panther, fox, wolf, dog, pig, beaver, wolverine, two species of civet cats, pencilled cat and crab-eating mongooses.

Morphology, Biology and Life Cycle

The Adult Worm.—The Oriental lung fluke resides normally in fibrous capsules in the lungs but it may also develop in other soft tissues of the body. This worm (Fig. 151) is a plump, ovoidal object, rounded anteriorly and somewhat tapering posteriorly, reddish-brown in the living state, gray or grayish-brown after preservation. It measures 7.5 to 12 mm. in length, 4 to 6 mm. in breadth and 3.5 to 5 mm. in thickness. The cuticle is provided with scale-like spines which are single-toothed or multidentate. The oral sucker (*os*) and the ventral acetabulum (*vs*) are subequal (0.75 to 0.8 mm.) in diameter.

The eggs of *P. westermani* (Fig. 152 *A*) are broadly ovoidal, relatively thick-shelled, golden-brown in color, with a somewhat flattened operculum, and measure 80 to 118 microns by 48 to 60 microns. They are unembryonated when laid by the parent worm.

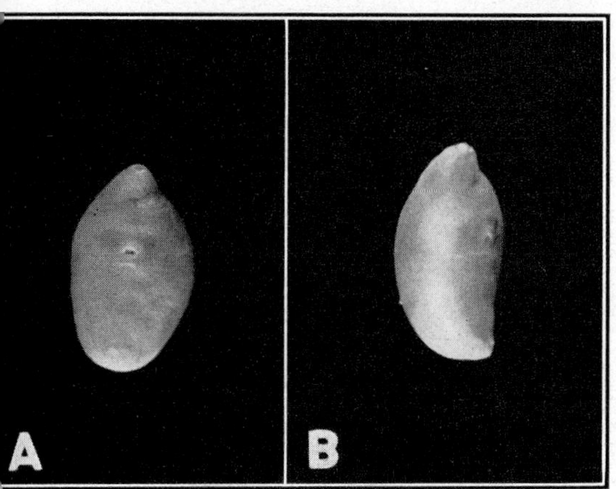

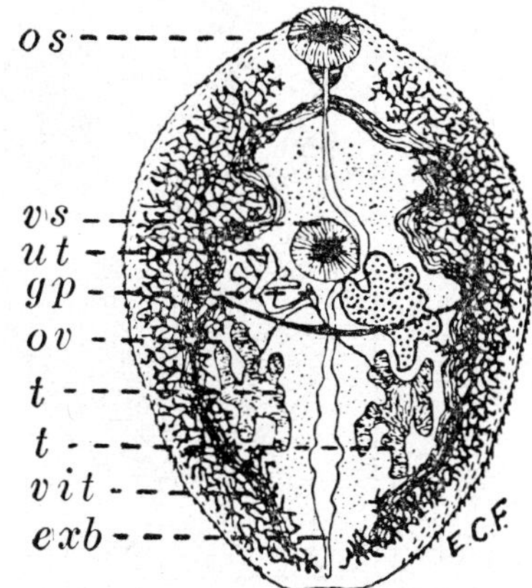

FIG. 151.—Adult *Paragonimus westermani*. *A*, ventral view and *B*, ventrolateral view of worm obtained from brain, × 2 (courtesy Lt.-Colonel L. E. Zimmerman, Armed Forces Institute of Pathology, Washington, D. C.); *right*, compressed, stained specimen, ventral view, × 5. *exb*, excretory bladder; *gp*, genital pore; *os*, oral sucker; *ov*, ovary; *t*, *t*, testis; *ut*, uterus; *vit*, vitellaria; *vs*, ventral acetabulum. (Original adaptation from Leuckart, in Faust's *Human Helminthology*, Lea & Febiger, Philadelphia.)

Life Cycle.—When deposited in the pulmonary capsules the eggs usually accumulate around the worm. Due to openings from the capsular pockets into the bronchioles, some of the eggs reach the respiratory passages and are coughed up, imparting a rusty tinge, resembling minute iron filings, to the sputum. Many of them are swallowed, pass down the digestive tract and are evacuated in the feces. In order to develop, the eggs must reach clear, usually cool, running water, in which they embryonate in 16 or more days, then hatch (Fig. 152 *B*). The free-swimming miracidia then enter suitable operculate snails, including several species of *Semisulcospira*, one of *Tarebia* and one of *Assimenia*. Within these snails the miracidium transforms into a first-generation sporocyst, in which redias are developed. The redia, in turn, produces a brood of cercarias, which escape from the snail and are temporarily free in the water.

The cercaria of *P. westermani* is a flattened oval object with a relatively large oral sucker beset with a dorsal stylet, a smaller ventral acetabulum somewhat posterior to the equatorial plane, two conspicuous groups of penetration glands, a triangular excretory bladder and a delicate knob-like tail. These cercarias invade the viscera and muscles of fresh-water crabs (species of *Eliocheir, Potamon, Parathelphusa, Barythelphusa, Sesarma* and *Pseudothelphusa*) or, in Korea, species of crayfishes (*Astacus japonicus, A. similis*), in the soft tissues of which they become encysted.

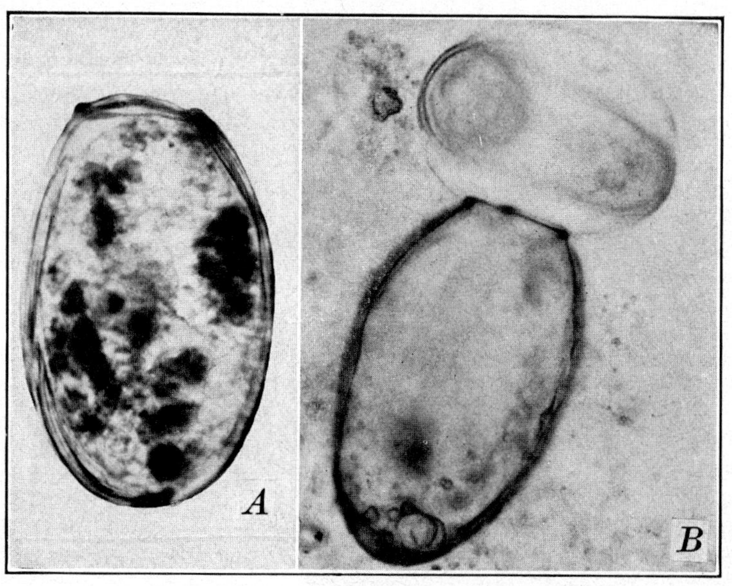

Fig. 152.—Eggs of *Paragonimus westermani.* *A*, immature egg from human sputum; *B*, miracidium hatching from egg, still within embryonic membrane. (*A*, after Faust in Brennemann's *Practice of Pediatrics; B*, photomicrograph by Dr. O. K. Khaw, from Faust's *Human Helminthology*, Lea & Febiger, Philadelphia.)

When the viable cysts are ingested by the definitive host, excystation occurs in the duodenum and the young worms migrate through the intestinal wall to the peritoneal cavity, burrow through the diaphragm, enter the lungs, and finally settle down near a bronchiole where they develop into adult worms within a fibrous capsule laid down by the host (Yokogawa, 1919). The circuitous migration from the duodenum to the peribronchial tissues provides abundant opportunity for the worms to become side-tracked or to wander into organs and tissues far removed from the typical residence of the adult worms.

Pathogenicity and Symptomatology

If the lung fluke reaches the pulmonary parenchyma, the host-tissue reaction consists of an eosinophilic and neutrophilic infiltration around the growing worm, followed by the development of a thick fibrous envelope. Such cysts usually occur in the deeper lung tissue and are approximately 6 to 10 mm. in diameter. Almost invariably small blood vessels are present in the capsule and there is leakage from the cystic cavity into a bronchiole, so that with the irritation caused by discharge of the eggs and the fluke's metabolites into a bronchiole, paroxysmal coughing occurs, frequently resulting in hemorrhage, with the expulsion of blood in the sputum.

Worms have also been discovered in many ectopic locations, including the liver, intestinal wall, mesenteric lymph nodes, peritoneum, visceral and somatic muscles, testes, pleura and the brain. In these abnormal sites there is a tendency for development of abscesses and pseudo-tubercles, or the lesion may be suppurative or frankly ulcerative (Musgrave, 1907).

Paragonimiasis of the lungs is usually insidious in its onset and mildly chronic in its course. There may be no symptoms other than the occasional coughing up of rusty sputum, but there may be a history of periodic hemoptysis or at least of occasion discharge of blood-tinged sputum. However, dyspnea, fever, malaise, easy fatiguability and anorexia have been observed in cases of extensive pulmonary involvement (Roque, Ludwick and Bell, 1953). Secondary anemia rarely occurs as a result of the hemopysis.

Paragonimiasis in ectopic locations usually causes significant symptoms. In the pleura there may be a thick purulent effusion and aspirated material may contain an abundance of the fluke's eggs. Glandular involvement characteristically provokes a notable leukocytosis with fever. In the brain the worms reside in granulomatous tissues characteristically producing a Jacksonian type of epilepsy such as occurs in cysticercosis of the brain (page 352) or cerebral schistosomiasis (page 413). Numerous cases of cerebral paragonimiasis are reported in the medical literature from Japan and Korea (Mitsuno, Takeya-Sikô, Inanaga and Zimmerman, 1952).

Diagnosis

Specific diagnosis can readily be made by recovery of the eggs of *P. westermani* (Fig. 152 *A*) in rusty or blood-tinged sputum, or from the feces (Komiya and Yokogawa, 1953), pleural aspirate or peritoneal abscesses. Clinically the roentgenogram may be helpful in making a tentative diagnosis of pulmonary paragonimiasis, although the chest shadows strongly parallel those of pulmonary tuberculosis. Roque, Ludwick and Bell (1953) suggest that paragonimiasis should be considered seriously in endemic areas *only* in those cases in which the sputum is negative for tubercle bacilli. Cerebral paragonimiasis can be determined only after exploratory operation and recovery of the worm or its eggs.

Treatment

No chemotherapeutic agent has been developed or tested which is specifically lethal for *P. westermani*. Emetine hydrochloride, administered as in fascioliasis (page 383), is symptomatically helpful but has not been demonstrated to be curative (Komiya *et al.*, 1952).

Prognosis

In benign infections involving the lungs, the prognosis is fair to good. In other cases, it is equivocal.

Control

For the individual in endemic areas, the disease may be prevented by meticulous care not to eat the soft tissues of crabs or crayfishes unless they have been thoroughly heated. No public health program has been developed to control the infection.

PARAGONIMUS KELLICOTTI Ward, 1908

This lung fluke is a natural parasite of a number of mammals in the Mississippi River drainage of the United States and of northern Canada. It is found in the mink, the pig, dog, muskrat, opossum, cat, wild cat, goat, and man (single case). The molluscan host is the snail *Pomatiopsis lapidaria* and the crustacean host, crayfishes of the genus *Cambarus* (Ameel, 1934). In most respects infection with this lung fluke parallels that of *P. westermani*.

SUMMARY

1. Trematodes, or flukes constitute a distinct class of the flatworms (Phylum Platyhelminthes). Only the digenetic trematodes parasitize man and higher vertebrate animals. These organisms have a minimum of three generations in their life cycle; they utilize a molluscan host (usually a snail) for the development of the first two of these generations and the early part of the third generation. Eggs laid by the mature worm in the body of the definitive host and discharged in the host's excreta hatch in water (or other appropriate media), liberating ciliated larvas (miracidia), which develop within the molluscan host into sporocysts (or redias). A second generation of sporocysts (or redias) is produced within the body of the first-generation organisms, and tailed larvas (cercarias) are developed within the second-generation organisms. The cercarias escape from the molluscan host into the water and (1) invade the skin of the definitive host in which they mature, or (2) encyst upon aquatic vegetation which serves as a source of infection for the definitive host, or (3) enter and encyst in the soft tissues of an aquatic animal, which provides the inoculum for the definitive host.
2. The mature digenetic trematode has a digestive system, a primitive nervous system, an excretory system, in some groups a lymphatic system, and elaborately developed genital organs. Most digenetic trematodes are hermaphroditic.
3. The most important intestinal trematode infecting man is *Fasciolopsis buski*, a large fleshy worm which also parasitizes hogs in extensive areas throughout the Orient. The cercarial stage encysts on buffalo nuts, "water chestnuts" and other aquatic plants eaten by man.

The worms become attached to the duodenal and jejunal wall, producing ulceration, systemic intoxication and in heavy infections intestinal obstruction. The symptoms are those of acute dyspepsia, diarrhea and profound intoxication. Diagnosis is made on recovery of the large typical eggs of the worm in the patient's stool. Specific treatment consists in administration of hexylresorcinol crystoids by mouth. Control requires that only sterilized fertilizer be used in the fields in which the edible plants are grown.

4. Additional intestinal flukes which parasitize man are *Watsonius watsoni* and *Gastrodiscoides hominis,* acquired from eating vegetation; several echinostomate species, acquired from eating raw snails, clams or limpets, fresh-water fish or tadpoles containing the encysted larvas; species of *Plagiorchis,* the larvas of which are encysted in the grubs of insects, and *Troglotrema salmincola,* acquired from eating raw salmon and trout.
5. Many species of heterophyid flukes parasitize man. All are acquired from eating uncooked fish which harbor the encysted larvas. The most common species infecting man are *Heterophyes heterophyes* and *Metagonimus yokogawai.* These minute flukes live in the mucosal crypts of the duodenum and jejunum and at times are buried deeply in the glands.

   Heavy infections produce duodenal colic and mucous diarrhea. Diagnosis is based on recovery of the eggs in the feces. The worms may be expelled by administration of hexylresorcinol crystoids by mouth as in ascariasis, or tetrachlorethylene by mouth as in hookworm infection. Prevention consists in the thorough cooking of fish before it is served as food.
6. The most cosmopolitan hepatic trematode is the sheep liver fluke *Fasciola hepatica,* which is a common parasite of sheep and many other herbivorous and omnivorous animals. Human infection is acquired in most countries from eating water-cress as salad greens. The metacercarias taken into the digestive tract excyst in the duodenum, burrow through the intestinal wall, migrate across the peritoneal cavity to the liver, then burrow through the hepatic parenchyma to the proximal bile ducts and the gall bladder, where they develop into relatively large worms.

   The young migrating worms produce traumatic and necrotic damage. Within the bile passages they provoke extensive hyperplasia of the epithelium and fibrous encapsulation of the ducts, with symptoms of cholangitis, cholecystitis, or cholelithiasis, digestive disturbances and systemic intoxication. Occasionally the migrating young worms develop in ectopic locations. Diagnosis is based on recovery of the large, typical eggs in the feces or preferably from biliary drainage. Emetine hydrochloride administered subcutaneously is a relatively satisfactory anthelmintic. Prevention of human infections can be accomplished by refraining from eating raw water-cress.

   Fasciola gigantica of the camel, cattle and water buffalo has occasionally been reported from man.
7. The lancet fluke, *Dicrocœlium dendriticum,* common in the bile ducts of herbivorous mammals, utilizes species of land snails and a species of foraging ant as intermediate hosts. Accidental ingestion of infected

ants provides the source of infection for the mammal. A number of genuine human infections have occurred, none in the United States. The worms are medium-sized, thin and transparent; their presence in the distal bile passages provokes hyperplastic and fibrotic changes.

8. *Clonorchis sinensis*, with extensive distribution in the Sino-Japanese area, *Opisthorchis felineus*, with distribution in eastern and southeastern Europe, northern Asia and Indochina, and *O. viverrini*, limited to northern Thailand, are closely related species of liver flukes, infection of which is acquired by man and many mammals from consumption of uncooked fresh-water fish. Human excreta constitute an important factor in the hyperendemicity of *Clonorchis* infection. The eggs of these three species of flukes which reach fresh water are ingested by certain snails, in which cercarias are later produced. These tailed larvas enter fishes in the vicinity and encyst in the flesh.

   The metacercarias ingested in the uncooked fish excyst in the duodenum of the definitive host, migrate through the ampulla of Vater into the bile passages and settle down in the distal bile ducts near the surface of the liver, where they provoke hyperplasia of the epithelium and fibrous thickening around the ducts. The worms live for 20 to 25 years and superinfection is common in hyperendemic areas, so that the eventual damage is usually significant. The symptoms evoked are proportional to the number of worms. Heavy infection produces symptoms of gall bladder disease or peptic ulcer. Diagnosis is based on recovery of the typical eggs in the patient's stools. Although gentian violet medicinal by mouth and tartar emetic by vein will eradicate most early infections, no chemotherapeutic has been found to kill the worms in chronic infections. Abstinence from eating inadequately cooked fresh-water fish will prevent human exposure.

9. The Oriental lung fluke, *Paragonimus westermani*, is prevalent in many parts of the Orient and Southwest Pacific islands and has also been reported from northern and central Africa and countries in northern South America. Exposure results from eating fresh-water crabs or crayfishes which are the second intermediate hosts of this worm. The metacercarias excyst in the duodenum and typically migrate through the intestinal wall, peritoneal cavity, diaphragm and pleural cavity to the lungs, where they settle down in the parenchyma near a bronchiole and develop into fleshy ovoidal worms. Because of the long devious journey the larvas at times become sidetracked in the peritoneal cavity or may migrate to such distant foci as the brain.

   In the lungs the worms provoke cellular infiltration and fibrous tissue encapsulation. Eggs are commonly discharged into a bronchiole and coughed up in sputum. If the worms lodge in the pleural cavity there will be purulent effusion; in the peritoneum, abscessing or ulcerating lesions; in the brain, granulomatous lesions. In the brain the characteristic symptom is Jacksonian epilepsy. Clinical diagnosis must be confirmed by recovery of the typical eggs. There is no specific chemotherapeutic. Prevention in endemic areas consists in meticulous care not to eat uncooked or inadequately cooked crab or crayfish meat.

10. *Paragonimus kellicotti,* a North American lung fluke, is a natural parasite of fur-bearing mammals, cats, dogs and hogs. A single human infection has been reported.

REFERENCES

AFRICA, C. M. 1937. Ova in the Spinal Cord of Man. Philippine J. Sci., *62*, 393–399.

AFRICA, C. M., GARCIA, E. Y., and DE LEON, W. 1935. Intestinal Heterophyidiasis with Cardiac Involvement. Philippine J. Pub. Health, *2*, 1–22.

ARENAS, R., ESPINOSA, A., and PADRÓN RUIZ, E. 1948. Fascioliasis Hepática con Carácter de Brote Epidémico. Rev. Kuba, *4*, 92–97.

BARLOW, C. H. 1925. The Life Cycle of the Human Intestinal Fluke *Fasciolopsis Buski* (Lankester). Am. J. Hyg., Monogr. Ser. No. 4, 98 pp.

BILHARZ, T. 1852. Ein Beitrag zur Helminthographia Humana. Zeitschr. f. Wissensch. Zool., *4*, 53–72.

BONNE, C., BRAS, G., and LIE KIAN JOE. 1948. Five Human Echinostomes in the Malayan Archipelago. Med. Maandblad, No. 23, June, 1948. 10 pp.

CORBY, D. R., and GORHAM, J. R. 1950. The Pathology and Etiology of Salmon Disease in the Dog and Fox. Am. J. Path., *26*, 617–637.

CORT, W. W. 1944. The Germ Cell Cycle in the Digenetic Trematodes. Quart. Rev. Biol., *19*, 275–284.

FAUST, E. C. 1949. *Human Helminthology.* 3rd ed., 744 pp., Lea & Febiger, Philadelphia.

FAUST, E. C., and KHAW, O. -K. 1927. Studies on *Clonorchis Sinensis* (Cobbold). Am. J. Hyg., Monogr. Ser., No. 8, 284 pp.

FRIESS, M. 1946. Distomatose Hépatique à *Fasciola Hepatica.* Infestation Familiale. Algérie Méd., May-June, No. 3, 247–253.

KOBAYASHI, H. 1918–1921. Studies on the Lung Fluke in Korea. I. On the Life History and Morphology of the Lung Fluke. II. Structure of the Adult Worm. III. Development in the First Intermediate Host. Mitt. Med. Hochsch. Keijo, pp. 1–21, 5–16, 97–115,.

KOENIGSTEIN, R. P. 1949. Observations on the Epidemiology of Infections with *Clonorchis Sinensis.* Trans. R. Soc. Trop. Med. & Hyg., *42*, 503–506.

KOMIYA, Y., and YOKOGAWA, M. 1953. The Recovering of Paragonimus Eggs from Stools of Paragonimiasis Patients by AMS III Centrifuging Technic. Japanese J. Med. Sci., and Biol., *6*, 207–211.

KOMIYA, Y., YOKOGAWA, M., *et al.* 1952. Studies on Paragonimiasis in Schizuoka Prefecture. II. Studies on the Treatment of Paragonimiasis. Japanese J. Med. Sci. and Biol., *5*, 433–445.

KRULL, W. H., and MAPES, C. R. 1952. Studies on the Biology of *Dicrocœlium Dendriticum* (Rudolphi, 1819) Looss, 1899 (Trematoda: Dicrocœliidæ), Including Its Relationship to the Intermediate Host *Cionella Lubrica* (Müller). VII. The Second Intermediate Host of *Dicrocœlium Dendriticum.* Cornell Veterinarian, 42, 603–604.

LEUCKART, R. 1882. Zur Entwicklungsgeschichte des Leberegels. Arch. f. Naturgesch., *1*, 80–119.

McCOY, O. R., and CHU, T. C. 1937. *Fasciolopsis Buski* Infection among School Children in Shaohsing and Treatment with Hexylresorcinol. Chinese Med. J., *51*, 937–944.

MANSON, P. 1881. *Distoma Ringeri.* Chinese Customs Gaz., Med. Repts. No. 20, pp. 10–12.

MITSUNO, T., TAKEYA-SIKÔ, INANAGA, K., and ZIMMERMAN, L. E. 1952. Cerebral Paragonimiasis. A Neurosurgical Problem in the Far East. J. Nerv. & Mental Dis., *116*, 685–714.

MUSGRAVE, W. E. 1907. Paragonimiasis in the Philippine Islands. Philippine J. Sci., B, *2*, 15–63.

NEGHME, A., and OSSANDON, M. 1943. Ectopic and Hepatic Fasioliasis. Am. J. Trop. Med., *23*, 545–550.

Otto, J. H. 1935. Clinical, Pathophysiological and Therapeutic Aspects of Human Clonorchiasis. Trans. 9th Congr. Far Eastern Assn. Trop. Med., *1*, 543–561.

Prats, F., *et al.* 1953. Urticaria Cronica por Distomatosis Hepatica. Bol. Inform. Parasit. Chilenas, *8*, 55–57.

Roque, F. T., Ludwick, R. W., and Bell, J. C. 1953. Pulmonary Paragonimiasis. Ann. Int. Med., *38*, 1206–1221.

Stemmermann, G. M. 1953. Human Infestation with *Fasciola Gigantica*. Am. J. Path., *29*, 731–759.

Stephenson, W. 1947. Physiological and Histochemical Observations on the Adult Liver Fluke, *Fasciola Hepatica* L. Parasitol., *38*, 116–144.

Strong, R. P. 1942. *Stitt's Diagnosis, Prevention and Treatment of Tropical Diseases.* 6th ed., 1747 pp. The Blakiston Co., New York.

Stunkard, H. W. 1937. On the Life Cycle of *Himasthla Quissetensis* (Miller and Northup, 1926) Stunkard, 1934 (Trematoda). Festschrift Skrjabin, pp. 689–698.

Thomas, A. P. W. 1883. The Life History of the Liver Fluke (*Fasciola Hepatica*). Quar. J. Micr. Sci., *23*, 99–133.

Vogel, H. 1934. Die Entwicklungszyklus von *Opisthorchis Felineus* (Riv.), nebst Bemerkungen über Systematik und Epidemiologie. Zoologica, *33*, 1–103.

Yokogawa, S. 1919. A Study of the Lung Distoma. Third Rept., Formosan Endoparasitic Dis. Research. 289 pp. (Japanese text.)

Chapter 15

The Blood-Flukes or Schistosomes

Introduction

The group of digenetic trematodes which inhabits the blood stream of vertebrate hosts are commonly referred to as blood flukes or schistosomes. The latter designation is applied to the worms because of the long sex canal on the ventral side of the male, in which the female is held during insemination and the much longer period of oviposition. All blood flukes are diecious. However, at times the blood-inhabiting species exhibit a tendency to hermaphroditism (Vogel, 1934; Short, 1951).

Epidemiology.—The free-living cercarias of these flukes become attached to the skin of their definitive host, which they actively enter, and in which after a period of migration through the bloodvessels they develop to maturity in this host. The usual methods of human exposure consist in wading, swimming, bathing or washing clothes in shallow water near the infected snail hosts.

The excreta of man and reservoir hosts containing viable schistosome eggs provide the inoculum which initiates the extrinsic phase of the life cycle of the parasites. The eggs hatch in fresh water, the escaping miracidia enter snails in the vicinity, undergo two sporocyst generations of development and multiplication within the snails, and the fork-tailed cercarias are then discharged into the water. For *Schistosoma japonicum* there are many mammalian reservoirs, yet the use of human feces as fertilizer for crops in endemic areas probably constitutes the most important source of eggs. In contrast, *S. mansoni* and *S. hæmatobium* have no important natural reservoirs; infection with these parasites is perpetuated almost exclusively by the promiscuous discharge of human wastes into nearby water (feces in the case of *S. mansoni,* urine and feces in the case of *S. hæmatobium*).

The Adult Blood Flukes.—These worms live typically in portal venous bloodvessels or in the vesical venules of the caval system. They occur characteristically in pairs in small mesenteric venules (intestinal types) and vesical veins (urinary type). At times, however, they become dislodged from these sites and are carried into the intra-hepatic portal vessels, pelvic veins, pulmonary arterioles, or even reach distant ectopic sites (Faust, 1948). In so far as has been demonstrated, the adults never migrate through blood capillaries except in the rich anastomoses between the portal and caval systems.

The mature schistosomes are delicate cylindroidal objects accommodated to the smaller bloodvessels, and usually lie with their anterior extremities directed towards the capillaries. The somewhat larger, more muscular male

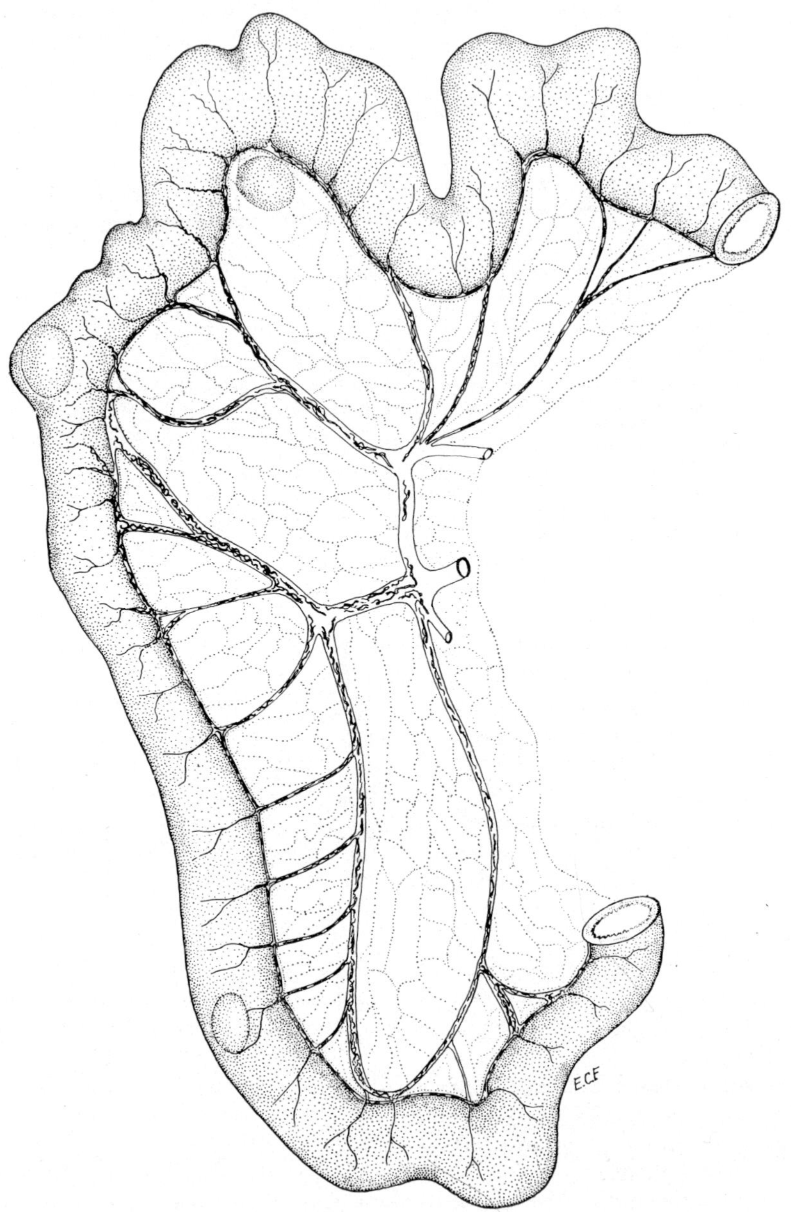

FIG. 153.—Loop of small intestine with terminal branches of mesenteric vein, showing pairs of blood flukes (*Schistosoma japonicum*) in the venules. A majority of the eggs deposited by the female worms are still within the blood vessels, blocking the flow of venous blood, but some have escaped through rupture of the vessels into the submucosa and mucosa and are filtering through to the intestinal canal. Diagrammatic representation based on sections from experimental infection of dogs by Faust and Meleney (1924). (Original from Faust's *Human Helminthology*, Lea & Febiger, Philadelphia.)

is attached by its suckers to the wall of the vessel, holding the thread-like female in its sex canal, thus enabling the female to extend its anterior extremity into the smaller-calibered venules in which it deposits eggs (Fig. 153).

The blood flukes which parasitize man secure nutriment from glucose (Bueding, 1950), and from other soluble substances in the plasma. The worms may live for 20 to 30 years or more in the human host, provided the patient does not die meanwhile of an intercurrent disease.

The Life Cycle.—The eggs of schistosomes are relatively thin-shelled, non-operculate, and contain a partially developed miracidium at the time of oviposition. Since the eggs are usually somewhat larger than the di-

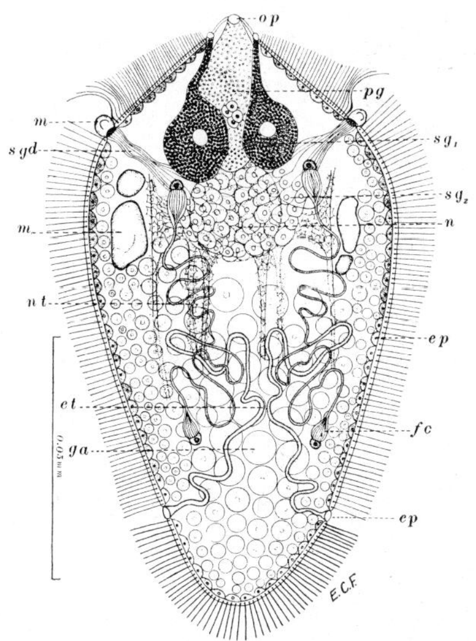

FIG. 154.—Miracidium of *Schistosoma japonicum*, hatched from egg in fresh water. *ep*, excretory pore; *et*, excretory tubule; *fc*, flame cell (solenocyte); *ga*, germ cell of second-generation sporocyst; *m*, metabolic secretions; *n*, nerve center; *nt*, posterior nerve trunk; *op*, opening of primitive gut; *pg*, primitive gut; sg_1, anterior secretory (penetration) gland; sg_2, lateral group of secretory glands; *sgd*, lateral secretory gland duct. × 550. (After Faust and Meleney, from Faust's *Human Helminthology*, Lea & Febiger, Philadelphia.)

ameter of the venules in which they are laid, they tend to remain temporarily as a chain of short sausage links, distributed in a fan-shaped pattern in the smaller venules, in which they obstruct the normal flow of blood. A combination of mechanical obstruction of the venules produced by the eggs, enzymes secreted by the miracidia and hypermotility of the parasitized organ causes weakening and rupture of the wall of the bloodvessel and discharge of the eggs into the surrounding tissues. Where eggs are deposited in previously undamaged mucosa they are extruded into the lumen of the organ and are evacuated in the stool (intestinal types) or the urine (vesical type).

When egg-laden stools or urines are discharged into fresh water, hatching occurs through a rent in the shell, and the miracidia become free-swimming organisms (Fig. 154). If appropriate species of snails are in the immediate vicinity, the miracidia attack the snail's soft tissues, penetrate a short distance and transform into first-generation sporocysts. Within each sporocyst several second-generation sporocysts are developed and on escape from the parent sporocyst migrate further into the snail's tissues (Fig. 155).

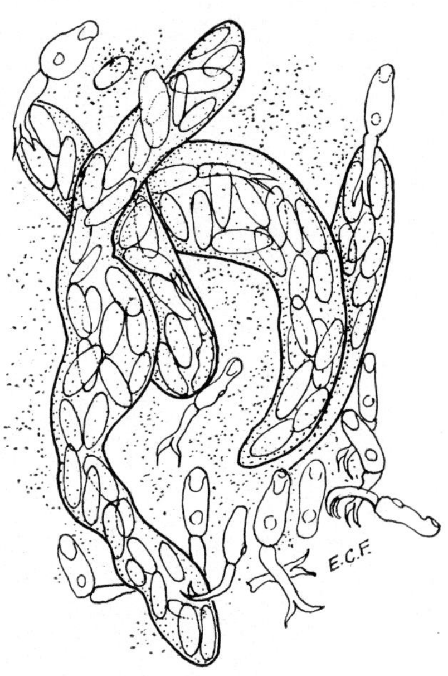

FIG. 155.—Second-generation sporocysts of *Schistosoma japonicum* with escaping cercarias, dissected out of *Oncomelania quadrasi*, the intermediate host in the Philippines. × ca, 100. (Original, from Faust's *Human Helminthology*, Lea & Febiger, Philadelphia.)

Here a brood of many fork-tailed cercarias is produced over a period of several weeks. When mature these larvas escape from the second-generation sporocysts, break out of the snail and swim about in the water (Fig. 156).

In contact with the skin of man or other susceptible animals the cercarias burrow and digest their way into the skin, meanwhile discarding their tails. After penetration into cutaneous blood capillaries or venules, the larvas are carried in the blood stream through the right chambers of the heart into the pulmonary arteries. They reach and slowly squeeze through the pulmonary capillaries, following which they are carried through the left chambers of the heart into the aorta and large arterial vessels. A majority are usually carried into the mesenteric artery and pass through the capillaries into intra-hepatic portal blood. Here the little larvas feed and grow. About 16 days later they begin migrating against incoming portal blood to the locations where they are destined to reside. The young *Schistosoma japonicum* reach the smaller branches of the superior mesenteric vein and soon mature (*e. g.*, 4 to 5 weeks after skin penetration). *S. mansoni* adolescents typically require 6 to 7 weeks to reach and mature in the inferior mesenteric vein. Those of *S. hæmatobium* pass first *via* the inferior mesenteric into the rectal veins, then through anastomoses into hemorrhoidal and pudendal veins and eventually reach the vesical venous system.

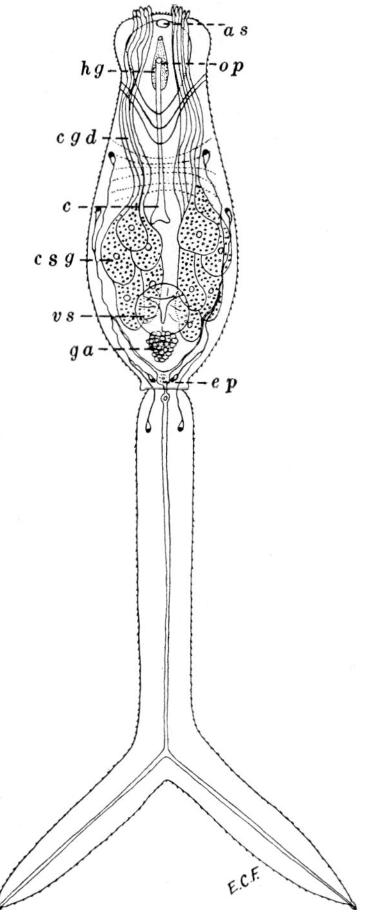

FIG. 156.—Cercaria of *Schistosoma japonicum*. *as*, opening of anterior sucker; *c*, primitive gut; *cgd*, penetration gland duct; *csg*, penetration gland; *ep*, excretory pore; *ga*, genital primordium; *hg*, head gland; *op*, opening of primitive gut; *vs*, ventral sucker. × 340. (Original, from Faust's *Human Helminthology*, Lea & Febiger, Philadelphia.)

Although *S. hæmatobium* at times mature and oviposit *en route* through the rectal vessels, those in the vesical veins begin to oviposit considerably later (*e. g.*, 10 to 12 weeks after skin penetration).

The life cycle of the human blood flukes is illustrated diagrammatically in Figure 157.

Pathogenesis.—Pathologic changes resulting from blood-fluke infection in a susceptible host are divided into three consecutive periods, *viz.*, (1) *biologic incubation*, from skin penetration until the worms have arrived and matured in the venules of the intestine or urinary bladder and the females are ready to oviposit; (2) the *acute stage*, which is one of active egg deposi-

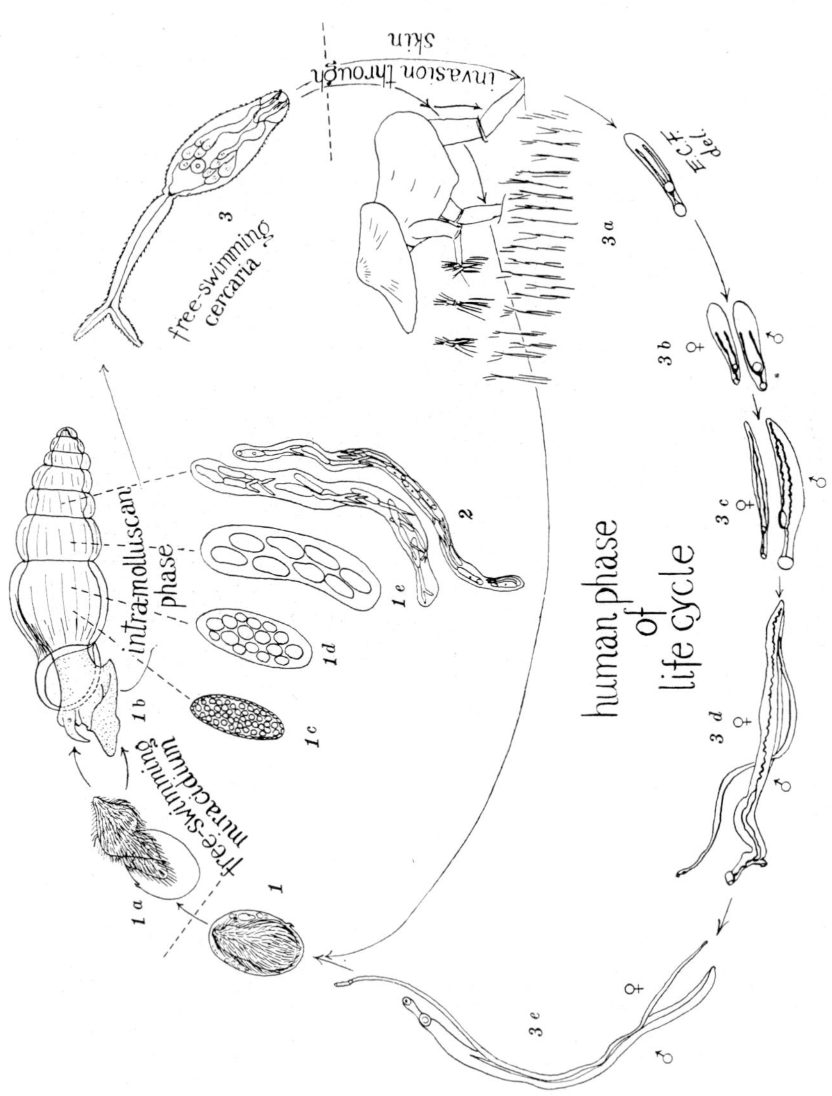

FIG. 157.—Life cycle of a human blood fluke, *Schistosoma japonicum*. *1*, *1a–e*, first generation, *e. g.*, egg →miracidium→first-generation sporocyst; *2*, second generation sporocyst; *3*, *3a–e*, third (definitive) generation, *e.g.*, cercaria→metacercaria→developing worms→adult schistosome. (Original, from Faust's *Human*

tion and extrusion, and (3) the *chronic stage*, that of tissue proliferation and repair.

(1) *Biologic Incubation.*—Minute hemorrhages are produced at the sites of penetration from the surface of the skin into the cutaneous venules. Next, during 4 or 5 days while the larvas are squeezing through pulmonary

capillaries, there is considerable infiltration around the delicate blood-vessels through which the worms are passing, with a predominance of eosinophils and at times of giant cells. Larvas which break out of the capillaries are responsible for acute inflammatory reaction around each strayed larva and its rapid destruction. Similarly, larvas which are carried in arterial blood to sites unfavorable for development are attacked and destroyed by phagocytes. On arrival in intra-hepatic portal blood the worms' metabolites provoke an acute hepatitis and systemic intoxication and sensitization. These reactions continue throughout biologic incubation into the two later stages.

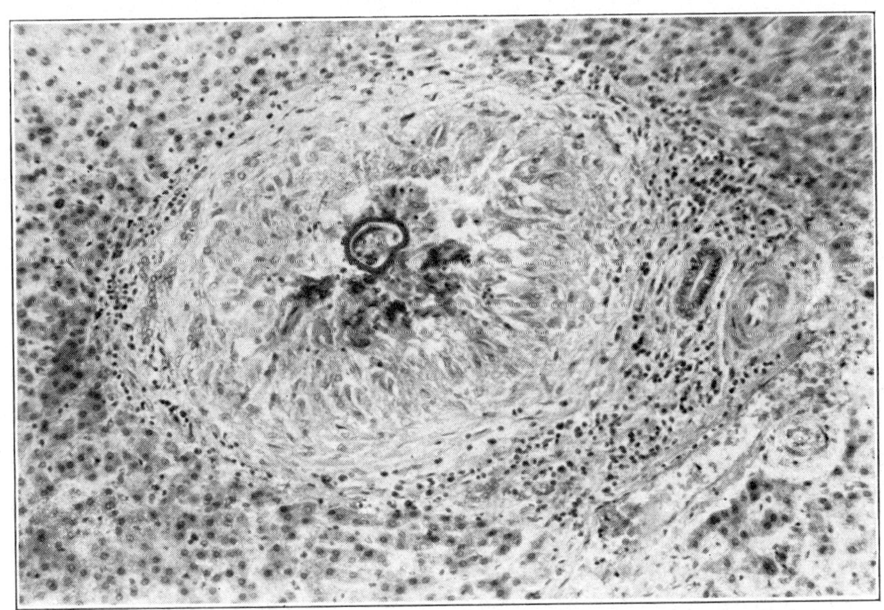

Fig. 158.—Organizing pseudo-tubercle around egg of *Schistosoma mansoni* in intestinal wall. (After Ash and Spitz.)

(2) *The Acute Stage.*—With the production and extrusion of eggs from the mesenteric or vesical venules and filtration of the eggs through the perivascular tissues into the lumen of the intestine or bladder, there is traumatic damage and hemorrhage. In a few weeks if the patient observes complete rest during this stage of the disease, the intestinal and bladder lesions tend to heal, but on resumption of physical exercise they are reactivated by extrusion of new batches of eggs.

Meanwhile, some of the eggs which escape from the venules become trapped in perivascular tissues by the development of a pseudo-abscess around each egg and the transformation of this acute pathologic process into a pseudo-tubercle (Fig. 158). As the smaller intestinal venules become blocked with eggs (*S. japonicum* and *S. mansoni*), the worms retreat into the larger mesenteric veins, so that many of the eggs are now swept into the intra-hepatic portal vessels, are trapped in the small portal venules, filter into periportal tissues, and provoke pseudo-tubercle formation. In *S. hæmatobium* infection eggs and at times the worms themselves are carried out of the vesical plexus into adjacent pelvic veins, or *via* the inferior vena cava reach the pulmonary arterioles, where they produce similar lesions. Moreover, *S. mansoni* and *S. japonicum* adults and eggs may pass from portal to caval blood and *S. hæmatobium* from caval to portal blood. Occasionally worms and eggs of all three species may be recovered at distant sites in the skin, myocardium or central nervous system.

(3) *The Chronic Stage.*—This consists of continued host-cell proliferation and fibrous repair of damage produced by eggs. In infection with *S. japonicum* and *S. mansoni,* the intestinal wall becomes fibrosed, the lumen reduced in diameter, and at times almost obliterated. The liver, originally enlarged as a result of inflammatory changes, gradually develops extensive periportal fibrosis. Characteristically there is a compensatory congestive enlargement of the spleen and distention of collateral veins, particularly the superficial abdominal vessels.

In the chronic stage of the vesical type of schistosomiasis, the wall of the urinary bladder becomes gradually thickened and fibrosed, phosphatic deposits cover the mucosal lining, uric acid concentrations develop around eggs free in the bladder, and the urethra becomes thickened and its lumen reduced by strictures. These same chronic processes extend at times into adjacent pelvic organs and into the external genitalia.

To a somewhat lesser degree, eggs of *S. hæmatobium*, *S. mansoni* and *S. japonicum*, in the order named, infiltrate perivascularly in the lungs, where they stimulate pseudo-tubercle formation and cirrhotic changes. Nests of schistosome eggs which are deposited by mature female worms that reach the brain (particularly *S. japonicum*) and spinal cord (*S. mansoni*) provoke granulomas; those that arrive in cutaneous bloodvessels are responsible for ulcerating abscesses. Carcinomas of the rectum, liver and urinary bladder are not infrequently found in chronic blood-fluke disease.

Symptomatology, Diagnosis, Treatment and Prognosis.—These topics will be considered separately under each of the etiologic agents presented below (*Schistosoma japonicum,* page 412; *S. mansoni,* page 419, and *S. hæmatobium,* page 424).

Control.—See separate discussion under *S. japonicum* (page 415), *S. mansoni* (page 420) and *S. hæmatobium* (page 425).

SCHISTOSOMA JAPONICUM Katsurada, 1904

(The Oriental blood fluke, causing intestinal and hepatic schistosomiasis, Oriental schistosomiasis or schistosomiasis japonica)

Historical and Geographical Notes

A mature worm was first recovered from man by Fujinami (1904) and worms of both sexes from dogs and cats in the same year by Katsurada, who described the worm, which he named and incriminated as the causative agent of the disease. In 1905, Logan reported the infection in Central China. Fujinami and Nakamura (1909) demonstrated that the skin was the portal of entry into the definitive host, Miyairi and Suzuki (1913–1914) elucidated the extrinsic stages of the life cycle, from the hatched miracidium through the small amphibious snail *Oncomelania nosophora* to the emergence of the fork-tailed larva into water, and Miyagawa (1912–1913) traced the migration route in the definitive host. Valuable experience concerning the early stages of the disease and their sequelæ was obtained as a result of study of approximately 2000 American and 500 Australian military personnel who were exposed to the infection on Leyte, Philippine Islands late in 1944 and early in 1945.

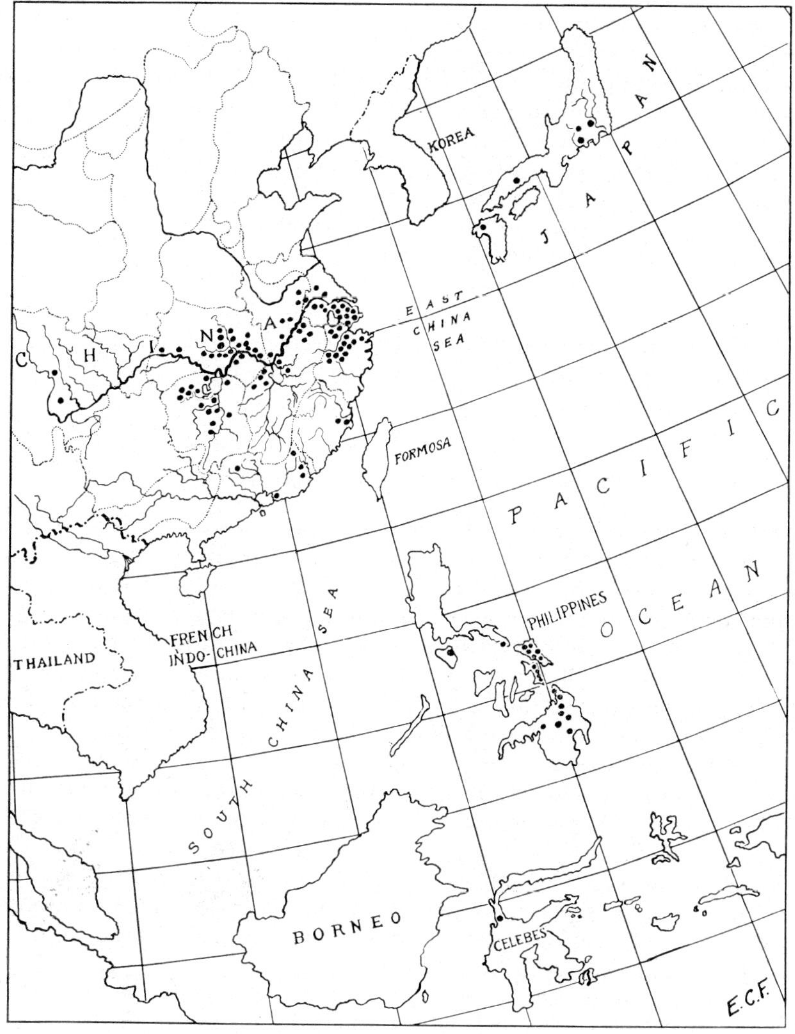

FIG. 159.—Map of the Far East, showing distribution of *Schistosoma japonicum* infection in Japan, China, Formosa, Philippines and Celebes. (Original from Faust's *Human Helminthology*, Lea & Febiger, Philadelphia.)

Schistosomiasis japonica is confined to the Far East, coëxtensive with the distribution of snails of the genus *Oncomelania* (Fig. 159). In Formosa *S. japonicum* is found in the west-central part; it is enzoötic and has not been demonstrated to produce patent infection in man (Hsü *et al.*, 1952.)

Stoll (1947) has estimated that the total incidence of infection with *S. japonicum* is 46 million persons, all of whom acquired the disease in the Far East.

Epidemiology

All mammals naturally exposed to the cercarial stage of the parasite are susceptible hosts. In addition to man these include cats, dogs, cattle, water buffaloes, pigs and several species of rodents. Exposure occurs when the cercarias in infested water come in contact with unprotected skin, most frequently during the planting of rice seedlings, but wading, bathing or washing clothes in infested canals contribute measurably to human infection, while the principal source of inoculum consists of eggs of *S. japonicum* in human feces spread as fertilizer on the fields. Additional eggs are provided in the feces of reservoir mammals, particularly the beasts of burden used to prepare the fields for cultivation.

In the Philippines, McMullen *et al.* (1953) have found the susceptible snail host, *Oncomelania quadrasi*, in streams in virgin forests in alluvial plains suitable for rice culture when the forests are cut down. This suggests potential opportunity for extension of old areas of endemicity or the development of new ones.

Morphology, Biology and Life Cycle

The Adult Worms.—The adult males of *S. japonicum* (Fig. 160) measure 12 to 20 mm. in length by about 0.50 mm. in greatest breadth. Their cuticle lacks tuberculations. Conspicuous features of the body are the subequal oral sucker and ventral acetabulum, the latter situated not far behind the former; the long ventral sex canal originating just behind the acetabulum and extending to the posterior end of the worm, and the relatively large, compressed, ovoidal testes (usually 7) piled on top of one another behind the ventral acetabulum.

The females are much more delicate than the males, with a length of about 15 to 30 mm. and a breadth of 0.1 to 0.3 mm., depending on the degree of elongation of the body within a small venule. The ventral acetabulum is somewhat larger than the oral sucker and lies close behind the latter. Details of the primary female genitalia are illustrated in Figure 160 *B*. Embryonation is completed after oviposition, so that eggs discharged in the stool are usually rotund, measure 70 to 100 microns by 50 to 65 microns, and contain a ciliated miracidium.

The normal habitat of the young adult *S. japonicum* is the superior mesenteric vein, particularly the tributaries adjacent to the small intestine. Several months later some of the worms migrate into the branches of the inferior mesenteric vein, or even into the caval system. In all of these locations, the females continue to lay a considerable number of eggs daily over a long period of time. Although males can mature without females, the latter remain dwarfed and immature unless some males are present.

The Life Cycle.—Fully embryonated viable eggs of *S. japonicum* (Fig. 161) soon hatch in fresh water and the miracidia attack and enter the soft tissues of species of small operculate snails of the genus *Oncomelania* (*O.*

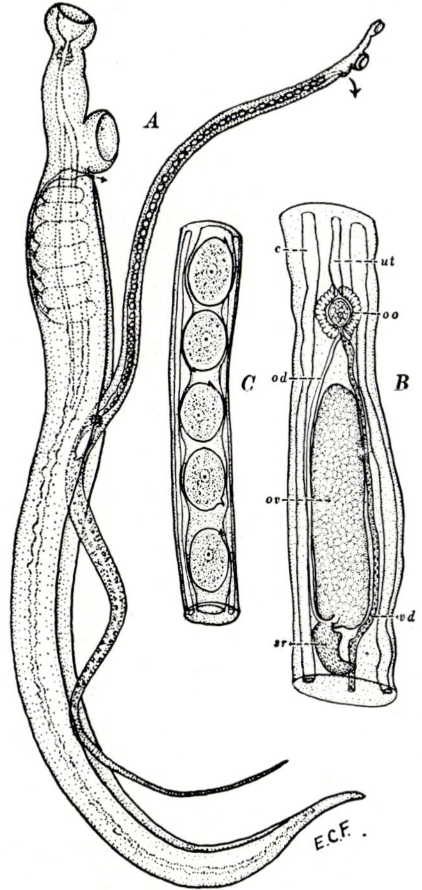

FIG. 160.—Adult male and female *Schistosoma japonicum*. *A*, female in sex canal of male, in position for egg laying; testes of male are compactly piled on one another just behind ventral acetabulum; arrows indicate genital pores of male and female worms; *B*, segment of female showing important genitalia; *C*, detail of proximal end of uterus filled with immature eggs. *c*, cecum; *od*, oviduct; *oo*, oötype; *sr*, seminal receptacle; *ut*, uterus; *vd*, vitelline duct. (After Faust, from *Human Helminthology*, Lea & Febiger, Philadelphia.)

nosophora in Japan and South China coast, *O. hupensis* in the Yangtze valley, *O. formosana* in Formosa, *O. quadrasi* in the Philippines and probably other species in inland China). After approximately four weeks of development within the snail the intra-molluscan phase is completed and cercarias begin to emerge into the water; but during dry weather the cercarias remain within the snail, the operculum of which is sealed tightly by secretion of mucus. On contact with the skin of man or other mammals which frequent the water, the cercarias become attached to the skin and, as the water drains off, get under epidermal scales, or enter hair follicles or sweat glands, penetrate into cutaneous capillaries and begin their blood migration. Approximately 4 to 5 weeks later they have matured in the smaller branches of the superior mesenteric vein and egg-laying is initiated. (See Faust and Meleney, 1924.)

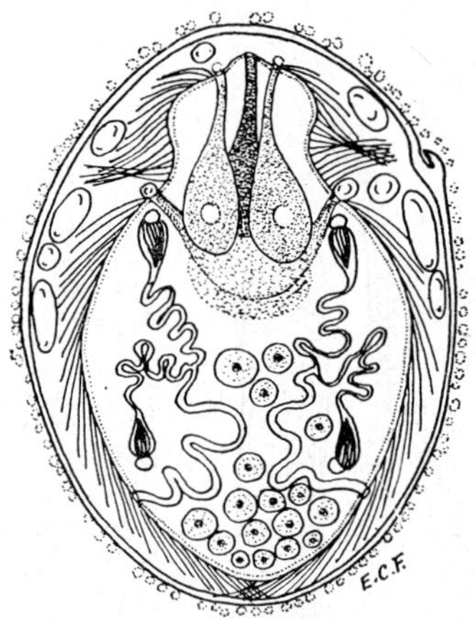

Fig. 161.—Fully embryonated egg of *Schistosoma japonicum*, with enclosed miracidium and host cells adherent to the sticky surface of the shell. × 60. (Original, from Faust's *Human Helminthology*, Lea & Febiger, Philadelphia.)

Pathogenesis and Symptomatology

Pathogenesis.—The tissue and humoral changes produced by *S. japonicum* in the human body conform to the general picture described earlier in this chapter (page 406), and can be traced through the successive periods of (1) incubation, (2) egg extrusion and (3) tissue proliferation around eggs infiltrated perivascularly. However, the following points require special emphasis in schistosomiasis japonica: The biologic incubation period is relatively short, *e. g.*, 4 to 5 weeks; the number of eggs produced by each female *S. japonicum* is larger than in infection with the other two species commonly parasitizing man, and the brunt of the damage is borne by the small intestine and the liver.

Traumatic damage is produced as each egg escapes from a venule, filters through the tissues and is extruded into the lumen of the small intestine, with accompanying hemorrhage. Even a few pairs of *S. japonicum* can produce significant damage because of the considerable ovipositing capacity of each female. The eggs pass down the intestinal canal and are evacuated in the stool in a menstruum of bloody mucus (Fig. 162). Little by little some of the worms migrate through the venules to undamaged areas, including the colon and the rectum. Meanwhile the worms' metabolites continue to produce toxic hepatitis and systemic sensitization, the latter demonstrated by the eosinophilic leukocytosis which occasionally reaches 90% of the total leukocyte count.

In an infection of a few dozen worms during a period of 5 years, the picture may assume grave proportions, with the development of fibrosis, papillomas and stenosis of the intestinal tract, hepatic cirrhosis with ascites, splenomegaly, and at times moderate pulmonary cirrhosis. Occasionally nests of eggs will be deposited in ectopic sites, as in the brain where granulomatous lesions envelop nests of eggs (Faust, 1948). In lighter infections, the terminal stage will develop more slowly; in heavy infections death may supervene as a result of overwhelming intoxication before the acute stage has gotten well underway and even before eggs are being passed in the feces. During the chronic stage there are characteristically a monocytosis, neutropenia and moderate eosinophilia.

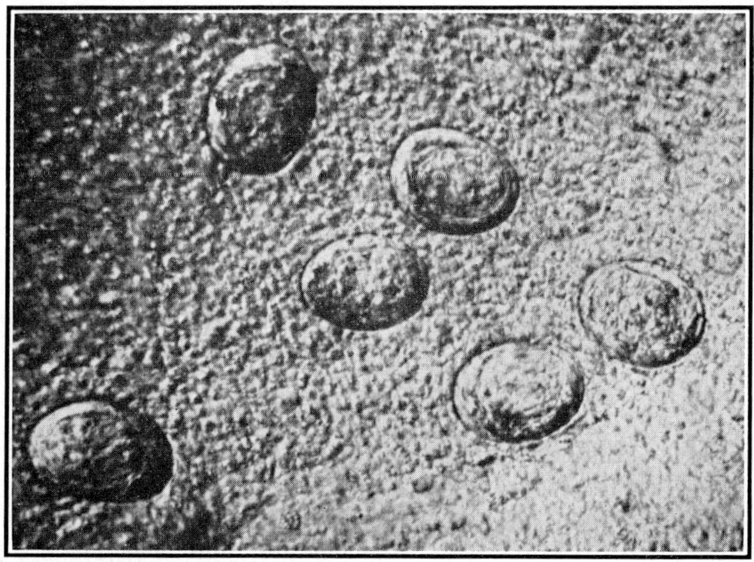

Fig. 162.—Eggs of *Schistosoma japonicum* in dysenteric portion of patient's stool during acute stage of infection. × 200. (After Faust and Meleney, from *Human Helminthology*, Lea & Febiger, Philadelphia.)

Symptoms.—Towards the end of the biologic incubation period the patient begins to manifest toxic symptoms, with late afternoon fever and night sweats. He usually has an enlarged, tender liver, complains of epigastric distress and pain in the back, groin or legs. Some cases develop giant urticaria about this time or somewhat later. Characteristically there is a prodromal toxic diarrhea.

The acute stage is characteristically ushered in with dysentery and the appearance of eggs in the stools. There are daily fever, excruciating epigastric pain and continued increase in the size of the liver. The patient loses appetite and weight and takes to his bed, but after a few weeks may feel better and return to work, only to have a recurrence of symptoms on physical exertion. The blood picture indicates a microcytic hypochromic type of anemia and an increase in serum globulin, with continued high eosinophilia (Faust *et al.*, 1946).

As the chronic stage develops, palpation of the liver reveals an increasingly cirrhotic organ with multiple minute granules (*e. g.*, pseudo-tubercles) on the surface. The mesentery and omentum may be thickened so as to bind down the colon and separate the abdomen into an upper and a lower portion. Somewhat later there is increasing evidence of ascites, severe emaciation, hepatic facies, dyspnea on slight exertion, dilatation of the superficial abdominal veins, and in some patients a hypertensive myocarditis due to infiltration of eggs in the cardiac wall. The patient gradually goes into a decline and may die of exhaustion or a supervening infection.

Among natives in endemic areas reëxposure is common, so that new infections are superimposed on older ones, complicating the clinical picture.

Diagnosis

During the biologic incubation period specific diagnosis is not possible. With the development of the acute stage eggs of *S. japonicum* can usually be recovered in bloody mucus discharged in the stool. This method of diagnosis is available as long as eggs are extruded, although sedimentation or acid-ether concentration technics may be required to recover the eggs. (See "Technical Aids," pages 581 and 582.) Intradermal and complement fixation tests with schistosome antigen (see "Technical Aids," pages 615 and 616) will provide additional evidence of the causative agent of the disease (Expert Committee on Bilharziasis, 1953). In chronic cases rectal biopsy will often provide demonstration of eggs when they are not found in the stools.

Treatment

The only satisfactory drugs for treating schistosomiasis japonica are *potassium antimony tartrate* (tartar emetic) and *sodium antimony tartrate*, administered slowly by vein in a filtered 0.5% solution. If the sodium salt is used it must be prepared fresh each time it is administered. The treatment schedule developed by U. S. Army hospitals in 1945 for military personnel who acquired the disease in the Philippines in 1944–1945, employing tartar emetic, is as follows: 1st day, 8 cc. (14.4 mgm. Sb); 3rd day, 12 cc. (21.6 mgm. Sb); 5th day, 16 cc. (28.8 mgm. Sb); 7th day, 20 cc. (36 mgm. Sb); 9th, 11th 13th, 21st, 23rd, 25th, 27th and 29th days, 24 cc. each (43.2 mgm. Sb); total, 320 cc. (576 mgm. Sb). One course provides about 84 per cent cures (Most *et al.*, 1950). Solutions stronger than 0.5% are not tolerated because of the extensive liver damage produced in this disease. Very slow administration is advised to minimize paroxysmal coughing, nausea and vomiting.

Surgical exploration is indicated in cases of suspected schistosomiasis of the brain or spinal cord. In selected chronic cases splenectomy may be considered.

Prognosis

This is fair to good if a full course of one of the antimony tartrates is administered during the patent acute stage or early chronic stage; poor in the late chronic stage irrespective of treatment, because of the amount of hepatic cirrhosis. During the prepatent period specific treatment is contraindicated because of the toxic hepatitis.

Control

Schistosomiasis japonica is most difficult to control because of the numerous reservoir hosts. Moreover, it is impractical for natives in endemic-enzoötic areas to avoid contact with infested water.

A method of control which may become practical in the extensive endemic territories in the Far East is the application of chemicals to kill the snail hosts. The most effective molluscicide (2-cyclohexyl-4:6-dinitrophenol), when applied to the irrigation ditches of rice fields in the spring before the fields are planted and again in the fall after harvest, kills most of the *Oncomelania* snails (90% or more) at each application. This chemical has been tested in Japan and in the Philippines and appears to have sufficient promise to justify extensive application (McMullen, 1952).

SCHISTOSOMA MANSONI Sambon, 1907

(Manson's blood fluke, causing schistosomiasis mansoni)

Historical and Geographical Notes

Although the original clinical investigation of Bilharz (1852) on human blood fluke infection in Egypt indicated that some of the female worms which he recovered contained lateral-spined eggs, it was not until 1907 that Sambon proposed the name *mansoni* for this type of schistosome. Da Silva (1908) found a greater number of testes in *Schistosoma mansoni* than in *S. hæmatobium*, the earlier-named species. Flu (1911) in Surinam and Risquez (1918) in Venezuela, demonstrated that *S. mansoni* had a predilection for the mesenteric veins and *S. hæmatobium* for the vesical and pelvic plexuses, and finally Leiper (1918) found a series of morphologic and life-cycle differences between the two species.

Manson's blood fluke is fundamentally a parasite of the Continent of Africa (Fig. 163) in which man is the important and almost exclusive host. It is heavily endemic in the Nile delta but is elsewhere much less prevalent in Egypt. It is common throughout practically all of tropical Africa from west to east and from the upper Nile valley through Mozambique and Southern Rhodesia. It is established further south in Natal and on the east coast of Madagascar. In Africa it is frequently coëxistent with *S. hæmatobium*. It is present in the Yemen, southwest Arabia, and possibly other foci of the Arabian peninsula. Importation of infected African slaves to tropical America provided opportunity for establishment of the disease in extensive areas of Brazil, in Surinam and Venezuela, and in several of the West Indies (Republica Dominicana, Puerto Rico, Vieques, St. Christopher, St. Martin, Montserrat, Nevis, St. Kitts, St. Lucia, Martinique and Guadeloupe). Stoll (1947) has estimated that 39.2 million persons are infected with this blood fluke, for the most part living in Africa.

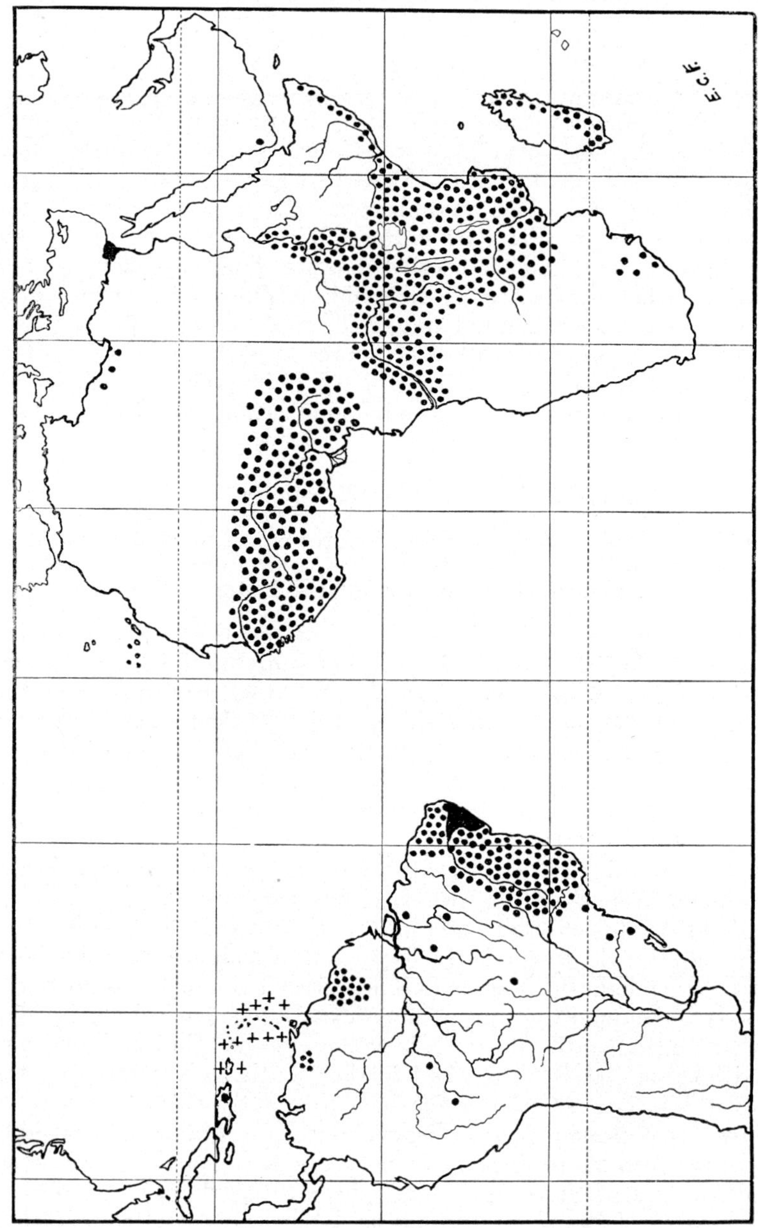

Fig. 163.—Map showing distribution of *Schistosoma mansoni* in Africa, an adjacent area of Arabia, Madagascar, South America and the West Indies (+). Hyperendemic regions in lower Egypt and Brazil are indicated in solid black. (Original, from Faust's *Human Helminthology*, Lea & Febiger, Philadelphia.)

Epidemiology

Although on rare occasions African and West Indian monkeys have been found to harbor *S. mansoni, Rattus rattus frugivorus* in Pernambuco, Brazil (Barbosa *et al.*, 1953) and other rodents in Brazil (Pimental, 1953) have been found naturally infected, and the desert gerbille (*Gerbillus pyramidum pyramidum*) has been found infected once (Kuntz, 1952), the only important definitive host is man. The molluscan intermediate hosts are planorbid snails, including several species of *Biomphalaria* throughout Africa and *Australorbis glabratus* in the Americas.

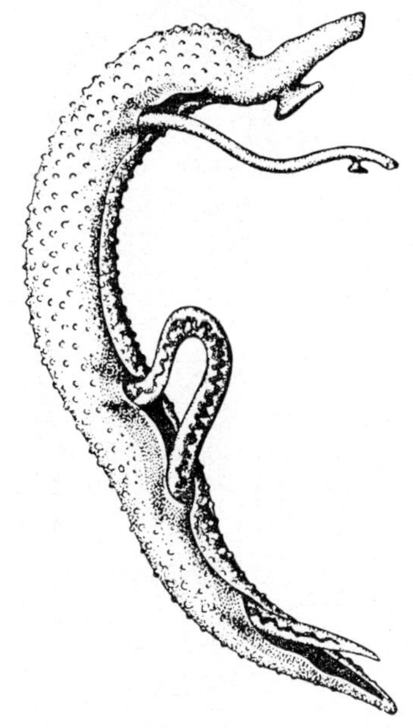

Fig. 164.—Adult male and female *Schistosoma mansoni* in copula. Note the cuticular tuberculations on the male. × 10. (After Gonnërt, from Craig and Faust's *Clinical Parasitology*, Lea & Febiger, Philadelphia.)

Human exposure to Manson's schistosomiasis results from wading, bathing, swimming, washing clothes, and by a variety of agricultural pursuits in which hands or legs are immersed in cercaria-infested water. Kuntz (1952) has reported that in the Yemen the Moslem ablution pools are infested with *S. mansoni* and *S. hæmatobium*.

Morphology, Biology and Life Cycle

The Adult Worms.—The adults of *S. mansoni* (Fig. 164) are considerably shorter than those of *S. japonicum*. The males have a length of 6.4 to 9.9 mm., and the females, 7.2 to 14 mm. The cuticle of the male is provided with numerous warty excrescences. The testes, numbering 6 to 9, are minute bodies lying in a grape-like cluster a short distance behind the ventral acetabulum. The most striking internal feature of the female is the short uterus, providing storage space for very few lateral-spined eggs. The worms usually reside in the tributaries of the inferior mesenteric vein adjacent to the lower colon, although they may be found at higher levels of the intestine, in intra-hepatic portal blood, in the vesical venules, in the pulmonary arterioles and rarely in ectopic foci (Faust, 1948).

The fully developed eggs of *S. mansoni* as recovered in the stool (Fig. 165) are large, elongated-ovoidal objects, rounded at both ends and pro-

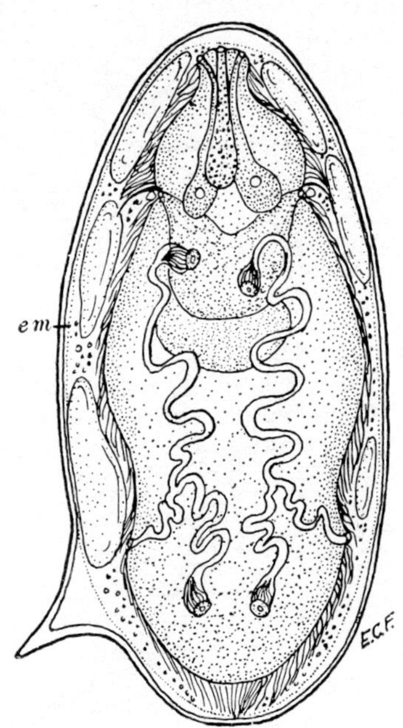

Fig. 165.—Fully embryonated egg of *Schistosoma mansoni*, with enclosed miracidium, lateral view. *em*, embryonic membrane. × 500. (Original, from Faust's *Human Helminthology*, Lea & Febiger, Philadelphia.)

vided with a conspicuous, lateral spine near one pole, extending at an obtuse angle from the shell's long axis. They measure 114 to 175 microns by 45 to 68 microns.

The Life Cycle.—On dilution of the host's excreta with fresh water the fully embryonated eggs hatch within a few hours and are soon found attached to the soft parts of planorbid snails in the immediate vicinity. The cercarias which later emerge from the snail enter human skin and migrate *via* blood vessels to the mesenteric-portal blood. However, after a preliminary meal within portal blood, they pass into the hepatic veins and circulate through the lungs at least once before congregating again in the intra-hepatic portal blood for further development (Faust and Hoffman, 1934; Koppisch, 1937). The time required for migration of the adolescent worms from the intra-hepatic portal vessel to the branches of the inferior mesenteric vein, their maturity and initiation of egg laying is 3 to 4 weeks in the human host, so that the total incubation period is 6 to 7 weeks.

Pathogenesis and Symptomatology

Pathogenesis.—The humoral and tissue changes caused by *S. mansoni* closely resemble those due to infection with *S. japonicum* (page 412) but (1) The biologic incubation period is about two weeks longer; (2) the early intestinal lesions develop typically in the colon rather than the small intestine, and (3) the number of eggs produced by *S. mansoni* is about $\frac{1}{10}$, hence there are comparably fewer eggs extruded from the intestinal wall and fewer which later become trapped in the perivascular tissues of the intestine and liver. As a result the traumatic damage and the proliferative and fibrotic changes are considerably less, worm-for-worm, than in schistosomiasis japonica; hence intestinal fibrosis and hepatic cirrhosis develop more slowly in Manson's schistosomiasis.

Symptomatology.—There is no notable difference in the prepatent symptoms between infection with *S. mansoni* and *S. japonicum*. Although toxic manifestations continue through the acute into the chronic period, the usual intestinal symptoms are diarrhea or dysentery. Hepatic cirrhosis develops much more gradually than in schistosomiasis japonica, frank ascites is less frequent and fibrosis of the mesentery-omentum is rarely demonstrated. Nevertheless, very heavy infections with *S. mansoni* produce severe toxic symptoms and rapidly developing dysfunction of the intestinal wall and periportal tissues (Pons, 1937). Moreover, pulmonary lesions and symptoms are relatively common in Manson's schistosomiasis (Jaffé, 1944; Meira, 1951).

Diagnosis

This is usually made on demonstration of the characteristic eggs of *S. mansoni* with their distinct lateral spine (Fig. 165), evacuated in the stool. More frequently than in infection with *S. japonicum* concentration methods, *e. g.*, sedimentation and acid-ether technics (see "TECHNICAL AIDS," pages 581 and 582) are required because of the scanty number of eggs. Likewise, rectal biopsy is a particularly fruitful procedure (Ottolina and Atencio, 1943; Hernández-Morales and Maldonado, 1946). Intradermal and complement-fixation reactions with schistosome antigen are at times valuable. Rarely the eggs escape from pulmonary arterioles, are extruded through the tissues into a bronchiole and coughed up in sputum as are the eggs of *Paragonimus westermani* (page 587).

Treatment

The only satisfactory chemotherapeutics in Manson's schistosomiasis are potassium antimony tartrate (tartar emetic) and sodium antimony tartrate, administered intravenously as a 0.5% solution, in the dosage schedule recommended for schistosomiasis japonica (page 414). Neoantimosan (Fuadin) and lithium antimony thiomalate (Anthiomaline), given intramuscularly, are temporarily helpful but not curative. Miracil D (Nilodon) is ineffective in this disease (Greany, 1952).

Control

Since there are no important reservoir hosts for Manson's schistosomiasis, control should be relatively simple. Yet the insanitary disposal of human excreta constitutes a very great obstacle. Rice fields and sugar cane plantations under irrigation, truck gardens using human nightsoil as fertilizer and other cultivated areas provide a challenge to the sanitary engineer. Some public health workers regard copper sulfate as the most practical molluscicidal agent for the planorbid-snail intermediate hosts of this infection; others consider the newer molluscicide, sodium pentachlorophenate, to be the most promising and economical (McMullen, 1953; Wright and Dobrovolny, 1953), since it destroys the eggs as well as the young adults of these snails in flowing water, at a cost of approximately one-half cent *per capita* each application. A biological method of snail destruction, namely, by exposing the snails to a lethal bacterium (*B. pinottii* Cruz and Dias, 1953), is being investigated by Dias in Brazil (1953). Preliminary field tests have shown approximately 90% kill.

SCHISTOSOMA HÆMATOBIUM (Bilharz, 1852) Weinland, 1858

(The vesical blood fluke, causing vesical schistosomiasis or vesical bilharziasis, endemic hematuria)

Historical and Geographical Notes

Vesical blood fluke disease was prevalent in Lower Egypt in ancient times, as demonstrated by pathologic studies on mummies dating many centuries B. C. The earliest recorded epidemic occurred among Napoleon's troops in the Nile delta in 1799. The adult worms were first recovered by Theodor Bilharz, in 1851, from the mesenteric veins of a native of Cairo. In 1864 Harley, in South Africa, regarded the blood flukes present in vesical veins as causal agents of hematuria. In 1918 Leiper provided conclusive experimental evidence that *S. hæmatobium* and *S. mansoni* were separate species.

Because of the early work of Bilharz on Egyptian blood fluke disease, Cobbold (1859) created the genus *Bilharzia* for the species *hæmatobium*, without knowing that the genus *Schistosoma* had been proposed a year earlier. A number of European and Egyptian workers continue to employ *Bilharzia* without regard to the Law of Priority. These workers use the term bilharziasis for infections with *S. hæmatobium* and *S. mansoni*.

The ancient home of *S. hæmatobium* was the lower Nile Valley, where infection with this worm is still hyperendemic. The present-day distribution (Fig. 166) includes practically the entire African Continent, even oases in several deserts; the island of Madagascar; numerous areas in the Arabian peninsula; a focus in southern Palestine among the Moslem population; several centers in Syria near the Turkish border; the lower Tigris-Euphrates valley; the coast of Iran adjacent to the Persian Gulf; an endemic focus on the west coast of India about 140 miles south of Bombay (Gadgil and Shah, 1952), and two endemic centers on the south coast of Portugal.

Epidemiology

Man is the almost exclusive definitive host of *S. hæmatobium*. Eggs of this worm are commonly extruded from the wall of the urinary bladder and excreted in the urine. Promiscuous urination into bodies of fresh water including ponds and irrigation canals, primitive latrines situated over small rivers or ponds and the emptying of excreta from night pails into small

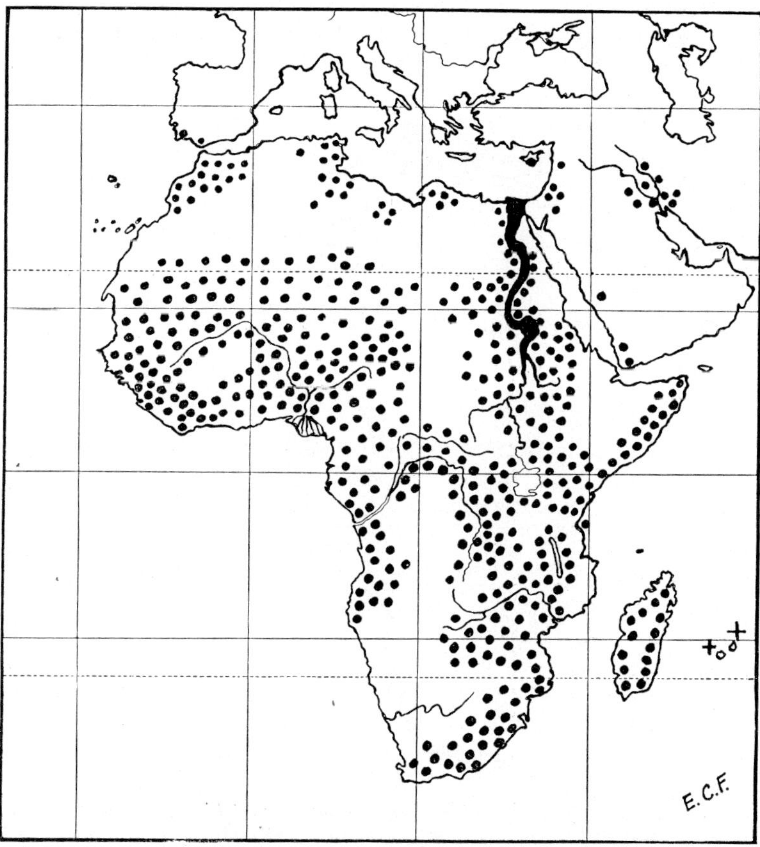

Fig. 166.—Map showing distribution of *Schistosoma hæmatobium* in Africa, Near East, Middle East, Madagascar and southern Portugal. The solid black along the Nile River indicates hyperendemicity. (Original, from Faust's *Human Helminthology,* Lea & Febiger, Philadelphia.)

village streams all provide infection for the snail hosts. Moreover, the studies of Gelfand and Ross (1953) confirm those of other recent workers in Africa, that *S. hæmatobium* eggs are as commonly deposited in the wall of the colon and rectum as in the urinary bladder, indicating that the stools of infected individuals are a potential medium for the evacuation of eggs into fresh water.

The incidence of schistosomiasis hæmatobia varies from small percentages to near saturation of a native population. The infection is particularly prevalent in villages, and the incidence highest among young boys who wade or swim in polluted water. The snails which serve as intermediate hosts with few exceptions belong to the genera *Bulinus* and *Physopsis*, especially *Bulinus truncatus* and *Physopsis africana,* but in Morocco and southern Portugal *Planorbis dufourii* is the susceptible mollusc.

Extension of irrigation projects throughout Africa and in the Tigris-Euphrates valley is responsible for the spread of vesical schistosomiasis into previously uninfected contiguous areas due to carriage of the snail hosts into the new canals.

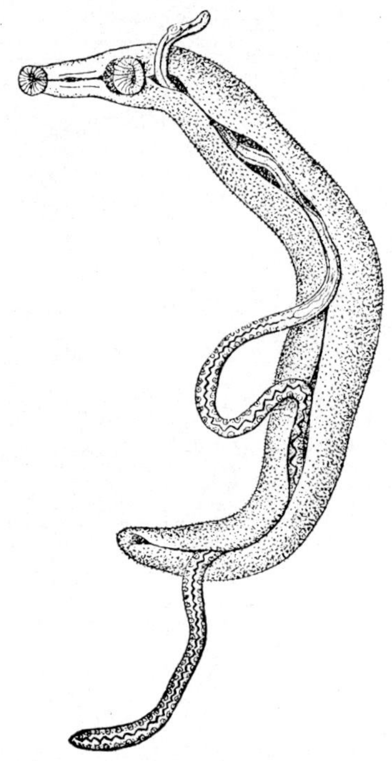

Fig. 167.—Adult male and female *Schistosoma hæmatobium.* Note fine cuticular tuberculations on male. × 12. (After Looss, in Faust's *Human Helminthology,* Lea & Febiger, Philadelphia.)

Morphology, Biology and Life Cycle

The Adult Worms.—The male is considerably stouter than its mate (Fig. 167), measuring 10 to 15 mm. in length by about 1 mm. in greatest girth. The ventral acetabulum is appreciably larger than the oral sucker. Minute cuticular spines are present on both suckers and the entire cuticle, including the lining of the ventral sex canal, is provided with small tuberculations. Four or at times 5 small subglobose testes can be demonstrated close to one another immediately behind the ventral acetabulum.

The female is delicately cylindrical, with a length measurement of about 20 mm. and a diameter of 0.25 mm. The genital organs, exclusive of the vitellaria, occupy the median longitudinal field, beginning with the genital pore just behind the ventral acetabulum and extending posteriorwards about two-fifths of the body length. On oviposition the eggs of *S. hæmatobium* are incompletely embryonated but by the time they are excreted they have usually become fully embryonated.

Life Cycle.—The fully mature egg of *S. hæmatobium* (Fig 168) is elonggated ovoidal, rounded at the anterior pole and is provided posteriorly with a terminal spine. It measures 112 to 170 microns in length by 40 to

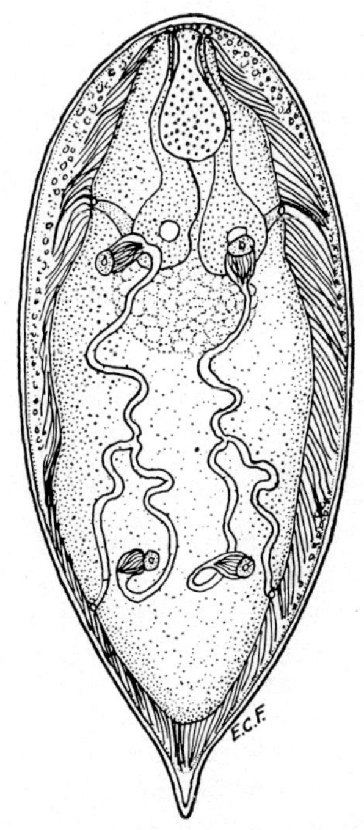

Fig. 168.—Fully embryonated egg of *Schistosoma hæmatobium*, with enclosed miracidium. × 640. (Original, in Faust's *Human Helminthology*, Lea & Febiger, Philadelphia.)

70 microns in breadth, is straw-colored and relatively transparent. When these eggs reach fresh water they soon hatch and the escaping miracidia, after a short free-swimming period, are attracted too, and penetrate the soft tissues of appropriate snails, in which they undergo development and multiplication, with the emergence of fork-tailed cercarias 4 to 8 weeks after exposure of the snails.

On contact with human skin the cercarias penetrate and migrate in blood vessels into portal blood, where they feed and grow, then about 3 weeks after skin exposure begin to migrate against the venous current into the inferior mesenteric vein, and into the rectal vessels. In this location some of the adolescent worms mature and oviposit (Barlow and Meleney, 1949).

Possibly a majority migrate through the hemorrhoidal anastomoses and pudendal vein to the vesical plexus, which is apparently the optimum location for this species. Usually a total of 7 to 9 weeks intervene between the exodus of the adolescent worms from the intra-hepatic portal blood until eggs first appear in the urine, *e. g.*, 10 to 12 weeks following skin penetration.

S. hæmatobium, like *S. japonicum* and *S. mansoni*, may live for 20 to 30 years provided the host survives that long.

Pathogenesis and Symptomatology

Pathogenesis.—The prepatent incubation period in schistosomiasis hæmatobia parallels that of the two intestinal types of the disease, but there is usually less evidence of acute hepatitis and systemic intoxication. Moreover, unless the adolescent worms mature in the rectal veins inflammation and edema of the intestinal tract is much less pronounced.

Egg deposition and extrusion cause local traumatic damage and hemorrhage, either in the wall of the rectum or the urinary bladder. In the bladder there is first hyperplasia of the wall, then deposition of patches of gritty phosphatic salts on the surface and dense fibrosis of the muscular and submucous coats, through which it is increasingly difficult for the eggs to filter. Small calculi of oxalates or uric acid crystals, sloughed portions of a papilloma or clots of blood in the bladder cavity form around eggs, so that sizable bladder stones are formed. Meanwhile the urethral lumen becomes greatly constricted, at times completely closed. Similarly the ureters and the pelves of the kidneys may become affected. The penis or scrotum may develop an elephantoid appearance due to obstruction of the scrotal lymphatics, and fistulas may break through the skin. In women the vulvæ are frequently hyperplastic and indurated. Advanced cases of vesical schistosomiasis usually have septic involvement.

Finally, there is a high correlation between chronic schistosomiasis of the bladder and malignancies of this organ (Ferguson, 1913; Makar and Fawzy, 1947).

Symptomatology.—During the biologic incubation period, the patient may be essentially symptomless or he may have an increasing malaise with late afternoon fever, moderate hepatic pain or epigastric distress, and an elevated eosinophil count. If the worms mature in the rectal veins there may be severe tenesmus with dysentery. More often the first evidence of the infection is the painless passage of blood at the end of the period of micturition. This symptom (hematuria) continues throughout the course of the disease but more and more there is also discharge of pus cells and necrotic tissue débris, decrease in the interval between periods of urination, and eventual incontinence, or anuria due to urethral stricture. Bladder colic is a cardinal symptom.

Schistosomiasis hæmatobia may be responsible for symptoms referable to the kidneys, testes or prostate, lungs, heart, central nervous system and eye, appendix or liver.

Diagnosis

This is most easily accomplished in a majority of cases by recovery of the characteristic eggs (Fig. 168) in the sediment which settles out of urine in an inverted conical glass container. At times a small bladder biopsy specimen will provide positive evidence not present in the urine. The diagnostician must be mindful of the relatively high involvement of the rectum in this infection (Gelfand and Ross, 1953), so that stool examination, if necessary with concentration technics (see "TECHNICAL AIDS," pages 581 and 582), or at times rectal biopsies, are indicated. Intradermal and other immunologic tests appear less needful than examination of the excreta for *S. hæmatobium* eggs.

Treatment

As in the other types of human schistosomiasis, the most effective drugs in vesical schistosomiasis are potassium antimony tartrate (tartar emetic) and sodium antimony tartrate. Unless there is evidence of liver involvement the drug may be concentrated as much as 6% for intravenous injection; however the lesser concentration (0.5%) recommended for the intestinal types of schistosomiasis will be better tolerated. (For dosage schedule see page 414.) Because of difficulty in getting dispensary patients to return for repeated treatment over a period of several weeks, attempts have been made to accelerate the time schedule by increasing the daily dosage, from an intensive course of 6 slow injections during a 48-hour period to a 10-day course (Girgis and Magid, 1952). Neoantimosan (Fuadin) and lithium antimony thiomalate (Anthiomaline) produce a relatively low percentage of cures. Miracil D (Nilodon) apparently has considerably usefulness in *S. hæmatobium* infection. Its advantages are that it is administered orally and a complete course requires only 3 to 5 days; its disadvantages are unpleasant taste and disagreeable side effects such as nausea, abdominal pain, constipation and mental depression. It lends itself to treatment of small children whose veins are difficult to enter by needle and to use in dispensary practice in rural areas.

Prognosis

This is good to grave, depending on the number of worms in the infection, their location in the tissues, the chronicity of the infection, and septic or neoplastic complications.

Control

Schistosomiasis hæmatobia is amenable to practical control, since there are essentially no reservoir mammalian hosts. The molluscicidal drug sodium pentochlorophenate is particularly satisfactory in attacking the nonoperculate snail hosts of this schistosome which live in flowing as well as still water (McMullen, 1953). Correction of the insanitary habits and customs of native peoples with respect to the discharge of their excreta will require long-time health education.

Other Blood Flukes Reported as Human Parasites

Several additional species of *Schistosoma* have been reported as human parasites. The evidence provided by Gelfand and Ross (1953), that *S. hæmatobium* eggs are as frequently present in the tissues supplied with mesenteric-portal blood as in those in the caval blood drainage, together with the knowledge that *S. hæmatobium* eggs vary remarkably in size and the length of the terminal spine, suggest that some of these diagnoses may refer to *S. hæmatobium*.

Schistosoma Bovis (Sonsino 1876) Blanchard, 1895

This is a common parasite in the mesenteric-portal system of cattle and sheep in southern Europe, Iraq and Africa. The eggs (Fig. 169, *4*) are much narrower, more spindle-shaped and considerably longer (230 to 380 microns by 70 to 90 microns) than those of *S. hæmatobium* (Fig. 169, *2*), and in the reservoir hosts can not be easily misdiagnosed. Eggs believed to be those of *S. bovis* have been found in human urine in South Africa but the worms have not been recovered from man.

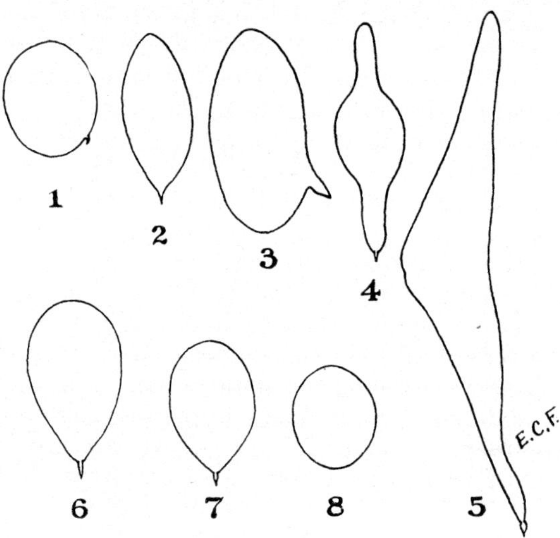

Fig. 169.—Eggs of representative blood flukes parasitizing man and other mammalian hosts. *1. Schistosoma japonicum; 2, S. hæmatobium; 3, S. mansoni; 4, S. bovis; 5. S. spindale; 6, Ornithobilharzia bomfordi; 7, S. indicum; 8, Schistosomatium douthitti* (syn. *pathlocopticum*). Drawn to scale, much enlarged. (Original, from Faust's *Human Helminthology*, Lea & Febiger, Philadelphia.)

Schistosoma Spindale Montgomery, 1906

This is a relatively common parasite in the caval blood of cattle, water buffaloes, sheep and goats in India, Sumatra and South Africa. The elongated fusiform eggs (Fig. 169, *5*) are very large (400 microns by 72 microns). Eggs considered to be those of *S. spindale* have been reported from human urine in South Africa but not in India where the infection is much more heavily enzoötic.

Schistosoma Intercalatum Fisher, 1934

This species was created for cases of human infection in tropical Africa in which terminal-spined *Schistosoma* eggs were found exclusively in the stools and the symptoms were referable only to the organs drained by mesenteric-portal blood. Chesterman (Fisher, 1934), has observed several hundred cases in the Belgian Congo and studied at autopsy the distribution of the worms, their eggs and the tissues parasitized. No involvement of the bladder was discovered. The eggs (140 to 240 microns by 50 to 85 microns) are intermediate in size and shape between those of *S. hæmatobium* and *S. bovis*. Experimentally *Physopsis africana* has been found to be a satisfactory molluscan host.

Schistosoma Matthei Veglia and Le Roux, 1929

This schistosome is probably identical with *S. hæmatobium* or *S. bovis*. It is a natural parasite in the mesenteric-portal blood of sheep and monkeys in southern Rhodesia, where Blackie (1932) has diagnosed the worm in human infections on the basis of terminal-spined eggs (210 to 240 microns by 40 to 70 microns) recovered in the urine, and adult worms in association with *S. hæmatobium* at two human autopsies.

Schistosoma Incognitum Chandler, 1926

Chandler (1926) created this species on the basis of eggs measuring 95 to 100 microns by 41 to 50 microns, somewhat resembling those of *S. indicum* (Fig. 169, *7*), with a small terminal spine, diagnosed twice from human stools in India. Saunders (1934) recovered similar eggs from fecal droppings of pigs in Madras, and Bhalerao (1934) described male and female adults from the mesenteric-portal bloodvessels of a Calcutta pig. The dog is also a reservoir host.

Schistosoma Faradjei Walkiers, 1928

This species, the validity of which is very doubtful, was proposed for eggs of a schistosome recovered from the stools of natives in the Belgian Congo. The eggs were somewhat smaller than those of *S. mansoni* and lacked a spine.

SCHISTOSOME DERMATITIS

(Swimmer's itch, clam digger's itch, Gulf Coast itch, cercarial dermatitis)

Historical, Geographical and Biological Notes

In 1928 Cort demonstrated that the cercarias of certain non-human blood flukes were the causal agents of an aggravating form of dermatitis. Intensive investigations in many geographical regions have demonstrated that this skin infection usually occurs during the warm months and is due to skin penetration of the schistosome cercarias; that non-operculate snails in bodies of fresh water serve as intermediate hosts for these blood flukes, the adults of which are usually parasitic in migratory birds; that transient birds pollute the water with their excreta containing the eggs of the parasite, and that miracidia hatched from the eggs initiate infection in the snails.

Schistosome dermatitis resulting from contact with cercaria-infested fresh water has been reported from several foci in Michigan, Wisconsin, Minnesota, Oregon, Washington, southern California, Montana, Canada, Germany, Switzerland, France, Wales, El Salvador, Cuba, Argentina, Burma, India, Japan, Australia, and New Zealand. Species of *Lymnæa*, *Stagnicola*, *Physa*, *Physella*, *Planorbis*, *Polyplis*, *Chilina*, etc. serve as intermediate hosts and the definitive hosts are commonly ducks and geese but passerine birds are naturally infected with some of these avian schistosomes. The adult worms which develop from cercarias producing the dermatitis belong to the genera *Trichobilharzia* (McMullen and Beaver, 1945), *Gigantobilharzia* (Cort, 1950; Hunter *et al.*, 1950) and *Ornithobilharzia* (Szidat, 1951).

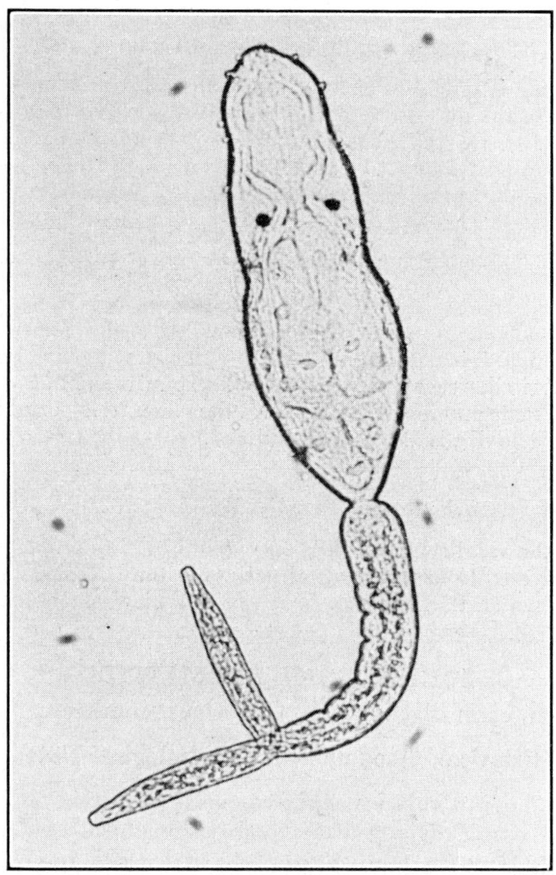

FIG. 170.—Oculate cercaria of avian blood-fluke producing schistosome dermatitis in Hawaii. Penetration glands and ducts are clearly shown. (Photomicrograph courtesy of Dr. George Chu.)

Other areas of schistosome dermatitis are found along salt water beaches in Hawaii, southern California, Florida, Rhode Island, and Connecticut. In these areas marine snails are the molluscan hosts of the blood flukes (Fig. 170) and terns, as well as other water and migratory birds, are the natural definitive hosts. Stunkard and Hinchliffe, (*l. c.*) identified the adult worm of their cercaria as a species of *Microbilharzia.*

A third epidemiologic type of schistosome dermatitis is due to invasion of the human skin with non-human mammalian schistosomes. Buckley

(1938) described this infection among paddy workers in Malaya, resulting from contact with water infested with cercarias of the cattle blood fluke, *Schistosoma spindale*. Cort (1950) lists the cercaria of the rodent schistosome, *Schistosomatium douthitti*, as a potential causal agent, and Alves (1953) has experimentally produced dermatitis in man with cercarias of *S. matthei*.

Both Olivier (1949) and Macfarlane (1949) regard schistosome dermatitis as a sensitization reaction which is intensified by repeated exposure. Furthermore, the dermatitis is much more likely to develop with exposure to blood flukes not adapted to development in man than to those commonly developing to maturity in the human host.

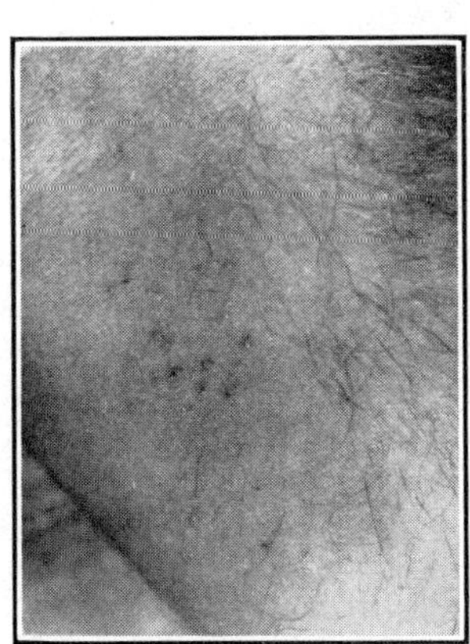

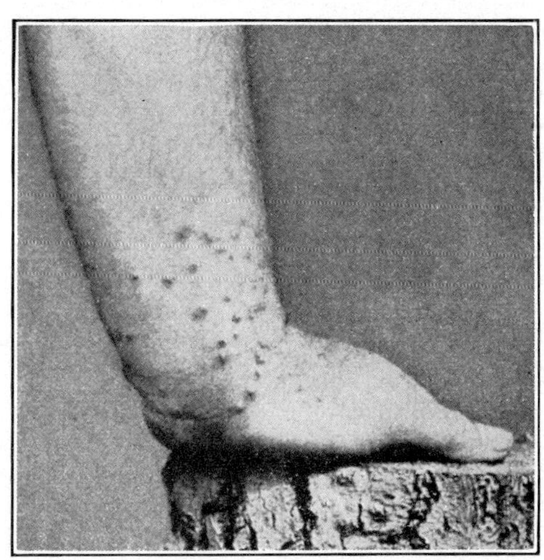

Fig. 171.—Experimental lesions of schistosome dermatitis. *Left*, a few sites of skin invasion on the forearm, with developing papules (photograph courtesy of Dr. George Chu, Hawaii); *right*, multiple pustules on the wrist, with some local edema (after Cort, from Faust's *Human Helminthology*, Lea & Febiger, Philadelphia.)

Clinical Aspects of Schistosome Dermatitis

The lesions produced in schistosome dermatitis (Fig. 171) conform to the following pattern. As the water containing the schistosome cercarias drains off the skin a prickling or nettling sensation is experienced. This may be accompanied by erythema of the invaded area and in highly sensitive individuals, especially those who have been previously exposed, by local or generalized urticaria. Soon the initial irritation subsides, leaving only a macule at each site of penetration, but in a few hours there is intense itching of the involved area and the macules transform into papules. The reaction reaches its maximum between the second and third day, then gradually decreases. However, rubbing of the infected site tends to reactivate the itching.

Treatment consists in the topical application of palliatives such as calamine lotion, to relieve the itching, and, if required, sedation to reduce nervousness.

Control

If the schistosome cercarias responsible for the dermatitis utilize fresh-water snails as intermediate hosts, a molluscicidal chemical such as copper sulfate or copper carbonate may be dissolved in the water along the shore of lakes or in canals and ditches where the snails are found. McMullen and Beaver (1945) urge that beaches in endemic areas be protected from migratory birds, to reduce the opportunity for infection of the snails and thus provide considerable reduction in the dermatitis the following summer.

The control of schistosome dermatitis along salt-water beaches poses a more difficult problem, the solution to which has not been explored.

SUMMARY

1. The digenetic trematodes which inhabit the bloodvessels of vertebrates are called blood flukes. They are also designated as schistosomes because of the long trough on the ventral side of the male which holds the female during insemination and oviposition. The blood flukes are typically diecious; the mated pairs normally inhabit the mesenteric-portal and caval blood systems, in the smaller branches of which they lay non-operculate, partially embryonated eggs. These escape into perivascular tissues, commonly filter into the lumen of the intestine or urinary bladder and are then evacuated in the excreta, meanwhile completing embryonation. On reaching fresh water they soon hatch. The miracidia swim for a brief time in the water, then become attached to, and enter appropriate species of snails, in which they metamorphose and multiply, with the production of cercarias, which swarm out of the snail and infest the water. On contact with the skin of man or other susceptible vertebrates, the cercarias become attached, penetrate down to the cutaneous venules which they enter, and initiate infection in the definitive host. Three blood flukes, *Schistosoma japonicum*, *S. mansoni* and *S. hæmatobium*, are important parasites of man.
2. Pollution of water with the excreta of infected human beings or other definitive hosts provides opportunity for the blood-fluke eggs to hatch in the water and infect susceptible snails. The fork-tailed cercarias which emerge into the water constitute the inoculum for definitive hosts. Eggs of *Schistosoma japonicum* and *S. mansoni* are excreted almost always in the stools; those of *S. hæmatobium*, principally in the urine. Man is the almost exclusive host of *S. mansoni* and *S. hæmatobium* but *S. japonicum* utilizes many domestic mammals as reservoirs. Human exposure results from wading, bathing, swimming, washing clothes and carrying on agricultural pursuits in endemic areas.
3. The cercarias of human blood flukes after cutaneous penetration migrate in bloodvessels through the lungs, are transported into the abdominal and mesenteric arteries and pass through the mesenteric capillaries into

intra-hepatic portal blood. Here they feed and grow, and about 3 weeks after skin penetration begin to migrate back into the mesenteric veins, *Schistosoma japonicum* to the smaller branches of the superior mesenteric vein, *S. mansoni* to the inferior mesenteric vein and *S. hæmatobium* through the inferior mesenteric and rectal veins, then *via* the hemorrhoidal plexus or pudendal vein into the vesical venules. In these locations the worms mature and produce eggs.

4. The pathologic changes in the human host resulting from schistosome infection are (1) intoxication and sensitization, which begin with entry into the skin, gradually increase during the biological incubation period and are continued as long as the parasite or its eggs reside in the host's body; (2) traumatic damage resulting from extrusion of the eggs from bloodvessels through the tissues, and (3) pseudo-tubercle formation around eggs which becomes trapped.

5. *Schistosoma japonicum* (Oriental blood fluke) occurs in Japan, China, Formosa (enzoötic disease but without evidence of patent human infection), the Philippines and Celebes. Possibly as many as fifty millions suffer from the disease throughout the endemic territory. Several species of small operculate snails of the genus *Oncomelania* are the intermediate hosts.

   The early symptoms in *Schistosoma japonicum* infection consist in systemic intoxication and sensitization, together with acute hepatitis, followed by epigastric distress, with dysentery, hepatomegaly and splenomegaly, and later evidences of profound intestinal and hepatic dysfunction. Diagnosis is based on recovery of the characteristic ovoidal eggs in the stool or by rectal biopsy. Treatment consists in administering potassium antimony tartrate (or sodium antimony tartrate) by vein in a $\frac{1}{2}\%$ solution. Control of this infection is difficult because of the large number of reservoir hosts and the custom of using human excreta to fertilize rice and other crops. A practical method of control is to treat the banks of the snail-inhabited canals twice yearly with a potent molluscicide such as 2-cyclohexyl-4-6-dinitrophenol.

6. *Schistosoma mansoni* (Manson's blood fluke) occurs in many areas of Africa and is widely distributed in tropical America. The adult worms typically inhabit the smaller branches of the inferior mesenteric vein. The eggs filter through the intestinal wall and are evacuated in the stools. Planorbid snails of the genera *Biomphalaria* (Africa) and *Australorbis* (tropical America) serve as intermediate hosts.

   The pathologic changes in Manson's schistosomiasis parallel those of *S. japonicum* infection but with the following differences: (1) the large bowel bears the brunt of traumatic damage during egg extrusion, and (2) the much smaller number of eggs produced by *S. mansoni* provokes fewer fibrotic changes in the intestinal wall, liver and other organs. Symptoms are referable principally to the colon, rectum and liver, but may indicate damage to the tissues of the lungs, urinary bladder or other organs. Diagnosis is based on recovery of the characteristic elongated-ovoidal eggs with a conspicuous lateral spine, in the stools or by rectal biopsy. Treatment consists in the administration of antimony tartrates by vein. Satisfactory control can be obtained by applying the potent molluscicide sodium pentachlorphenate to water inhabited by the snail hosts.

7. *Schistosoma hæmatobium* (vesical blood fluke) is extensively distributed throughout Africa, the Near East and Middle East, and is also endemic in southern Portugal. The adult worms typically inhabit the vesical venous plexus. The eggs are extruded through the bladder wall and are excreted in the urine; but these blood flukes at times mature in the rectum, or they may migrate through the caval blood to various pelvic organs and the lungs. The intermediate hosts are non-operculate snails belonging to the genera *Bulinus, Physopsis,* and *Planorbis* in Morocco and Portugal.

   Vesical schistosomiasis causes hematuria. Later the bladder wall becomes fibrosed, bladder stones develop, the urethra becomes constricted and the genitalia, ureters, kidneys and lungs may be involved. Symptoms are primarily referable to dysfunction of the urinary bladder and urethra. Diagnosis is made by recovery of the characteristic elongated-ovoidal eggs with a terminal spine, in the urine or the stool. Antimony tartrates, administered by vein, are the most efficacious chemotherapeutics but Miracil D, given by mouth, provides considerable therapeutic promise. Control can be achieved by attacking the snail hosts with sodium pentachlorophenate.

8. Other blood flukes which have been reported from man include: *Schistosoma bovis, S. spindale, S. intercalatum, S. matthei, S. incognitum* and *S. faradjei.*

9. Schistosome dermatitis results from skin penetration of cercarias of blood flukes poorly adapted to the human host. In many fresh-water lakes and streams of the Americas, Europe and Asia summer epidemics have occurred when persons waded or swam in water infested with these cercarias, which for the most part develop to maturity in avian hosts. Occasionally the cercarias of non-human mammalian schistosomes also produce this type of dermatitis. In addition, the disease has resulted from wading (or swimming) in salt water along the shores of Hawaii, southern California, southern Florida and New England. Terns and other marine birds are the natural definitive hosts of these blood flukes.

   Schistosome dermatitis consists of a severe prickling as the non-human blood-fluke cercarias enter the skin from the infested water, a macule at each point of penetration, at times with local edema or generalized urticaria; later an intense nettling as each lesion changes into a pustule. No over-all effective control has been demonstrated, although molluscicidal agents have been employed in a few infested fresh-water areas.

REFERENCES

Bang, F., Ferguson, M. S., Hairston, N. G., and Graham, O. H. 1925. Hyperendemicity of Schistosomiasis Japonica on Leyte Island, P. I. Am. J. Trop. Med., *25*, 407.

Barbosa, F. S., Dobbins, J. E., Jr., and Vasconcelos, C. M. 1953. Infectação Natural de *Rattus Rattus Frugivorus* por *Schistosoma Mansoni* em Pernambuco. Pub. Avul. Inst. Aggeu Magalliães, *2*, 63–67.

Barlow, C. H., and Meleney, H. E. 1949. A Voluntary Infection with *Schistosoma Hæmatobium.* Am. J. Trop. Med., *29,* 79–87.
Brumpt, E. 1949. *Précis de Parasitologie.* 6th ed. 2138 pp., Masson et Cie, Paris.
Buckley, J. J. C. 1938. On a Dermatitis in Malaya Caused by the Cercariæ of *Schistosoma Spindale* Montgomery, 1906. J. Helminthol., *16,* 117–120.
Bueding, E. 1950. Carbohydrate Metabolism of *Schistosoma Mansoni.* J. Gen'l Physiol., *33,* 475–495.
Chandler, A. C. 1926. A New Schistosome Infection of Man, etc. Indian J. Med. Res., *14,* 179–183.
Chu, G. W. T. C. 1952. First Report of the Presence of a Dermatitis-producing Marine Larval Schistosome in Hawaii. Sci., *115,* 151–152.
Cort, W. W. 1928. Schistosome Dermatitis in the United States. J. Am. Med. Assn., *90,* 1027–1029.
————1950. Studies on Schistosome Dermatitis. Am. J. Hyg., *52,* 251–307.
Dias, E. 1953. Nova Possibilidade de Combate aos Moluscos Transmissores das Esquistossomoses. 22 pp., Bambuí, Minas Gerais (Brasil).
Expert Committee on Bilharziasis. 1953. First Report. World Health Org. Techn. Ser. No. 65. Geneva. 45 pp.
Faust, E. C. 1948. An Inquiry into Ectopic Lesions in Schistosomiasis. Am. J. Trop. Med., *28,* 175–199.
————1949. *Human Helminthology.* 3rd ed., 744 pp. Lea & Febiger, Philadelphia.
Faust, E. C., and Meleney, H. E. 1924. Schistosomiasis Japonica. Am. J. Hyg., Monogr. Ser., No. 3. 339 pp.
Faust, E. C., Wright, W. H., McMullen, D. B., and Hunter, G. W., III. 1946. The Diagnosis of Schistosomiasis Japonica. I. The Symptoms, Signs and Physical Findings Characteristic of Schistosomiasis Japonica at Different Stages in the Development of the Disease. Am. J. Trop. Med., *26,* 87–112.
Faust, E. C., *et al.* 1933–1934. Studies on Schistosomiasis Mansoni in Puerto Rico. I–III. Puerto Rico J. Pub. Health & Trop. Med., *9,* 154–168.
Fisher, A. C. 1934. A Study of the Schistosomiasis of the Stanleyville District of the Belgian Congo. Trans. R. Soc. Trop. Med. & Hyg., *28,* 277–306.
Gadgil, R. K., and Shah, S. N. 1952. Human Schistosomiasis in India. Discovery of an Endemic Focus in the Bombay States. Indian J. Med. Sci., *6,* 760-763.
Gelfand, M., and Ross, W. F. 1953. The Distribution of Schistosome Ova in the Alimentary Tract in Subjects of Bilharziasis. Trans. R. Soc. Trop. Med. & Hyg., *47,* 215–217.
Hernández-Morales, F., and Maldonado, J. F. 1946. Diagnosis of Schistosomiasis Mansoni by Rectal Biopsy Technique. Am. J. Trop. Med., *26,* 811–820.
Hsü, H. F., Li, S. Y., Wang, C. K., and Fan, P. C. 1952. Schistosomiasis Japonica in Formosa. Am. J. Trop. Med. & Hyg., *1,* 287–301.
Katsurada, F. 1904. *Schistosomum Japonicum,* ein Neuer Menschlicher Parasit. Annot. Zool. Japan., *5* (Pt. 3), 1–14.
Koppisch, E. 1937. Studies on Schistosomiasis Mansoni in Puerto Rico. IV. The Pathological Anatomy of Experimental Schistosomiasis in Puerto Rico. Puerto Rico J. Pub. Health & Trop. Med., *13,* 1–114.
Kuntz, R. 1952. *Schistosoma Mansoni* and S. *Hæmatobium* in the Yemen, Southwest Arabia: with a Report of an Unusual Factor in the Epidemiology of Schistosomiasis Mansoni. J. Parasitol., *38,* 24–28.
Leiper, R. T. 1918. Report on the Results of the Bilharzia Mission in Egypt. 140 pp. J. Royal Surg. Med. Corps., London.
McMullen, D. B. 1952. Schistosomiasis and Molluscacides. Am. J. Trop. Med. & Hyg., *1,* 671–679.
————1953. (See Expert Committee on Bilharziasis.)
McMullen, D. B., and Beaver, P. C. 1945. Studies on Schistosome Dermatitis. IX. The Life Cycles of Three Dermatitis-Producing Schistosomes from Birds and a Discussion of the Subfamily Bilharziellinæ (Trematoda: Schistosomatidæ). Am. J. Hyg., *42,* 128–154.
McMullen, D. B., Hubendick, B., Pesigan, T. P., and Bierstein, P. 1953. Observations Made by the World Health Organization Schistosomiasis Team in the Philippines. J. Parasitol., *39* (No. 4, Sec. 2), 17.

28

MEIRA, J. A. 1951. Esquistosomiase Mansoni Hépato-Esplênica. Tese, Fac. de Med., Univ. S. Paulo (Brasil). 607 pp.

MIYAIRI, K., and SUZUKI, M. 1914. Der Zwischenwirt des *Schistosomum Japonicum* Katsurada. Mitteil. Med. Fak. Kaiserl. Univ. Kyushu, *1*, 187–197.

MOST, H., *et al.* 1950. Schistosomiasis Japonica in American Military Personnel. Am. J. Trop. Med., *30*, 239–299.

OLIVIER, L. 1949. Schistosome Dermatitis, a Sensitization Reaction. Am. J. Hyg., *49*, 290–301.

OTTOLINA, C. 1951. Valor Absoluto de la Biopsia Rectoscopica por Transparencia. Estudio en 138 Rectos Humanos Enteros Preparados con una Technica Adecuata. Rev. Policl. Caracas, *19*, 79–151.

PESIGAN, T. P., and MASILUNGAN, V. A. 1950. Studies on Schistosomiasis. Experiments on the Chemical Control of *Oncomelania Quadrasi* Snails. J. Philippine Med. Assn., *26*, 17–30.

PIMENTAL, J. 1953. Infestação Experimental e Natural de Murídeos pelo *Schistosoma Mansoni.* Rev. Brasil. de Malariol. e Doenças Tropicais, *5*, 219–222.

PONS, J. A. 1937. Studies on Schistosomiasis Mansoni in Puerto Rico. V. Clinical Aspects. Puerto Rico J. Pub. Health & Trop. Med., *13*, 171–254.

SAMBON, L. W. 1907. Remarks on *Schistosoma Mansoni.* J. Trop. Med. & Hyg., *10*, 303–304.

SHORT, R. B. 1951. Hermaphroditic Female *Schistosomatium Douthitti* (Trematoda: Schistosomatidæ). J. Parasitol., *37*, 547–555.

STOLL, N. R. 1947. This Wormy World. J. Parasitol., *33*, 1–18.

STUNKARD, H. W., and HINCHLIFFE, M. C. 1952. The Morphology and Life History of *Microbilharzia Variglandis* (Miller and Northrup, 1926) Stunkard and Hinchliffe, 1951, Avian Blood-flukes Whose Larvæ Cause "Swimmer's Itch" of Ocean Beaches. J. Parasitol., *38*, 248–265.

SZIDAT, L. 1942. Was Ist *Cercaria Ocellata* La Valette? Morphologische und Entwicklungsgeschichte Untersuchungen ueber der Erreger der Europäischen Cercarien-Dermatitis des Menschen. Deutsh. Trop. Zeitschr., *46*, 481–597; 509–524.

VOGEL, H. 1947. Hermaphrodites of *Schistosoma Mansoni.* Ann. Trop. Med. & Parasitol., *41*, 266–277.

WRIGHT, W. H., and DOBROVOLNY, C. G. 1953. Experiments in the Control of Schistosomiasis in Brazil. Pub. Health Repts., *68*, 1156–1160.

WRIGHT, W. H., MCMULLEN, D. B., BENNETT, H. J., BAUMAN, P. M., and INGALLS, J. W., JR. 1947. The Epidemiology of Schistosomiasis Japonica in the Philippine Islands and Japan. III. Surveys of Endemic Areas of Schistosomiasis Japonica in Japan. Am. J. Trop. Med., *27*, 417–447.

WRIGHT, W. H., MCMULLEN, D. B., FAUST, E. C., and BAUMAN, P. M. 1947. The Epidemiology of Schistosomiasis Japonica in the Philippine Islands and Japan. II. Surveys for Schistosomiasis Japonica on Mindanao, Philippine Islands. Am. J. Hyg., *45*, 164–184.

SECTION V

Other Helminths Parasitizing Man

Chapter 16

Thorny-Headed Worms (Acanthocephalans)

THESE worms differ so fundamentally from other invertebrate forms that they are placed in a separate phylum, the Acanthocephala. Van Cleave (1941, 1947, 1948) has shown that they resemble the tapeworms, although in no way is there evidence of close kinship.

All species of acanthocephalans are parasitic throughout their life cycle except for the interval required for completion of embryonation of the eggs on the ground or in water. The sexes are separate. The designation "thorny-headed" refers to the armature of spines on the proboscis.

The adult acanthocephalans (Fig. 172) are elongated, somewhat flattened sacs, rounded posteriorly and provided anteriorly with a spinose proboscis which serves as an efficient organ for attachment to the host's intestinal wall. This organ may be introverted into a proboscis sheath located in the anterior part of the body proper. The living worms are chalky to milky white or light pink in color. They lack segmentation but may have superficial transverse constrictions (*Macrocanthorhynchus hirudinaceus*) or bead-like annulations (*Moniliformis moniliformis*). They vary in size from a few millimeters to several centimeters in length. They have no digestive tract and their body cavity lacks a mesothelium. They possess one or more pairs of very elongate, possibly glandular organs called lemnisci. In some species primitive nephridial structures have been described. There is a central nerve mass in or on the internal margin of the proboscis sheath.

The males (Fig. 172 *A*) are considerably smaller than the females. The male genitalia consist of the following structures: a *genital pore* at the posterior extremity, surrounded by a campanulate *bursa;* two ovoidal *testes*, each with a *vas efferens*, several *cement glands* opening into a *cement-gland receptacle*, and a *suspensory ligament* which anchors the male organs in the body cavity.

The females (Fig. 172 *B*) are likewise provided with a *suspensory ligament.* The primary genital organ consists of a number of ovarian follicles or floating *ovaries*, from which many eggs are produced and float in the body cavity. After 3 (or at times 4) egg envelopes have been provided, the eggs are withdrawn from the body cavity through a muscular bell-shaped structure, the *selective apparatus* into the *uterus*. They pass into the *vagina* and are discharged through a terminal pore.

Acanthocephalans are parasites of the intestine of their definitive hosts. The eggs are evacuated in the feces and deposited on the ground or in water, where they complete embryonation. On being ingested by species of arthropods, including dung beetles and cockroaches, the eggs hatch in the midgut, whereupon the emerging larvas migrate through the gut wall

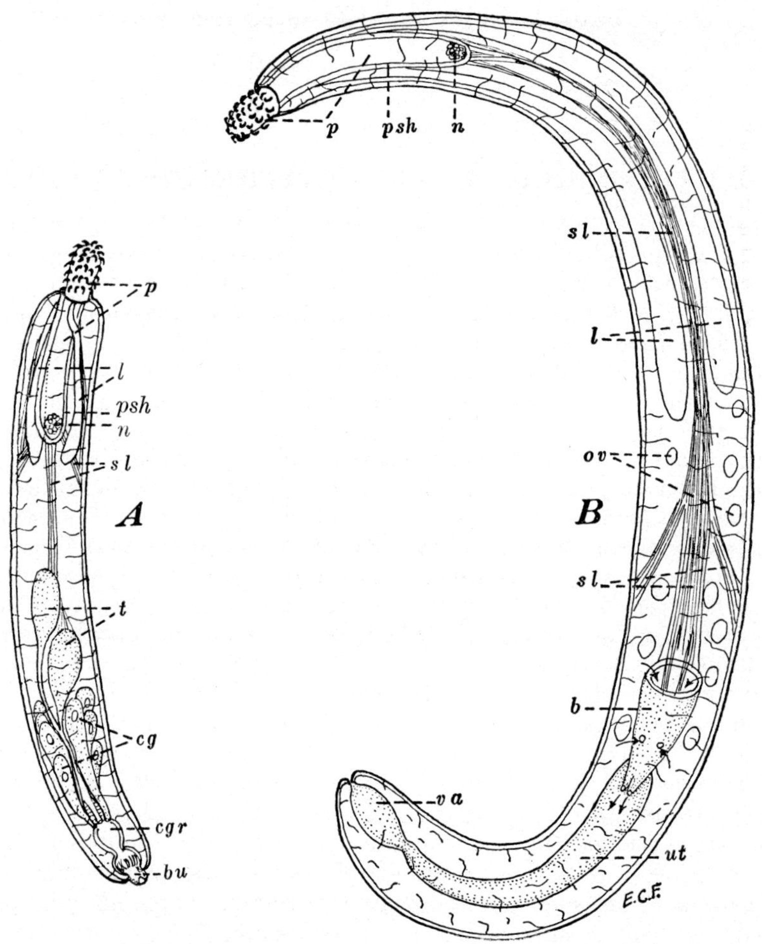

Fig. 172.—Morphology of male (*A*) and female (*B*) acanthocephalans. *b*, muscular bell; *bu*, bursa; *cg*, cement glands; *cgr*, cement gland receptacle; *l*, lemnisci; *n*, nerve mass; *ov*, floating ovaries; *p*, proboscis; *psh*, proboscis sheath; *sl*, suspensory ligaments; *t*, testes; *ut*, uterus; *va*, vagina. (Original, from Faust's *Human Helminthology*, Lea & Febiger, Philadelphia.)

into the hemal cavity and undergo development into *acanthor*, hatched from the egg; *acanthella*, the second larval stage, in which a rudimentary proboscis is developed, and *juvenile*, in which indications of adult structures may be found. When an appropriate vertebrate ingests an arthropod containing the juvenile forms, the young worms are digested out of their intermediate host, become attached to the definitive host's intestine, develop to maturity, mate, and egg-laying begins.

Two species of acanthocephalans have been reported as parasites of man, *e. g.*, *Macracanthorhynchus hirudinaceus* and *Moniliformis moniliformis*.

MACRACANTHORHYNCHUS HIRUDINACEUS (Pallas, 1891) Travassos, 1917

(The giant spiny-snouted leech-like worm)

This large acanthocephalan is milky-white or somewhat pinkish in color, cylindroidal, slightly flattened dorsoventrally and has transverse striations of its cuticle. The proboscis is provided with 5 or 6 series of recurved spines

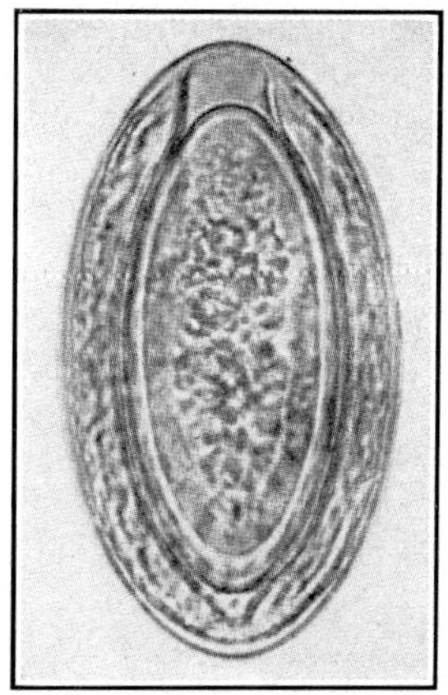

FIG. 173.—Photomicrograph of partly embryonated egg of *Macracanthorhynchus hirudinaceus*. × 500. (Original, from Faust's *Human Helminthology*, Lea & Febiger, Philadelphia.)

arranged in counterclockwise spirals. The males measure 5 to 10 cm. in length by 3 to 5 mm. in breadth and the females, 20 to 35 cm. in length by 4 to 10 mm. in breadth. The posterior end of the females is obtusely rounded.

M. hirudinaceus has a cosmopolitan distribution. Pigs, wild boars, the peccary, and occasionally dogs and monkeys are the natural definitive hosts. The ellipsoidal eggs (Fig. 173) measure 80 to 100 microns in length by about 40 to 50 microns in diameter. They have 3 embryonic envelopes and are fairly mature when evacuated in the host's feces. Coprophagous beetles are the intermediate hosts.

Human infection with *M. hirudinaceus* has been reported only once (Lambl, 1859), based on an immature female worm recovered at autopsy of a 9-year-old child who died of leukemia in Prague (1857). Brumpt (1949) considers that this was probably a mistaken diagnosis and that the worm may have been a species of acanthocephalan parasitic in fish which had been poorly cleaned before being consumed. Gonzaga (1921) reported recovery of the eggs of *M. hirudinaceus* in 2 of 1,236 stool specimens examined in northern Brazil but these may have been cases of false infection which resulted from ingestion of parasitized hog's intestines.

In the natural hosts the attachment of *M. hirudinaceus* to the intestinal wall produces a marked local inflammation, with infiltration of many eosinophilic leukocytes, followed by necrosis of the area and at times perforation.

MONILIFORMIS MONILIFORMIS (Bremser, 1811) Travassos, 1915
(The moniliform acanthocephalan)

The adults of this species are milky white in color and somewhat attenuate at both extremities. The body is superficially constricted into a considerable number of bead-like pseudo-segments. The proboscis is armed with 12 to 15 spiraling rows of recurved hooklets, 7 to 8 in each row. The males have a length of 4 to 5 cm. and the females, 10 to 27 cm.

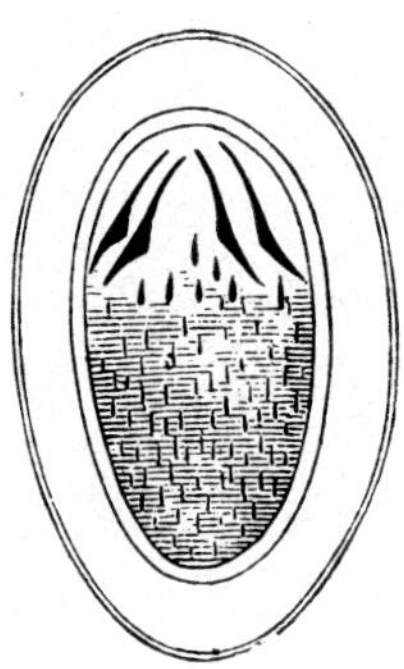

Fig. 174.—Egg of *Moniliformis moniliformis*, fully embryonated. × 500. (After Grassi and Calandruccio, from Faust's *Human Helminthology*, Lea & Febiger, Philadelphia.)

M. moniliformis is a cosmopolitan parasite in the small intestine of domestic and wild rodents. The ellipsoidal eggs (Fig. 174), measuring 85 to 118 microns in length by 40 to 52 microns in diameter, are provided with three embryonic envelopes. Various species of cockroaches and coprophagous beetles serve as intermediate hosts. Infection of the mammalian host is due to ingestion of the infected insect. Sita (1949) reported that the biological incubation period of *M. moniliformis* in laboratory rats is 22 to 38 days.

Authentic human infection has been reported from Italy (1 natural and 1 experimental infection), the Sudan (1 case) and British Honduras (1 case).

The clinical aspects of *M. moniliformis* infection were carefully studied by Calandruccio (Grassi and Calandruccio, 1888) who inoculated himself experimentally. Nineteen days after swallowing several larvas, he developed severe gastro-intestinal pain, with diarrhea, exhaustion, sleepiness and tinnitus. Eggs first appeared in his stools about 5 weeks after inoculation. Extract of male fern produced evacuation of all of the worms, but the symptoms did not disappear for an additional 2 days.

SUMMARY

1. The thorny-headed worms, or Acanthocephala, are elongated, somewhat flattened, sacculate organisms, measuring from a few millimeters to many centimeters in length, and are provided anteriorly with a spinose proboscis. They lack segmentation but at times have superficial transverse constrictions. They also lack a digestive tract and a mesothelial lining of the body cavity. The sexes are separate. The adults are intestinal parasites of vertebrates.
2. Eggs laid by the female worms are evacuated in the host's feces. When fully-embryonated eggs are ingested by a coprophagous arthropod they hatch (acanthor stage), migrate to the hemocele and transform into the acanthella and then the juvenile stage; when the definitive host ingests the infected larval host, opportunity is provided for completion of the cycle.
3. Two species of acanthocephalans have been reported as human parasites, *Macracanthorhynchus hirudinaceus*, a large form commonly found as an adult in the pig and using dung beetles as intermediate hosts, diagnosed once on the basis of an immature specimen obtained post-mortem from a child in Prague, and *Moniliformis moniliformis*, a parasite of rodents with larval stages in roaches, recovered in human infections once each in Italy, the Sudan and British Honduras. Following a self-imposed experimental infection with this species Calandruccio, in Italy, experienced severe intestinal distress and systemic intoxication, which subsided after evacuation of the worms.

REFERENCES

Brumpt, E. 1949. *Précis de Parasitologie.* 6th ed. p. 1037. Masson et Cie, Paris.

Grassi, B., and Calandruccio, S. 1888. Ueber einen Echinorhynchus Welcher Auch in Menschen Parasitiert und Dessen Zwischenwirth ein Blaps Ist. Centralbl. Bakt., *3*, 521–525.

Sita, E. 1949. The Life-Cycle of *Moniliformis Moniliformis* (Bremser, 1811), Acanthocephala. Current Sci. (India), *18*, 216–218.

Van Cleave, H. J. 1941. Relationships of the Acanthocephala. Am. Naturalist, *75*, 31–47.

———1947. A Critical Review of Terminology for Immature Stages in Acanthocephalan Life Histories. J. Parasitol., *33*, 118–125.

———1948. Expanding Horizons in the Recognition of a Phylum. J. Parasitol., *34*, 1–20.

Chapter 17

Gordiid Worms or "Hair Snakes"

THIS group of diecious worms constitutes a division (Class Gordiacea) of the Phylum Nematomorpha. Superficially gordiid worms resemble the true roundworms (Phylum Nematoda) but their internal anatomy is different in the following respects: (1) their body cavity is lined with mesothelium; (2) there are no longitudinal cords; (3) the digestive tract is atrophied in mature worms; (4) a cloaca is present in the female as well as in the male, and (5) the ovaries are not continuous with their ducts, so that the eggs are first discharged into the body cavity and then enter the ducts.

The adult worms (Fig. 175) are elongated wiry objects, creamy-yellow to dark brown in color, intensely opaque and measure from 10 to 50 cm. in

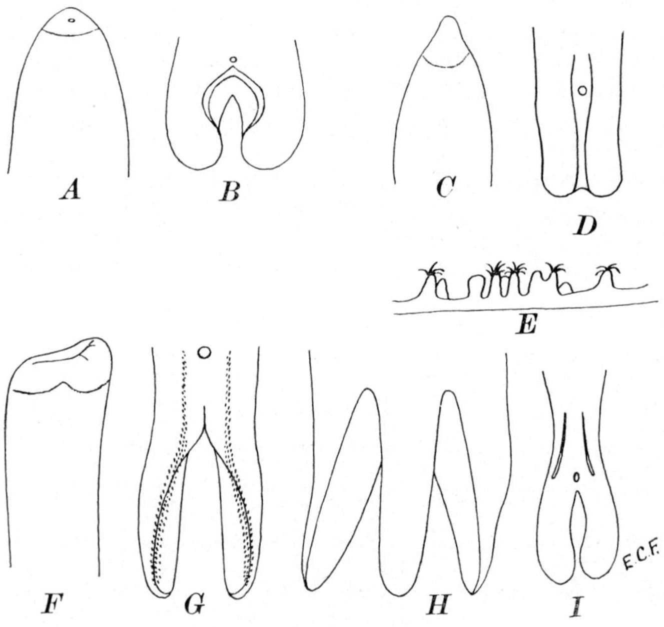

FIG. 175.—Diagnostic characters of some gordiid worms. *A*, anterior end and *B*, posterior end of male *Gordius villoti*, enlarged; *C*, anterior end and *D*, posterior end of male *Chordodes*, enlarged; *E*, section through cuticular papillæ and hairs of *Chordodes*, greatly enlarged; *F*, anterior end and *G*, posterior end of male *Paragordius varius*, enlarged; *H*, posterior end of female *P. varius*, enlarged; *I*, posterior end of male *Parachordodes*, enlarged. (*A*, *B*, *C*, *D*, *I*, adapted from Camerano; *E*, adapted from Römer; *F*, *G*, *H*, adapted from Stiles, from Faust's *Human Helminthology*, Lea & Febiger, Philadelphia.)

length. Their anterior ends are either somewhat elliptically pointed or bluntly rounded. The posterior end of the male is bifurcated behind the anus (Fig. 175, *B, G, I*) or at least grooved (Fig. 175, *D*), while that of the female is either entire or trifurcated.

The mature worms live in fresh water, where they slowly move about in a stiff, wiry fashion. Here they mate and the females discharge strings of eggs into the water. After a period of embryonation in water a larva breaks out of the egg shell. Provided with a beaked proboscis having retractile stylets and three rows of reversed spines, it bores into animal tissue. In a grasshopper or cricket, it proceeds to the hemocele of this insect and transforms into a snake-like worm which is coiled back and forth on itself. As it approaches maturity the gordiid ruptures the body wall of the insect and becomes a free-living aquatic worm.

Human "Parasitism" with Gordiid Worms

There are many accounts of gordiid worms parasitic in man. While some of these reports suggest that the worms were only a contamination of human excreta, there are instances of indubitable passage of the living organisms in the vomitus or feces and of a few discharged *per urethram*. Infested water used as a vaginal douche may account for urethral discharge of mature gordiids from female subjects (Baylis, 1941; Carvalho, 1942) but no plausible explanation has been advanced in the case of several quite immature specimens passed *per urethram* on several occasions by an adult male patient in South Carolina (Craig and Faust, 1951, page 443).

Apparently authentic instances of gordiid worms evacuated from the human body have been reported from Europe, Africa, and North and South America. In none of these is there evidence of true parasitism or that the presence of a gordiid in the digestive tract produced serious harm. In each of the three reported cases of urethral exit of the worms there was a history of pain in the bladder or inguinal region which was relieved on spontaneous escape of the worms.

The 1 reported instance of tissue invasion of man by a gordiid worm is that from Florida reported by Sayad, Johnson and Faust (1936). An immature female *Gordius* (probably *G. robustus*) was partly removed surgically and partly left in place in a tumorous tissue pocket which had developed on the lower border of the orbit of an adult white male resident of Miami, Florida. The worm had caused considerable local host cell reaction, with dense infiltration of eosinophils, epithelioid and giant cells. There was no indication in the patient's history as to how the worm had become established in this location.

SUMMARY

1. Gordiid worms, or "hair snakes," belonging to the Class Gordiacea, Phylum Nematomorpha, superficially resemble the true roundworms (Nematoda) but differ in the following fundamental characteristics: a body cavity lined with mesothelium; lack of longitudinal cords; digestive tract atrophied in the mature worms; cloaca in the female as well as the

male, and ovaries discontinuous with their ducts. Furthermore, gordiid worms are parasitic only during their larval development and the adult worms are free-living in fresh water.

2. The adult males and females are elongated, creamy-yellow to dark brown wiry objects which measure 10 to 50 cm. in length. After fertilization the female discharges strings of eggs that embryonate in the water and give birth to larvas that actively penetrate into the hemocele of the intermediate hosts (grasshoppers and crickets), where they gradually metamorphose into the adult stage, following which they escape into water.
3. Human "parasitism" with "hair snakes" has been reported from many parts of the world. In most instances the worms have been spontaneously passed in the feces or have been vomited. Twice they have been voided *per urethram* by female subjects and once by a male subject. In none of these cases is there evidence of true parasitism. There is one record of an immature female specimen which had become lodged in tissue on the lower border of the orbit of an adult white male, with resultant inflammatory reaction.

REFERENCES

Baylis, H. A. 1927. Notes on Two Gordiids and a Mermithid Said to Have Been Parasitic in Man. Trans. R. Soc. Trop. Med. & Hyg., *21*, 203–206.

Carvalho, J. C. M. 1942. Studies on Some Gordiacea of North and South America. J. Parasitol., *28*, 213–222.

Sayad, W. Y., Johnson, V. M., and Faust, E. C. 1936. Human Parasitization with *Gordius Robustus*. J. Am. Med. Assn., *106*, 461–462.

Chapter 18

The Leeches or Hirudineans

Introduction

THE leeches, Class Hirudinea of the Phylum Annelida, are predatory or parasitic invertebrates which have true segmentation. They have a very muscular body, which is elongated-ovoidal, and are provided with two suckers, one surrounding the mouth and one at the posterior end of the body (Fig. 176), by which they are enabled to perform locomotion like the "measuring worms" (larvas of geometrid moths). Leeches utilize blood of vertebrate animals as their primary source of food and most species are avidily sanguivorous. Like ticks, the leeches are capable of ingesting a comparatively large quantity of blood, which they temporarily store in greatly distended ceca and later digest. Some leeches are aquatic, others terrestrial in rain-forest areas and still others are amphibious.

Morphology, Biology and Life Cycle

Morphology.—Leeches vary in size from small macroscopic objects to those many centimeters in length, and in shape from elongated cylindroidal to broadly ovoidal or pyriform objects. They have an antero-posterior axis, bilateral symmetry and are dorso-ventrally compressed, but frequently have a convex dorsum and a concave ventral side. There are a maximum of 34 true segments in the body, distinguished by a similar number of median ventral, paired nerve ganglia and a similar number of rows of sensory papillæ; however in each true somite there are from three to many external annulations.

A thin, smooth, tough cuticle covers the body. In the median annulus of each metamere there are numerous minute sensory papillæ. Seventeen pairs of excretory apertures, or nephridiopores, are located in the median annulus of metameres 7 to 23. On the dorsal face of each of the first 5 metameres in most leeches there are minute pairs of "eye-spots" or light-sensitive end organs. Cuticular setæ are developed only in the genus *Acanthobdella*. Depending on the species, the surface of the leech may be essentially colorless, *e. g.*, leukodermatous, striped longitudinally or symmetrically patterned in colors.

The *digestive system* (Fig. 177) is provided anteriorly with a protrusile proboscis (order Rhynchobdellida) or three very muscular jaws with marginal denticles (order Gnathobdellida). The small mouth leads into a muscular pharynx, which is surrounded by many unicellular secretory glands that provide anticoagulin (*hirudin*) when the leech is taking a blood meal. Behind the pharynx there is a long, thin-walled median crop, with

11 pairs of distensible diverticula or ceca. The distal end of the crop joins the midgut, where digestion of the stored blood takes place. Further posteriorly there are first a short intestine and then a short rectum which opens through a small anal pore.

The *excretory system* (Fig. 177) consists of 17 pairs of nephridia in segments 7 to 23.

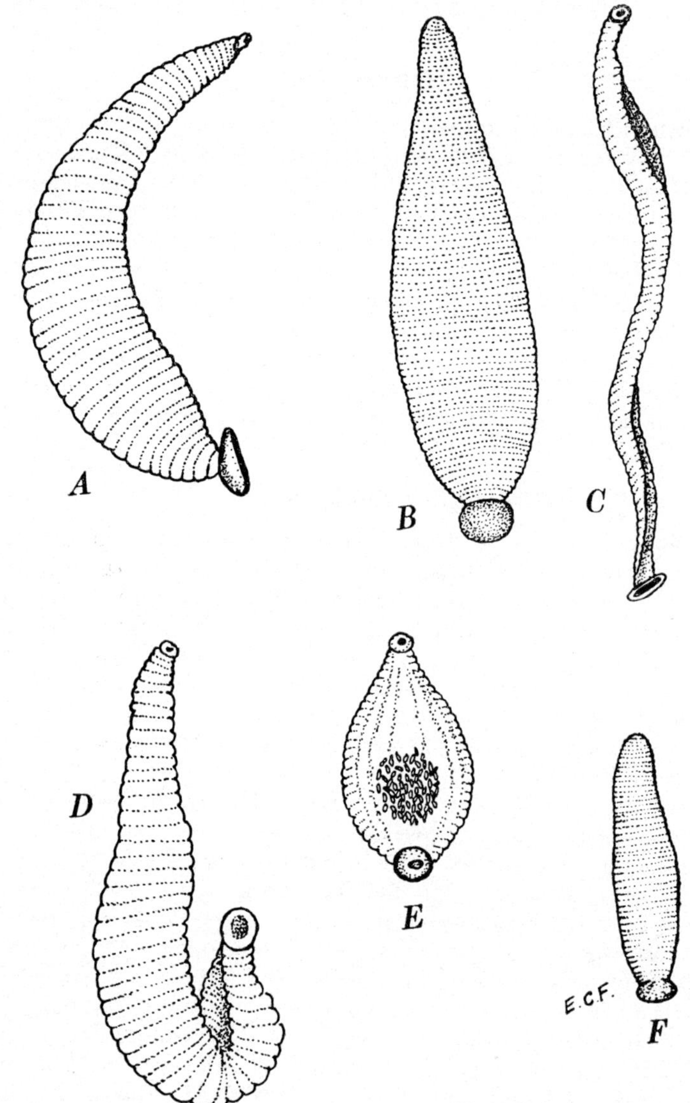

FIG. 176.—Habit sketches of leeches. × 1. *A*, *Limnatis nilotica* (adapted from Brumpt); *B*, dorsal view and *C*, lateral view of extended specimen of *Hirudo medicinalis* (adapted from Schmidt); *D*. *Hæmopis sanguisuga* (adapted from Blanchard); *E*, *Placobdella parasitica*, ventral view, with brood of attached young (adapted from Hemingway in Nachtrieb); *F*, *Hæmadipsa zeylanica*, dorsal view (adapted from Brumpt).

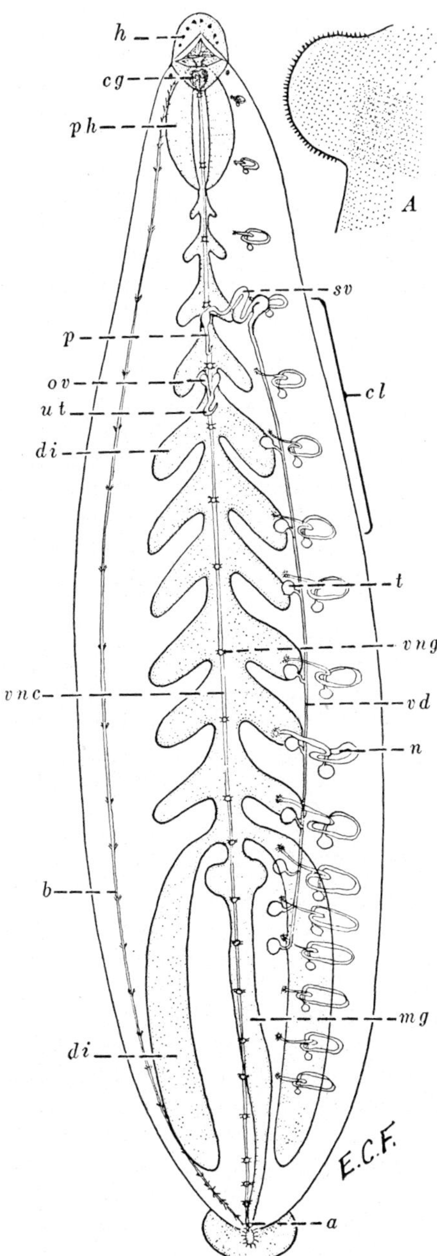

Fig. 177.—Internal anatomy of the "medicinal leech," *Hirudo medicinalis*. Bilaterally symmetrical nephridia and male genitalia are shown only on the right side, the lateral blood vessel only on the left side. *a*, anus; *b*, blood vessel; *cg*, cephalic ganglion or "brain"; *cl*, clitellar metameres; *di*, diverticula of the crop; *h*, head with "eye-spots"; *mg*, midgut; *n*, nephridium; *ov*, ovary; *p*, penis; *ph*, pharynx; *sv*, seminal vesicle; *t*, testis; *ut*, uterus; *vd*, vas deferens; *vnc*, ventral nerve cord; *vng*, ventral nerve ganglion. × 2. *A*, detail of one of the 3 hammerhead jaws with marginal denticles, greatly enlarged. (Original adaptation, from Faust's *Human Helminthology*, Lea & Febiger, Philadelphia.)

The *blood-vascular system* is composed of bloodvessels with muscular walls and two blood sinuses (one dorsal and one ventral) which represent the greatly reduced body cavity. Branches and capillaries extend to all parts of the organism. The circulating blood contains plasma, at times with free hemoglobin, and colorless corpuscles.

The *nervous system* (Fig. 177) consists of a pair of median ventral, partially fused ganglia for each metamere, with connecting longitudinal twinned nerve cords, and at the anterior end a large cephalic ganglion having commissures around the anterior end of the pharynx to the small, dorsally situated "brain." Nerves arising from the ganglia extend to all important organs and tissues, including the "eye-spots," sensory papillæ, suckers, etc.

The *reproductive organs* of both sexes are found in the same worm. Each organism (Fig. 177) possesses 1 to 10 (or more) pairs of small spherical *testes*, a *vas efferens* for each testis, a pair each of *vasa deferentia*, *seminal vesicles*, *prostate glands*, *ejaculatory ducts* and muscular *penial organs;* one pair of *ovaries* with *oviducts* which unite and join a muscular *uterus* that opens through a short *vagina* one metamere behind the male genital pore.

Life Cycle.—Insemination is characteristically accomplished by cross-fertilization, either by reciprocal copulation in which the penis of one is introduced into the vagina of another, or by implantation of a horny spermatophore containing the spermatozoa of one onto the cuticle of another. Fertilization therefore always precedes oviposition. In some groups the eggs are deposited soon after fertilization; in other groups (Fig. 176, *E*) the eggs and even the hatched young are carried for some time in a cocoon secreted by special glands in the 9th to 11th metameres. As soon as the little leech is able to suck blood, it leaves its parent and fends for itself.

Medical Importance of Leeches

Since the days of early Greek medicine the "medicinal leech" (*Hirudo medicinalis*) has been employed by physicians to extract blood from patients (Fig. 176, *B*, *C*). The medicinal leech is still dispensed in some pharmacies of Europe and Latin America.

Leeches Injurious to Man.—These belong to two ecologic groups, aquatic and terrestrial. Aquatic forms are responsible for internal hirudiniasis, and the terrestrial species for external hirudiniasis.

Internal Hirudiniasis.—Small, unengorged leeches, which get into the mouth in unfiltered or unstrained drinking water, reach the posterior pharynx, the larynx, epiglottis and esophagus, or may wander into the nasopharynx, become attached and suck blood. They increase greatly in size, cause congestion and inflammatory swelling of the area, at times producing occlusion of the respective passages. They produce intense pain and tenderness of the affected region. If the leech is attached to the posterior pharynx or the larynx, sudden deep inhalation of air may carry it into the trachea or a bronchus, producing blockage of the air passage and at times suffocation.

Internal hirudiniasis involving the pharynx and upper respiratory tract has been widely reported from southern Europe, northern Africa, the

Azores and Canary Islands, Turkey, Syria, Palestine, Iran, Baluchistan, Seistan, Afghanistan, Turkestan, southwest China, and on the northwest frontiers of India. In many of these regions the leech is *Limnatis nilotica* (Fig. 176, *A*), which is so small as to be hardly noticed in clear water of quiet brooks, pools, ponds or lakes; but after attachment to mucous membranes and engorgement it may reach a length of 8 to 12 cm. and a width of 1 to 1.5 cm. near the posterior end. The mouth is surrounded by a relatively weak sucker but is armed with 3 powerful jaws provided with many marginal denticles and with sensory papillæ. The posterior sucker is large and powerful. The upper side of the worm is dark olive green, at times with longitudinal striping, the lower side dark gray. *L. maculosa* (reported from Malaya), *L. africana* (Senegal and the Congo basin), *L. mysomelas* (Senegal) and *L. granulosa* (India) are other species of *Limnatis* with similar histories of attachment to mucous membranes. *Dinobdella ferax* is a common culprit in India, Burma, southern China and Formosa (Chin, 1949). Undiagnosed species have been reported from Java and Sumatra.

Internal hirudiniasis may also occur as a result of bathing, swimming or standing waist-high in leech-infested fresh water, with involvement of the vagina (Woolnough, 1928), labium majus (Hamilton, 1933) or male urethra (Ghosh, 1933). Moreover, bathers whose eyes come in contact with leeches free in the water may develop corneal (Mazzola, 1929) or conjunctival (Kuwahara, 1903) lesions.

Leeches lodged in the nasal passages may be visualized with a speculum. If the worm is located in the nares, naso-pharynx or upper pharynx, the area may be injected with procaine and the intruder removed with a probe having a sharp hook on its inner end. Considerable skill is required to snare the slippery object. If the leech has become attached to the posterior pharynx, larynx, trachea or bronchus, conservative treatment requires that the patient be placed in the Trendelenburg position before attempts are made to remove it. In the event of lodgment in the trachea, tracheotomy may be required. For leech infestation of the genito-urinary tract, strong saline irrigation is advised to evacuate the worm.

All drinking water from areas where aquatic leeches are known to occur should be boiled, filtered or strained through several layers of cheese cloth.

External Hirudiniasis.—Leech infestation of the skin is a relatively common occurrence among persons who travel through tropical rain-forests. Moreover, it has been reported from the Chilean Andes, Australia and Micronesia. A considerable number of terrestrial leeches have been incriminated, including the notorious *Hæmadipsa zeylanica* of India, Ceylon and Burma, *H. japonica* of Japan, *H. talagalla* of the Philippines, *H. javanica* of Java, *H. fallax*, *H. morsitans* and *H. vagans* of Madagascar, a species of *Philæmon* in Australia and many undiagnosed species from other areas.

H. zeylanica (Fig. 176, *F*) attains a length of 2 to 3 cm. According to the naturalist Tennent (1860) this leech is a veritable scourge of man and beast. "Their size is so insignificant, and the wound they make is so skillfully punctured, that both are generally imperceptible, and the first intimation of their onslaught is the trickling of blood, or a chill feeling of the leech when it begins to hang heavily on the skin from being distended with its repast." Worth (1951) doubts the ability of these leeches to leap on their victim, although he admits that they "may at times 'drop' onto hosts from overhanging vegetation." He states that "final lodgment on a host results from initial awareness of the host's presence and resultant crawling activity in the host's direction." The first man in a group passing through a leech-infested region activates the leech, "leading to infestation of individuals subsequently traversing the disturbed path."

Travelers through leech-infested tropical rain-forests are frequently plagued by these worms, which are able to get inside closely-woven pants or insinuate themselves into tightly laced, stout, knee-length leather boots. At times so much swelling of the feet is produced as a result of the infestation that it is very difficult to remove the boots at the end of the day.

Although the leech's puncture of the skin is essentially painless, there may be a serous discharge from the wound for some time, due to secretion of hirudin into the puncture site. Healing is slow and is frequently complicated by invasion of pyogenic organisms. Leeches found attached to the skin should not be pulled off without first applying a few drops of brine or procaine to the worm or touching it with a match flame, after which it can be removed by gentle traction. The wound should then be staunched and covered with an aseptic dressing. As a prophylactic, dimethyl phthalate, when applied to clothing in the amount of 4 cc. per square foot, and to the tongue, lace holes and neck of shoes or boots, repels terrestrial leeches up to 6 days (Ribbands, 1946).

SUMMARY

1. Leeches (Class Hirudinea, Phylum Annelida) are aquatic or terrestrial invertebrate forms, predatory or parasitic and typically blood-sucking in their habits. They have true segmentation but are provided with three or more superficial annulations for each metamere. They vary in size from small macroscopic objects to several centimeters in length, are elongated, bilaterally symmetrical, dorso-ventrally compressed, and have a sucker at the anterior and posterior extremities. One group (Rhynchobdellida) have a protrusile proboscis but the species of medical importance (Gnathobdellida) have three muscular jaws with marginal denticles.
2. Leeches have a complete digestive tract, with 11 pairs of distensible diverticula from the thin-walled crop, capable of storing a considerable amount of blood.
3. Leeches are hermaphroditic but cross-fertilization is characteristic. In some species the eggs are laid as soon as they are fertilized; in other species the eggs or even the hatched young are carried for some time on the ventral side of the parent.
4. Leeches are injurious to man by internal or external attachment. Species which live in water may be accidentally taken into the mouth and become attached to the mucous lining of the pharynx or upper respiratory passages, producing painful inflammatory swellings and at times blockage of the respiratory passages, or may enter the urethra or infest the conjunctiva. This type of injury is called internal hirudiniasis. Other species in tropical rain-forests fasten themselves to the skin of

persons passing along jungle paths, frequently getting under clothing or within leather boots, where they suck blood and produce relatively painless swelling of the affected areas. This type of infestation is called external hirudiniasis.

5. In cases of internal hirudiniasis of the pharynx or upper respiratory passages, the worm should first be visualized, anethesized by injection of procaine into the parasitized area, then skillfully removed with a hooked probe, but great care must be exercised that the patient does not inhale the leech into the trachea or a bronchus. For urethral infestation irrigation with strong salt solution is usually effective. In cases of external hirudiniasis a few drops of procaine or strong salt solution or a match flame should be applied to the worm to cause its partial relaxation, after which it may be removed by gentle traction. The bleeding is then staunched and the would dressed aseptically.
6. Prophylaxis in internal hirudiniasis of the pharynx or respiratory organs consists in drinking only boiled or filtered water. The application of dimethyl phthalate to the skin, clothing and the inside of boots is usually effective in preventing external hirudiniasis.

REFERENCES

Chin, T. H. 1949. Further Note on Leech Infestation in Man. J. Parasitol., *35*, 215.

Ghosh, M. M. 1933. A Leech in the Male Urethra. Indian Med. Gaz., *68*, 574.

Hamilton, C. S. P. 1933. Leech Bite of Labium Majus. Indian Med. Gaz., *68*, 87–88.

Kuwahara, Y. 1903. Ueber Lebende Hirudineen im Bindehautsack des Menschlichen Auge. Centralbl. f. prakt. Augenheilk., *27*, 262–263.

Ribbands, C. R. 1946. Experiments with Leech Repellents. Ann. Trop. Med. & Parasitol., *40*, 314–319.

Salzberger, M. 1928. Leeches as Foreign Bodies in the Upper Air Passages in Palestine. Laryngoscope, *38*, 27–32.

Seyfarth, C. 1917. Tropische und Subtropische Süsswasserblutegel als Parasiten im Menschen. Centralbl. Bakt., *79*, 89–96.

Woolnough, S. J. 1928. Intractable Bleeding from a Leech Bite. Med. J. Austral., *i*, 115.

Worth, C. B. 1951. Description and Discussion of the Biting of an Indian Land Leech (Annelida: Hirudinea). J. Bombay Natural Hist. Soc., Dec., 423–425.

SECTION VI

Arthropods as Agents and Vectors

Chapter 19

Arthropods and Human Disease

INTRODUCTION

ARTHROPODS (Phylum Arthropoda) constitute the largest group of related organisms in the Animal Kingdom. They are segmented invertebrates which are bilaterally symmetrical, have an antero-posterior axis, are provided with an exoskeleton and have paired jointed appendages. In the ancestral arthropod (Fig. 178) all of the segments (metameres) were sepa-

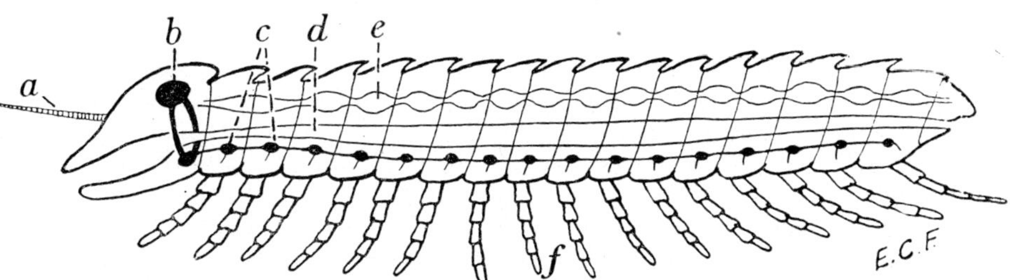

FIG. 178.—An ancestral arthropod (lateral view). *a*, antenna; *b*, brain; *c*, ventral nerve cord with twinned ganglion for each segment. *d*, digestive tract; *e*, dorsal blood vessel; *f*, jointed appendages of one side. (Adaptation by Faust, from Craig and Faust's *Clinical Parasitology*, Lea & Febiger, Philadelphia.)

rated from one another, with a twinned nerve ganglion and a pair of jointed appendages of similar type for each body segment; but as evolutionary changes developed, the 5 (or 6) anteriormost segments became consolidated into a head portion, and the head appendages became modified into sense organs (*antennæ*), jaws (*mandibles*), piercing organs (*cheliceræ*), etc., while those of the remainder of the body became transformed in terrestrial species into *walking legs* and in aquatic species into biramous paddle-like *swimming appendages*.

The Adult.—All arthropods possess a *digestive tract* divided into three portions, *viz.*, (1) a foregut lined with chitin, divided successively into a mouth cavity, a muscular pharynx, esophagus and proventriculus, for the ingestion and trituration of food; (2) a non-chitinized midgut or "stomach," in which nutriment is digested and from which it is absorbed, and (3) a chitinized posterior portion, consisting of hindgut and rectum for the accumulation and elimination of excreta.

The *excretory organs*, present in all but a few arthropods, consist of the Malpighian tubules, usually 2 or more in number, which lie freely in the hemocele and open into the hindgut near its junction with the midgut. They serve to collect liquid wastes, which are then discharged into the hindgut.

There is a *blood vascular system* consisting of a dorsally situated pumping organ (heart), aorta and paired vessels, and a hemal cavity (hemocele) which extends into all parts of the body and communicates with the heart. The blood consists of plasma and corpuscles and is usually provided with hemocyanin rather than hemoglobin.

The *respiratory system* has been developed into one or the other of two main types, *viz.*, gills for aquatic species and a tracheal system for terrestrial forms. The "book lungs" of scorpions and spiders constitute a special adaptation of gills to a non-aquatic environment.

The *central nervous system* consists of a dorsally-situated "brain" composed of 5 or 6 fused cephalic ganglia, circum-esophageal commissures to the median ventral paired nerve trunks, and twinned ganglia for each post-cephalic body segment. Nerve fibers extend from the central nervous system to all important organs and tissues. In many groups there are light-sensitive organs in the head, either individual "eye-spots" (ocelli) or compound eyes (ommatidia).

Arthropods have no trace of a ciliated epithelium. The musculature which is mostly striated is highly developed in many species, particularly in the organs of locomotion.

The sexes are separate and are frequently distinguishable by external morphologic differences.

The Life Cycle.—The simplest type of life cycle consists of egg, one or more larval stages resembling the adult except for smaller size and lack of sex organs, and the adult. Some groups have one or more nymphal stages between larva and adult, while others have a much more complicated development, with the interpolation of a pupal stage between the last larva and the adult. In the latter type there is little resemblance between the larva and the adult, so that during the pupal period complete internal and external reörganization is required. During each stage of growth the entire exoskeleton as well as the chitinous lining of the foregut and hindgut are shed and a new exoskeleton is secreted.

Biology of Arthropods.—There is agreement among entomologists that arthropods were originally aquatic. Groups like the copepods and the larger crustaceans have continued to inhabit the water and respire through gills. Many species have become terrestrial and as a result have developed a tracheal type of respiration. Others which are aquatic during their larval and pupal stages and aërial during their adult life employ tracheal respiration during both immature and sexually mature stages.

Medical Importance of Arthropods.—Some types of arthropods are beneficial to man; others produce great economic loss, and still others are themselves harmful in causing disease, in serving as intermediate hosts of parasites or in transmitting pathogenic microörganisms.

Classification of Arthropods.—For the systematic classification of arthropods and the major morphologic character of different groups the reader is referred to Chapter 3, page 31. The species of medical importance belong to the following groups.

CRUSTACEA (mostly aquatic). Examples: copepods (*Cyclops* and *Diaptomus*); decapods (crabs and crayfishes). [Intermediate hosts.]

CHILOPODA (terrestrial). Example: centipedes. [Venomous.]

ARACHNIDA (terrestrial). Examples: scorpions, spiders, ticks and mites. [Venomous, biological vectors, intermediate hosts.]

PENTASTOMIDA (strictly endo-parasitic). Examples: the tongue worms. [Parasitic.]

INSECTA (Aquatic, terrestrial or parasitic during larval development; terrestrial, aërial or parasitic in adult stage). Examples: sucking lice, true bugs, beetles, bees, wasps and ants, moths, flies and gnats, fleas. [Venomous, biological and mechanical vectors, intermediate hosts, parasitic.]

ARTHROPODS AS AGENTS OF HUMAN DISEASE

Many arthropods are agents of disease when the adult or larval stage of the organism feeds on the skin or underlying tissues, withdrawing blood, producing traumatic or necrotic damage, or causing sensitization. And in a few groups the arthropod introduces a potent venom into the skin of the victim, producing local, systemic and neurotoxic injury.

CENTIPEDES (CHILOPODA)

Adult Morphology.—Centipedes (Fig. 179) are elongated terrestrial forms ranging from 5 to 25 cm. or more in length, with one pair of jointed appendages and one pair of tracheal openings (spiracles) for each body segment behind the head. The genital pores are found ventrally on the penultimate body segment. The head appendages consist of a pair of long, many-jointed antennæ, a pair of stout mandibles, an anterior pair of biramous maxillæ, and a posterior pair of leg-like maxillæ. A pair of poison claws arise from the first body segment just ventro-lateral to the mouth. The terminal joint of each claw is a strong, sharply-pointed, incurved, piercing fang, with a subterminal pore for secretion from the poison gland which is situated in the base of the claw. The opalescent discharge consists of venom and a much larger amount of digestive enzymes.

Clinical Notes.—The size of the centipede, its activity and the time which has elapsed since the last "bite" are usually related to the amount of venom introduced into the skin of the victim. Many centipedes have considerable difficulty in piercing the skin of the human finger (Baerg, 1929) and at most produce a sharp pain at the site of inoculation, with local erythema and occasionally induration, papule formation or superficial necrosis (Pawlowsky and Stein, 1935; Buecherl, 1946). No human deaths have been reported as a result of uncomplicated centipede bites.

On a number of occasions small centipedes have been found to be accidental invaders of the human nares, frontal sinuses, digestive tract and urethra, causing temporary painful congestion or occlusion of the organ (Garzia, 1938).

Millipedes (Diplopoda), the "thousand-legged worms," which typically have two pairs of jointed appendages for each body segment, are harmless.

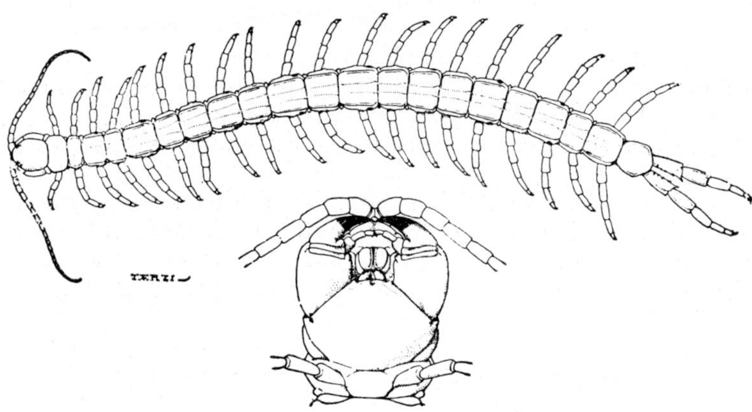

FIG. 179.—The centipede *Scolopendra morsitans*. *Above*, dorsal view of entire centipede; *below*, anterior view of head. (After Castellani and Chalmers, from Craig and Faust's *Clinical Parasitology*, Lea & Febiger, Philadelphia.)

SCORPIONS (SCORPIONES)

Adult Morphology.—Scorpions, like crabs and crayfishes, have their body divided externally into a fused, unsegmented cephalothorax and an abdomen with distinct evidence of segmentation. True scorpions (Fig. 180) have a long anterior pair of pinchers (pedipalps) with their conspicuous terminal claws, 4 pairs of long, sprawling, cephalothoracic legs behind the pinchers, and the division of the abdomen into a broad anterior, 7-segmented portion and a much narrower, 5-segmented posterior portion with a terminal segment (the telson) which is modified into a sting apparatus. The male can be differentiated from the female because of broader claws in the pedipalps and a longer posterior abdomen. (Whip scorpions, which are harmless, have a uniformly broad abdomen which ends in a long, whip-like caudal extremity.) Between the bases of the pinchers there are a pair of small jaws or cheliceræ. Also at the anterior end of the scorpion there are a pair of conspicuous median compound eyes and 2 to 10 lateral "eye-spots." Just behind the base of the last pair of legs on the ventral side there are a pair of comb-like tactile organs.

Bionomics.—Scorpions lurk in dark places, where they may be resting, or they may move about actively. They can turn the caudal stinger in any direction, but characteristically the stinger is curved over the back or to one side. Their natural habitat is under rocks, old logs, piles of sand, or under any type of protective covering. Within homes they seek out dark corners of earthen floors, the underside of mattresses, crevices of walls or between floor boards. Many species of scorpions live in hot arid regions, but they can not survive dryness or intense heat. This is why they migrate into houses or under cool moist covering during midday. Other species live in moist tropical climates.

The preferred food of the scorpion consists of the water roach (*Blatella germanica*), small spiders or beetles. But they will eat centipedes or other scorpions, even of their own species, provided their prey has just molted and has a soft cuticle (Stahnke, 1949).

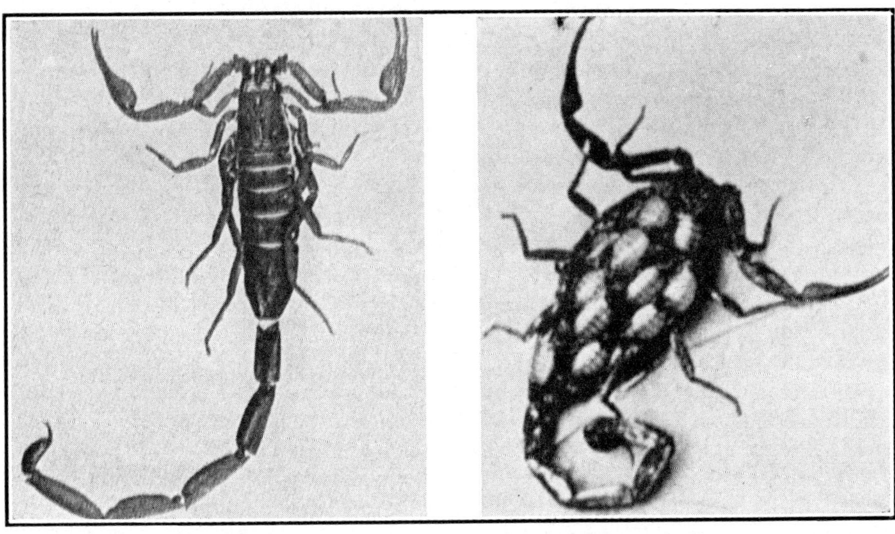

A *B*

Fig. 180.—*A*, male *Centruroides*, × 1 (after Dr. C. C. Hoffmann); *B*, female *C. sculpturatus* with newly born young, × 1 (after Stahnke). (From Craig and Faust's *Clinical Parasitology*, Lea & Febiger, Philadelphia.)

The Life Cycle.—Scorpions are viviparous. Following several months of intra-uterine development, the young are born with an embryonic envelope which facilitates parturition. Immediately after birth the mother removes the membrane with her pedipalps and the little scorpions crawl onto her back, where they remain for some time (Waterman, 1939). (See Fig. 180 *B*.)

Venenation.—Human beings come in contact with scorpions by accidentally stepping on them with bare feet or by bringing the hand or forearm in contact with them, usually when they are concealed in dark places. The dirt floor of adobe huts is a common place of exposure. But in these areas as in the moist Tropics, scorpions may be found in vegetation near human habitations, inside dwellings near water containers, or concealed inside boots or shoes, clothing or any other damp dark object.

Scorpion venom is elaborated in two glands which lie in the swollen portion of the telson, and is discharged through the hollow, sharp, curved tip. It is a clear, colorless toxalbumin, containing hemorrhagic, hemolytic, neurotoxic and other toxic fractions. Small species of scorpions are less likely to pierce human skin than larger forms, but once the stinger has penetrated, the amount of the different toxic components in the venom determines the type and severity of the reaction. If the venom consists primarily of hemorrhagin the lesion will be mostly local at the site of its introduction, like that of many species of vipers and pit vipers (Chapter 24, page 569); if it consists primarily of neurotoxin, the reaction will be systemic. Species of *Vejovis, Hadrurus, Superstitionia* and *Diplocentrus* of Mexico and southwestern United States, *Prionurus* of the eastern Mediterranean area and *Euscorpius* of southern Europe belong to the first group, while species of *Centruroides* of Mexico and southwestern United States, *Buthus quinquestriatus* of southern Europe, the eastern Mediterranean and northern Africa, *Buthus martensi* of Manchuria, *Parabuthus* of Bechuanaland, *Scorpio maurus* of northern Africa, *Tamulus* of India and *Tityus trinitalis* of Trinidad all belong to the latter group. Some of these scorpions are only medium-sized but have very potent venom.

Children of preschool age are most liable to venenation and the highest mortality occurs in this age group. The mortality from *T. trinitalis* in young children in Trinidad is 25%, even though a majority of stings occur in older children and adults (Waterman, 1938). The death rate from *Centruroides suffusus* in central northern Mexico averages 100 per 100,000 population yearly; most of the victims are children 1 to 7 years old. Arizona physicians diagnosed and treated 1,573 cases of scorpion sting during a 10-month period (1948). Of the 233 patients hospitalized, 193 were in a convulsive condition. During the 20-year period 1929-1948, there were 64 deaths reported in this State from scorpion sting, all due to species of *Centruroides* (*C. sculpturatus* or *C. gertschi*). These constituted 68% of all deaths from venomous animals (Stahnke, 1949).

Pathogenesis and Symptomatology.—At the site of the sting there is a single, small puncture wound, accompanied by sharp, aching, local pain. In many instances the essential toxic fraction is hemorrhagin. This produces an erythematous swelling at the site, frequently with induration, with a small area of hemorrhage. This may involve a forearm if the sting was on a finger, or the ankle and lower part of the leg if the sting was on the foot, with swelling of the member but rarely extending further than the axial or popliteal lymph nodes respectively. But unless the wound becomes secondarily infected, the symptoms subside in a few hours or at most in 1 or 2 days.

Scorpions which inject neurotoxic venom produce systemic manifestations. Stahnke (1949) states that this type of scorpion venom "does not produce a swelling or discoloration at the site of the sting." In addition to an immediate, intense, aching local pain, a radiating, burning sensation, and inflammation of the nearby lymph nodes, there is relatively rapid development of generalized numbness, throbbing and spastic twitching of the muscles, with convulsive attacks, like symptoms of strychnine poisoning. Small children may become extremely nervous and physically almost unmanageable. There may be vomiting, continuous rhinorrhea and profuse frothy salivation. Cerebral symptoms include hallucinations, strabismus, temporary monoplegia, hemiplegia, or temporary blindness. There may be extreme thirst, urinary incontinence or anuria, tachycardia, weak shallow respiration and a fever up to 40° C. (104° F.). The symptoms may gradually subside, may last for many weeks, or the patient may succumb to respiratory paralysis.

Diagnosis.—In a scorpion-infested region, clinical diagnosis may be made from the patient's local or systemic symptoms, history of contact with a scorpion, and demonstration of a small reddened local wound having a single point of skin puncture. This type of venenation must be differentiated from spider bite (page 459), tick paralysis (page 462), bee sting (page 480) and reptile venenation (pages 566, 569).

Treatment.—Therapeutic measures should be undertaken at the earliest possible moment. A tight tourniquet should be placed near the site so as to isolate it from the body, but this must be released every 20 to 30 minutes so as not to embarrass blood and lymphatic flow. If an ice-pack is available it should be placed over the puncture wound; or in a hospital ethyl chloride may be sprayed over the immediate area (Stahnke, 1953). Special medical care is indicated for patients under school age, those who have a history of cardiac symptoms, in cases of multiple stings on different parts of the body or on the external genitalia, and whenever there are severe neurotoxic symptoms. Sedation is indicated in the more serious cases and pituitrin administered by vein for patients in shock. Antivenin should be reserved for persons manifesting systemic intoxication. This is available in most Pasteur institutes in scorpion-infested countries, and in the United States at the Poisonous Animals Research Laboratory, Arizona State College, Tempe, Arizona.

Prognosis.—The outcome is favorable in cases of sting with scorpions which inject only hemorrhagic venom; grave to equivocal in cases of neurotoxic venenation unless effective medical care is rapidly made available.

Control.—Eradication of scorpions over wide areas is impractical. For homes or restricted localities Stahnke (1949) recommends residual spraying of a mixture of insect toxicants consisting of 10% DDT, 2% Chlordane and 0.2% pyrethrum in a light oil base. The pyrethrum provides rapid knockdown and the other ingredients slower residual effect. This combination of insecticides also kills other insects on which the scorpions depend for their food.

SPIDERS (ARANEÆ)

Adult Morphology.—Spiders are arachnids which have a cephalothorax and an abdomen separated by a conspicuous constriction (the pedicel). They lack external evidence of segmentation (Figs. 181, 182), although at times there is a cervical groove or furrow between the head and the thorax. The exoskeleton is relatively thin but tough; it may be smooth or be provided with hairs or setæ. Several simple "eye-spots" are present on the front of the head. The mouth parts consist of a pair of poison jaws (chelicerae) just above the mouth, an upper lip (labrum), a median epipharynx immediately ventral to the labrum, a median lower lip and a pair of pedipalps. The poison jaws have a short, broad, basal segment and a clawed terminal segment through the tip of which the poison gland opens. In the males the pedipalps are greatly modified for transfer of seminal fluid to the female. There are 4 pairs of walking legs arising from the ventral side of the thorax. The abdomen is sacculate and is much larger than the cephalothorax. Typically there are 1 or 2 pairs of slits on the ventral side of the abdomen which are the openings of primitive book lungs. Most species of true spiders also have a pair of spiracles leading into a tracheal system of respiration.

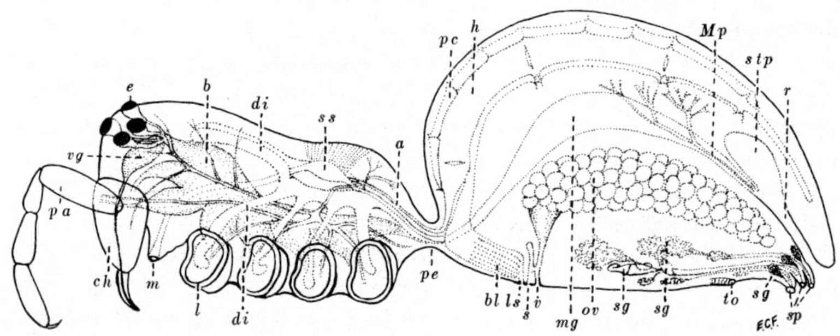

Fig. 181.—Diagram of a spider (lateral view), showing external and internal organs on left side. *a*, aorta; *b*, brain; *bl*, book lung; *ch*, chelicera; *di*, diverticulum of midgut; *e*, eyespot; *h*, heart; *l*, thoracic leg attachment; *ls*, lung slit; *m*, mouth; *mg*, midgut; *Mp*, Malpighian tubule; *ov*, ovary; *pa*, pedipalp; *pc*, pericardial cavity; *pe*, pedicle; *r*, rectum; *s*, opening of spermatheca; *sg*, silk gland; *sp*, spinnerets; *ss*, sucking stomach; *stp*, stercoral pocket; *to*, tracheal opening (spiracle); *v*, vagina; *vg*, venom gland. (Original adaptation from Comstock.)

Fig. 182.—Female black-widow spider (*Latrodectus mactans*) with cocoon containing eggs. (After G. H. Needham, from Craig and Faust's *Clinical Parasitology*, Lea & Febiger, Philadelphia.)

Bionomics.—Spiders are provided with spinning organs, usually 3 pairs of glands, which open ventrally near the posterior end of the body. All spiders are carnivorous and many are cannibalistic. They trap their victims, including flies and other relatively small, soft-bodied insects or their own kind, then pounce on them and render them helpless by injecting venom through the tips of their poison jaws, after which they proceed to suck out the body juices. All true spiders employ this method of obtaining food but relatively few species are capable of piercing tough cuticle.

Spiders live in a variety of locations on the ground, under fallen trees, in piles of rocks, or outside and within human habitations. They require moisture and during long dry seasons will migrate considerable distances from an arid to a moist habitat.

The Life Cycle.—The fertilized eggs are laid in masses, usually within a spun cocoon. The eggs soon hatch, but the 8-legged spiderlings usually remain within the cocoon for weeks or months. To permit growth they shed their cuticle repeatedly and possibly never outgrow this habit, even after they have become sexually mature (Baerg, 1938).

Spiders Harmful to Man.—Relatively few of the many species of spiders are able to puncture human skin, so that most spiders are medically unimportant. Those which attack man do so accidentally when the hand or other exposed part of the body comes in contact with the spider or its web.

Pathophysiologically spiders belong to two groups, namely, those which are responsible for a local necrotizing ulcer and those which cause systemic symptoms.

Only one species, *Loxosceles laëta*, has been definitely incriminated as the cause of *necrotic arachnidism.* This spider is almost exclusively domestic in its habits and has been reported as a common species in northern Chile and in Uruguay. According to Schenone (1953) it is about 1.5 cm. in length, is yellowish-brown in color and has the body and appendages covered with fine hairs. It lives in the walls of old houses, but is also found in closets or wardrobes of newer dwellings among the clothing (Mackinnon and Witkind, 1953).

A considerable number of species of spiders in many parts of the world produce *systemic arachnidism.* There are the large hairly, ferocious-looking tarantulas of the Tropics, which are less harmful than their size would suggest, and the dangerous smaller forms with potent venom. The latter include several species of *Latrodectus*, among them the "black widow" (*L. mactans*), distributed in the Americas from eastern Canada to Chile; also *Atrax robustus* and *A. formidabilis* of Australia; *Sericopelma communis* of Panama, and species of *Lycosa* and *Ctenus* of Brazil. These spiders are not primarily domestic in their habits but during severe droughts will be found under stone walls or lumber piles and, in the case of *L. mactans,* on the under-side of outdoor privy seats, where the web comes in contact with the external genitalia of persons using the privy.

The venom of *L. mactans* and probably of related species contains a transparent, lemon-colored, oily thermolabile toxalbumin and digestive enzymes (D'Amour, Becker and Van Riper, 1936). That of *L. mactans* is about one-third as potent as rattlesnake venom, while that of *L. indistinctus* is at least as toxic as Cape cobra venom. The poisonous fraction is a neurotoxin (Hall and Vogelsang, 1932).

Pathogenesis and Symptomatology.—(1) *Necrotic Arachnidism.*—Mackinnon and Witkind (1953) and Schenone (1953) confirm the earlier reports of Macchiavello (1937, 1947), that *Loxosceles laëta* invariably produces cutaneous necrosis at the site of its bite. Almost immediately following the bite there is intense local pain and ecchymotic swelling, followed by general malaise and a febrile reaction. The puncture wound becomes indurated, then transforms into a cellulitis of extensive diameter. The center first becomes blanched, then hemorrhagic and breaks down, leaving an indolent ulcer which heals very slowly and leaves an ugly cicatricial scar, measuring up to 30 cm. in width. At times associated hemoglobinuria and jaundice have been noted.

(2) *Systemic Arachnidism.*—At the site of the bite there is an immediate sharp pain but little if any swelling, although later the puncture wound may become reddened and edematous. The bitten member burns and aches. The venom will soon reach the lymphatics and then the circulating blood, with the development of motor disturbances, including weakness, cramps, and spastic contraction of the muscles, particularly those of the abdomen. Gajardo-Tobár (1941) reported marked clonic and tonic motor disturbances, exaggerated reflexes, rapid shallow respiration, early tachycardia and increditably high arterial pressure. Convulsions may occur in small children, and delirium, stupor, complete prostration or shock in all age groups. Death from respiratory failure is not uncommon when diagnosis and treatment are delayed.

Diagnosis.—In its early stage necrotic arachnidism must be differentiated from bee sting, localized erysipelas and malignant buboes; later it must be distinguished from cellulitis and cutaneous ulcers of pyogenic origin. Systemic arachnidism must be differentiated from scorpion sting or cobra-type venenation. In both kinds of arachnidism the history of a spider in contact with the skin, and the early demonstration of two small punctures close to one another will suggest spider bite.

Treatment.—For necrotic arachnidism conservative measures are indicated, reserving antibiotics for cases with secondary complications. Schenone (1953) reports good results with cortisone in 3 daily doses of 200 mgm., thereafter 100 mgm. daily for several days. For systemic arachnidism vasodilatation and sedation are frequently indicated. In both types specific antivenin should be administered if available as soon as possible following the accident.

Control.—DDT and benzene hexachloride (Gammexane) are effective in killing all types of spiders when these insect toxicants are sprayed in a kerosene medium or dusted onto active webs and sites where the spiders reside. Children should be warned not to reach with unprotected hands into old piles of lumber or under stones.

TICKS AND MITES (ACARI)

Adult Morphology and Bionomics.—These arthropods are more or less broadly oval, without distinct superficial separation between cephalothorax and abdomen and with no external evidence of segmentation. They have 4 pairs of legs arising from the ventral side of the thorax, the front 2 pairs extending anterolaterally and the hind 2 pairs posterolaterally. The head structures (capitulum) consist of a median hypostome situated below the mouth and a pair of cheliceræ (both arising from a capitular base), together with an outer pair of palps. The cheliceræ open an incision for the hypostome to penetrate into softer tissues so that the animal may then suck tissue juices. Salivary gland secretions may aid in the procurement of this nutriment. Most acarids do not enter the host tissues but a few species (*e. g.*, mange mites and demodectic mites) are parasitic in the skin.

The Life Cycle.—The females lays their eggs singly or in batches, depending on their egg-producing capacity. After embryonation and hatching the emerging active 6-legged larva feeds and grows, then sheds its cuticle and becomes an 8-legged nymph, which resembles the adult except that it lacks sexual organs. There is a second-stage nymph in some groups of mites, and a few species of mites have 3 nymphal stages. The last nymphal stage transforms into the 8-legged adult.

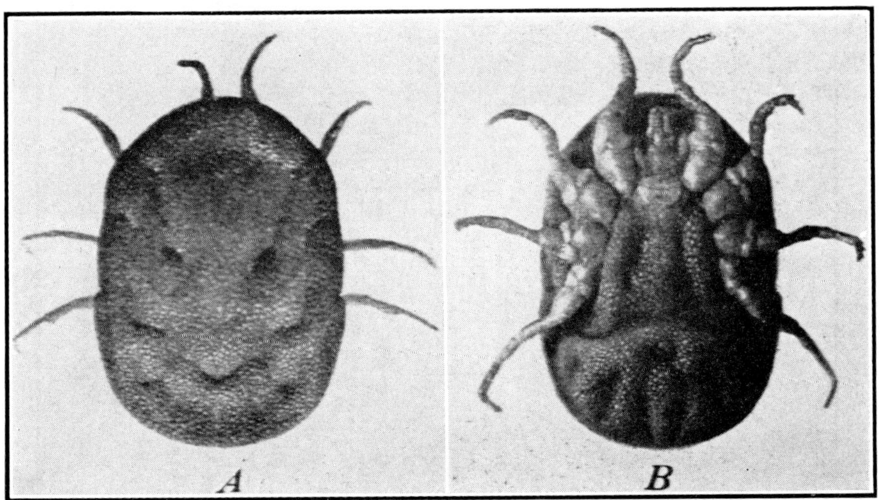

Fig. 183.—Soft-bodied tick (*Ornithodoros moubata*). *A*, dorsal view; *B*, ventral view. $\times 6\frac{2}{3}$. (After Professor O. Jírovec, Prague, from Craig and Faust's *Clinical Parasitology*, Lea & Febiger, Philadelphia.)

Ticks (Ixodoidea)

Definition.—Ticks are large mites which have a leathery integument, a large hypostome beset with recurved teeth, a furrowed ventral side and tracheæ which open externally through a pair of spiracular (stigmal) plates near the bases of the third and fourth legs. All ticks feed on vertebrate blood during each of their active stages. Two family groups are recognized, the Argasidæ or soft-bodied ticks (Fig. 183), which lack a hard dorsal shield, have their mouth parts under the anterior extremity of the body and like bedbugs hide in cracks during the daytime and feed intermittently at night, and the Ixodidæ or hard-bodied ticks (Fig. 184), which have a shield covering the entire dorsum of the male but only the anterior part of the female, have mouth parts visible in front of the body and in most species remain on the host for a prolonged period to take blood. Like the leeches (page 443) ticks have several distensible diverticula of the crop to accommodate a big meal. During engorgement the tick swells up to many times its fasting size.

Ticks as Causative Agents.—Ticks produce two types of damage to their hosts, *viz.*, (1) local traumatic and inflammatory at the site of attachment and (2) systemic.

Local traumatic and inflammatory damage is produced by all ticks when they puncture the skin and suck blood. The large hypostome with its recurved teeth serves as an effective anchoring organ in the skin after the sharply toothed cheliceræ cut an opening through the epidermis. The palps do not enter the wound but serve as a counter-anchor. Through a tubular

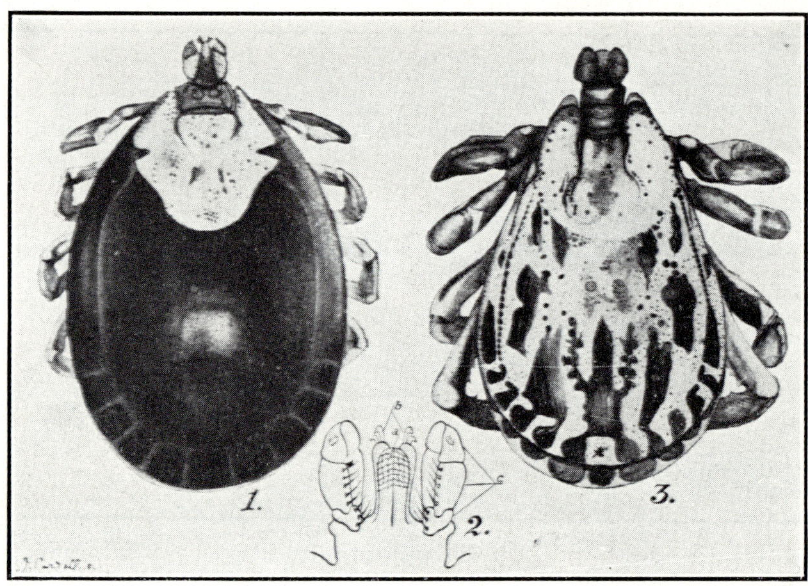

FIG. 184.—Hard-bodies tick (*Dermacentor andersoni*), dorsal views. *1*, female; *2*, head showing hypostome (a), cheliceræ (b) and palps (c); *3*, male. Enlarged. (From Stitt's Diagnostics, Prevention and Treatment of Tropical Diseases, in Craig and Faust's *Clinical Parasitology*, Lea & Febiger, Philadelphia.)

stylet lying within the mouth cavity blood is sucked into the muscular pharynx. Secretion into the wound from a pair of salivary glands prevents coagulation of blood. The combined mechanical and digestive action provokes an inflammatory reaction in the perivascular tissues of the corium, with local hyperemia, edema and hemorrhage, together with a thickening of the stratum corneum (Hoeppli and Feng, 1933).

Systemic damage may consist solely in a sensitization reaction to the salivary secretions of the tick. Much more serious is *"tick paralysis,"* which is characterized by an ascending flaccid motor paralysis, with generalized intoxication, elevation of temperature to 40° C. (104° F.), difficulty in swallowing and respiration, and at times fatal termination. This syndrome may appear rapidly or be delayed for 5 days or more following the bite, depending principally on whether the site of the tick's attachment is on the neck at the base of the skull, further down the spinal cord or on a more distant site. Young children are particularly apt to develop tick paralysis but adults are not immune.

The cause of the paralysis is probably some fraction of the tick's saliva introduced into the skin, since tests have ruled out the likelihood of a filtrable virus. Most cases of tick paralysis in North America have been associated with bites of the hard-bodied Rocky Mountain wood tick, *Dermacentor andersoni* and the dog tick, *D. variabilis*. Species of *Ixodes* have produced similar symptoms in Europe, South Africa and Australia. Likewise, soft-bodied ticks of the genus *Ornithodoros* have been found to produce the same syndrome in the U. S. S. R. The adult female is more often responsible than the male or the immature stages.

Tick paralysis (Landry's type) requires differentiation from poliomyelitis, encephalomyelitis and ascending motor paralysis resulting from venenation of other arthropods or snakes having neurotoxin in their venom. There is no specific treatment but palliative and supportive therapy is helpful. The prognosis is grave if the tick's attachment is at the base of the brain. Dusting of DDT inside the shoes and pants will serve as a partial prophylaxis in preventing the tick from attaching to the skin. Children or adults who walk through tick-infested areas should remove all clothing as soon as they return to their home or camp and all attached or crawling ticks should be removed at once to minimize danger.

For a consideration of ticks as vectors of pathogenic agents, please consult pages 518–519.

MANGE MITES (SARCOPTOIDEA)

Morphology and Bionomics of Sarcoptes Scabiei.—Several species of mange mites parasitize the skin of mammals. Some of these are important in veterinary medicine. Only one species, *Sarcoptes scabiei*, commonly produces human disease.

S. scabiei was first described and incriminated by Renucci in 1834. This minute, broadly oval mite (Fig. 185) superficially resembles a microscopic turtle with the head organs and the 4 pairs of legs protruding from the main portion of the body. The anterior 2 pairs of legs have delicate, terminal, stalked sucking pads; in the female the posterior 2 pairs end in bristles, while in the male the 3rd pair is provided with bristles and the 4th pair with sucking pads. On the dorsal surface of the body there are many, more or less transverse, parallel ridges, except medially, just behind the head and, also numerous tooth-like and finger-like spines as well as bristles, all of which are important in identifying the species. *S. scabiei* lacks special respiratory organs. The females are somewhat larger than the males, *e. g.*, 330 to 450 microns by 250 to 350 microns and 200 to 240 microns by 150 to 200 microns respectively.

These mites live in slightly serpiginous cutaneous burrows. The gravid female is usually found at the inner, blind end of the tunnel, where she deposits one to a few large, broadly ovoidal eggs daily for 4 to 5 weeks. The males reside in lateral burrows. Three to 5 days after oviposition a

6-legged larva escapes from the egg shell. It either produces a lateral tunnel or crawls out of the mouth of the tunnel, starts a new one by burrowing down a hair follicle or develops a moulting pocket under epidermal scales. In 2 or 3 days the larva moults and becomes a first-stage nymph. After a second nymphal period the mite becomes sexually mature. A complete life cycle requires 8 to 17 days. In a cool environment *S. scabiei* will live for at least 1 week off the host's body, the females will oviposit and the eggs will hatch.

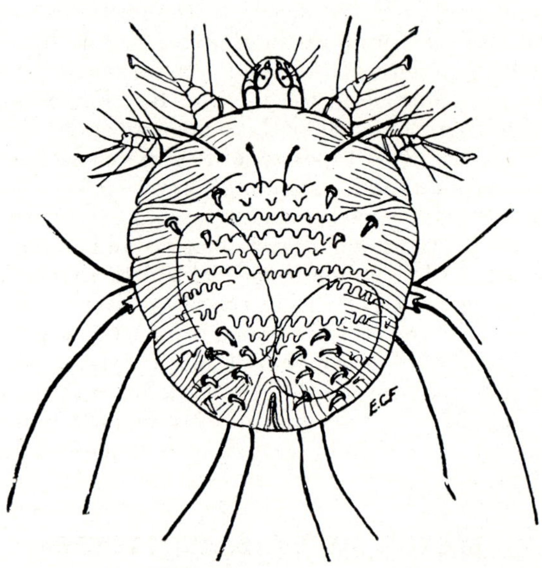

Fig. 185.—Human mange mite (*Sarcoptes scabiei*), gravid female (dorsal view), containing 2 immature eggs. Greatly enlarged. (After Faust in Brennemann's Practice of Pediatrics, from Craig and Faust's *Clinical Parasitology*, Lea & Febiger, Philadelphia.)

Epidemiology of Human Sarcoptic Mange.—Exposure to sarcoptic mange is due almost exclusively to contact with infested persons, their clothing, bed linen, towels or other fomites contaminated with gravid females of *S. scabiei* or their offspring. Rarely the infestation with non-human varieties of this mite is acquired from infested horses, sheep, goats, cattle or the alpaca (Mellanby, 1947; Matheson, 1950.)

Pathogenesis and Symptomatology.—The cutaneous lesion is developed in just a few days. It may be only a few millimeters or several centimeters in length, but eventually it usually has several lateral extensions. It is most frequently located between the fingers, on the back of the hands, at the elbows, axillæ, groin, or on the breast. The tunnel lies in the deeper part of the epidermis and is slightly lower at its inner end. As the mites feed on the tissues they deposit microscopic fecal pellets, which are responsible for the vesiculations and the associated pruritus. The itching is intensified by warmth and moisture. The first objective evidence is the small, reddish, slightly raised track in the skin, with a minute vesicle at the inner end. Scratching opens the tunnels and produces a bloody-serous exudation, permits bacteria to enter the lesion and frequently spreads the parasites to other skin areas. The chronic stage consists of multiple lesions with vesicles, papules, pustules and excoriation, and a weeping eczema of the area.

Diagnosis.—The physician can make a relatively satisfactory diagnosis on the basis of the clinical picture. Sarcoptic mange must be differentiated from the dermatomycoses, various types of cutaneous larva migrans and several other dermatitides.

Treatment.—The most satisfactory treatment consists in the application of 2 ounces of lindane ointment (1% gamma isomer of benzene hexachloride in vanishing cream) to all parts of the body below the head following a soaking hot soapy bath. After 24 hours the patient takes a second bath and puts on clean clothes. Occasionally a second treatment may be required. Lindane kills the eggs as well as the active stages of the mite, which is not the case in sulfur, pyrethrin, rotenone or benzyl benzoate therapy.

Control.—Sarcoptic mange tends to be hyperendemic in jails, armies, school children and isolated families who do not practice good personal and group hygiene. Prescription of specific therapy in dispensaries and by visiting nurses in schools and homes provides a method of practical control.

Follicular Mites (Demodecoidea)

Demodex Folliculorum and Follicular Mange.—Although related species infest dogs and other domestic mammals, *D. folliculorum* is the only follicular mite of man. The adult is an elongated, vermiform organism, having a length of 0.1 to 0.39 mm. It is provided with a small, inconspicuous hypostome, a pair of stylet-like cheliceræ and a pair of relatively large palps having a terminal claw. There are 4 pairs of short, stumpy, thoracic legs having a sucking cup and 2 claws on the terminal joint, a long median genital slit in the female between the last pair of legs, and many parallel transverse striations on the abdomen.

Clinical Notes.—Follicular mites burrow into the hair follicles and sebaceous glands where they provoke a fibrous tissue reaction, causing a mild pruritus, possibly an acne-like dermatitis or localized keratosis, and providing an opportunity for bacteria to enter the skin. Ayres and Anderson (1932) reported 30 cases, most of which were in women who used facial creams instead of soap to cleanse the skin. Application of lindane ointment (1% gamma isomer of benzene hexachloride in vanishing cream) to the affected area, following a thorough cleansing with hot soapy water to open the pores, constitutes specific treatment.

PARASITOID MITES (PARASITOIDEA)

Adult Morphology and Bionomics.—Members of this group (Fig. 186) are small macroscopic mites, oval or pyriform in contour, and are more closely related to the ticks than to other mites. Like other mites they have an unarmed, sharply pointed hypostome and are considerably smaller and more delicate than ticks. The legs have a sucking pad and 2 claws on the terminal joint. The species of particular medical interest belong to the genera *Bdellonyssus*, *Allodermanyssus* and *Dermanyssus*. The cheliceræ of *Bdellonyssus* are spear-like and have a terminal joint opposed to the end portion of the subterminal one, while in the other two genera the cheliceræ have a single needle-like termination. The species which attack man most frequently are the rat mite (*Bdellonyssus bacoti*), the mouse mite (*Allodermanyssus sanguineus*) and the chicken and pigeon mite (*Dermanyssus gallinæ*). *B. bacoti* not only infests rats but is also found on squirrels. *A. sanguineus* is found on domestic mice and other small rodents in the eastern and southwestern United States and Egypt. *D. gallinæ* is a cosmopolitan pest in chicken houses and dove cotes. These mites attack man when opportunity is provided.

Life Cycle.—Parasitoid mites typically have a larval stage hatched from the egg followed by two nymphal stages, then the adult. Under optimum conditions of 24 to 26° C. and 47% relative humidity the life cycle of *B. bacoti* is completed in 11 to 16 days, the adults survive 62 days and the females each lay 99 eggs (Skaliy and Hayes, 1949).

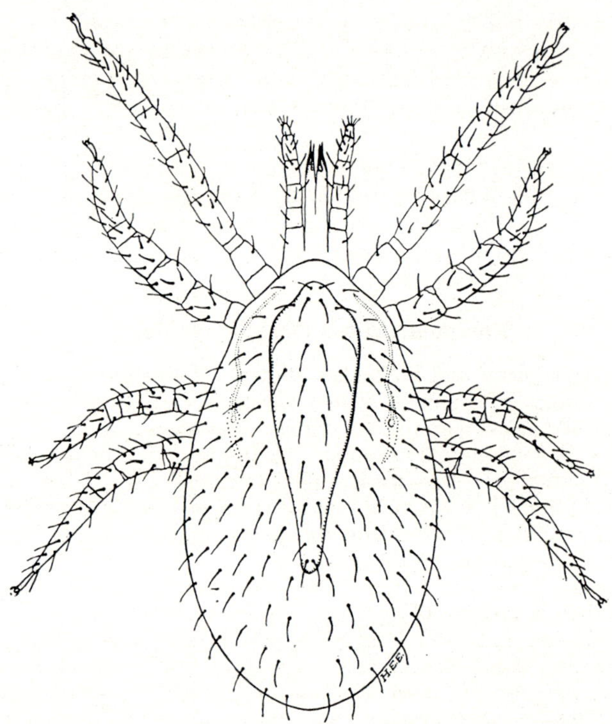

FIG. 186.—Adult parasitoid mite, *Bdellonyssus bacoti*, dorsal view. Greatly enlarged. (After Ewing, from Craig and Faust's *Clinical Parasitology*, Lea & Febiger, Philadelphia.)

Medical Importance.—All three species of parasitoid mites mentioned above are biological vectors of pathogenic microörganisms which affect man. This subject is considered in a subsequent chapter (pages 518, 535). These mites also produce an aggravating dermatitis.

B. bacoti feeds only on blood and drops off its host after a full meal. It takes at least 4 blood meals, one for each active stage. It infests persons working in granaries, food-supply houses, basements of homes and other places commonly frequented by rats. The dermatitis consists of urticarial wheals, papules and vesicles which develop at the site where each mite has fed. The intense itching frequently leads to scratching, with opportunity for secondary infection.

A. sanguineus and *D. gallinæ* probably do not suck blood but depend for their nourishment on tissue juices sucked out of the lower epidermis. They, too, produce a severe dermatitis and papular eczema due to the very toxic salivary secretions which they introduce into the skin.

Diagnosis of parasitoid mites is based on a history of contact with premises which harbor the natural hosts of these mites, and on demonstration of the particular mite recovered from the body of the victim. Treatment is topical and palliative in nature. Control consists in dusting DDT or other arthropod toxicants not harmful to children in infested localities, such as chicken houses, rat runs and basements of homes, and campaigns to reduce domestic rodents.

Several other species of parasitoid mites have from time to time been described as accidental human parasites, puncturing the skin and producing a dermatitis.

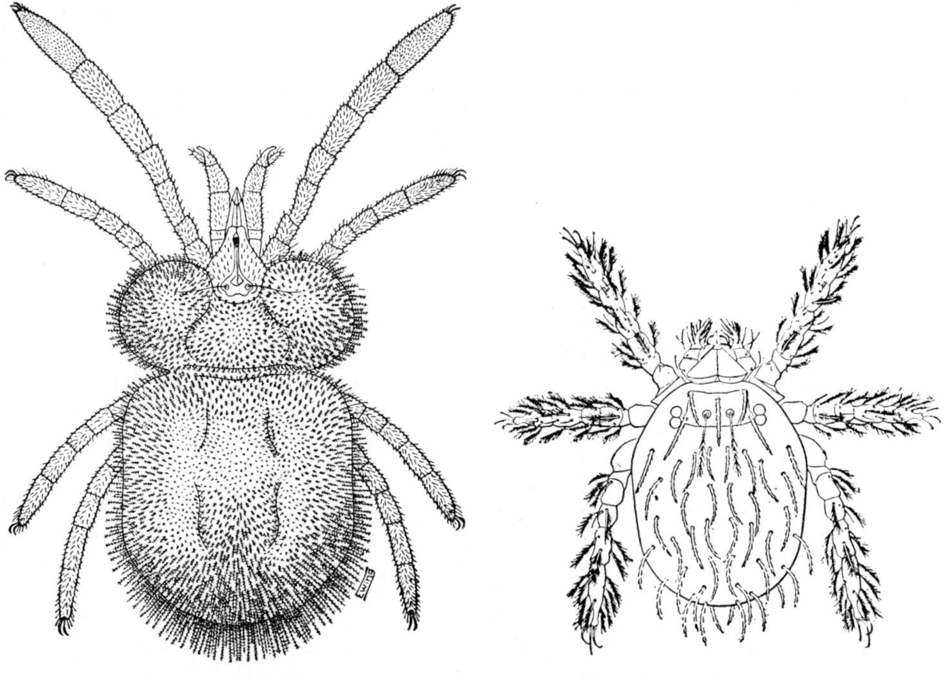

Fig. 187 Fig. 188

Fig. 187.—Adult red mite, *Trombicula alfreddugèsi*, dorsal view. Greatly enlarged. (After Ewing, from Craig and Faust's *Clinical Parasitology*, Lea & Febiger, Philadelphia.)

Fig. 188.—Larval stage of *Trombicula akamushi*, dorsal view. Greatly enlarged. (After Nagayo, *et al.*, from Craig and Faust's *Clinical Parasitology*, Lea & Febiger, Philadelphia.)

CHIGGERS, HARVEST MITES, RED MITES, "RED BUGS"

(TROMBIDOIDEA, Family TROMBICULIDÆ)

Adult Morphology and Bionomics.—The common names applied to this group refer to the larval stage which sucks tissue juices from man and a large variety of vertebrate hosts. The adults (Fig. 187) are about 1 mm.

long and figure-8-shaped. Both body and legs are covered with dense, velvety, pilose hairs. The cheliceræ have a blade-like distal joint provided dorsally with a row of saw teeth. There is a well-marked constriction of the body between the 2nd and 3rd pairs of legs. The food of the nymphs and adults consists of eggs or the juices which these predators extract from other arthropods.

Life Cycle.—The eggs of trombiculid mites are laid on the ground and on the lower stems and leaves of grass or bushes. Upon maturity a 6-legged larva (Fig. 188) emerges from the egg shell and usually crawls upon a small rodent but may become attached to any terrestrial vertebrate including larger rodents, domestic mammals or persons who enter infested vegetation. The larval mite sinks its cheliceræ and hypostome into the skin and proceeds to suck tissue juice until engorged. Then it releases its attachment, crawls down to the ground, transforms into a nymphochrysalis, then into a nymphal stage. Following an imagochrysalis stage the mite becomes sexually mature. North American species require a minimum of 55 to 71 days to complete a cycle. The larvas of the related family Trombidiidæ feed only on other arthropods, never on vertebrates.

The common species of trombiculids in the United States are *Trombicula* (*Eutrombicula*) *alfreddugèsi*, *T.* (*E.*) *splendens* and *T.* (*E.*) *batatas;* in Australia, *T.* (*Eutrombicula*) *sarcina*; in New Guinea, species of *Schöngastia;* in Europe, *T.* (*Neotrombicula*) *autumnalis*; in Japan, *T.* (*Leptotrombidium*) *akamushi;* in Malaya, *Ascoschöngastia malayensis*. The cuticle of the larva is usually red, hence the designation "red mite" or "red bug," but in some species it is practically colorless.

Medical Importance.—*Trombicula akamushi, T. deliensis, T. fuji* and *Ascoschöngastia indica* have been incriminated as reservoir hosts and biological vectors of *Rickettsia tsutsugamushi,* etiologic agent of scrub typhus. This subject is considered in a subsequent chapter (pages 533–534). The larvas of *Trombicula* and *Schöngastia* and probably other related genera produce a type of dermatitis in man. While some infested persons are relatively immune, others develop a severe local reaction which is first noted several hours after the mite has become attached and has begun to feed, accompanied by an almost insufferable pruritus. Soon a wheal forms around the site, frequently with hemorrhage. Scratching causes scarification and bleeding. The regions most frequently attacked are the ankles and legs, external genitalia and groin, the waistline, axillæ and breasts.

Treatment and Prophylaxis.—Topical application of phenolated camphor in mineral oil materially relieves the pruritus. Dusting of DDT into clothing, particularly socks and trouser cuffs provides considerable temporary protection. If persons find it necessary to travel through red mite-infested areas the impregnation of clothing with dimethyl phthalate or dibutyl phthalate will greatly reduce the likelihood of bites. Cutting of high grass in the infested regions is an important control measure. Continued residence in the region usually provides tolerance to the bites.

Predaceous Mites (Tarsonemoidea)

Adult Morphology and Bionomics.—Members of this group have a distinct separation between cephalothorax and abdomen, with external evidence of segmentation on the abdomen. The cheliceræ are stylet-like and the palps are inconspicuous. Several species are predaceous on insects which infest grain crops. *Pediculoides (Pyemotes) ventricosus,* frequently referred to as the grain itch mite, is of medical importance.

Life Cycle.—*Pediculoides ventricosus* is produced viviparously and is mature at birth. The male immediately fertilizes the female, which then looks for a suitable host, piercing its skin to suck tissue juices. As it feeds the abdomen becomes greatly swollen. Eggs are produced, become mature and hatch within the distended sac, then pass through larval and nymphal stages before emergence.

Epidemiology.—*P. ventricosus* is cosmopolitan in its distribution in grain-raising regions of the world. Epidemic dermatitis due to this mite occurs seasonally in Italy, the Balkans, Egypt, Algeria, India, South Australia, the north-central plains area of the United States and adjacent Canada.

Clinical Notes.—When persons handle mite-infested grain or hay during harvest time or in storage, or sleep on infested wheat, barley or rye straw, especially in hot dry weather, the mites avidly attack all parts of the skin, to which they become attached but are unable to penetrate. Dozens to hundreds of the mites may be involved. A wheal develops at each site of attachment to the skin, causing an intense pruritus. The lesion is a whitish raised area surrounding a central vesicle. Rubbing or scratching aggravates the condition. Systemic symptoms mimicking serum sickness may develop in cases of heavy infestation or in particularly sensitive individuals. Diagnosis can be made by obtaining the occupational history or habits of the patient, together with the character of the dermatitis and at times by recovery of the female mites from the skin. Scabies (page 564), pediculosis (page 584) and allergic dermatitis must be ruled out. Treatment consists first of all in topical application of a mild anti-pruritic, accompanied or followed by an antiseptic lotion.

Control.—Little or no immunity is developed to this infestation. Persons may be attacked several times during one harvest season. Use of sulfur or other insect toxicant to infested granaries to kill the insects on which the mites normally feed, together with burning of the stubble in grain fields, will reduce exposure.

Food Mites (Tyroglyphoidea)

Adult Morphology and Bionomics.—The small, stout body is separated into a cephalo-thorax and an abdomen by a transverse groove but there is no external evidence of segmentation on the abdomen. The surface of the body is smooth and glistening, without transverse parallel lines. The legs typically have terminal claws and lack stalked suckers. Males have a sucking pad on each side of the genital opening. The adults are never true predators or parasites but feed on cheeses or cereals and a variety of organic substances.

Life Cycle.—The following stages are recognized: egg, larva, 2 (or 3) nymphal stages, adult female, and normal or heteromorphic male. If there are 3 nymphal stages, the second one is provided with suckers or claspers for grasping insects, allowing the mite to be dispersed to other localities.

Epidemiology.—The group has very extensive distribution. Accidental human infestation results from handling or eating infested plant products. The more common mites which infest the skin are *Tyroglyphus siro,* from handling vanilla pods and beans; *T. longior* var. *castellanii,* from contact with copra; *Glyciphagus prunorum,* contracted in grocery stores, and *Rhizoglyphus echinopus,* associated with flower bulbs. If infested cheeses and other foods are eaten they provide a means for the mites to get into the alimentary tract.

Clinical Notes.—Dermatitis results when the skin of the hands or other body areas come in contact with infested plant products. The mites crawl under epidermal scales or enter cracks in the skin, where they lodge and produce a temporary pruritus, *e. g.*, "copra itch," "grocer's itch," "vanilla worker's itch," etc. Almost invariably this is an occupational disease which must not be confused with scabies. Tyroglyphoid mites may temporarily lodge in the intestinal crypts and produce irritation of the mucous membrane. If they should be accidentally breathed into the lungs, they may provoke bronchial asthma with an associated eosinophilia (Carter and D'Abrera, 1946; Soysa, 1949).

Treatment of cutaneous food-mite infestation consists in thoroughly cleansing of the affected skin with soap and water and application of lindane ointment (0.5% gamma isomer of benzene hexachloride in vanishing cream). Intestinal infestation can usually be eliminated by saline purgation. Pulmonary infestation may possibly respond to arsenical treatment.

Control.—No practical measures have been demonstrated.

"TONGUE WORMS" (PENTASTOMIDA)

Adult Morphology and Biology.—The adults of this group are elongate, linguiform or moniliform objects which have superficial annulations that do not correspond to the internal segments (metameres). They are legless, but near the mouth there are 2 pairs of hollow, curved, retractile hooklets (rudimentary appendages), which have basal glands that produce digestive and possibly hemolytic secretions. There is no external separation into head, thorax and abdomen. The males are somewhat smaller than the females. The adults are endoparasitic in the mouth, esophagus or respiratory organs of vertebrates, where they feed on blood and mucosal cells.

Life Cycle.—In the genus *Linguatula* (*L. serrata*), which is tongue-shaped, the females deposit their eggs in the posterior nares of the mammalian host. They are discharged in nasal secretions and on reaching water or moist vegetation complete embryonation. When ingested by herbivorous mammals, the eggs hatch in the digestive tract, the emerging larvas migrate through the intestinal wall and lodge in the liver or other viscera. There they transform in about 5 to 6 months into nymphs which lie within a capsule of host tissue. If the infected larval host is eaten by carnivorous animals, the nymphs are digested out of the tissue and migrate to the nasal passages where they develop into adults. The common larval hosts are rabbits, sheep and goats; the common definitive host is the dog.

In the genera *Armillifer* (*A. armillatus*, *A. moniliformis*), and *Porocephalus*, which superficially resemble a string of beads, the females live and deposit their eggs in the respiratory passages of pythons and other snakes. Animals which consume infected raw snakes, or ingest the "worm's" eggs that have been discharged in nasal secretions into water or on vegetation, serve as intermediate hosts in which the larval and nymphal stages develop.

Clinical Notes.—*Linguatula serrata* has been found as a human parasite in Africa, Germany, Switzerland, Panama, Brazil, Chile, and once in Dallas, Texas (U. S. A.). Gajardo Tobár (1943) reported that the encapsulated immature stages occur with considerable frequency in necropsies at Valparaiso and Concepción, Chile. Species of *Armillifer* and *Porocephalus* have been recovered in immature stages from man in many locations in tropical Africa, and in Egypt, India, Java, and China. In most cases the "worms" produce no demonstrable symptoms and are incidental autopsy findings. Rarely multiple infection provokes marked inflammation of the intestinal wall or the liver. Diagnosis is almost invariably post-mortem. No satisfactory treatment has been developed.

Control.—This requires discontinuance of the custom of eating raw flesh and refraining from drinking raw water or eating polluted raw vegetation in enzoötic areas.

SUMMARY

1. Arthropods (Phylum Arthropoda) constitute the largest group of organisms in the Animal Kingdom. They are characterized by bilateral symmetry, true segmentation, an exoskeleton and paired jointed appendages. In the ancestral arthropod all segments of the body were similar, but with evolution the 5 (or 6) anteriormost ones became consolidated into a head and the appendages of the head, thorax and abdomen became modified for special uses.
2. The adults have a complete digestive tract, an excretory system, a blood vascular system, a respiratory system (in most species), a central nervous system and male or female genitalia.
3. The life cycle of arthropods may be very simple, with only egg, larval and adult stages; it may be somewhat more complex, with one or more nymphal stages between larva and adult, or it may be highly complex, with a complete metamorphosis during a pupal stage between larva and adult.
4. Originally all arthropods were aquatic. Many groups have become adapted to a terrestrial life; some are either aquatic or terrestrial during their immature stages and terrestrial or aërial as mature forms.
5. Species of arthropods of medical importance may serve as intermediate hosts or vectors of other organisms pathogenic for man; or they themselves may produce human illness as internal or external parasites, or as a result of venomous and salivary secretions which they introduce into the body.
6. Centipedes (Chilopoda) are elongated forms having one pair of jointed appendages for each body segment. On the head there are 1 pair each of antennæ and mandibles and 2 pairs of maxillæ. The first postcephalic appendage bears a pair of poison jaws with a terminal fang, through which digestive enzymes and venom are injected into the victim, with sharp localized pain and occasionally a regional lymphangitis, but rarely if ever with fatal termination. Occasionally small centipedes have been recovered from the upper respiratory passages, digestive tract and urethra.
7. Scorpions (Scorpiones) have a fused dorsal exoskeleton covering the head and thorax, and separate abdominal segments. They have long, clawed pedipalps and inconspicuous jaws on the head, four long cephalothoracic legs, and a broad anterior and narrow posterior portion of the abdomen ending in a curved caudal sting apparatus. Scorpions are viviparous. They live in arid or moist warm climates and shun extreme dryness and sunlight. Their natural food is soft-bodied insects but they also venenate larger animals as a protective mechanism. Human scorpion sting occurs in many parts of the world, including the southwestern United States. The venom of some species of scorpions produces only localized reaction at the site of the sting. In other species the venom is primarily neurotoxic, resulting in an ascending motor paralysis, at times resulting in death, particularly in children of preschool age who are the most common victims. Insect toxicants sprayed within and around homes provide considerable protection.

8. Spiders (Araneæ) have a cephalothorax separated from a much larger abdomen by a conspicuous constriction, and 4 pairs of long thoracic legs. The mouth parts include a pair of poison jaws with a hollow clawed termination, through which digestive enzymes and venom are secreted.

   All spiders elaborate venom but very few species are able to puncture human skin. Those which venenate man belong to two groups, one having secretions which produce a local indolent ulcer (necrotic arachnidism) and the other with a neurotoxic fraction causing an ascending motor paralysis (systemic arachnidism). The black-widow spider (*Latrodectus mactans*) is the most notorious and widely distributed species which elaborates potent neurotoxins and causes systemic arachnidism, at times ending fatally, particularly in children. For this type treatment consists of vasodilatation, sedation and administration of specific antivenin. Residual spraying of DDT or benzene hexachloride (Gammexane) where the spiders live provides satisfactory control.
9. Ticks and mites (Acari) are 8-legged arthropods which are usually broadly oval in contour and have no external separation between cephalothorax and abdomen. They possess a head portion which is characterized by a median hypostome below the mouth, a pair of chelicerae and a pair of palps. The life cycle includes the egg, a 6-legged larval stage, one or more 8-legged nymphal stages and the adult.
10. Ticks are large mites with a leathery integument and a conspicuous hypostome provided with sharp recurved hooklets. They have a larval and one nymphal stage between the egg and the adult. All ticks feed on vertebrate blood during each active stage. The soft-bodied forms (Argasidæ) feed intermittently and the hard-bodied forms (Ixodidæ) take a prolonged feeding.

    Ticks are medically important (1) as biological vectors of microörganisms pathogenic for man, (2) as the agents of painful cutaneous wounds, and (3) as the cause of tick paralysis resulting from the injection of their salivary secretions into the punctured skin. Paralysis is most apt to occur if the tick is attached at the base of the brain. Dusting of DDT into socks and trouser cuffs will materially reduce the liability of tick infestation.
11. Mange mites are true tissue parasites in the skin. The species which infests man (*Sarcoptes scabiei*) is a very small macroscopic object, broadly oval, with a head projecting forward like a turtle's, 2 pairs of anteriorly-projecting legs and 2 pairs of posteriorly-projecting legs. The female lives at the inner end of a tunnel, where she lays a few large eggs each day for 4 to 5 weeks.

    Human sarcoptic mange is almost always contracted from close contact with infested persons or their clothing, rarely from infested horses, cattle or other large domestic animals. The female burrows into the skin, producing a tunnel in the deeper epidermis, feeding on the cells and depositing small fecal dejecta, which produce the vesiculation at the inner end of the tunnel and cause intense pruritus. Scratching results in scarification and spread of the mite's progeny to other cutaneous areas. Treatment consists in thorough soaking of the lesions with warm soapy water, then application of lindane (benzene hexachloride) ointment. The disease can be controlled by apprehending and treating all persons who develop the infestation.

12. The follicular mange mite (*Demodex folliculorum*) is a microscopic vermiform object which invades the hair follicles and sebaceous glands, particularly of the face, producing an inflammatory reaction of an acniform type, accompanied by moderate pruritus. Use of warm soapy water on the infested skin followed by application of lindane (benzene hexachloride) ointment is remedial.
13. Parasitoid mites (*Bdellonyssus*, *Allodermanyssus* and *Dermanyssus*) are small macroscopic forms which commonly infest rodents or birds to suck blood or tissue juice from the skin. All of these species are biological vectors of pathogenic microörganisms and also produce a pruritic dermatitis. Control consists in dusting DDT or other insect toxicants in infested locations and campaigns against domestic rats and mice.
14. Chiggers or red mites (family Trombiculidæ) are small macroscopic mites, having adults which obtain food from small invertebrates and larvas which infest vertebrate hosts to suck tissue juices. A few species in the Orient are biological vectors of scrub typhus. Several species of *Trombicula* and *Schöngastia* are aggravating pests of man, producing severe local reaction at their sites of attachment, with intense pruritus. Topical application of phenolated camphor in mineral oil relieves the itching. Dusting of DDT into socks and clothing provides considerable temporary protection from the mites.
15. Predaceous mites commonly prey on insects which infest cereal crops. One cosmopolitan species, *Pediculoides ventricosus*, is a serious human pest, particularly at harvest time. The mites cause a severe, intensely pruritic dermatitis. Topical application of palliative lotions relieves the pruritus.
16. Food mites are small forms which are neither truly parasitic nor predaceous, feeding on organic substances such as cheeses and cereals. They infest the skin of persons who handle green grocery stocks, cheeses, copra and other infested objects, causing a temporary mild pruritus. Rarely they may be inhaled and cause bronchial asthma.
17. "Tongue worms" (pentastomes) are worm-like arthropods with superficial annulations. They require two hosts to complete a life cycle. The immature stages are found in the visceral organs, the mature stage in the upper respiratory passages of the host. Man occasionally serves as intermediate hosts of *Linguatula serrata* ("tongue worm") and species of *Armillifer* and *Porocephalus* (moniliform pentastomes).

REFERENCES

Ayres, S., and Anderson, N. P. 1932. *Demodex Folliculorum.* Its Rôle in the Etiology of Acne Rosacea. Arch. Derm. & Syph., *25*, 89–98.

Baerg, W. J. 1929. Some Poisonous Arthropods of North and Central America. Trans. 4th Internat'l Congress Entomol., Ithaca, N. Y., Vol. II, 418–438.

————1938. Tarantula Studies. J. New York Entomol. Soc., *46*, 31–43.

Baker, E. W., and Wharton, G. W. 1952. *An Introduction to Acarology.* 465 pp. Macmillan Co., New York.

Carter, H. F., and D'Abrera, V. St. E. 1946. Mites (Acarina)—a Probable Factor in the Aetiology of Spasmotic Bronchitis and Asthma Associated with High Eosinophilia. Trans. R. Soc. Trop. Med. & Hyg., *39*, 373–396.

D'Amour, F. E., Becker, F. E., and Van Riper, W. 1936. The Black Widow Spider. Q. Rev. Biol., *11*, 123–160.

Efrati, P. 1949. Poisoning by Scorpion Sting in Israeli. Am. J. Trop. Med., *29*, 249–257.

Garjardo-Tobár, R. 1943. Observaciones acerca de la *Linguatula Serrata.* Med. Moderna (Valparaiso, Chile), Año XVI, No. 8, 1–4.

Mackinnon, J. E., and Witkind, J. 1953. Arachnidismo Necrótico. An. Fac. de Med., Montevideo, *38*, 75–100.

Matheson, R. 1950. *Medical Entomology.* 2nd ed., 612 pp. Comstock Publishing Co., Ithaca, N. Y.

Rogers, G. K. 1943. Grain Itch. J. Am. Med. Assn., *123*, 887–889.

Schenone, F., H. 1953. Mordeduras de Arañas. Bol. Inform. Parasit. Chileñas, *8*, 35–36.

Skaliy, P., and Hayes, W. J. 1949. The Biology of *Liponyssus Bacoti* (Hirst, 1913). (Acarina, Liponyssidæ). Am. J. Trop. Med., *29*, 759–772.

Soysa, E. 1949. The Eosinophilic Respiratory Syndrome. J. R. Army Med. Corps, *92*, 1.

Stahnke, H. L. 1949. Scorpions. 23 pp. Tempe, Arizona.

———1953. The L-C Treatment of Venomous Bites or Stings. Am. J. Trop. Med. & Hyg., *2*, 142–143.

Waterman, J. A. 1938. Some Notes on Scorpion Poisoning in Trinidad. Trans. R. Soc. Trop. Med. & Hyg., *31*, 607–624.

Wilson, W. H. 1904. The Physiological Action of Scorpion Venom. J. Physiol., *31*, 1–53.

Chapter 20

Arthropods as Agents of Human Disease (*Concluded*)

INSECTS

INSECTS (Class Insecta) are the most numerous of the arthropods and comprise about 70% of all the known species of animals. Both economically and medically insects constitute the most important group in the Animal Kingdom.

Adult Morphology.—All adult insects have 3 pairs of thoracic legs, hence the frequent reference to this class as "hexapods." Moreover, insects have three distinct portions of the body, *e. g.*, head, thorax and abdomen (Fig. 189).

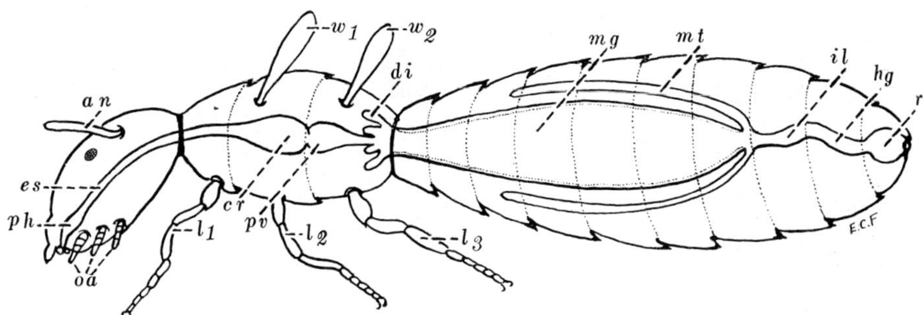

FIG. 189.—Schematic representation of an insect, viewed from the left side. *an*, antenna; *cr*, crop; *di*, food diverticulum; *es*, esophagus; *hg*, hindgut; *il*, ileum; l_1, l_2, l_2, thoracic legs; *mg*, midgut; *mt*, Malpighian tubule; *oa*, oral appendages; *ph*, pharynx; *pv*, proventriculus; *r*, rectum; w_1, w_2, wings. (Original adaptation.)

The *head* is developed from 6 fused segments. The paired appendages are all highly modified from the jointed legs of the primitive arthropod (Fig. 178, page 451). The anteriormost pair are the antennæ. The mouth parts consist of 1 pair each of palps, mandibles and maxillæ and a posteriormost fused pair, the labium or lower lip (Fig. 190). In the grasshopper, cockroach and beetles, these are adapted for chewing, whereas in sucking lice, bugs, moths and butterflies, flies and fleas they have been transformed into a tubule adapted for lapping or for piercing and sucking.

The *thorax* contains 3 segments, prothorax, mesothorax and metathorax, each with a pair of walking legs (Fig. 189). Most insects also have wings. The full number of wings consists of 2 pairs, 1 pair each on the mesothoracic and metathoracic segments. Flies have retained only the mesothoracic pair.

The *abdomen* consists of 12 original segments, a majority of which can be seen on external examination of the insect, although the first two are not apparent, and the distalmost ones are modified as external genital organs.

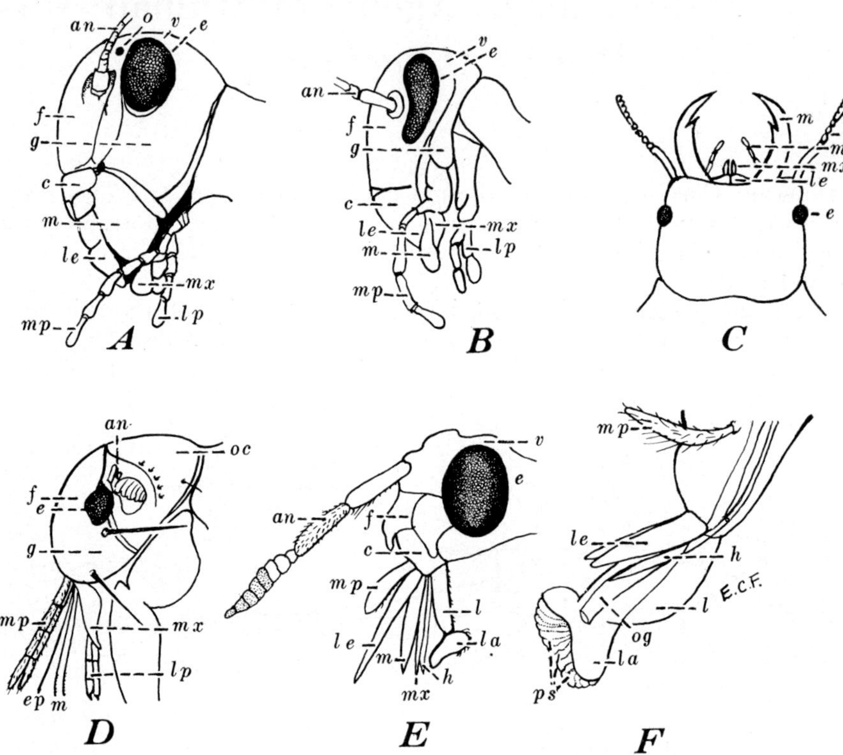

FIG. 190.—Representative head appendages of several insects. *A*, *B*, *C*, chewing types; *D*, *E*, *F*, sucking types. *A*, grasshopper; *B*, cockroach; *C*, lucanid beetle; *D*, human flea; *E*, deer fly; *F*, calliphorid fly. *an*, antenna; *c*, clypeus; *e*, compound eye; *ep*, epipharynx; *f*, frons; *g*, gena (cheek); *h*, hypopharynx; *l*, labium; *la*, labellum; *le*, labrum or labrum-epipharynx; *lp*, labial palp; *m*, mandible; *mp*, maxillary palp; *mx*, maxilla; *o*, ocellus (eyespot); *oc*, occiput; *og*, oral groove; *ps*, pseudo-tracheæ; *sd*, salivary duct; *v*, vertex. (Original adaptations, *A*, from Folsom, *B* and *C* from Comstock, *D* from Fox, *E* and *F* from Imms.)

The digestive tract with its component organs is shown in Figure 189.

Life Cycle.—In the ancestral insect the stage hatched from the egg was essentially adult in character. Some present-day groups, such as the chewing and sucking lice, have only an inconspicuous metamorphosis between larva and adult. Others, like the true bugs, resemble the ticks and mites in having larval and/or nymphal stages before transformation to the adult. In still other groups, *e. g.*, beetles, ants, butterflies, flies and fleas, the larva is worm-like and has chewing mouth parts. In these insects, following the last larval stage there is a pupal period during which a profound reorganization of internal and external structures takes place before the adult emerges from the pupal skin or cocoon.

For more detailed information on the morphology of adult and immature stages of insects the reader should consult standard textbooks on entomology.

Insects as Causal Agents of Disease

From a medical point of view, emphasis is usually focused on the insect as host and transmitter of pathogenic microörganisms. This subject is considered in Chapter 21, p. 516. But many insects are likewise important causal agents of disease. The types of injury which they produce may be classified as follows:

1. Vesicating, *e. g.*, discharge of body fluids which produce blisters on the skin or mucous membranes. Example: Blister beetles.
2. Urticating, *e. g.*, nettling from poison "hairs" which come in contact with the skin or mucous membranes. Example: Caterpillars.
3. Venenating, *e. g.*, introduction of poison fluid into the skin as a protective mechanism of the insect. Examples: Bees, wasps, hornets and ants.
4. Sensitizing, *e. g.*, introduction of salivary or other secretions into the skin with resultant sensitization phenomena. Examples: Bloodsucking insects (sucking lice, true bugs, flies and fleas).
5. Tissue-invading, *e. g.*, specific or accidental invasion of the skin by the larval or adult stage of the insect. Examples: Myiasis-producing flies, the chigœ flea, beetles.

Each of these topics will be considered in sequence.

1. Vesicating Insects

Insect vesication is confined to a few families of beetles (Order Coleoptera), in which the adults have chewing mouth parts. There are 2 pairs of wings, of which the first pair are thickened to form a protective covering (elytra) over the membraneous second pair when the wings are at rest over the abdomen.

The most notorious of the vesicating beetles belong to the Family Meloidæ, the adults of which produce cantharidin, a substance present in all body tissues but most concentrated in the genitalia. The effective principle is a volatile fluid of pungent odor and weakly acid taste which has been used for centuries as a rubefacient, diuretic and aphrodisiac. The commonest cantharidin-producing species is *Lytta* (*Cantharis*) *vesicatoria* ("Spanish fly"). When this beetle (Fig. 191 *A*) is accidentally crushed or discharges its body fluids on the skin, or is therapeutically applied to the skin, an epidermal blister develops, in which histamine-like substances can be demonstrated. If toxic doses of cantharidin are swallowed, there is a syndrome of severe gastro-intestinal irritation, with nausea, vomiting, profuse diarrhea and occasional collapse (Hinman, 1933).

A more potent vesicating fluid (not containing cantharidin) is elaborated by adults of certain rove beetles (Family Staphylinidæ), including members of the genus *Pæderus* (Fig. 191 *B*) which are cosmopolitan in their distribution. Likewise species of the Family Paussidæ in South Africa develop vesicant substances. Both of these types of fluids cause intensely painful blisters when they come in contact with the skin or conjunctiva.

If a vesicating beetle alights on the skin, it is much safer to blow it off rather than to crush it. Well-screened sleeping quarters will prevent accidental vesication during sleep. Calamine lotion applied topically partly alleviates the burning pain caused by the vesicating fluid.

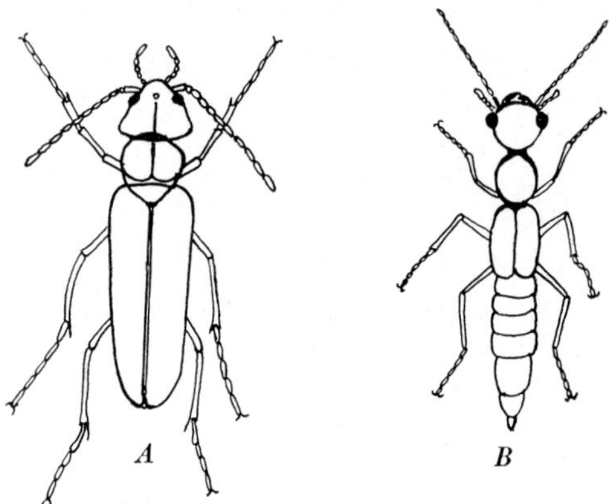

Fig. 191.—Vesicating beetles. *A*, *Lytta vesicatoria* ("Spanish fly"); *B*, *Pæderus sabæus* (rove beetle). (Original adaptations from Smart.)

2. Urticating Insects

Urtication among insects is a protective mechanism of the larval stages (caterpillars) of one family of butterflies and several families of moths (Order Lepidoptera). The adults typically have 2 pairs of membranous wings covered with overlapping patterned scales and maxillæ adapted to sucking juices such as the nectar of flowers. Butterflies fold their wings together vertically when at rest and moths usually fold their wings around their abdomen or roof-like above their body. The females oviposit on or near vegetation which is used as food by the larval stages. The larvas feed ravenously and develop into successively larger larval instars, then form a horny case or spin a cocoon which houses the pupal stage. After a period of weeks or months, metamorphosis is completed and the adult emerges from the pupal covering.

The specialized mechanism for urtication found in several families of lepidopterans is confined to certain hairs or spines employed in protecting the caterpillars from their enemies. These venom-producing organs (Fig. 192) originate in the hypodermis and project through the cuticle. They are of two main morphologic types, primitive and modified (Gilmer, 1925). In the former, each seta is connected with a single unicellular poison gland at its base, which has a minute duct extending into the center of the hair. In the latter, the seta has a bulbous base lined or filled with a number of poison-producing cells. This type may be tipped with a sharp terminus or have a plug which opens to discharge the contents; some species have barbed or branched spines or setæ. Poison setæ may be widely distributed over the larva's body or may be confined to tufts. They may be easily seen or may be concealed among longer non-poisonous, silky hairs. The more common urticating lepidopterans caterpillars include a few butterflies, flannel moths, slug caterpillars, processionary caterpillars, tussock moths, tiger moths, owlet moths and giant silkworms.

All larval stages of poisonous species have urticating hairs. Accidental contact with the living caterpillar causes urtication. In the case of the puss caterpillar (*Megalopyge opercularis*), which frequently feeds on leaves of tall bushes, nettling will result when the larva drops onto the face or neck of a person underneath. Moreover, poison hairs incorporated into the cocoon or remaining in the cocoon may become attached to the wings or body of the emerging adults and be carried to persons who accidentally brush against the moths; or residual hairs may be blown in air currents and make contact with unprotected human skin and mucous membranes.

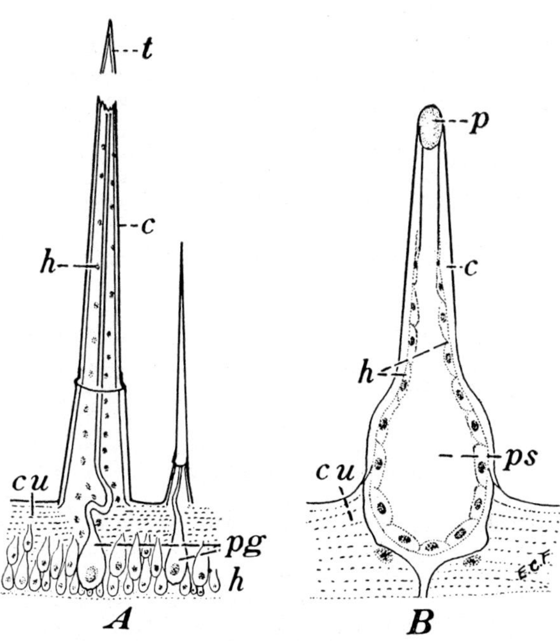

Fig. 192.—Primitive (*A*) and modified (*B*) types of urticating hairs of caterpillars. *c*, chitinous covering of spine; *cu*, cuticle; *h*, hypodermis; *p*, canal plug; *pg*, poison gland cell; *ps*, poison sac; *t*, tip of spine. (Adapted from Beyer and from Foot, in Craig and Faust's *Clinical Parasitology*, Lea & Febiger, Philadelphia.)

The sharp poison setæ readily penetrate into tender skin, the conjunctivæ, nasal or buccal mucosa. If the tip of the seta is open, the poison is discharged directly into the tissues; if it is closed, the hair usually breaks off and releases the toxic substance. The chemical composition of the poison is not known, although it appears to be neither cantharidin or formic acid. Both Tyzzer (1907) and Baerg (1925) have demonstrated a hemolytic constituent.

Pathogenesis and Symptomatology.—The amount of injury and the severity of symptoms in caterpillar urtication depend on the species of caterpillar and its type of poison, the number of setæ which have pierced the body surface, the age of the patient (since the skin of small children is more delicate than that of older persons), whether the setæ have penetrated into the conjunctivæ or mucous membranes, and the individual sensitivity of the victim.

At the time the poison is introduced, there is a local burning, stinging sensation, the affected area becomes erythematous, then elevated and whitish, with a reddish border extending radially as much as 2.5 centimeters and a peripheral reddish macular zone 2 cm. beyond (Mills, 1925; Lucas, 1942). Occasionally an entire hand or arm may become swollen, or urticarial wheals may develop over the entire body, accompanied by systemic manifestations suggesting a neurotoxic syndrome (Lucas, *l. c.*). Rarely, the poison setæ enter the corneal conjunctivæ or deeper tissues of the eyeball, producing excruciating pain, a swollen inflamed organ, at times superficial ulceration and scarring which affects normal vision. De Schweinitz and Shumway (1904) reported development of pseudotubercle reaction around setæ in the cornea and iris. A similar type of urtication was seen in the Charity Hospital, New Orleans in 1952. Cheverton (1936) has described superficial gangrene of the lids of the right eye, with corneal ulceration and chronic conjunctivitis in a boy who had accidentally gotten hairs of a processionary caterpillar in the conjunctivæ.

Persons in contact with the eggs and caterpillars of the range caterpillar (*Hemileuca oliviæ*) have developed hay fever and asthma, with coryza, coughing and severe wheezing (Caffrey, 1918; Randolph, 1934).

Treatment.—There is no satisfactory treatment other than topical application of palliative lotions. The lesion heals slowly like a chemical burn. Caterpillar urtication must be distinguished from allergy dermatitis. Surgery may be required if the eye is involved.

Control.—Area control of moths is indicated, both as an economic measure and as a potential disease preventative. Several insect toxicants are valuable when power-sprayed over affected outdoor areas. DDT and chlordane require no special precautions but dieldrin and thiocyanates, and particularly parathion, which are probably more effective, are very toxic so that there must be special protection for man and higher animals in the area.

3. Venenating Insects

Specific insect venenation is confined to the bees, wasps, hornets and ants (Order Hymenoptera). These insects have 2 pairs of membranous wings, mouth parts adapted to sucking or lapping nectar (bees), or for lancing and chewing (ants). In the worker (a modified female) the ovipositor at the caudal extremity is transformed into a sting apparatus. Metamorphosis in these insects is complete.

The Sting Apparatus.—As described for the honey bee, the venenating mechanism (Fig. 193) consists of a pair of tubular acid glands, the contents of which are conducted through a long duct into a venom receptacle, a single alkaline gland which opens at the outer end of the venom receptacle, a strong muscular bulb below the venom receptacle, and the chitinized sting, consisting of a dorsal sheath, a pair of ventro-lateral lancets which have sharp recurved teeth and fit into the grooved lower side of the sheath, and a pair of lateral palps. The puncture is made by the sheath and lancets, then a mixture of the poison secretions is injected into the wound. All species of bees, hornets, wasps and several species of ants have an efficient sting mechanism and potent venom.

Venenation.—The workers of the honey bee and of some wasps leave the posterior tip of their abdomen, including the entire sting mechanism, in the victim's skin. Muscle attachments continue to contract for some time, forcing the sting more deeply into the wound and setting additional venom free. None of these individuals are able to sting again. Bumble bees retain their sting and produce less severe trauma.

The active venom fraction, *apitoxin*, is present in the acid gland secretion. It is a "dialyzable protein of low molecular weight with an isoëlectric point of about pH

9.7" (Wigglesworth, 1939). Immunologically bee venom is related to viper venom, *e. g.*, its principal toxic constituent is hemorrhagin (Phisalix, 1922, Essex, 1932).

Pathogenesis and Symptomatology.—In some individuals the sting of hymenopterans produces only a temporary local swelling with moderate pain which disappears in a few hours. In other persons the entire member becomes swollen and systemic symptoms of considerable or even profound nature develop. Subsequent venenation may have a rapid, fatal outcome resulting from voluminous emphysema of the lungs, overdistention of the right side of the heart, splanchnic dilatation and liver engorgement (Jex-Blake, 1942).

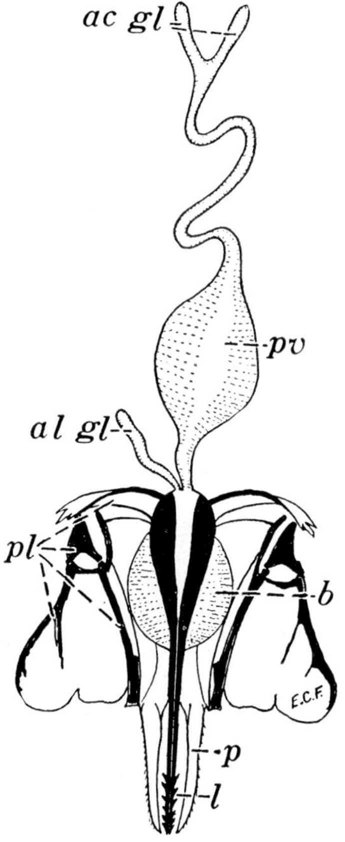

Fig. 193.—Venenating mechanism (modified ovipositor) of honey bee. *ac gl*, acid venom glands; *al gl*, alkaline venom gland; *b*, bulb; *l*, lancet; *p*, palp; *pl*, chitinized plates, *pv*, acid venom receptacle. (Adapted from Patton and Evans, in Craig and Faust's *Clinical Parasitology*, Lea & Febiger, Philadelphia.)

Ants which produce particularly painful wounds are the large aggressive species found in the Tropics, such as the tucandeira (*Paraponera clavata*) of South America, which at times literally sting their victims to death. The "fire ant" (*Solenopsis sævissima* var. *richteri*), a relatively small species recently introduced into the southern United States, is a vicious stinger. Its venom produces a vesicle at the site of skin puncture, with a peripheral reddish macule and at times an indurated swelling up to 2 cm. in diameter.

Treatment.—In case of honey-bee sting, the sting is extracted by use of a sharp needle or knife blade. Local injection of an antihistaminic drug will ease the pain resulting from the accumulation of histamine-like substances at the wounded site. In cases of systemic involvement, epinephrin should be administered as promptly as possible. Ice packs and palliative lotions applied topically to bumble-bee, wasp, hornet and ant venenation may be helpful in reducing the swelling and relieving the pain.

Control.—Accidental sting by bees, wasps and hornets is sometimes unavoidable. However, sensitized persons should avoid exposure by wearing protective clothing, gloves, and nets for face and neck when they approach swarms or active hives. Hypersensitized individuals should receive desensitizing treatment carried out with honey-bee venom extract, which is group-specific. Sprinkling of powdered chlordane (6% in inert powder) on ant nests in the ground followed by wetting, to allow penetration of the toxicant into the soil, is effective against ants.

4. Salivary Sensitization

Introduction

Sensitization phenomena result from the injection of salivary secretions into the human skin by sucking lice, hemophagous bugs, blood-sucking flies and fleas. These secretions usually contain only digestive enzymes or related foreign proteins but the reniform salivary glands of sucking lice apparently produce a special toxic principle (Pawlowsky and Stein, 1925).

SUCKING LICE (ANOPLURA)

Adult Morphology.— Lice are small macroscopic, wingless, dorsoventrally flattened insects which have 3- to 5-jointed stubby antennæ and 3 pairs of conspicuous legs each ending in a sharp curved claw. The "biting lice" (Mallophaga) have chewing mouth parts, a head broader than the thorax and feed on feathers, hairs and epidermal scales of birds and mammals but do not infest man. In contrast, the sucking lice (Anoplura) have mouth parts adapted to piercing and sucking, their head is narrower than the thorax, their legs terminate in claws used for clinging to hairs or fibers, and they are restricted to an ectoparasitic life on mammals. (See Fig. 194.)

The anteriormost portion of the head is the clypeus, which is prolonged into an upper lip (labrum), below which is the sucking apparatus (haustellum). This is provided with 6 pairs of minute teeth which, when everted, anchor the mouth of the louse to the host's skin. Within the haustellum are a chitinized food channel leading into the pharynx and a stylet sac containing a dorsal pair of stylets (maxillæ), a median tubular hypopharynx through which saliva is secreted and a ventral gutterlike structure (lower lip or labium) that supports the parts of the piercing mechanism which enter the skin. In preparation for taking blood the louse applies its haustellum to the skin surface, inserts its teeth into the epidermis, then introduces the stylets and hypopharynx, deposits a drop of saliva, and by alternate contraction and distention of the pharynx pumps blood through the mouth funnel into the esophagus and midgut.

Externally neither the head nor the thorax exhibits evidence of segmentation but several of the abdominal segments are distinct. The abdomen of the male is narrower than that of the female and is rounded posteriorly, while the caudal extremity of the female is provided with a pair of blunt processes (cerci) for grasping a hair or fiber onto which an egg is then attached. Blood and possibly cutaneous cell juices constitute the food of adult sucking lice.

Life Cycle.—The female begins to oviposit in a day or two after she has matured and has been fertilized. Head lice (*Pediculus humanus* var. *capitis*) characteristically cement their eggs to the hair of the head or back of the neck; body lice (*P. humanus* var. *corporis*), to the fibers of body clothing;

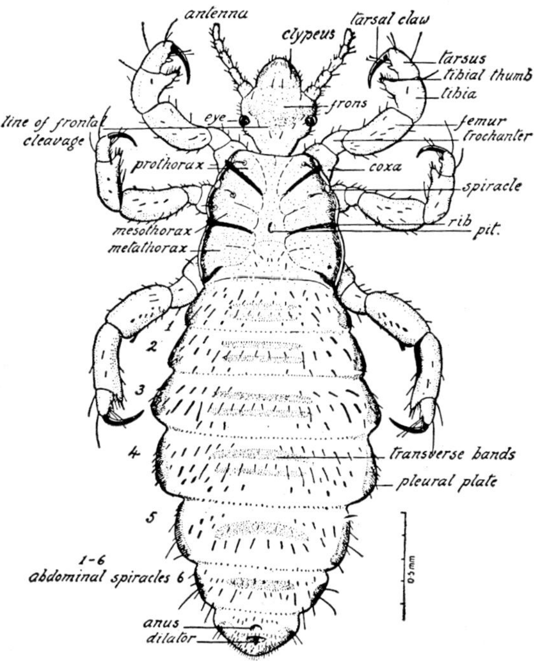

FIG. 194.—Human body louse (*Pediculus humanus* var. *corporis*), male, dorsal view, enlarged. (After Nuttall in Matheson's Medical Entomology, from Craig and Faust's *Clinical Parasitology*, Lea & Febiger, Philadelphia.)

pubic lice (*Phthirus pubis*), to the hairs of the pubic region, chest, axilla, eyebrows and eyelashes. These eggs, the so-called "nits" (Fig. 195), hatch in 4 to 14 days at body temperature, with emergence of the first nymphal stage, which feeds, moults and passes through a second and third nymphal stage before becoming adult 12 to 28 days after oviposition. The adults live about 30 days, during which time each female produces 5 to 10 eggs daily.

Bionomics.—Lice are host specific. The head, body and pubic lice found on man are exclusively human parasites. Their nymphs and adults depend on man for food and warmth but actively transfer from one person to another. They rapidly leave a patient with high temperature; at low temperatures they become inactive but will survive for several days off their victims. Body lice engorge at frequent intervals, discharging relatively large pellets of dark red excrement as they feed.

Infestation with lice is most common among groups in the population living in crowded quarters or observing poor personal hygiene. The body louse (*P. humanus* var. *corporis*) is usually found on individuals in cold climates who wear heavy clothing and seldom bathe. The head louse (*P. humanus* var. *capitis*) is more often found on long-haired girls and women than on males with short hair. The pubic louse (*Phthirus pubis*) is named because it is usually associated with the pubic hairs; it is also called the crab louse because of its broad thorax and abdomen and the large clawed tarsal

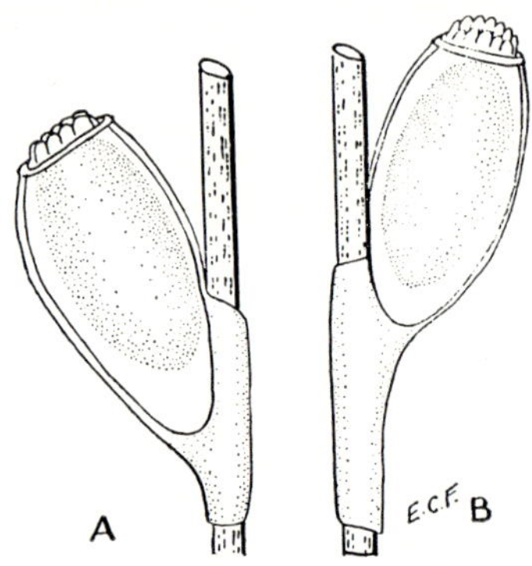

Fig. 195.—Eggs of human lice. *A*, *Pediculus humanus* var. *capitis*; *B*, *Phthirus pubis*. (Original adaptations, from Craig and Faust's *Clinical Parasitology*, Lea & Febiger, Philadelphia.)

joint on each leg resembling that of a crab. Like the head louse, it is more intimately associated with the body hairs and takes a more prolonged feeding than the body louse, which lives among the wool or cotton fibers of clothing except when it is feeding on the skin.

Louse-bite.—Louse infestation is referred to as *pediculosis*. The local lesion produced by human body lice develops at any site on the body where the nymphs or adults are feeding. Head lice usually confine their activities to the back of the neck but they may feed on any hair-covered area of the scalp. Pubic lice frequent the pubic or other hairy regions of the body.

Saliva introduced by the louse into the puncture wound results in the development of a roseate elevated papule, accompanied by intense pruritus. Involuntary scratching of the lesion almost always occurs, with the production of an eczematous dermatitis, striated scarring from use of the fingernails and at times induration and bronzing of the area, the so-called "vagabond's disease." Topical application of soothing lotions relieves the pruritus and allows the lesions to heal.

For consideration of lice as transmitters of pathogenic microörganisms please see Chapter 21, pages 531, 535 and 541.

Control.—For persons infested with head or pubic lice, lindane ointment ($\frac{1}{2}$% benzene hexachloride in vanishing cream) rubbed into the parasitized skin is a practical, specific measure. For body lice, dusting of the body and clothing with 5% DDT in pyrophyllite has proved most effective as a control measure except recently in Japan, Korea and North China, where resistance to DDT has developed (Barnett and Knoblock, 1952). Extensive tests are being conducted to provide satisfactory safe insecticide substitutes to control these resistant strains (Eddy, 1952). Considerable resistance to DDT has also been demonstrated by body lice in Egypt (Hulbert *et al.*, 1954). Chlordane is possibly the most effective, safe alternative. All clothing and other fomites of infested persons should be sterilized by fumigation with methyl bromide, using necessary precautions.

TRUE BUGS (HETEROPTERA)

Adult Morphology.—Members of this order of insects typically have 2 pairs of wings, of which the anterior pair are thickened basally and membranous distally and the posterior ones are entirely membranous. Bedbugs have only wing buds which never develop into functional organs. The most conspicuous external feature of the true bugs is the hinged proboscis, which lies under the head and thorax when at rest but is directed ventrally at right angles to the body when engaged in piercing and sucking.

The head appendages consist of a pair of 3-jointed antennæ and the proboscis with its enclosed structures. Palps are lacking. The protective portion of the proboscis is the sheath (lower lip or labium), a relatively long, 3- or 4-jointed, flexible tube which is almost completely closed on its anterior face. Covering the basal portion of the proboscis there is a short, rhomboidal, upper lip (labrum). Within the proboscis sheath there are a pair each of long, terminally-toothed, bristle-like mandibles and slightly larger, grooved maxillæ that form the food canal. Below the maxillæ there is a minute hypopharynx. (See Geigy and Kraus, 1952.)

The prothorax occupies the greatest part of the thoracic region. The legs are 3-jointed and terminate in 2 small claws.

The digestive tract of true bugs conforms for the most part to that of insects as a whole (Fig. 189, page 475).

Life Cycle.—Metamorphosis is incomplete and almost as inconspicuous as it is in the sucking lice. Following the hatching of the eggs there are several larval (or nymphal) stages, then the sexually mature males and females.

Bionomics.—In the bedbugs (Family Cimicidæ) the adults and immature stages hide in dark cracks and crevices within human habitations during the daytime and come out to suck blood from their victims at night. Each female lays about 100 to 500 glutinous eggs in batches over a period of several weeks. The female requires 4 to 12 minutes to become engorged. The two types of bedbugs which commonly attack man are the Temperate Zone species, *Cimex lectularius*, and the Tropical species, *C. hemipterus*. The former is more urban, the latter more rural in its habitat (Lewis, 1949). Both are shiny, mahogany brown in color, with a body about 5 mm. long and 3 mm. broad, flattened dorso-ventrally; they lack wings, are covered with many hair-like spines and have conspicuous compound eyes (Fig. 196).

The assassin or cone-nosed bugs (Family Triatomidæ) and their relatives of the Superfamily Reduvidoidea are more elongated and considerably larger than the bedbugs (Fig. 197). They have conspicuous, well-developed wings, a pair of compound eyes, and immediately postero-dorsal to each eye a small "eye-spot." Seen from above, the head is roughly diamond-shaped but from a lateral view it is more or less conical. The abdomen is elongated-ovoidal and is not conspicuously flattened. While assassin bugs have a relatively wide geographical distribution, those which are medically important reside in somewhat restricted zones in arid warm regions. Some

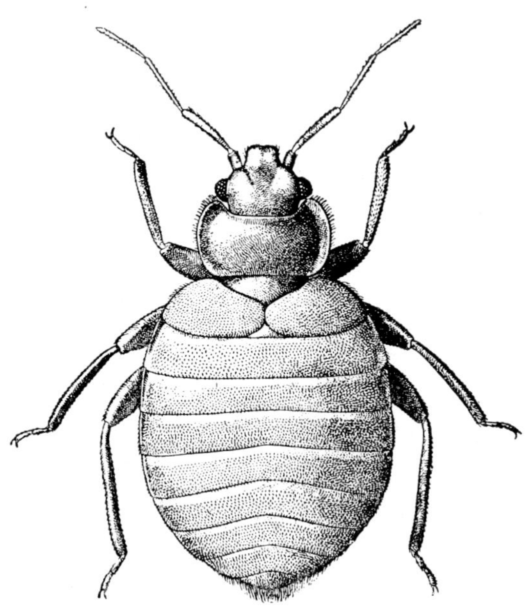

Fig. 196.—Bedbug (*Cimex lectularius*), adult female, dorsal view. × 10. (After MacGregor, in Byam and Archibald's Practice of Medicine in the Tropics, from Craig and Faust's *Clinical Parasitology*, Lea & Febiger, Philadelphia.)

species, such as *Triatoma infestans*, *Panstrongylus megistus* and *Rhodnius prolixus* of South America are primarily domestic in their habits and lay their non-glutinous eggs in cracks and crevices of poorly constructed adobe and thatched homes, from which the active stages sally forth at night to feed on sleeping victims.

Bedbug and Assassin-Bug "Bite."—All of these species are avid blood suckers. Bedbugs are usually more annoying than they are injurious, but in some persons their "bites" are responsible for a swollen, inflamed, cutaneous lesion with an indurated circumference at the site of each puncture, occasionally accompanied by systemic sensitization. Some species of assassin bugs inflict painful wounds, with local swelling, induration, oozing of blood and serum from the puncture site and generalized urticaria. *Reduvius* *personatus* has a potent salivary toxin which produces intense local pain when introduced into the skin. Other species like *Panstrongylus megistus* expertly puncture the skin and withdraw blood almost painlessly from the victim. The common location of their "bites" is the face, particularly on the lips and outer angle of the eyes. Topical application of soothing lotions or ointments relieves the dermatitis.

The importance of bugs as vectors of pathogenic microörganisms is considered in Chapter 21, page 544.

Control.—Since bedbugs which suck human blood are domestic in their habits, their control is limited to human dwellings. The most satisfactory method of control consists in spraying a 2% emulsion of chlordane in

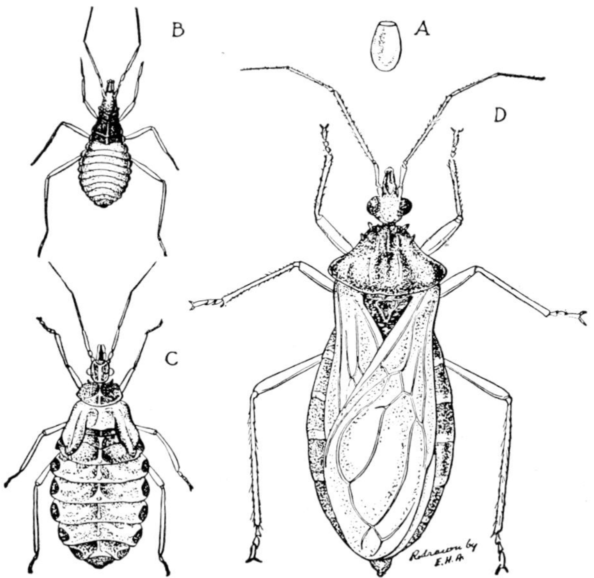

FIG. 197.—Stages in the life cycle of an assassin bug, *Panstrongylus megistus*. *A*, egg; *B*, one-day-old larva hatched from egg; *C*, 3-months-old larva; *D*, adult female. (Adapted from Pinto, in Shattuck's Diseases of the Tropics, Appleton-Century-Crofts, Inc., N. Y.)

kerosene with $\frac{3}{10}$% Triton X-45 emulsifier into cracks and crevices of walls, bedbug-infested mattresses, beds, or other furniture. In old plastered walls the potency of chlordane deteriorates rapidly because of the lime content of the plaster, so that several applications may be required to kill all of the bugs.

Assassin bugs are domestic and wild, depending on the particular species. The practical problem is limited to eradication of those which inhabit homes. The most efficient insecticide for this purpose is benzene hexachloride (Gammexane), employing an emulsion consisting of 5% technical grade gamma isomer in kerosene with $\frac{3}{10}$% Triton X-45 emulsifier. The emulsion is sprayed on inside walls and into the thatch or other roof covering of the home. In dry climates the residual effect is prolonged for at least 6 months, considerably less in moist climates.

Both types of bug infestation are commonly associated with homes of the low economic segment of a population. The fundamental preventive measure consists in the construction or rebuilding of domiciles free of wall cracks and with a roof which does not attract the breeding of bugs.

FLIES (DIPTERA)

Introduction

Flies are insects which as adults typically have a single pair of membranous wings arising from the dorso-lateral angle of the 2nd thoracic segment. In place of a 2nd pair of wings on the 3rd thoracic segment there

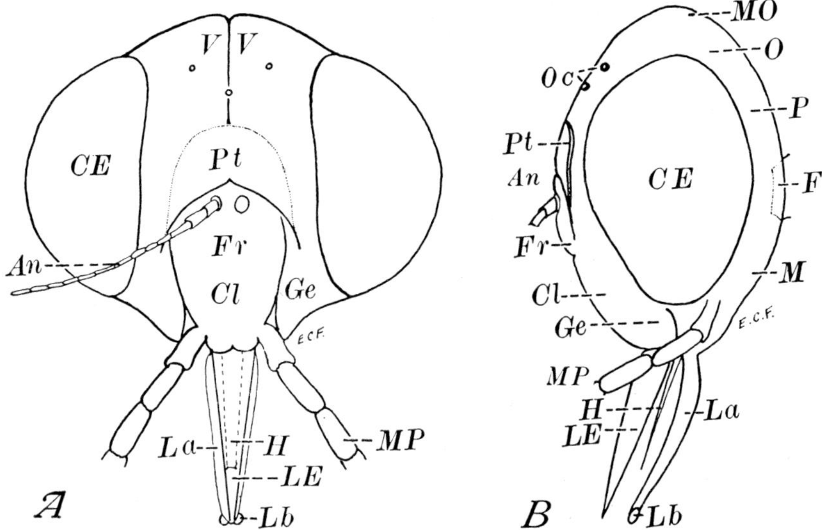

FIG. 198.—Schematic representation of the head of a fly. *A*, frontal view; *B*, lateral view. *An*, antenna; *CE*, compound eye, *Cl*, clypeus; *F*, foramen between head and thorax; *Fr*, frons; *Ge*, gena (cheek); *H*, hypopharynx; *La*, labium; *Lb*, labellum; *LE*, labrum-epipharynx (upper lip); *M*, metacephalon; *MO*, mid-occiput; *MP*, maxillary palp; *O*, occiput; *Oc*, ocelli (eyespots); *P*, paracephalon; *Pt*, ptilinum; *VV*, vertex. (Original adaptation, from Craig and Faust's *Clinical Parasitology*, Lea & Febiger, Philadelphia.)

are a pair of minute club-shaped "balancing organs" (halteres). The mouth parts of flies are adapted to sucking or lapping liquid or fine particulate nutriment, and in several families to piercing the skin in order to obtain a meal of blood or tissue juice. All flies have complete metamorphosis, with egg, several larval instars, pupa and adult.

Adult Morphology.—Some flies, *viz.*, mosquitoes, sandflies and midges, are delicate forms, while others, *viz.*, horse flies, flesh flies and warble flies, are relatively large and quite robust.

The Head.—This is a relatively large, moveable part of the body, connected with the thorax by a constriction, and covered with several well-defined chitinous plates (sclerites). From frontal or lateral view (Fig. 198) the most conspicuous feature is the compound eyes, which are usually separated from one another (dichoptic) by a median frontal plate but in some males are essentially contiguous (holoptic). The antennæ, which arise from the frontal plate (frons) have a remarkable variety of forms. The maxillary palps are attached to the lower lateral angles of the clypeus, a ventral continuation of the frons. The mouth parts extend from the under side of the clypeus and are developed into a sucking proboscis, which is short and stout in some groups and long and slender in others. Its anteriormost component is the unpaired labrum-epipharynx, while the lowermost one is the labium or lower lip that is provided with terminal labellæ, one for each of the two fused parts. The labium is deeply troughed and forms the protective sheath of the proboscis. Internally between the labrum-epipharynx and the labium is the hypopharynx with its salivary duct. These mouth structures constitute the channel through which food is taken into the digestive tract.

In species like the house fly (*Musca domestica*), which feeds by lapping and sucking, the lower portion of the proboscis is modified into a haustellum, with an expanded terminal portion adapted for adhesion to surfaces and provided with minute channels (pseudo-tracheæ) for directing nutriment centrally into the food canal (Fig. 190, *F*, p. 476). In contrast, species which feed by piercing and sucking, as illustrated by the female mosquito, have a sharply-pointed labrum-epipharynx and hypopharynx, together with a pair each of lanceolate mandibles and maxillæ, all lying within the labium, which supports the other mouth parts as they enter the skin preparatory to sucking blood.

The Thorax.—The conspicuous region is the second segment which bears the wings, thin, membranous extensions of the tergal cuticle, usually naked but in some groups covered with hairs, setæ or scales. The vein patterns of the wings are important in classification of flies. A pair of small "balancing organs" arising from the metathoracic segment replaces the second pair of wings. Each of the 3 pairs of legs has 5 distinct portions, with a terminal pair of claws, sucking pads (pulvilli) and at times a median bristled or feathered empodium.

The Abdomen.—The first two segments are atrophied or greatly reduced. In some but not all groups segments 3 through 11 can be distinguished. In the female, segments 7 to 10 are modified into an ovipositor; in the male, segments 9 and 10 form the complicated external genitalia (hypopygium). Adult flies have no abdominal leg-like appendages.

Internal Anatomy.—In most respects the digestive tract is similar to that of other insects. (See Fig. 189, page 475.)

Life Cycles.—A majority of flies are oviparous but flesh flies, tsetse flies and the Pupipara are viviparous. There are 3 or more larval instars, then a pupal stage and the adult. The larvas are more or less worm-like, with 12 or fewer distinct body segments, have a head (*e. g.*, mosquitoes) or lack a definite head (*e. g.*, house fly, flesh flies, etc.). They have chewing rather than sucking mouth parts. In a few species the larvas have no spiracular openings; in some groups only the posterior abdominal pair of spiracles are functional, as in the mosquitoes; in many groups both the anterior and posterior pairs are open, and in a few primitive groups there are a pair of spiracles for each or most of the body segments.

The last larval skin becomes the pupal case, as in the house-fly, or it is shed and the pupa forms its own protective cuticle. Following complete metamorphosis during the pupal stage the adult emerges from the pupal covering.

While adult flies are adapted to life in the air, they obtain their food from sources on the ground. The female deposits her eggs or living young on the ground, on the bodies of vertebrate animals, in excreta or in water, depending on the adaptations of the particular species.

Classification of Flies

Taxonomic Classification.—The main division is into two sub-orders, *viz.*, the Orthorrhapha ("straight-seamed flies"), in which the adults emerge from a T-shaped split in the dorsal cuticle of the mid-thoracic segment of the pupa, and the Cyclorrhapha ("circular-seamed flies"), in which emergence is through a circular opening in the anterior portion of the dorsal covering of the pupa. All flies which have mouth parts adapted to piercing the skin and sucking blood, with the exception of a few of the muscids, the tsetse flies and Pupipara, belong to the first group. The filth flies, flesh flies, warble flies, tsetses and Pupipara belong to the second group. The families within each of the two major groups are separated primarily on the basis of the type of antennæ, wing pattern and disposition of diagnostically important setæ (chetotaxy).

Medical Classification.—From a medical viewpoint it is convenient to classify flies corresponding to their rôle in the production of injury and disease, *viz.*, (1) as biological or mechanical vectors of pathogenic organisms; (2) in the causation of sensitization, and (3) in the production of myiasis. The first of these topics is presented in Chapter 21, pages 524–529.

Flies as Sensitizing Agents

All flies which puncture human skin for the purpose of sucking blood introduce droplets of saliva consisting primarily of digestive enzymes. These secretions contain foreign protein substances which may produce considerable local reaction in the skin and in some individuals systemic sensitization. The flies which pierce the skin and suck blood belong to four major groups, *viz.*, (1) the Nematocera, which have many-jointed thread-like antennæ and include the mosquitoes (Culicidæ), "moth" flies (Psychodidæ), midges (Chironomidæ), and coffee-flies or black-gnats (Simuliidæ); (2) the Brachycera, which have 3-jointed short antennæ, and include the horse flies, gad flies and deer flies (Tabanidæ); (3) "circular-seamed" flies in which the axillary basal lobe of the wings is well developed, represented by the biting stable-fly or dog-fly, *Stomoxys calcitrans*, of the family Muscidæ, and the tsetse flies (Glossinidæ), and (4) all of the Pupipara, which have short, non-retractile mouth parts, highly developed, toothed or spined claws on broadly separated legs, and are commonly ectoparasitic on several species of mammals and birds.

THE MOSQUITOES (CULICIDÆ)

Adult Morphology.—Mosquitoes are slender, delicate flies which have a cosmopolitan distribution and number several thousand species. The

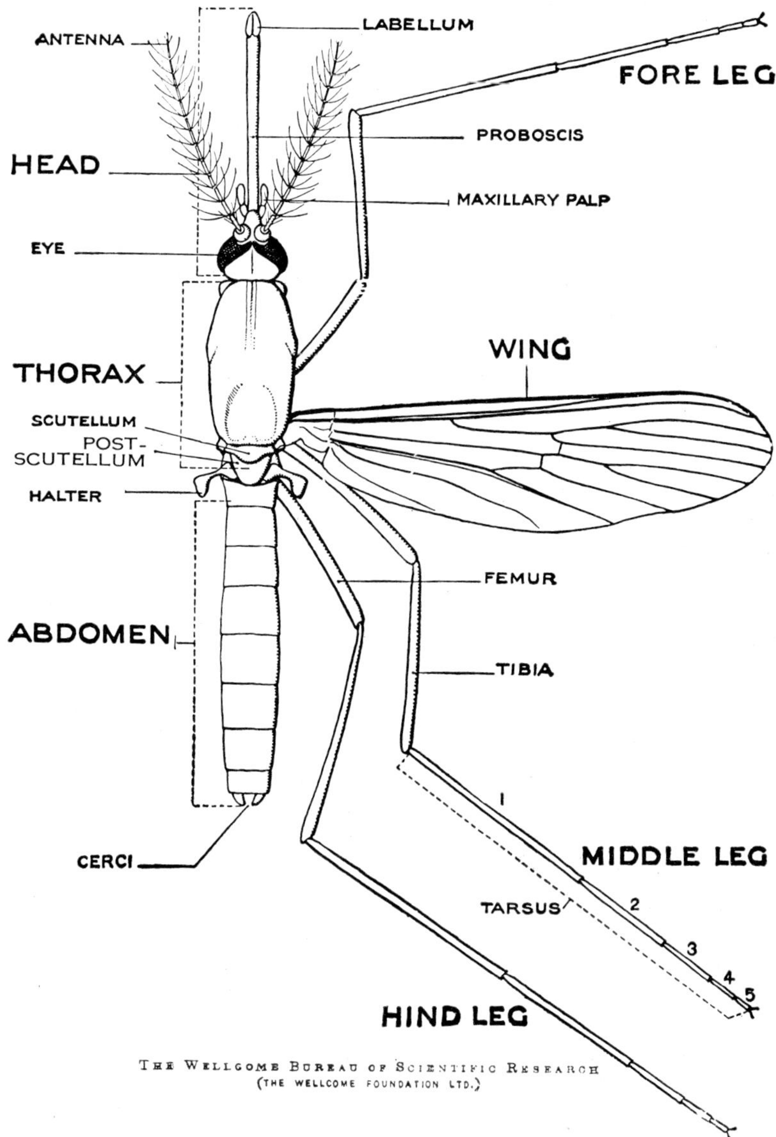

FIG. 199.—Diagram of a female culicine mosquito, dorsal view. (After MacGregor, from Craig and Faust's *Clinical Parasitology*, Lea & Febiger, Philadelphia.)

antennæ are long, 15-jointed and are provided with whorls of hairs at the nodes, which are plumose in the male, scantier in the female. The mouth parts are long and in the female of most species (but not the male) are adapted to piercing and sucking blood (Fig. 199). The head is subglobose and the compound eyes are conspicuous. The maxillary palps in the male (except in the tribe Sabethini) are nearly as long as the proboscis; the palps in female anophelines are equally long while those in female culicines are short. The thorax is elongate-ovoidal or rectangular from the dorsal aspect and is covered almost completely by the mesothoracic plate (mesonotum), which is separated posteriorly by a suture from the scutellum. The legs which are long and slender terminate in 2 tarsal claws. The wings are long and narrow and frequently have species-distinctive scale patterns.

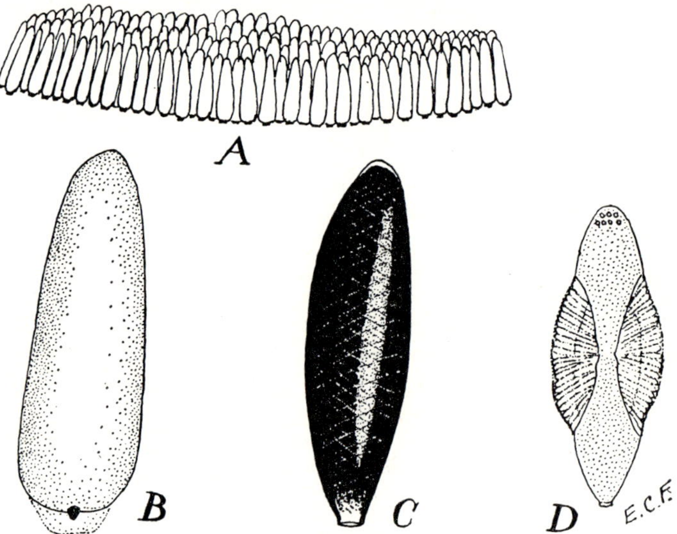

Fig. 200.—Mosquito eggs. *A*, raft of *Culex pipiens* eggs; *B*, single egg of *C. pipiens; C*, egg of *Aëdes ægypti; D*, egg of *Anopheles quadrimaculatus*. Enlarged. (Original adaptations, from Craig and Faust's *Clinical Parasitology*, Lea & Febiger, Philadelphia.)

When at rest they lie one on the other over the abdomen. Of the 10 functional abdominal segments 8 are clearly visible. In the female the 9th segment is greatly reduced, while the 10th is shortened, narrowed and bears two caudal cerci. The last 3 segments in the male are twisted 180° and are modified into a very complicated external genital apparatus (hypopygium) which is of specific diagnostic importance.

In many species insemination of the females occurs during or immediately following a prenuptial swarming of the males in a quiet area at sundown some distance above the ground, shortly after emergence of the adults from their pupal case. Females which enter the swarm are grasped by the males and are inseminated. The males are able to suck only plant juices and probably die soon after mating but the females survive for several weeks.

Life Cycle.—Egg production and egg laying are typically dependent on a previous blood meal. Most females oviposit in a wet or moist location but *Aëdes* may select a dry site where water will accumulate later. The eggs are laid singly until a complete brood has been discharged. *Anopheles* and *Aëdes* eggs remain isolated on the surface of the water but those of *Culex* become aggregated into floating rafts (Fig. 200). Most mosquitoes utilize fresh water during their aquatic stages but a few are adapted to brackish water. Under favorable conditions of moisture and temperature the eggs hatch in 24 to 48 hours. At the moment of hatching the egg breaker, a chisel-shaped organ on the top of the head of the first-stage larva, produces a slit in the shell and the larva emerges into the water.

The larva has a head, thorax and abdomen, with a siphon tube (culicines) or much shorter stigmal apparatus (anophelines), bearing the openings of 2 tracheal tubes, arising from the 8th abdominal segment. Culicines feed at an angle below the water surface while anophelines must lie parallel to the surface and obtain their food close to the surface, usually with their head turned as much as 180° from its normal position (Fig. 201, *A*, *B*, *C*). These larvas have chewing mouth parts with which they crush small particulate food that the mouth brushes sweep in in currents of water. Following four larval instars, the mosquito transforms into a megalocephalic pupa, which is strongly curved ventrally and has a pair of thoracic breathing trumpets (Fig. 201, *D*, *E*, *F*). As it matures the pupa becomes darker and more buoyant. When metamorphosis is complete the thoracic cuticle splits, and the thorax, head and finally the abdomen emerge. Meanwhile the wings have unfolded and the legs have stretched out, and in 5 to 10 minutes the body is dried so that the mosquito is ready for flight.

Figure 202 illustrates the characteristic appearance of the adult *Culex pipiens*, *Aëdes aegypti* and *Anopheles quadrimaculatus* when resting on a surface, together with the dorsal view of head and thorax of the females. (For more detailed information on species identification the reader is referred to Matheson's *Medical Entomology*, 2nd ed., 1950.)

Bionomics.—The females of some species of mosquitoes, of which *Anopheles gambiæ* is one of the best examples, have a preference for human blood, *e. g.*, they are *anthropophilous*. Many other species will feed without preference on the most available vertebrate, *e. g.*, they are *zoöphilous*.

Mosquitoes are more avid for blood when the atmospheric temperature and humidity are high than when they are low (Brown, Sarkaria and Thompson, 1951), and are attracted to skin moisture, particularly perspiration.

Mosquito "Bite" and Sensitization.—Griffiths and Gordon (1952) found that after the piercing apparatus of the mosquito's proboscis penetrates beneath the epidermis it probes persistently and rapidly until a blood supply is tapped; meanwhile droplets of saliva are secreted at short intervals. After a capillary has been penetrated the feeding may be directly from the bloodvessel or from the pool of extravasated blood.

Goldman, Johnson and Ramsey (1952) report that the intensity of the tissue reaction to the "bite" is dependent on the sensitivity of the individual, the species of mosquito (or other arthropod) and the duration of the feeding, but it is not due primarily to the mechanical effects of the puncture.

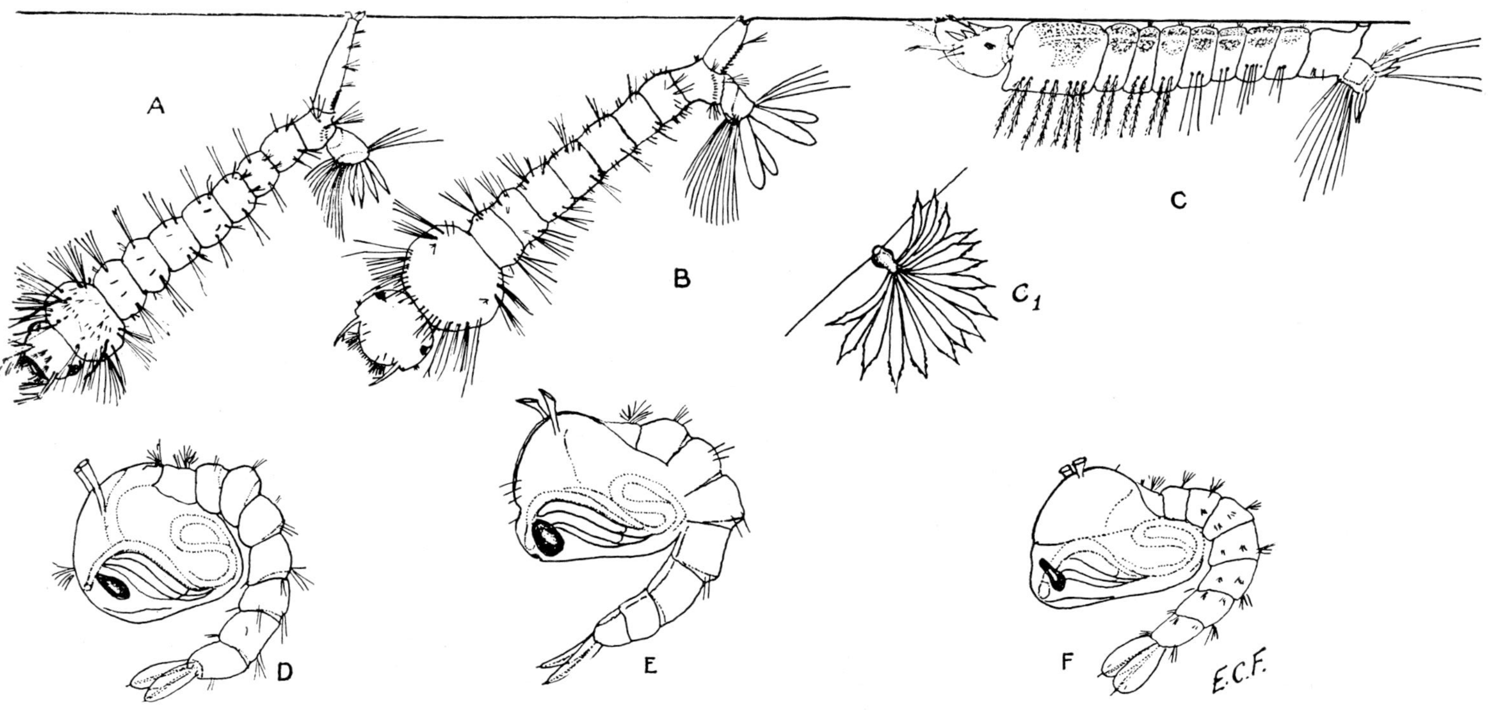

Fig. 201.—Larvas (*A*, *B*, *C*) and pupas (*D*, *E*, *F*) of *Culex pipiens*, *Aëdes ægypti* and *Anopheles quadrimaculatus* respectively, showing breathing position of larvas and resting position of pupas. C_1, palmate hair tuft from dorsum of 3rd abdominal segment of *A. quadrimaculatus.* (Original, in Craig and Faust's *Clinical Parasitology*, Lea & Febiger, Philadelphia.)

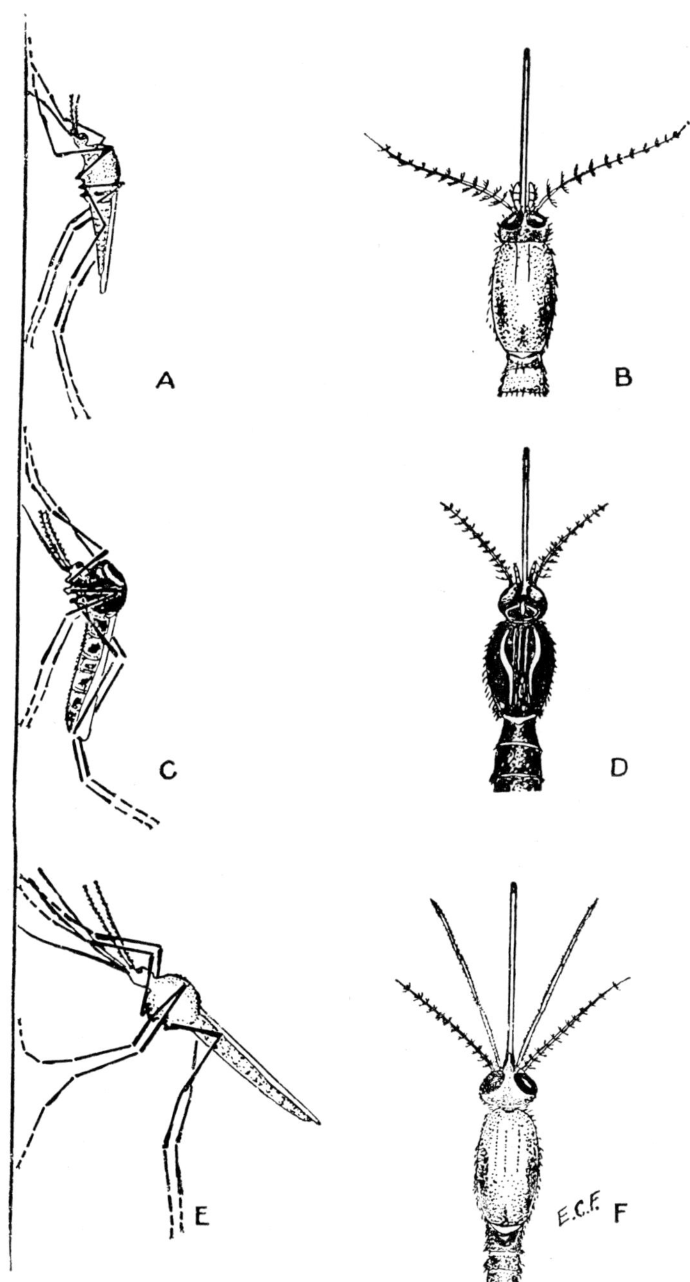

Fig. 202.—Adult resting position, and dorsal view of head and thorax of *Culex pipiens* (*A*, *B*), *Aëdes ægypti* (*C*, *D*) and *Anopheles quadrimaculatus* (*E*, *F*). (Original, in Craig and Faust's *Clinical Parasitology*, Lea & Febiger, Philadelphia.)

Typically there is an initial edema at the site, followed by perivascular polymorphonuclear and lymphocytic infiltration. In sensitive individuals eosinophils, plasma cells and histiocytes invade the area. Scratching and rubbing prolong the reaction and increase the tissue damage. Rockwell and Johnson (1952) demonstrated three clinical types of allergic reaction to mosquito "bites," *viz.*, urticarial, tuberculoid and eczematoid, which they surmise result from multiple antigens, often correlated with other hypersensitivities.

Application of Quotane ointment to the affected skin is palliative.

The rôle of mosquitoes in the transmission of pathogenic microörganisms is presented in Chapter 21, pages 525–529.

Control.—The control of mosquitoes has engaged the thought and energy of medical entomologists, sanitary engineers and parasitologists for many decades. The measures which have been employed include attack on the breeding sites by naturalistic methods and larvicides, use of DDT as a residual spray to kill adults in homes and out-buildings, and protection of persons by screening, bednets, etc. In so far as these mosquitoes cause sensitization, control can be effective. However, this does not take into account the pest mosquitoes belonging to the genera *Culex*, *Aëdes* and *Mansonia*, swarms of which are carried many miles by prevailing winds to feed on human populations. Area control by periodic fogging of residential areas with insect toxicants provides considerable relief to these pest mosquitoes but does not appreciably affect their breeding.

SAND-FLIES (Psychodidæ)

Adult Morphology and Bionomics.—All of the blood-sucking members of this family belong to the genus *Phlebotomus*, *e. g.*, "vein cutters," which have widespread distribution in warm and temperate climates. The adults (Fig. 203) are small, hump-backed, tawny in color, with conspicuous black compound eyes, a pair of long delicate antennæ, long, narrowly obovate wings which form a V-shaped outline above the thorax when the fly is resting on a surface, long, straggling legs, and many delicate tawny hairs on the body, wings and legs. Sand-flies prefer to hop rather than fly and ordinarily are not found more than 5 meters above the ground or far from their breeding sites. Only the females puncture skin and take a blood meal. Sand-flies feed at night and hide in dark places in the daytime. An adult female will take a blood meal one-third of its unfed weight.

Life Cycle.—Long ovoidal eggs are laid in batches of about 50 in moist dark sites, at times on the shaded side at the base of buildings, in rank vegetation or in hollow tree trunks. They hatch in 9 to 12 days and the emerging worm-like larvas, carrying a pair of long caudal bristles, feed on organic débris and the excreta of lizards, but never in a strictly aquatic medium (Hertig, 1948). There are 4 larval instars and a naked pupal stage. Thirty to 40 days after oviposition the cycle is completed.

Sand-fly Sensitization.—The "bite" of a female sand-fly produces a local, frequently indurated inflammation, at times with a wheal 1 to 2 cm. in diameter. This is accompanied by a needling pain, which may be followed by an irritating local pruritus lasting hours or weeks. Some persons develop a severe allergic reaction, with swelling of the bitten member, fever, nausea and general malaise. Topical application of phenolated camphor in mineral oil or Quotane ointment alleviates the local pruritus.

For transmission of pathogenic microörganisms by *Phlebotomus* please see Chapter 21, pages 530, 537 and 544.

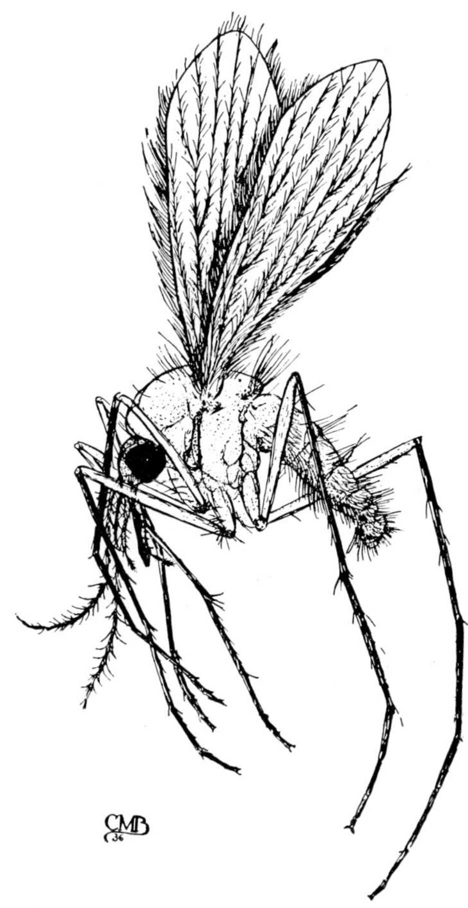

FIG. 203.—Adult female sand-fly (*Phlebotomus chinensis*). Greatly enlarged. (Original in Craig and Faust's *Clinical Parasitology*, Lea & Febiger, Philadelphia.)

Control.—DDT as a residual spray around doors and windows and on the inside walls of human dwellings has proven very effective in killing the adult sand-flies and thus eliminating their "bites" (Hertig, 1948, 1949).

"BITING" MIDGES (Chironomidæ)

Adult Morphology and Bionomics.—The species of medical importance belong to the genus *Culicoides*. The adult *Culicoides* is a small dark fly, with long delicate antennæ, moderately long maxillary palps, humped thorax, a pair of short, broadly obovate wings, and moderately long legs. The hairs on the body, wings and legs are short and relatively scanty compared with those of *Phlebotomus*.

Life Cycle.—Eggs are laid in decaying vegetation in water, in tree holes, crab holes, in the scum of a wet sand bed or even in piles of wet manure. Some species breed in brackish water. The larvas are delicate worm-like objects, which have caudal gills and hooks. The pupa is elongate, chrysalis-like, and has a pair of conspicuous breathing trumpets.

Culicoides Sensitization.—Swarms of these minute midges attack man or mammals, usually at dusk when there is little or no breeze, "biting" on all exposed surfaces of the body and producing multiple lesions which at times disappear after a few hours and cause only temporary needling pain, but in some persons produce severe local pruritus which lasts several days and is intensified by rubbing or scratching. Topical application of phenolated camphor in mineral oil or Quotane ointment is palliative.

For a consideration of *Culicoides* as transmitter of filaria infections please consult Chapter 11, pages 310–311.

Control.—Ordinary screens and bednets will not prevent unfed females from reaching the skin of persons inside dwellings. DDT residual spraying inside homes and periodic area spraying with this insecticide will greatly reduce the annoyance caused by these midges.

BLACK FLIES, BLACK GNATS, COFFEE FLIES (Simuliidæ)

Adult Morphology and Bionomics.—The adults are small, stout, hump-backed forms, with relatively short, stout legs, moderately short, 11-jointed antennæ, outwardly curved maxillary palps, conspicuous eyes (holoptic in the male, dichoptic in the female), and a pair of large unpatterned wings. These gnats are not found at great distances from their breeding grounds unless they are carried in currents of air. Only the females suck blood. They usually take their blood meals in bright light and typically do not "bite" inside dark dwellings or in dense shade. Several species are found in the vicinity of coffee plantations in tropical Africa and tropical America, but other species live in temperate and cool climates. All members of the family belong to the genus *Simulium* (*sensu lato*). Some species are black but others are yellowish-brown or metallic in color.

Life Cycle.—The females lay batches of minute, triangular-shaped eggs in running, well-oxygenated water, at or just below the water surface, where they are glued to bare rocks, dead branches of trees, or stems of aquatic grass. In 4 to 12 hours the eggs hatch, and the larvas emerge and become attached to objects in the water by a caudal hooked disc. There are 7 larval instars, requiring 13 or more days before the mature larva spins an incomplete cocoon around itself. The pupa has a pair of conspicuous, branched external breathing tubes. Following a period of metamorphosis lasting several days the adult fly emerges from the pupal case and takes to the air.

Simulium Sensitization.—Swarms of female *Simulium* attack man and domestic animals throughout the year in warm climates and during warm months in cooler climates. The "bite" itself is not particularly painful, but frequently it produces an intensely pruritic raised lesion. Typically a little pool of extravasated blood produced by the puncture remains in the skin for days or weeks until it is resorbed. Individuals who are repeatedly "bitten" may develop hypersensitization with swelling of an arm or face, generalized urticaria, fever and malaise. No desensitizing measures have been developed. Application of Quotane ointment to the affected skin will relieve the pruritus.

For the role of *Simulium* in the transmission of onchocerciasis please consult Chapter 11, pages 302–303.

Control.—This requires surveys to determine the exact breeding places of the *Simulium*, then larvicidal treatment of the water at pool stage during the dry season with concentrates of DDT. Dimethyl phthalate, when rubbed on the exposed skin, is frequently an effective temporary repellent.

HORSE FLIES, GAD FLIES, DEER FLIES, MANGO FLIES (Tabanidæ)

Adult Morphology and Bionomics.—All of these flies are much larger and more robust than mosquitoes and other gnats, and in size and appearance more nearly resemble the house-fly, stable-fly and warble-fly. Tabanids have prominent irridescent eyes and rather dull-colored bodies which are relatively free of bristles. They have a pair of very powerful wings, a head which is broader than the thorax, short, stout, 3-segmented antennæ, a proboscis which is short in *Tabanus*, medium-long in *Chrysops* and very long in *Pangonia*. Only the females have mouth parts adapted to piercing and sucking blood.

Life Cycle.—The females lay batches of 100 or more elongated-ovoidal eggs which are attached to plants or rocks over clear, frequently running water. In 5 to 7 days the larvas hatch, drop into the water, where they feed and pass through 7 larval instars in the course of a year, then migrate to dry ground to pupate. The chrysalis-like pupas are completely quiet for one to 3 weeks, after which the adults emerge and soon mate.

Tabanid "Bites."—The relatively large proboscis produces an ugly puncture wound, which is painful and heals slowly. Sensitization occasionally develops from saliva secreted into the wound but the trauma produced is frequently more serious. At times surgical dressing of the puncture sites is required.

For the rôle of tabanids as transmitters of pathogenic microörganisms please consult Chapter 11, pages 308–310, and Chapter 21, page 544.

Control.—No effective control measures have been formulated.

BLOOD SUCKING MUSCID FLIES (Muscidæ)

Adult Morphology and Bionomics.—Muscid flies, of which the common house-fly, *Musca domestica*, is the best known example, are medium-sized, stout individuals, frequently of a general dusky-gray color. The blood-sucking species which commonly "bites" man and has a cosmopolitan distribution is *Stomoxys calcitrans*. It somewhat resembles *M. domestica* but can be distinguished by its long, stabbing proboscis, which projects conspicuously in front of the mouth. Both males and females are vicious "biters" and blood suckers.

Life Cycle.—The whitish ovoidal eggs are laid one at a time in manure, decaying straw or rotting vegetation. The maggot-type larvas hatch in one to 3 days, feed, and after passing through 3 larval instars in 11 to 30 days, crawl to a drier location and pupate. After 6 to 20 days the adults emerge from the pupal case and soon mate.

Stomoxys "Bites."—*Stomoxys* readily attacks man, stabbing into exposed skin, and like tabanid females produces sharp pain at the time of the puncture. A small pool of blood characteristically wells up over the wound. Although this fly is an aggravating pest, it seldom produces serious local or systemic sensitization.

For the rôle of *S. calcitrans* in myiasis please refer to page 505; and as a disease transmitter, see Chapter 9, page 170.

Control.—This can best be obtained by preventing the breeding of the fly. Concrete drains under manure piles, power-spraying of DDT or other insect toxicants into piles of rotting straw and area-spraying of DDT on rotting vegetation constitute important control measures.

TSETSE FLIES (Glossinidæ)

Adult Morphology and Bionomics.—These flies, which are limited in their natural distribution to the tropical belt of Africa, are about the size of the common house-fly but are honey-brown in color. When at rest they may be readily recognized by the position of the proboscis extended in front of the head and the way in which the wings are folded over one another straight across the back of the abdomen (Fig. 204). The piercing and penetrating parts of the proboscis are similar to those of *Stomoxys*, although during the act of feeding they are flexible like those of mosquitoes. Tsetses not only suck blood from cutaneous capillaries but also that which wells up from the wound onto the surface of the skin (Gordon and Crewe, 1949). Both males and females are efficient "biters" and voracious blood suckers.

The adults are hardy, long-lived and fly considerable distances but are indigenous to two general types of biotic environments, *viz.*, (1) tropical rain-forests from the west coast of Africa to lakes Albert, Victoria and Tanganyika on the east, and (2) the high savannas of East Africa from the southern Sudan to Southern Rhodesia and Mozambique, where they feed on wild game animals. *Glossina palpalis* is the most abundant and widely distributed tsetse in the rain-forest belt and *G. morsitans* in the eastern highlands.

Life Cycle.—Eggs produced by the females hatch *in utero*, where 3 successive larval stages feed on "milk" secreted by special intra-uterine glands. After 9 to 12 days the mature 3rd-stage larvas are deposited on the ground one at a time and transform into pupas by a hardening of the last skin. Metamorphosis to the adult requires 21 to 60 days, depending on the species.

Tsetse "Bites".—In nature tsetse flies have an abundance of wild mammals from which they secure blood. They are most common in dense vegetation along waterways in the rain-forest belt and in the high grasses of the uplands. Man is "bitten" when he builds his villages near these breeding grounds or enters the areas to fish, hunt or cut wood. They "bite" only during the daytime. They produce stinging pain when they puncture the skin but they are primarily important because they are the vectors of trypanosomiasis to man and domestic mammals. (See Chapter 9, pages 187, 190.)

Control.—Because tsetse flies have an abundance of wild mammals which serve as a ready source of food, control is difficult. Clearing of the bush around native villages, ford and boat landings, planned grass fires in certain areas, trapping of the flies in game preserves, and fumigation of vehicular transportation are useful in one area or another, but no single control program is thoroughly effective.

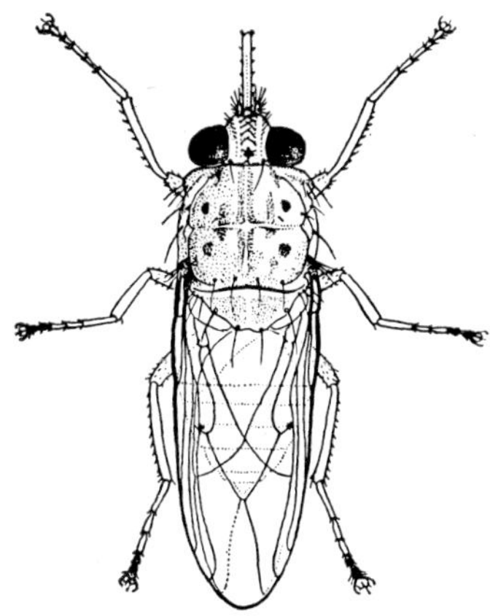

Fig. 204.—Adult tsetse-fly (*Glossina* sp.) in resting position. (From Matheson's Medical Entomology, in Craig and Faust's *Clinical Parasitology*, Lea & Febiger, Philadelphia.)

HIPPOBOSCIDS AND SHEEP KEDS (Pupipara)

These flies have a tough, leathery cuticle, are flattened dorsoventrally, have an efficient skin-piercing proboscis and as adults are more strictly ectoparasitic than other flies. They are larviparous and like tsetse flies the larvas pupate soon after they are deposited by the females. Species of *Hippobosca* have a pair of functional wings; these flies parasitize dogs, cattle, horses and other large mammals. *Melophagus ovinus*, the sheep ked, has lost its wings as a result of its parasitic habits. None of the Pupipara are anthropophilous but they readily attack persons associated with infested domestic animals, become attached to the hair, particularly at the back of the neck, and voraciously suck blood. The puncture produces considerable pain and hemorrhage. Control involves spraying of effective insect toxicants on the natural mammalian hosts.

FLEAS (Siphonaptera)

Adult Morphology.—Fleas are small, wingless, medium- to dark-brown, shiny insects, which are compressed from side to side. They are provided with long legs for hopping and jumping, and both sexes have a proboscis adapted for piercing the skin and sucking blood (Fig. 205). Compound eyes are present in some species, lacking in others. Each of the pair of antennæ is situated in an oblique groove connected with a stricture sepa-

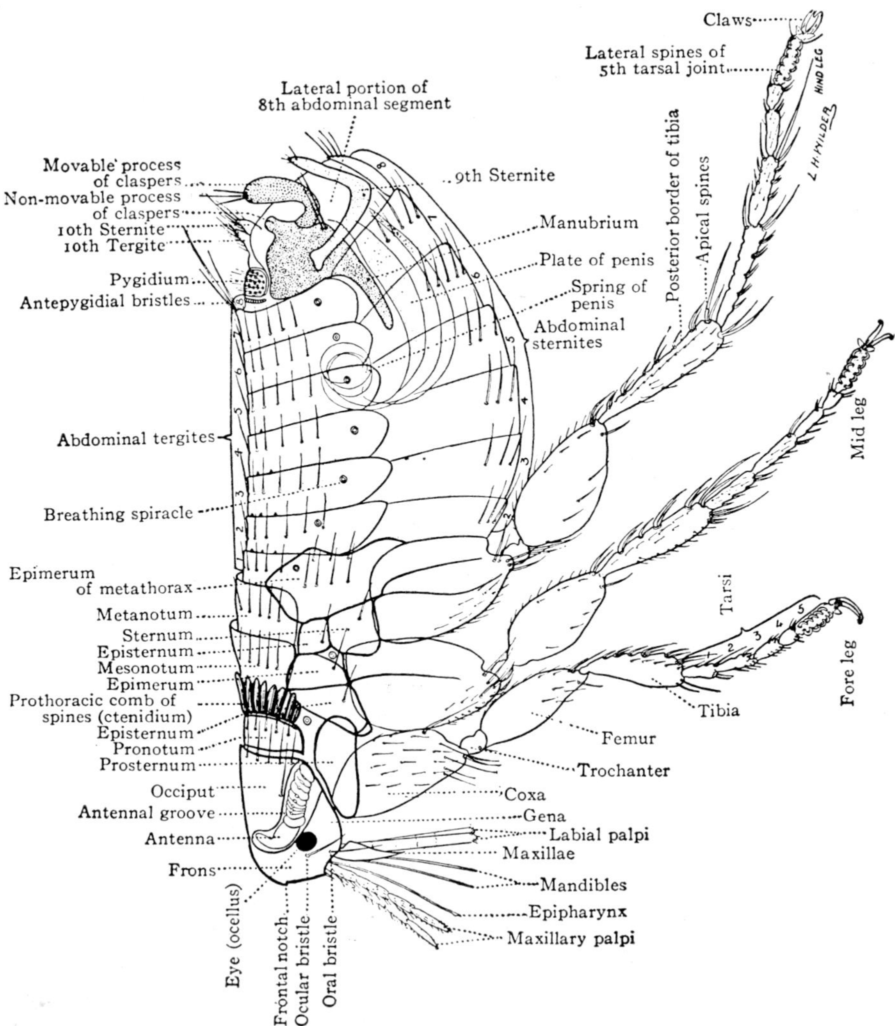

FIG. 205.—External anatomy of a male rat flea (*Nosopsyllus fasciatus*). (From Fox's Insects and Diseases of Man, in Craig and Faust's *Clinical Parasitology*, Lea & Febiger, Philadelphia.)

rating the side of the head into two distinct parts. The following mouth parts can be demonstrated: an anterior pair of jointed maxillary palps, a posterior pair of jointed labial palps, a pair of minutely barbed, needle-like mandibles, a pair of blade-like maxillæ, and a single, stylet-shaped labrum-epipharynx, which with the mandibles forms the food channel. The 3 thoracic segments, each bearing a pair of 5-jointed legs terminating in 2 claws, are easily recognized. The abdomen is composed of 10 segments, of which the last 3 are modified into external genital structures. The 9th seg-

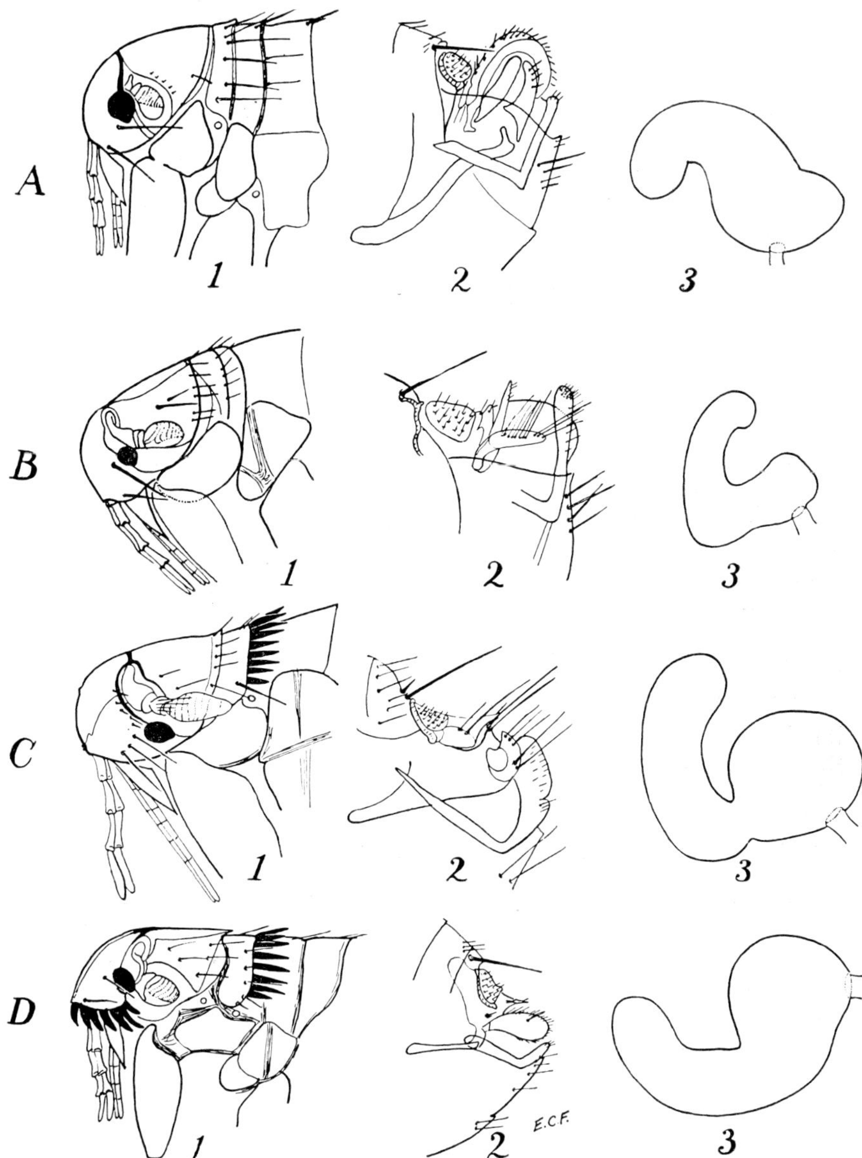

Fig. 206.—Head (*1*), caudal extremity of male (*2*) and seminal receptacle (*3*), of common fleas. *A*, *Pulex irritans; B*, *Xenopsylla cheopis; C*, *Nosopsyllus fasciatus; D*, *Ctenocephalides canis*. (Original adaptations, from Craig and Faust's *Clinical Parasitology*, Lea & Febiger, Philadelphia.)

ment contains a dorsal prominence, the pygidium, which is considered to be sensory in function.

The digestive tract resembles that of most insects (Fig. 189, page 475); however, the proventriculus is provided with particularly long chitinous teeth.

Bionomics.—Unlike lice, fleas are not host-specific although they are usually found on certain hosts. A majority of species of fleas are ectoparasites of rodents. A few of these such as *Xenopsylla cheopis* and *Nosopsyllus fasciatus* of domestic rats have as widespread distribution as their hosts, but most rodent fleas have rather limited geographic distribution. The human flea (*Pulex irritans*), the dog flea (*Ctenocephalides canis*) and the cat flea (*C. felis*) are cosmopolitan.

Life Cycle.—The minute, ovoidal, glistening white eggs are usually deposited on the ground or in infested nests. The larvas are delicate, wormlike organisms with long delicate setæ. They have chewing mouth parts but feed mostly on bloody dejecta of the parent fleas. There are 3 larval instars, following which the mature larva spins a cocoon around itself and pupates. The larval period may require only a week in a warm climate or as much as 3 months in a cool climate; the pupal period may be as short as a week or as long as a year. The adults survive for a year or more under favorable conditions.

Species-diagnostic characteristics of the 4 fleas commonly infesting man are illustrated in Figure 206.

The Chigœ Flea.—Unlike other fleas which puncture the skin of man and other mammals to obtain blood, the chigœ, *Tunga penetrans*, invades the skin. The chigœ may be distinguished from other fleas by the sharp upper angling of the front portion of its head (the frons), the long, stiff, barbed mandibles, the lack of a distinct suture from the antennal groove to the top of the head and the foreshortened thoracic segments. The female sucks juices from cutaneous tissues and develops a tremendous distension of its abdomen. It lays eggs in the tissues or on the ground. Occasionally both males and hatched larval stages may be found in the lesions. This flea is a common parasite of the feet of hogs and dogs throughout tropical America and parts of tropical Africa. It has been described from San Diego County, California and as far south as Uruguay. Barefooted persons who walk on ground polluted from infested animals are liable to become parasitized by chigœs. Clinical consideration of chigœ infestation of man is provided on page 513.

Flea Sensitization.—Many persons are not seriously inconvenienced by the "bites" of fleas. In other individuals a local sensitization reaction develops at the puncture site. The lesion is roseate, raised, frequently edematous and indurated. It is intensely pruritic, and becomes inflamed and scarified as a result of scratching. At times it provides a worrisome problem for the family physician and dermatologist (Lunsford, 1949).

For a consideration of fleas as transmitters of pathogenic microörganisms, please see Chapter 21, pages 532, 538.

Control.—Dogs, cats and domestic rodents provide the common sources for fleas which get on human skin and produce flea dermatitis. Periodic dusting of dogs with DDT, as well as the rugs and cushions in the home on which dogs and cats walk or lie, will greatly reduce the flea population within the house. DDT dusting of courtyards and lawns is also effective prophylaxis. Similar dusting of basements, rat runs and nests will help to prevent the breeding of rodent fleas around the home. The wearing of stout leather shoes will prevent most human infestation with the chigœ.

5. Tissue-Invading Insects

Three groups of insects are involved as intentional or accidental invaders of human and other animal tissues. These are the flies, beetles and the chigœ flea (*Tunga penetrans*).

FLIES (DIPTERA) AND MYIASIS

Myiasis is infestation of the body with the larvas (maggots) of flies. With rare exceptions, as in the "biting" stable fly (*Stomoxys calcitrans*), none of the adults of the myiasis-producing flies have mouth parts able to puncture skin and suck blood, although most of them will avidly lap up blood when opportunity is afforded (Herms, 1932). Myiasis is (1) *specific*, resulting from obligate selection of living tissues by the mother fly as a source of nourishment for the larvas; (2) *semi-specific*, in which oviposition or larviposition in tissues is stimulated by foul or fetid odors emanating from purulent discharges or contaminated wounds, and (3) *accidental*, in which the larvas or the eggs by chance are deposited in superficial sites or contaminate the gastrointestinal or urinary passages.

The flies which cause myiasis belong to a number of families, including the flesh flies (Sarcophagidæ), the screw-worm or blow flies (Calliphoridæ), the warble or bot flies (Gasterophilidæ, Hypodermatidæ, Cuterebridæ, Œstridæ), the filth flies, *e. g.*, house-fly (*Musca domestica*), lesser house-fly (*Fannia canicularis*), latrine-fly (*F. scalaris*), non-biting stable-fly (*Muscina stabulans*) and related muscids (Muscidæ), the drone-flies (Syrpidæ), the cheese-skipper (Piophilidæ), vinegar-flies (Drosophilidæ), and occasionally representatives of several other families. Some of the more important species (Fig. 207) will be presented as examples of myiasis-producing flies.

The larva of myiasis-producing species is armed with a pair of sharp, curved mandibular hooks for abrading and entering tissues. Mature maggots of a number of species are illustrated in Figure 208.

For more detailed description of the adults of myiasis-producing flies the monographic study by James (1947) is highly recommended.

Specific Myiasis

Flesh Flies (Sarcophagidæ).—*Wohlfahrtia Vigil.*—This medium-sized grayish fly (Fig. 207, *1*) lacks longitudinal stripes on the thorax and has 6 small, light-colored triangular areas on the back of its dark-gray abdomen. It is distributed in the northern United States and adjacent Canada, and is the Nearctic counterpart of *W. magnifica* of Europe and northern Asia. The females are larviparous, the larvas mature in 7 to 9 days, the pupal stage

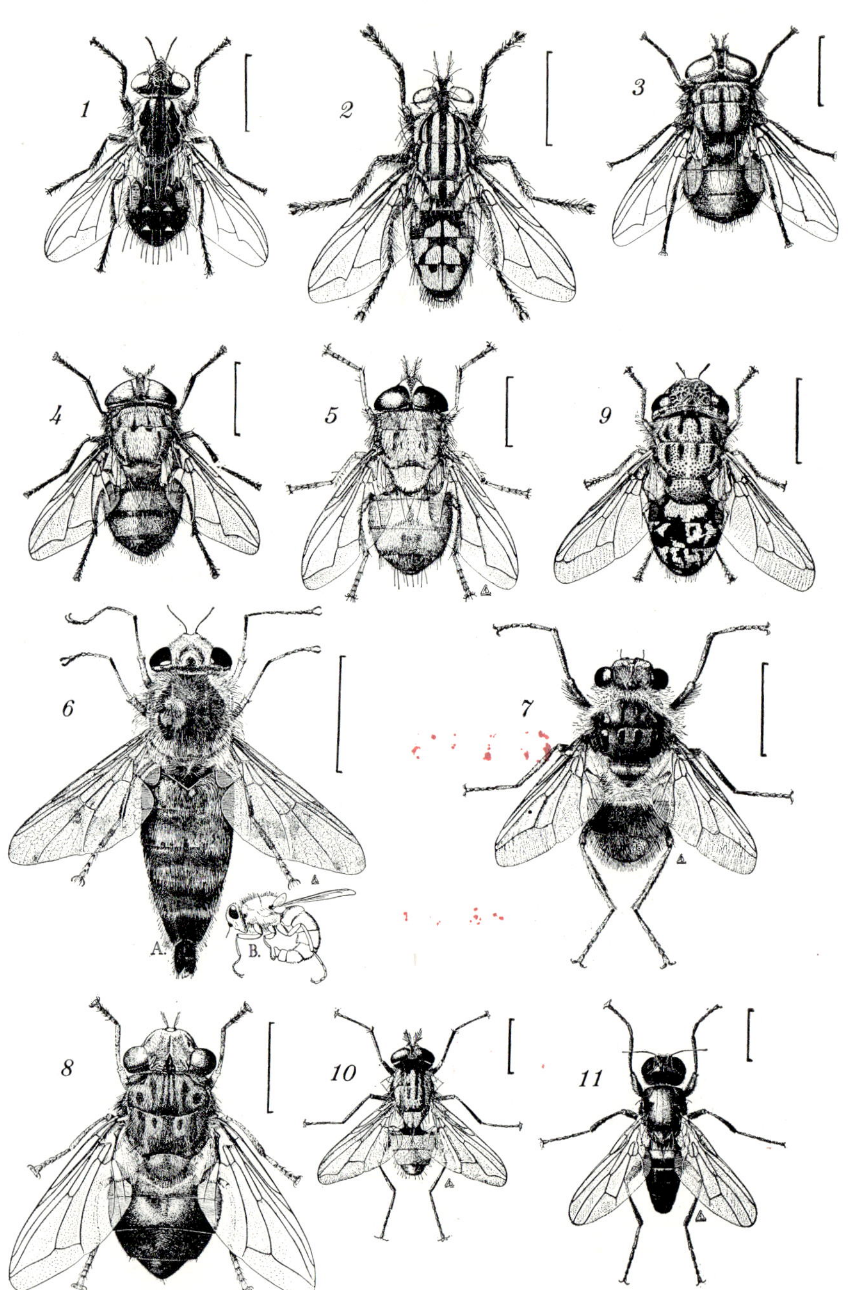

FIG. 207.—Adults of several important or relatively common myiasis-producing flies. *1, 3–9,* involved in specific myiasis (*1, Wohlfabrtis vigil,* female; *3, Callitroga hominivorax,* female; *4, Chrysomya bezziana,* female; *5, Cordylobia anthropophaga,* male; *6, Gasterophilus intestinalis,* female; *7, Hypoderma lineatum,* female; *8, Dermatobia hominis,* female; *9, Œstrus ovis,* female. *2,* involved in semi-specific myiasis (*Sarcophaga hæmorrhoidalis,* male). *10, 11,* involved in accidental myiasis (*10, Musca domestica,* male; *11, Piophila casei,* female). The line adjacent to each drawing indicates the natural size of the fly. (All figures from James' *The Flies That Cause Myiasis in Man,* courtesy Bureau of Entomology and Plant Quarantine, U. S. Dept. Agriculture.)

requires 10 to 12 days and females begin to deposit their young in 11 to 17 days after they emerge from the pupal case. The adults have well-developed mouth parts but apparently feed solely on nectar of wild flowers.

The larvas are deposited in masses on exposed, undamaged body surfaces but usually migrate some distance before entering the unbroken skin, which

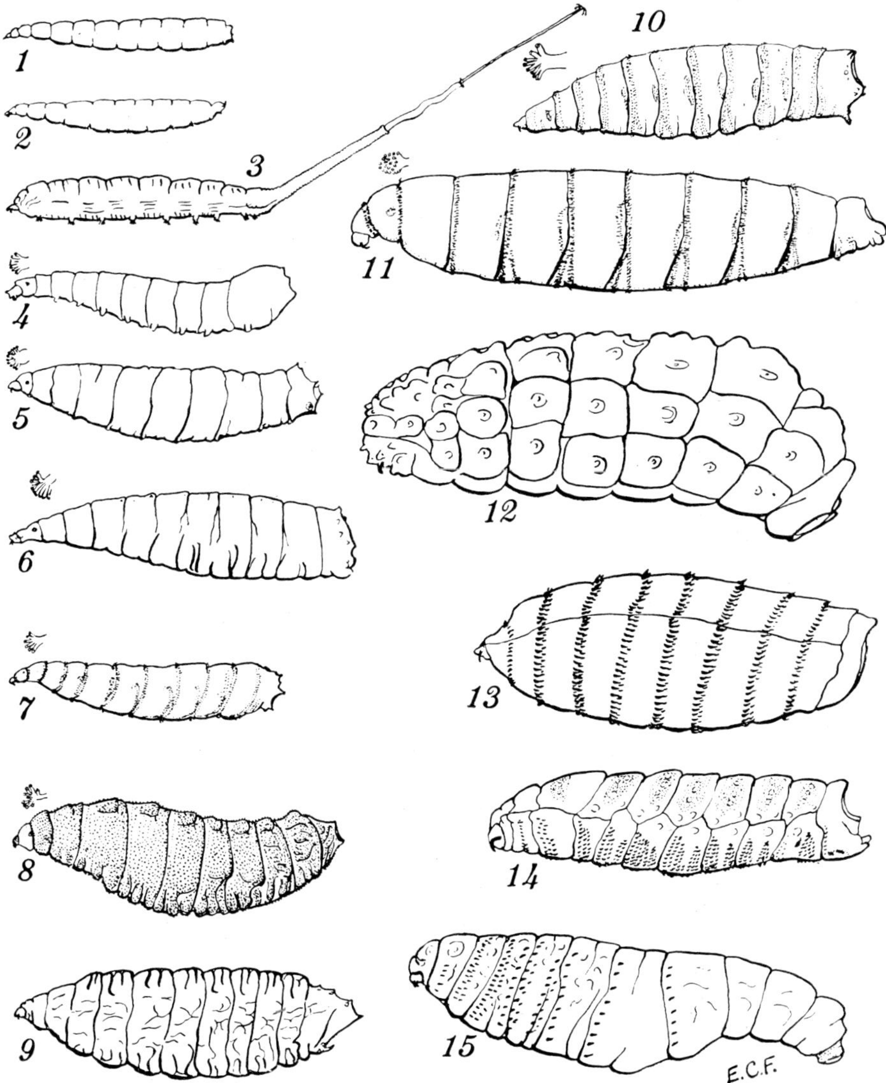

Fig. 208.—Appearance of the mature larvas of several myiasis-producing flies, lateral view. *1*, *Sepsis* sp.; *2*, *Piophila casei; 3*, *Tubifera tenax; 4*, *Musca domestica; 5*, *Phænicia sericata; 6*, *Calliphora vicina; 7*, *Chrysomya bezziana; 8*, *Cordylobia anthropophaga; 9*, *Auchmeromyia luteola; 10*, *Callitroga hominivorax; 11*, *Wohlfahrtia magnifica; 12*, *Hypoderma bovis; 13*, *Gasterophilus intestinalis; 14*, *Œstrus ovis; 15*, *Dermatobia hominis*. × $3\frac{1}{3}$. Anterior spiracle at upper left of *4*, *5*, *6*, *7*, *8*, *10* and *11*. (Original adaptations, from Craig and Faust's *Clinical Parasitology*, Lea & Febiger, Philadelphia.)

must be tender in order for them to penetrate. This limits human infestation to young infants who are left out of doors without protection of mosquito nets. The involved areas include the neck, chest, shoulders, cheeks, palms, navel and eyelids. Once under the epidermis the maggot produces a small raised abscess in the subcutaneous tissues with an opening to the surface. The head is at the inner end and the caudal extremity nearest the external pore. The furuncles are usually multiple and may be mistaken for an advanced type of impetigo. The reported symptoms include irritability, fever, dehydration and loss of weight. Diagnosis should be made at the earliest possible moment to prevent the entrance of pyogenic bacteria as well as extensive mutilation. Under aseptic precautions the maggots may be squeezed out by slight pressure, the wounds cleaned and then covered with surgical dressing. These flies are not attracted by fetid odors and do not feed on dead flesh. Unscreened infants should not be left out of doors during the summer months when the flies are larvipositing.

Screw-worm Flies (Calliphoridæ).—*Callitroga Hominivorax* (Syn. *C. Americana*) (Primary Screw-worm Fly).—This bluish or bluish-green fly (Fig. 207, *3*) is 8 to 10 mm. long and has black hairs on the more lateral areas of the lower part of the front of the head. *C. hominivorax* is widely distributed throughout the Americas from the southern half of the United States to Chile and Argentina. The female is oviparous, gluing her eggs in masses to clean skin near a wound. The eggs hatch in 11 to 21 hours and groups of the young maggots penetrate in pockets down to the underlying tissues. After 4 to 8 days of voracious feeding, the mature maggots drop to the ground and pupate. Seven to 54 days later the adults emerge and feed on manure, meat and serous or purulent exudates, but the maggots require clean flesh for their nourishment.

This maggot is the most important member of the screw-worm family affecting livestock and man. The hatched larvas enter scarified, bruised, inflamed or even undamaged skin and may tunnel deeply into the viscera. They also infest the vagina, the nasal and frontal sinuses, eyes, ears and mouth. The furuncular lesions which they produce are extremely painful and characteristically become secondarily infected, so that extensive mutilation commonly results. The more serious human cases terminate fatally. This species requires differentiation from its close relative, *C. macellaria*, the larva of which is typically saprozoic rather than an obligate parasite.

Chrysomya Bezziana (Old World Screw-worm Fly).—This fly (Fig. 207, *4*) has a black head except for the orange color on its face, cheeks, antennæ and palps. The thorax and abdomen are green to bluish-purple, with three black transverse stripes on the top of the abdomen. The adults measure 8 to 12 mm. long. This species has an extensive distribution through southern Asia and in Africa south of the Sahara. The female glues batches of eggs to dry, unbroken skin, either within the edge of a wound, over bruises or abscesses, or on surface membranes exuding purulent serum or blood. The larvas hatch in 24 hours and at first feed near the surface, then burrow deeply into the flesh, causing a liquefaction necrosis. On the 6th day they have matured and emerge from the lesion to pupate on the ground. After a varying period, depending on the season, the adults come out of the pupal case and start a new cycle. There are 8 or more yearly generations, each with a potential of several hundred eggs.

C. bezziana maggots attack open wounds in large numbers, and produce deep mutilation. In man they most frequently infest the head but have been reported from the nasal and frontal sinuses, ears, eyes and mouth, as well as exposed genitalia. The infestation may cause the loss of an eye or an ear, or erosion of the entire nares, at times with fatal outcome (Patton, 1920, 1922).

Cordylobia Anthropophaga (Tumbu-Fly).—This yellowish-colored fly (Fig. 207, *5*), smaller than most screw-worm flies, has a length of 8 to 10 mm. or somewhat less. It is widely distributed throughout Africa except on the Mediterranean coast. The adults deposit their eggs on dirt soiled with excrement, including the floors of native huts. Hatching occurs in 48 hours and the young maggots enter skin which comes in contact with the infested ground, producing indurated furuncles in the dermis. The mature larva emerges on the 8th or 9th day, buries itself in the soil and pupates. Twelve to 14 days later the adult breaks out of the pupal case, soon mates and a new cycle is started.

Although domestic rats and dogs are most often infested, man is also a common host. The young maggot invades the epidermis almost painlessly, so that the first sign is a reddish papule which soon develops into a boil that is open at the surface to permit breathing of the maggot. There is little pus but much serous exudate from the relatively large cavity of the furuncle. The infested skin area is indurated and very tender. Natives expel the maggots by firm pressure between thumb and finger. Control requires thorough washing and ironing of all contaminated clothing and bedding, and sterilization of floors of native huts.

Auchmeromyia Luteola (Congo Floor-Maggot).—The adult closely resembles *C. anthropophaga* (Fig. 207, *5*). It frequents shady places, including native huts in the African tropics which constitute its enzoötic area. After hatching the maggot attacks human victims who sleep directly on the floors, although it is unable to climb on cots or beds, voraciously sucks blood like a tick or bedbug, and like these arthropods is more of a nuisance than a true parasite. Control consists in sterilization of the floors of huts and use of raised platforms for sleeping.

Warble or Bot Flies (Gasterophilidæ, Hypodermatidæ, Cuterebridæ, Œstridæ).—*Gasterophilus Intestinalis* (Common Horse-Bot).—This brownish-yellow fly (Fig. 207, *6*) has a short, deep head, which is heavily pilose, with small antennæ and mouth parts that are vestigial and non-functional. The thorax is densely hairy and well developed. The hirsute abdomen is elongate-ovoidal and tapers towards the posterior end, which is characteristically curved under the anterior abdominal segments (Fig. 207, *6B*). The general appearance is that of a bee rather than a fly. Its length is 12 to 17 mm. This species is widely distributed in North America, Europe, Africa, Asia, Australia, New Zealand and Hawaii. The horse is the usual host, on which eggs are glued to the body hairs, especially those on the hocks, under the knees and abdomen. In an attempt to relieve the itching the horse bites the area with his lips, causing the eggs to hatch. The little spinose maggots adhere to the lips, penetrating below the surface. When mature the maggots emerge from the lips or tongue and either crawl out and drop to the ground to pupate, or are swallowed and pass out in the feces.

Although the larvas of *G. intestinalis*, *G. hæmorrhoidalis* and *G. nasalis* are much more frequent parasites of the horse, from time to time they infest the human skin and mucous membranes, causing a swelling at the site of entry and later a raised serpiginous tunnel just superficial to the stratum germinativum, in which the maggot travels several mm. daily for a period of several months. Macroscopically the lesion resembles that of cutaneous larva migrans produced by *Ancylostoma braziliense* (Chapter 9, page 274), with which it is coëxtensive in distribution. Moreover, both kinds of agents produce intense pruritus. Differential diagnosis can readily be made by massaging mineral oil over the invaded skin and demonstrating as many as 8 or 9 transverse bands of dark scales which are present at the anterior end of most body segments (see Fig. 208, *13*). Once identified the maggot can be removed with a sharp needle introduced into the head of the tunnel. Human infestation is usually on the extremities but there is one report of ophthalmomyiasis interna due to *G. intestinalis* (Anderson, 1935). Control is primarily a veterinary problem, requiring the treatment of infested horses with appropriate insecticides to kill the maggots as they hatch.

Hypoderma Bovis (Northern Cattle-Bot-Fly).—James (1947) refers to the adult of this species as "a dark, rather robust bumblebee-like fly, about 12 mm. in length," with an abundance of long yellow hairs on the head, thorax and abdomen. It has extensive distribution in the cooler parts of North America, Europe and Asia, and is frequently carried on cattle to other areas. The related species, *H. lineatum* (Fig. 207, *7*), is somewhat less robust and hirsute. The adult flies take no food. As the eggs are laid they are glued to the hairs of the legs or abdomen of cattle. On hatching 3 to 7 days later the young larvas immediately burrow into the skin, migrating through interstitial tissue between somatic muscles to the back of the animal, where they produce subcutaneous pockets (warbles). When the larvas are mature, they perforate through the skin, drop to the ground and pupate. A year is required for a complete cycle, most of which is in the tissues of the host. Persons associated with infested cattle may become parasitized by *H. bovis* or *H. lineatum* (common cattle-grub or heel-fly).

The skin lesion in man is furuncular rather than serpiginous. The larva lives in the subcutaneous tissues, producing considerable inflammation and pain; and it often migrates some distance from the site where it entered the skin. There are also several reports of ophthalmomyiasis interna resulting from infestation with *H. bovis* and *H. lineatum* (Anderson, 1935). In patients giving a history of close contact with infested cattle and with one or more deep furuncles under the skin, a strong suspicion of myiasis is justified. After local procaine anesthesia has been produced the lesion should be incised and the larva, if present, removed while still alive, so that an abscess will not develop from a sequestered dead maggot. Control is almost exclusively a veterinary problem, including spraying of cattle with insecticides which will kill the young larvas as soon as they hatch and before they enter the skin.

Dermatobia Hominis (Tropical Warble-Fly).—This is a robust fly (Fig. 207, *8*), about 12 mm. long, which resembles the common blue-bottle fly (*Calliphora vomitoria*). The adults do not feed. They live in forests in tropical America and rarely venture far afield into clearings. They employ a unique way of transporting their egg to distant vertebrate hosts, *e. g.*, by cementing batches of eggs to the abdomen of certain mosquitoes (*Psorophora*), *Stomoxys calcitrans*, and less commonly ticks and assassin bugs. Or they may oviposit on wet laundry hung out of doors near a forest. When the vicarious arthropod vector settles on the skin the eggs of *D. hominis* are set free. Likewise when persons put on egg-infested clothing a similar opportunity is provided. They soon hatch and the young larvas bore down to the subcutaneous tissues where each produces an inflamed pocket with a pore to the surface so that the posterior end of the larva may from time to time come out to breathe. A period of 6 weeks or more is required for the larva to mature, then it emerges and drops to the ground to pupate. Following 14 to 24 days on the soil the adults emerge from the pupal case, copulate, and the females oviposit, possibly only once.

In man the lesions develop most often on the hands, wrists, ankles, neck and face. The invasion of the tissues is perpendicular to the surface, and never serpiginous in type. At first a small itching pimple appears, then the active larva grows and discharges its irritating metabolites. The area becomes inflamed, hyperemic and its surface is tightly stretched so that there is intense, throbbing pain. Considerable skill is required to extract the larva intact. No effective control program has been developed.

Œstrus ovis (Sheep-Bot or Gad-Fly).—The yellowish head of this fly (Fig. 207, *9*) has prominent pock-like pits between and below the eyes. The thorax has a grayish bloom with 4 dorsal, blackish, longitudinal stripes which are interrupted between the 1st and 2nd segments. The abdomen is irregularly patterned black and gray. The legs are yellow. This fly has a cosmopolitan distribution where domestic sheep and goats are raised. The adults take no food. In nature the gravid female darts into the nares of its victim and deposits living young, which migrate to the adjacent sinuses, where they feed on mucous membranes, mature, then return to the surface, drop to the ground and pupate. In 3 or 4 weeks the adults emerge, copulate and the females begin to larviposit. At least one and probably 2 developmental cycles occur annually.

Human infestation with *Œ. ovis* is often encountered in Italy, Palestine, North Africa, Cape Verde Islands, U. S. S. R. and less frequently in the western United States. The mother fly commonly deposits the young larva on the conjunctiva. It may migrate into the lacrymal duct, or work its way deeply into the orbit, rarely into the eyeball. Superficial infestation is very irritating and painful; deep penetration may cause the loss of the eye. Nasal and oral myiasis produced by this fly is encountered mostly in Mediterranean countries, causing painful congestion similar to internal leech infestation (Chapter 18, page 446). Rarely the larva has been found attached to the external membrane of the ear (James, 1947). The related gad-fly of northern Europe and Asia, *Rhinœstrus purpureus*, has also been recovered in the larval stage from the human conjunctivæ. Removal of the maggot at an early stage of its development usually assures rapid, uncomplicated recovery. Control measures are primarily concerned with periodic spraying or dipping of sheep and goats with larvicidal toxicants.

Semi-specific Myiasis

A majority of the flesh flies and screw-worm flies deposit their young or eggs in carrion which constitutes the source of nutriment for the growing maggots, but foul-smelling open wounds provide an equally favorable attraction and source of food. The maggots proceed to liquefy and consume the diseased tissues and often invade adjacent undamaged flesh or bone.

The most notorious of the flesh flies is *Sarcophaga hæmorrhoidalis.*

Sarcophaga hæmorrhoidalis (Red-tailed Flesh-Fly).—The adults (Fig. 207, *2*) are large grayish flies, 10 to 14 mm. long, with 4 black longitudinal stripes on the thorax and a checkered upper surface of the abdomen. They have a cosmopolitan distribution and feed on decaying meat and flesh, or on feces. The females are larviparous and deposit their young on foul-smelling media or at times on the anus of persons sitting on outdoor latrines. Or the maggots may be ingested in contaminated cold meat. They develop through 3 larval instars, then drop or crawl to drier surroundings on the ground and pupate.

The maggots of *S. hæmorrhoidalis* ingested in infested cold food are capable of producing severe gastrointestinal disturbances, with griping abdominal pains, nausea, vomiting and fever, due sometimes, as Bryan demonstrated sigmoidoscopically (1937) to ulceration produced by the maggots which became attached to the intestinal wall. This fly is capable of completing its entire larval development within the human intestinal tract.

Several of the screw-worm flies feed on decaying flesh and foul-smelling wounds, including those of man. The reports of *Callitroga* attacking undamaged human tissues undoubtedly refer to *C. hominivorax* (see page 508) and not to the common screw-worm fly, *C. macellaria*, which is essentially saprozoic rather than parasitic. Other species of this group which are scavengers but may invade injured human tissues are: the black blow-fly (*Phormia regina*), the green-bottle flies (*Lucilia cæsar, Phænicia cuprina, P. sericata*), and the blue-bottle flies (*Calliphora vomitoria, C. vicina*). In most instances the damage produced by these maggots is traumatic, *e. g.*, extension of preëxisting wounds, but there are several records of at least temporary parasitism in the nares, adjacent sinuses and buccal cavity, intestinal tract and external ear.

Accidental Myiasis

Almost any fly that oviposits or larviposits in manure, decaying vegetation or other feeding site for its larval stages provides the opportunity for accidental myiasis in case the eggs or maggots are carelessly ingested in contaminated food or get into the bladder or vagina of persons who are unclean in their personal hygiene.

BEETLE INFESTATION (Canthariasis)

There are numerous records of infestation of man by eggs, larvas and adults of several species of beetles (Théodoridès, 1948). Most of these cases involve the intestinal and urinary tracts, in which the larvas or adults have become accidentally and temporarily lodged, with mild to severe disturbances in digestion or urination. Beetle eggs have been recovered once from the human nares and the larval stage has been removed once from the human eye.

CHIGŒ FLEA INFESTATION

The distinguishing morphologic characters of the chigœ flea (*Tunga penetrans*) have been described earlier in this chapter (page 504). Both males and females suck blood but only the females burrow into skin, where they become engorged until they may swell up to the size of a pea. The common sites of infestation are the soles of the feet and spaces between the toes, but no body surface is exempt from invasion. The pocket developed by the females may extend deeply into the dermis, causes great pain and inconvenience, and characteristically becomes secondarily infected. The female is carefully teased out of the wound with a sharp needle, then the wound is cleansed and provided with surgical dressing. The most satisfactory prophylaxis consists in wearing good stout leather shoes, but natives in the Tropics, who share this infestation with their pigs and dogs, are neither willing nor financially able to provide this means of health security.

SUMMARY

1. Insects have a distinct separation into head, thorax and abdomen. The head of the adult has a pair of antennæ and mandibulate type of mouth parts. The thorax is composed of 3 segments, each with a pair of 5-jointed legs. Typically there are wings on the 2nd and 3rd segments. The abdomen has 12 original segments, of which the first 2 are atrophied or rudimentary and the distalmost ones are modified as genital structures. Larval stages of insects are more or less worm-like and have chewing mouth parts.
2. The life cycle of insects varies from one in which the larva hatched from the egg is hardly distinguishable from the adult, to a very complex type in which a complete metamorphosis occurs during the pupal stage between the larval and the adult.
3. In the rôle of causal agents of disease, insects may be classified as (1) vesicating, (2) urticating, (3) venenating, (4) sensitizing and (5) tissue-invading.
4. Vesication is produced by certain families of beetles, which have a fluid that causes blisters when it comes in contact with the skin and mucous membranes.
5. Urtication is produced by the nettling hairs of the caterpillars of one family of butterflies and several families of moths. In contact with the

skin or mucous membranes, these hairs penetrate or break off, releasing a poison-gland secretion which causes a chemical type of burn.

6. Venenation is due to the introduction into the skin or mucous membranes of the venom of bees, wasps, hornets and ants. The venom apparatus is found only in the worker. The venom substance (apitoxin) produces considerable local reaction and in hypersensitized individuals an anaphylactic reaction which may cause death.
7. Sensitization is produced by insects which have mouth parts adapted for piercing the skin and sucking blood. The introduction of salivary secretions into the puncture wound results in a local tissue reaction in many individuals and intense systemic symptoms of an allergic type in some persons. The groups of insects which provoke sensitization in man are head lice, body lice, pubic lice, bedbugs, assassin-bugs, mosquitoes, sand-flies, "biting" midges, black-gnats, horse-flies and their relatives, "biting" stable-fly, tsetse-flies, hippoboscids and sheep-keds, and fleas.
8. Tissue invasion on the part of insects is due to specific, semi-specific or accidental entry of an immature or adult stage of the insect into the skin or mucous membrane of man or other animals. The most common agents are flies, which deposit living young (maggots) or eggs on undamaged or injured tissues. The larvas penetrate into the tissues, on which they feed, produce severe, at times mutilating damage, and occasionally cause death.

Larval and adult stages of beetles have been found temporarily lodged in the digestive tract or urinary bladder, and a larva has been recovered once from the eye. A mass of beetle eggs was once removed from the human nares.

The chigœ flea (*Tunga penetrans*) produces a dermatitis usually on the sole of the foot or between the toes. Only the females burrow deeply into the skin and produce a painful swelling.

REFERENCES

Anderson, W. B. 1935. Ophthalmomyiasis. Am. J. Ophthalm., *18*, 699–705.

Barnett, H. C., and Knoblock, E. C. 1952. Chemical and Biological Studies on DDT Resistance of Lice. U. S. Armed Forces Med. J., *3*, 297–304.

Blacklock, D. B., and Thompson, M. G. 1923. A Study of the Tumbu Fly, *Cordylobia Anthropophaga* Grünberg, in Sierra Leone. Ann. Trop. Med. & Parasitol., *17*, 443–502.

Bryan, W. J., Jr. 1937. Myiasis. J. Am. Med. Assn., *109*, 573–574.

Caffrey, D. J. 1918. Notes on the Poisoning Urticating Spines of *Hemileuca Olivia* Larvæ. J. Econom. Entomol., *11*, 363–367.

Cheverton, R. L. 1936. Irritation Caused by Contact with the Processionary Caterpillar. Trans. R. Soc. Trop. Med. & Hyg., *29*, 555–557.

Eddy, G. W. 1952. Effectiveness of Certain Insecticides Against DDT-resistant Body Lice in Korea. J. Econ. Entomol., *45*, 1043–1051.

Geigy, R., and Kraus, C. 1952. Rüssel und Stechakt von *Rhodnius Prolixus*. Acta Tropica, *9*, 272–276.

Gilmer, P. M. 1925. A Comparative Study of the Poison Apparatus of Certain Lepdopterous Larvæ. Ann. Entomol. Soc. Am., *18*, 203–239.

Goldman, L., Johnson, P., and Ramsey, J. 1952. The Insect Bite Reaction. I. The Mechanism. J. Investig. Derm., *18*, 403–417.

Gordon, R. M., and Crewe, W. 1949. The Mechanism by Which Mosquitoes and Tsetse Flies Obtain Their Blood Meals. Ann. Trop. Med. & Parasitol., *42*, 356.

GRIFFITHS, R. B., and GORDON, R. M. 1952. An Apparatus Which Enables the Process of Feeding by Mosquitoes to be Observed in the Tissues of a Live Rodent; Together with an Account of the Injection of Saliva and Its Significance in Malaria. Ann. Trop. Med. & Parasitol., *45*, 311–319.

HERMS, W. B. 1932. Non-bloodsucking Flies as Vectors of Pathogenic Microorganisms. Ann. Entomol. Soc. Am., *25*, 623–628.

HERTIG, M. 1948. Sandflies of the Genus *Phlebotomus*—A Review of Their Habits, Disease Relationships and Control. Proc. 4th Internat'l Congr. Trop. Med. & Malaria, Vol. II, 1609–1615.

————1949. *Phlebotomus* and Residual DDT in Greece and Italy. Am. J. Trop. Med., *29*, 773–802.

HULBERT, H. S., PEFFLY, R. L., and ABDEL AZIZ SALAH. 1954. DDT Resistance in Egyptian Body Lice. Am. J. Trop. Med. & Hyg., *3*, 922–929.

JAMES, M. T. 1947. The Flies that Cause Myiasis in Man. U. S. Dept. Agr. Misc. Publ., No. 631. Washington, D. C. 175 pp.

JEX-BLAKE, A. J. 1942. Bee Stings. E. Afr. Med. J., *19*, 74.

LUCAS, T. A. 1942. Poisoning by *Megalopyge Opercularis* ("Puss Caterpillar"). J. Am. Med. Assn., *119*, 877–880.

MATHESON, R. 1950. *Medical Entomology*. 2nd ed., 612 pp. Comstock Publishing Co., Ithaca, N. Y.

MILLS, R. G. 1925. Some Observations and Experiments on the Irritating Properties of the Larva of *Parasa Hilarata* Staudinger. Am. J. Hyg., *5*, 342–363.

PATTON, W. S. 1921. Notes on the Myiasis-Producing Diptera of Man and Animals. Bull. Entomol. Res., *12*, 239–261.

————1922. Some Notes on Indian Calliphorinæ. VI. How to Recognize the Indian Myiasis-producing Flies and Their Larvæ, Together with Some Notes on How to Breed Them and Study Their Habits. Indian J. Med. Res., *9*, 635–653.

PAWLOWSKY, E. N., and STEIN, A. K. 1925. Ueber die Ursachen der Wirkung der Läuse der Gattung *Pediculus* auf die Integumenta des Menschen. Russian Entomol. Soc., *19*, 17–20.

PECK, S. M., WRIGHT, W. H., and GANT, J. Q. 1943. Cutaneous Reactions Due to the Body Louse (*Pediculus Humanus*). J. Am. Med. Assn., *123*, 821–825.

PHISALIX, M. 1922. *Animaux Venimeux et Venins*. 1600 pp. Paris.

ROCKWELL, E. M., and JOHNSON, P. 1952. The Insect Bite Reaction. II. Evaluation of the Allergic Reaction. J. Investig. Derm., *19*, 137–155.

THÉODORIDÈS, J. 1948. Les Coleopteres Parasites Accidentels de l'Homme. Ann. de Parasitol., *23*, 348–363.

TYZZER, E. E. 1907. The Pathology of the Brown-tail Moth Dermatitis. J. Med. Res., *16*, 43–64.

WIGGLESWORTH, V. B. 1939. *The Principles of Insect Physiology*. 434 pp. London, (See "Venoms," page 331.)

Chapter 21

Arthropod Vectors of Human Disease

Introduction

THE term *vector means carrier.* The rôle of the vector may be purely accidental, *e. g., mechanical,* as in the spread of enteric bacteria by the house-fly, *Musca domestica.* On the other hand, the vector may have a fundamental and frequently an obligate relationship to the life cycle of the pathogen, in which case its rôle is *biological.* Arthropods constitute the most important carrier group in the Animal Kingdom, not excluding man, in the transmission of organisms producing human disease.

Arthropods as Mechanical Vectors

Source of Inoculum.—The most frequent source of the infectious agent is the medium on which the arthropod is feeding or is preparing to deposit its offspring. Many times it consists of human or animal excreta, or it may be the sero-purulent discharge from the nares, eyes or cutaneous lesions. In other instances the mechanical vector has mouth parts adapted to piercing the skin and sucking up blood or tissue juices containing the pathogen.

Relationship of the Arthropod to the Pathogen.—The contact of the mechanical vector with the pathogen may result from contamination of body surfaces with the inoculum, followed by deposition of the contaminant in food or drink intended for human use, or on mucous membranes; or it may ingest the microörganism and later void it in fecal dejecta or vomit drops.

In all of these types of transmission there is no required incubation and frequently no multiplication of the infectious agent on or in the body of the arthropod. The efficiency of the transmission depends on the ability of the agent to survive under the prevailing conditions and usually in the rapidity with which the transfer is made.

Disease Agents Mechanically Carried by Arthropods.—*Enteric Bacteria.*—The unusually high prevalence of the common house-fly *Musca domestica* during earlier epidemics of typhoid fever has been a matter of observation for more than half a century, so that this pest has in years past been referred to as "the typhoid fly." It, and to a somewhat lesser extent other flies which characteristically breed in human excreta have been proven to be mechanical vectors not only of the typhoid organism (*Salmonella typhosa*) but also of other enteric bacteria, including *S. paratyphi A, S. enteritidis, S. schottmülleri, S. typhimurium, Escherichia coli* and *Shigella dysenteriæ.* Watt (1949) states that improvement of water, milk and shell-fish supplies in the United States has practically eliminated typhoid fever in many areas without fly control, but that "these measures have not been as effective in the reduction of infections with the *Salmonella* and *Shigella* groups of organisms, and while the fly has been suspected in the spread of these bacteria, until recently we have never known just how important they were in the dissemination of these microörganisms."

In tropical countries shigellosis ("bacillary dysentery") is frequently disseminated by filth flies, which breed in open latrines containing the etiologic agent and after picking up filth on their hairy bodies are ideal vectors of the *Shigella* organisms to human food and drink or directly to the lips of the victims.

The house-fly and other filth flies are likewise very important in the spread of cholera in tropical and Oriental countries. Napier (1946) regards these flies "by far the most, and probably the only, important active agent, though the cockroach and the rat should not be entirely excluded as possible mechanical conveyers of morbid material."

The rôle of cockroaches in the potential spread of enteric bacteria has been tested experimentally. Janssen and Wedberg (1952) employed the common house roach, *Blatella germanica,* to which they fed a diet of culture medium containing *Salmonella typhimurium* and *S. typhosa.* With the former bacillus the stools were positive for 7 days but with the latter they became negative between the 12th and 15th hour after the meal. Another study employing the roach *Periplaneta americana* was conducted by Jung and Shaffer (1952), who fed *S. typhimurium* and *S. montevideo* in raw feces. When the roach ingested 10,000 or more organisms, the contents of the digestive tract were positive for at least 7 days. These experiments provide support for the view that roaches may at times be disseminators of enteric bacteria, provided a large number of the organisms have been ingested.

S. enteritidis has been passed in fecal dejecta of the tick *Dermacentor andersoni* 35 days after oral contamination (Parker and Steinhaus, 1943), and living *S. typhosa* has been recovered from the feces of human body lice.

Non-enteric Bacteria.—Domestic flies have been demonstrated to be potential vectors of *Mycobacterium tuberculosis, Bacillus anthracis, Pasteurella pestis, P. tularensis* and *Brucella* species, and tabanid flies are suspect in the spread of anthrax. Bedbugs, the deer-fly (*Chrysops discalis*) and mosquitoes (*Aëdes ægypti, Culex apicalis* and *Anopheles maculipennis*) are suitable experimental transmitters of tularemia.

Species of eye-gnats of the genus *Hippelates* have been incriminated in epidemics of acute conjunctivitis (epidemic "pink eye") in California, Florida and Georgia (Herms, 1932; Davis and Pittman, 1950). Eye-gnats of the genus *Siphunculina* are regarded as important disseminators of conjunctivitis in Egypt and India.

Viruses.—The virus of yellow fever can be mechanically transmitted by ticks (*Ornithodoros moubata* in Africa, *Amblyomma cajennense* in Brazil) for a period of 4 to 8 hours during an interrupted blood meal. Bedbugs feeding on an acute yellow fever case pass the virus in their feces (Biraud, 1935); they are likewise potential vectors of smallpox virus.

Spirochetes.—The serous discharges of open lesions of yaws (frambesia), caused by *Treponema pertenue,* are favorite feeding sites of *Musca spectanda,*

Table 11 Arthropods Which are Biological

(Adapted from Craig and Faust's Clinical Parasitology)

Class Group	*Order*	*Species*
CRUSTACEA	COPEPODA ("water fleas")	*Cyclops* spp.
		Diaptomus spp. *Cyclops* spp.
		Cyclops spp.
		Cyclops spp.
	DECAPODA (crayfishes, crabs, lobsters, etc.)	Fresh-water crabs and crayfishes
DIPLOPODA ("millipedes")		*Julus* sp., *Fontaria virginiensis*
ARACHNIDA (spiders, ticks, mites, etc.)	ACARI (ticks and mites)	*Dermacentor* spp., *Amblyomma* spp., *Rhipicephalus* spp., *Hyalomma* sp., *Hæmaphysalis* spp. (hard-bodied ticks); also *Ornithodoros* spp. (soft-bodied ticks)
		Rhipicephalus sanguineus, *Dermacentor andersoni*, *Hæmaphysalis humerosa*, et al.
		Amblyomma americanum, *Dermacentor* spp. and many other ticks
		Ornithodoros spp. (soft-bodied ticks)
		Trombicula spp. (red mites)
		Allodermanyssus sanguineus
		Bdellonyssus bacoti (rat mite)

Vectors of Important Human Pathogens

Disease Transmitted	*Etiologic Agent*	*Relation of Arthropod to Pathogen and to Human Infection*
Dracontiasis (Medina worm infection)	*Dracunculus medinensis*	Intermediate host, with no multiplication of pathogen; man acquires infection by swallowing water containing infected *Cyclops*
Diphyllobothriasis (fish tapeworm infection)	*Diphyllobothrium latum*	First intermediate host, with no multiplication of pathogen; source of infection for freshwater fishes which produce infection in man
Gnathostomiasis	*Gnathostoma spinigerum*	
Sparganosis	*Diphyllobothrium* (subgenus *Spirometra*) spp.	As in *D. latum.* Man becomes infected from accidentally swallowing infected *Cyclops* or from second intermediate host which is never a fish
Paragonimiasis (pulmonary distomiasis, endemic hemoptysis)	*Paragonimus westermani*	Second intermediate host, with no multiplication of pathogen; man acquires infection by eating infected crabs and crayfish
Rat tapeworm infection	*Hymenolepis diminuta*	Pathogen develops from embryo to larva in hemocele of arthropod; definitive host infected by accidentally swallowing infected adult arthropod
Spotted fever	*Rickettsia rickettsi, R. conori, R. australis*	Pathogen multiplies in wall of tick's mid-gut; congenitally transmitted in tick; man inoculated through "bite" of tick
"Q" fever	*Coxiella burneti*	Pathogen multiplies in wall of tick's midgut; man may be inoculated through "bite" of tick
Tularemia	*Pasteurella tularensis*	Pathogen multiplies in gut and hemocele of tick; congenitally transmitted in some ticks; man inoculated through "bite" or crushing of tick
Enzoötic-endemic relapsing fever	*Borrelia duttoni*	Pathogen multiplies in tissues of tick outside gut; man inoculated through "bite" of tick
Scrub typhus (Japanese river fever)	*Rickettsia tsutsugamushi*	Pathogen multiplies in gut of mite; congenitally transmitted in mite; man infected from "bite" of larval mite
Rickettsialpox	*Rickettsia akari*	Pathogen multiplies in mite; congenital transmission in mite not demonstrated; man inoculated through "bite" of mite
Murine typhus fever (experimental)	*Rickettsia typhi*	Pathogen multiplies in gut of mite; experimental animal inoculated through "bite" of mite

Table 11 Arthropods Which are Biological

Class Group	*Order*	*Species*
		Dermanyssus gallinæ
		Oribatid mites
INSECTA (insects)	ANOPLURA (sucking lice)	*Pediculus humanus* var. *corporis* (body louse)
		Idem.
		Idem.
	MALLOPHAGA (chewing lice)	*Trichodectes canis* (dog louse)
	ORTHOPTERA (grasshoppers, crickets and roaches)	*Periplaneta americana* and *Blattella* spp.
		Idem.
		Idem.
	DERMAPTERA (earwigs)	*Anisolabis annulipes* (earwig)
	HETEROPTERA (true bugs)	*Triatoma* spp., *Panstrongylus* spp. et al. (cone-nosed bugs)
	DIPTERA (flies)	*Anopheles* spp. (mosquitoes)
		Anopheles spp., *Mansonia* spp.
		Culex spp., *Aëdes* spp., *Anopheles* spp.
		Aëdes spp. et al.

Vectors of Important Human Pathogens—(Continued)

Disease Transmitted	*Etiologic Agent*	*Relation of Arthropod to Pathogen and to Human Infection*
St. Louis encephalitis, Western equine encephalomyelitis	*Erro* spp.	Pathogen multiplies in gut of mite and is congenitally transmitted; mite transfers infection to fowls, possibly to man, at time of "bite"
Anoplocephaline tapeworms	*Bertiella studeri, Inermicapsifer cubensis*	Pathogen matures from embryo to larva, without multiplication, in hemocele of mite; man inoculated by accidentally swallowing infected mite
Epidemic typhus fever	*Rickettsia prowazeki*	Pathogen multiplies in epithelium of louse's mid-gut; man inoculated through "bite," feces or crushing of louse on skin
Trench fever	*Rickettsia quintana*	Pathogen probably multiplies in mid-gut of louse; man inoculated by feces or crushing of louse on skin
Epidemic relapsing fever	*Borrelia recurrentis*	Pathogen multiplies in tissues of louse outside gut; man inoculated by crushing of louse on skin
Dog tapeworm infection	*Dipylidium caninum*	Pathogen develops from embryo to larva, without multiplication, in hemocele of louse; man possibly inoculated by swallowing infected louse
Rat tapeworm infection	*Hymenolepis diminuta*	Pathogen matures from embryo to larva, without multiplication, in hemocele of cockroach; man inoculated by swallowing infected insect
Gongylonema infection	*Gongylonema pulchrum*	Idem.
Acanthocephaliasis	*Moniliformis moniliformis*	Idem.
Rat tapeworm infection	*Hymenolepis diminuta*	Idem.
Chagas' disease	*Trypanosoma cruzi*	Pathogen multiplies in mid-gut of bug; man inoculated through feces of bug rubbed into conjunctiva or onto skin
Malaria	*Plasmodium vivax, P. malariæ, P. falciparum, P. ovale*	Pathogen completes sexual cycle, then multiplies by sporogony in mosquito; man inoculated through "bite" of mosquito
Malayan filariasis	*Wuchereria malayi*	Pathogen matures from embryo to larva, without multiplication, in tissues of mosquito; man inoculated through "bite" of mosquito
Bancroft's filariasis	*Wuchereria bancrofti*	Idem.
Yellow fever	*Charon evagatus*	Pathogen multiplies in tissues of mosquito; man inoculated through "bite" of mosquito

Table 11 Arthropods Which are Biological

Class Group	*Order*	*Species*
		Aëdes spp., *Armigeres obturbans*
		Aëdes spp., *Culex* spp., *Mansonia titillans*, et al.
		Culicoides spp.
		Simulium spp. (black gnats, black flies, coffee flies)
		Chrysops spp. (mango flies)
		Chrysops spp. and *Tabanus* spp. (horse flies)
		Phlebotomus spp. (sand-flies)
		Phlebotomus spp.
		Phlebotomus spp.
		Glossina spp. (tsetse flies)
	SIPHONAPTERA (fleas)	*Xenopsylla cheopis* et al. (rodent fleas); possibly *Pulex irritans* (human flea)
		Xenopsylla cheopis and occasionally other fleas
		Xenopsylla cheopis and other rat fleas
		Ctenocephalides canis, *C. felis*, *Pulex irritans*
	COLEOPTERA (beetles)	Many species of dung beetles
		Many species of dung beetles
		Many species of dung beetles
	LEPIDOPTERA (moths and butterflies)	A few species of moth larvas

Vectors of Important Human Pathogens—(Concluded)

Disease Transmitted	*Etiologic Agent*	*Relation of Arthropod to Pathogen and to Human Infection*
Dengue	*Charon* sp. (?)	Idem.
Encephalitides	*Erro* spp.	Idem.
Acanthocheilonematiasis, Ozzard's filariasis	*Acanthocheilonema perstans*, *A. streptocerca*, *Mansonella ozzardi*	Pathogen matures from embryo to larva, without multiplication, in tissues of gnat; man inoculated through "bite" of gnat
Onchocercosis (filariasis)	*Onchocerca volvulus*	Idem.
Loaiasis (filariasis)	*Loa loa*	Idem.
Tularemia	*Pasteurella tularensis*	Pathogen in gut of fly; man inoculated through "bite" of fly
Visceral leishmaniasis, cutaneous leishmaniasis, mucocutaneous leishmaniasis	*Leishmania donovani*, *L. tropica*, *L. brasiliensis*	Pathogen multiplies in mid-gut of fly; man inoculated through "bite" of fly
Bartonellosis (Carrion's disease, verruga peruana)	*Bartonella bacilliformis*	Idem.
Sand-fly fever	*Charon* sp. (?)	Pathogen multiplies in tissues of fly; man inoculated through "bite" of fly
African trypanosomiasis	*Trypanosoma gambiense*, *T. rhodesiense*	Pathogen multiplies in mid-gut and salivary glands of fly; man inoculated through "bite" of fly
Plague	*Pasteurella pestis*	Pathogen multiplies in gut of flea; man inoculated primarily through "bite," occasionally from feces of flea
Murine typhus fever	*Rickettsia typhi*	Pathogen multiplies in epithelium of mid-gut of flea; man inoculated through "bite" and feces of flea
Rat tapeworm infection	*Hymenolepis diminuta*	Pathogen develops from embryo to larva in hemocele of flea; man inoculated by swallowing infected flea
Dog tapeworm infection	*Dipylidium caninum*	Idem.
Rat tapeworm infection	*Hymenolepis diminuta*	Pathogen develops from embryo to larva in hemocele of beetle; man inoculated by swallowing infected beetle
Gongylonema infection	*Gongylonema pulchrum*	Idem.
Acanthocephaliasis	*Macracanthorhynchus hirudinaceus*, *Moniliformis moniliformis*	Idem.
Rat tapeworm infection	*Hymenolepis diminuta*	Pathogen develops from embryo to larva in hemocele of larval moth; man inoculated by swallowing infected insect

M. sorbens and *Hippelates pallipes,* all of which contaminate their proboscis with the spirochetes and may soon deposit them on broken skin or clean mucous membranes of healthy persons. *Aëdes ægypti* is also a strong suspect as a mechanical transmitter of this spirochete.

Amebic Cysts.—Circumstantial and experimental evidence indicates that the house-fly and other filth flies, as well as cockroaches, are good mechanical vectors of the cysts of *Endamœba histolytica* and other protozoa of the human intestinal tract. This subject has been considered in Chapter 7, page 81.

Non-enteric Protozoa.—Many species of ticks may serve as mechanical vectors of *Trypanosoma cruzi,* while *Stomoxys calcitrans* has been similarly incriminated in the transmission of *Leishmania tropica, Trypanosoma gambiense* and *T. rhodesiense.* The organisms, picked up from the blood of an active case, soil the arthropod's mouth parts, where they are viable for a few hours and during this time may be introduced into the skin of the next appropriate host during completion of a blood meal. Tsetse-flies (*Glossina*), which are the biological vectors of the African trypanosomes of man, may also serve as mechanical vectors of these organisms during an interrupted feeding (Chapter 9, page 524).

Helminth Eggs and Larvas.—When human feces containing eggs of *Ascaris lumbricoides, Trichocephalus trichiurus,* hookworms and tapeworms are deposited on the ground, cockroaches, ants, wasps and dung beetles frequently break up the fecal sump quite rapidly and disseminate the eggs widely through the top soil, thus serving as mechanical disseminators of these parasite objects.

Arthropods as Biological Vectors

Reference to Table 11 shows that 4 separate class groups of arthropods, *e. g.,* Crustacea, Diplopoda, Arachnida and Insecta, are biological vectors of microörganisms parasitic in man. In some instances the arthropod serves as an essential or at least a satisfactory intermediate host of the pathogen, and human infection develops when man accidentally ingests the arthropod. The parasite is digested out of its arthropod host and proceeds to develop in the human body. Less commonly man consumes the infected arthropod as a regular item of food (*e. g.,* uncooked crabs and crayfishes) and in this way acquires the infection. These methods constitute a characteristic and essential mechanism for completing the life cycle of the parasite.

In contrast to the passive transfer of the disease-producing agent by the arthropod as a biological vector, there is a wealth of instances in which the transfer is active. All of these involve arthropods which have mouth parts adapted to skin penetration permitting a feeding on blood or tissue juices. This group of vectors consists of the ticks, red mites, parasitoid mites, sucking lice, true bugs, blood-sucking flies and fleas.

Consideration of arthropods as biological vectors will be focused primarily on the pathogenic agents and the ways in which they are transmitted by the arthropod. For reference to a majority of these etiologic agents arranged according to the arthropod vector, please consult Table 11.

VIRUSES AND VIRAL INFECTIONS

Viruses are ultramicroscopic, obligate parasites of host cells. The pathogenic species which are arthropod-transmitted include the agents of yellow fever, dengue, the encephalitides, Rift Valley fever, sand-fly fever, Colorado tick fever, and a number of others. Except for the viruses of sand-fly fever, Colorado tick fever and the encephalitides mosquitoes are the sole natural biological vectors.

Yellow Fever

The Agent.—This virus measures 17 to 28 $\mu\mu$ in diameter. It dies within 5 minutes at 55° C., within 2 to 3 hours at usual room temperature and is readily destroyed by standard disinfectants, but it survives for months or

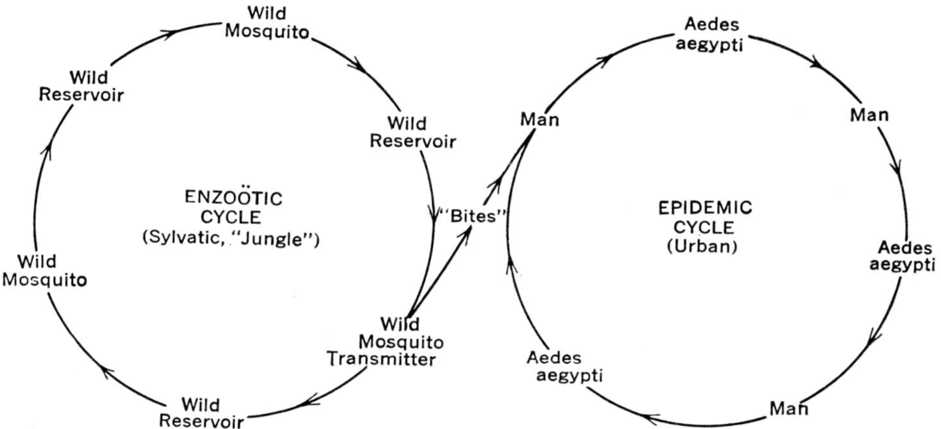

Fig. 209.—The enzoötic and epidemic transmission cycles of yellow fever. (Original, from Craig and Faust's *Clinical Parasitology*, Lea & Febiger, Philadelphia.)

years in the frozen state. It may be viscerotropic or neurotropic (Theiler, 1951). Its arthropod hosts are domestic and sylvatic mosquitoes. Several species of monkeys and at least one marsupial constitute the natural mammalian hosts, and previously non-immunized human beings on exposure also contract the infection.

Historical, Geographical and Epidemiologic Notes.—Yellow fever has probably existed in the rain-forests of tropical Africa and possibly also tropical America from prehistoric times. This is *sylvatic* or "jungle" *yellow fever*. The *enzoötic cycle* (Fig. 209) involves primarily wild monkeys and wild mosquitoes and is essentially one of the forest canopy. In enzoötic areas the infected mosquitoes transmit the infection to the wild mammal which dies of the infection or develops a fast immunity. In a broad sense the mosquito constitutes the true reservoir (Bugher *et al.*, 1944).

Man is exposed (1) when he enters the forest, (2) when infected sylvatic mosquitoes or monkeys leave the forests temporarily for nearby clearings and bring the infection to his rural habitation, or (3) when domestic mosquitoes, particularly *Aëdes ægypti,* become infected and transmit the virus to human beings. Then the disease becomes *epidemic yellow fever.*

Epidemic or urban yellow fever was known for approximately two centuries before the enzoötic type was discovered. During the 18th and 19th centuries the disease developed to epidemic proportions in the port cities of West Africa and from there was carried to Continental Europe. Similarly, in the Atlantic ports of northern South America, the Caribbean ports of Central America, the Gulf ports of Mexico, and in the West Indies urban yellow fever became an ever-present scourge. From these centers it reached the Atlantic and Gulf ports of the United States, where severe epidemics occurred during the warm months of the year. The essential difference between urban yellow fever in the Tropics and temperate regions was that it was almost constantly present in the former communities but never survived cold weather in the latter.

Although Carlos J. Finlay in Havana had advocated mosquito transmission of yellow fever and had provided experimental proof that a mosquito, probably *Aëdes ægypti,* was responsible for the urban epidemics, Walter Reed and his colleagues of the U. S. Army Yellow Fever Commission in Cuba (1900) used human volunteers as experimental subjects and demonstrated that the "Stegomyia" mosquito was essential for man-to-man transmission. (See Fig. 209, epidemic cycle.) This investigation led to control in urban areas by preventing the breeding of *Aëdes ægypti.* By 1925 there was substantial evidence that yellow fever no longer existed. However, relatively silent zones of enzoötic infection were then discovered in tropical forests of South America and Africa, which from time to time spread to human settlements.

In the Western Hemisphere the present-day enzoötic area covers vast regions in the Amazon Valley from Brazil and Bolivia northwards through Peru and Ecuador to Colombia and Venezuela, and in the Caribbean drainage of Colombia, Venezuela and the Guianas, and recently (1948–1954) a northward extension from Panamá through Costa Rica to Honduras, with epidemic outbreaks in villages adjacent to the jungle (Soper, 1952; Elton, 1952). In Africa the sylvatic area extends from the Atlantic to the Indian Ocean between 10° S. and 15° N. latitude, except for Tanganyika.

In South America the mosquitoes which are primarily responsible for maintaining the sylvatic infection are *Hæmagogus spegazzinii falco* and *Aëdes leucocelænus* (Kumm and Cerqueira, 1951). In Africa the mosquitoes belong to the genera *Aëdes* (several wild and two semi-domestic species, *A. simpsoni* and *A. africanus*), *Culex, Tæniorhynchus, Anopheles* and a number of sabethine forms.

In the mammalian host the virus circulates in the blood during the last 6 to 10 hours of the incubation period and the first 3 or 4 days thereafter. Susceptible mosquitoes become positive in 8 to 14 days and are infective for the rest of their life. The virus multiplies in the mosquito, is present in all tissues and cavities but produces no detectable ill-effects. *A. ægypti* may contain 100 infective doses.

Pathogenesis and Symptomatology.—The characteristic lesions are early mid-zonal necrosis and fatty degeneration of the liver, followed by extensive hemorrhages in the viscera and toxic nephrosis.

The incubation period of 3 to 6 days is succeeded by a sudden onset of symptoms, with profound malaise, intense headache, muscle pains and fever (39° to 40° C.). After 2 to 4 days of acute infection the temperature declines and the symptoms partly subside, only to return as a result of profound intoxication. With the return of fever the pulse rate decreases (Faget's sign). When there is extensive vomiting of blood accompanied by marked peptonuria or anuria the prognosis is grave; but if the fever gradually subsides and there are no severe complications a period of long convalescence leads to complete recovery and life-long immunity. The disease in small children may be essentially asymptomatic.

Diagnosis.—This must be made on the patient's history and the symptoms, since there is no specific diagnostic test during the incubation and symptomatic periods.

Treatment.—This is exclusively symptomatic and palliative.

Control.—Persons who have had yellow fever, have a life-long immunity. Those who are subject to exposure through contact with the disease in or near enzoötic zones should be vaccinated with attenuated neurotropic virus (17D grown on chick embryo). Typically full protection to infection is provided for several years (Dick and Gee, 1952), possibly for a lifetime.

In order that urban communities may be spared epidemic outbreaks of yellow fever, the breeding of *Aëdes ægypti* must be reduced essentially to zero. This control program is the one barrier which will prevent periodic urban epidemics. Many countries require evidence of yellow fever vaccination if persons have traveled through enzoötic zones.

Dengue

The Agent.—Dengue or "breakbone fever" is due to infection with a specific filtrable virus which is an obligate protoplasmic parasite.

Historical, Geographical and Epidemiologic Notes.—The disease was first described by Benjamin Rush, in 1780, during an epidemic in Philadelphia. Ashburn and Craig (1907) demonstrated the filtrable nature of the causative agent, while Siler, Hall and Hitchens (1926) confirmed earlier studies that *Aëdes ægypti* is the usual mosquito vector. In the Orient and Hawaii *A. albopictus* is involved and in Formosa, *Armigeres obturbans*. Moreover, *Aëdes hebrideus* appears to be the transmitter in the New Hebrides, and *A. polynesiensis* in Samoa and Tahiti.

The disease is commonly limited to warm climates, where it is endemic among natives and develops epidemically in non-immune persons. Man is the only proven natural mammalian host of the virus.

The mosquito is able to acquire the infection only during the first 3 days of the patient's illness. A period of 8 to 11 days is then required for incubation, after which the mosquito remains infective throughout the remainder of its life.

Clinical Notes.—Dengue virus has a predilection for parenchymatous organs and the endothelial lining of bloodvessels, where it produces degenerative changes and hemorrhage. Following an incubation of 4 to 10 days there is typically an abrupt onset, with a chill, excruciating pain in the joints, loins, epigastric region and behind the eyes, hyperemic swelling of the face and a fever of 39.5° to 40° C. lasting for 4 to 7 days, accompanied by increased pulse rate and at times extreme prostration. There is then a sudden remission, with a drop in temperature and profuse sweating. Within a few hours there is a return of fever (hence "saddle-back" designation), extreme malaise, nervous depression and a terminal rash, progressing from the extremities to the trunk, lasting 2 or 3 days and terminating in a pruritic desquamation. Then there is slow convalescence.

Diagnosis is made on the patient's history of exposure in an endemic area, the "saddle-back" temperature curve if it occurs, the rash which is practically pathognomonic, and the leukopenia, with a shift to the left in the Schilling count and relative monocytosis. Treatment is symptomatic and palliative. The disease is rarely fatal. One attack confers considerable although not solid immunity.

Control.—This consists exclusively in measures directed against the breeding of *Aëdes ægypti* and other mosquito transmitters. No vaccine has been developed for general prophylactic use.

The Encephalitides

This group of diseases includes St. Louis encephalitis, Japanese B encephalitis, Eastern, Western and Venezuelan equine encephalomyelitis, West Nile encephalitis, Russian spring-summer encephalitis and other geographically limited infections. The viral agents of these diseases are immunologically closely related and all produce lesions in the central nervous system.

St. Louis encephalitis is widely disseminated in the United States west of the Appalachian Mountains. In nature the infection occurs primarily in birds and is transmitted for the most part by the chicken mite, *Dermanyssus gallinæ*, the bird mite, *Bdellonyssus sylviarum*, and the mosquito, *Culex tarsalis* (Smith *et al.*, 1948; Reeves *et al.*, 1947; Hammon and Reeves, 1943). Several other species of *Culex*, *Aëdes* and *Anopheles* have been reported as positive in nature. Horses and human beings, on exposure, develop the disease. Epidemics have occurred in Cincinnati, Ohio and Paris, Illinois (1932), in St. Louis (1937) and in several western states since that time (Lennette, 1946). The virus measures 20 to 33 $\mu\mu$ in diameter. In man there is an incubation period of 4 to 21 days, a sudden onset with raging headache, high fever, muscular rigidity and tremors lasting for 7 to 10 days, then rapid complete recovery if the patient survives.

Japanese B encephalitis has an extensive distribution in Sino-Japanese areas, the Philippines, other Southwest Pacific islands and the Maritime Provinces of Siberia, and probably in India. This disease is immunologically a close relative of St. Louis encephalitis, and the virus is of similar size (20 to 30 $\mu\mu$). Dogs, horses, cows and goats, but not birds, appear to be natural reservoirs. Transmission in nature has been demonstrated in *Culex pipiens* var. *pallens*, *C. tritæniorhynchus* and *Aëdes togoi*. Serious epidemics have occurred, at times with high mortality. The acute manifestations include nuchal rigidity, disorientation and other neurologic evidences of lesions in the cerebellar cortex. Subsequently there is a relatively prolonged subacute or chronic period and fairly frequently permanent neurological symptoms. Treatment is entirely symptomatic. Control efforts are directed almost exclusively against the breeding of the mosquito hosts.

Eastern and Western equine encephalomyelitis are due to closely related but immunologically distinct strains of a neurotropic virus which has a diameter of about 50 to 57 $\mu\mu$. In nature the disease occurs in many wild and domestic birds, in which it may be symptomless, and in horses, in which it is highly pathogenic. The Eastern strain is present on the Atlantic Coast of the United States, the Western strain west of the Appalachian Mountains. The most frequent transmitter of the former is the mosquito, *Mansonia perturbans*. The disease may be epidemic in character. The onset is sudden and the symptoms are typically severe, with high fever, convulsions, twitching and signs of high intracranial pressure. Critically ill patients may not survive. Mental and neurological sequelæ are fairly common in the survivors.

Venezuelan equine encephalomyelitis is present enzoötically in Venezuela and the West Indies. It is highly contagious for horses and man. The natural transmitters are *Aëdes tæniorhynchus, Anopheles neomaculipalpis* and *Mansonia titillans*. The symptoms are more characteristic of influenza than of a neurotropic disease.

West Nile encephalitis was first identified in Uganda by Smithburn *et al.* (1940). Since that time human infection has been found in rural Egypt, epidemically in Israeli villages since 1950, and probably in India. It may be a widely prevalent disease in the Middle East. *Culex molestus* is believed on epidemiologic and immunologic grounds to be the natural transmitter in Israeli (Med. News Letter, U. S. N., 22, No. 1, 10 July, 1953, 35–36). The disease usually runs a mild course. Morbidity is high, but no fatal cases have been reported.

Russian (Far Eastern) spring-summer encephalitis is an infection of wild rodents throughout the forests of the U. S. S. R. Immune sera from natives of India indicate it is indigenous to that country. It is transmitted by ticks (*Ixodes persulcatus, Dermacentor sylvarum* and *Hæmaphysalis concinna*) in which it is congenital. Man is first exposed during the spring when the hibernating tick becomes active and again during the summer months. After 8 to 18 days incubation there is an acute stage of 2 to 10 days with symptoms of headache, pain in the cervical region, fever, nausea and vomiting, muscle paralysis, vertigo and coma (Warren, 1946). About 30% mortality has been reported.

Other viral encephalitides which are arthropod-transmitted include *Semliki Forest encephalitis* in Uganda, transmitted by *Aëdes abnormalis* (Smithburn, Haddow and Mahaffy, 1946); *Mengo encephalomyelitis* of rats, monkeys and man in Uganda, and *Ilhéus encephalitis* in Brazil, transmitted by *Aëdes ægypti, A. serratus* and *Psorophora ferox* (Laemmert and Hughes, 1947).

Colorado Tick Fever

This viral disease is prevalent in Colorado, Oregon, Utah and Wyoming, where it is contracted from infestation with *Dermacentor andersoni* in which it occurs congenitally. The same viral agent has also been isolated from *D. variabilis* on Long Island. The onset is sudden. Symptoms include myositis, temporal headache, malaise, chills and fever followed by defervescence, then a return of the symptoms, and finally complete recovery (Collins, 1944).

Rift Valley Fever

This disease of cattle, sheep, goats and man is widely distributed from the Sudan to South Africa. Dick (1953) suggests that possibly there is a sylvatic cycle in wild animals. Natural infection has been found in the mosquitoes *Eretmapodites chrysogaster, Aëdes tarsalis* and *A. de-boëri.* Human infection is accidental and occurs only from "bites" of infected mosquitoes while in intimate contact with infected mammals. The most striking symptoms are ophthalmic, including retinitis and temporary loss of vision. No fatal uncomplicated human cases have been reported. Recovery is complete.

Sand-fly Fever

(Phlebotomus Fever, Pappataci Fever)

This disease is prevalent in moist lowlands of the subtropical regions of the Eastern Hemisphere between 20° and 45° N. latitude. The virus measures 25 to 60 $\mu\mu$ in diameter. The transmitters are certain species of sandflies, particularly *Phlebotomus papatasii.* The disease develops epidemically during the summer and fall following the emergence of a new brood of adult sandflies. Man is the only known mammalian host.

Following an incubation period of $2\frac{1}{2}$ to 6 days, there is a sudden onset, a chilly sensation, fever for 1 to 4 days, severe frontal and post-orbital headache, general malaise, pain and stiffness in muscles and joints and abdominal discomfort, then slow recovery. Although there is a distinct shift to the left in the Schilling count, no marked leukopenia occurs as in dengue. This disease is never fatal. Diagnosis must be made on clinical and epidemiologic grounds. Treatment is symptomatic.

Control consists in residual spraying of doors, window frames and inside walls of houses with DDT to kill the adult sandflies (Hertig, 1949).

RICKETTSIAS AND RICKETTSIAL INFECTIONS (RICKETTSIOSES)

Rickettsias are microscopically small, rod-shaped, spherical, ovoidal or pleomorphic, Gram-negative, usually non-filtrable organisms intimately associated with arthropods. They live and multiply only in living tissues or body fluids containing tissue cells. Many rickettsias are non-pathogenic symbionts of arthropods but some are highly pathogenic when introduced into man and domestic mammals. These species belong to two families, the Rickettsiaceæ and the Bartonellaceæ.

Rickettsiaceæ.—Philip (1953) provides the following classification for species of the family causing human disease:

Genus *Rickettsia*.

1. *R. prowazeki*, causing louse-borne epidemic typhus.
2. *R. typhi*, causing flea-borne murine typhus.
3. *R. tsutsugamushi*, causing trombiculid mite-borne or scrub typhus.
4. *R. rickettsi*, causing tick-borne American spotted fever.
5. *R. conori*, causing tick-borne typhus fever of the Mediterranean basin, Africa and India.
6. *R. australis*, causing North Queensland typhus (presumably tick-borne).
7. *R. akari*, causing parasitoid mite-borne rickettsialpox.
8. *R. quintana*, causing louse-borne trench fever.

Genus *Coxiella*. *C. burneti*, causing Q fever, at times transmitted by ticks.

BARTONELLACEÆ.—The single species of this family which is infective for man is *Bartonella bacilliformis*, causing sand-fly-borne bartonellosis (Carrion's disease, verruga peruana).

Louse-borne Epidemic Typhus Fever

The Agent.—*Rickettsia prowazeki*, a coccus-like or short rod-like body measuring 300 to 500 $\mu\mu$, is an obligate cytoplasmic parasite, especially of the endothelium of small bloodvessels. It was first isolated and described by da Rocha Lima in 1916.

Historical, Geographical and Epidemiologic Notes.—From the dawn of history epidemic typhus has caused a tremendous toll of human lives. It is much more prevalent in cool than in warm climates.

Demonstration of the body louse as the causative agent of epidemic typhus was first provided by Nicolle in 1909. In nature the cycle involves only man and the human louse. When *P. humanus* var. *corporis* (or less commonly *P. humanus* var. *capitis*) sucks blood from a typhus-infected patient towards the end of the incubation period or during the first few days of the acute infection, the rickettsias rapidly enter the lining cells of its midgut and multiply extensively, producing swelling and then rupture of these cells. The organisms are present in the minute fecal dejecta on the second day and in the saliva after the sixth day. Once infected, the louse remains infective for life but usually dies within 12 days because of the damage produced by the rickettsias to its midgut. Man is exposed from (1) contact of the rickettsia-laden feces with the skin or mucous membranes either by direct deposition or by contaminated fingers, (2) crushing of the louse on the skin and (3) the "bite" of the louse. The rickettsias in the feces remain viable for a considerable time on soiled clothing or skin and may produce infection through scarified skin or following inhalation from contaminated air.

Pathogenesis and Symptomatology.—Following introduction into the skin or mucous membranes, the typhus rickettsias invade the cytoplasm of the endothelial cells of the small bloodvessels, produce acute inflammation and mural thrombi, and provoke perivascular infiltration and hemorrhage. After an incubation period of 5 to 7 days and prodromal malaise there is a sudden onset of symptoms, with chills and a fever of 40° C. (104° F.) or more lasting 6 to 8 days, then defervescence by lysis or crisis. There are raging frontal and post-orbital headache, flushed cheeks, congested conjunctivæ, pain in the back and legs, hyperesthesia, tremors and twitching, mental lethargy or delirium, and prostration. Gangrene of the tips of the fingers, toes and nose may develop. The exanthem, appearing on the third to fifth day and reaching a maximum in 2 or 3 days, is relatively discrete, one to 4 mm. in diameter, at first bright red, then changing to dark red or purplish and becoming petechial.

Brill's disease is an exacerbation of epidemic typhus in persons who many years earlier had the acute infection (Murray and Snyder, 1951).

Diagnosis.—Since typhus develops epidemically in louse-infested groups, diagnosis can be made on clinical grounds and the epidemiologic history. However, typhus requires differentiation from the common exanthematous diseases, other rickettsioses, louse-borne relapsing fever, Weil's disease, dengue and occasionally plague. Beginning on the 4th to 6th day increasing agglutination titer with Proteus OX 19 (Weil-Felix reaction) and a specific complement-fixation test (Bengtson, 1944) provide confirmation.

Treatment.—Symptomatic treatment and good nursing care are required during the acute stage. Specific therapeusis with one of the newer antibiotics (chloramphenicol, Aureomycin, Terramycin, etc.) is indicated (Knight and Ruiz-Sanchez, 1952). These rickettiostatic drugs prevent overwhelming intoxication, resolve the fever fairly rapidly and shorten the period of convalescence.

Prognosis.—With early diagnosis, good nursing care and appropriate antibiotic medication the prognosis is excellent. Otherwise the mortality may be very high.

Control.—Delousing of the individual with DDT powder, or other effective, safe insecticide, and fumigation of his clothing constitute basic control procedures. Immunization with Cox-type typhus vaccine every 6 months in epidemic areas provides relatively high protection for persons in louse-borne typhus areas.

Flea-borne Murine Typhus Fever

The Agent.—*Rickettsia typhi* is morphologically indistinguishable from *R. prowazeki* but can be differentiated by the complement-fixation test.

Geographical and Epidemiologic Notes.—Murine typhus is widely distributed throughout temperate and warm climates. It is essentially an infection of domestic rodents and their ectoparasites. Other mammals (rabbit, squirrel, opossum, skunk, weasel, cat and dog), and possibly even birds, have been found naturally infected in the southeastern United States. In the rat and its fleas there is no evidence that the infection causes serious tissue damage. Human infection is sporadic and is associated with rat infestation of homes, workshops, warehouses, granaries, etc. Exposure usually results from rubbing the infected feces into the puncture wound made by the flea.

Clinical Notes.—The lesions produced by *R. typhi* are similar to those due to *R. prowazeki* but are usually much less extensive. After an incubation period of 4 to 14 days there is an acute onset of symptoms, with chills, fever of 38.5° to 40° C. (100° to 104° F.), headache, rash on the 5th day and then slow convalescence. Diagnosis of murine typhus fever can be made beginning on the 6th day when the Weil-Felix test becomes positive. Specific evidence that it is murine typhus is obtained by complement-fixation using *R. typhi* antigen (Bengtson, 1944). Treatment is similar to that described for epidemic typhus (Knight and Ruiz-Sanchez, 1952). Except for the aged and infirm the prognosis is excellent.

Control.—Prevention of murine typhus requires active campaigns to prevent the breeding of domestic rats, together with the use of DDT in rat runs and harborages.

Scrub Typhus (Tsutsugamushi Disease)

The Agent.—*Rickettsia tsutsugamushi* is morphologically similar to *R. prowazeki.*

Geographical and Epidemiologic Notes.—Scrub typhus has an extensive distribution in the Southwest Pacific islands (including the Philippines), Malaya, Thailand, Burma, several states of India, in Ceylon, Indochina, southwest China, and is present in Queensland (Australia) and Japan. Its enzoötic cycle is primarily in two species of trombiculid mites, *Trombicula akamushi, T. deliensis,* and to a limited extent also in *T. fuji* and *Euschöngastia indica.* In these mites the etiologic agent is congenitally transmitted. The mites (see Chapter 19, page 468) suck mammalian tissue juices only during their larval stage and are therefore able to become infected from, or to transmit the infection to a vertebrate host exclusively during this stage. In nature they feed on wild rodents which are susceptible to the infection but do not develop symptoms (Philip, 1949). Man is exposed when he enters marshy flood plains near the mouth of rivers (Japan), the extensive lush grass in the moist Tropics, or at times dry rocky areas (Pescadores).

Clinical Notes.—The inoculated rickettsias tend to multiply locally in the skin, where frequently but not invariably they produce an ulcer, covered with a reddish-black eschar surrounded by a pink margin. From the primary site they become extensively disseminated throughout the body, causing damage to the walls of the small bloodvessels, particularly in the lungs, myocardium and brain. One to 2 weeks following exposure there is a sudden onset of symptoms, with chills, dizziness, headache and a fever which reaches 40° C. (104° F.) or more in 2 or 3 days. The temperature then gradually returns to normal over a period of 2 to 3 days. A petechial exanthem may develop on the 4th or 5th day. It appears first on the face, then on the trunk and extremities, and fades about a week later. Seriously ill cases end fatally or have a long convalescence. Natives who are repeatedly exposed exhibit considerable immunity.

Diagnosis is made presumptively on clinical and epidemiologic grounds and is confirmed by agglutination of Proteus OXK (and not OX19 or OX2) by patient's serum. Treatment is similar to that described for epidemic typhus (page 532), and the prognosis is essentially the same.

Control.—Power-spraying of jungle or swamp grass with crude Gammexane (benzene hexachloride), then cutting it provides considerable protection for native populations, since the mites are sensitive to drying and sunlight. Hand-spraying of rodent burrows and rocky caves aids in killing the mites. Individual protection from attacks of the mites is obtained by wearing clothing impregnated with 45 parts benzyl benzoate, 45 parts dibutyl phthalate and 10 parts detergent emulsifier. Dusting of 10% DDT into shoes and socks also provides a safeguard for the wearer (Philip, 1949). Suppressive (but not true prophylactic) therapy is obtained by taking 0.5 Gm. daily doses of chloramphenicol during the period of potential exposure in enzoötic areas and for at least 10 days thereafter (Bailey and Ley, 1952). No satisfactory vaccine has been developed.

Tick-borne Typhus Fevers

The Agents.—Three closely related but immunologically different rickettsias, *R. rickettsi, R. conori* and *R. australis,* are the agents of tick-borne typhus. These microörganisms are pleomorphic short rods or ovoidal bodies about 0.3 microns in length. They invade the nucleus as well as the cytoplasm of mammalian cells, particularly the endothelial lining of bloodvessels.

Geographical and Epidemiologic Notes.—Tick-typhus produced by *R. rickettsi* has an extensive distribution in the United States, adjacent western Canada, Mexico, Colombia and Brazil. That caused by *R. conori* occurs in the Mediterranean basin, in South Africa, East Africa and India. That due to *R. australis* is found in North Queensland (Australia). In all of these areas the reservoirs and transmitters are hard-bodied ticks (see Chapter 19, page 461). Man is typically exposed from "bites" of the adult tick, most often during its activation following a hibernating period. The common method of inoculation is through the introduction of the tick's hypostome into the skin.

In nature the following species of ticks are known transmitters: *Dermacentor andersoni,* Western U. S. and adjacent Canada; *D. variabilis,* Central and Eastern U. S.; *Amblyomma americanum,* Texas and Oklahoma; *A. cajennense,* Panamá, Colombia, Brazil; *Rhipicephalus sanguineus,* Mexico, Mediterranean Basin, Crimea, Abyssinia, Kenya; *Hæmaphysalis leachi* and *Hyalomma ægyptium,* S. Africa.

Clinical Notes.—The agents of tick typhus invade and destroy the endothelial cells of the bloodvessels, first near the site of inoculation, then in multiple foci throughout the body. They produce mural thrombi, and provoke perivascular infiltration, frequently resulting in local gangrene (Lillie, 1941). Following an incubation period of 2 to 5 days in severe cases (3 to 14 days in milder ones), there are prodromes of malaise and chills, then typically rigors, intense headache, pains in the joints, hyperesthesia, photophobia, and a fever which may reach 41° C. (105.8° F.). In many cases resulting from exposure to *R. conori* a persistent button-like primary eschar develops at the site of the tick's "bite." Characteristically in tick typhus there is a roseate macular rash of a petechial type, which develops at the time of onset of symptoms, first on the wrists and ankles, then extending to all skin areas and adjacent mucous membranes. In the more severe infections there are delirium, stupor and toxic coma. In many cases the fever declines or becomes remittent by the beginning of the 3rd week of illness and a prolonged convalescence ensues.

Diagnosis in endemic areas is based on a history of tick infestation followed in a few days by a sudden onset of symptoms and accompanied by the exanthem proceeding centrally from the extremities. Confirmation is provided by the agglutinating property of patient's serum for Proteus OK19 and OK2, with rising titer to 1:320 or more. Species diagnosis of the rickettsial agent can be obtained by complement-fixation (Bengtson, 1944). Treatment (Harrell, 1952) and prognosis are the same as for epidemic typhus (page 532).

Control.—The disease may be avoided by keeping out of tick-infested areas except in the case of the dog ticks, *Dermacentor variabilis*, *Amblyomma americanum* and *Rhipicephalus sanguineus*, which are brought into the home on dogs. Previous to entering a tick-infested area the socks, inside of the shoes and trouser cuffs should be dusted with DDT. On returning to the house all clothing should be removed and careful inspection made for ticks on the skin. In highly endemic areas, biennial immunization with Cox-type *R. rickettsi* vaccine has proven very effective.

Rickettsialpox

The Agent.—*Rickettsia akari* is immunologically a close relative of the rickettsias which produce tick-borne typhus fever.

Geographical and Epidemiologic Notes.—The disease has been reported only from the metropolitan area of New York City, Boston and West Hartford, Connecticut. The enzoötic cycle involves domestic mice and their parasitoid mite, *Allodermanyssus sanguineus* (Chapter 19, page 465). Whenever the mite becomes infected from the mouse and then "bites" man the rickettsia is inoculated into the human skin (Huebner, *et al.*, 1946).

Clinical Notes.—At the site of inoculation a small vesicle or pustule develops. Thereafter a mild train of symptoms is observed, consisting of fever, sweats, regional adenitis and a maculate rash resembling the exanthem of chickenpox. Diagnosis is made presumptively on the dermatitis and fever, and can be confirmed by specific complement-fixation. Treatment is usually symptomatic but chloramphenicol, Aureomycin or Terramycin may be employed to advantage in moderately severe cases (Rose, 1952). Prognosis is excellent.

Control.—The dusting of DDT throughout mice-infested premises will temporarily keep down the mite population. Extermination of mice constitutes the fundamental preventive measure.

Trench Fever

The Agent.—The status of *Rickettsia quintana* remains in dispute as the agent of trench fever.

Geographical and Epidemiologic Notes.—Trench fever (Wolhynian fever or five-day fever) was first observed in epidemic form on the Eastern front during World War I. During the next 2 decades only a few sporadic cases were reported. During World War II, it broke out again in eastern Europe. More recently the infection has been found to be endemic in parts of Mexico.

Its transmission has been studied experimentally by Weyer in Hamburg (1949) and more recently by Mooser and Weyer (1953). Lice become infected from feeding on human cases from the first day of acute symptoms and extending over a long period, even after clinical recovery. Incubation in the louse requires 5 to 9 days, during which the rickettsias multiply on the cuticular surface of the midgut and not within the epithelial cells. When the louse feeds the organisms are introduced into the skin, either from rubbing in the fecal dejecta or possibly from the saliva.

Clinical Notes.—Following an incubation period of 10 to 30 days, there is a sudden onset of symptoms, with severe headache, pain and hyperesthesia in the back and lower extremities, and prostration. The fever is remittent approximately every 5 days, hence the designation "*quintana.*" In most patients there is a transient roseolate macular exanthem. Diagnosis is based on epidemiologic grounds and the clinical findings. Specific treatment probably can be obtained by administering chloramphenicol, Aureomycin or Terramycin. The disease is extremely incapacitating but the eventual prognosis is excellent even without specific treatment.

Control.—Prevention can be obtained by delousing measures which have proven effective in epidemic typhus (page 532).

Q FEVER

The Agent.—*Coxiella burneti* is a short rod measuring 0.4 to 1.0 micron in length. It develops in micro-colonies in the cytoplasm of reticuloendothelial cells.

Geographical and Epidemiologic Notes.—The disease was first described by Derrick (1937) from Queensland, Australia and the agent almost simultaneously in the tick *Dermacentor andersoni* in western Montana. It has been reported in enzoötic or epidemic form in practically every country where search has been made for it. In the enzoötic cycle cattle, sheep and goats are the usual mammalian hosts, while many species of hard-bodied and a few species of soft-bodied ticks are efficient vectors. Man may develop infection from the "bite" of an infected tick but much oftener he acquires the disease from inhaling the organisms in tick's fecal dejecta floating in the air, or even on soiled clothing, at times considerable distances from enzoötic regions. The disease is particularly prevalent on the Pacific Coast of the United States.

Clinical Notes.—The notable cellular pathology in *Q* fever consists in hypertrophy and hyperplasia of the fixed histiocytes of the spleen and Kupffer cells of the liver, and in fatal cases a mononuclear pneumonitis (Perrin, 1949). After a variable incubation period, in moderate to severe cases there is a sudden onset of symptoms, with a fever of 39.5° to 40° C. (103° to 104° F.) lasting 6 to 24 days, a slow pulse, raging headache, chills or rigors followed by drenching sweats, photophobia, pain in the back and legs, and prostration. There is no rash and the blood picture is normal. Tenderness of the spleen is elicited on deep inspiration. In some patients, there is a viral-like pneumonia (*viz.*, Balkan "grippe"). Probably there are many inapparent infections for every clinical case. Diagnosis is made on the epidemiologic and clinical history, confirmed by agglutination of *C.*

burneti obtained from spleens of infected laboratory mice with patient's serum diluted 1:10. Treatment consists of symptomatic relief, good nursing care and administration of chloramphenicol, Aureomycin or Terramycin (Clark and Lennette, 1952). Prognosis is good except for patients with severe pulmonary complications.

Control.—Preventive measures are difficult to formulate and to carry out because a preponderance of human exposures result from inhaling the causal agent. Use of insecticide sprays on cattle, sheep and goats should reduce the tick population and decrease the amount of the enzoötic disease. In this way it will eventually provide less opportunity for human exposure.

Bartonellosis

The Agent.—*Bartonella bacilliformis* is a minute, pleomorphic, bacillus-like organism which is primarily a parasite of red blood corpuscles, secondarily of reticulo-endothelial cells.

Geographical and Epidemiologic Notes.—This disease occurs in certain mountain valleys in northwestern South America (Rimac and Eulalia valleys above Lima, Peru; Province of Loja, Ecuador and Department of Nariña, Colombia near the Ecuadorian border). The characteristic cycle involves man as the vertebrate host and Andean species of sandflies. Natives who survive childhood infection appear to have considerable immunity.

Clinical Notes.—When introduced into the human skin, *B. bacilliformis* almost immediately enters red blood cells, in which the organism multiplies, causing destruction of the cells. Reduction in circulating red cells and toxic absorption of the pathogen's metabolites produce secondary anemia of considerable magnitude and a febrile reaction. Soon the parasites invade the fixed histiocytes, which increase in number and cause enlargement of the liver, spleen and lymph nodes, engorgement of the bone marrow and hyperplasia of the endothelial lining of the smaller bloodvessels and lymphatic vessels, likewise verrucous eruptions of the skin.

Following an incubation period of 10 to 21 days there is usually an insidious onset, with symptoms suggestive of a septic condition, lasting from a few days to more than 2 months. The anemia increases, jaundice is common and bleeding occurs from mucous membranes, but there is no leukocytosis. This period is called *Carrion's disease.*

Following the acute febrile stage, or before its termination, warty eruptions appear on the skin and in subcutaneous tissues. They are hemangiomatous and tend to break down and ulcerate, then become granulomatous or indolent. This condition lasts for weeks or months and may recur after apparent healing. Fulminating infection is frequently fatal, recovery with lasting immunity is fairly common, and low-grade clinical infection is a frequent occurrence in the native population.

Diagnosis can be made clinically in patients who have a history of exposure in endemic zones and present either the febrile-anemic state or the verrucous condition. Administration of chloramphenicol in the amount of 4 Gm. daily for 4 days, then 2 Gm. daily for 4 to 6 days provides rapid clinical improvement and possible cure (DeVault, 1952).

Control.—Hertig and Fairchild (1948) have demonstrated the highly lethal effect of DDT for the adult sand-fly vectors when the insecticide is used as a residual spray on doors, windows and inside walls of human habitations. This measure effectively limits exposure to bartonellosis.

BACTERIA AND BACTERIAL INFECTIONS

Only species of *Pasteurella* (*P. pestis* and *P. tularensis*) are commonly picked up by blood-sucking arthropods and usually after a period of multiplication in the midgut are introduced into the skin of man and other susceptible mammals.

Plague

The Agent.—*Pasteurella pestis* is a Gram-negative, non-motile, pleomorphic, bipolar bacillus which does not form spores but is usually provided with a capsule.

Historical and Geographical Notes.—Plague is a disease as ancient as mankind. From time to time in the ancient world and during medieval times, epidemics and pandemics of plague with high mortality broke out in Asia and Europe. Among these were the "Black Death" which visited Europe during the 14th and 17th centuries and left uncounted dead in its wake. The latest pandemic originated in Yünnan Province, southwest China and reached Hong Kong in 1894. From this port city, either directly or indirectly, the disease was carried on ships to all parts of the world and became established for the first time in the Western Hemisphere. In 1894, Yersin, in Hong Kong, described the etiologic agent, while Simond (1898) in Bombay, Bautier and Raybaud (1902) in Marseilles, Liston (1905) in Bombay and the Plague Commission in India (1907–1916) conclusively demonstrated the rôle of rodent fleas in its transmission.

Today there are many enzoötic foci of plague, with periodic outbreaks in the human population. The more important foci are Manchuria, southeastern China, Indochina, Java, Thailand, Burma, India, Iran, Iraq, Asia Minor, Egypt, Morocco, Senegal, the Azores, Belgian Congo, East and South Africa and Madagascar. Plague also exists in Hawaii, northeastern Brazil, northern Argentina, Bolivia, Peru, Ecuador, and the western third of the United States.

Epidemiology.—Plague is essentially a disease of rodents and their fleas. There are two epidemiologic rodent types, *viz.*, (1) that in domestic and semi-domestic rats (*Rattus norvegicus*, *R. rattus*, *R. alexandrinus* and other species) and (2) wild rodent plague. In both domestic and wild rodents there is an underlying, relatively quiescent, enzoötic infection which periodically becomes epizoötic. In the domestic rats this provides opportunity for the development of epidemics. First the brown rat (*R. norvegicus*) is involved, then the black rat (*R. rattus*). Opportunity for human contact with the disease in the wild rodents (so-called "sylvatic plague") is much less; as a result only occasional human infection is derived from this source.

Fleas (see Chapter 20, page 501) are the responsible vectors of bubonic plague from rodent to rodent, from rodent to man, and possibly from man to man. When plague bacilli are present in the blood meal one or more of the following situations develops: (1) After an interrupted feeding the flea may regurgitate the bacilli into the skin of the next host; (2) the bacilli may reach the flea's midgut, multiply and be evacuated in fecal dejecta in or near the puncture wound made by the flea in its new host; (3) multiplication of the organisms in the flea's midgut may produce a "block" in the proventriculus, so that subsequently the flea in wandering from one host

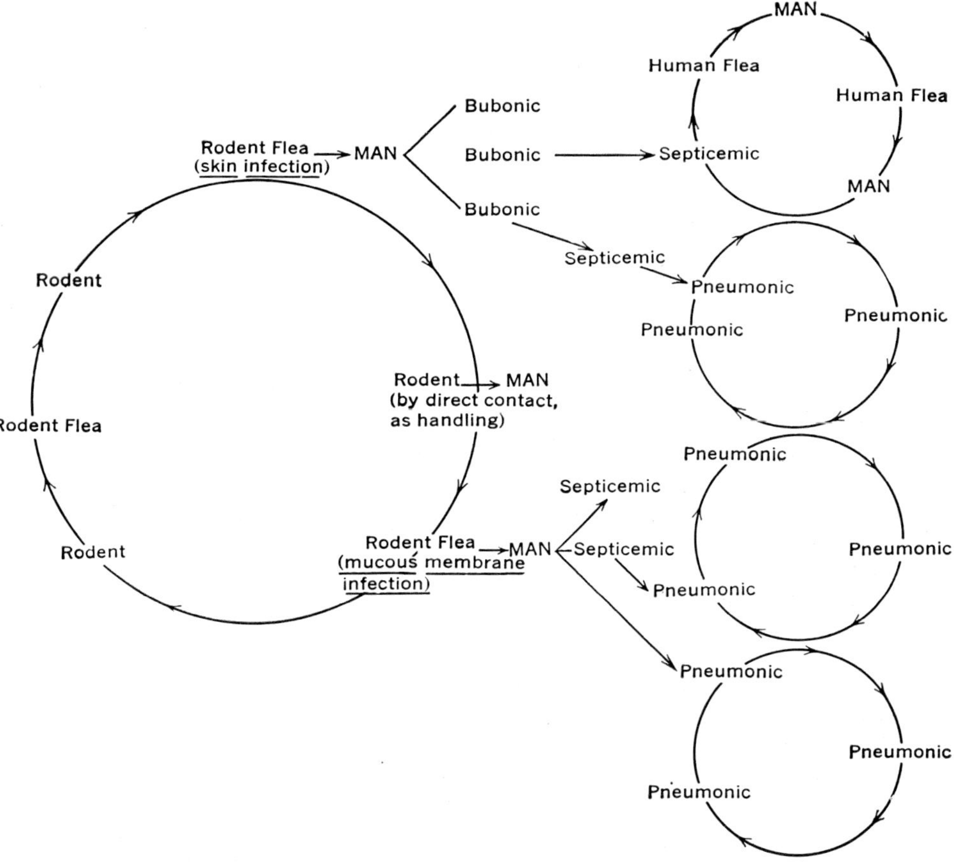

Fig. 210.—The transmission cycles of rodent and human plague. (Original, from Craig and Faust's *Clinical Parasitology,* Lea & Febiger, Philadelphia.)

to another in an attempt to satisfy its hunger contaminates the puncture wounds which it makes in a number of hosts, and (4) "blocked" fleas may transfer bacilli directly from an infected to a clean host. Most exposures result from transmission by "blocked" fleas. The domestic rodent flea, *Xenopsylla cheopis,* is primarily responsible for plague epidemics.

Once the disease has become epidemic, cases of pneumonic plague will usually develop after a few to several passages in man. Pneumonic plague is contagious and requires no transfer through fleas.

The rodent and human cycles of plague are illustrated in Figure 210.

Pathogenesis and Symptomatology.—In bubonic plague the usual portal of entry of the bacilli is through the puncture site made by the flea. The typical lesion develops in the nearest lymph node, where the characteristic bubo appears as a raised, very tender abscess with a blood-stained cheesy center containing a mass of multiplying *P. pestis,* surrounded by a hemorrhagic zone and then an outer zone of blood-stained serum. Rarely the lesion is encapsulated ("pestis minor"). In 60% of cases the bubo is located in the groin, in 20% in the axilla, in 10% in the neck and in 10% it is scattered. From the bubo, the organisms usually get into the blood stream, in which they continue to multiply (septicemic plague), and at times become filtered out in the lungs to multiply and produce pneumonic plague. Occasionally, the bacilli are introduced by the flea directly into a bloodvessel, producing primary septicemia. The symptoms which develop are due to the pathogen's extremely toxic metabolites which are disseminated throughout the patient's body. Within 3 to 5 days after inoculation and the gradual development of the bubo, there are aches and pain in the immediate vicinity of the bubo, a feeling of malaise, mental apathy, slurred or staccato speech, ataxia and stupor, accompanied or soon followed by chills and fever of a remittent type, rapid pulse and rapid shallow respiration. Patients who develop a septicemic infection are more seriously affected, and those whose infection becomes pneumonic invariably die unless treated early by modern methods.

Presumptive *diagnosis* in an area of epidemic plague may be made on the basis of the characteristic bubo with attendant symptoms. Material aspirated from the bubo, the blood of a suspected plague case and bloody sputum from a pneumonic case should be cultured on appropriate media and inoculated parenterally into guinea pigs. Infected rodents and pooled speciments of their fleas provide material for demonstrating their degree of involvement in enzoötic plague.

Treatment has been transformed during the past three decades from a relatively hopeless to an eminently satisfactory status. Administration of sulfadiazine reversed the prognosis of bubonic plague from 70% fatalities to about 80% recovery, although the sulfa drugs had little effect on the fatal outcome of septicemic and pneumonic plague. Streptomycin administered in daily doses of 2 to 4 Gm. until the fever has subsided produces practically 100% cures in all types of the disease, *provided* the patient is diagnosed and treated early in the disease. Chloramphenicol, Aureomycin and Terramycin are equally effective (Smadel *et al.,* 1952).

Control.—The control and prevention of plague involve the following procedures: (1) Quarantine, (2) domestic rodent-flea destruction, (3) domestic rat eradication, (4) prophylaxis and (5) containment of wild-rodent plague.

Quarantine.—This measure was first instituted specifically against rat-infested and plague-infected ships as soon as there was proof following the pandemic of 1894–1905 concerning the rôle of rat fleas in the transmission of the disease to man. Quarantine has greatly reduced the introduction of the disease into clean areas.

In the event of an epidemic outbreak of plague in a community, quarantine should be established peripherally to prevent the spread of the disease.

Domestic Rodent-flea Destruction.—This is effectively carried out by dusting DDT (10% in inert powder) into rat runs, burrows and nests. The insecticide kills the fleas and breaks the cycle. This must always precede rat eradication.

Rat Eradication.—Since domestic rats are the important urban reservoirs of plague, their breeding must be controlled. Rat-proofing of warehouses, stores and homes is basically important. Rat trapping and rat poisoning with red squill, alpha naphtha-thiourea (Antu), "1080," Warfarin and other rodenticides are valuable in reducing the domestic rat population, but rat eradication has never been entirely successful. This essential is still the most serious handicap to effective plague control.

Prophylactic Measures.—Prophylactic administration of sulfadiazine, streptomycin, Aureomycin or Terramycin to contacts of plague patients provides considerable security against the contacts developing fatal infection. Immunization with potent, killed *Pasteurella pestis* vaccine or with the avirulent living organisms has been demonstrated to be a valuable prophylactic although it is not always completely protective. To be effective vaccination must be carried out at least 5 days before exposure and repeated every 6 months.

Containment of Wild-rodent Plague.—In many regions of the world, including much of the western United States, there are extensive areas where plague is established in wild rodents. Only occasional human cases develop as a result of direct contact with these flea-infested, plague-infected rodents.

Tularemia

Although tularemia is most often contracted from dressing rabbits infected with *Pasteurella tularensis*, the blood-sucking deer-fly, *Chrysops discalis*, and other species of this genus are good transmitters of the bacillus from infected wild mammals to man (Jellison, 1950).

SPIROCHETAL DISEASES

Arthropods are the essential vectors of two types of relapsing fever in man, the one produced by *Borrelia recurrentis* and transmitted by human body lice, the other produced by *Borrelia duttoni* and transmitted by soft-bodied ticks.

Louse-borne Epidemic Relapsing Fever

The Agent.—The etiologic agent is *Borrelia recurrentis* (syn. *B. obermeieri*, *B. carteri*), a spirochete of the human blood stream and body fluids, which multiplies by longitudinal binary fission. It has three or more body undulations and distinctly sharp ends and has a length approximately two to five times the diameter of a red blood cell (Fig. 211).

Geographical Distribution and Epidemiology.—Epidemic relapsing fever is a disease of louse-infested human populations. Hence its distribution parallels that of epidemic typhus fever (page 531). In parts of tropical Africa it coëxists with tick-borne relapsing fever. There is no evidence that it occurs indigenously in North America today.

Human infection is acquired from the body louse (*Pediculus humanus* var. *corporis*) and is epidemic in character, as distinguished from enzoötic-endemic tick-borne relapsing fever. Lice (see Chapter 20, page 482) become infected from feeding on infected human blood. Within two hours the organisms are found in all parts of their body. Here they multiply as typical spirochetes (Feng and Chung, 1936). Once infected the louse remains infected for life. The parasites are transmitted to man when the louse is crushed on the skin at the site of its puncture.

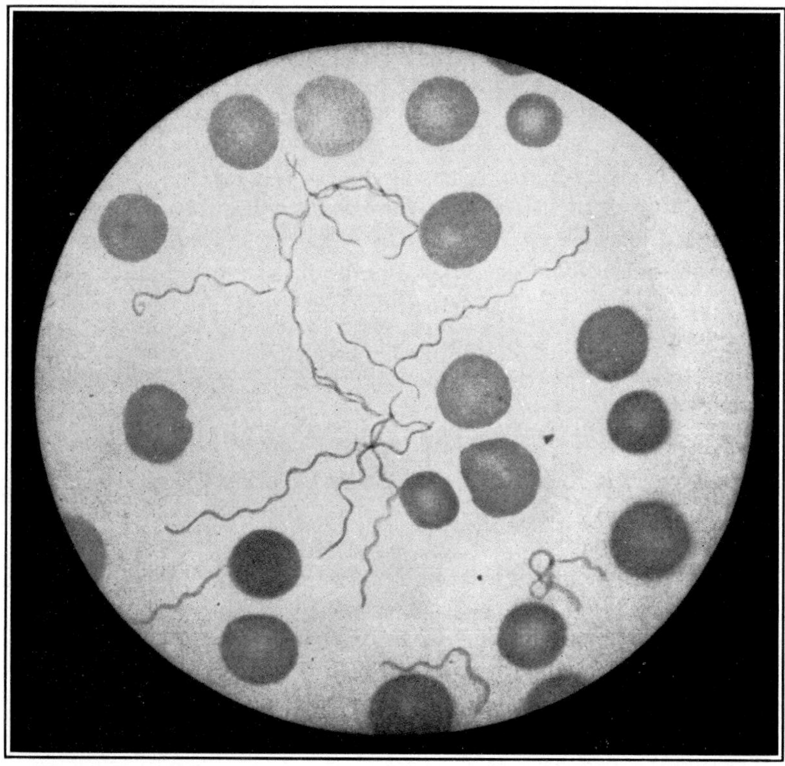

Fig. 211.—Tick-borne relapsing fever spirochetes (*Borrelia duttoni*) in peripheral blood during a clinical attack. (After Dr. S. B. Wolbach, in Shattuck's *Diseases of the Tropics*, Appleton-Century-Crofts, Inc.)

Clinical Notes.—Once *B. recurrentis* has been introduced into the skin, the organism circulates in the blood stream and in tissue fluids but does not penetrate undamaged cells. The toxic metabolites cause necrosis of the parenchyma cells of the liver and spleen, degenerative changes in the bone marrow and kidneys, and the endothelial lining of small bloodvessels in which the pathogen multiplies. The spirochete circulates in peripheral blood only during the primary and recurrent attacks; at other times it is concentrated in visceral organs.

Following an incubation period of 4 to 8 days, there is typically a sudden onset of symptoms, consisting of a shaking chill and fever of 40° to 41° C. (104° to 105.8° F.), severe headache, pain in the back and legs, joints, liver and spleen, hemorrhage from the smaller bloodvessels in the skin and mucous membranes and profuse epistaxis. There may be extreme prostration. After 4 or 5 days, the temperature drops by crisis to subnormal. Sweating and weakness but relief from pain are then experienced. Within 5 to 15 days, there is a second clinical episode which is usually less intensive and of shorter duration than the primary attack. Characteristically there are several alternating periods of clinical bouts and remissions before the infection becomes inapparent. *B. recurrentis* consists of several strains, each of which is responsible for a specific clinical episode of the disease.

Diagnosis is made presumptively on the clinical course of the disease during an epidemic outbreak among louse-infested populations. Specific diagnosis consists in demonstrating a *Borrelia*-type of spirochete in peripheral blood at the time of clinical attacks. Treatment requires symptomatic care and administration of penicillin in 0.5% glucose solution (1 million units daily for 5 to 7 days. Unlike arsenical drug therapy penicillin treatment may be undertaken at any stage of the disease. Prognosis is usually good, even in untreated patients unless there is supervening disease.

Control.—Prevention of epidemic relapsing fever can be accomplished by unremitting war on human body lice.

Tick-borne Relapsing Fever

The Agent.—The causative agent, *Borrelia duttoni*, is morphologically indistinguishable from *B. recurrentis*, the agent of epidemic relapsing fever. There are many synonyms of *B. duttoni* based on tick hosts in various geographical areas. These are possibly varieties but are not true species (Davis, 1940).

Geographical Distribution and Epidemiology.—This disease is widely distributed in parts of Africa, the Near East, Middle East, the table lands of Central Asia, Spain, the western half of the United States and Latin America. In some regions both louse-borne and tick-borne relapsing fever occur and in still other regions the evidence as to the type of the infection is still unsatisfactory.

Tick-borne relapsing fever is an enzoötic infection involving soft-bodied ticks of the genus *Ornithodoros* (see Chapter 19, page 461) as transmitters, and wild rodents, monkeys and other mammals as susceptible vertebrate hosts. Within a few hours after the tick ingests *B. duttoni* in a blood meal the spirochetes have penetrated from the intestine into all parts of the tick's body, where they multiply. Once the tick becomes infected it retains the organisms for life and transmits them congenitally. Any active stage of the tick is then able to transmit the spirochetes to a susceptible mammal through its "bite" or secretion of its coxal fluid on the punctured skin. Human infection is accidental, sporadic or mildly endemic, rarely if ever epidemic.

Clinical Notes.—The pathogenesis and symptomatology in tick-borne relapsing fever are similar to that of the epidemic type (page 542). Toxic inflammation and necrosis are particularly marked in the liver, spleen and glomeruli of the kidneys (Kemp *et al.*, 1942).

Diagnosis and treatment are the same as in *B. recurrentis* infection (page 543).

Control.—Since species of *Ornithodoros* are widely distributed throughout the world and in many areas are reservoirs of *B. duttoni*, avoidance of exposure to "bites" of these ticks is advisable wherever this is possible. Dusting of DDT into clothing and residual spraying of DDT or benzene hexachloride inside tick-infested homes constitute moderately satisfactory prophylaxis. (See Chapter 19, page 463.) Vaccination has not been developed.

PROTOZOAN DISEASES

The protozoan diseases which are transmitted by arthropods have been considered in Section 2, Chapters 8 and 9. They will be briefly summarized here from the viewpoint of the arthropods as biological vectors.

Malaria.—Anopheline mosquitoes (Chapter 20, page 491) are the obligate vectors of all four species of human malaria parasites (*Plasmodium vivax, P. falciparum, P. malariæ* and *P. ovale*).

The Leishmaniases.—Species of *Phlebotomus* or sand-flies (Chapter 20, page 496) are the intermediate hosts of *Leishmania donovani* (producing visceral leishmaniasis or kala-azar), *L. brasiliensis* (producing mucocutaneous leishmaniasis) and *L. tropica* (producing cutaneous leishmanisais).

African Trypanosomiasis.—Species of *Glossina* or tsetse flies (Chapter 20, page 500) serve as necessary hosts for the metacyclic development of the etiologic agents, *Trypanosoma gambiense* and *T. rhodesiense*.

Chagas' Disease (American Trypanosomiasis).—Species of triatomid bugs, particularly *Triatoma infestans, Panstrongylus megistus* and *Rhodnius prolixus*, all of which breed in human habitations, are obligate transmitters of *Trypanosoma cruzi* (Chapter 20, page 486).

HELMINTHIC DISEASES

Certain helminthic infections are passively transmitted to man when the infected arthropod is accidentally swallowed or serves as an article of food in its essentially raw state. In the former category are dracunculosis (page 312), sparganosis (page 360), rat tapeworm infection (page 338), dog tapeworm infection (page 339) and several incidental helminthiases. In the latter category is paragonimiasis (page 392). In contrast the filaria infections are actively transmitted by blood-sucking arthropods. These will be briefly summarized here.

Bancroft's and Malayan Filariasis.—Mosquitoes (Chapter 20, pages 289 to 301) are the obligate intermediate hosts of *Wuchereria bancrofti* and *W. malayi*, the causative agents respectively of these two diseases.

Loaiasis.—*Loa loa* is transmitted by mango flies of the genus *Chrysops* (Chapter 20, page 307).

Onchocercosis.—*Onchocerca volvulus* has unsheathed microfilarias which are not found in circulating blood but migrate in peripheral lymph vessels and interstitially in cutaneous tissue juices. The intermediate host is the small hump-backed fly *Simulium* (Chapter 20, page 301), which picks up the microfilarias when feeding on tissue juices in the skin.

Infections with Acanthocheilonema and Mansonella.—The intermediate hosts of these filarias are species of biting gnats of the genus *Culicoides* (Chapter 20, pages 310-311).

SUMMARY

1. In the rôle of carriers of disease-producing organisms arthropods serve as mechanical or biological vectors.
2. As a mechanical vector the arthropod contaminates the external parts of its body or its digestive tract with excreta or secretions containing the infectious agent. In the alimentary tract the pathogen may multiply. Within hours or days the inoculum is deposited in food or drink intended for human consumption, or on mucous membranes, and in this way the arthropod transfers the pathogen.
3. The most frequent examples of mechanical transmission are the enteric bacteria, including those of the *Salmonella* group, *Shigella* and the cholera vibrios by the house-fly and other filth flies.
4. Non-enteric bacterial diseases disseminated by filth-feeding arthropods include tuberculosis, plague, tularemia, brucellosis, anthrax and acute epidemic conjunctivitis. Filth flies and cockroaches are good mechanical vectors of the cysts of *Endamœba histolytica,* while blood-sucking arthropods may transmit the virus of yellow fever, and the protozoa which live in the blood stream and tissues.
5. Arthropods are of unique importance as biological vectors of microörganisms which produce human disease. At times the arthropod serves merely as a good incubator and transmitter. In a few instances transmission is accidental from swallowing the infected host. A much larger group of pathogens utilize blood-sucking arthropods both as essential host and active transmitters of viruses, the rickettsias, *Pasteurella pestis, P. tularensis, Borrelia recurrentis* and *B. duttoni,* the leishmanias and trypanosomes.
6. The arthropod-transmitted virus diseases include principally yellow fever, dengue, the encephalitides and sand-fly fever.
7. Yellow fever in urban areas requires *Aëdes ægypti* as the biological vector and is epidemic in character, but in its enzoötic habitats in tropical rain-forests it utilizes wild mosquitoes which transmit the disease to monkeys which live in the treetops. The eradication of *Aëdes ægypti* keeps urban communities free of the disease but the sylvatic disease remains. Vaccination provides protection for man exposed to the sylvatic type of the disease.
8. Dengue is an epidemic disease of warm climates usually transmitted by *Aëdes ægypti.* The disease can be controlled by eliminating the breeding of the transmitters.
9. Sand-fly fever is an epidemic disease of subtropical and tropical countries of the Eastern Hemisphere and is transmitted by species of the sand-fly *Phlebotomus.* Use of DDT as a residual spray in and around homes to kill the sand-flies provides protection.

10. The viruses of St. Louis and Japanese B encephalitis, Eastern, Western and Venezuelan equine encephalomyelitis, West Nile encephalitis, Russian spring-summer encephalitis, and several tropical rain-forest encephalitides of Africa and Brazil, are transmitted by wild mosquitoes. In these as in the other arthropod-transmitted encephalitides, infection of man and other mammals results from "bites" of infected mosquitoes.
11. Colorado tick fever virus is transmitted by *Dermacentor andersoni* and Rift Valley fever of eastern Africa by several species of vectors.
12. Eight separate rickettsial diseases of man involve arthropods as biological vectors. These are louse-borne and flea-borne typhus fever, scrub typhus, three types of tick-borne typhus, rickettsialpox and trench fever.
13. Epidemic typhus fever is produced by *Rickettsia prowazeki* and is a disease exclusively of lice and men. It is transmitted from the infected louse's bite, fecal dejecta or by crushing the louse on the skin. Cox-type vaccine provides relatively satisfactory immunity. Eradication of lice from human communities by DDT dusting is basic to epidemic typhus control.

    Murine typhus is caused by *R. typhi*. It is transmitted from rat to rat and from rat to man principally by the tropical rat flea *Xenopsylla cheopis*. The disease is enzoötic-endemic, but may become epidemic if the rickettsia becomes adapted to transmission by body lice. Control consists in use of DDT to kill the rodent fleas and intensive campaigns to eradicate the rodent reservoirs.
14. Scrub typhus (tsutsugamushi disease) is produced by *Rickettsia tsutsugamushi*, an enzoötic infection among rodents in the Southwest Pacific islands, Malaya, Thailand, Burma, several states of India, Ceylon, Indochina, southwest China, and is present in Queensland (Australia) and Japan. It is transmitted by trombiculid mites, especially *Trombicula akamushi* and *T. deliensis*, in which the infection is congenital. Only the larva transmits the rickettsia. Control consists in measures to kill the mites and in protection against exposure.
15. The tick-borne typhus fevers are produced by *Rickettsia rickettsi* in the Western Hemisphere, *R. conori* in the Mediterranean countries, South Africa, East Africa and India, and *R. australis* in North Queensland (Australia). The natural reservoirs and transmitters are hard-bodied ticks belonging to several genera, in which the infection is congenital. Transmission is through the "bites" of all active stages of these ticks. Control consists in avoiding tick infestation in enzoötic areas, dusting of clothing with DDT before entering these areas and biennial vaccination against the disease.
16. Rickettsialpox is produced by *Rickettsia akari*, an agent of infection in domestic mice, and is transmitted by the mouse mite *Allodermanyssus sanguineus*. It is contracted when the infected mites "bite" man. It has a mild course and typically requires only symptomatic treatment. Control consists in eradication of mice and their ectoparasites in human habitations.
17. Trench fever is produced by *Rickettsia quintana* and is contracted from "bites" of infected body lice. There are no known reservoirs. Control is effected by delousing measures as in epidemic typhus fever.

18. Q fever is produced by *Coxiella burneti* and may be contracted from "bites" of infected ticks but much more frequently results from inhalation of the rickettsias polluting air or fomites. Control requires anti-tick measures where cattle, sheep and goats harbor the infection and precautions against inhaling the rickettsias in polluted air.
19. Bartonellosis is produced by *Bartonella bacilliformis* in the inter-Andean regions of Peru, Ecuador and Colombia, and is transmitted by species of the sand-fly *Phlebotomus*.
20. The most important bacterial disease transmitted by blood-sucking arthropods is plague, produced by *Pasteurella pestis*. Fundamentally this is a disease of rodents and is transmitted by their fleas. It has extensive distribution in wild rodents (*viz.*, sylvatic or wild-rodent plague) and in domestic rodents. The former is responsible for occasional human cases, the latter for periodic epidemics of the disease in India, China, Java, East and South Africa and Madagascar, and to a lesser extent in other countries. The common transmitter from domestic rodents to man is *Xenopsylla cheopis*, the tropical rat flea. Pneumonic plague is commonly transmitted from man to man by droplet spray. Control consists in quarantine, use of DDT to kill the rat fleas, anti-rat measures, vaccination and prophylactic use of sulfonamides for contact cases.
21. The spirochetal diseases transmitted by blood-sucking arthropods are the relapsing fevers, transmitted by the body louse, and by soft-bodied ticks of the genus *Ornithodoros*. The former is exclusively a man-louse-man infection and is typically epidemic in character. The latter is fundamentally enzoötic with occasional cases in the human population. Control differs in the two types: in the louse-borne infection it consists in effective delousing measures; in the tick-borne type measures must be directed against the tick.
22. Protozoan infections of man involving blood-sucking arthropods as biological vectors include malaria, produced by species of *Plasmodium* and transmitted by *Anopheles* mosquitoes; three types of leishmaniasis, produced by species of *Leishmania* and transmitted by the sand-fly *Phlebotomus*; African trypanosomiasis, produced by *Trypanosoma gambiense* and *T. rhodesiense* and transmitted by tsetse flies (*Glossina*), and Chagas' disease, produced by *Trypanosoma cruzi* and transmitted by triatomid bugs.
23. The helminthic infections of man transmitted by arthropods include: (1) those in which the arthropod is a required intermediate host but the causative agents are passively introduced into the human digestive tract, and (2) those in which the parasite is actively introduced into the skin by a blood-sucking arthropod. The filaria infections are the important members of the second group, Bancroft's filariasis, produced by *Wuchereria bancrofti*, and Malayan filariasis, produced by *W. malayi*, are transmitted by mosquitoes; loaiasis, produced by *Loa loa*, is transmitted by the mango fly *Chrysops;* onchocercosis, produced by *Onchocerca volvulus*, is transmitted by the hump-backed fly *Simulium*, and infections with *Acanthocheilonema* and *Mansonella* are transmitted by the gnat *Culicoides*.

REFERENCES

Ashburn, P. M., and Craig, C. F. 1907. Experimental Investigations Regarding the Etiology of Dengue Fever, with a General Consideration of the Disease. Philippine J. Sci., *2*, 93–152.

Bailey, C. A., and Ley, H. L., Jr. 1952. Treatment and Prophylaxis of Scrub Typhus with Antibiotics. Ann. New York Acad. Sci., *55*, 983–994.

Bengtson, I. A. 1944. Complement Fixation in the Rickettsial Diseases—Technic of the Test. Pub. Health Repts., *59*, 402–405.

Bugher, J. C. 1951. In *Yellow Fever*, G. K. Strode, Editor, pp. 303–384. McGraw-Hill, New York.

Bugher, J. C., Boshell-Manrique, J., Roca-Garcia, M., and Osorno-Mesa, E. 1944. Epidemiology of Jungle Yellow Fever in Eastern Colombia. Am. J. Hyg., *39*, 16–51.

Clark, W. H., and Lennette, E. H. 1952. Treatment of Q Fever with Antibiotics. Ann. New York Acad. Sci., *55*, 1004–1018.

Collins, J. D. 1944. Colorado Tick Fever. Bull. U. S. Army Med. Dept., No. 80, 81–85.

Davis, D. J., and Pittman, M. 1950. Acute Conjunctivitis in the South. CDC Bull., Apr. 1950, pp. 18–19.

Davis, G. E. 1940. Ticks and Relapsing Fever in the United States. Pub. Health Repts., *55*, 2347–2356.

De Vault, V. T. 1952. Treatment of Bartonellosis with Antibiotics. Ann. New York Acad. Sci., *55*, 1222–1227.

Derrick, E. H. 1937. "Q" Fever, a New Fever Entity: Clinical Features, Diagnosis and Laboratory Investigation. Med. J. Australia, *ii*, 281.

Dick, G. W. A. 1953. Epidemiological Notes on Some Viruses Isolated in Uganda (Yellow Fever, Rift Valley Fever, Bwamba Fever, West Nile, Mengo, Semliki Forest, Bunyamwera, Ntaya, Uganda S and Zika Viruses). Trans. R. Soc. Trop. Med. & Hyg., *47*, 13–48.

Dick, G. W. A., and Gee, F. L. 1952. Immunity to Yellow Fever Nine Years after Vaccination with 17D Vaccine. Trans. R. Soc. Trop. Med. & Hyg., *46*, 449–458.

Dutton, J. E., and Todd, J. L. 1905. The Nature of Human Tick Fever in the Eastern Part of the Congo Free State. Liverpool School Trop. Med. Mem., No. 17, pp. 1–18.

Elton, N. W. 1952. Yellow Fever in Panama: Historical and Contemporary. Am. J. Trop. Med. & Hyg., *1*, 436–456.

Feng, L. C., and Chung, H. L. 1936. Studies on the Development of *Spirochæta Duttoni* in *Ornithodorus Moubata*. Chinese Med. J., *50*, 1185–1190.

Hammon, W. McD., and Reeves, W. C. 1943. Laboratory Transmission of St. Louis Encephalitis Virus by Three Genera of Mosquitoes. J. Exp. Med., *78*, 241–253.

Harrell, G. T. 1952. Treatment of Rocky Mountain Spotted Fever with Antibiotics. Ann. New York Acad. Sci., *55*, 1027–1042.

Hawley, J. E., Penner, L. R., Wedberg, S. E., and Kulp, W. L. 1951. The Rôle of the House-fly *Musca Domestica*, in the Multiplication of Certain Enteric Bacteria. Am. J. Trop. Med., *31*, 572–582.

Herms, W. B. 1932. Non-bloodsucking Flies as Vectors of Pathogenic Microörganisms. Ann. Entomol. Soc. of Am., *25*, 623–628.

Hertig, M. 1949. *Phlebotomus* and Residual DDT in Greece and Italy. Am. J. Trop. Med., *29*, 773–802.

Hertig, M., and Fairchild, G. B. 1948. The Control of *Phlebotomus* in Peru with DDT. Am. J. Trop. Med., *28*, 207–230.

Huebner, R. J., Jellison, W. L., and Pomerantz, C. 1946. Rickettsialpox—A Newly Recognized Rickettsial Disease. IV. Isolation of a Rickettsia Apparently Identical with the Causative Agent of Rickettsialpox from *Allodermanyssus Sanguineus*, A Rodent Mite. Pub. Health Repts., *61*, 1677–1682.

Janssen, W. A., and Wedberg, S. E. 1952. The Common House Roach *Blatella Germanica* Linn., as a Potential Vector of *Salmonella Typhimurium* and *Salmonella Typhosa*. Am. J. Trop. Med. & Hyg., *1*, 337–343.

Jung, R. C., and Shaffer, M. F. 1952. Survival of Ingested *Salmonella* in the Cockroach *Periplaneta Americana.* Am. J. Trop. Med. & Hyg., *1,* 990–998.

Kemp, H. A., von Haam, E., Fisher, W. M., and Evans, H. L. 1942. Pathology and Immunology in Relapsing Fever, in *Relapsing Fever in the Americas,* pp. 117–124. Lancaster, Pa.

Knight, V., and Ruiz-Sanchez, F. 1952. Treatment of Endemic and Epidemic Typhus with Antibiotics. Ann. New York Acad. Sci., *55,* 992–1003.

Kumm, H. W., and Cerqueira, N. L. 1951. The Role of *Aëdes Leucocelænus* in the Epidemiology of Yellow Fever in Brazil. Bull. Entomol. Res., *42,* 195–199.

Lennette, E. H. 1946. Isolation of St. Louis Encephalitis Virus from a Fatal Human Case in California. Proc. Soc. Exp. Biol. & Med., *61,* 206–210.

Lillie, R. D. 1941. Pathology of Rocky Mountain Spotted Fever. Nat'l Inst. Health Bull. No. 177, Washington. 59 pp.

Murray, E. S., and Snyder, J. C. 1951. Brill's Disease. II. Etiology. Am. J. Hyg., *53,* 22–32.

Napier, L. E. 1946. *The Principles and Practice of Tropical Medicine.* 917 pp. Macmillan Co., New York.

Parker, R. R., and Steinhaus, E. A. 1943. *Salmonella Enteritidis:* Experimental Transmission by the Rocky Mountain Wood Tick, *Dermacentor Andersoni* Stiles. Pub. Health Repts., *58,* 1010–1012.

Philip, C. B. 1953. Nomenclature of the Rickettsiaceæ Pathogenic to Vertebrates. Ann. New York Acad. Sci., *56,* 484–494.

Rose, H. M. 1952. Treatment of Rickettsialpox with Antibiotics. Ann. New York Acad. Sci., *55,* 1019–1026.

Sabin, A., Philip, C. B., and Paul, J. R. 1944. Phlebotomus (Pappataci or Sandfly) Fever. A Disease of Military Importance. Summary of Existing Knowledge and Preliminary Report of Original Investigations. J. Am. Med. Assn., *125,* 603–606; 693–699.

Siler, J. F., Hall, M. W., and Hitchens, A. P. 1926. Dengue. Its History, Epidemiology, Mechanism of Transmission, Etiology, Clinical Manifestations, Immunity, and Prevention. Manila. 476 pp.

Simond, P. L. 1898. La Propagation de la Peste. Ann. Inst. Pasteur, *12,* 625–687.

Smadel, J. E., Woodward, T. E., Amies, C. R., and Goodner, K. 1952. Antibiotics in the Treatment of Bubonic and Pneumonic Plague in Man. Ann. New York Acad. Sci., *55,* 1275–1284.

Smith, M. G., Blattner, R., Heys, R., and Miller, A. 1948. Experiments on the Rôle of the Chicken Mite, *Dermanyssus gallinæ,* and the Mosquito in the Epidemiology of St. Louis Encephalitis. J. Exp. Med., *87,* 119–138.

Soper, F. L. 1952. Yellow Fever in the Caribbean. Bol. San. Panam., *32,* 197–204.

Theiler, M. 1951. In *Yellow Fever,* G. K. Strode, Editor. pp. 43–136. McGraw-Hill, New York.

Warren, A. J. 1951. In *Yellow Fever,* G. K. Strode, Editor, pp. 24–26. McGraw-Hill, New York.

Warren, J. 1946. Epidemic Encephalitis in the Far East. Am. J. Trop. Med., *26,* 417–436.

Watt, J. 1949. Fly Control and the Acute Diarrheal Diseases. Bol. Ofic. San. Panam., *28,* 249–256.

Weyer, F. 1949. Laboratoriumsinfektionen in Beziehung zu Aetiologischen und Epidemiologischen Fragen beim Fleckfieber und Wolhynischen Fieber. Zeitschr. Trop. Med. u. Parasitol., *1,* 2–32.

Whitman, L. 1951. In *Yellow Fever,* G. I. Strode, Editor, pp. 233–298. McGraw-Hill, New York.

SECTION VII

Other Invertebrate and Vertebrate Agents of Human Disease

Chapter 22

Invertebrate Agents of Human Disease Other Than the Protozoa, Helminths and Arthropods

Introduction

SEVERAL phyla of invertebrates other than the Arthropoda are provided with mechanisms which they employ defensively or for stunning their prey. Even some groups of the Protozoa possess nettling organelles. These protozoa are small macroscopic or submacroscopic objects which are harmless to man, but the development of a venenating apparatus in these one-celled animals indicates that such structures of defense are evolutionarily very old.

Metazoan invertebrates which harm man belong to three phyla, the Cœlenterata, Echinodermata and Mollusca.

The Celenterates

Morphology and Bionomics.—The celenterates (Cœlenterata) are metazoa which possess a radial symmetry, an ectoderm and an endoderm. The latter borders on a single cavity, the celenteron, which represents the digestive tract and the as-yet-undifferentiated body cavity (celom). Especially characteristic of the celenterates are tentacles which are typically provided with nettling cells or cnidoblasts, each of which contains a nettling mechanism, the nematocyst. Three classes of celenterates, the Hydrozoa, Scyphozoa and the Anthozoa, are provided with nematocysts; only in the class Ctenophora are they wanting.

The HYDROZOA are represented by the sessile fresh-water hydras and the colonial salt-water hydroid polyps. The latter produces bell-like free-swimming medusæ. The Siphonophora (an order of the Hydrozoa) are large, pelagic, colonial forms which are practically transparent, are frequently brilliantly colored, and are provided with a float and a swim bell. The most notorious members of this group are the Portuguese man-of-war and other species of *Physalia*. In the Hydrozoa the asexual, frequently sessile stage plays a predominant rôle.

In contrast to the Hydrozoa, in the SCYPHOZOA the sexual stage or medusæ are dominant. These are the jelly fishes which measure from 10 to 120 cm. or more in diameter and may weigh several kilograms.

The third class of celenterates which has a nettling mechanism is the ANTHOZOA, including the sea anemones and the corals. These are sessile colonial organisms which often develop to enormous size, as in the Great Barrier Reef off the northeast coast of Australia.

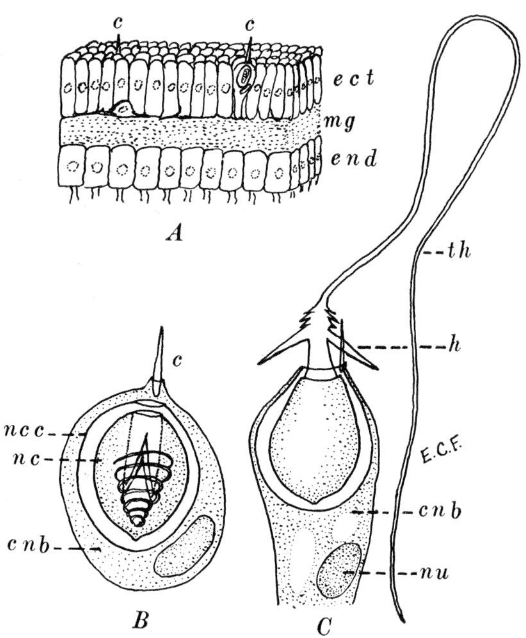

FIG. 212.—The nettling apparatus of the celenterate hydra. *A*, section through the body wall, showing ectodermal layer (*ect*), mesoglea (*mg*) and endodermal layer (*end*), with two cnidoblasts each having a cnidocil (c) extending beyond the surface; *B*, unexploded mechanism, and *C*, exploded mechanism. *c*, cnidocil; *cnb*, cnidoblast; *h*, harpoon; *nc*, nematocyst; *ncc*, nematocyst capsule; *nu*, nucleus; *th*, trigger hair. Greatly magnified. (*A*, adapted from Phisalix, *Animaux Venimeux et Venins*, Masson & Cie., Paris, 1922; *B*, *C*, adapted from Schneider, in Parker and Haswell, *Textbook of Zoölogy*, The Macmillan Co., London.)

The Urticating Mechanism.—The nematocysts of celenterates may be found only in restricted bands or clumps within the enteric cavity. They may be confined to a corona below prehensile tentacles or may be developed on the extremity of the tentacles. In the simple, more generalized type such as hydra they are distributed throughout the entire body surface.

The *cnidoblast* (Fig. 212) is a swollen cell with reduced cytoplasm and a nucleus compressed and pushed to one side to accommodate the ovoidal *nematocyst*. This structure has a double capsule, is filled with urticating fluid, and contains an invaginated, tightly coiled, hollow thread provided with barbs at its attachment end. The outer margin of the cnidoblast is flush with the ectodermal surface, but lateral to the nematocyst it has a spinose projection called the *cnidocil*, the trigger mechanism for eversion of the hollow thread and discharge of the urticating fluid.

Early students of zoölogy attributed the eversion of the nettling thread and discharge of the urticating fluid solely to surface contact with the cnidocil or to mechanical pressure on the cnidoblast. In 1896, Iwanzoff postulated that the "explosion" resulted from osmotic pressure due to swelling of the gelatinous contents of the semi-permeable capsule of the nematocyst. Experimental studies of later workers support the latter view.

Pathogenesis.—The toxic substances in the urticating fluid which have been demonstrated are a thermolabile, non-dialyzable hypnotoxin, a thermo-stable complex containing a neurotoxin, a hemorrhagin and an anaphylactogen (congestin), and an antagonistic urticating fraction (thalassin). These toxins produce different physiologic reactions, depending on the proportion of the different fractions, the mode of administration and individual idiosyncrasy of the victim (Phisalix, 1922).

Pathology and Sympatomatology of Celenterate Urtication.—The giant discomedusa *Cyanea* of the North Atlantic coast of Europe is described by Phisalix (1922) as "a terror to bathers of delicate skin . . . difficult to avoid, since the tentacles are transparent and invisible, trailing obliquely in the water." On contact they cause violent pain. Species of *Rhizostoma* which appear at intervals in shallow water along the Atlantic Coast of France and in the Mediterranean produce urtication and edema at the site of the sting and at times alarming systemic manifestations, including severe dyspnea, a state of depression and extreme muscular fatigue. In Philippine waters, one of the most dangerous forms is *Dactylometra quinquecirrha*, which has its nematocysts on long, ribbon-like oral palps. On contact of the skin with the urticating filaments there is an immediate stinging sensation as if the skin had been suddenly burned, followed in 10 to 60 minutes by marked anxiety and restlessness, pain in the chest, abundant mucoid sputum, coryza and lacrymation. This condition may soon abate, may last for a day or two, or the victim may die in a few hours of cardiac and respiratory failure (Wade, 1928). Species of the genus *Dactylometra* are widely distributed along temperate and tropical coasts of both the Atlantic and Pacific Oceans.

Another medusa in Philippine waters is *Chiropsalmus quadrigatus*, which occurs in shallow waters and is especially dangerous since bathers can not avoid it because of its transparency. Its nematocysts "are so numerous in a small area that the aggregate amount of poison discharged into the tissue must be considerable" (Light, 1914). In 1 case described by Light involving this species, the long tentacles were wrapped several times around the legs of a bather, producing immediate intense pain. At times urtication by this species is fatal, particularly in children.

Physalia, the Portuguese man-of-war, is common in tropical waters. In contact with the skin of swimmers, this large colonial polyp causes severe local burning pain, sudden fright and hysteria, and occasionally severe systemic reactions. In 1 case reported by Frachtman and McCollum (1945) from Hawaii, about 90 minutes after being stung the patient began to experience nausea and muscular weakness, followed by spasms of the abdominal muscles and diaphragm. The contractions increased in magnitude, changed from a clonic to an almost tonic character and extended to the muscles of the shoulders, neck and extremities, suggesting strychnine poisoning. There was evidence of central nervous system depression and for a while respiratory failure seemed imminent. Although some improvement was noted in 24 hours, the condition did not clear up completely until eight days later.

Corals, belonging to the ANTHOZOA, also have nettling cells which produce severe dermatitis. In his classical volume *Corals and Coral Islands,* Dana (1872) described the action of the urticating mechanisms. The tubular nematocysts turn themselves inside out with lightning-like rapidity, with the basal harpoon appearing last. These nettling cells are present in great numbers not only on the tentacles of the anemone-like living portion of the coral but also around the mouth and within the enteric cavity. Levin and Behrman (1941) reported a case of a deep-sea coral diver in the West Indies, who, in 1939, experienced a distinct stinging sensation on the inner surface of the forearm when he picked up a new type of coral, *Madrepora palmata.* Soon a clear fluid was oozing from his venenated skin, after which the affected area became red, edematous and pruritic. Within 24 hours the skin sloughed off, leaving an indolent ulcer which required several months to heal. Roentgen radiation was employed in obtaining relief from the pruritus and in resolving the ulcer.

Control.—Sea bathers in areas where celenterates occur should abstain from bathing and swimming during seasons when the animals are particularly numerous. It is especially important that they should not be alone, since multiple urtication may cause rapid pain, hysteria and fatigue, so that good swimmers may drown unless they are immediately rescued.

The Echinoderms

The echinoderms (Phylum Echinodermata) are triploblastic marine invertebrates which have radial symmetry, an exoskeleton and a relatively extensive body cavity (celom). The sea-urchins (Class Echinoidea), occasionally produce human disease. They are subglobular, have a calcareous shell or testa, are more flattened on the oral than on the aboral side, and possess movable, articulated spines except immediately around the mouth and the anus. Many sucker-like tube feet among the spines serve as a means of attachment to objects and surfaces.

Castellani and Chalmers (1919) and Phisalix (1922) describe the spines of the common sea-urchin of the Red Sea, *Strongylocentrus lividus,* as poisonous. In the Caribbean area the spines of the white sea-urchin (*Triponeustes esculentus*) and of the black sea-urchin (*Centrechinus antillarum*) produce lesions only when they are forced into the skin of the hands or feet of bathers or divers (Earle, 1940), at times breaking off in the wound and producing suppuration. Removal of the spines, cleansing of the wound and antiseptic dressing usually allow clean healing.

The eggs of sea-urchins are usually non-poisonous but the consumption of immature eggs during the spawning season may cause severe gastrointestinal distress by "direct irritation of the nerve-endings in the mucosa of the stomach and intestine" (Alvarez and Hinshaw, 1935).

Molluscs

Molluscs (Phylum Mollusca) comprise a group of the higher invertebrates which are characterized by lack of segmentation and usually by the possession of a horny exoskeleton which is frequently impregnated with calcium carbonate. Molluscs which are injurious to man are limited to a few species of snails (Class Gastropoda). Gastropods usually have a shell consisting of a single piece and a mantle not divided into two lateral folds such as is present in mussels, clams and oysters (Class Lamellibranchia); they lack symmetry because of the one-sided development of the visceral mass, have a head with two tentacles in front of the foot, and are provided with a toothed radula in the buccal chamber. Some species are marine, others live in fresh-water and still others are terrestrial.

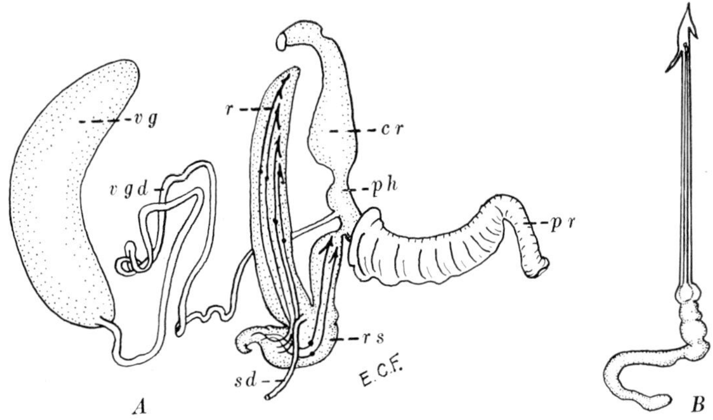

Fig. 213.—The poison apparatus of the cone-shell snail, *Conus striatus*. *A*, entire mechanism; *B*, radular spear. *cr*, crop; *ph*, pharynx; *pr*, proboscis; *r*, radula; *rs*, radular tooth; *sd*, salivary gland duct; *vg*, venom gland; *vgd*, venom gland duct. Enlarged. (Adapted from Clench and Yoshio Kondo.)

Species of the genus *Conus* (Family Conidæ of the subdivision Toxoglossa) have been responsible for serious, and occasionally fatal accidents among persons collecting the beautiful and prized shells of these marine snails. All known cases have been from the Pacific and Indian Oceans.

The venenating apparatus of these snails is associated with the mouth organs and in nature is employed in the procurement of food. It consists of a reniform poison gland opening into the pharynx through a long slender tortuous duct, a radular sheath which also leads into the pharynx, a number of hollow barbed radular teeth on long stems, and a very muscular proboscis capable of eversion beyond the anterior margin of the shell (Fig. 213). When prey or enemies come within striking distance, the proboscis is instantaneously projected and the sharp barbs of the teeth penetrate into the surface of the victim, discharging the poison fluid, probably through rupture of the barbs by slight retraction of the tooth so as to allow discharge of the venom through the hollow stem into the wound (Clench and Yoshio Kondo, 1943). The specific substances in cone-shell venom have apparently not been determined.

Hermitte (1945) has provided a summary of published records of illness and deaths resulting from venenation by species of *Conus, viz., C. aulicus,* 1 case, Moluccas; *C. textile,* 5 cases, 2 deaths, New Hebrides, New Caledonia, Loyalty Islands, New Guinea; *C. marmoreus,* 1 case, New Hebrides; *C. tulipa,* 3 cases, New Caledonia, Paumotu Islands; and *C. geographicus,* 6 cases, 2 deaths, Seychelles, New Britain, Japan, Australia, Fiji. Clench and Yoshio Kondo (*l. c.*) surmise that "the number of unrecorded deaths from this cause may be fairly extensive as the original 'bite' may not have been noticed, particularly if the collector has suffered the usual cuts and scratches that one encounters while reef collecting, especially among live coral."

SUMMARY

1. Invertebrates other than arthropods capable of producing human disease include the celenterates, echinoderms and mollusca.
2. Three classes of celenterates (Phylum Cœlenterata) *viz.,* Hydrozoa, Scyphozoa and Actinozoa, are provided with a nettling mechanism consisting of specialized ectodermal cells (cnidoblasts), each containing a nematocyst capsule or stinging apparatus. Within the capsule there is a coiled hollow thread with a harpoon base, venom fluid, and at the surface of the cnidoblast a spinose process (cnidocil). When stimulated the nettling thread is everted, discharging the poison fluid onto or into the skin of the victim. Most commonly they are on the tentacles, which are a characteristic structure of members of the phylum. The venom substances which have been isolated consist of a hypnotoxin, neurotoxin, hemorrhagin, anaphylactogen and an antagonistic urticating fraction.
3. Human injury and occasional death result from skin contact with marine celenterates, including free-swimming medusæ, colonial jelly-fishes and corals. The most dangerous symptom is respiratory failure but severe multiple urtication may produce shock and hysteria in good swimmers and divers, resulting in drowning unless the victims are promtply rescued.
4. Sea-urchins, a class of the Phylum Echinodermata, may cause injury when their calcareous spines penetrate tender skin and break off. A few species may have poison glands associated with these spines. Consumption of unripe sea-urchin eggs is responsible for severe gastroënteritis, allergy or anaphylaxis.
5. A few species of gastropods, all belonging to the genus *Conus* (cone-shell snail), prevalent in the warm waters of the Pacific and Indian Oceans, are capable of stabbing their victims with special long-stemmed radular teeth provided with a special venom secretion. Several cases and a few deaths have occurred among collectors of these beautiful but dangerous living cone shells.

REFERENCES

Castellani, A., and Chalmers, A. J. 1919. *Manual of Tropical Medicine.* 3rd Ed. p. 205. London.

Clench, W. J., and Yoshio Kondo. 1943. The Poison Cone Shell. Am. J. Trop. Med., *23*, 105–120.

Frachtman, H. J., and McCollum, W. T. 1945. Portuguese Man-of-War Stings. Am. J. Trop. Med., *25*, 499–500.

Hermitte, L. C. D. 1946. Venomous Marine Molluscs of the Genus *Conus.* Trans. R. Soc. Trop. Med. & Hyg., *39*, 485–512.

Iwanzoff. 1896. Ueber den Bau die Wirkungsweise und die Entwickelung der Nesselkapseln der Coelenteraten. Bull. Soc. Nat., Moscou, Ser. 3, *10*, 95–161.

Jordan, E. O. 1931. *Food Poisoning and Food-Borne Infection.* 2nd Ed., 286 pp., Univ. of Chicago Press, Chicago.

Levin, O. L., and Behrman, H. T. 1941. Coral Dermatitis. Arch. Derm. & Syphil., *44*, 600–603.

Light, S. F. 1914. (Cited by Wade, 1928.)

Phisalix, M. 1922. *Animaux Venimeux et Venins.* Chap. II. Cœlentérés, pp. 15–76; Echinodermes, pp. 77–99; Chap. VIII. Mollusques, pp. 465–485. Paris.

Wade, H. W. 1928. Post-mortem Findings in Acute Jelly-fish Poisoning with Sudden Death in Status Lymphaticus. Am. J. Trop. Med., *18*, 233–241.

Chapter 23

Fishes as Causative Agents of Human Disease

Introduction

From earliest historical times there have been numerous reports of poisoning by certain groups of fishes, occasionally with fatal outcome. Phisalix (1922) and Gudger (1930) classify fish poisoning in three categories, *viz.*, (1) ingestion of poisons present in tissues of the fish, (2) introduction into the body of poisons in their blood plasma and (3) through wounds inflicted by their ectodermal spines which have associated glandular poisons.

Poisoning from Ingestion of Fish

Consumption of the flesh of fishes, whether fresh-water or marine species, not infrequently causes acute food poisoning resulting from partial bacterial decomposition. Certain marine fishes, when eaten, may produce a more specific type of poisoning due to toxins elaborated in the tissues of the fish. Often it is difficult or practically impossible from case histories to distinguish between the two varieties.

Fish poisoning due to putrefaction, so-called "ptomaine poisoning," is common in the Tropics. The illness is relatively short following complete emptying of the digestive tract, with residual gastrointestinal soreness for several days.

In contrast, some marine fishes, such as the barracuda (*Sphyræna barracuda* of the West Indies), large mackerels (*Scomberomorus regalis* of the West Indies, *S. sierra* of the West Coast of America), the toad fish or fugu (*Tetrodon maculata* of Japanese waters), salt-water pikes (*Paratractus crysos* of Atlantic waters, *P. caballus* of the Pacific, *Caranx hippos* of Tropical America), and herrings (*Clupea venenosa*, *C. perforata*, *C. fimbricata*, of the South and Southwest Pacific), possess a poison which is present in concentrated form in the ovaries and testes, but is found in lesser amounts in other viscera and the flesh, particularly during the spawning season (Fig. 214). The venom is probably a neurotoxin; it produces *ichthyotoxicosis* (fugism of Japan, ciguatera of Cuba), an ascending motor and sensory paralysis, with slowed respiration, reduced blood pressure, dilatation of the pupils and sluggish reaction to stimulation, together with acute gastrointestinal symptoms. In fatal cases the bloodvessels of the brain and meninges become highly injected, the lungs congested and the alimentary tract violently inflamed, with evidence of gangrene. Lee and Pang (1945) have described two epidemic outbreaks among Hawaiians who consumed fried sea bass (*Variola louti* and *Serranus fascoguttatus*), which were fresh but had "inherent toxin in the living fish." Cohen *et al.* (1946) have reported a similar syndrome in 52 persons who ate fried barracuda-like fish in the Mariana Islands. Treatment is entirely symptomatic and palliative.

Strong (1944, page 1546) refers to prohibitions or warnings concerning poisonous fishes which are issued in regions where these fishes are abundant or during the spawning season.

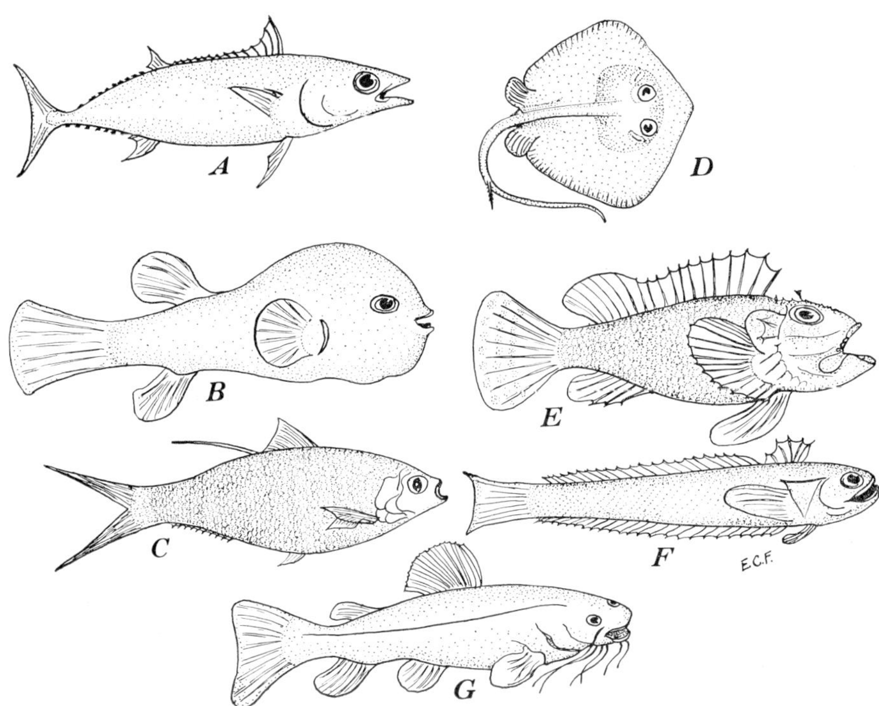

Fig. 214.—Poisonous fishes. *A*, barracuda (*Sphyræna picuda*); *B*, puffer fish (*Tetrolon*); *C*, herring (*Clupea*); *D*, stingray; *E*, *Scorpæna scrofa; F*, *Trachinus draco; G*, catfish. Reduced, not drawn to scale. (Adapted from Phisalix *Animaux Venimeux et Venins*, Masson & Cie., Paris, 1922, Strong *Stitt's Diagnosis, Prevention and Treatment of Tropical Diseases*, The Blakiston Co., Philadelphia, and Halstead and Bunker, Am. J. Trop. Med.)

Poisoning from Substance in Blood Plasma of Fishes

Several species of cyclostomes (*e. g.*, lamprey eels), cartilaginous fishes (*e. g.*, sharks and rays) and a few bony fishes (particularly the true eels) have a hemolytic substance in their blood. This has been demonstrated experimentally but evidence is lacking concerning its effect on man.

Venenation from Poison Spines

Many fishes are provided with spines which produce painful wounds in contact with the surface of the human body. In some species, these spines have poisonous secretions which are introduced at the time the spine produces the puncture. The most important groups of fishes which are provided with this type of venenating mechanism are the stingrays, catfishes, scorpion fishes and weeverfishes.

Stingray Venenation.—Halstead and Bunker (1953) consider stingrays to be "some of the most venomous fishes known to man." These fishes (Fig. 214) have a cartilaginous skeleton and are distinctly flattened and widened. A few species live in fresh water but most of them are found partially or completely buried on the sandy or muddy floor near the shores of salt-water coves or inlets in tropical and subtropical areas. They belong to two family groups, the stingrays proper and the bat-rays. Some species are no larger than the palm of the hand, others are several feet in length and breadth.

The venom apparatus is a part of the tail, usually in the basal or middle third of this appendage. In some species the tail is short, in others it is relatively long and whip-like. The mechanism consists of a serrated spine and its integumentary covering. The spine is rigid, having a pointed tip, margins with sharp, recurved denticles, shallow longitudinal grooves on the dorsal side and two distinct ventrolateral ones. The venom is produced in rows of specialized glandular cells below the epithelial surface, primarily in the ventrolateral grooves.

Stingray venenation usually occurs when a barefooted wader in shallow water accidentally steps on the base of the tail of the fish which is frequently the same color as the bottom sand or mud. Thereupon the spine is projected into the victim's foot, producing an ugly, very painful wound, sometimes extending deeply into the flesh. The puncture tears the sheath of the spine so that the dentate edges lacerate the tissues into which the venom is released, "producing a violent tissue reaction" (Halstead and Bunker, *l. c.*). At first it may feel like the burn due to a high-voltage electric discharge, then intense throbbing, with extension to the entire leg. Evans (1945), reporting on a stingray injury in India, describes early severe local pain and numbness of the member, then labored respiration, spasm of the abdominal muscles, restlessness, tingling of the extremities, nausea and syncope. The local wound frequently becomes infected and may slough. It heals very slowly, even with antiseptic dressings and modern antibiotic treatment.

The catfishes (Family Siluridæ) have poison glands attached to the base of the spines of the pectoral fins. The dragon fishes or weevers (*Trachina draco*, *T. viperus*), which resemble sea trout, have a long, sharp, grooved spine with an associated venom gland on the dorsal margins of their two gill covers and additional poison spines supporting the dorsal fin. The scorpion fish (*Scorpæna scropha*) is a vicious-looking red "devil" with venomous spines in the anterior portion of the dorsal fin. The lion fish (*S. plumieri*), a West Indian species, hides in nooks covered by weeds on bathing beaches, where bathers may step on its sharp dorsal spines.

The wound produced by the spines of these fishes is extremely painful, the site becomes inflamed and purpuric, and frequently sloughs. Systemic symptoms include tachycardia, chills and fever, excitability, convulsions and syncope.

The eels of the genus *Muræna* are notorious for the wounds which they inflict with their teeth. When a victim handling them allows the slippery animal to bite a finger, the sharp teeth penetrate deeply, at times to the bone.

SUMMARY

1. Fishes produce human disease due to (1) their consumption and (2) introduction of their poisonous spines into the skin.
2. Fish-food poisoning is of two kinds, the one an acute "ptomaine" type of gastro-intestinal irritation resulting from consumption of bacterial decomposition of the flesh, the other, severe digestive disturbances accompanied by motor and sensory paralysis resulting from toxins in the sex glands, other viscera and flesh, particularly at the breeding season.
3. Venenation from poison spines of fishes is produced when these spines pierce the skin, with the introduction of venom elaborated at the base of the spines. The most common offenders are the stingrays, the catfishes, the dragon fishes or weevers, and the vicious scorpion fishes with poison spines in the anterior portion of the dorsal fin. Eels of the genus *Muræna* bite the fingers of unwary victims, introducing a slimy secretion deeply into the tissues.
4. The wounds produced by poison spines of fishes are extremely painful, at times lacerating, become inflamed, frequently slough and heal slowly. Systemic reaction to the venom may include both motor and sensory disturbances.

REFERENCES

Cohen, S. C., Emert, J. T., and Goss, C. C. 1946. Poisoning by Barracuda-like Fish in the Marianas. U. S. Naval Med. Bull., *46*, 311.

Evans, H. M. 1945. Toxic Properties of Sting-Ray's Sting. Brit. Med. J., *ii*, 165.

Gudger, E. W. 1930. Poisonous Fishes and Fish Poisoning, with Special Reference to Ciguatera in the West Indies. Am. J. Trop. Med., *10*, 43–55.

Halsted, B. W., and Bunker, N. C. 1953. Stingray Attacks and Their Treatment. Am. J. Trop. Med. & Hyg., *2*, 115–128.

Lee, R. L. C., and Pang, H. Q. 1945. Ichthyotoxism-Fish Poisoning. Am. J. Trop. Med., *25*, 281–285.

Phisalix, M. 1922. *Animaux Venimeux et Venins.* Paris. Chap. IX, Poissons Toxicophores, pp. 487–628.

Strong, R. P. 1944. *Stitt's Diagnosis, Prevention and Treatment of Tropical Diseases.* 7th ed., pp. 1544–1547. The Blakiston Co., New York.

Chapter 24

Reptiles as Causative Agents of Human Disease

Introduction

REPTILES (Class Reptilia) are vertebrate animals which possess an amnion and allantois in embryonic life. They lack respiratory gills and are therefore necessarily adapted to terrestrial life. Their skin is strongly cornified and is provided with epidermal scales. They have a distinct caudal appendage behind the cloacal opening. Their quadrate bone serves as a suspensor for a distensible lower jaw.

In addition to many prehistoric species the reptiles include turtles, crocodiles, alligators, lizards and snakes. The last two groups are important in the causation of human disease.

LIZARDS (LACERTILIA)

Most lizards possess two pairs of limbs although these are lacking in a few forms. The only species harmful to man are the gila monsters (*Heloderma suspectum* and *H. horridum*), both of which are found exclusively in the Western Hemisphere. *H. suspectum,* the true gila monster, has a geographic range throughout the semi-desert areas of the southwestern United States west of the Rocky Mountains and the less elevated parts of Sonora State, Mexico. *H. horridum* has a more southerly distribution, from central Mexico through Guatemala and Honduras. The length of the former species varies from 16 to 24 inches and of the latter species, 36 to 54 inches. Their relatively flat head resembles a truncated triangle, their neck is short and thick, their body is considerably larger and longer, and their tail is thick, shorter than the body and tapers to a conical tip. The belly is covered with scales; elsewhere the skin is patterned with bead-like excrescences, with an alternation of black or purplish-black and yellow, orange or salmon-pink coloration in *H. suspectum,* black or brownish-black with splotches of bright yellow in *H. horridum.* The legs of the gila monster are spread far apart like those of an alligator, so that it crawls close to the ground, usually in a slow, lazy manner, but on approach of a large moving object it usually scurries out of danger.

The Venom Apparatus and Gila Monster Venenation.—The venom is produced in large submaxillary glands which give a swollen appearance to the proximal portion of the lower jaws. It is discharged from each gland through 4 small ducts which open at the base of 4 grooved, backward-curved teeth on each mandible. These teeth are matched by ungrooved teeth in the apposed maxillary bone (Arington, 1930). When apparent danger nears the monster is first impassive but with attentive, beady eyes. It may attempt to run away in sideways movements but if unsuccessful it will hiss, open its jaws wide, pivot itself on its hind legs and strike the object repeatedly. Once in contact it clamps the jaws shut, the sharp teeth pierce the skin and venom is expelled into the puncture sites. The essential venom is a neurotoxin resembling snake venom (Loeb, 1913) but is usually much less potent.

Pathogenesis and Symptomatology.—The wound made by a gila monster is invariably on a hand or foot. It is ugly and lacerating, producing a purpuric swelling. The local pain is sharp, poignant and radiates to the entire extremity, which develops a tingling sensation together with a general numbness, but these symptoms do not involve the other extremities, trunk or head. Profuse perspiration, dizziness and partial narcosis frequently develop, but no deaths have occurred due solely to gila monster venenation (Storer, 1931; Stahnke, 1949).

Diagnosis and Treatment.—The nature of the wound is relatively pathognomonic. First-aid measures consist of ligature, the application of ice-pack or ethyl chloride spray at the site, and cleansing and antiseptic dressing of the wound to prevent pyogenic infection. Palliative drugs may be used to relieve pain and caffein to prevent narcosis. There is no particular need for a specific antivenin.

Control.—This consists in care not to provoke the gila monster to bite.

SNAKES (SERPENTES)

Morphology and Bionomics.—Snakes are elongated, cylindroidal, limbless reptiles which have a horny covering of epidermal scales, a very flexible mouth, a forked tongue which is frequently projected in an excited manner through the closed mouth, an external auditory chamber, eyes lacking lids, a transvere cloacal opening and a paired penis in the male. Due to the mobility of the quadrate bones and their rather loose attachment to the maxillæ, as well as the elastic ligament joining the 2 mandibles anteriorly, the mouth can be opened very wide, at times as much as 180°.

There are approximately 2,400 species of snakes. Only 4 families, the Boidæ, Colubridæ, Elapidæ and the Viperidæ, contain species harmful to man.

The Boidæ are relatively huge forms, some of which reach a length of 30 feet. They have powerful muscles which they use when they coil around their prey to crush or strangle it. Species of the genera *Python* and *Eryx* occur in tropical Asia and Africa; the boas (*Boa*), anacondas (*Eunectes*) and *Ungalia maculata* are found in tropical South America, particularly in the Amazon valley. Authentic records of human deaths due to crushing by these several species are very rare. In the genus *Eryx*, several species of which have been described in an area from Greece and Egypt through Arabia and Afghanistan to India, Phisalix (1922, page 395) describes a temporal (rather than parotid) venom gland. One species in India, *E. conicus*, is reportedly very aggressive, attacking man and beast in the fashion of a python but having additionally a venomous bite (Phisalix, *l. c.*, page 289).

Venomous Snakes

All snakes elaborate venom but the majority of species have only unspecialized secretions which are discharged around the palatine teeth just as occurs in the eel, *Muræna* (Chapter 23, page 561). Those which are harmful to man are provided with modified teeth or fangs, which are developed on the maxillæ and not on the mandibles as they are in the gila monsters (see above). The dangerous species belong to three families, the Colubridæ, Elapidæ and the Viperidæ.

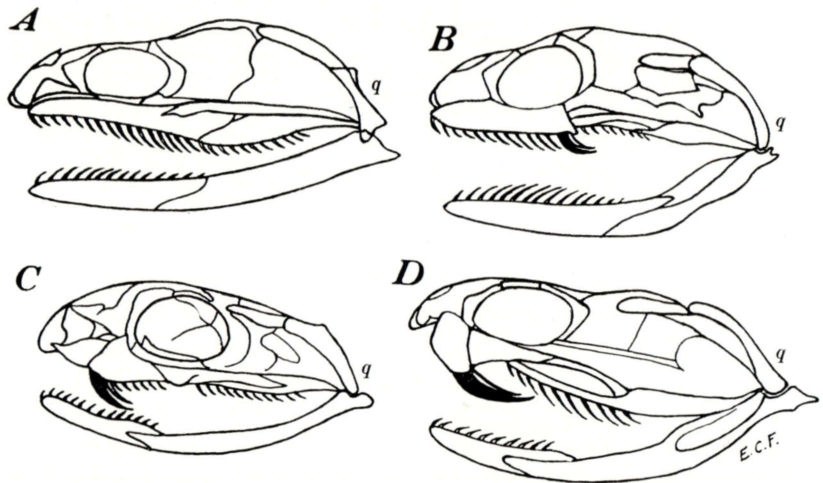

Fig. 215.—Lateral view of the skull bones of different types of snakes. *A*, *aglyphous* (without specialized fang), harmless to man; *B*, *opisthoglyphous* (with posterior fang on maxilla), usually harmless to man; *C*, *proteroglyphous* (with anterior fang), very dangerous to man; *D*, *solenoglyphous* (single fanged), very dangerous to man. Poison fang shown in solid black, with replacement fang directly behind. *q*, quadrate bone. (Adapted from Faust, *Oxford Loose-Leaf Medicine.*)

The Colubridæ are provided with broad, plate-like ventral scales visible from lateral view, symmetrically patterned large scales on top of the head and numerous maxillary teeth. On the basis of the types of maxillary teeth they are divided into two sections, *viz.:*

I. Aglypha (lacking true fangs).—There are more than 700 species, mostly terrestrial but some live in fresh or marine waters. All of the maxillary teeth are unspecialized for injecting salivary venoms, hence these species are harmless to man and other large animals (Fig. 215 *A*.) This group includes the black, milk and garter snakes of North America and the ring snakes of Europe, but not the very poisonous tiger snake, *Notechis scutatus*, of Australia.

II. Opisthoglypha (back-fanged).—These species possess 1 curved, specialized fang developed as the posteriormost of numerous teeth on each of the long maxillæ. There are about 300 species, most of which are relatively harmless to man because the fang is too far back to engage and penetrate into the skin. The boomslang ("tree snake") and *Tarbophis semiannulatus* of Central, East and South Africa are notable exceptions (Fig. 215 *B*).

THE ELAPIDÆ.—These are venomous species which have one curved specialized front fang developed as the anteriormost of several teeth on a shortened maxilla (PROTEROGLYPHA). The fang has 2 ventral (anterior) openings, one at its base where the venom is introduced, and one near the

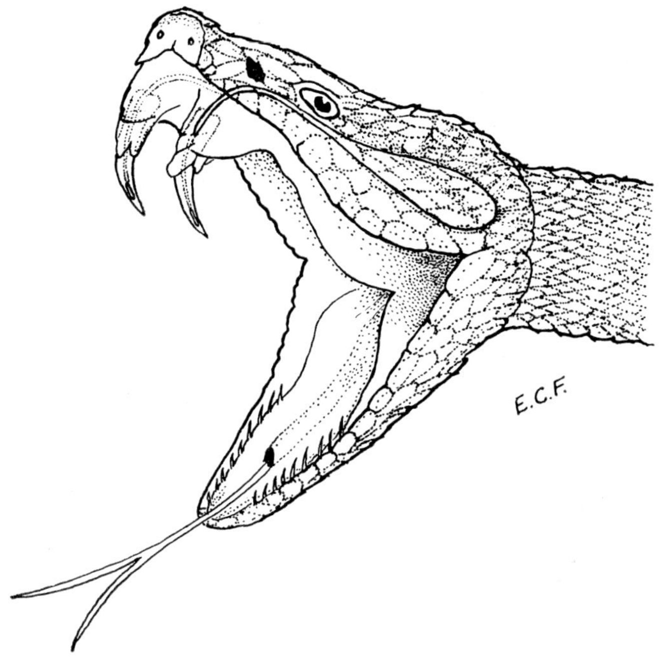

FIG. 216.—Head of a North American rattlesnake (solenoglyphous type), poised to strike. Note that the fangs are erect, with vaginal membrane somewhat retracted. Poison gland and gland duct leading into fang canal, with subterminal opening, likewise sensory pit between nostril and eye, are demonstrated. (Adapted from Faust, *Oxford Loose-Leaf Medicine.*)

sharp tip where it is discharged (Dunn, 1951). (Fig. 215 *C*.) All elapids are very dangerous to man. There are two subfamilies, the Elapinæ, with 250 species, which have a cylindrical tail and live on the land, and the Hydrophinæ, with 50 species, which have a laterally compressed, paddle-like tail and live in the sea.

THE VIPERIDÆ (vipers).—They are characterized by having a very short maxilla containing only a single, large, tubular, canalized fang and lack unspecialized maxillary teeth. Because of this unique feature they are referred to as SOLENOGLYPHA (single-toothed). (Fig. 215 *D*.) There are about 170 species of vipers, grouped in the sub-families Viperinæ (true vipers) and the Crotalinæ (pit vipers). The former species lack, and the latter species possess a conspicuous sensory pit between the nostril and the eye. (Fig. 216.)

The snakes which will be specially considered are the proteroglyphs and the solenoglyphs.

The Venom Apparatus and Venenation.—The 2 venom glands are modified parotid glands, each provided with a duct which passes into the base of the specialized fang (Fig. 216). The gland consists of a large number of terminal alveoli in which the venom is elaborated, with small ducts which coalesce and empty into a central cavity. A tough, semi-elastic fibrous capsule surrounds each gland. In many of the dangerous colubrids and in all but one of the vipers the enlarged venom gland produces a bulging at the postero-lateral angle of the jaw.

The mechanism of venenation is a *strike* or *stab*, not a "bite." It is somewhat different in the cobra (a proteroglyph) and the rattler (a solenoglyph). In the cobra, the back-curved fang protrudes from an ankylosed maxilla and the mandible aids the tooth in piercing the skin. In the rattlesnake, the fang is usually longer and is firmly embedded in a very mobile maxilla. When at rest it lies back against the roof of the mouth; when the mechanism becomes activated, the maxilla with its fang revolves forward, the point of the fang is freed of its membrane, becomes erect and is ready to strike. The greater mobility of the quadrate bone in solenoglyphs enables them to open their mouth at a greater angle so that the strike is effected without assistance from the mandible. In both groups, preparatory to stabbing the snake raises its neck in an S- or inverted ?-loop, above the posterior portion of its body which is coiled on the ground. Then the mouth is opened as widely as possible, the fangs are erected and strike into the victim, with release of the venom. In proteroglyphs, the venom canal within the fang is not closed at its base as it is in the solenoglyphs. In both groups the venom is discharged through a subterminal opening on the anterior face of the fang.

The Venom.—There are two types of venom, neurotoxin and hemotoxin. Proteroglyphs are provided primarily with the former and solenoglyphs primarily with the latter but there are exceptions. Neurotoxins are extremely rapid in their paralytic action on respiration and at times the motor centers controlling the circulation, the eye, the cervical region and locomotion. Hemotoxins are essentially endotheliolytic, producing destruction of the walls of the smaller bloodvessels, causing extensive hemorrhage both at the site of introduction of the venom and in the viscera. At times they also contain hemolysin, coagulants or anticoagulants.

The amount of the venom and its potency vary in the different species; these also depend on whether the particular snake has an accumulation of venom or has recently expended most of its supply.

The most venomous snakes are not necessarily the most prevalent species. In Panamá (Jutzy *et al.*, 1953) confirm the earlier report of Clark (1942) that the fer-de-lance (*Bothrops atrox*) is the most common cause of snake venenation and that the reportedly much more dangerous bushmaster (*Lachesis muta*) is relatively rare. Nor are the most deadly species necessarily the largest ones. True coral snakes are as dangerous as the Indian cobras, but are only one-tenth as lethal as the relatively small death adder of Australia. Another important factor in snake venenation is the aggressiveness or non-aggressiveness of the species.

The most harmful species in different geographical regions, arranged with reference to their neurotoxic or hemotoxic properties, venenating potencies, their prevalence and aggressiveness are summarized in Table 12.

Table 12. Important Species of Snakes Harmful to Man

(N, neurotoxic, H, hemotoxic, venenating potencies compared with Indian cobra as 1; C, common; U, uncommon; A, aggressive; NA, non-aggressive)

NEARCTIC (North America)	Coral Snake (*Micrurus fulvius*) southeastern U. S.	4 ft. long	N	1	U	NA
	Copperhead (*Agkistrodon mokasen*) eastern and southeastern U. S.	4 " "	H	<1	C	A
	Water moccasin (*A. piscivorus*) southeastern U. S.	6 " "	H	<1	C	A
	Massasauga (*Sistrurus catenatus*) northern and southwestern U. S.	$3\frac{1}{2}$ " "	H	<1	C	NA
	Timber rattler (*Crotalus horridus*) eastern half of U. S.	5 " "	H	<1	C	NA
	Eastern diamond-back (*C. adamanteus*) southeastern U. S.	7–$8\frac{1}{2}$ " "	H	1	C	A
	Western diamond-back (*C. cinereus*) southwestern U. S.	7 " "	H	1	C	A
NEOTROPICAL (Latin America)	Coral Snake (*Micrurus nigrocinctus*) Mexico to Argentina	4 " "	N	1	U	NA
	Tropical rattler (*Crotalus terrificus*) Mexico to Argentina	6 " "	N + H	1	C	NA
	Fer-de-lance (*Bothrops atrox*) Mexico to Brazil; W. Indies	8 " "	H	3–10	C	NA
	Jararaca (*B. jararaca*) Brazil	5 " "	H	<1	C	A
	Bushmaster (*Lachesis muta*) Costa Rica to Brazil; Trinidad	10–14 " "	H	<1	U	A
PALEARCTIC (Europe, Northern Asia, Mediterranean coast of Africa	Many species of vipers (*Vipera*, spp.)	2–5 " "	H	<1	C–U	NA
	Sand viper (*Vipera ammodytes*) Austria and Balkans	2 " "	H	1	C	A
ORIENTAL (southern Asia)	Indian or spectacled cobra (*Naja naja*) India to south China and southwestern Pacific	7 " "	N	1	C	NA
	King cobra or hamadryad (*Ophiophagus hannah*) India to Southwestern Pacific	18 " "	N	1	U	A
	Kraits (*Bungarus candidus, B. fasciatus*) India, Ceylon, Malaya	6 " "	N	15	C	NA
	Russell's viper or daboia (*Viper russelli*) India to Formosa	$5\frac{1}{2}$ " "	H	$\frac{1}{5}$	C	NA
	Saw-toothed viper or phoosa (*Echinatus carinatus*) northwestern India, Ceylon	$2\frac{1}{2}$ " "	H	5	C	A
	Malay pit viper (*Agkistrodon rhodostoma*) Malaya, Indonesia	3 " "	H	<1	?	A
	Oriental bamboo vipers (*Trimeresurus gramineus, T. flavoviridis* et al.) southwest Pacific, China Sea	5 " "	H	<1	C	A

Table 12. Important Species of Snakes Harmful to Man—(Continued)

ETHIOPIAN (Africa)	Cobras (*Naja haje* et al.)	7 " "	N	1	C	NA
	Mambas (*Dendroaspis angusticeps*) Central and South Africa	13 " "	N	1	C	A
	Saw-toothed viper (*Echis carinatus*) North and East Africa	2½ " "	H	5	C	A
	Puff adder (*Bitis lachesis*) Sudan to South Africa	5 " "	H	1	C	NA
	Gaboon viper (*B. gabonica*) Central Africa	6 " "	H + N	1	C	NA
AUSTRALIAN (Australia and adjacent islands)	Death adder (*Acanthophis antarcticus*) Indonesia to North Australia	2 10/12 " "	N	10	C	A
	Tiger snake (*Notechis scutatus*) Australia	5 " "	N	25	C	A
	Giant brown snake (*Oxyuranus scutellatus*) southern New Guinea, North Australia	11 " "	N	1	C	A
	Brown snake (*Demansia textilis*) New Guinea, Australia	6 " "	N	10	C	NA
	Black snake (*Pseudechis porphyriacus*) Australia	6 " "	N	⅓	C	NA
	Copperhead (*Denisonia superba*) southeastern Australia	4½ " "	N	2½	C	NA
TROPICAL OCEANS (Coasts of Africa, Asia, Southwest and South Pacific Islands, Australia, New Zealand, Pacific)	Sea snakes	2–5 " "	N	1	U	NA
	Pelamis platurus Pacific coast of America, Lower California to Ecuador	2½ " "	N	1	U	NA

Epidemiology

Most snake poisoning is accidental and is due to carelessness on the part of adults or children, at work or at play, who disturb the snake by stepping on or near it in the brush or jungle or by reaching an unprotected hand into grass or under rocks in which the snake is resting or looking for food. Some species frequent swampy bottom land, others live in highland timber and still others are found only in desert areas. In warm climates of both hemispheres, there are arboreal forms with prehensile tails; these species may drop on persons passing through jungle trails and produce serious intoxication. In tropical Asia and Africa, a few of the most venomous species prefer human habitations but do not usually attack unless they are frightened. Spitting cobras of East Africa spray their venom for several feet. Many snakes are active only during certain seasons of the year while others are constantly active in search of food.

Snake mortality is highest in Burma, *viz.*, more than 30 per 100,000 population annually. There are no venomous land snakes in Polynesia, on Madagascar, New Zealand, the Azores, Canary Islands, Cape Verde Islands, Puerto Rico, Haiti, Cuba, Jamaica, Ireland, Iceland, the Orkneys or Shetland Islands (Swaroop and Grab, 1954).

Pathogenesis and Symptomatology of Snake Venenation

Pathogenesis.—The type and degree of human injury produced by venomous snakes depends on the character, potency and quantity of the venom, the site and type of tissues venenated, and the age of the victim. The small death adder of North Australia is 10-fold as venomous and the equally small saw-toothed viper of Mediterranean countries 5 times as venomous as the much larger Indian cobra, and young rattlers have caused the death of small children.

In the cobras, kraits, asps, mambas, corals and the sea snakes, as well as the tropical rattler of Latin America, the principal poisonous substance in the venom is a neurotoxin. Fairley (1929) states that this has "a special affinity for the cells of the respiratory centre and the bulb, though it also involves nervous tissues elsewhere in the cord and brain." This investigator described the clinical picture as a progressive bulbar paralysis, with early respiratory embarrassment, palatal paralysis causing discharge of vomitus through the nares, and loss of laryngeal sensory reflex so that vomitus is inhaled into the respiratory tract. Death is due to respiratory failure. The venom of some elapine species also contains thrombase, hemolysin and a fibrolysin (Calmette, 1908), with evidence of hemorrhage at the site of the strike and internally, as well as hemoglobinemia, hemoglobinuria and anticoagulability of the blood. However, the local injury is typically unimportant compared with the rapidly developing neurotoxic effect. In contrast, in viperine poisoning the local wound is of primary or at least early importance. Later endotheliolysis of the visceral bloodvessels contributes largely to fatal tissue damage, *e. g.*, multiple internal hemorrhages. (Porges, 1953.)

Symptomatology.—In *elapine poisoning*, there is first an intense burning sensation at the site where the venom is introduced, with edema and congestion. Soon prostration and semiconsciousness, incontinence, profuse salivation, nausea, vomiting and cold perspiration develop. Speech and swallowing are seriously impaired. Respiration is at first rapid, with dyspnea and anoxia, then slow and feeble. Ocular symptoms include ptosis, diplopia, pupillary dilatation and lack of response to bright light. When lethal amounts of venom have been introduced, particularly if the neurotoxin has entered a cutaneous bloodvessel, coma and convulsions ensue rapidly and the patient dies of asphyxiation. If smaller doses of venom have reached the respiratory regulatory centers, death may be postponed or the condition may rapidly improve and the patient recover.

In *viperine poisoning* there is characteristically an immediate, sharp, burning pain at the site of the stab, with a rapidly developing bluish or purplish swelling. There is frequently local hemorrhage. As the venom is carried centralwards in the lymphatics, the patient develops nausea and weakness, tingling and numbness of the injured member, then experiences a feeling of suffocation. Multiple hemorrhages develop wherever the venom reaches peripheral or visceral bloodvessels; these lesions are particularly evident in the conjunctivæ and lips. Then there are extreme thirst, prostration, rapid, weak pulse, and dyspnea, but no evidence of central nervous system damage. With lethal amounts of the venom the patient dies of circulatory collapse; with smaller amounts he usually recovers, although the original wound may remain unhealed for a long time.

Diagnosis

The local wound will suggest some type of venenation. A pair of puncture points indicates that a scorpion (Chapter 19, page 455) is not involved, and the punctures are farther apart than in spider venenation (Chapter 19, page 457). However, the local edema may mask the puncture sites or the snake's fangs may be so small as to leave practically no evidence. In elapine poisoning, the rapid development of neurotoxic symptoms and in viperine poisoning the local swelling with ecchymosis are helpful in providing a clinical diagnosis, but wherever possible it is desirable to catch and identify the snake.

Treatment

Treatment of snake poisoning consists of local and supportive management and administration of specific antivenin. *Local treatment* helps to remove, destroy or immobilize the venom so as to prevent lethal doses from entering the general circulation. It is usually far more effective in viperine than in elapine poisoning. The first procedure is to tie a tight ligature around the member above the puncture but at 10- to 15-minute intervals the ligature must be temporarily loosened to prevent gangrene. The next orthodox steps have been to open the wound by making a cruciform incision, allowing free bleeding, and to suck out the venom or apply a mammary-gland pump to the site. Stahnke (1953) and Allen (1953) have recommended that refrigeration is probably the most effective local measure. Allen (*l. c.*) comments that "ice probably minimizes tissue damage and is certainly the best local anesthetic." As soon as possible thereafter Hoback and Green (1953) advise administration of cortisone "due to its remarkable ability to inhibit local tissue reactivity to foreign protein," and later following sensitivity reaction to antivenin.

Supportive treatment includes absolute quiet for the victim who should be placed in a horizontal position, warmly covered and have the benefit of sedatives to lessen pain, caffein to prevent collapse and infusion of large amounts of blood plasma to counteract shock. Alcohol should not be administered, since it dilates the bloodvessels and hastens diffusion of the venom.

Specific Treatment.—In every case it is desirable to administer *antivenin* at the earliest possible moment. This is particularly urgent in elapine poisoning since localization of the venom at the site of inoculation is rarely successful. In most countries a monovalent, bivalent or polyvalent antivenin is available. In the Unites States a polyvalent crotalic antivenin is stocked in most pharmacies. This is effective against all snake venoms in the country except that of coral snakes, which rarely attack human beings. This biological product is put up in 10 cc. syringes. Within the first hour or two, 2 to 3 cc. should be introduced subcutaneously around the wound to protect the tissues. In another hour or two and at 2- to 3-hour intervals thereafter larger amounts should be introduced subcutaneously at successively more proximal sites on the injured extremity. If collapse is imminent or has occurred the injection should be intravenous. A total of 30 to 50 cc. may be needed. Children require at least as large doses as adults.

Control

When walking in snake-infested regions it is desirable to wear substantial, knee-length leather boots, with heavy khaki pants securely tucked into the top. This provides protection against most venomous snakes, which do not strike above knee height. Venenation by snakes like the king cobra, arboreal species and the African spitting cobras which spray their venom will not be prevented by these precautions. When passing through jungle paths it is advisable to wear a substantial helmet to protect the head and neck. In spitting-cobra territory eye glasses may prevent the sprayed venom from getting into the eyes. Venomous snakes which are encountered in human habitations usually reside there to feed on domestic rodents. Anti-rat campaigns may cause these snakes to look elsewhere for their food. Children and adults should not reach with unprotected hands under brush or into piles of stones. Out-of-door sleeping quarters should be located some distance from the potential hiding places of harmful snakes.

SUMMARY

1. Reptiles have a strongly cornified epithelium provided with scales, a caudal appendage behind the cloacal opening and a distensible lower jaw hinged on the quadrate bone.
2. Two species of poisonous lizards, the gila monsters (*Heloderma suspectum* and *H. horridum*), are found in semi-desert areas in southwestern United States and adjacent Mexico. They have submaxillary poison glands which discharge venom at the base of 4 grooved teeth on each side of the mandible. The gila monster strikes and then clamps its jaw shut on the victim, introducing a mildly potent neurotoxic venom, causing local purpuric swelling and a tingling sensation of the injured member but essentially no systemic intoxication. Application of a ligature proximal to the wound, local ice packs and antiseptic dressings are indicated.
3. Snakes are limbless reptiles which have a covering of scales, a very flexible mouth, a forked tongue and a paired penis in the male. Only certain groups develop fangs, specialized maxillary teeth which are canalized, have an opening at their base for reception of venom from modified parotid glands and near their pointed tip an opening through which venom is discharged into the skin of a victim. In one group they are situated at the back of the maxilla, in another they are the anterior-most maxillary teeth and in a third group they are the only teeth developed on an extremely shortened maxilla. Very few posterior-fanged snakes are able to inflict wounds in man. On the other hand, all anterior-fanged species are dangerous.
4. Cobras, kraits, mambas, asps, true coral snakes and sea snakes elaborate neurotoxins which produce swelling and pain at the site of the wound but much more serious central nervous system damage. The true vipers of the Eastern Hemisphere, the copperhead of the United States, water moccasin, rattlesnakes, fer-de-lance, bushmaster, and related species having a sensory pit between the nostril and the eye, inject venom with endotheliolytic and hemolytic properties.

5. The most venomous snakes are not necessarily the largest, nor are they always the most prevalent in an area. The amount, quality and potency of the venom injected into the victim, the depth of penetration of the fangs and the age or peculiar intolerance of the victim determine the seriousness of the "bite."
6. Exposure frequently occurs when careless persons step on or near snakes hiding in dense grass or dead branches on the ground, or reach the unprotected hand under stones or into dense vegetation. Some arboreal snakes drop on the victim, attacking the head or neck. A few East African cobras spray venom a considerable distance. Some venomous snakes frequent human habitations in search for food.
7. Neurotoxic venom affects the respiratory center, with progressive bulbar paralysis, respiratory embarrassment and loss of muscular coördination of the throat. In contrast, the venom of vipers produces a more serious local lesion, multiple visceral hemorrhages, prostration, and may result in death from circulatory collapse.
8. The two distinct trains of symptoms provide relatively satisfactory evidence of neurotoxic or hemotoxic type of venenation.
9. Management of snake poisoning consists in local, palliative and specific antivenin treatment.
10. Control consists in wearing knee-length boots with khaki pants tucked well into the boots and other precautionary measures when persons are walking or camping in snake-infested regions.

REFERENCES

Allen, F. M. 1953. Tourniquet for Snake Bite. J. Am. Med. Assn., *151*, 1156.

Arington, O. N. 1930. Notes on Two Poisonous Lizards with Special Reference to *Heloderma suspectum*. Bull. Antivenin Inst. Am., *4*, 29.

Calmette, A. 1908. *Venoms, Venomous Animals and Antivenomous Therapeutics*. p. 1908, Wm. Wood & Co., New York.

Dunn, E. R. 1951. Venomous Reptiles of the Tropics, in Shattuck's *Disease of the Tropics*. pp. 741–754. Appleton-Century-Crofts, New York.

Fairley, N. H. 1929. The Present Position of Snake Bite and the Snake Bitten in Australia. Med. J. Australia, *i*, 296.

Hutchinson, R. H. 1929. On the Incidence of Snake-bite Poisoning in the United States and the Results of the Newer Methods of Treatment. Bull. Antivenin Inst. Am., *3*, 43.

———1930. Further Notes on the Incidence of Snake-bite Poisoning in the United States. Bull. Antivenin Inst. Am., *4*, 40.

Jutzy, D. A., Biber, S. H., Elton, N. W., and Lowry, E. C. 1953. A Clinical and Pathological Analysis of Snake Bite on the Panama Canal Zone. Am. J. Trop. Med. & Hyg., *2*, 129–141.

Loeb, L., *et al.* 1913. The Venom of *Heloderma*. Carnegie Inst. Washington, Publ. No. 177.

Phisalix, M. 1922. *Animaux Venimeux et Venins*. Pt. II, Chapter III, Serpentes, pp. 221–818. Paris.

Porges, N. 1953. Snake Venoms, Their Biochemistry and Mode of Action. Science, *117*, 47–51.

Stahnke, H. L. 1949. *Scorpions*. Arizona State College, Tempe.

———1953. The L-C Treatment of Venomous Bites or Stings. Am. J. Trop. Med. & Hyg., *2*, 142–143.

Swaroop, S., and Grab, B. 1954. Snakebite Mortality in the World. Bull. World Health Org. (Geneva), *10*, 35.

Chapter 25

Certain Mammals Harmful to Man

A LARGE number of mammals are at times dangerous to man. The bite of a dog, the clawing of a cat, the attack by an enraged bull, a wild boar, a rhinoceros or an elephant—all these may produce severe injury and at times death. Somewhat more unique are the ways in which two other types of mammals, one the duck-billed platypus and the other the vampire bat, produce harm to man and other animals.

The Duck-billed Platypus (Ornithorhynchus.)—This mammal, *Ornithorhynchus anatinus*, is a member of one of the two extant genera of monotremes, a group of primitive forms which have short legs, flat, webbed feet each terminating in 5 digits armed with long powerful claws, bill-like jaws lacking teeth, body fur resembling that of a beaver, and a stout flat tail. They are oviparous but are provided with a brood pouch for nursing their young. This species is found only in Australia and Tasmania. It lives in swamps, feeds on living earthworms, insect larvas, molluscs and other soft animals, and has an efficient venom apparatus.

Venom Apparatus and Venom.—This is composed of a relatively large, symmetrical, reniform gland situated in the femoral region on each side of the body, each with a long capillary duct leading to a curved canalized spine, which is fixed at its base to ligamentous tissue on the dorsal face of the tarsus of the posteriormost digit of the hind leg (Phisalix, 1922). The spine is directed upwards and backwards. This venenating mechanism is for defensive purposes, particularly against enemies during the breeding and nursing season when the female and her young are specially vulnerable. The secretion is potent only during this period. The venom is essentially hemotoxic in its action.

The Australian references cited by Phisalix (1923, pages 827–828) are dated from 1818 to 1906. Kellaway (1935) states that the venom acts as a vasodilator and is peripheral, not central in its effect.

The Vampire Bat.—This small, winged mammal, *Desmodus rotundatus*, feeds on blood of cattle, horses and man, usually at night. It is rather widely distributed from tropical southern Mexico through Central America to northern South America and the adjacent islands of the West Indies. Its teeth are extremely sharp and may penetrate a finger or toe painlessly. It sucks blood far in excess of its needs, so that quantities may be evacuated from its intestine in an essentially undigested state (Shattuck, 1951). Prolonged feeding of several bats on domestic animals may produce a secondary anemia.

D. rotundatus has been found to be a mechanical transmitter of *Trypanosoma hippicum*, the agent of mal de caderas. It is reportedly able to transmit rabies in a similar manner (Pawan, 1948).

Human protection from the vampire bat is afforded by good screening and bednets.

SUMMARY

While many mammals produce human injury by biting, goring and other traumatic methods, the duck-billed platypus, a primitive, almost extinct form of Australia and Tasmania, injects a hemotoxic venom through a claw on its hind feet. Vampire bats suck blood and may produce a secondary anemia.

REFERENCES

PAWAN, J. L. 1948. Fruit Eating Bats and Paralytic Rabies in Trinidad. Ann. Trop. Med. and Parasitol., *42*, 173–177.

PHISALIX, M. 1922. *Animaux Venimeux et Venins.* Pt. II, Chapter IV, Mammifère Venimeux, pp. 819–828.

SHATTUCK, G. C. 1951. *Diseases of the Tropics.* p. 759. Appleton-Century-Crofts, New York.

SECTION VIII

Technical Aids

Chapter 26

Parasitologic Diagnosis

Introduction

In order that the clinical and public health implications of parasites and vectors may be properly evaluated, it is necessary that the organisms involved be accurately diagnosed. Throughout the preceding chapters of this book emphasis has been placed on laboratory diagnosis as an essential component of the diagnostic problem, and in many instances as the *sine qua non* of accurate etiologic diagnosis. Thus, adequately trained personnel and suitable laboratory facilities are indispensable, whether the focus is on the individual patient or on epidemiologic surveys of population groups.

Parasitologic Equipment and Supplies

Unless the laboratory is devoted exclusively to parasitology, provision must be made in the general laboratory, preferably in a separate room, for performing the essential technics of coprologic, hematologic and other parasitologic diagnosis. There must be a sufficient footage of laboratory tables, an abundance of electric and gas outlets, sinks conveniently arranged with running cold and hot water, and adequate lighting of the room. In addition, there should be a full-sized clerical desk, as well as filing cabinets for records and for diagnostic specimens which are to be preserved.

Microscopic Equipment.—There must be one good compound microscope for each person doing parasitologic diagnosis. Each instrument should be equipped with a revolving nosepiece having low-power, high-dry and oil-immersion objectives in excellent condition, 5× and 10× oculars, mechanical stage and substage condenser. An inclined binocular microscope relieves eye strain of the diagnostician and therefore improves diagnostic capacity and reliability. For each microscope there should be a good electric lamp, preferably with "daylight" filter.

For study of macroscopic specimens such as helminths, surgical biopsies or entomological material, it is desirable to have at least one binocular dissecting microscope, with a series of paired oculars and objectives.

Additional microscopic equipment should include a micrometer disc to be placed in the eyepiece and a micrometer slide to calibrate the divisions in the micrometer disc for the particular microscope and for each of the eyepieces and objectives employed. If a micrometer slide is not available the units in a hemacytometer slide may be substituted in making the calibration.

Phase microscopic equipment is not necessary for routine diagnostic work.

Other Equipment.—There should be at least one good incubator, a drying oven, and one or more International clinical centrifuges, a steam sterilizer and a precision microtome with knives for cutting serial sections are needed.

Glassware.—Reagent bottles, petri dishes, pyrex-type beakers, flasks, funnels and pipettes of graded sizes, test tubes, graduate cylinders, microscope slides and coverglasses must be available in good supply. The *microscope slides* should be of hard, non-fogging white glass without sharp edges. For fecal examination the regular size (25 × 75 mm.) may be employed but a wider slide (37 × 75 mm.) is preferable. As soon as they become badly scratched or clouded slides should be discarded. Under no circumstances should those used in coprologic examination be employed for making blood films, for permanent-stained fecal films or for microscopic sections. The most convenient size of coverglass for routine use is the 22 mm. square. The No. 2 thickness is advised for fresh fecal film examination, since breakage is less than with the No. 1 thickness, which is used for permanent mounts of stained films and sections.

The *test tubes* routinely employed in the parasitology laboratory are the Wassermann tube (12 × 100 mm.) for concentration of parasite objects present in feces, 14 × 150 mm. and 25 × 200 mm. for culture of protozoa, and small serologic tubes for precipitin tests.

Staining dishes are required for making stained preparations of fecal films, blood films, parasite objects in aspirates or cultures and for sectioned material. The most convenient type of receptacle for all types of material fixed to the 25 × 75 mm. slide is a rectangular glass box with cover, provided with a removable, slotted glass tray for holding 20 slides back-to-back and a rust-resisting wire handle for lifting the tray out of the staining solution in the glass box. Two or three sets of 10 to 12 dishes each should be stocked. Smaller, slotted glass jars should be available for staining coverglass preparations. For *in toto* mounts embryologic glass dishes or crystals are convenient.

Specimen Containers.—A suitable type is a 2-oz. glass bottle with an aluminum or plastic screw top, which can be used for samples of stools, urine and sputum. For shipment it should fit into a mailing cylinder of heavy cardboard having a metal screw top. In addition, there is need for clear glass cylindrical jars with plastic tops for preservation of parasite objects. For large demonstration specimens or gross tissue pathology, rectangular or cylindrical museum jars are the most suitable.

Other Supplies.—Wooden specimen applicators and tongue depressors, surgical gauze or cheesecloth, dissecting and autopsy instruments and many other minor supplies are necessary for the properly functioning parasitology laboratory.

Reagents and Chemicals

For routine fresh fecal films each diagnostician requires conveniently placed dropping bottles of physiologic salt solution and iodine (filtered saturated iodine in one per cent potassium iodide or the more complicated D'Antoni's iodine stain). For concentration technics there should be at hand large bottles of zinc sulfate solution (sp. gr. 1.180) or brine (for certain common helminth eggs only).

For fixation of fecal films Schaudinn's fluid is most frequently employed. Other reagents are described later in this chapter. Formalin, Zenker's, Bouin's and other fixatives are routinely used for fixing tissues.

For staining of fecal films the iron-hematoxylin technic is probably the most satisfactory but there are other excellent technics for fixation and staining of feces in bulk and as smears on microscopic slides. Routine staining of sections is accomplished by the hematoxylin-eosin method. Best's carmine is used to demonstrate glycogen in these sections. Many other staining reagents have specific use in identifying certain types of tissue elements.

For blood films the usual stain is one of the Romanowsky eosin-methylene blue combinations. Best results are usually obtained with the Giemsa stain, although the Wright or Leishman stain is fairly satisfactory. Iron-hematoxylin provides an excellent demonstration of the "sheath" of some of the microfilarias.

The laboratory must have an adequate stock of ethyl alcohol, absolute ethyl alcohol, xylene, glycerol, neutral mounting media for microscopic mounts, distilled water and many other reagents used in daily or occasional diagnostic procedures.

For culturing protozoa there are several satisfactory types of media which will be considered later in this chapter. For culturing helminth larvas powdered or finely granulated animal charcoal is useful.

Laboratory Animals

Guinea-pigs, hamsters, white mice and rats, kittens and puppies are the most valuable for this purpose.

COPROLOGICAL EXAMINATION

Collection of the Specimen

The evacuation from the bowel is the *stool*. A normal stool consists almost exclusively of *feces* but in the diseased intestine a portion of the stool may consist of a bloody-mucous discharge or there may be a considerable amount of sloughed tissue. At times these portions of the stool provide evidence of parasitic infection when the feces are negative. Similarly *Ascaris*, *Enterobius* and proglottids of *Tænia* and *Dipylidium* may be passed without the presence of their eggs in the fecal part of the specimen. It is therefore important that the material submitted for examination be sufficient for dependable diagnosis. Gross inspection of the specimen should always precede microscopic examination.

Collection should be made in a clean container without contamination with the patient's urine. The specimen must be free of oil droplets, magnesia, powdered aluminum salts or barium.

Formed stools in which putrefaction is not taking place rapidly can usually be kept for one or more days, preferably in the ice-box, without loss of the diagnostic integrity of parasite objects which may be present. Unformed stools should be examined soon after they have been passed, if possible within a half hour and without chilling. Since these conditions can not always be met a representative sample of each unformed stool should be fixed in bulk. A very satisfactory technic for simultaneous preservation and staining of this type of stool is the MIF method, which is described later in this chapter (page 580).

Processing of the Specimen

1. **Direct Unpreserved Fecal Film.**—Routinely the unpreserved specimen should first be examined grossly and then microscopically as two coverglass preparations, thick enough to contain microscopic parasite objects which may be present in considerable numbers in the stool but thin enough to read newsprint without difficulty through the material. This amounts to about 5 to 10 mgm. of feces. These films should be free of air bubbles and macroscopic débris. The two preparations should be placed about 1 mm. apart in the middle two-thirds of the slide. One fecal film is made up in tepid physiologic salt solution and the other in 1 or more drops of iodine solution (sufficient to give a light yellowish-brown tinge to the film). Lugol's iodine solution is too strong and "burns" protozoa. Care must be exercised not to use too much diluent lest the preparation spill off the slide onto the microscope stage. The unstained film is useful particularly for motile trophozoites of intestinal protozoa, helminth eggs and *Strongyloides* larvas and has considerable diagnostic value for amebic cysts. The stained portion is most valuable in studying the internal diagnostic characteristics of protozoan cysts. (See Plate 3, page 56.)

2. **Preserved Stained Film.**—In case the stool sample has been prepared by the MIF method (page 580), a drop or two of the shaken suspension may be pipetted onto a clean slide and mounted with a coverglass.

If it is desired to make a permanent, stained film of the raw stool for study of intestinal protozoa, a representative fleck of the material is smeared as evenly as possible on an absolutely clean slide and is treated with a liquid fixative before the material has dried. The standard fixative is Schaudinn's solution (sat. sol. mercuric chloride in distilled water, 200 cc.; 95% ethyl alcohol, 100 cc.), to which glacial acetic acid, 15 cc. is added just before the fixative is to be used.

Lawless Permanent Mount Stain (1953).—This provides the following modification of standard technics: saturated solution of mercuric chloride in distilled water, 2 parts and 95% alcohol, 1 part, to make up 890 cc.; glacial acetic acid, 50 cc.; acetone, 50 cc., and formadehyde U.S.P., 10 cc. To this solution the following staining ingredients are added: acid fuchsin, 1.25 Gm. and fast green FCF, 0.5 Gm. This double-purpose fixative-stain is kept in a tightly-stoppered brown glass bottle. For use, the solution is transferred with a medicine dropper in sufficient quantity to cover the moist fecal film. The preparation is then heated over a laboratory flame until it begins to steam (not boil). It is then washed gently under tap water, drained, passed rapidly through 50%, 70%, 95% and absolute alcohol, cleared in xylol and mounted in neutral Canada balsam or in clarite. This technic provides excellent diagnosability for all protozoa (trophozoites and cysts) in the film.

Noble's Rapid Iron-Hematoxylin Stain (1944).—The following solutions are used:

1. *Mordant-fixative*, consisting of 10% formalin (4% formaldehyde) 3 parts; glacial acetic acid, 1 part, and 3 Gm. of ferric ammonium sulfate added for each 100 cc. of the formol-acid mixture.
2. *Stain*, consisting of 0.5% aqueous hematoxylin.

3 and 4. *Dehydrating and Clearing:* dioxane.

5. *Clearing:* dioxane and toluol half and half.

A thin fecal smear is made on a clean microscopic slide, is covered with a few drops of Solution 1 and is passed over a Bunsen or alcohol flame until it begins to steam. This is then quickly poured off, Solution 2 added to flood the film, warmed to steaming and the film rinsed thoroughly in running tap water. The excess water is next removed by draining and by drawing off with blotter or filter paper, the slide immersed in "3" and then in "4" for at least 1 minute, then in "5" for at least 30 seconds, and finally mounted in clarite.

Velat, Weinstein and Otto's Stain (1950).—This stain has been developed for the rapid study of the differential characters of the trophozoites of the intestinal amebas in fresh, wet preparations. It is a buffered aqueous solution of the precipitate obtained from the interaction of hematoxylin and crystal violet, using certified stains. The steps in preparation of the precipitate are as follows:

1. Make up a 2.5% solution of crystal violet in *warm* distilled water.
2. Make up a 1.0% solution of hematoxylin in *boiling* distilled water. Add 0.4 cc. of triethanoamine to 100 cc. of the boiling hematoxylin solution; boil for 2 to 3 minutes, then cool to approximately 50° C.
3. Add entire volume of warm hematoxylin-triethanoamine solution to Solution 1, with constant stirring, and resulting in rapid formation of a precipitate.
4. Filter several times through Whatman No. 2 filter paper. Save the precipitate on the filter paper and discard the filtrate. Wash down the precipitate into the cone of the filter paper, using small amounts of distilled water, totalling not more than 50 cc. Allow the precipitate to dry.
5. The dried precipitate is made up as a 0.05% solution in acetate buffer which is obtained by combining (*a*) 16.82 cc. glacial acetic acid in 983.18 cc. distilled water with (*b*) 19.72 Gm. sodium acetate ($NaC_2H_3O_2.3H_2O$) in 980.28 cc. distilled water, as follows: for pH 4.6, use 102 cc. sol. (*a*) and 98 cc. sol. (*b*); for pH 4.8, 80 cc. and 120 cc.; for pH 5.2, 42 cc. and 158 cc., and for pH 5.4, 29 cc. and 171 cc. Two to 3 weeks, with frequent shaking, are required for dissolving the precipitate. The solution is then filtered and the undissolved precipitate is discarded.
6. *For staining* a small quantity of fecal material is mixed into one or two drops of the stain. Gradually the chromatin material stains a purplish-black, while the cytoplasm takes on a light purplish color.

Faust's Iron-Hematoxylin Stain (1937).—1. Fix smears in Schaudinn's solution to which glacial acetic acid has been added, heated to a temperature of 60° C., for 2 minutes.

2. Immerse smears in 70% alcohol; 70% alcohol to which enough iodine has been added to give a port-wine color; 70 and 50% alcohol, leaving in each 2 minutes.
3. Wash in running water for 2 minutes.
4. Immerse smears in 2% aqueous iron-alum solution at 40° C. for 2 minutes.
5. Wash in running water 3 minutes.
6. Stain in 0.5% aqueous hematoxylin for 2 minutes.
7. Wash in running water 2 minutes.
8. Differentiate in *cold aqueous* iron-alum solution.
9. Wash in running water 10 to 15 minutes.

10. Immerse smears 2 minutes each in 70, 80, 90% and absolute alcohol.
11. Clear smears with xylol.
12. Mount in xylol-balsam or clarite.

Brooke and Goldman's PVA (Polyvinyl Alcohol) Fixative (1949).—This is a convenient method for fixing fecal films on microscopic slides. The fixative-preservative solution consists of: Schaudinn's sol., 93.5 cc.; glycerol, 1.5 cc.; glacial acetic acid, 5.0 cc. and powdered polyvinyl alcohol, 5 Gm. The polyvinyl alcohol is added by constant stirring when the other ingredients have been heated to 75° C. For use, 1 drop of well comminuted fecal suspension and 3 drops of the fixative are spread over the middle third of the microscopic slide, which is then dried overnight at 37° C. At a convenient time, the dry film is then placed in 70% alcohol containing iodine to remove excess mercuric chloride, then staining by the shorter iron-hematoxylin technic (Faust, 1937), or the standard longer technic of Heidenhain (1892).

MIF (Merthiolate-Iodine-Formaldehyde) Fixative-Stain of Sapero and Lawless (1953).—The stock solution consists of distilled water, 250 cc.; tincture of merthiolate No. 99 Lilly (1:1000), 200 cc., formaldehyde U.S.P., 25 cc., and glycerol, 5 cc., to which 10 to 15 parts of freshly prepared Lugol's solution (5% iodine in 10% potassium iodide in distilled water) is added. This may be used (*a*) in making direct fecal smears or (*b*) for collection and preservation of bulk stool specimens.

(a) *Direct Fecal Smears.*—Place 1 drop each of distilled water and 1 drop of MIF fixative-stain together on the slide, then add a small fleck of feces and mix thoroughly. Mount with a coverglass and examine.

(b) *Collection and Preservation of Bulk Specimen.*—For approximately each 0.25 Gm. of stool to be processed first introduce 0.15 cc. of Lugol's solution followed by 2.35 cc. of the MIF stock solution into a convenient-sized test-tube or other glass container, then add the stool specimen and mix thoroughly until there is a homogeneous suspension. This method is particularly adapted to field collections. All microscopic parasite objects are well preserved in a natural state and adequately stained for diagnostic reliability. Once preserved the material keeps well in a tightly-stoppered bottle for a year or more.

3. **Concentration Technics.**—Since microscopic parasite objects in the stool do not multiply as some of them do under conditions of *in vitro* cultivation, the rationale of their concentration from the stool is to separate them from the bulk of the material in the specimen, *e. g.*, bacteria, undigested food elements, etc. For this purpose two methods, sedimentation and flotation, or a combination of the two are employed.

I. SEDIMENTATION.—This is accomplished by suspending the stool in tap water and allowing natural settling to take place, or by accelerating the process mechanically through centrifugalization. This technic is primarily useful for concentration of protozoan cysts and helminth eggs, but by substituting physiologic salt solution amebic trophozoites may be concentrated by centrifugalization and retain their viability.

(*a*) *Simple Sedimentation.*—For the intestinal protozoa this method is tedious and provides little if any concentration over the direct fecal film (Faust *et al.*, 1938). On the other hand, for helminth eggs it has several advantages over other methods of concentration, since the eggs of all species settle to the bottom of the container in a viable, undistorted condition. It is especially recommended for eggs of *Schistosoma, Clonorchis, Opisthorchis,* and heterophyid flukes. Although the technic is relatively slow, there is ample compensation in the much larger amount of material which can be processed in a single container.

Ten or more grams of the fecal specimen are thoroughly comminuted in 10 to 20 times their volume of tap water, poured into 250 or 500 cc. urinalysis glasses and the sediment allowed to settle out. After an hour, the top two-thirds with the floating débris is either carefully poured off or siphoned off, water is added to near the top of the container and the fecal material thoroughly resuspended in it. This procedure is repeated once or twice until the supernatant fluid is relatively clear. After a final removal of water a small portion of bottom sediment is removed with a long pipette to a broad (fecal) slide (37 × 75 mm.) and examined for eggs.

Faust and Ingalls (1946) confirmed for *Schistosoma japonicum* the earlier observations of Faust and Hoffman (1934), that 0.5% glycerol added to tap water causes increased "wetting" and more rapid sedimentation, minimizes the number of eggs decanted and provides a yield up to about 25-fold that of the unprocessed stool. It is desirable to strain out the larger detritus in the stool through surgical gauze having about 22 meshes to the linear inch, using 2 to 4 thicknesses which have been previously soaked in water and the excess of water squeezed out. The gauze is then stretched loosely over a funnel of appropriate size and the emulsified feces poured through into the sedimentation glass. Very few eggs are trapped in the gauze unless there is considerable mucus in the stool. After 1 hour, the first decantation is made, 45 minutes later a second, and 30 minutes later a third and last one. Measured amounts of the sediment in the bottom are then removed to a microscopic slide and mounted with a 40 × 22 mm. cover-glass. Eggs of all types in the stool without loss of viability due to the technic are present in unusually high concentrates in the sediment (Maldonado and Acosta-Matienzo, 1953). It is probably the most practical method for obtaining immature, fully mature and degenerate eggs of *Schistosoma japonicum* and *S. mansoni* for diagnosis in the same proportion in which they occur in the stool.

Jahnes and Hodges (1947) claim that 10% ethyl alcohol in water (sp. gr. 0.986), is twofold superior to 0.5% glycerinated water for recovery of *Schistosoma* eggs, that the eggs obtained are not damaged and later hatch.

(*b*) *Centrifugalization.*—This method is fairly useful for concentration of protozoan cysts and helminth eggs in the stool, and if isotonic salt solution is substituted for tap water amebic trophozoites concentrate in a living state from 15- to 40-fold.

A 2- to 3-Gm. fecal specimen is thoroughly mixed with about 10 parts by volume of tap water, and is then strained through 2 layers of 16- to 20-mesh cheesecloth (to remove débris) into a 13 × 100 mm. serological pyrex glass tube. These tubes are cheap, are not easily broken and fit into the 9.5-cm. metal carrying tubes of the smaller electric-powered centrifuges of the International clinical centrifuge type. Because of their rounded bottoms they are better for fecal concentrates than the conventional 15-cc. centrifuge tubes, since the material does not easily pack in the base of the tube. The tubes are revolved in the centrifuge at a moderate speed (*ca.* 1500 to 2300 rpm.) for 1 to 2 minutes, are then removed, the supernatant liquid poured off, the tubes filled with water which is mixed with the fecal material, and are again centrifugalized. Theoretically, the centrifugalization should be repeated until the supernatant fluid is clear, but in practice 2 to 3 spinnings are usually satisfactory. This technic was used by Pepper (1908) and was extensively utilized by Howard (1915, 1919) in hookworm surveys in British Guiana. Lane states (1928) that its effective concentration is much less than was originally supposed.

For the diagnosis of *Schistosoma* eggs in the stool, Baroody and Most (1946) developed a *macro-centrifugalization technic,* comparable in the quantity of feces processed to sedimentation but more rapid. The steps are as follows: (1) 10 to 15 Gm. feces are shaken up thoroughly for 1 or 2 minutes in a 125 cc. Erlenmeyer flask containing about 100 cc. tepid tap water; (2) the suspension is strained through two layers of wet gauze into a 50 cc. centrifuge tube with a teated bottom; (3) this is spun in the centrifuge for 30 seconds at 1500 rpm; (4) the supernatant fluid is poured off, 40° C. water is added and centrifugalization is repeated; (5) repeat step (4) until supernatant fluid is clear; (6) 4 drops of sediment are examined under a 22 × 40 mm. coverglass; (7) if not positive for *Schistosoma* eggs, add 10 drops of water to the sediment and allow to stand until morning, then look for hatched miracidia.

Ritchie (1948) adds formalin for fixation and preservation of the parasite objects, and ether to remove fats and oils. The stool specimen is first comminuted in sufficient physiologic salt solution to provide 10 to 12 cc. of stool suspension, which is strained through 2 layers of surgical gauze into a 15 cc. centrifuge tube. The suspension is then centrifugalized, the supernate decanted and the particulate matter resuspended repeatedly until the supernate is clear. After an additional decantation the sediment is mixed with 10 cc. of 4% formaldehyde U.S.P. and allowed to stand for 5 minutes, after which 3 cc. of ether are added and the suspension is shaken vigorously. Following an additional period of centrifugalization at about 1500 rpm for 2 minutes, the entire supernate is poured off. A thin film of the sediment is placed on a microscopic slide, a drop of 2% iodine solution is mixed with it and the preparation mounted with a coverglass for examination. This method provides a good concentrate of protozoan cysts and helminth eggs which are diagnostically satisfactory.

Other methods of centrifugalization in which ether is employed with acid or sodium sulfate have been developed as follows: HCl and ether (Telemann, 1908; Mathieson and Stoll, 1945); HCl, ether and a detergent (Weller and Dammin, 1946; Hunter *et al.*, 1945–1948; Faust and Ingalls, 1946); citric acid and ether (Carles and Barthelemy, 1917); acetic acid and ether (De Rivas, 1928); HCl, ether and xylol (Loughlin and Stoll, 1946); Na_2SO_4, ether and detergent (Hunter *et al.*, 1946; Faust and Ingalls, 1946). The HCl-ether-detergent and Na_2SO_4-ether detergent technics are particularly useful in concentrating eggs of *Schistosoma mansoni* and *S. japonicum* from small samples of stools containing considerable blood and mucus.

II. FLOTATION.—In contrast to sedimentation, in which microscopic parasites that are heavier than bacteria and undigested food particles in the stool sink to the bottom of a container, flotation utilizes a liquid suspending medium heavier than the parasite objects so that they rise to the surface and can be skimmed out of the surface film. This method of concentration was introduced by Bass (1906) for recovery of hookworm eggs present in small numbers in the stool. For diagnostic usefulness, the suspending medium must not only be heavier than the object to be floated; it must not produce shrinkage sufficient to render the object undiagnosable.

The floating medium originally employed was brine, *e. g.*, concentrated solution of NaCl, having a specific gravity of approximately 1.200. Eggs of the common intestinal helminths, such as the hookworms, *Ascaris* and *Trichocephalus*, are not damaged by this process, but those of *Schistosoma*, hookworm and *Strongyloides* larvas, and protozoan cysts become badly shrunken; furthermore, eggs of *Clonorchis*, *Opisthorchis* and heterophyid species have a specific gravity higher than 1.200 and do not float in brine.

The pioneer work of Bass (*l. c.*) was supplemented and modified by Kofoid and Barber (1918), who removed helminth eggs in the surface float by means of a wire loop, and by Willis (1921), who superimposed a clean microscope slide on the top of the surface film and in that way obtained a concentrate of hookworm eggs. These relatively simple technics proved very useful in obtaining rapid diagnostic evidence of the presence (but not the quantity) of hookworm, *Ascaris* and *Trichocephalus* eggs in a stool sample.

Otto, Hewitt and Strahan (1941) used direct flotation in zinc sulfate solution having a specific gravity of 1.180, as originally developed by Faust *et al.* (1938, 1939). In this medium fertile eggs of the common helminths and protozoan cysts rise to the surface in a recognizable, essentially unshrunken condition, but infertile *Ascaris* eggs which have a higher specific gravity are rarely recovered.

III. Centrifugal-Flotation.—This method combines the principles of gravitation and flotation. A sample of stool is suspended in approximately 10 times its volume of water, strained through gauze to remove the larger objects, placed in a centrifuge tube and by means of 2 or 3 successive centrifugalizations, decantations of the supernate and resuspensions is cleared of the fine particulate material. After the last centrifugalization the entire supernate is drained off, the sediment is then resuspended in the floating medium, recentrifugalized and after the centrifuge tube has been at rest for approximately 5 minutes, the surface film is removed with a bacteriologic loop or a superimposed microscope slide. This technic provides high concentration of parasite objects practically free of detritus. The diagnosability of the parasites depends on the floating medium employed and the species of parasite.

1. *Lane's Direct Centrifugal-Flotation* (1924).—The technic was developed by Lane in an attempt to overcome some of the difficulties inherent in the simpler methods. Without question it is one of the most precise and delicate methods thus far devised and concentrates in the surface film all but a negligible amount of the eggs of hookworms, *Ascaris, Trichocephalus* and *Trichostrongylus* from a specimen. It is an elaboration and refinement of the Bass method of 1910, in which feces are first strained through a sieve, then successively centrifugalized in water, heavy salt solutions, and water again.

The method is, however, too complicated for field work, although it is suitable for a central diagnostic laboratory where maximum accuracy is desired and good technical assistance is available.

2. *Zinc Sulfate Centrifugal-Flotation of Faust et al.* (1938, 1939).—This technic was developed to meet the needs of the clinical laboratory for heavy concentration of protozoan cysts, helminth eggs and larvas present in the stool, in a readily diagnosable condition. All of these parasite objects, except for operculate eggs, those of blood flukes and eggs heavier than the floating medium, are recovered in unusual concentration and in a viable condition. The most useful concentration of zinc sulfate for floating the common parasite objects has a specific gravity of 1.180. Sawitz (1942) determined that the specific gravity of viable hookworm eggs is 1.055, of whipworm eggs, 1.150, of fertile *Ascaris* eggs, 1.110 and of infertile *Ascaris* eggs, >1.200. The specific gravity of *Endamoeba histolytica* and *Endolimax nana* is approximately 1.065–1.070, of *Endamœba coli* slightly higher, of *Chilomastix mesnili* possibly close to 1.180 and of *Giardia lamblia*, 1.060 or somewhat less (based on unpublished data in the author's laboratory).

The steps in the technic, employing zinc sulfate solution of 1.180 sp. gr. (approximately 33% dry granular $ZnSO_4$ U.S.P.), are as follows:

(*a*) Prepare a fecal suspension by comminuting about 10 parts of lukewarm tapwater with 1 part of the stool specimen (about the size of a small pecan).

(*b*) Approximately 10 cc. amount of the suspension is strained through 1 layer of *wet* cheesecloth (in a small funnel) into a Wassermann tube.

(*c*) The preparation in the tube is then centrifugalized for 45 to 60 seconds at top speed of an International clinical centrifuge (*ca.* 2300 rpm.). The supernatant fluid is poured off, 2 or 3 cc. of water added, the sediment broken up by shaking or tapping, and additional water added to fill the tube.

(*d*) Repeat "*c*" (usually 2 or 3 times) until the supernatant fluid is clear.

(*e*) The last supernatant fluid is poured off, 3 to 4 cc. of zinc sulfate solution of specific gravity 1.180 added, the packed sediment broken up and enough zinc sulfate solution added to fill the tube to about one-half inch of the rim.

(*f*) The tube is centrifugalized for 45 to 60 seconds at top speed and is brought to a stop for one or two minutes.

(*g*) Several loopfuls of diagnostic material floating in the surface film are removed by means of a bacteriologic loop onto a clean slide, 1 drop of D'Antoni's iodine stain (or saturated iodine in 1% KI) is added and the preparation agitated manually to insure uniform staining.

(*h*) The preparation is mounted with a coverglass and is now ready for examination.

Tobie *et al.* (1951) have demonstrated remarkable efficiency for the zinc sulfate centrifugal-flotation technic. Sacramento (1940), Garcia and Pesigan (1940), Otto, Hewitt and Strahan (1941) and Sanches (1952) have developed modifications or simplifications of the method. All experienced diagnosticians who have employed the original technic subscribe to its general applicability and usefulness for the concentration at one time of protozoan cysts, several species of helminth eggs, as well as hookworm and *Strongyloides* larvas present in the stool. Elsdon-Dew (personal communication, 1953) comments particularly on its value for recovery of small numbers of *Isospora* cysts in the stool. These small, almost transparent objects of low specific gravity concentrate in the zinc sulfate medium as satisfactorily as the cysts of *Giardia lamblia.* This technic is not satisfactory for concentration of eggs of *Schistosoma,* which become badly shrunken and usually remain in the sediment, for operculate eggs of *Fasciola, Fasciolopsis, Paragonimus* or *Diphyllobothrium,* and for eggs of species which have a specific gravity greater than 1.180. For effective concentration of these eggs sedimentation and simple or specialized centrifugalization technics must be employed.

Quantitative Egg-Count Technics.—While the several technics described above provide opportunity for efficient recovery and accurate identification of most parasite objects in the stool, there is need for estimating the parasite burden of the patient, to determine the degree of infection, whether incidental, moderate or heavy. Methods have been developed for relatively accurate calculation of hookworm, *Ascaris* and to a lesser degree of *Trichocephalus* worm burden by counting the eggs present in the stool.

Beaver's Direct Egg-Count Technic (1949–1950).—The method of making egg-counts by direct smear is based on the observations that eggs of hookworms, and probably those of other species which inhabit the small intestine or upper colon, have random distribution in the stool, and that any series of direct smears of equal density taken from the same stool contain equal quantities of fecal solids and statistically equal numbers of eggs. A method of making uniform smears has been devised and the factor for converting eggs per slide to eggs per cc. of formed stool has been determined for the type of smear which is regarded tentatively as being of ideal density. This involves the use of a photo-electric type of light meter which is adapted to measuring the turbidity of the fecal smear. A wooden block 18 mm. in thickness and of any convenient diameter is fitted to the light meter's window and a 16 mm. hole is drilled into the center of the block. This serves as a platform for the microscope slide on which the smear is made and provides a mask which reduces the window to a convenient size for preparing and spreading the smear.

An electric lamp is suspended directly over the reduced window and made adjustable so that arbitrary whole number readings can be obtained.

When the original light meter reading is adjusted to 20 the interference readings of 7.5, 10, 11.5, 13 and 16 correspond to uniform fecal smears containing respectively 1/200, 1/300, 1/400, 1/500 and 1/1000 cc. For standardization 1 drop (0.05 cc.) of a mixture of 2N Na_2SO_4 + N/1 $BaCl_2$, each previously mixed with $\frac{1}{2}$ part pure glycerol, in the following proportions, provides density readings equivalent to the fecal smears: 3:2, 1/200 cc.; 2:3, 1/300 cc.; 1:2, 1/400 cc.; 1:3, 1/500 cc., and 1:6, 1/1000 cc. For routine smears 1/500 cc. amounts of fecal suspension are most useful; for stools with large numbers of eggs, 1/1000 cc. smears are more satisfactory, and for those with very few eggs it is desirable to use the thicker smears. For the number of eggs per cc. of stool the egg count is multiplied by the denominator, *viz.*, when the smear contains 1/200 cc. the factor is 200, etc. Calculation of hookworm burden is similar to that described immediately below, and the accuracy of the calculation is approximately the same.

Stoll's Dilution Egg-Count Technic (1923).—The technic is as follows: four grams of feces are weighed out and placed in a graduated small Erlenmeyer flask or large test-tube having a mark indicating a 60-cc. level, and decinormal sodium hydroxide is poured in up to the 60-cc. mark. Several small glass beads are now added, the container closed with a rubber stopper and the contents shaken until the feces are thoroughly comminuted. A hard fecal specimen should be left in the liquid over night to secure adequate disintegration. When proper comminution has been obtained, the mixture is thoroughly shaken up and 0.15 cc. of the supension is drawn up into a capillary pipette, discharged onto a clean fecal slide and covered with a 22 × 40 mm. coverglass. The total number of eggs of the particular species of helminth under observation is then counted, and this number multiplied by 100 to obtain the number of eggs per gram of feces. The estimated daily output of eggs can then be secured by multiplying the number per gram by the total weight of a 24-hour fecal specimen. The estimate obtained is usually accurate within 10 to 20%, but varies per gram of feces for a particular species of helminth, depending on the consistency of the feces (whether liquid, semiformed, formed or hard) and in total daily output per female worm in a given period of time.

The Stoll technic has been employed in conjunction with worm-counts in *Necator, Ancylostoma, Ascaris, Clonorchis* and *Fasciolopsis* infections in order to determine the egg-laying capacity of these species of worms per unit of time or per unit of formed fecal output. The following figures may be considered as relatively accurate estimates for these worms: *Necator, ca.* 9000 eggs per female *per diem* (Stoll, 1923); *Ancylostoma*, several times that of *Necator* (Sweet, 1924; Cort, Stoll and Grant, 1926); *Ascaris, ca.* 72,000 to 245,000 eggs per female *per diem* (Brown and Cort, 1927); *Clonorchis*, 2400 eggs per worm *per diem* in cats, 1600 in guinea-pigs, *e. g.*, egg-laying capacity variable with the host (Faust and Khaw, 1926, 1927); *Fasciolopsis*, 25,000 eggs per worm *per diem* (Stoll, Cort and Kwei, 1927).

Zinc Sulfate Centrifugal-Flotation Technic for Egg Counts.—Hood (1947) employed the zinc sulfate technic as a quantitative check on the Stoll dilution counts (see above, "Stoll's Dilution Egg-Count Technic"), using 500 hookworm-positive stool specimens. She found that in light infections (*i. e.*, 1 to 40 eggs per slide by the zinc sulfate technic) 61.2% were missed by the Stoll method. Since the zinc sulfate concentrate provided an average count 12-fold that of the Stoll count, a conversion formula, *viz.*, $\frac{ZnSO_2 \text{ count} \times 200}{12}$ = eggs per cc. of stool, is employed.

Worms Migrating Out of the Anus

In the case of *Enterobius* infection, it is not usual for the gravid female worms to oviposit within the bowel. Adult females habitually migrate out of the anus and their eggs commonly are shed onto the perianal and perineal skin. The worms may be passed in the feces but more commonly crawl out of the anus at night. Mature and immature *Ascaris* are frequently passed spontaneously by the host. They should be preserved in alcohol or formalin and properly identified. Tapeworm proglottids (species of *Tænia* or *Dipylidium caninum*) singly or in chains, are usually discharged periodically in the stools of infected patients. Specific identification of these worms can most readily be made from the moist proglottids. Patients should be warned not to wrap them in toilet paper, which dries them out and usually renders identification difficult or impossible.

Anal Scrapings and Swabs

Amebiasis cutis of the perianal area may be diagnosed by scraping out the contents of suspected ulcers, removing the material to a slide in a drop or two of tepid physiologic salt solution, mounting with a coverglass and demonstrating typical *E. histolytica* motility in cells resembling amebic trophozoites.

Heller (1876) apparently first recommended the use of an anal scraper or swab to obtain material for microscopical examination for *Enterobius* eggs. Hall (1937) devised a much more convenient swab, which provides consistently high diagnostic yields. The applicator consists of a glass rod tipped with cellophane held in place with a rubber band, and is employed to swab the perianal area of the patient. The cellophane with adhering material is removed from the rod, is flattened between two glass slides and examined for eggs under low power of the microscope.

In 1941 Graham introduced a *Scotch cellulose tape technic* for obtaining eggs of *Enterobius* from the anal and perianal areas. A length of the tape is held adhesive-side-out on the end of a wooden tongue blade by the thumb and index finger, or the tape may be looped adhesive-side-out on the end of the microscope slide and after "swabbing" is placed adhesive-side-down, in a drop of toluene, on the slide for examination. Most workers regard this as considerably more efficient than the Hall technic.

In 1943, Schüffner and Swellengrebel first reported on a *glass pestle swabber* made from a 10 cm. length of heavy glass tubing and blown out at one end into a globe which is then ground rough. It is massaged over the perianal region, the adherent mucus, tissue cells, eggs, etc. are then transferred to a drop of water on a slide and the deposit examined under a microscope. The pestle is easily cleaned in water and can be used repeatedly.

Scott and other workers claim that perianal swabbing has high efficiency in recovering eggs of *Schistosoma mansoni*, while Mazzotti regards it as the preferred technic in obtaining eggs of *Tænia solium*.

PURGED AND ENEMA SPECIMENS

The purpose of examining this type of material is to obtain diagnostic evidence of infection with *Endamœba histolytica,* usually in the cecal area of the intestine, when routine examination of the stools has been consistently negative and yet there is strong clinical suspicion of intestinal amebiasis. For diagnostic purposes, the purgative agent should be a salt solution. Although magnesium sulfate (Epsom salts) is usually employed, sodium sulfate (Glauber salts) or phospho-soda is probably better for delivering the amebic trophozoites in an undamaged, motile condition. For reliable diagnosis the examination must be made while the specimen is fresh. The material to be examined is the mucus and tissue detritus in the liquid portion following the evacuation of the fecal material. With a pipette, small amounts of the mucus or other sediment are transferred to microscope slides with as little water as possible, mounted with coverglasses and examined in the unstained condition. Typical pseudopodial activity and locomotion must be demonstrated in order to make a specific diagnosis of *E. histolytica* and care must be taken not to confuse trophozoites of *E. coli*, *Endolimax nana*, *Dientamœba fragilis* or host tissue macrophages with those of *E. histolytica*.

Enema specimens should be obtained by high instillation of tepid physiologic salt solution, to irrigate the cecal area. As in purged material, the mucus settlings in the liquid portion of the evacuation will provide the greatest likelihood of obtaining positive evidence of *Endamœba histolytica*.

EXAMINATION OF URINE

The pathogenic flagellate, *Trichomonas vaginalis,* is frequently recovered from urine sediment in both female and male patients who are infected. Rarely trophozoites of *Endamœba histolytica* may be present in urine of persons who have amebic ulceration of the genitalia.

Urine is the common excretion in which eggs of *Schistosoma hæmatobium* are discharged. Eggs of *Dioctophyma renale,* a rare parasite of man, are also recovered from the urine. In both of these infections the specimen of urine is collected in a urinalysis or sedimentation glass and the eggs allowed to sink to the bottom, together with erythrocytes and pus cells. The bottom sediment is then pipetted onto a fecal slide and examined microscopically. In Bancroft's filaria infection with chyluria the microfilarias are discharged in the urine. They may readily be recovered from centrifugalized specimens. There are rare occasions when *Strongyloides* larvas have been identified in the urine.

EXAMINATION OF SPUTUM

In pleuropulmonary amebiasis, the rupture of the amebic abscess into a bronchus characteristically results in coughing up the contents containing blood, mucus, necrotic tissue cells and trophozoites of *Endamœba histolytica*. Similarly, rupture of a pulmonary hydatid cyst is followed by discharge of its contents, in which there will be fragments of the laminated membrane and germinal layer of the cyst wall, and usually many free scolices of *Echinococcus granulosus*. Sputum is the most common discharge from which eggs of the lung fluke, *Paragonimus westermani,* are recovered. Occasionally eggs of blood flukes are coughed up.

RECOVERY OF PARASITES IN THE BLOOD

Next to the feces, the blood provides the most common medium for recovery of various stages of animal parasites. From this source, diagnosis is routinely made of malaria, African trypanosomiasis and most types of filariasis, less frequently of Chagas' disease and rarely kala-azar and toxoplasmosis. It is necessary to remember that in a particular infection these etiologic agents are not consistently present, at least in high density.

Protozoa in the Blood.—The standard procedure to obtain material for diagnosis of protozoa in the circulating blood is to make microscope slide preparations. The older method consisted in obtaining only thin blood films but for rapid examination thick films are needed. Preferably a combined thin- and thick-film should be made on the outer thirds of the same slide. The slide should be smooth and free of all blemishes, oil, lint and finger marks. In making the thin film a small drop of blood from a finger, toe (of children) or ear lobe is brought in contact with one end of the slide and is immediately drawn out into a smooth film one-cell-thick with the smooth straight edge of another slide. In making the thick film a somewhat larger drop of blood is deposited near the other end of the slide and is spread out evenly to the size of about 20 mm. diameter. Both films must be allowed to dry thoroughly, if necessary in a drying oven at about 37° to 40° C. overnight, without opportunity for contamination from dust or deposits of flies or roaches. Unless the slide is meticulously clean the thick film is likely to flake off. Freshly prepared films always stain best.

Giemsa's Stain.—The most valuable single stain for blood films which are to be examined for protozoa or microfilarias is that developed by Giemsa, prepared from azure blue and eosin. The thin-filmed end of the slide must first be fixed in absolute ethyl alcohol or absolute methyl alcohol for 2 to 3 minutes to avoid dehemoglobinization. The thick film requires no fixation, since dehemoglobinization is necessary to see through the several layers of cells. When ready for staining the slide should be immersed for a period of 10 to 30 minutes in a mixture of 1 drop of the concentrated stain to each cc. of neutral distilled water, then washed off, and dried in the air or with non-linty blotting paper. It is now ready for examination with oil-immersion objective, but if it is to be preserved each portion should be covered with clarite and mounted with a No. 1 coverglass.

Wright's Stain.—Since blood films for differential white cell counts are usually stained by the Wright technic, in some laboratories it may be convenient to employ this stain in searching for protozoa in the blood. For the thin blood film enough of the undiluted stock solution is placed on the slide in sufficient amount to cover the film. This fixes the hemoglobin in the red cells. In 3 to 5 minutes, a sufficient amount of distilled water is added to produce a greenish metallic surface. After 5 to 20 minutes, the stain is thoroughly washed off in running water, the film is dried and is ready for oil-immersion examination. For the thick film Wright's stain may be diluted with distilled water 1:30, but most modern workers prefer Giemsa's or Field's stain.

Field's Stain.—This stain was developed by Field (1941) for thick blood films in the diagnosis of malaria. As in the Giemsa method for staining thick-blood films, no preliminary fixation is required but the films must be completely dry and should be freshly prepared.

Preparation of Stain.—Two solutions are utilized, both isotonic and adjusted to a pH of 6.6.

Solution 1:

Methylene blue	0.8 Gm.
Azure B	0.5 "
Disodium hydrogen phosphate (anhydrous) .	5.0 "
Potassium dihydrogen phosphate (anhydrous)	6.25 "
Distilled water	500 cc.

Solution 2:

Eosin	1.0 Gm.
Disodium hydrogen phosphate (anhydrous) .	5.0 "
Potassium dihydrogen phosphate (anhydrous)	6.25 "
Distilled water	500 cc.

The phosphate salts are first made up in solution in the distilled water and the respective stains added. (The azure B is first ground in a mortar with a little of the phosphate solution.) Let each dye solution stand for twenty-four hours, then filter. If scum or precipitate forms later, refiltration is required. The stains may be kept for several weeks and used over and over, if they are in covered staining jars. When the eosin solution becomes greenish, it should be renewed.

Technic of staining:

(1) Dip film for one second in Solution 1.
(2) Rinse immediately in clean water until stain ceases to flow from film.
(3) Dip for one second in Solution 2.
(4) Rinse in clear water.
(5) Place in vertical position to dry.

Walker's Stain.—This stain, as reported to the Expert Committee on Malaria, World Health Organization (1952), is designed for thick blood films. The technic is as follows:

Make thick blood films by merely spreading blood so when slide is tilted at right angles the blood does not make an immediate drop at the lower border but rather crawls slowly to low point.

Place *flat* on desk *until dry*. Use no heat; a fan speeds drying.

To stain:

1. Dip slide in dilute methylene-blue phosphate for 1 second only.
2. Wash gently in one or two changes of distilled water to remove excess blue.
3. Place slide *face downward* on curved plate.
4. Run *fresh* dilute Giemsa (1 drop Giemsa per cc. buffer solution) under slide. Allow to act 6 to 8 minutes.
5. Dip in distilled water, drain briefly, dry with heat, examine under oil immersion.

The two steps which distinguish this method from other procedures are that (1) the preliminary treatment with methylene blue-phosphate solution helps the thick film to stick to the slide, maintains the integrity and morphology of the leukocytes and the parasites if present, reduces staining time by Giemsa to less than 10 minutes, and (2) after removing the excess blue by several dips in distilled water, the slides are placed *face downward* on a curved staining plate, or over any glass depression which will allow 4 to 5 mm. space below the point where the blood is spread. Since the hemoglobin molecule is so heavy, it falls completely out of the preparation instead of dragging through lower portions of the drop.

Blood elements so treated have a much sharper appearance than thick films stained with the Giemsa method alone. Differential counts of the leukocytes can be rapidly and confidently done. In addition, the blue staining accentuates those red blood cells which do not completely dehemoglobinize and are seen as bluish masses of irregular density, or dark blue stippling scattered among the leukocytes and platelets.

The required chemicals are mixed in the following proportions:

	A	*B*
Medicinal Methylene Blue,	1 Gm.	–
Na_2HPO_4 anhydrous,	3 "	7
KH_2PO_4	1 "	4

Take 1 Gm. of *A* to 300 cc. distilled water to prepare the methylene blue phosphate mixture.
1 Gm. of *B* to 1000 cc. makes satisfactory buffer water.

Microfilarias in Blood and Cutaneous Tissue Juice.—In most instances microfilarias circulating in the peripheral blood (or in cutaneous tissue juices, *viz.*, those of *Onchocerca volvulus*) are satisfactorily stained by the Giemsa technic. The thick film is recommended. After the material has been flattened into a circular area about 20 mm. in diameter on an absolutely clean microscope slide and has been thoroughly dried, the slide is placed vertically in the diluted Giemsa stain (see above). In approximately 30 minutes the staining is completed, the slide is removed, washed gently in tap water and dried. Overstaining is not likely to occur.

Hematoxylin Stains.—Some workers prefer hematoxylin to the Giemsa stain. The dried thick film is dehemoglobinized in 0.5% HCl, washed in 1% lithium carbonate solution and then stained by the iron-hematoxylin technic (see page 579), or by the Bullard technic. Bullard's hematoxylin is prepared as follows:

1. Fifty % alcohol, 144 cc.; glacial acetic acid, 16 cc.; hematoxylin crystals, 8 Gm.
2. Heat the above and add: distilled water, 250 cc.; ammonium alum, 20 Gm.
3. Heat to boiling and add slowly: red mercuric oxide, 8 Gm.
4. Cool quickly, filter and add: 95% alcohol, 275 cc.; glycerol, 330 cc.; glacial acetic acid, 18 cc.; ammonium alum, 40 Gm.
5. Keep in bright light for about one week for ripening and filter again before using.

The staining process is similar to that employing Harris' hematoxylin, *viz.*, immerse in the full-strength staining solution for 12 to 15 minutes, wash in tap water or 1% lithium carbonate solution until the film is distinctly blue, then dry.

Concentration of Microfilarias.—Defibrinated and dehemoglobinized blood, lymph or chylous urine is concentrated by centrifugalizing for about one minute at 1000 or more revolutions per minute, the supernatant fluid decanted and the sediment examined for embryos or larvas. These may be vitally stained or the film air-dried, fixed and permanently stained.

Knott (1939) has modified this technic as follows: 2 cc. of blood are thoroughly shaken with 10 cc. of a 2% solution of formaldehyde, centrifugalized for 5 minutes at 2,000 rpm., the supernatant fluid decanted and the sediment stained in bulk, then examined microscopically for microfilarias.

For the *quantitative estimation of microfilarias* in blood samples Brady and Lawton (1944) recommend the following procedure:

"Twenty cubic millimeters of blood are drawn up into a pipette such as is employed for the hemoglobin estimation by the acid hematin technique. After wiping the tip of the pipette with cotton, the volume of blood is expelled into the chamber of the Sedgwick-Rafter counting cell. This cell was designed for enumerating organisms in water and consists of a slide with a depression 0.1 cm. in depth and 2 × 5 cm. in area, thus capable of holding 1 cc. of fluid. One cc. of 0.1 *N* hydrochloric acid is added, the suspension stirred with a dissecting needle, and a coverslip applied without leaving an air bubble in the chamber. The microfilariæ settle rapidly to the bottom of the chamber and little focusing is thus required. With the aid of a mechanical stage, the entire area of the chamber is examined with the use of a 15 or 25 mm. objective.

"The method permits the examination of quantities of blood up to 0.1 cc., obviates the possibility of loss of microfilariæ in the test sample and requires only a single piece of equipment. The only disadvantage encountered is that objectives providing magnification higher than 8 mm. cannot be used because of the thickness of the preparation."

RECOVERY OF PARASITES FROM ASPIRATES

Recovery of protozoa and helminths from aspirated material constitutes a very important part of the diagnostic problem.

Proctoscopic aspirates and scrapings are valuable in confirming suspicion of amebic ulcers in the lower sigmoid colon and rectum, but diagnosis of the cellular content of the aspirate is frequently a difficult problem, since host tissue cells are often confused with non-motile trophozoites or cysts of *Endamœba histolytica*.

Duodenal aspiration is employed in the demonstration of infections with *Giardia lamblia*, *Strongyloides stercoralis* (which may not be evident in stool examination), *Fasciolopsis buski* (eggs) and parasites located in the gall bladder or biliary tract. However, to avoid incorrect diagnosis or inference, when there is suspicion of biliary infection it is preferable to obtain samples of pure bile uncontaminated with duodenal juices.

Aspirates from lesions in the liver and lungs are particularly helpful in obtaining material for diagnosis of amebic hepatitis and amebic liver abscess, as well as hydatid cyst. In the hepatic abscess, trophozoites of *Endamœba histolytica* are more likely to be demonstrated in aspirates obtained from the wall of the enlarging lesion than from the completely necrotic center of the abscess. In searching for diagnostic evidence of hydatid cysts the fluid content of the cyst usually contains numerous scolices ("heads") of daughter hydatids.

Aspirates from lymph nodes, spleen, liver, bone marrow and spinal fluid frequently provide diagnostic evidence of African trypanosomiasis, visceral leishmaniasis (kala-azar), Chagas' disease and toxoplasmosis. The material obtained should be used in part for direct, unstained, coverglass preparations to demonstrate motile organisms (trypanosomes), in part for impression smears which are processed by the Giemsa technic (see above, page 588), and in part for culturing the organisms which may be present. (See Chapter 27, pages 605–606.)

BIOPSIED MATERIAL

Biopsy is becoming increasingly useful and common in the diagnosis of parasitic infections. This may be the most convenient and at times is the only method of confirming clinical suspicion of the infection.

Skin biopsies are employed for demonstration of amebiasis cutis, cutaneous leishmaniasis, and microfilarias of *Onchocerca volvulus*. In the former two infections a representative portion of the entire lesion should be removed; this should be fixed in Zenker's solution and processed for serial, or at least several sections to be stained by the hematoxylin-eosin technic. For microfilarias of *O. volvulus* only small, superficial biopsies are required. These thin samples of skin are each placed in a drop of tepid physiologic salt solution, mounted with a coverglass and examined for microfilarias emerging from the tissue fragment. Occasionally in areas where other types of filariasis are endemic other microfilarias may be present, particularly if the biopsy has been deep enough to rupture cutaneous blood vessels.

Superficial lymph node biopsies are designed for demonstration of the organisms of African trypanosomiasis, kala-azar, Chagas' disease and toxoplasmosis. While impression smears should be made for staining with the Giemsa technic, a representative portion should be fixed in Zenker's solution, sectioned and stained with hematoxylin-eosin.

Muscle biopsy is employed for demonstration of *Trichinella* larvas and at times the cysticercus larvas of *Tænia solium.* Some of the former material may be compressed between glass slides and examined directly for *Trichinella* cysts, but a portion should be digested in artificial gastric juice at 37° C. and the excysted larvas concentrated by centrifugalization. (If the specimen is adequate, a portion can be fed to a laboratory rat for evidence of the viability of the larvas which may be present.) Usually muscle biopsy for demonstration of trichinosis is less common than immunologic technics. (See Chapter 28, pages 612–613.) If a cysticercus larva is present in the specimen, it should be carefully dissected out of its capsule deflated with a needle and compressed between a slide and coverglass to demonstrate the characteristic scolex with four suckers and an anterior circlet of hooks.

Proctoscopic biopsy may be performed in an attempt to confirm suspicion of amebic colitis, but it is less commonly undertaken than proctoscopic aspiration. On the other hand, proctoscopic biopsy is a most valuable procedure for demonstrating eggs of *Schistosoma mansoni*, *S. japonicum* and *S. hæmatobium* which have been deposited in the lower mesenteric and rectal venules and have filtered into adjacent tissues of the sigmoid colon and rectum.

Meira and Soares (1948) state that biopsied rectal material taken from the level of the first valve of Houston, rendered transparent by KOH and examined microscopically under compression, provides a simple, harmless procedure. It is particularly valuable in chronic cases of intestinal schistosomiasis and as a follow-up of treatment, when stools are frequently negative for eggs of the parasite. It should always be employed as a check on immunologic tests. Similar technic, using the cystoscope to obtain biopsy of the bladder, is useful in diagnosing *S. hæmatobium* infection.

Visceral biopsy, particularly from the surface of the liver, provides the only practical clinical diagnostic procedure for demonstration of visceral larva migrans produced by dog and cat ascarids (*Toxocara canis, T. felis*). The technic is simple and safe (Beaver *et al.*, 1952).

SPECIMENS OBTAINED FOLLOWING CHEMOTHERAPEUSIS

The most common post-treatment examinations are made in helminthic infections of the intestinal tract, particularly those due to hookworms, *Ascaris*, *Trichocephalus*, the tapeworms, and intestinal trematodes. Depending on whether the anthelmintic is only anesthetizing or is lethal in its effect, the worms will be evacuated in an undamaged, living condition or may be badly damaged.

AUTOPSY MATERIAL

Protozoan Infections.—Since post-mortem tissue autolysis occurs rapidly and with it speedy degeneration of the parasites in the tissues, for good diagnostic evidence it is imperative that autopsy be obtained as soon as possible, preferably within four hours after death. Representative blocks of abnormal tissues should be fixed in formalin, or preferably in Zenker's solution, and then processed for sectioning and staining. Delayed autopsies may provide negative or equivocal information concerning any protozoön which may be involved. In the event the gross lesions strongly suggest amebic infection and necropsy has been delayed, routine sections first stained with hematoxylin-eosin and then with Best's carmine may allow identification of the amebas by their strawberry pink staining reaction.

Helminthic Infections.—While it is always desirable to make necropsy examination for helminths as soon as possible after death, these parasites frequently survive for a considerable time in a diagnosable condition, especially if the body has been kept cold. A majority of helminths will be recovered from the intestinal tract and adjacent viscera, but filaria worms, *Paragonimus* and tapeworm larvas will be located elsewhere.

Gastro-intestinal Infections.—After the gastro-intestinal tract has been removed from the body it should be opened along the line of lesser curvature and the contents from the several levels collected separately for subsequent examinations. Hookworms and whipworms should be removed by gentle traction from their attachment to the bowel wall. *Strongyloides* in the wall may be obtained by careful scraping of the mucosa, particularly of the duodenum and jejunum, but blocks of supposedly infected tissue should always be cut and fixed as soon as possible in Zenker's fluid, later sectioned and examined microscopically. Minute worms, as *Strongyloides* and heterophyoid flukes, are most readily obtained by placing the opened bowel in luke-warm physiologic salt solution, shaking vigorously and examining the liquid for the worms in a large flat petri dish, or by passing the liquid through a fine bronze screen or bolting cloth. For *Clonorchis, Opisthorchis, Fasciola* and *Dicrocœlium* infections, the gall-bladder and biliary passages must be opened and carefully examined.

Helminthic Infections in Other Locations.—In *Schistosoma mansoni, S. japonicum* and *S. hæmatobium* infections, the liver should be removed intact with its connections to the entire intestinal tract, and the mesenteric and rectal venules carefully perfused. Likewise, the intra-hepatic portal vein should be opened and search made there for the worms. Representative blocks of intestine, mesenteric lymph nodes and liver should always be fixed and sectioned. For *S. hæmatobium* and *S. mansoni,* the urinary bladder and other organs of the pelvic region together with their blood supply, should be removed and similarly examined. All three species of *Schistosoma* may likewise be present at times in the pulmonary arterioles. *Paragonimus* is most commonly found within cystic tumors in the depth of the lungs but the worms may have developed in the abdominal viscera or even in the brain. *Echinococcus* cysts most frequently occur in the liver but have been recovered from practically every organ and tissue of the body. The adult Bancroft's filaria worms may develop in lymph nodes and lymphoid tissue in any portion of the body, but are most commonly located in the groin, medially above the testes or at the proximal end of obstructed lymph tracts.

Preservation of Helminths.—Most helminths do not require delicate technics for satisfactory preservation. Tapeworms and trematodes usually fix well in steaming (not boiling) 2% formaldehyde (5% formalin), and nematodes may be fixed in the same medium to which glycerol (1 part to 10 by volume) has been added before the fixative is heated. In case large tapeworms are desired for demonstration specimens, they should be chilled and should be placed in the desired position before fixation.

Sections of tissues containing helminths and their eggs or larvas should be fixed in Zenker's fluid. For museum specimens, in which it is desirable to retain the natural color of tissues, the Kaiserling technic may be employed. For staining microscopic sections containing helminths, Delafield's hematoxylin with eosin is fairly good but Bullard's hematoxylin-eosin is better.

For large tapeworms Roudabush (1947) recommends relaxation of the living worms in water in the icebox so that they will not move when touched. Attached fecal débris should be removed, knots in the worms untangled and the worms wound around the outside of a cylinder in a relaxed state. Then the fixative solution should be gently poured over the worm until complete killing of the tissues has been accomplished. Roudabush (*l. c.*) uses the following fixative formula: Ethyl alcohol, 95%, 24 parts; commercial formalin, 15 parts; glacial acetic acid, 5 parts; glycerol, 10 parts; tap water, 46 parts.

Glycerogel Permanent Mounts for Helminths.—Yetwin (1944) has developed the following medium for making permanent mounts of small nematodes and states that Wotten (1936) employed a similar medium for trematodes.

10% Bacto gelatin, granular (Difco)	150 cc.
Glycerol, reagent (Merck)	50 cc.
1% chromium and potassium sulfate, C. P., granular (Merck)	100 cc.
Phenol, U. S. P., Liquid	1 cc.

The gelatin is dissolved in boiling water and the glycerol added and thoroughly mixed, after which the chrome solution and phenol are similarly introduced. The medium will jell at room temperature but liquefies in 15 minutes at 65° C. Specimens may be transferred directly from glycerol or formalin solutions to the mounting medium which hardens into a permanent mount. In 18 hours, the parasite objects are clear and ready for examination.

For delicate fixation of helminths, needed for study of the more detailed histology and cytology of the worms, Gilson's or Bouin's fluid is recommended. In the preparation of *in toto* mounts of trematodes, tapeworm proglottids or small nematodes, Bullard's hematoxylin may be used for staining, although good results are more difficult to obtain than with acid carmine solutions. Description of the methods will be found in any good manual on microtechnic. For studying the internal anatomy of nematode larvas, a saturated solution of iodine in 1% potassium iodide provides a satisfactory stain for temporary mounts. Living miracidia and cercarias of trematodes, and hexacanth embryos hatched from tapeworm eggs, may be studied to advantage in a 0.1% aqueous solution of brilliant cresyl blue, or in the Velat-Weinstein-Otto stain (*vide* p. 579).

Eggs of helminths obtained from centrifugalization or sedimentation of feces or urine are satisfactorily fixed and preserved in steaming 4% formaldehyde. *Paragonimus* eggs in sputum may be preserved in a phenol-glycerol solution (phenol, 1%; glycerol, 5%; distilled water, 94%).

MATERIAL FROM THE ENVIRONMENT

Material obtained from the environment may be useful in providing evidence of specific causal relationship of an animal agent or vector to the disease in a particular patient, as, for example, recovery of an arthropod or vertebrate animal in connection with host venenation. In this connection, data concerning the presence of protozoan or helminth parasites in reservoir or alternate hosts may provide a clue with respect to the sources of these parasites in man.

Recovery of Parasite Objects from Fomites.—Protozoan parasites are rarely recovered from fomites. Gross fecal pollution of underclothing and furniture may furnish evidence of *Endamœba histolytica* cysts following immersion of these objects in water and concentration of the sediment by macro-centrifugalization (Ivanhoe, 1943).

In contrast to the protozoan parasites, eggs of intestinal helminths are not uncommonly obtained from underclothing, household furniture, green vegetables, topsoil of potted house plants and from paper money. The most common of these eggs in the immediate environment are those of the seatworm, *Enterobius vermicularis*. Likewise it is frequently possible to obtain eggs of *Ascaris*, *Trichocephalus*, human hookworms, *Hymenolepis nana* and *Tænia* on the floors and in other locations within the homes of infected individuals.

Recovery of Parasite Objects from Water.—There is good circumstantial evidence that *Endamœba histolytica* may gain entry to the human digestive tract in drinking water grossly polluted with human excreta, but direct proof by isolation of amebic cysts from the water has only recently been provided (Artigas, 1953). The recovery of eggs of *Ascaris*, *Trichocephalus* and *Tænia* by macrocentrifugalization of sewage has been demonstrated both in natural and experimental studies.

Recovery of Parasite Objects from the Soil.—While it is possible and even probable that under certain conditions in moist tropical countries cysts of intestinal protozoa deposited on the soil in human excreta may survive and later get into the human digestive tract on contaminated objects (Beaver and Deschamps, 1949), no eminently practical method has been developed for recovery of these organisms from the soil.

In epidemiologic investigations of intestinal helminthic infections, it is frequently necessary to obtain direct evidence of soil pollution by demonstration of the eggs or larvas. When first deposited these parasite objects may be present in the fecal sump on top of the ground, but rain, coprophagous insects and other agents soon cause disintegration, with dissemination of the eggs, and the larvas tend to migrate actively in the topsoil.

A satisfactory method of isolating helminth eggs from the soil is described by Headlee (1936) as an adaptation of the Caldwell and Caldwell technic, modified by Spindler (1929). A representative 5 to 10 Gm. sampling from a pint of suspected soil is first placed in a 50 cc. centrifuge tube and treated for an hour with 10 cc. of 30% antiformin solution. The mixture is stirred frequently, to bring the antiformin in contact with every particle of soil. The tube is then filled with sodium dichromate (1.35 specific gravity), the mixture thoroughly shaken, and then centrifugalized at 1000 revolutions per minute for 2 minutes. After being allowed to rise to the surface film the eggs are looped from the film, transferred to a 15 cc. centrifuge tube with a conical bottom, and the tube nearly filled with distilled water. After shaking, the tube is centrifugalized as before, the supernatant fluid pipetted off, and the sediment at the bottom of the tube, containing the eggs, is placed within a rectangular area on a fecal slide and examined microscopically.

Isolation of nematode larvas from the soil is accomplished by the *Baermann technic*, which depends on the principle that a large proportion of nematode larvas will migrate out of the soil into water of a somewhat warmer temperature when this water is brought into contact with the lower surface of the soil. The simple apparatus used consists of a glass filter funnel of 15 to 23 cm. diameter (preferably ribbed), placed in a convenient rack or ring stand, and connected at its lower end with a short rubber tube, provided with a pinch-cock. The soil sample to be tested is placed in a little basket made of 1 mm. mesh bronze or aluminum screening lined with cheesecloth. Luke-warm water is placed in the funnel and its height so adjusted that the lower level of the soil will come in contact with the upper level of the water when the wire basket is set into the funnel. Within 10 to 15 minutes nematode larvas in positive soils may be observed migrating down the stem of the funnel. The maximum yield takes place within the first hour, after which the pinch-cock should be opened, about 25 to 50 cc. of water drawn off into a test-tube, the suspension centrifugalized, the supernatant fluid pipetted off immediately and the sediment poured onto a fecal slide for examination. The examiner needs considerable training to differentiate hookworm and *Strongyloides* larvas from nematodes free-living in the soil.

REFERENCES

Artigas, J. J. 1953. Hallazgo de "*Entamœba Histolytica*" en Muestra de Agua Potable de Osorno. Nueva Technica de Investigación. Bol. Inform. Parasit. Chilenas, *8*, 44.

Baroody, B. J., and Most, H. 1946. The Relative Efficiency of Water Centrifugal Sedimentation and Other Methods of Stool Examination for Diagnosis of Schistosomiasis Japonica. J. Lab. & Clin. Med., *31*, 815–823.

Bass, C. C. 1906. Uncinariasis in Mississippi. J. Am. Med. Assn., *47*, 185–189.

———1910. The Diagnosis of Hookworm Infection with Special Reference to the Examination of Feces for Eggs of Intestinal Parasites. Arch. Diagn., *3*, 231–236.

Beaver, P. C. 1949. A Nephelometric Method of Calibrating the Photoelectric Meter for Making Egg-counts by Direct Fecal Smear. J. Parasitol., *35* (2nd section), 13.

———1950. The Standardization of Fecal Smears for Estimating Egg Production and Worm Burden. J. Parasitol., *36*, 451–456.

Brady, F. J., and Lawton, A. H. 1944. A New Method for Quantitative Estimation of Microfilariæ in Blood Samples. J. Parasitol., *30*, 34.

Brooke, M. M., and Goldman, M. 1949. Polyvinyl Alcohol-fixative as a Preservative and Adhesive for Protozoa in Dysenteric Stools and Other Liquid Material. J. Lab. & Clin. Med., *34*, 1554–1560.

Craig, C. F., and Faust, E. C. 1937. *Clinical Parasitology*, 5th ed., p. 864. Lea & Febiger, Philadelphia.

Faust, E. C., D'Antoni, J. S., Odom, V., Miller, M. J., Peres, C., Sawitz, W., Thomen, L. F., Tobie, J., and Walker, J. H. 1938. A Critical Study of Clinical Laboratory Technics for the Diagnosis of Protozoan Cysts and Helminth Eggs in Feces. Am. J. Trop. Med., *18*, 169–183.

FAUST, E. C., and HOFFMAN, W. A. 1934. Studies on Schistosomiasis Mansoni in Puerto Rico. II. The Epidemiology and Geographical Distribution of Schistosomiasis Mansoni in Puerto Rico. 2. A Survey of Intestinal Parasites in Endemic Schistosomiasis Areas in Puerto Rico. Puerto Rico J. Pub. Health & Trop. Med., *9*, 447–471.

FAUST, E. C., and INGALLS, J. W., JR. 1946. The Diagnosis of Schistosomiasis Japonica. III. Technics for the Recovery of the Eggs of *Schistosoma Japonicum*. Am. J. Trop. Med., *26*, 559–584.

FAUST, E. C., SAWITZ, W., TOBIE, J., ODOM, V., PERES, C., and LINCICOME, D. R. 1939. Comparative Efficiencies of Various Technics for the Diagnosis of Protozoa and Helminths in Feces. J. Parasitol., *25*, 241–262.

FIELD, T. W. 1941. Further Note on a Method of Staining Malarial Parasites in Thick Blood Films. Trans. R. Soc. Trop. Med. & Hyg., *35*, 35–42.

GRAHAM, C. 1941. A Device for the Diagnosis of Enterobius Infection. Am. J. Trop. Med., *21*, 159–161.

HALL, M. C. 1937. Studies on Oxyuriasis. I. Types of Anal Swabs and Scrapers, with a Description of a New Type of Swab. Am. J. Trop. Med., *17*, 445–453.

HEADLEE, W. H. 1936. The Epidemiology of Human Ascariasis in the Metropolitan Area of New Orleans, Louisiana. Am. J. Hyg., *24*, 469–521.

HERNÁNDEZ-MORALES, F., and MALDONADO, J. F. 1946. Diagnosis of Schistosomiasis Mansoni by a Rectal Biopsy Technique. Am. J. Trop. Med., *26*, 811–820.

HOOD, M. 1947. The Practical Handling of Parasitology by the Clinical Pathologist. South. Med. J., *40*, 523–530.

JOHNSON, A. S., JR., and BERRY, M. G. 1945. Asiatic Schistosomiasis: Clinical Features, Sigmoidoscopic Picture and Treatment of Early Infections. War Med., *8*, 156–162.

KNOTT, J. I. 1939. A Method for Making Microfilarial Surveys on Day Blood. Trans. R. Soc. Trop. Med. & Hyg., *33*, 191–196.

KOFOID, C. A., and BARBER, M. A. 1918. Rapid Method for Detection of Ova of Intestinal Parasites in Human Stools. J. Am. Med. Assn., *71*, 1557–1561.

LANE, C. 1924. The Mass Diagnosis of Ankylostome Infestation. Trans. R. Soc. Trop. Med. & Hyg., *17*, 407–436.

LAWLESS, D. K. 1953. A Rapid Permanent-Mount Stain Technique for the Diagnosis of the Intestinal Protozoa. Am. J. Trop. Med. & Hyg., *2*, 1137–1138.

MALDONADO, J. F., and ACOSTA-MATIENZO, J. 1953. A Comparison of Fecal Examination Procedures in the Diagnosis of *Schistosoma Mansoni*. Exp. Parasitol., *2*, 294–310.

MEIRA, J. A., and SOARES, J. C. DE M. 1948. A Biopsia Retal no Diagnostico da Esquistosomiase Mansoni. Arq. Fac. Hig. e Saude Púb., Univ. São Paulo, *2*, 45–90.

NOBLE, G. A. 1944. A Five-minute Method for Staining Fecal Smears. Science, *100*, 37–38.

OTTO, G. F., HEWITT, R., and STRAHAN, D. E. 1941. A Simplified Zinc Sulfate Levitation Method of Fecal Examination for Protozoan Cysts and Hookworm Eggs. Am. J. Hyg., *33*, 32–37.

OTTOLINA, C., and ATENCIO, M. H. 1943. Nuevas Caminas para el Diagnostico Clínico Preciso de la Schistosomiasis Mansoni. Rev. Policlin. Caracas, *12*, 35 pp.

PEPPER, W. 1908. A New Method for Examination of the Feces for the Ova of Uncinaria. J. Med. Research, *13*, 75.

RITCHIE, L. S. 1948. An Ether Sedimentation Technique for Routine Stool Examinations. Bull. U. S. Army Med. Dept., *8*, 326.

ROUDABUSH, R. L. 1947. A Method for Relaxing and Fixing Large Tapeworms. J. Parasitol., *33* (2nd Sec.), 17.

SAPERO, J. J., and LAWLESS, D. K. 1953. The "MIF" Stain-preservation Technic for the Identification of Intestinal Protozoa. Am. J. Trop. Med., and Hyg., *2*, 613–619.

SAWITZ, W. 1942. The Buoyancy of Certain Nematode Eggs. J. Parasitol., *28*, 95–102.

SAWITZ, W., ODOM, V., and LINCICOME, D. R. 1939. The Diagnosis of Oxyuriasis. Comparative Efficiency of the NIH Swab Examinations and Stool Examination by Brine and Zinc Sulphate Flotation for *Enterobius Vermicularis* Infection. Pub. Health Repts., *54*, 1148–1158.

SCHÜFFNER, W., and SWELLENGREBEL, N. H. 1943. Eine Zweizeitige Methode zur Nachweis von Oxyuris-Eiern. Ihre Leistung gegenüber dem Amerikanischen NIH-Wischer. Zentralbl. Bakt. Parasit. u. Infektionskr., *151*, 71–80.

Spindler, L. A. 1929. On the Use of a Method for the Isolation of *Ascaris* Eggs from the Soil. Am. J. Hyg., *10*, 157–164.

Stoll, N. R. 1923. An Effective Method of Counting Hookworm Eggs in Feces. Am. J. Hyg., *3*, 59–70.

Tobie, J. E., Reardon, L. V., Bozicevich, J., Shih, B.-C., Mantel, N., and Thomas, E. H. 1951. The Efficiency of the Zinc Sulfate Technic in the Detection of Intestinal Protozoa by Successive Stool Examinations. Am. J. Trop. Med., *31*, 552–560.

Velat, C. A., Weinstein, P. O., and Otto, G. F. 1950. A Stain for the Rapid Differentiation of the Trophozoites of the Intestinal Amœbæ in Fresh, Wet Preparations. Am. J. Trop. Med., *30*, 43–51.

Weller, T. H., and Dammin, G. J. 1945. An Improved Method of Examination of Feces for the Diagnosis of Intestinal Schistosomiasis. Am. J. Clin. Path., *15*, 496–500.

Willis, H. H. 1921. A Simple Levitation Method for the Detection of Hookworm Ova. Med. J. Australia, *8*, 375–376.

Yetwin, I. J. 1944. A Simple Permanent Mounting Method for *Necator Americanus*. J. Parasitol., *30*, 201.

Yolles, T. K., Moore, D. V., DeGiusti, D. L., Ripsom, C. A., and Meleney, H. E., 1947. A Technique for the Perfusion of Laboratory Animals for the Recovery of Schistosomes. J. Parasitol., *33*, 419–426.

Chapter 27

Culture Technics

THE cultivation of animal agents or vectors of human disease serves a threefold purpose *viz.*, (1) to supplement other methods of laboratory diagnosis, (2) for use in teaching and (3) to provide organisms in quantity for investigation. Diagnostically, it is sometimes possible to obtain the parasite or its vector in culture in an identifiable stage when other material for diagnosis may fail to furnish specific evidence. Culture technics are available for protozoan and helminthic parasites and many of the arthropods.

In Vitro Cultivation of Protozoan Parasites

Intestinal Protozoa.—Numerous media have been developed for the cultivation of intestinal amebas, flagellates and the ciliate *Balantidium coli.* To initiate a culture fresh stools uncontaminated with urine are required. Formed stools containing the cysts may be employed, or liquid specimens with trophozoites. In the latter case elements of mucus and tissue detritus are more likely to contain the pathogen than the diluted fecal portion. To prevent rapid overgrowth of enteric bacteria it is frequently helpful to add penicillin when the stool sample is inoculated into the culture medium, and it is necessary to introduce considerably more inoculum than in bacteriologic cultures.

In general, the inoculum should consist of representative portions of the several components of the stool, saline-purged specimen, enema specimen, proctoscopic aspirate, liver aspirate or other material obtained from the patient. About ½ cc. of the material is inoculated into the medium and the culture is incubated at 37° C. Aseptic technic is recommended. Subcultures are usually made at 48-hour intervals. At times no evidence of the suspected organism is found in samplings of the original culture but subcultures may be positive. The following media are selected from the many good ones which have been developed. (For other technics please consult Craig's *Laboratory Diagnosis of Protozoan Diseases*, 2nd ed., 1948.)

CULTURE MEDIA

Balamuth's Monophasic Medium (1946)

A. *Preparation*

1. Weigh 288 Gm. dehydrated egg yolk.
2. Add 288 cc. distilled water and 1000 cc. 0.85% saline, and with an electric mixer (or similar instrument) emulsify until suspension is smooth.

3. Heat over an open flame in the top part of a double boiler, stirring constantly until coagulation begins (5–10 min.).
4. Heat the mixture over boiling water, stirring occasionally until coagulation is complete (about 20 min.). Add 160 cc. distilled water to offset loss from evaporation.
5. Filter the mixture through a muslin bag. When the bag cools it may be squeezed gently to obtain the maximum volume of filtrate.
6. Measure filtrate and add 0.85% saline to bring volume to 1000 cc.
7. Dispense the filtrate into 2 one-liter Erlenmeyer flasks. Autoclave for 20 min. at 15 lbs. (121° C.).
8. Place the flasks in the refrigerator overnight or until the solution is thoroughly chilled.
9. Filter while cold through a Buchner funnel, preferably using negative pressure to facilitate filtration. Use 2 pieces of Whatman qualitative filter paper of suitable size and pour the mixture in small amounts through the funnel, replacing the papers frequently.
10. Measure the filtrate. Add an equal volume of Balamuth's buffer solution.
11. Add 0.5% crude liver extract (Lilly, No. 408) (5 cc. per liter of medium).
12. Dispense in 5–7 cc. amounts in tubes; autoclave for 20 minutes at 15 lbs. (121° C.). Add sterile rice powder and incubate for 24 hours at 37° C. before using. The medium may be left in flasks in large amounts, autoclaved, and stored in the refrigerator. It can be kept for a month or more without deterioration, though there may be an accumulation or sediment which should be removed by filtration. Re-autoclaving produces no harmful effects, and may even be beneficial.

B. *Solutions*

1. Balamuth buffer solution

(*a*) 1*M* K_2HPO_4	174.180 Gm.
Distilled water to make . . .	1000.0 cc.
(*b*) 1*M* KH_2PO_4	136.092 Gm.
Distilled water to make . . .	1000.0 cc.

2. Mix these solutions in a ratio of 4.3 parts 1*M* K_2HPO_4 to 0.7 parts 1*M* KH_2PO_4. To one part of this mixture add 14 parts of distilled water to prepare the *M*/15 buffer. This final solution is the one used in (10) above in the directions for preparation of the medium.

Boeck and Drbohlav's Diphasic (L.E.S.) Medium (1925)

Preparation.—Four eggs are washed, brushed with alcohol, and broken into a sterile flask containing glass beads. Fifty cc. of Locke's solution (see below) are then added and the mixture broken up by shaking. Test tubes are then filled with enough of the mixture to produce slants about 1 to 1.5 inches in length upon coagulating by heat. The tubes are slanted in an inspissator and heated at 70° C. (158° F.) until the mixture is solidified, after which they are autoclaved at 15 lb. pressure for twenty minutes. The tubes are then covered to a depth of about 1 cm. with a mixture of equal parts of sterile Locke's solution and 1 part of sterile inactivated human blood serum after the mixture has been passed through a Berkefeld filter and incubated to determine sterility.

Medium No. 2. Locke-egg-albumin (L.E.A.) Medium.—The above medium was modified by Drbohlav by using crystallized egg albumin instead of human blood serum. A 1% solution of crystallized egg albumin in Locke's solution was sterilized by passage through a Berkefeld filter, and then added to the tubes containing the egg slants as described for the L.E.S. medium.

The initial reaction of these media varies from *p*H 7.2 to *p*H 7.8 and requires no adjustment.

Locke's Solution.—The Locke solution used in the above media has the following formula:

NaCl	9.0 Gm.
$CaCl_2$	0.2 "
KCl	0.4 "
$NaHCO_2$	0.2 "
Glucose	2.5 "
Distilled water . . .	1000 cc.

The solution is sterilized in the Arnold sterilizer or the autoclave.

Modified Diphasic Medium (As utilized by the Amebiasis Research Unit, Dept. Trop. Med. & Pub. Health, Tulane Univ.)

A. Preparation

1. Emulsify 4 whole hen's eggs with 50 cc. of Ringer's Solution.
2. Filter the emulsion through several thicknesses of cheesecloth or surgical gauze.
3. Dispense 2–3 cc. amounts into 16 × 150 mm. Pyrex test tubes.
4. Place several layers of paper in the bottom of the autoclave and slant the tubes at an angle of 30°. (Place the tubes in baskets so that the rows are not more than 2–3 deep.)
5. Inspissate for 10 minutes at 15 lb. in the autoclave. (Set valves according to directions which accompany the machine.) Cool.
6. Overlay each slant with approximately 5 cc. of buffered saline (*p*H 7.0), or normal saline containing 0.5% crude liver extract (Lilly, No. 408).
7. Sterilize slants in the autoclave for 20 minutes at 15 lb. (121° C.). (Wrap the baskets in paper to minimize breaking of the slants during sterilization.)
8. Add about one loopful of sterile rice powder to each sterile overlayed slant.
9. Incubate medium for 24 hrs. at 37° C. just prior to use, to demonstrate sterility.

B. Solutions.

1. Stock Ringer's Solution

NaCl	70.0 Gm.
CaCl	3.0 "
KCl	2.5 "
Distilled water . . .	1000 cc.

Dilute the stock solution 1:10 with neutral distilled water for use.

2. Buffered Saline (*p*H 7.0)

0.85% Saline	450.0 cc.
M/15 KH_2PO_4	19.0 cc.
M/15 Na_2HPO_4	31.0 cc.
M/15 KH_2PO_4, prepared as follows:	
KH_2PO_4	0.07 Gm.
Distilled water to make . .	1000 cc.
M/15 Na_2HPO_4, prepared as follows:	
Na_2HPO_4	9.46 Gm.
Distilled water to make . .	1000 cc.

Nelson's Medium (1947)

Preparation.—The material consists of human, calf, beef or guinea-pig liver, cat intestine, or egg yolk; all give about the same result when extracted.

The extraction of the selected tissue is made with 95% ethyl alcohol by adding 10 parts of the tissue or egg yolk to 90 parts of the alcohol. The tissue used is cut into small pieces and placed in the alcohol; if egg yolk is used the yolk is separated from the white which gives an inert extract.

The flask or bottle containing the alcohol and tissue is shaken several times a day and is ready for use in 48 hours. At the time of use place 10 cc. of the stock alcoholic extract in a small flask and drive off the alcohol by heating in a water bath; then add 20 cc. of a melted 2% agar in buffered 0.5% saline, tube the mixture in 2 cc. quantities and slant. No serum supplement is required. Cover the agar slants with buffered 0.5% saline, inoculate and incubate. (The agar mixture can be autoclaved before slanting if desired.) The *p*H of the medium should be 7.4 if tissue extracts are used and 7.6 if egg-yolk extract is used. Rice flour sterilized at 150° C. is added to the medium at the time of inoculation.

Shaffer, Ryden and Frye's Transparent Medium (1948–1949)

Components per tube:

1. Saline: 2 cc.
2. Horse serum: 0.25 cc.
3. Supernate of streptobacillus: 2.5 cc.
4. Penicillin: 500 units per tube.

Preparation.—Since large numbers of cultures are usually transferred at one time, the required quantity of medium is prepared as follows:

1. Twenty-four hours before the transfers are to be made, large tubes (25 mm. × 200 mm.) of thioglycollate medium (containing 30 cc.), plus starch and overlaid with petrolatum, are inoculated with 0.5 cc. from a 48-hour culture of streptobacillus (also in thioglycollate medium). The petrolatum is resealed with heat, and the tubes are incubated for 24 hours at 37° C.

   These tubes of thioglycollate each have approximately 4 loopfuls of rice flour added 24 hours or more before they are to be used. They are incubated for 24 hours after the addition of starch to ascertain whether or not contaminants are present. Since the tubes are sealed with petrolatum, they can be stored for a long period of time without the medium oxidizing.
2. When the streptobacillus is 24 hours old, the following steps are performed:
   a. The streptobacillus cultures are put into 50 cc. centrifuge tubes, overlaid with petrolatum, and centrifugalized at 2000 rpm. for 45 minutes.
   b. While the streptobacillus is in the centrifuge, physiologic salt solution and serum are measured into a flask in the desired amounts. Stock solutions containing 200 cc. of the salt solution and 25 cc. of horse serum are prepared aseptically approximately 10 days or more previous to the transfers. Immediately after they are prepared, 1 cc. from each solution is introduced into a tube of thioglycollate, then incubated for 10 days to insure the sterility of the solutions. The solutions may be stored in the refrigerator for considerable periods of time. The horse serum is preserved with merthiolate, 1 to 10,000.
   c. Ten minutes before the streptobacillus is to be taken from the centrifuge, penicillin is added to the saline-horse serum mixture.
   (1) 500 units penicillin per tube are used in routine transfers in which there are no bacteria present other than the streptobacillus.

(2) In cultures that are being transferred from a medium other than Shaffer-Ryden-Frye, or in those that have bacteria present other than streptobacillus, both streptomycin and penicillin are used: *viz.*, 10,000 units streptomycin and 5,000 units penicillin per tube for the first three or four transfers, or until the contaminants are killed.

d. The streptobacillus is then taken from the centrifuge, and the supernate is removed with a pipette (do not disturb sediment in bottom of tube) and immediately added to the flask containing the saline-horse serum and penicillin.

e. The medium is then dispensed into test tubes (16 mm. × 150 mm.) in 4.5 cc. amounts.

f. 0.5 cc. inoculum is then added to each tube. The tubes are sealed with petrolatum and incubated at 37° C.

g. Transfers are made at 72 or 96 hours.

Note.—The entire procedure requires aseptic technic.

Sadun, Krupp and Everritt's Embryonic Fluid Medium (1952)

This was developed to provide a transparent medium which could be prepared in quantity and stored for some time before use, in which large numbers of *Endamœba histolytica* could be grown sufficiently free of bacteria and particulate matter so that precise metabolic studies could be carried out. This method, like that of Shaffer, Ryden and Frye, is principally for research use.

Preparation.—Chicken eggs which have embryonated 9 to 13 days are candled and drilled, the shell opened, the shell membrane teased away, and the amniotic and allantoic fluids removed aseptically with a Pasteur pipette. In pooled amounts of 3.8 cc. the fluid is then introduced into 125 × 14 mm. tubes. *E. histolytica* trophozoites grown in Balamuth's or L.E.S. medium for 48 hours are transferred in 0.2 cc. amounts to each tube. Penicillin and streptomycin are then added to make a final dilution of 1,000 units of each antibiotic per cc. of medium. The tubes are sealed with petrolatum and incubated at 37° C. for 48 hours. Sterility tests should indicate no viable bacteria at the end of the incubation period, and 5- to 10-fold increase in amebas may be anticipated. For subculturing 0.3 cc. of sediment containing the amebas, 0.3 cc. of bacterial culture with which the amebas have been previously associated and 0.1 cc. of antibiotic solution (1000 units each of penicillin and streptomycin per cc. of final volume) are introduced into each tube, which is sealed with petrolatum and incubated for 48 hours.

Phillips' Medium (1950)

This differs from all other *in vitro* culture media for *Endamœba histolytica* in the substitution of *Trypanosoma cruzi* as the metabolic associate. The amebas previously grown in a Shaffer-Ryden-Frye type of medium are inoculated into a thioglycollate preparation with horse serum and a rich suspension of *T. cruzi* which has been grown on diphasic blood agar. Penicillin is added to provide bacterial sterility, and petrolatum overlay to reduce O_2 tension. Transfers are made at 48-hour periods.

Hogue's Medium for Intestinal Flagellates (1921)

Preparation.—The whites of 6 hen's eggs are placed in a flask containing glass beads and thoroughly shaken, after which 600 cc. of a 0.7% sodium chloride solution are added. The mixture is heated over a water-bath for 20 to 30 minutes, being constantly agitated while cooking, passed through coarse cheesecloth, and then filtered through cotton with a suction pump. Five cc. of the filtrate are placed in each culture tube, the tubes are stoppered with cotton plugs and autoclaved for 20 minutes at 15 lb. pressure.

This medium has proved valuable in the cultivation of *Trichomonas hominis*, *Embadomonas intestinalis*, *Chilomastix mesnili* and other flagellates. The portion of fecal material to be cultured may be collected upon a toothpick, and, when an amount about the size of an apple-seed has adhered, the tooth-pick can be dropped into the test-tube containing the medium, and the whole incubated at about 36° C. The medium should be examined in 24 hours for flagellates, which are most numerous on the surface of the medium.

Adler and Pulvertaft's Medium (1944)

This is very satisfactory for growth of *Trichomonas vaginalis* free of bacteria.

Preparation:

Locke's solution	4.0 cc.
Goat's or sheep serum, inactivated	0.5 "
Septamide (Heyden), 17% sol.	0.1 "
Rice powder	
Penicillin, 90 units per cc.	

Subcultures grow well on a modified Trussell and Johnson medium (1941), consisting of:

1. Proteose peptone 2%
   NaCl 0.5%
   Make up in distilled water, adjust to *p*H 6 and autoclave.
2. Add: Normal human serum . . 5%
   Sodium thioglycollate . . 0.1%

Rees' Medium for Balantidium Coli (1927)

Preparation.—A modified Ringer's Solution is made up as follows:

NaCl	6.50 Gm.
KCl	0.14 "
$CaCl_2$	0.12 "
$NaHCO_3$	0.20 "
Na_2HPO_4	0.01 "
Distilled water	1000 cc.

To each 18 cc. of this solution placed in a test tube and autoclaved at 15 lb. pressure for 10 minutes, 2 cc. of sterile human or horse serum and a small sprinkling of sterile rice powder are added. The inoculum is then introduced, the culture incubated at 36° C., and transfers made every 72 hours.

Blood and Tissue Flagellates.—The inoculum consists of blood, aspirates or small amounts of biopsied or post-mortem samples from glands, spleen, liver or bone marrow, obtained aseptically from patients suspected of having infection of *Leishmania donovani*, *L. brasiliensis*, *L. tropica*, *Trypanosoma gambiense*, *T. rhodesiense*, *T. cruzi* or other hemoflagellates. To insure bacterial sterility it is desirable to introduce 500 units of penicillin into each tube at the time of inoculation.

Novy, MacNeal and Nicolle's (NNN) Medium (1904–1908)

This method was developed for cultivation of the leishmanias but is equally satisfactory for *Trypanosoma cruzi.*

Preparation.—The formula is as follows:

Agar	14 Gm.
Sodium chloride . .	6 "
Distilled water . .	900 cc.

Mix and bring to the boiling-point, then distribute in tubes and sterilize in the autoclave.

In using the tubed medium, it is melted and then cooled to 48° C. and to each tube of medium one-third of its volume of sterile defibrinated rabbit blood is added. This is well mixed with the medium by rotating the tube, after which the tubes are slanted and allowed to cool. This is best done on ice, as more water of condensation is obtained, and it is in this supernate at the bottom of the tubes that the organisms develop most rapidly and in greatest numbers. Before using, the tubes should be tested for sterility by placing them in the incubator at 37° C. for twenty-four hours.

Senekji's Medium (1939)

This was developed for cultivation of the leishmanias and *T. cruzi.*

Preparation.—The technic is as follows:

I. *Blood Culture Medium.*—Bacto beef extract, 50 parts is dissolved in distilled water 1000 parts and heated at 50° C. for 1 hour, then at 80° C. for 5 minutes. The solution is passed through filter paper and the following ingredients added: neopeptone, 20 parts; agar (Nobel), 20 parts, NaCl (c.p.), 5 parts. Adjust to a *p*H of 7.2–7.4. Autoclave at 15 pounds for 20 minutes. When cool, add defibrinated rabbit's blood to make 10% of the medium.

II. *Egg-liver Extract.*—Four eggs are emulsified with glass beads in a sterile flask. Add 50 cc. of the following solution:

NaCl, 0.02 Gm.; $CaCl_2$, 0.02 Gm.; KCl, 0.02 Gm.; $NaHCO_3$, 0.02 Gm.; distilled water, 100 cc. Emulsify, filter and make into test-tube slants or put in flasks; sterilize at 90° C. at 1-lb. pressure for 10 minutes. Reduce autoclave pressure very slowly to avoid bubbles. Overlay solidified base with sterile 0.5% liver extract in normal physiologic salt solution. Incubate 24 hours to test sterility.

On the blood medium the leishmanias and *T. cruzi* form luxuriant colonies. Contaminated cultures can be purified by adding penicillin, 500 units/cc.

Brutsaert and Henrard's Medium (1938)

This was developed for cultivation of the African trypanosomes.

Preparation.—Two basic solutions are employed: 0.6% each of Ringer's and Tyrode's. These are dispensed in amounts of 2 to 2.5 cc. in test tubes, autoclaved, and to each tube there are added 2 cc. of 1% citrated human blood. The tubes are then incubated at 37° C. for 24 hours to test their bacterial sterility. Blood from infected patients or animals is drawn up into a syringe and discharged in 0.5 cc. amounts into the culture tubes, which are incubated at 25° to 28° C. Growth should be demonstrable in ten to twenty days by microscopic examination.

Weinman's Medium (1944)

This was developed for cultivation of *Trypanosoma gambiense.* It is a modification of the Noguchi-Battistini medium (1926) for culturing *Bartonella bacilliformis.*

Preparation.—The medium consists of (*a*) NaCl 8 Gm. and distilled water to make up 900 cc.; (*b*) citrated human plasma 100 cc. and human hemoglobin (made by taking 1 part of blood with 3 parts of distilled water) 20 cc. (*a*) is autoclaved and (*b*) added and the medium adjusted to *p*H 7.4 to 7.5. It is dispensed in rubber-stoppered test tubes and, when inoculated, incubated at 26° to 28° C. The cultures become positive in 7 to 10 days.

Malaria Parasites.—*No simple,* satisfactory *culture method has been developed* for the *in vitro* cultivation of malaria parasites. Relatively complicated media, apparatus and technics have led to success in survival and asexual multiplication of *Plasmodium vivax*, *P. falciparum*, *P. knowlesi* and *P. cynomolgi* in a medium consisting of inorganic salts, carbohydrates, liver extract, ascorbic acid, and whole-blood mixtures containing the parasites (Geiman, 1951).

Toxoplasma.—*T. gondii* has not been cultivated under *in vitro* conditions.

In Vitro Cultivation of Parasitic Helminths

Attempts have been made to culture parasitic helminths in nutrient media, in some instances attended with partial success. In general, aseptic technics in bacteria-free media have prolonged the life of the worms and in some species have resulted in development from a larva to a more mature larval stage or to sexual maturity. The complexity of helminth metabolism and inability to meet essential environmental conditions undoubtedly account for failure to complete the life cycles of these organisms under artificial conditions.

In contrast to the above-mentioned parasitic helminths, it is relatively easy to obtain the complete extrinsic, *e. g.*, free-living stages, of strains of *Strongyloides stercoralis* or of other species of this genus exhibiting indirect development. Rhabditoid larvas (or eggs) of these strains, recovered from the stools of the natural hosts, provide the inoculum. The media consist of host's feces or other suitable nutriment, containing the associated enteric bacteria or free of bacteria. If conditions of moisture, *p*H and nutrition are properly maintained, development may be continued through several free-living generations, and theoretically for an indefinite period before the organism produces filariform larvas (Beach, 1936; Graham, 1939).

Development of Arthropods in the Laboratory

For diagnostic purposes, it is at times desirable to develop certain arthropods from larval to adult stages. While there are keys for the identification of the larval stages of mosquitoes, fly maggots, beetle larvas and certain other arthropods of medical importance, such identification is usually made by experts in taxonomic entomology. Many of these arthropods and others can be developed and maintained in the laboratory if they are needed for teaching and research purposes. The common species of mosquitoes, particularly *Aëdes ægypti* and *Culex pipiens* or *C. quinquefasciatus*, and some species of *Anopheles*, are good examples.

In Vivo Cultivation of Parasites

Some animal parasites which have thus far been refractory to *in vitro* cultivation may be developed in appropriate animal tissues. This latter method is essential for direct demonstration of living *Toxoplasma gondii* outside the host and provides an opportunity for studying host-tissue relationship and pathogenicity of many other parasites under controlled conditions.

Cultivation in Chick Embryos and Tissue Explants.—Attempts to culture *Endamœba histolytica* free of bacteria in living chick embryos have been unsuccessful (Everritt *et al.*, 1953), but Shaffer *et al.* (1953) have reported satisfactory growth and multiplication in minced tissue-culture media, free of microbial associates.

Romaña and Meyer (1942) and Hawking (1946) have studied the mammalian phase of the life cycle of *Trypanosoma cruzi* in tissue culture, employing a technic which is adaptable to similar investigation of human leishmaniasis (Tchernomoretz, 1946; Hawking, 1948) and may possibly be useful in studies of the African trypanosomes.

Plasmodia of avian and primate malarias have been successfully cultivated in chick embryonic tissue and mammalian tissue explants, and in some instances have been found in preërythrocytic stages when the inoculum consisted of sporozoites of the appropriate plasmodium obtained from infected mosquitoes (Hawking, 1945; Tonkin and Hawking, 1947; Hawking *et al.*, 1948).

The studies of MacFarlane and Ruchman (1948) and of Jacobs (1953) indicate that "chick embryos serve well for the propagation of *Toxoplasma.* Inoculation into the yolk sac results in dissemination of the parasite which can be recovered from the chorioallantoic and other membranes and from the embryonic tissues in one week or earlier" (Jacobs, *l. c.*).

Development of the Parasite in Experimental Hosts.—The procedure is so well known and so extensively documented that it needs no elaboration. All types of laboratory animals have been employed to carry on these investigations (Faust, 1953), so that human volunteers have been spared the hazards of the disease except for critical clinical studies after the basic investigations have been completed.

REFERENCES

Adler, S., and Pulvertaft, J. V. 1944. The Use of Penicillin for Obtaining Bacteria-free Cultures of *Trichomonas Vaginalis* Donné, 1837. Ann. Trop. Med. & Parasitol., *38*, 188–189.

Balamuth, W. 1946. Improved Egg Yolk Infusion for Cultivation of *Entamœba Histolytica* and Other Intestinal Protozoa. Am. J. Clin. Path., *16*, 380–384.

Boeck, W. C., and Drhbolav, J. 1925. The Cultivation of *Endamœba Histolytica.* Am. J. Hyg., *5*, 371–407.

Everritt, M. G., Sadun, E. H., and Carrera, G. M. 1953. Cultivation of *Endamœba Histolytica* in the Chick Embryo. Exp. Parasitol., *2*, 141–146.

Faust, E. C. 1953. Animal Research in Tropical Medicine. Bull. Med. Res., *8*, 2–5.

Geiman, Q. M. 1951. The Cultivation of Malarial Parasites, in *Parasitic Infections in Man*, edited by Harry Most, pages 130–149. Columbia University Press, New York.

Hall, M. C. 1917. The Longevity of Adult Ascarids Outside the Body of the Host: Its Bearing in Anthelmintic Treatment. J. Am. Med. Assn., *68*, 772–773.

Hawking, F. 1945. Growth of Protozoa in Tissue Culture. I. *Plasmodium Gallinaceum*, Exoërythrocytic Forms. Trans. R. Soc. Trop. Med. & Hyg., *39*, 245–263.

———1946. Growth of Protozoa in Tissue Culture. II. *Plasmodium Relictum*, Exoërythrocytic Forms. Trans. R. Soc. Trop. Med. & Hyg., *40*, 183–188.

———1948. Growth of Protozoa in Tissue Culture. V. *Leishmania donovani.* Trans. R. Soc. Trop. Med. & Hyg., *41*, 545–554.

Hawking, F., Perry, W. L. M., and Thurston, J. P. 1948. Tissue Forms of a Malaria Parasite, *Plasmodium cynomolgi.* Lancet, *i*, 783–789.

Hogue, M. J. 1921. The Cultivation of *Trichomonas Hominis.* Am. J. Trop. Med., *1*, 211–214.

Jacobs, L. 1953. The Biology of *Toxoplasma.* Am. J. Trop. Med. & Hyg., *2*, 365–389.

MacFarlane, J. O., and Ruchman, I. 1948. Cultivation of *Toxoplasma* in the Developing Chick Embryo. Proc. Soc. Exp. Biol. & Med., *67*, 1–4.

Nelson, E. C. 1947. Alcoholic Extract Medium for the Diagnosis and Cultivation of *Endamœba Histolytica.* Am. J. Trop. Med., *27*, 545–552.

NOVY, F. G., and MACNEAL, W. J. 1904. On the Cultivation of *Trypanosoma Brucei*. J. Infect. Dis., *1*, 1–30.

PHILLIPS, B. P. 1950. Cultivation of *Endamœba Histolytica* with *Trypanosoma Cruzi*. Science, *111*, 8–9.

REES, C. W. 1927. Balantidia from Pigs and Guinea-pigs: Their Viability, Cyst Production and Cultivation. Science, *66*, 89–91.

SADUN, E. H., KRUPP, I. M., and EVERRITT, M. G. 1952. Cultivation of *Endamœba Histolytica* in Embryonic Fluids. Proc. Soc. Exp. Biol. & Med., *80*, 272–275.

SENEKJI, H. A. 1939. Studies on the Culture of *Leishmania Tropica*. Trans. R. Soc. Trop. Med. & Hyg., *33*, 267–269.

SHAFFER, J. G., SIENKIEWICZ, H. S., and WASHINGTON, J. E. 1953. The Propagation of *Endamœba Histolytica* in Tissue-Bearing Culture without Accompanying Bacteria or Other Microörganisms. Am. J. Hyg., *57*, 366–379.

SHAFFER, J. G., RYDEN, F. W., and FRYE, W. W. 1948. The Growth and Multiplication of *Endamœba Histolytica* in a Transparent Medium, without the Addition of Rice Flour or Other Particulate Matter and Without Demonstrable Bacteria. Am. J. Hyg., *47*, 345–350.

SMYTH, J. D. 1946. Studies on Tapeworm Physiology. III. Aseptic Cultivation of Larval Diphyllobothriidæ *in Vitro*. J. Exp. Biol., *24*, 374–386.

————1947. Studies on Tapeworm Physiology. II. Cultivation and Development of *Ligula Intestinalis in Vitro*. Parasitol., *38*, 173–181.

TCHERNOMORETZ, I. 1946. The Tissue Culture of L. D. Bodies of *L. Donovani* and *L. Infantum* from Flagellates. Harefuah, *30*, No. 4. (Cited by Hawking, 1948.)

TONKIN, I. M., and HAWKING, F. 1947. Growth of Protozoa in Tissue Culture. IV. *P. Lophuræ*, Exoerythrocytic Forms *in Vivo* and *in Vitro*. Trans. R. Soc. Trop. Med. & Hyg., *41*, 407.

WEINMAN, D. 1944. Cultivation of *Trypanosoma Gambiense in Vitro* in Cell-free Medium. Proc. Soc. Exp. Biol. & Med., *55*, 82–83.

Chapter 28

Immunologic Diagnosis

Introduction

IMMUNOLOGIC diagnostic tests are available in a considerable number of protozoan and helminthic infections. In some animal parasitoses immunologic reactions provide the only, or the most practical methods of demonstrating the presence of a particular organism.

The parasite and its products constitute the antigen and the substances elaborated by the host are the antibodies. In general, the more intimate the tissue relationship is between parasite and host, the greater is the amount of antibody which is produced.

Immunologic reactions may result from one or more of three components in the antigen, *viz.*, protein, lipoid and polysaccharide. The protein is generally recognized as the fraction indicating species-specificity; the lipoid shows group relationships of the parasite, and the polysaccharide provides evidence of strain specificity. All three of these fractions are present in every protozoan or metazoan parasite which has been investigated. However, antigens which are artificially prepared for testing purposes differ greatly in their specificity and potency, depending on the method of their preparation, the care with which the antigens have been isolated, and particularly their purity. Furthermore, the types of tests which are made with the antigen are not necessarily subject to similar interpretation. For example, an intradermal reaction may be positive and the precipitin or complement-fixation reaction negative. The latter is more indicative of present host activity to the parasite, while the former provides information that the parasite is or has provoked host reaction.

In some infections, notably amebiasis, the immunologic antibody response is transient and disappears soon after the causal agent has been eradicated. In many parasitic infections, however, a positive test may be elicited many years after the infection was acquired.

In this chapter immunologic tests will be considered only for those parasitic diseases in which other diagnostic procedures can not be more readily carried out, or in which the immunologic evidence adds materially to the diagnosis.

Immunologic Tests for Protozoa

Intestinal Protozoa.—The only species of intestinal protozoön for which immunologic tests may have practical significance is *Endamœba histolytica*. Dependable clinical laboratory diagnosis of this infection by immunologic technics has not yet been developed. This method should never be regarded as a substitute for recovery of *E. histolytica* in the stools, in purged, enema or aspirated material, but it would serve a very useful purpose in suspected cases in which no definite evidence of infection has been obtained by these procedures. And it would be particularly helpful in amebic hepatitis (Hussey and Brown, 1950) as well as in follow-up examinations after anti-amebic therapy.

Craig (1929) prepared antigen for the *complement fixation test* by extraction with alcohol of abundant trophozoites of *E. histolytica,* either grown in culture or obtained from dysenteric mucoid material in the stools of artificially infected dogs. The test in approximately 1000 human cases closely paralleled the coprologic examinations made by the present author and his associates, and there were very few false positives or negatives. The technic for preparing antigen and conducting the test has been described by Craig in his *Laboratory Diagnosis of Protozoan Diseases* (1948), pages 95–115. Results obtained by other workers employing Craig's technic have been contradictory or equivocal.

Bozicevich and associates have used the saline extraction technic and obtained a positive correlation of approximately 80 per cent with coprologic diagnosis. These workers grew their ameba in cultures in association with a single non-pathogenic bacterium.

Thus far the complement fixation technic for diagnosing amebiasis is still relatively unsatisfactory, due to difficulty in obtaining a sufficiently potent antigen rather than to its non-specificity. The antigen prepared by Eli Lilly and Company appears to surmount much of the difficulty.

No practical method has been developed for employing amebic antigen in conducting precipitin or intradermal tests.

Malaria Parasites.—Several workers have developed technics for serologic tests in malaria. *Complement fixation* has been obtained in simian and human malarias (Coggeshall and Eaton, 1938; Dulaney and Stratman-Thomas, 1940; Kligler and Yoeli, 1941; Dulaney and Watson, 1945). *Precipitin reaction* has been carried out with antigens prepared from human and simian infections by Taliaferro and Fisher (1927), Taliaferro and Taliaferro (1928) and Stratman-Thomas and Dulaney (*l. c.*). Another serologic test to diagnose malaria is *flocculation* (Akashi and So, 1941; Chorine and Prudhomme, 1934; Henry, 1927 and Naidu, Rao and Rajagopal, 1942). In addition, Proske and Watson (1939) have reported a specific *tyrosin-staining test* which is claimed to provide a higher diagnostic yield (97.4 per cent) than examination of thick blood films (81.9 per cent).

Blood and Tissue Flagellates.—*The Leishmanias.*—Although *Leishmania donovani, L. tropica* and *L. brasiliensis* are morphologically indistinguishable from one another, they may be differentiated by agglutination tests, employing the leptomonas stage of the respective organisms grown in blood-agar culture and sera from immunized rabbits (Nicolle and Manceaux, 1909; Pavoni, 1914; Noguchi, 1926; Wagener and Koch, 1926).

Practical diagnosis of leishmaniasis may be obtained by agglutination, precipitin or complement-fixation reactions.

Nonspecific Tests.—In kala-azar there is characteristically a notable increase in serum globulin, so that the addition of a small amount of distilled water, antimony or formalin to patient's serum produces precipitation or cloudiness of the serum. The test is performed in a serologic tube, into which approximately 1 cc. of patient's serum is introduced. If 2 or 3 volumes of distilled water are then introduced a white precipitation occurs in a half hour or less in positive cases. This is the *serum-euglobulin test* of Bramachari (1917) and Sia (1921). A similar precipitate is formed (*antimony test*) in the sera of positive cases when urea stibamine (4% sol.) or stibosan is allowed to trickle down the side of the tube (Chopra, das Gupta and David, 1927). Likewise, if 1 drop of commercial formaldehyde is added to 1 cc. of positive serum in the tube and the mixture is shaken well, an opaque opalescent whitish gel is soon formed. This is the *formol-gel test* or *aldehyde test* of Napier (1921).

Complement fixation has also become a very efficient method of diagnosis in kala-azar. Sen Gupta (1943), who made extensive clinical trial of the tubercle-antigen complement-fixation test developed by Greval, Sen Gupta and Napier (1939), states that this test is of high diagnostic significance.

More recently it has been demonstrated by several observers that complement fixation with the antigen devised by Witebsky, Klingenstein and Kuhn, prepared from the acid-fast bacillus of Kedrowsky, gives a very high percentage of positive results with the blood serum in early cases of kala-azar. Sen Gupta (1944) has reported that in 900 cases of kala-azar and other diseases, 93% of the 240 cases of kala-azar gave a positive reaction, while in 664 patients suffering from other diseases liable to be confused with kala-azar 99% gave a negative reaction. He concluded that this test is even superior to sternal puncture in the early diagnosis of kala-azar.

Attempts should always be made to support positive serologic reactions by recovery of the leishmania in material obtained by aspiration from enlarged glands, bone marrow or spleen, either by demonstration of the organism in Giemsa-stained smears or after culture in blood agar media.

The *intradermal reaction* has been tested in all three types of leishmaniasis and has potential diagnostic usefulness. The antigen is obtained by physiologic saline extraction of cultured leishmanias. Positive diagnosis may be obtained before the organisms themselves are demonstrable in the patient's tissues. The reaction is of the delayed type but usually appears within 24 hours following the introduction of antigen into the skin. In 1926, Montenegro demonstrated the diagnostic value of this test, with confirmation by Gomes (1939), Pessôa and Pestana (1940) and Battistini and Herrer (1945) for *L. brasiliensis* and Dostrovsky and Sagher (1946) for *L. tropica*. Its particular diagnostic value in *L. brasiliensis* infection is after extension of the primary lesion to the muco-cutaneous junctions, in which the leishmanias may be difficult to demonstrate.

African Trypanosomes.—Although attempts have been made since the beginning of the present century to develop immunologic tests for the detection of infection with *Trypanosoma gambiense* and *T. rhodesiense*, no practical serologic method has been developed.

Trypanosoma Cruzi.—The three immunologic methods which have been explored are the intradermal reaction, agglutination and complement fixation. Mayer and Pifano (1941) and Mazza *et al.*, (1942) developed an *intradermal test*, employing as antigen cultured *T. cruzi* concentrates killed in 0.5 per cent phenol in physiologic salt solution. These workers reported a specific local reaction which reached its climax in 48 hours.

Agglutination has been demonstrated experimentally by Packchanian (1940) and Senekji (1943) and is highly specific, but this diagnostic procedure has not been widely tested in human infections.

Complement fixation constitutes a very valuable diagnostic method for diagnosis of *T. cruzi*, particularly in relatively occult chronic infections. As originally developed by Guerreiro and Machado (1913), *e. g.*, the so-called *Machado test*, antigen was obtained as an aqueous extract of the spleens of experimentally infected puppies, and the test was conducted by the usual complement-fixation technic. Kelser (1936) refined the procedure by obtaining antigen from cultured organisms. Although Dussert *et al.* (1939) consider the test to be a practical one, they indicate that it is not species-specific.

Toxoplasma.—In detection of *Toxoplasma* in experimental animals and human cases, Sabin (1949) developed a highly specific *complement-fixation test* in which antigen is obtained from centrifugalized concentrates of the organism grown on the chorioallantoic membranes of chick embryos. However, the *Sabin-Feldman dye test* (1948) is equally satisfactory and is much easier to perform. It is carried out as follows: Living toxoplasmas from peritoneal exudate of an experimentally infected laboratory mouse are placed as a thin wet film on a test plate in a small amount of normal human serum, and a similar test plate is prepared with serum of a suspected case of toxoplasmosis. A drop or two of alkaline methylene blue stain are now mixed with the film on each plate. In the control plate the cytoplasm and nuclear material of all cells are rather deeply stained. If the second plate is from a *Toxoplasma* patient (either with active, chronic or inapparent infection), the patient's serum will contain neutralizing antibodies which will prevent the cytoplasm of the free parasites from taking the stain (although the cytoplasm of the parasites still within macrophages will be protected and will stain normally). In experimental animals, this test develops in three to five days after inoculation with *Toxoplasma.*

Immunologic Tests for Helminths

Many helminths produce antibody reactions in the human host. A majority of these parasites do not require diagnosis by immunologic technics, since they or their progeny are readily detected in the excreta. However, in some helminthic diseases immunologic tests are both practical and useful, and at times provide the only clinical laboratory procedures or the most dependable ones available. At other times positive tests indicate the need for more thorough examination of the excreta or provide a helpful guide preceding exploratory operations.

The tests which have the greatest practical usefulness are the intradermal reaction, precipitin test and complement fixation. Each of these will be considered under the headings of the respective parasites.

Trichinella Spiralis.—*Intradermal Test.*—The intradermal test is particularly helpful in mild cases, which manifest only vague symptoms. The following adaptation of the Bachman technic (1929) was used by Sawitz (1937).

Antigen is prepared from laboratory rats infected with *Trichinella.* For each 80 grams of meat from the sacrificed rat 1500 cc. of a 0.6% pepsin—0.3% HCl solution are used to digest the larvas out of the meat, the material being kept at 37° C. for 5 to 12 hours and shaken from time to time. The digest is then poured through 6 layers of cheesecloth, diluted with an equal amount of water and allowed to stand in a graduate for 2 hours. The upper third of the liquid is drawn off and replaced with warm tap water. The process is repeated 6 or 8 times until the supernatant fluid is clear. The purified material is left in a sedimentation glass overnight and next morning is placed in a petri dish, allowed to dry and then transferred to a beaker with ether to remove lipoids. After 24 hours, the ether is removed from the top and the residue dried *in vacuo* over sulfuric acid for 48 hours. The dry yield is pulverized in a clean dry mortar and kept in sterile ampules or dissolved in Coca's or McCoy's solution, 1 to 100 parts by weight. This latter constitutes the stock solution.

For intradermal tests the stock antigen is diluted 1 to 50 to secure a 1 to 5000 dilution. This is kept on ice until used. In the test, 0.1 cc. of antigen is introduced intracutaneously on one forearm and an equal amount of the solution lacking the antigen is injected intracutaneously on the other forearm. In positive cases (whether clinical or subclinical), a small white swelling appears immediately around the injected site, surrounded by an unraised irregular erythematous area of about 5 cm. diameter. The reaction reaches its maximum in about 10 minutes and begins to fade in 15 to 20 minutes. In negative cases, there is no reaction. Although, under carefully controlled technic, false positives do not commonly occur, it is always desirable to supplement the intradermal test with a precipitin test (*see below*), especially to determine if the infection has been of recent origin.

Precipitin Test.—Antigen is obtained from laboratory infected animals (rats, rabbits, guinea-pigs), from the lean meat of which the larvas are obtained by peptic digest technic, then concentrated by centrifugalization and desiccated in a partial vacuum.

Oliver González (1941) discovered that there are two types of antibody reaction in trichinosis, one which is anti-larval and one anti-adult. The latter forms a precipitate *in vitro* around the mouth, vulva and anus of adult trichinas, is detectable 15 days after infection, reaches its maximum about the 25th to 35th day and terminates on the 50th day. The anti-larval type of antibody produces a precipitate which reaches a maximum between the 45th and 60th day.

Roth (1945, 1946) developed a slide precipitin test which he stated is more reliable than the orthodox test. The procedure is as follows. About 100 sterile living *T. spiralis*, obtained by muscle digestion of laboratory hosts, are placed in a sterile, hollow-ground slide in 0.5 cc. of patient's serum to be tested, and the preparation is then mounted with a coverglass. The slide is set in a moist chamber and is incubated for 24 hours at 37° C. Bubbles and granules appear around the mouth of the larvas in positive sera. A particular advantage of this test is that it becomes positive 10 to 20 days after symptoms first appear. It is claimed to be more delicate and more trustworthy than other serologic tests for trichinosis.

Suessenguth and Kline (1944) have adapted the Kline test for syphilis to trichinosis. They report early, accurate diagnosis.

Complement Fixation.—Alcoholic extract of trichinized flesh is stated to give a negative reaction. Ströbel (1911) digested the flesh in a warm chamber with caustic soda and antiformin, neutralized the digest with hydrochloric acid, filtered it and obtained an extract which was potent for 2 weeks, if kept in the ice-box. The experimental work of Bachman (1929), using antigen prepared as for the precipitin test, indicates this test does not become specific until the 25th day after inoculation of an experimental animal. In clinical diagnosis it is not as satisfactory as the intradermal and precipitin reactions.

Filaria Worms.—*Intradermal Test.*—This is most probably a group reaction. Antigen can be prepared from any true filaria worm. The best yield is obtained from the dog heart worm, *Dirofilaria immitis*, living specimens of which should be freed of blood and serum, and washed in distilled water. They should then be dried, separated from lipoids, thoroughly dried again, pulverized and diluted with Coca's solution or physiologic salt solution, 1 to 200 parts by weight. For *Wuchereria bancrofti*, Taliaferro and Hoffman (1930) used 0.025 cc. of the stock solution, but Fairley (1931) who confirmed this study, used 0.25 cc. of a 0.1% solution.

Bozicevich and Hutter (1944) used a precise technic with *Dirofilaria immitis* antigen for testing infection with Bancroft's filaria (*W. bancrofti*). In preparation of the antigen living adults of *D. immitis* were obtained aseptically from the right ventricle of the infected dog, were washed in sterile physiologic salt solution, then in sterile distilled water, immediately placed in sterile test tubes and frozen with dry ice. The worms were then thawed, cut in small pieces, ground moist in a mortar, then dried in a desiccator and finally reground. Extraction was carried out in physiologic salt solution 1 to 100 parts by weight for 24 hours in the ice-box. The material was next frozen and thawed twice, then incubated at 56° C. for 4 hours with occasional shaking. Thereafter it was centrifugalized at 15,000 rpm. for 15 minutes, fractionally sterilized at 56° C. for 1 hour and tested for bacterial sterility. Finally, 0.03% phenol was added for preservation. When this stock antigen was needed for intradermal tests it was diluted to 1 to 8000 with physiologic salt solution. In 25 prepatent cases of the infection, using 0.01 cc. of the diluted antigen, positive reaction was obtained in all cases in fifteen minutes (immediate reaction), with a wheal of 3 mm. in diameter in excess of the control phenolized saline injection. There were no false positives with this dilution which rules out reaction to other helminths that may be present in the tested individual.

Chandler, Milliken and Schuhardt (1930) used *Dirofilaria* antigen for *Loa loa* infection, while Rodhain and Dubois (1932) used adult *Onchocerca volvulus* and *Loa loa* extracts as antigen to test infection with these two filaria worms. The immediate reaction, characterized typically by a diffuse erythema, wheal formation and pseudopodial extensions, covering an area of not less than 2 cm., was used in reading the test, which has an accuracy of at least 90%.

During the epidemic of Bancroft's filariasis among American troops in the South Pacific area (1943–1944), immunologic tests were carried out on many hundreds of individuals who had early clinical manifestations of the disease before the parent worms had matured and were shedding microfilarias. Antigen prepared from *Dirofilaria immitis* was employed by Huntington, Fogel, Eichold and Dickson (1944) and several other groups for intradermal tests, with an approximate 90% positive diagnosis. Wharton (1947) used similar antigen in skin-testing 215 exposed individuals in British Guiana. Employing the antigen in 1:10,000 dilution and with diluted negative dog's serum as a control, he obtained 89.8% positive reactions, 5.1% negatives and 5.1% which were equivocal. Of the 28 cases with elephantiasis, 26 reacted positively, 1 was negative and 1 was sensitive to dog's serum.

Skin testing of individuals in the *Onchocerca*-endemic area in Guatemala by Bozicevich *et al.* (1947) with antigens prepared from *D. immitis*, *Setaria equina Litomosoides carinii* and *O. volvulus* demonstrated that the *O. volvulus* antigen was more sensitive and more specific than the others, while *D. immitis* came next in producing satisfactory results.

Complement Fixation.—Van Hoof (1934) has obtained positive complement-fixation reactions in patients harboring *Onchocerca volvulus* in Africa. In a series of tests on *Onchocerca* patients in Guatemala, Bozicevich *et al.* (*l. c.*) found *O. volvulus* antigen much more sensitive than antigens prepared from other filaria worms.

Strongyloides Stercoralis.—*Intradermal Test.*—The application of powdered *Strongyloides* to a scarified area of the skin produces an immediate urticarial wheal in animals positive for this worm, even in very light infections which require culture methods for diagnosis (Fülleborn, 1926).

Brannon (1943) utilized as antigen washed filariform larvas of *Strongyloides* obtained from cultured feces of a naturally infected chimpanzee. The larvas were ground up with emery powder, and the antigen extracted in Coca's solution, dried to powder form, and then diluted 1:100 in Coca's solution. Similarly prepared antigens from hookworm larvas and bacteria in the original fecal specimen served as controls. Approximately 4 million larvas produced 15 to 25 mgm. of powdered antigen. The powder was dissolved in Coca's solution to make a dilution of 1:100 which was demonstrated to be bacteriologically sterile. An amount of 0.1 cc. of this solution was then employed in making the intradermal tests, which were carried out on 25 individuals with chronic strongyloidiasis. All tests provoked positive reactions, while all controls were negative except for one suffering from severe, exfoliative dermatitis and one moribund individual (Brannon and Faust, 1949).

Precipitin Test.—Brannon (1943) used this test as a check on the intradermal reaction carried out on 25 patients harboring *Strongyloides stercoralis.* The antigen titer ranged from 1:5,000 to 1:30,000. All sera showed precipitins varying in degree from + to ++++. In 4 persons previously known to have the infection but at the time without demonstrable larvas, the reaction ranged from equivocal to +++.

Ascaris Lumbricoides.—*Intradermal Test.*—The test consists in placing a few drops of body fluid of *Ascaris lumbricoides* on a scarified area of the skin. In sensitized individuals there is an immediate local reaction, consisting of an erythematous wheal at the site of application, and frequently extensive lymphatic and systemic involvement. The more alarming symptoms disappear in the course of an hour or two but generalized edema may persist for some days. It is important to note that *Ascaris*-sensitization does not necessarily mean infection with *Ascaris* at the time of the test, but may be the result of a previous infection or, in the case of workers in a laboratory, merely contact with fresh or preserved worms (Ransom, Harrison and Couch, 1924).

Complement Fixation.—Antigen may be prepared by extracting in physiologic salt solution the macerated adult worms which have been evacuated from human or porcine infections, then filtering and desiccating the solute. The fact that the serum of *Ascaris*-infected individuals gives a positive reaction is of little but academic diagnosis, except in purely male infections.

Schistosoma Species.—*Intradermal Test.*—This is a schistosome-group reaction. The antigen may be obtained from molluscs infected with mammalian schistosomes or in a more purified state from adult schistosomes, removed from an experimentally infected laboratory mammal. The dried antigen may be employed as a 0.5 or 1% saline extract, sterilized by passage through a Seitz filter and stored in sterile ampules in the ice-box. The technic of making the test has been described by Fairley and Williams (1927) and by Taliaferro and Taliaferro (1931). When molluscan tissues infected with the schistosome are used, it is necessary to use uninfected molluscan-tissue extract for the control.

Oliver González and Pratt (1944), testing 96 persons infected with *S. mansoni*, obtained 100% positive skin reactions and no false positives. These workers utilized antigens prepared from the cercarias and adult worms, with titers ranging from 1:10,000 to 1:200,000. They found that the antigen could be stored at 0° to 10° C. for as long as 12 months without impairing its specificity (Pratt and Oliver González, 1947). Alves and Blair (1946) state that cercarial antigen provides a higher degree of accuracy than routine microscopic examination of stools.

Wright, Bozicevich, Brady and Bauman (1947) failed to elicit any positive skin reactions in American military personnel exposed to schistosomiasis japonica on Leyte, P. I. late in 1944 and early in 1945, 4 to 5 months before the tests were conducted. The antigen was prepared from adult *S. mansoni* and was employed in a dilution of 1:1,000, dry weight basis. This might suggest that the intradermal test in schistosomiasis does not develop until the infection becomes chronic.

Precipitin Test.—Employing antigens prepared from cercarias and adults of *S. mansoni* and testing 86 patients harboring this parasite, Oliver González and Pratt (1944) obtained 93% positive precipitin reactions and no false positives in persons having other parasites. The titer used ranged from 1:3,200 to 1:4,000.

Complement Fixation.—The antigen is usually prepared as an alcoholic extract of molluscan tissues infected with mammalian schistosome cercarias (1 cc. 95 to 96% alcohol for each infected snail liver). After extraction at 37° C. for 24 hours, it is filtered, the filtrate then evaporated and thoroughly dried, weighed and dissolved in physiologic salt solution (1 to 40 by weight). An alternative technic consists in evaporating the filtrate to the point of turbidity, adding just enough absolute alcohol to clarify it, and placing it in 1 cc. ampules in the ice-box until needed, when it is diluted 1 to 39 with physiologic salt solution. Most authorities agree that the antigen is a lipoid rather than a protein. This test is most useful in patients passing through the incubation period of the disease before eggs are being discharged, and in old chronic cases in which extensive fibrosis of the bowel or bladder wall usually prevents evacuation of eggs. Positive cases should be checked with a routine Wassermann test to preclude syphilis.

Williams (1947), in testing 560 Australian troops who had been exposed to *S. japonicum* infection on Leyte, P. I. in 1944–1945, utilized antigen prepared in 1927 by Fairley from snails infected with *S. spindale*. In one group of 169 individuals, all with positive reaction, 25 were negative by stool examination. Of 365 persons previously regarded as negative, 34 had positive tests, 27 had positive stools and 26 of the 27 were positive by both technics. No false positives were encountered in unexposed persons or in those with positive Wassermann sera.

Serum-Globulin Reaction.—This is a nonspecific test due to the excess of serum euglobulin elaborated in the animal body in the presence of certain disease-producing organisms. In India and China, it has been utilized as a presumptive test for cases of kala-azar. It may be conducted as an aldhyde (formol-gel) test (Napier, 1922, 1943) or a precipitation reaction (Sia, 1921, 1924).

Faust and Meleney (1924) found this test positive in schistosomiasis japonica patients free of kala-azar, while Faust, Jones and Hoffman (1934) obtained 8 positive tests in 11 patients suffering from chronic schistosomiasis mansoni in Puerto Rico.

In nonspecific seriologic tests of 104 schistosomiasis cases on Leyte, P. I., Wright *et al.* (1947) obtained positive reactions in 77.3% of 75 military personnel and all of 29 Filipino civilians (chronic cases). There were 11 of 70 individuals not known to have schistosomiasis who gave positive tests. Lal (1924) and Khalil and Hassan (1932) have obtained positive findings in other cases of schistosomiasis.

Paragonimus Westermani.—*Complement Fixation.*—The antigen is prepared by physiologic saline extraction of macerated adult *Paragonimus westermani*, obtained from human cases at autopsy, from naturally infected reservoir hosts or from experimentally infected laboratory animals (Ando). It is particularly useful in detecting cases with abdominal or cerebral involvement, where the eggs are not voided in the sputum or feces.

Echinococcus Granulosus.—*Intradermal Test.*—Since 1911, when Casoni first described the specificity of the intradermal test in persons parasitized by the hydatid cyst, it has been used as a clinical diagnostic procedure, and became a particularly valuable test after it was refined by Dew, Kellaway and Williams (1925). The antigen employed consists of sterile hydatid fluid obtained by puncture of unilocular hydatid cysts of sheep, pigs, oxen or human cases. The liquid antigen is filtered, incubated to test its sterility, and placed in sealed ampules on ice. With these precautions it is potent up to 6 months. For the test, 0.2 cc. of the antigen is introduced intradermally on the upper arm after sterilization of the area with alcohol, and is controlled by the injection of a like amount of sterile physiologic salt solution into the skin several centimeters distant or on the opposite arm. The control fades almost immediately, while the tested site of positive cases develops a typical wheal within ½ hour. This test is particularly useful pre-operatively. In postoperative tests, an intense skin reaction may result, even though the cyst may have been removed many months previously.

The most potent hydatid antigen is that provided by the Dennis technic.

Dennis' Technic (1937).—Freshly aspirated, bacteriologically sterile, hydatid fluid from cysts of the liver and lungs of infected cattle and sheep constitutes the source of the antigen. About 1 liter of the fluid is chilled, acidified by the addition of 5% trichloracetic acid, and placed in the ice-box overnight to accelerate flocculation. The precipitate is obtained by repeated centrifugalization and is next washed in distilled water to remove excess acid. It is then suspended in about 50 cc. of distilled water and 10% sodium hydroxide added, drop by drop, until practically all of the protein is in solution. The insoluble residue is collected by centrifugalization and discarded. The solution is chilled, the protein reprecipitated by the addition of 1 *N* glacial acetic acid and left in the ice-box overnight. It is then re-centrifugalized, washed free of acid and evaporated in a drying oven at 37° C. or over calcium chloride. The dry precipitate is ground in a mortar and stored over calcium chloride in a desiccator. About 100 mgm. of purified antigen may be obtained from each liter of hydatid fluid. Stock antigen solution is made up 1 to 1000 in slightly alkalinized physiologic salt solution. It may be sterilized by filtration through a Seitz EK filter or by adding 0.5% chloroform. This solution is about 10 times as potent as unpurified hydatid fluid.

For intradermal tests the purified powdered Dennis antigen is diluted 1 to 10,000 in physiologic salt solution and 0.2 cc. of this solution employed. Possibly the most specific skin test may be obtained by using the polysaccharide portion of antigen extracted from hydatid scolices.

Precipitin Test.—The precipitin test, which has been particularly studied by Australian investigators, closely parallels the complement-fixation reaction. In practice, fresh hydatid fluid is obtained aseptically from infected sheep. It may be preserved by the addition of 0.05% phenol or 1:1000 merthiolate solution and will remain stable for several months. Add 0.4 cc. of patient's fresh serum to an equal amount of the antigen in small agglutination tubes and allow to stand for 36 hours at room temperature. In a serum with high precipitin-content (*e. g.*, high serum globulin) a precipitate forms in 2 or 3 hours. Thick flocculation has been designated as +++; fine precipitate with granules in suspension, ++; and microscopic granularity, +.

Complement Fixation.—The antigen consists of hydatid fluid removed aseptically from known infected human cases or from infected domestic mammals. Fairley (1922) found antigen obtained from sheep having cysts with viable scolices to be most satisfactory. Contaminated antigen must not be used. For this test the Dennis purified powdered antigen is diluted 1 to 5000 and is utilized as in the Kolmer modification of the Wassermann test. This antigen is sensitive, specific, not anticomplementary and apparently gives no false positive tests.

Cysticercus Cellulosæ.—*Intradermal Test.*—This is a group-specific test. In testing for *C. cellulosæ* in man, antigen may be obtained from fluid of various species of cysticerci in domestic animals.

Precipitin Test.—The reaction is carried out as in testing hydatid infection. Antigen fluid is obtained from cysticerci from previous human cases, or, more practically, from the bladder worms of *Tænia solium* or other species of *Tænia*, the larvas of which develop in hogs, rabbits and other intermediate hosts.

Immunologic Tests Involving Arthropods

Although Blacklock and Thompson (1923) demonstrated that invasion of the tissues of experimental laboratory animals by the larvas (maggots) of the tumbu-fly, *Cordylobia anthropophaga,* calls forth notable immune response to subsequent attack, this phenomenon has not been employed as a clinical laboratory test in this or other arthropod infestations. The only practical use which has been made of the sensitization reaction to arthropod metabolites concerns the venom of the honey bee. Persons who develop hypersensitivity to bee sting may be desensitized and thus freed of the liability of fatal anaphylactic shock. (See Chapter 20, page 482.)

Precipitin Tests for Blood Ingested by Arthropods.—Malariologists and other workers frequently need to know whether a mosquito or other blood-sucking arthropod is selective in animals on which it feeds, to determine whether a particular species is dangerous as a transmitter of infectious agents from person to person. Precipitin tests and other standard methods of blood sampling provide the methods for obtaining this information.

Additional application of the precipitin test has been made by Weitz and Buxton (1953), to determine the period of digestion of blood meals by various arthropods. Mosquitoes and the midge *Culicoides* usually gave positive tests up to 24 hours; some tsetse flies (*Glossina morsitans*) up to 3 days but another species (*G. swynnertoni*) only within a much shorter time; the soft-bodied tick, *Ornithodoros moubata,* more than 6 months, and the rat mite, *Bdellonyssus bacoti*, only 1 day.

Tests for Virus Neutralizing Antibodies in Mosquitoes.—In the study of arthropod-borne viruses, it is important to know how long species which have fed on immune vertebrate hosts retain the specific antibodies and what effect this may have on subsequent blood meals containing active virus of the same kind. Scrivani *et al.* (1953) studied this problem with *Aëdes nigromaculis* and *Culex tarsalis*, which are natural transmitters of Western equine encephalomyelitis. They found that immune antibodies do not remain active beyond a 24-hour period. This indicates that these mosquitoes collected in the field should be kept in the laboratory at room temperature for that period before they are pooled and frozen to test whether they are carrying the live virus.

REFERENCES

BACHMAN, G. W. 1929. An Intradermal Reaction in Experimental Trichinosis. J. Prev. Med., *2*, 513–523.

BLACKLOCK, D. B., and THOMPSON, M. G. 1923. A Study of the Tumbu-fly, *Cordylobia Anthropophaga* Grünberg, in Sierre Leone. Ann. Trop. Med. & Parasitol., *17*, 443–510.

BOZICEVICH, J. 1950. Discussion of "The Complement Fixation Test for Hepatic Amebiasis." Am. J. Trop. Med., *30*, 154–157.

BOZICEVICH, J., and HUTTER, A. M. 1944. Intradermal and Serological Tests with *Dirofilaria Immitis* Antigen in Cases of Human Filariasis. Am. J. Trop. Med., *24*, 203–208.

BRAHMACHARI, U. 1917. *Kala-Azar, Its Treatment.* 123 pp., Butterworth & Co., Calcutta.

BRANNON, M. J. C., and FAUST, E. C. 1949. Preparation and Testing of Specific Antigen for Diagnosis of Human Strongyloidiasis. Am. J. Trop. Med., *29*, 229–239.

CHOPRA, R. N., DAS GUPTA, J. C., and DAVID, J. C. 1927. The Antimony Test in the Diagnosis of Kala-azar. Indian Med. Gaz., *62*, 688–691.

COGGESHALL, L. T., and EATON, M. C. 1938. The Complement Fixation Reaction in Monkey Malaria. J. Exp. Med., *67*, 871–882.

CRAIG, C. F. 1929. The Technique and Results of a Complement Fixation Test for the Diagnosis of Infections with *Endamœba Histolytica.* Am. J. Trop. Med., *9*, 277–296.

————1948. *Laboratory Diagnosis of Protozoan Diseases.* 2nd ed., 384 pp. Lea & Febiger, Philadelphia.

DENNIS, E. W. 1937. A Stable Concentrated Purified Antigen for the Immunological Study of Hydatid Disease. J. Parasitol., *23*, 62–67.

DEW, H. R., KELLAWAY, C. H., and WILLIAMS, F. E. 1925. The Intradermal Reaction in Hydatid Disease and Its Clinical Value. Med. J. Australia, *i*, 471–478.

DOSTROVSKY, A., and SAGHER, F. 1946. The Intracutaneous Test in Cutaneous Leishmaniasis. Ann. Trop. Med. & Parasitol., *40*, 265–269.

DULANEY, A. D., and STRATMAN-THOMAS, W. K. 1940. Complement Fixation in Human Malaria: Results Obtained with Various Antigens. J. Immunol., *29*, 247–255.

FAIRLEY, N. H. 1922. The Complement-Fixation Test for Hydatid Disease and Its Clinical Value. Med. J. Australia, *i*, 341–346.

————1931. Serological and Intradermal Tests in Filariasis. Trans. R. Soc. Trop. Med. & Hyg., *24*, 635–648.

FAIRLEY, N. H., and WILLIAMS, F. E. 1927. A Preliminary Report on an Intradermal Reaction in Schistosomiasis. Med. J. Australia, *ii*, 811–818.

Faust, E. C., and Meleney, H. E. 1924. Studies on Schistosomiasis Japonica. Am. J. Hyg., Monogr. Ser. No. 3, 339 pp.

Frisch, A. W., Whims, C. B., and Oppenheim, J. M. 1947. Intradermal Reactions in Trichinosis. Am. J. Clin. Path., *17*, 16–23.

Guerreiro, C., and Machado, A. 1913. Da Reacção de Brodet e Gengou na Molestia de Carlos Chagas como Elemento Diagnostico. Brazil Méd., *27*, 225–226.

Hussey, K. L., and Brown, B. W. 1950. The Complement Fixation Test for Hepatic Amebiasis. Am. J. Trop. Med., *30*, 147–154.

Kelser, R. A. 1936. A Complement Fixation Test for Chagas' Disease Employing an Artificial Culture Antigen. Am. J. Trop. Med., *16*, 405–415.

Napier, L. E. 1921. Kala-azar. Indian Med. Gaz., *56*, 401–404.

Noguchi, H. 1926. Comparative Studies of Herpetomonads and Leishmanias. II. Differentiation of the Organisms by Serological Reactions and Fermentation Tests. J. Exp. Med., *44*, 327–337.

Oliver González, J. 1941. The Dual Antibody Basis of Acquired Immunity in Trichinosis. J. Infect. Dis., *69*, 254–270.

Pratt, C. K., and Oliver González, J. 1947. Intradermal Reactions to Fresh and Stored Antigens Prepared from Cercaria of *S. Mansoni.* Puerto Rico J. Pub. Health & Trop. Med., *22*, 254–256.

Proske, H. O., and Watson, R. B. 1939. The Protein Tyrosin Reaction: A Biochemical Test for Malaria. J. Med., *20*, 279–288.

Ransom, B. H., Harrison, W. T., and Couch, J. F. 1924. Ascaris Sensitization. J. Agr. Research, *28*, 577–582.

Roth, H. 1945. Serodiagnosis of Trichinosis by Microscopical Testing with Live Trichinæ Larvæ. Nature, *23*, 758–759.

Sabin, A. B. 1949. Complement Fixation Test in Toxoplasmosis and Persistence of the Antibody in Human Beings. Pediatrics, *4*, 443–453.

Sabin, A. B., and Feldman, H. A. 1948. Dyes as Microchemical Indicators of a New Immunity Phenomenon Affecting a Protozoön Parasite. Science, *108*, 660–663.

Scrivani, R. P., Reeves, W. C., and Brookman, B. 1953. Duration of Activity of Western Equine Encephalomyelitis Neutralizing Bodies in *Aëdes Nigromaculis* and *Culex Tarsalis.* Am. J. Trop. Med. & Hyg., *2*, 457–463.

Taliaferro, W. H., and Hoffman, W. A. 1930. Skin Reactions to *Dirofilaria Immitis* in Persons Infected with *Wuchereria Bancrofti.* J. Prev. Med., *4*, 261–280.

Taliaferro, W. H., and Taliaferro, L. G. 1931. Skin Reactions in Persons Infected with *Schistosoma Mansoni.* Puerto Rico J. Publ. Health & Trop. Med., *7*, 23–35.

Van Hoof, L. 1934. Serological Reactions in Onchocerciasis. Trans. R. Soc. Trop. Med. & Hyg., *27*, 609–617.

Weitz, B., and Buxton, P. A. 1953. The Rate of Digestion of Blood Meals of Various Hematophagous Arthropods as Determined by the Precipitin Test. Bull. Ent. Research, *44*, 445–450.

Williams, F. E. 1947. The Complement Fixation Reaction in Asiatic Schistosomiasis Employing Cercarial Antigen (*Schistosoma Spindale*). Trans. R. Soc. Trop. Med. & Hyg., *40*, 421–434.

Wright, W. H., Bozicevich, J., Brady, F. J., and Bauman, P. M. 1947. The Diagnosis of Schistosomiasis Japonica. V. The Diagnosis of Schistosomiasis Japonica by Means of Intradermal and Serological Tests. Am. J. Hyg., *45*, 150–163.

Chapter 29

Entomological Material, Intermediate and Reservoir Hosts

Introduction.—The usefulness of this material is threefold. The organism may be the causative agent, the suspected transmitter or an important host harboring the agent of human disease. It may prove to be a valuable demonstration for teaching medical students, sanitary officers or technicians. And it may provide opportunity for carrying out a research problem. In spite of the fact that much is known about the epidemiologic aspects of infections produced by animal parasites, a great deal remains to be learned. Specimens obtained in the hospital, brought in by patients to the clinic or collected in the field should be given careful examination, even though many of them are plentiful and have no particular medical interest; a few may be important.

First of all, it is necessary to distinguish between living and dead specimens. In the former case it may be desirable to keep the material alive or to culture it to a more mature stage, to observe its habits, to learn about its requirements of food, moisture or other environmental conditions. This applies particularly to a great variety of arthropods, fresh-water molluscs, and to the smaller mammals which may serve as reservoirs of human parasites. If it is desirable to keep these animals alive, appropriate vivaria must be provided for them, *viz.*, cages, aquaria, etc.

If the specimens are dead and there is need to preserve them, it will be helpful to know whether they keep well as dry objects or should be preserved in liquid media such as alcohol or formalin. If the specimens are captured alive and are to be preserved, then it is necessary to know the most satisfactory methods of anesthetizing them so that their exhibit value will be retained.

Collection and Preservation of Arthropods.—The technic of collecting arthropods varies, depending on the type or group concerned. Centipedes, scorpions, ticks, spiders and assassin-bugs are brought into the laboratory by interested persons for identification. If placed in a dry container they are usually not damaged when they arrive. Trombiculid mites (*e. g.*, "red bugs"), sarcoptoid mites and human lice are most commonly obtained by general practitioners or dermatologists in charity clinics, and may be preserved in small vials containing alcohol. Bed-bugs can be obtained by careful search in infested homes. Adult fleas can be removed from dogs and cats by touching them with a camel's hair brush moistened with xylol or chloroform and removing them with a fine forceps to a vial or jar. Rats caught in traps may be placed in an air-tight chloroform chamber for removal of rodent fleas, mites and lice. Flea larvas are readily obtained by sieving the sweepings from the floors of dwellings occupied by infested persons, dogs or cats.

Adult living female mosquitoes, sand-flies and *Culicoides* may be captured uninjured by carefully placing a wide-mouthed bottle over the exposed skin when these blood-sucking flies are beginning to feed; then, when they have left the feeding site, slipping a small piece of cardboard over the mouth of the bottle, placing the bottle right-side-up and substituting a cork or cap for the pasteboard. They may be secured in a like manner from walls or furniture on which they are resting. Or they may be bred in cages from larvas previously brought into the laboratory. *Culex* and *Aëdes* mosquitoes may be bred through several generations in the laboratory, so that students may have complete demonstrations of their life cycles. Most species of anophelines require larger, better controlled breeding quarters, which are not usually practical except in special laboratories under expert direction. However, eggs, larvas and pupas may be taken from aquatic breeding grounds and brought in for observation and study. For these and other insects, insect collecting nets, adapted for use in catching adults and larvas, are indispensable.

Filth flies, which breed in garbage, human and animal manure, and decaying meat, may be obtained as adults from unsanitary latrines, garbage piles and dead animals lying on the ground, or the gravid females may be induced to oviposit (or larviposit) in the laboratory, on decaying food or manure as culture media. Larvas recovered from human lesions or excreta may be bred out on appropriate culture media, or may be fixed in hot 70% alcohol-glycerol, 10 to 1 parts by volume, and identified as larvas.

Large arthropods with hard exoskeletons may be killed in cyanide gas chambers or chloroform chambers and may then be preserved in 70% alcohol, or dried and thinly shellacked and mounted in a suitable demonstration box or jar. Ticks and spiders will shrink badly if allowed to dry out. No insects or other arthropods should be stored in formaldehyde solution, since this preservative causes disintegration of the exoskeleton.

The scales of delicate adult insects, as mosquitoes, are badly damaged by rough handling. These insects should be killed in a chloroform or cyanide jar, mounted with entomological pins before they completely dry, and should be placed in suitable entomological boxes, in case they are desired for demonstration. For transportation to specialists for identification, unmounted specimens of small biting Diptera (including mosquitoes) should preferably be placed between pieces of lens paper in a well-buffered pill-box. For dry mounting, these delicate insects are ruined if they are placed in alcohol.

Collecting and Preservation of Molluscs.—While the clinical laboratory usually has no special need for preserving snails or other molluscs, the laboratorian may be called upon to make identification of the specimens. This is a task for specialists, frequently at a distance from the laboratory, and molluscs ordinarily do not survive shipment in a living condition. They can be killed by plunging them into steaming, not boiling water, then transferred through 25% and 50 to 70% alcohol, in which they will keep well.

Collection and Preservation of Vertebrate Animals.—The curiosity of human beings, particularly children, in the collection of natural objects should be encouraged. Occasionally, it stimulates a high school student to take basic scientific training leading to the profession of medicine or public health. Hence diagnostic laboratories may expect to have fishes, reptiles, birds or small mammals brought in for indentification. At times identification is not difficult and may be made without consulting a specialist, but more frequently the services of such a person are required.

Fishes and reptiles may be preserved either in 4% formaldehyde or 70% alcohol and will keep well, provided slits have been made beforehand into the animal's body cavities so that the viscera will be adequately fixed. Although it is not usual to preserve the entire bird or mammal, this may be done and the animal mounted if the technician is a good taxidermist. More frequently only the "skins" of birds and the pelts and skulls of mammals are kept. These, too, require some skill to prevent their deterioration and considerable care that they do not become infested with maggots before they are "cured."

Identification of Specimens.—The time has long since passed when it is sufficient to identify an arthropod as a tick, mite, fly or mosquito. Similarly there is need for adequate identification of molluscs and vertebrate animals, especially if they have a connection with disease in man or domestic animals. In case such expert service is not available in the immediate vicinity and the specimen seems worthy of diagnosis, it should be shipped to a specialist. The one institution in the United States, in which there is a corps of experts always willing to make identification of adequately preserved specimens, is the U. S. National Museum, Washington, D. C. It will be well first to address a letter to "The Curator of [Arthropods, Molluscs, Fishes Reptiles, Birds, Mammals, etc.]," at the U. S. National Museum, advising him of the need for identification and requesting instructions for packaging and prepaid shipment. Although several weeks may be required before the identification has been made, it can be depended on as being accurate, provided the material sent is in identifiable condition and arrives in an undamaged state.

The Mounting of Arthropods as Permanent Preparations.—Some of the smaller arthropods and early larval stages of larger ones are sufficiently clear and transparent so that *in toto* mounts may be made by passing them through dehydrating and clearing agents into balsam or clarite. Others, which have tissues that are too dense for satisfactory slide preparations without special treatment, should be placed in 10% cold aqueous potassium hydroxide solution for 24 hours. If rapid diagnosis is essential, the specimens may be punctured with finely pointed needles, placed in the caustic solution and heated to steaming for a few minutes, care being exercised not to cause their disintegration. After thorough washing they are ready for dehydration and clearing. For sectioning of arthropods or arthropod parts, the organism should be carefully punctured to allow rapid penetration of the fixing fluid. Bles' fixative (alcohol-formalin-acetic acid) is recommended.

Chloral Hydrate Mounting Medium.—Probably the simplest practical method for killing, fixing, dehydrating, staining, clearing and mounting small arthropods (as Cyclops and Diaptomus, mites, unfed stages of ticks, fleas, lice, bedbugs, mosquito larvas, pupas and adults, other small blood-sucking or filth flies, as well as their dissected diagnostic parts) consists in using Doetschman's modification of the Berlese technic (Doetschman, 1944). The formula is as follows:

Distilled water . . .	35 cc.
Chloral hydrate . .	20 Gm.
Gum arabic . . .	20 Gm.
Glycerol	20 cc.
Glucose syrup . . .	3 cc.
Basic fuchsin . . .	10 drops or more

The gum arabic will dissolve readily if the solution is heated in a water bath. This method likewise prevents carbonization of the chloral hydrate and caramelization of the glucose. The water in the solution should be evaporated until a desired viscosity has been obtained. Living specimens or those previously fixed and preserved in 70% alcohol may be utilized. The mounts should have little slivers of glass between the slide and coverglass to prevent too much compression of the mounted object. The preparation clears almost immediately and may be utilized as a temporary mount, or it may be heated in a drying oven at 37° to 40° C. for permanency. Air bubbles in the preparation will be minimized if 1 drop of the medium is placed on the slide, the object to be mounted centered therein and a second drop of the medium placed on the lower side of the coverglass to be superimposed on the object.

Larger arthropods which remain in good condition as demonstration objects following dehydration may be successfully mounted in clear plastic medium. Instructions and material for plastic mounts may be obtained from several biological supply houses, including General Biological Supply House, Chicago, Illinois and Ward's Natural Science Establishment, Rochester, N. Y.

Care of Demonstration Collections.—Demonstrations and mounted specimens which are preserved as dry mounts must be kept in tight boxes away from dust and breeze. Precautions must be constantly taken to prevent the small, plump, hairy larvas of *Anthrenus museorum* and *A. verbasci* (dermestid beetles) from eating the specimens. Crystals of paradichlorobenzene, placed in a little cardboard or paper cup in one corner of each box and renewed 3 or 4 times a year, will guard against such danger.

REFERENCES

Abbott, R. T. 1948. Handbook of Medically Important Mollusks of the Orient and Western Pacific. Bull. Mus. Comp. Zoöl., Harvard Coll., *100*, 246–328.

Banks, N. 1909. Directions for Collecting and Preserving Insects. U. S. National Museum. Bull. No. 67, pp. 1-135, figs, 1–188.

Bequaert, J. 1928. Mollusks of Importance in Human and Veterinary Medicine. Am. J. Trop. Med., *8*, 165–182, 215–232.

Doetschman, W. H. 1944. Some Suggestions in Microtechnique Particularly Useful in Microëntomology and Parasitology. Trans. Am. Micr. Soc., *63*, 175–178.

Eltringham, H. 1930. *Histological and Illustrative Methods for Entomologists.* Clarendon Press, Oxford (England), 139 pp.

Faust, E. C., and Khaw, O.-K. 1927. Fishes Involved in *Clonorchis* Infection. In *Studies on Clonorchis Sinensis* (Cobbold). Am. J. Hyg., Monogr. Ser. No. 8, pp. 70–86.

Fox, C. 1925. *Insects and Diseases of Man.* Chap. 22, "A Few Notes on Technique." P. Blakiston's Son & Co., Philadelphia.

Frings, H. 1947. A Simple Method for Rearing Blowflies without Meat. Science, *105*, 482.

Fuller, H. S., Murray, E. S., and Snyder, J. C. 1949. Studies of Human Body Lice, *Pediculus Humanus Corporis.* 1. A Method for Feeding Lice through a Membrane and Experimental Infection with *Rickettsia Prowazeki, R. Mooseri* and *Borrelia Novyi.* Pub. Health Repts., *64*, 1287–1292.

Lankester, E. R., and Harmer, S. F. 1921. *Handbook of Instruction for Collectors.* Brit. Museum Nat. Hist., London. 222 pp.

Neveu-Lemaire, M. 1927, 1928. Essai de Mammalogie Médicale. II. Les Mamiféres Hôtes Intermédiaires ou Hôtes Définitifs des Helminthes Parasites de l'Homme et Ceux qui Hébergent des Parasites qui leur Sont Communs avec l'Espèce Humaine. Ann. Parasitol., *5*, 356–380; *6*, 107–131.

Peterson, A. 1934, 1937. Entomological Equipment and Methods. Ann Arbor (Michigan). 21 + 334 pp., 138 pl.

Simmons, J. S., and Gentzkow, C. J. 1955. *Medical and Public Health Laboratory Methods.* 6th ed. Lea & Febiger, Philadelphia. *In press.*

Smart, J. 1940. Instructions for Collectors. No. 4a. Brit. Museum of Nat. Hist., London. 164 pp.

INDEX OF AUTHORS

C

SUBJECT INDEX

D

E

G

I

M

N

O

NORTHERN
3 1211 00784538 7